The Quantum Theory
of
Molecular Electronic Structure

FRONTIERS IN CHEMISTRY

Ronald Breslow and Martin Karplus, Editors
Columbia University

THERMODYNAMICS OF SMALL SYSTEMS:
Parts I and II

T. L. Hill *University of Oregon*

LECTURES ON QUANTUM THEORY OF MOLECULAR ELECTRONIC STRUCTURE

R. G. Parr *The Johns Hopkins University*

OXIDATION MECHANISMS: Applications to Organic Chemistry

R. Stewart *University of British Columbia*

THE BIOSYNTHESIS OF STEROIDS, TERPENES, AND ACETOGENINS

J. H. Richards *California Institute of Technology*
J. B. Hendrickson *Brandeis University*

The Quantum Theory of Molecular Electronic Structure

A lecture-note and reprint volume

Robert G. Parr
The Johns Hopkins University

W. A. BENJAMIN, INC.
1964
New York Amsterdam

QUANTUM THEORY OF MOLECULAR ELECTRONIC STRUCTURE
A lecture-note and reprint volume

Library of Congress Catalog Card Number 63–11728
Manufactured in the United States of America

The publisher is pleased to acknowledge the assistance of Cecilia Duray-Bito, who produced the illustrations, and William Prokos, who designed the cover and dust jacket.

Final manuscript was received on November 5, 1962; this volume was published on June 10, 1963; second printing with corrections, April 24, 1964.

W. A. BENJAMIN, INC.
2465 Broadway, New York 25, New York

Editors' Foreword

It has become increasingly clear that developments in chemistry are moving so rapidly that new means are needed to report the current status of active fields of research. The person who wishes to appreciate the significance of current research or who desires to enter a new field often requires some aid in negotiating the difficult path through the voluminous series of original articles. Attempts to provide the necessary guidance have been made by review journals and by edited volumes composed of chapters written by a number of experts. Unfortunately, the best research scientists have sometimes been unwilling to write the reviews. Furthermore, since the review journals usually do not form a part of a scientist's personal library, the existing articles have not had the desired availability to students and research workers. Although the edited volumes avoid the latter difficulty, they do so at the expense of serious time delays resulting from the participation of many authors; the books are often out of date upon publication.

To overcome these problems in scientific communication we have initiated the series "Frontiers in Chemistry." It is expected that the series will consist primarily of brief monographs written by active workers in the various fields of chemistry. These will not be exhaustive treatises so much as critical reviews, in which an author indicates his opinion of the current status and future direction of a field. It is also our intent to publish occasional collections of reprints with an evaluation of the relationship of the articles to the current status of the field. We hope that the resulting series of monographs and reprint volumes will provide authoritative summaries that are readily available to both students and research scientists.

Any advice that will assist us in this purpose will be greatly appreciated. We particularly welcome suggestions of fields that should be included in the series or authors who should be invited to contribute.

R. BRESLOW
M. KARPLUS

New York, New York
February 1963

Preface

This book deals with the quantum theory of the electronic structure of molecules, at a level designed to take the reader to the borderlines of research in this part of chemistry. The contents are a set of lectures and a group of reprints of research papers. A knowledge of elementary quantum mechanics is presumed.

The subject matter is the body of theoretical research done since World War II, dedicated to the development of methods for precisely determining electronic wave functions for molecules. In the lectures I have attempted to provide practical understanding both of the purely theoretical methods currently used for small molecules and of the semiempirical methods currently used for large conjugated organic molecules. As important, I have tried to show how these methods are in process of continuous modification and improvement. A discussion is included of very recent work on the many-electron theory of atoms and molecules, and I have not excluded speculation as to how the various methods may develop in the future.

These lectures were presented at the University of Illinois during the spring semester of 1961–1962, while I was a visiting member of the faculty of the Department of Chemistry and Chemical Engineering and a member of the Center of Advanced Study. I am very grateful to Dean F. T. Wall, Professor H. E. Carter, and Professor H. S. Gutowsky for their invitation and hospitality.

I have selected the papers reprinted in order to document and round out the limited picture that I myself see. I have given several hundred additional references to the recent periodical literature, which should provide a much broader base for further study.

I would like to dedicate this book to my graduate students at Carnegie Institute of Technology over a period of fourteen years, Peter Hauk, Hubert Joy, Oliver Ludwig, Peter Lykos, Joe Parks, Tony Saturno, Larry Snyder, and Russ Taylor, and to my senior research co-workers there, Tadashi Arai, Werner Bingel, David Bishop, Audrey Companion, Giuseppe Del Re, Frank Ellison, Fausto Fumi, Murray Geller, Henk Hameka, Jim Hoyland, John I'Haya, Teturo Inui, Leonello Paoloni, Klaus Ruedenberg, Al Turner, and Carl Wulfman.

ROBERT G. PARR

Baltimore, Maryland
January 1963

Acknowledgments

The publisher wishes to acknowledge the assistance of the following organizations in the preparation of this volume:

The American Institute of Physics, for permission to reprint the articles from *Reviews of Modern Physics* and *Journal of Chemical Physics;* The National Academy of Sciences, for permission to reprint the articles from the *Proceedings of the National Academy of Sciences* (*U. S.*); The Faraday Society, for permission to reprint the articles from the *Transactions of the Faraday Society;* The Chemical Society of Japan, for permission to reprint the article from the *Bulletin of the Chemical Society of Japan;* The Physical Society of London, for permission to reprint the articles from the *Proceedings of the Physical Society;* The Royal Swedish Academy of Sciences, for permission to reprint the article from *Arkiv for Fysik;* Taylor and Francis Ltd., for permission to reprint the articles from *Molecular Physics;* The Royal Society of London, for permission to reprint the article from the *Proceedings of the Royal Society*.

The author wishes to thank:

The many authors of the papers reprinted for permission to reproduce their work; Professor Peter Lykos, Professor David Bishop, Dr. Oliver Ludwig, and Mr. Robert Wyatt, for special help; Mrs. Sally Proemmel and Miss Linda Glidden for secretarial assistance; The University Research Board of the University of Illinois for a grant which made possible production of a preliminary mimeographed edition; His wife, Jane Bolstad Parr, for much help.

Contents

Reprints

The Quantum Theory
of
Molecular Electronic Structure

I. Introduction

1 PRELIMINARY REMARKS

The object of these lectures is to provide an understanding of the progress that is being made in current theoretical research on the question that Professor Robert S. Mulliken has stated: "What are the electrons really doing in molecules?"[1]† This question defines a dynamic research field at the heart of chemistry, which may be called the quantum theory of molecular electronic structure or, for short, the quantum theory of valence.[2-5] I want to describe to you the directions in which this field is moving and to share with you my optimism concerning the ultimate value of the work, for all of chemistry.

At the very start I must call attention to the profound effect of high-speed electronic computers on the quantum theory of valence. Suddenly, and most emphatically, much more accurate descriptions of the chemical bond are becoming available. A key problem that we should try to keep in the forefront of our discussion is to what extent the traditional, simple concepts of quantum chemistry can be preserved in the transition to descriptions of much-higher accuracy.

In the remainder of Part I of these lectures, I shall characterize the problem we are dealing with more definitely and fully, review the main tools from quantum mechanics that are available for dealing with it,[6-8] and discuss in some detail the electronic structure of the helium atom. In Part II, the hydrogen molecule will be considered; this is followed by the theory of antisymmetrized wave functions; finally, I shall discuss current methods for handling small molecules. In Part III planar unsaturated organic molecules will be treated at length. In Part IV three approaches to the many-electron correlation problem will be discussed: the method of atoms in molecules, the theory of separated electron pairs, and the very recent, many-electron theory of

†Numbered references are listed together at the end of the lectures.

molecules. Finally, in Part V, I shall try to summarize the current situation in quantum chemistry. Throughout the discussion many references will be given to the current periodical literature.

I shall be saying little about molecules in course of reaction and nothing at all about molecules in condensed states; the isolated single molecule, in itself, is problem enough. The account will be my personal one.

2 NATURE OF THE PROBLEM

Our problem was solved in principle before most of us were born, with the invention of quantum mechanics in the 1920s. For, the time-independent differential equation then written down by Schrödinger,

$$\mathcal{H}\Psi = W\Psi \tag{2-1}$$

combined with the Pauli exclusion principle, have been shown to account quantitatively for a host of atomic-level facts, and there is no reason to suspect that these basic principles are not sufficient for the ordinary chemistry† of the light elements.[9,10] The only difficulty is in the mathematics: Eq. (2-1) is hard to solve for systems of chemical interest.

In Eq. (2-1), the quantity $\mathcal{H}$ is the quantum-mechanical Hamiltonian operator for the system (obtained by specified rules), and Ψ is its wave function in the stationary state of energy W. The function Ψ depends on the spatial and spin coordinates of all particles. The quantity $|\Psi|^2$ measures the probability of finding the system in a given configuration. Suitable boundary conditions (including the Pauli principle) must be imposed on Ψ. When Eq. (2-1) is satisfied, Ψ is an energy *eigenfunction* for the system, and W is the corresponding energy *eigenvalue*. For a molecule, these quantities W are the ground- and excited-state energies known to the spectroscopist. For nonstationary states, the time-dependent wave functions can be constructed by superposition of stationary-state functions, using the Schrödinger equation which includes the time $\mathcal{H}\Psi_t = (ih/2\pi)\,\partial\Psi_t/\partial t$. For an actual molecule, with given $\mathcal{H}$, the solution of Eq. (2-1) is usually attempted by some method of successive approximations. Thus solution may be accomplished by the process‡

†The term "ordinary chemistry" is meant to exclude the many important phenomena in magnetic-resonance spectroscopies that are associated with special "weak interaction" terms in the Hamiltonian (see Ref. 9); "light elements" are the atoms lighter than, say, sodium, for which relativistic effects are negligible (see Ref. 10).

‡Volume elements including spin are written $d\tau$, without spin dv.

$$W = \min_\Phi \int \Phi^* \mathcal{H} \Phi \, d\tau / \int \Phi^* \Phi \, d\tau \qquad (2\text{-}2)$$

in which mutually orthogonal trial functions Φ, satisfying the appropriate boundary conditions, are guessed again and again, until the minimum values of the indicated quotient of integrals are found. Equation (2-2), the *variational theorem*, is basic for valence theory.

For any trial function Φ we may compute the quantity

$$E = \int \Phi^* \mathcal{H} \Phi \, d\tau / \int \Phi^* \Phi \, d\tau \qquad (2\text{-}3)$$

which is the expectation value of the energy of the system in the state Φ. Since each and every measurement of the energy must give some one of the energy eigenvalues, whatever Φ is, the average energy associated with it cannot be less than the actual lowest or ground-state energy level for the system W_0, so that

$$E \geqq W_0 \qquad (2\text{-}4)$$

This gives us a procedure, called the *variational method*, for obtaining an approximate ground-state energy and wave function: Given a form for Φ, depending on one or more parameters, minimize E as a function of the parameters. With luck, the Φ so obtained will be a good approximation to the true ground-state wave function; if it is not, it may be improved by further generalization of its functional form. For an excited state, however, the energy does not, in general, converge so nicely from above upon the exact energy.[11]

A particular variational method of very great importance is the *linear variational method*, in which the trial function Φ is linearly composed from some finite set of known starting functions Φ_i

$$\Phi = \sum_{i=1}^{M} C_i \Phi_i \qquad (2\text{-}5)$$

In this case, minimization of E gives M simultaneous homogeneous linear equations for the M unknown coefficients C_j,

$$\sum_{j=1}^{M} C_j (H_{ij} - S_{ij} E) = 0 \qquad (2\text{-}6)$$

where the quantities

$$H_{ij} = H_{ji}^* = \int \Phi_i^* \mathcal{H} \Phi_j \, d\tau \qquad (2\text{-}7)$$

$$S_{ij} = S_{ji}^* = \int \Phi_i^* \Phi_j \, d\tau \qquad (2\text{-}8)$$

are numbers which can be computed from the starting Φ_i and the known $\mathcal{H}$. The condition for existence of a nontrivial solution of these equations is that the determinant of the coefficients vanish; this is the *secular equation* for the problem,

$$|(H_{ij} - S_{ij}E)| = 0 \qquad (2\text{-}9)$$

This equation for the energy has M roots E_k; these converge on the true eigenvalues W_k from above, as M is increased by addition of more independent basic functions. These equations provide the quantum-mechanical basis for the theory of resonance,[12,13]† although this will not represent our main use of them.

Of course, we are interested in many properties of a molecule other than its energy, and a wave function that gives a good energy may not predict another property very well. But, as the wave function becomes more apropos the energy, it will ultimately become good for other properties as well.‡ And computation of any desired property, once the wave function is known, is much easier than the determination of the wave function itself.

Traditional and modern perturbation methods can also be employed to solve Eq. (2-1); examples abound in the literature of special molecular properties but are rare in ordinary valence theory.

The wave functions Ψ depend on both electronic and nuclear coordinates. Born and Oppenheimer have shown that, owing to the smallness of the ratio of the mass of an electron to that of any nucleus, one may, to a good approximation, proceed in a simplified way.[14] The wave function Ψ for each molecular state may be taken to be a product $\Psi_n\Psi_e$ of a part describing the nuclear motions Ψ_n, which depends on nuclear coordinates only, and a part describing the electronic motions Ψ_e, which depends on electronic coordinates and nuclear coordinates. The latter, Ψ_e, may be determined by solving an electronic Schrödinger equation

$$\mathcal{H}_e\Psi_e = W_e\Psi_e \qquad (2\text{-}10)$$

where $\mathcal{H}_e = (T_e + V_{ee} + V_{ne})$, and hence Ψ_e, depends parametrically on the nuclear geometry through the dependence on that geometry of the nuclear-electron potential-energy operator V_{ne}. The former, Ψ_n, can be found by subsequently solving an equation $\mathcal{H}_n\Psi_n = W\Psi_n$, where $\mathcal{H}_n = T_n + V_{nn} + W_e$ con-

---

†The Φ_i represent the various *contributing structures*, Φ the actual molecule, and the *resonance energy* is the energy increment $H_{11} - E_1$, where H_{11} is the smallest of the H_{ii} and E_1 is the lowest root of Eq. (2-9).

‡Of course, one should always realize that an approximate wave function may not be as good for one property as for another.

tains the electronic energy W_e as an effective potential; here, W most definitely is the total energy.

The problem of determining the various possible Ψ_e and W_e (or $W_e + V_{nn}$) is our central concern; the rest is the familiar problem of rotational-vibrational-translational motions of nuclei. To quote the variational equivalent of Eq. (2-10), our problem is to find, for various fixed nuclear configurations of a molecule, electronic wave functions Φ_e that minimize the expression†

$$E_e = \int \Phi_e^* \mathcal{H}_e \Phi_e \, d\tau_e / \int \Phi_e^* \Phi_e \, d\tau_e \tag{2-11}$$

Since $\mathcal{H}_e$ can ordinarily be written upon inspection, the problem thus stated may be viewed as a purely mathematical one. From this way of looking at valence, we may see that we must, for each nuclear configuration of a molecule of interest to us, (1) find suitable trial functions Φ_e; (2) calculate E_e and other properties of interest; and (3) change the parameters or otherwise change Φ_e so as to make E_e smaller, and iterate, until a satisfactory convergence has been obtained.

If one aspires after an accurate description of some complex molecular-electronic structure, this is the threefold nature of the problem.

Step (1) requires good chemical intuition or considerable quantum-chemical experience if extensive iteration is to be avoided; if one is willing to undergo the inconvenience of considerable iteration, one can tolerate a wider variety of choices at the first stage. Step (2) is mathematics pure but not simple; it may be exceedingly difficult and ponderous for even a very simple molecule. (As we shall see, the worst troubles come from the electron-electron repulsion terms V_{ee} in $\mathcal{H}_e$.) Step (3) is a matter of patience, systematization, and working time.

A remark should be made at this point about a fundamental dichotomy that exists in theories of valence, involving *purely theoretical* methods on the one hand, and *semiempirical* methods on the other. If one proceeds simply as described above, every molecular property will be computed in terms of the fundamental constants of physics. Indeed, I am sure that we would agree that that is the goal toward which we should strive. The enormous difficulty of carrying this task to fruition means, however, that alternative methods always will be useful, wherein some experimental data on molecules are used to ''calibrate'' a calculation. Such methods are called semiempirical. Carefully used, their value for predicting unknown properties of molecules can be very great.

In later section, we shall consider both theoretical and semiempirical methods. For small molecules, our emphasis will be on the first, for large molecules, on the second. But before we are done, we shall return to the dichotomy.[15]

---

†In subsequent applications subscripts e will sometimes be omitted.

3 THE HELIUM ATOM

To obtain a more concrete idea of the nature of the problem we are up against, we may consider the situation for simple atoms. Atoms, after all, are what molecules are made of, and any difficulty we find for atoms surely will persist for molecules. Everyone is familiar with the 1s, 2s, $2p_x$, $2p_y$, $2p_z$ orbitals of a hydrogen atom and with the fact that one can describe the helium atom by saying that two electrons occupy a 1s orbital with opposite spins. But are such descriptions precise, or sufficient for chemical purposes?

For hydrogen itself, or indeed for any light one-electron atom with nuclear charge Z, the simple orbital description is accurate; the Schrödinger equation [Eq. (2-10)] can be solved exactly, giving the well-known *hydrogen-like orbitals*

$$\psi_{n\ell m}(r,\theta,\phi) = N_{n\ell}(2Zr/na_0)^{\ell} L_{n+\ell}^{2\ell+1}(2Zr/na_0) \exp(-Zr/na_0) Y_{\ell m}(\theta,\phi) \tag{3-1}$$

Here, $N_{n\ell}$ is a normalizing factor, which we need not bother to write down, the $L_k^p(x)$ are associated Laguerre functions of the indicated argument and indices, the $Y_{\ell m}(\theta,\phi)$ are surface harmonics of the indicated arguments and indices, and r, θ, ϕ are spherical coordinates of the electron relative to the nucleus (in the Born-Oppenheimer approximation—more accurately, the motion is about the center of gravity of the system). The quantity a_0 is the atomic unit of length ($h^2/4\pi^2me^2 = 0.53$ A, where m is the electron mass) and n, ℓ, and m are quantum numbers, all integral, with $0 < n$, $0 \leqq \ell \leqq n-1$, $-\ell \leqq m \leqq \ell$. The electron also has a spin function, but, on the assumption that the Hamiltonian is spin free (which we make),[16] this merely multiplies the space function of Eq. (3-1).

The functions of Eq. (3-1) are eigenfunctions for the hydrogen-like atom associated with its *discrete* energy levels, in the atomic unit of energy (e^2/a_0)

$$W_n = -Z^2/2n^2 \tag{3-2}$$

There also are some possible positive energies, indeed an infinite number of them, the *continuum* levels, with corresponding wave functions that can be written down. The set of all the eigenfunctions for all the states, discrete and continuous, of a hydrogen-like atom of a given charge, is a complete orthonormal set of functions in the space of one electron.†

The orbitals of Eq. (3-1) are employed a great deal in quantum chemistry. The first several of them are, with a_0 taken as the unit of length,

---

†Completeness of a set of functions means that an arbitrary function of the same variables may be linearly expressed in terms of members of the set.

$$(1s) = \psi_{100} = (Z^3/\pi)^{\frac{1}{2}} \exp(-Zr)$$

$$(2s) = \psi_{200} = (Z^3/32\pi)^{\frac{1}{2}} (2 - Zr) \exp(-Zr/2)$$

$$(2p_0) = \psi_{210} = (Z^3/32\pi)^{\frac{1}{2}} (Zr) \exp(-Zr/2) \cos\theta \qquad (3\text{-}3)$$

$$(2p_1) = \psi_{211} = (Z^3/64\pi)^{\frac{1}{2}} (Zr) \exp(-Zr/2) \sin\theta \exp(i\phi)$$

$$(2p_{-1}) = \psi_{21-1} = (Z^3/64\pi)^{\frac{1}{2}} (Zr) \exp(-Zr/2) \sin\theta \exp(-i\phi)$$

The radial functions for these orbitals are powers of r times exponentials except for the 2s function, in which the radial factor has a node at $r = 2/Z$, which may be thought of as a consequence of the orthogonality of 2s to 1s. For many purposes it is convenient to use what is called the Slater 2s function,

$$(2s)^{\text{Slater}} = (Z^3/96\pi)^{\frac{1}{2}} (Zr) \exp(-Zr/2) \qquad (3\text{-}4)$$

This is not orthogonal to the 1s function, however, which is wise to keep in mind. More generally, we define the generalized *Slater orbitals* by the formula

$$S_{n\ell m}(r,\theta,\phi) = A_n r^{n-1} \exp(-\zeta r) Y_{\ell m}(\theta,\phi) \qquad (3\text{-}5)$$

With $A_n = (2\zeta)^{n+\frac{1}{2}}[(2n)!]^{-\frac{1}{2}}$, this is normalized to 1 if the $Y_{\ell m}(\theta,\phi)$ are. The parameter ζ is an *orbital exponent* and need not be identical with an effective nuclear charge divided by n; the parameter n is an effective total quantum number and need not be integral. The Slater 1s, $2p_0$, $2p_1$, $2p_{-1}$ orbitals are identical with hydrogen-like orbitals of appropriate Z values. The set of all orbitals of the form of Eq. (3-5), with n, ℓ, and m restricted to integral values but with all possible positive ζ values, is a complete (although not orthogonal) set of functions in the space of one electron.

Let us turn now to the problem of the electronic structure of the ground state of the helium atom. A properly antisymmetrized wave function for the two electrons will be a symmetrical space part times an antisymmetrical spin part, of the form $(\alpha_1\beta_2-\alpha_2\beta_1)/\sqrt{2}$, and we need consider only the former.† A reasonable guess would be that both electrons occupy a 1s orbital,

$$\Phi(1,2) = 1s(1)1s(2) = (1s)^2 \qquad (3\text{-}6)$$

where, because of screening, we anticipate some ζ value less than 2.

† The spin part integrates to unity when the Hamiltonian is spin free. We could also have an antisymmetrical space part times a symmetrical spin part, which indeed we do have for certain excited states of the atom.

To find out how good a description of helium this wave function provides, one needs to compute E from Eq. (2-11), with the Hamiltonian operator (in atomic units)

$$\mathcal{H} = T_e + V_{ne} + V_{ee} = \left[-\frac{1}{2}\nabla_1^2 - \frac{1}{2}\nabla_2^2\right] - [(2/r_1) + (2/r_2)] + (1/r_{12})$$

$$= \left[-\frac{1}{2}\nabla_1^2 - (\zeta/r_1)\right] + \left[-\frac{1}{2}\nabla_2^2 - (\zeta/r_2)\right] \qquad (3\text{-}7)$$

$$+ (\zeta - 2)\,[(1/r_1) + (1/r_2)] + (1/r_{12})$$

This gives, making use of the fact that (1s) is a normalized eigenfunction of the operator $-(1/2)\nabla^2 - (\zeta/r)$ with eigenvalue $-(1/2)\zeta^2$,

$$E = \iint 1s(1)1s(2)\mathcal{H}1s(1)1s(2)\,dv(1)\,dv(2)$$

$$= 2[-(1/2)\zeta^2] + 2(\zeta - 2)\int 1s(1)1s(1)(1/r_1)\,dv(1) \qquad (3\text{-}8)$$

$$+ \iint 1s(1)1s(1)(1/r_{12})1s(2)1s(2)\,dv(1)\,dv(2)$$

The first integral is easy:

$$\int 1s(1)1s(1)(1/r_1)\,dv(1) = (\zeta^3/\pi)4\pi\int_0^\infty r\exp(-2\zeta r)\,dr = \zeta \qquad (3\text{-}9)$$

The second can be obtained by first performing the integration over electron 2, and by employing the facts that the classical electrostatic potential outside a uniform spherical shell of charge is just what it would be if that charge were localized at its center and that the potential everywhere inside such a shell has the value at the surface. Thus

$$\int 1s(2)1s(2)(1/r_{12})\,dv(2) = 4\zeta^3\left[\int_{r_1}^\infty r_2\exp(-2\zeta r_2)\,dr_2 + (1/r_1)\int_0^{r_1} r_2^2\exp(-2\zeta r_2)\,dr_2\right] \qquad (3\text{-}10)$$

and

$$\iint 1s(1)1s(1)(1/r_{12})1s(2)1s(2)\,dv(1)\,dv(2)$$

$$= 16\zeta^6\int_0^\infty r_1^2\exp(-2\zeta r_1)\,dr_1\left[\int_{r_1}^\infty r_2\exp(-2\zeta r_2)\,dr_2 + (1/r_1)\int_0^{r_1} r_2^2\exp(-2\zeta r_2)\,dr_2\right]$$

$$= 32\zeta^6\int_0^\infty r_1^2\exp(-2\zeta r_1)\,dr_1\int_{r_1}^\infty r_2\exp(-2\zeta r_2)\,dr_2 = \zeta\int_0^\infty s^2e^{-s}\,ds\int_s^\infty te^{-t}\,dt$$

$$= \zeta\int_0^\infty s^2e^{-s}[(1 + s)e^{-s}]\,ds = \zeta[(1/8)2! + (1/16)3!] = (5/8)\zeta \qquad (3\text{-}11)$$

Equation (3-8) then gives

$$E = -\zeta^2 + 2(\zeta - 2)\zeta + (5/8)\zeta = \zeta^2 - (27/8)\zeta \qquad (3\text{-}12)$$

Upon differentiating this expression with respect to ζ and setting the result equal to zero, in accordance with the variational method, we obtain

$$\zeta_{best} = 27/16 = 1.6875 \qquad (3\text{-}13)$$

and

$$E_{best} = -\zeta^2_{best} = -2.848 \text{ au} \qquad (3\text{-}14)$$

The experimental value of the energy is -2.904 au, so this simple description of the electronic structure gives 98 per cent of the true energy. Not bad, so we tend to accept the description and say, giving a physical interpretation to Eq. (3-13): In the helium atom, each of the electrons occupies a hydrogen-like atomic orbital of effective charge about 1.7, which is the true nuclear charge 2.0 less a correction 0.3 for the "screening" of one electron by the other.

That will suffice for most qualitative and many quantitative purposes. However, we are interested in chemical processes, and chemical processes entail *changes* from one electronic environment to another, involving energy increments of the order of magnitude of a few kilocalories per mole. What we should look at is the absolute error in the above energy, to get a feeling for whether our accuracy is at the level that will make chemical predictions possible. Computing this we get a jolt: $2.904 - 2.848 = 0.056$ au is no less than 0.056×27 ev/au $\times$ 23 kcal/ev $\approx$ 35 kcal per mole. Not so encouraging after all!†

The essential weakness in Eq. (3-6) is the assumption that probability distributions for the two electrons simply multiply, which implies that each sees only an average field of the other. In fact, the $(1/r_{12})$ term in Eq. (3-7) implies rather that the electronic motions are *correlated* in a detailed fashion—when one electron is in a particular place, the other will tend to avoid that place. An accurate description, precisely agreeing with experiment, can indeed be obtained by introducing r_{12} itself explicitly into the variation function[17]; this was obtained long ago by Hylleraas. The mathematics of this method is most unwieldy, however, and nobody has succeeded in extending it to systems containing more than two electrons.[18]

Of considerably more interest are improvements that preserve the orbital concept. First, one may observe that the above treatment of the functional form of Eq. (3-6) does not fully test that form, for the specific Eq. (3-3) has been used for the orbital 1s—the simple exponential in r might not be as good

---

†This exaggerates our difficulties somewhat because, in chemical processes, 1s shells of atoms tend to remain sensibly unchanged.

as some more general form. We might, for example, use an ns Slater orbital, where n is not an integer. If we do so, we obtain, with $n = 0.955$, an energy of -2.854 au,[19] an appreciable improvement. Much more generally and with patience, one may numerically determine the best-possible single space orbital ϕ, in the simple-product description

$$\Phi(1,2) = \phi(1)\,\phi(2) \tag{3-15}$$

with no restrictions whatever on the functional form of ϕ. This, the Hartree-Fock method, gives -2.862 au for the energy,[20] still in error by 0.042 au, or 1.1 ev, or 26 kcal. For reasons that should be clear from the foregoing, this error is called the *correlation energy* of the atom; it is, you see, on the order of 1 ev for one electron pair. Table 1 summarizes these calculations on helium, plus those described in the following:

To begin to bring correlation effects into account, using orbitals, we must relax the restriction that the two-electron function is a simple product. Thus, if we use the still simple Eckart form

$$\Phi(1,2) = 1s(1)1s'(2) + 1s'(1)1s(2) = 1s1s' \tag{3-16}$$

where 1s and 1s′ are hydrogen orbitals of orbital exponents ζ and ζ', we get -2.876 au for the energy [the energy formula is a straightforward modification of Eq. (3-12)],[21] with an error of only 18 kcal.[22] Generalizing further in this particular way, including many products of functions of r_1 and r_2 only, there results the "S limit" of -2.879 au,[23] in error by 15 kcal/mole. Comparing this result with the Hartree-Föck result already quoted, we may say that, in helium, the *radial correlation energy* is $100(26 - 15)/26 = 41$ per cent of the total correlation energy.

Such a very complicated function of r_1 and r_2 allows one electron to be close to the nucleus when the other is far out. But it still neglects *angular correlation energy*, i.e., when one electron is on one side of the nucleus the other electron is more likely than not on the other side. The exact function depends on r_1, r_2, and r_{12}, and it can be expanded in a series[24]

$$\Psi(1,2) = \sum_{\ell=0}^{\infty} \Psi_\ell(r_1,r_2)P_\ell(\cos\theta_{12}) \tag{3-17}$$

where θ_{12} is the angle subtended at the nucleus by the radius vectors from the nucleus to electrons 1 and 2; the S limit just described represents only the $\ell = 0$ component of this expansion.

The higher terms in Eq. (3-17), which we denote by P, D, F, etc. (with S for the first term), can be brought into play by admixing with ss′-type terms one or more functions $(p)^2 = p_x(1)p_x(2) + p_y(1)p_y(2) + p_z(1)p_z(2)$, $(d)^2$, $(f)^2$,

TABLE 1
Some variation functions for the normal helium atom

Function[a]	Reference	Energy, au	Δ, au	Δ, ev	Δ, kcal/mole
1. Exact solution[b]	17	−2.9037	0	0	0
2. $(1s)^2$ with $\zeta = 1.6875$	Eq. (3-14) of text	−2.8477	0.0560	1.5	35
3. $(ns)^2$ with $\zeta = 1.61162$, $n = 0.955$	19	−2.8542	0.0495	1.3	31
4. $(\phi)^2$ Hartree-Fock	20	−2.8617	0.0421	1.1	26
5. $(1s1s')$ with $\zeta = 1.188530$, $\zeta' = 2.173171$	21	−2.8757	0.0281	0.8	18
6. S limit (no angular dependence)	23	−2.8790	0.0247	0.7	15
7. $(1s1s') + (2p)^2 + (3d)^2 + (4f)^2$	25, 26	−2.8974	0.0063	0.2	4
8. $(ss') + (p)^2 + (d)^2 + (f)^2$	26	−2.8979	0.0058	0.2	4
9. S (ten terms) + P (six terms) + D (three terms) + F (one term)	27	−2.9028	0.0009	0.0	1
10. Thirty-five terms, including G	28	−2.9032	0.0005	0.0	1

[a]The + sign in functions 7 through 9 indicates "mixed linearly with." Function 6 is the best function obtainable of the form $\Phi(r_1, r_2)$. Functions 9 and 10 are of the same form as functions 7 and 8, or Eq. (3-17) of the text, with the indicated number of terms of each type.

[b]The "exact solution" is that for the nonrelativistic Schrödinger equation in the Born-Oppenheimer approximation. The experimental value of the energy is −2.9033 au, which indicates the chemically negligible magnitude of the relativistic plus Born-Oppenheimer corrections. See Ref. 10.

and so on. Thus one could try, using Slater radial functions,

$$\Phi(1,2) = C_1(ss') + C_2(p)^2 + C_3(d)^2 + C_4(f)^2 + \cdots \tag{3-18}$$

where (ss') stands for a "split-s" function like Eq. (3-16). The result with one term of each of the indicated types and including f orbitals is −2.897 au if the principal quantum numbers are taken to be integral,[25] −2.898 au if they are allowed to be nonintegral,[26] in error only 0.2 ev or 4 kcal/mole. More elaborately, one can go all out to get the successive terms to full accuracy; by mixing ten S terms, six P terms, three D terms, and one F term, Nesbet and Watson have indeed reduced the error to just 1 kcal/mole[27]; by mixing a total of 35 terms, Weiss has done even better.[28]

This process is our first example of what is called *superposition of configurations* or *configuration interaction;* it will give the description of the atomic electronic structure to any desired accuracy. And, as we shall see, this method of improving wave functions may be extended to many-electron systems, in contrast with the explicit introduction of r_{ij} coordinates into the trial wave functions.

As has recently been discussed by Arai and Lykos,[29] correlation energy has both kinetic and potential energy components, related in accord with the virial theorem[30]

$$W_{corr} = T_{corr} + V_{corr} = -T_{corr} = \frac{1}{2}V_{corr} \tag{3-19}$$

The concept of correlation energy is an important one, of broad generality.[31] We shall make frequent allusions to it.

II. Small Molecules

4 THE HYDROGEN MOLECULE

We could now direct our discussion to many-electron atoms,[20,28,32-38] but instead let us proceed immediately to molecules.[39]

The hydrogen molecule-ion we certainly would expect to be favorable for calculation, for it has but one electron. Indeed, the H_2^+ Schrödinger equation in the Born-Oppenheimer approximation (which, in these lectures, we assume, henceforth, for all molecules) has been solved exactly. However, there seems little possibility of use of the rather complicated orbitals in elliptical coordinates thus obtained for other molecules, although attempts have been made,[40] and the direct integration of the Schrödinger equation for other molecular species would appear to be an unprofitable enterprise.

Many less elaborate treatments of H_2^+ have been carried out[41]; most of them use some kind of atomic-orbital approximation, and some have important bearing on valence theory for large molecules. Here we shall merely mention that the lowest state for the electron in H_2^+ has a wave function that can be written approximately as the sum of 1s orbitals on the two hydrogen nuclei, in normalized form

$$\phi(1) = \frac{1s_A(1) + 1s_B(1)}{\sqrt{2(1 + S)}} \tag{4-1}$$

where S is the *overlap integral*

$$\int 1s_A(1) 1s_B(1)\, dv(1)$$

This description is certainly correct for large distances, but, at the equilibrium distance $2a_0$, it accounts for only 81 per cent of the binding energy of the molecule relative to a proton plus a hydrogen atom, even if the orbital exponent is varied. This means that, again, higher atomic orbitals must be mixed in before high accuracy is obtained—call it configuration interaction, if you will.

The hydrogen molecule is perhaps more appropriate for our first detailed study, since it is the prototype for the normal covalent bond, the most essential link of all chemistry. We shall do well to ponder this case, for even *it* is "not as simple as some people seem to think."[42]

A comprehensive annotated bibliography of more than 40 calculations on the hydrogen molecule was published in 1960 by McLean, Weiss, and Yoshimine,[43] so we may be quite selective in our discussion. We shall consider, in turn, calculations in elliptical coordinates, calculations using atomic orbitals on the two atoms, and calculations in spherical coordinates at the molecular center. Table 2 presents the numerical results to be discussed.

TABLE 2
Some variation functions for the normal hydrogen molecule

Function	Ref.	D, ev[a]	Δ, ev	Δ, kcal/mole
Exact solution[b]	45	4.75	0	0
Elliptical coordinates,[c] no r_{12}	45	4.69	0.1	1
Hartree-Fock[d]	45	3.63	1.1	26
Heitler-London, $\zeta = 1.00$	Eq. (4-6)	3.20	1.6	36
Heitler-London, $\zeta = 1.166$	Eq. (4-6)	3.78	1.0	22
Simple LCAO, $\zeta = 1.00$	Eq. (4-7)	2.65	2.1	48
Simple LCAO, $\zeta = 1.197$	Eq. (4-7)	3.49	1.3	29
Weinbaum, $\zeta = 1.193$[e]	50	4.02	0.7	17
Configuration interaction, Slater-type orbitals[f]	43	4.55	0.2	5
One-center, Slater-type orbitals[g]	55, 56	4.31	0.4	10
One-center, special Laguerre radial factors[g]	57	4.39	0.4	8

[a]Energy at the equilibrium distance 1.4 a_0 or the predicted equilibrium distance, relative to that of two separated hydrogen atoms.

[b]Solution of nonrelativistic Schrödinger equation in the Born-Oppenheimer approximation, using Eq. (4-2). The actual computed energy was −1.1744 au at the equilibrium distance 1.4 a_0, corresponding to a dissociation energy D of 4.7467 ev, the experimental value being 4.7466. The Born-Oppenheimer correction amounts to 0.014 ev, however, which destroys the good agreement. See Ref. 45.

[c]Eq. (4-3) of text.

[d]Eq. (4-5) of text.

[e]Eq. (4-10) of text.

[f]See text. 1s, 2s, and 2p orbitals were employed.

[g]See Table 3 for details.

As with helium, the wave function for the ground state is a product of a symmetric space factor and an antisymmetric spin factor, and we consider only the former. The obvious approach, and the one that has given the best results, is to employ elliptical coordinates with the nuclei as foci to describe the electronic positions relative to the nuclei. If we take the coordinates for an electron

$$\xi = (r_A + r_B)/R, \qquad \eta = (r_A - r_B)/R$$

and an angle ϕ about the internuclear axis, we may write a trial variation function for hydrogen in the form

$$\Phi(1,2) = \sum_{pqrst} A_{pqrst}(\xi_1^p\eta_1^q\xi_2^r\eta_2^s + \xi_1^r\eta_1^s\xi_2^p\eta_2^q)\exp[-\alpha(\xi_1 + \xi_2)]r_{12}^t \tag{4-2}$$

and expect to get the correct answer if we include enough terms. Using a 13-term function of this form, James and Coolidge[44] way back in 1933 came within 0.02 ev of the full experimental binding energy, 4.75 ev (relative to two hydrogen atoms), at the equilibrium distance 1.4 a_0. Kolos and Roothaan[45] have very recently extended the expansion to 50 terms, and they obtain 4.75 precisely. These calculations give confidence that the Schrödinger quantum mechanics will be sufficient for a quantitative account of the electronic structure of simple molecules.

One can avoid the r_{12} terms in Eq. (4-2) by using in place of it an expansion

$$\begin{aligned}\Phi(1,2) = \sum_{pqrsm} & B_{pqrsm}(\xi_1^p\eta_1^q\xi_2^r\eta_2^s + \xi_1^r\eta_1^s\xi_2^p\eta_2^q) \\ & \times \exp[-\alpha(\xi_1 + \xi_2)]\cos[m(\phi_1 - \phi_2)]\end{aligned} \tag{4-3}$$

With 40 terms in such a series, Kolos and Roothaan obtain 4.69 ev for the binding energy, in error by only 1.4 kcal per mole.[45] Alternatively, one can employ a slightly different and more general form, which offers certain mathematical advantages:

$$\begin{aligned}\Phi(1,2) &= \sum_{ij} C_{ij}[\chi_a^i(1)\chi_b^j(2) + \chi_b^j(1)\chi_a^i(2)] \\ \chi_a(i) &= \exp(-\delta_a\xi_i - \alpha_a\eta_i)\xi_i^{n_a}\eta_i^{m_a}\exp(i\nu_a\phi_i)[(\xi_i^2 - 1)(1 - \eta_i^2)]^{\frac{1}{2}|\nu_a|}\end{aligned} \tag{4-4}$$

where a typical orbital $\chi_a(i)$, based on nucleus A, has the indicated many-parameter form. Harris[46] and Davidson[47] have recently reported calculations with such variation functions, on excited as well as ground states, at many internuclear distances. Especially interesting is the work of Davidson, in which conclusive evidence is presented that the first ${}^1\Sigma_g^+$ excited state of H_2 has a potential curve displaying a double minimum.

These calculations are difficult and tedious. The integrals that arise are hard, and they are many; just the organization of the computations is a major undertaking.

As a by-product of their calculations, Kolos and Roothaan did not find it difficult to extract the best wave function for hydrogen of the Hartree-Fock form

$$\Phi(1,2) = \phi(1)\phi(2) \tag{4-5}$$

with the molecular orbital ϕ expanded in elliptical coordinate components.[45] The energy found is 3.64 ev, showing that the correlation energy for hydrogen at the equilibrium internuclear distance is 1.1 ev, just what it was for helium—a result that we may hope represents more than just a coincidence.

What about the use of atomic orbitals for this problem, which we may anticipate would provide a method more easily extended to complex molecules than the use of complicated functions in elliptical coordinates? This is as old as quantum chemistry itself, for the very 1928-Heitler-London treatment of the hydrogen molecule, using 1s orbitals on each atom, may be thought of as the birth of the field.[48]

Given the orbitals $1s_A$ and $1s_B$ on the two atoms, let us say that, if each has, in general,[49] an effective charge ζ, we can immediately write down a wave function that would be accurate at very large internuclear distances, just as we did in Eq. (4-1) for H_2^+. This is the Heitler-London or *valence bond* (VB) wave function

$$\Phi_{VB}(1,2) = \frac{1s_A(1)1s_B(2) + 1s_B(1)1s_A(2)}{\sqrt{2(1 + S^2)}} \tag{4-6}$$

Alternatively, we could read Eq. (4-1) as telling us what sort of orbital each of our two electrons will be expected to occupy. This gives us a *molecular orbital* (MO) description of the form of Eq. (4-5) but with ϕ approximated in a certain way,

$$\Phi_{MO}(1,2) = \frac{[1s_A(1) + 1s_B(1)][1s_A(2) + 1s_B(2)]}{2(1 + S)} \tag{4-7}$$

More precisely we call this last the LCAO-MO wave function, indicating that each molecular orbital (MO) has been assumed to be a *linear combination of atomic orbitals* (LCAO).

Of these two descriptions, the valence bond one is a little better, being in error by 36 kcal/mole if ζ is set equal to 1, 22 kcal/mole if ζ is varied; the molecular-orbital function falls short by 48 kcal with $\zeta = 1$, by 29 kcal if ζ is varied. Neither description is really very good, although both do qualitatively account for binding.

We can readily see how to get a better description using just these same orbitals $1s_A$ and $1s_B$. We might emphasize the physical meaning of the terms that enter Eqs. (4-6) and (4-7) by introducing the notations

$$\Phi_{COVALENT} = 1s_A(1)1s_B(2) + 1s_B(1)1s_A(2)$$
$$\Phi_{IONIC} = 1s_A(1)1s_A(2) + 1s_B(1)1s_B(2) \qquad (4\text{-}8)$$

Then Eqs. (4-6) and (4-7) become

$$\Phi_{VB} = A\Phi_{COVALENT}$$
$$\Phi_{MO} = B(\Phi_{COVALENT} + \Phi_{IONIC}) \qquad (4\text{-}9)$$

and a better description than both is immediately apparent,

$$\Phi_{BETTER} = C\Phi_{COVALENT} + D\Phi_{IONIC} \qquad (4\text{-}10)$$

where C and D are determined by the linear variational method. In this way, Weinbaum[50] found an energy in error by only 16 kcal/mole, with C/D equal to 3.9. The valence-bond function may be said to contain too little *ionic character*, whereas the molecular orbital function contains too much.

We can arrive at Eq. (4-10) by another path, making use of the molecular-orbital description for the "doubly excited" configuration in which the two electrons have been promoted from the *bonding* molecular orbital of Eq. (4-1) to the *antibonding* molecular orbital

$$\phi'(1) = \frac{1s_A(1) - 1s_B(1)}{\sqrt{2(1 - S)}} \qquad (4\text{-}11)$$

The two-electron wave function is

$$\Phi'_{MO}(1,2) = \frac{[1s_A(1) - 1s_B(1)][1s_A(2) - 1s_B(2)]}{2(1 - S)} \qquad (4\text{-}12)$$

This function may be mixed linearly with the simple molecular orbital function of Eq. (4-7); the result is

$$\Phi_{BETTER} = E\Phi_{MO} + F\Phi'_{MO} \qquad (4\text{-}13)$$

But by just a little arithmetic it can be verified that this function is identical with that of Eq. (4-10): Starting from a given set of atomic orbitals, *the valence-bond method, including ionic terms, is equivalent to the molecular-orbital method including configuration interaction.*

Thus there is no difference between the valence-bond method and the molecular-orbital method, if each is fully refined. If one is going to the full limit in a given problem, the molecular-orbital method is almost always more convenient for the simple mathematical reason that the basic functions in the method (ϕ and ϕ' in this case) are orthogonal, whereas the basic functions in the valence-bond method ($1s_A1s_A$, $1s_A1s_B$, $1s_B1s_B$, in this case) are not.

Of course, there is a great deal of difference, mathematically and physically, between a simple-valence-bond description and a simple-molecular-orbital one, and one of our problems is to develop experience with these alternative approximations to the true situation. The role of the overlap integral in the two formulations provides a remarkable first example of the contrasts that exist. To see what this is, we require energy formulas. The Hamiltonian operator is

$$\mathcal{H} = -\frac{1}{2}(\nabla_1^2 + \nabla_2^2) - [(1/r_{A1}) + (1/r_{B1}) + (1/r_{A2}) + (1/r_{B2})] + (1/r_{12}) \tag{4-14}$$

For the valence-bond energy, including the nuclear-nuclear repulsion energy, from Eqs. (2-11) and (4-6) and taking $\zeta = 1$ for simplicity, this gives

$$E_{VB} = 2W_H + \frac{1}{R} + \frac{(aa|bb) - 2(a|bb) + (ab|ab) - 2S(a|ab)}{1 + S^2} \tag{4-15}$$

where

$$(aa|bb) = \iint 1s_A(1)1s_A(1)(1/r_{12})1s_B(2)1s_B(2)\,dv(1)\,dv(2) \tag{4-16}$$

$$(ab|ab) = \iint 1s_A(1)1s_B(1)(1/r_{12})1s_A(2)1s_B(2)\,dv(1)\,dv(2) \tag{4-17}$$

$$(a|bb) = \int 1s_B(1)1s_B(1)(1/r_{A1})\,dv(1) \tag{4-18}$$

$$(a|ab) = \int 1s_A(1)1s_B(1)(1/r_{A1})\,dv(1) \tag{4-19}$$

Similarly, the molecular-orbital energy, from Eqs. (2-11) and (4-7) and again taking $\zeta = 1$, is

$$E_{MO} = 2W_H + \frac{1}{R} + \frac{(aa|aa) + (aa|bb) + 2(ab|ab) + 4(aa|ab)}{2(1 + S)^2} - \frac{2(a|aa) + 2(a|ab)}{1 + S} \tag{4-20}$$

where

$$(aa|aa) = \iint 1s_A(1)1s_A(1)(1/r_{12})1s_A(2)1s_A(2)\,dv(1)\,dv(2) \tag{4-21}$$

$$(aa|ab) = \iint 1s_A(1)1s_A(1)(1/r_{12})1s_A(2)1s_B(2)\,dv(1)\,dv(2) \qquad (4\text{-}22)$$

$$(a|aa) = \int 1s_A(1)1s_A(1)(1/r_{A1})\,dv(1) \qquad (4\text{-}23)$$

All the integrals of Eqs. (4-16) through (4-19) and Eqs. (4-21) to (4-23) are inherently positive. Their evaluation is not easy, but it can be accomplished.[51]

The same general kinds of integrals enter the two formulas, nuclear-attraction integrals and electronic-repulsion integrals, but in quite different ways. In the valence-bond formula, the term responsible for the considerable stabilization energy relative to two separated hydrogen atoms is the term $-2S(a|ab)$, proportional to the overlap integral S and the energy of attraction of an electron in the overlap distribution $1s_A 1s_B$ for a nucleus. [The only other negative term in Eq. (4-15), $-2(a|bb)$, gives little binding.] Thus, one might generally suppose that the binding energy would be proportional to S and would be the larger, other things being equal, the larger S was. And, of course, arguments of this kind have been extraordinarily fruitful for chemistry.[12,52] In the molecular-orbital formula, on the other hand, S appears most innocuously just in energy denominators; the nuclear attraction terms (a|aa) and (a|ab) confer the stability.

The various components in the binding energy for hydrogen (and other molecules) have recently been analyzed in considerable detail by Ruedenberg,[53] who has shown that an important factor in binding that often has been overlooked is the pile-up of charge at the nuclei themselves, which accompanies atomic orbital contraction in molecule formation (note the $\zeta > 1$ values in Table 2).

But, to return to the problem of getting an *accurate* description of hydrogen using orbitals at the two atoms, it is clear that orbitals beyond the 1s level must be introduced before a truly good description can result. Because of the difficulty of integral evaluation, little progress was made on this problem until very recently. McLean, Weiss, and Yoshimine, in 1960, finally did obtain a dissociation energy of 4.55 ev,[43] in error only 5 kcal/mole, using a many-configuration wave function constructed from 1s, 2s, $2p_x$, $2p_y$, and $2p_z$ orbitals on the two atoms. Higher accuracy than this is certainly attainable by this method, although it will require evaluation of some difficult integrals involving d orbitals.

To circumvent the integrals problem, one possibility is to expand the molecular wave function not in orbitals centered on the *two* nuclei but in orbitals centered at *one* of them, or at the molecular center.[19] The first idea has not yet been fully explored,[54] but the second has. The results are interesting and encouraging; those of two sets of authors are summarized in Table 3.

Slater orbitals of nonintegral principal quantum numbers can be employed (integral n's give appreciably poorer results in this case); this was done by Joy and Parr in 1958.[55,56] With a seven-term function of the form

$$\Phi(1,2) = C_1(ss') + C_2(s''s''') + C_3(s^{iv}d_0) + C_4(s^{v}g_0) + C_5(p_0)^2 + C_6(p_1p_{-1}) + C_7(p_0'f_0) \qquad (4\text{-}24)$$

where the z axis is the internuclear axis, they obtained a dissociation energy of 4.31 ev, better than had been obtained up to that time using orbital functions. Hagstrom and Shull[57] a bit later obtained 4.36 ev by the same general method, but employed a much larger basic set of orbitals in which the radial factors are the functions (unnormalized)

$$r^{\ell} L_{n+\ell+1}^{2\ell+2}(2\eta r) \exp(-\eta r)$$

Here η is a scale factor, the same for all orbitals; these functions are a nice complete orthonormal set of functions in the variable r, and integrals involving them are reasonably easy.

These two calculations gave results in remarkable agreement, even for the various components of the energy, as is shown in Table 3. If we acknowledge the possibility that methods might be found to calculate residual errors in calculations done in this way, we may be optimistic about the use of such one-center-expansion methods elsewhere.

TABLE 3
One-Center-Variation Functions for the Normal Hydrogen Molecule

Term type[a]	Energy increment, au		Estimated exact[d]
	Joy-Parr[b]	Hagstrom-Shull[c]	
ss'	−1.0430	−1.0441	−1.0440
sd_0	−0.0798	−0.0782	−0.0805
sg_0	−0.0109	−0.0105	−0.0110
si_0		−0.0021	−0.0025
p_0p_0	−0.0154	−0.0160	−0.0160
p_0f_0	−0.0010		−0.0013
p_1p_{-1}	−0.0105	−0.0105	−0.0110
Other terms			−0.0081
Total	−1.1605	−1.1614	−1.1744

[a]Joy and Parr used two terms of the ss′ type, one each of the others. Hagstrom and Shull employed 11, 12, 6, 3, 6, and 6 terms of each of the indicated types.

[b]Reference 55, as corrected in Ref. 56, for $R = 1.38\ a_0$.

[c]Reference 57, for $R = 1.40\ a_0$.

[d]Naturally, these estimates must total the exact value −1.1744 au. In addition, if terms like p_1p_{-1}, d_1d_{-1} are excluded, the total must approximate the result obtained by James and Coolidge excluding r_{12} terms, −1.1577.

5 GENERAL CONSIDERATIONS ON MANY-ELECTRON PROBLEMS†

The many-electron problems presented by most molecules are not different in kind from the two-electron problem of hydrogen. One must find antisymmetric wave functions that are good approximations to solutions of Schrödinger's equation for a given case, with a Hamiltonian operator containing the kinetic-energy operator for the electrons, the potential-energy (operator) for electron-nuclear attractions, and the potential energy of electron-electron repulsions, with the nuclear configuration fixed.

Specifically, the Hamiltonian operator for each n-electron problem is taken to have the form

$$\mathcal{H}_e\,(1,2,\ldots,n) = \sum_{\zeta}\mathcal{H}_N(\zeta) + \sum_{\zeta < \eta}(1/r_{\zeta\eta}) \tag{5-1}$$

where the indices ζ and η run from 1 to n, the terms $(1/r_{\zeta\eta})$ represent the electron-electron repulsions, and $\mathcal{H}_N(\zeta)$ is the Hamiltonian operator for electron ζ in the field of the bare nuclei, comprising a kinetic-energy term plus an electron-nuclear attraction term:

$$\mathcal{H}_N(\zeta) = -\frac{1}{2}\nabla_\zeta^2 - \sum_{\alpha}(Z_\alpha/r_{\zeta\alpha}) \tag{5-2}$$

Here Z_α is the charge on nucleus α (in units of +e) and $r_{\zeta\alpha}$ is the distance of electron ζ from nucleus α.

With $\mathcal{H}_e$ given by Eq. (5-1), we set out to find approximate $\Phi_e(1,2,\ldots,n)$, which (1) minimize Eq. (2-11), (2) satisfy the Pauli principle, and (3) are constructed from one-electron orbitals by some scheme. Restriction (3) means that we shall be excluding from consideration wave functions that depend explicitly on the interelectronic coordinates $r_{\zeta\eta}$, or other functional forms not explicit in one-electron components.

Condition (2) introduces special complications for more than two electrons, for it is not possible, as it was in the two-electron case, to write every antisymmetric wave function as a simple product of a space part and a spin part. To illustrate this, suppose we had three electrons, one in space orbital ϕ_1 with spin function α, one in ϕ_1 with spin β, and one in another orbital ϕ_2 with spin α. Allowing the symbol λ to denote a *spin orbital*, we would in this case have three spin orbitals for an electron, $\lambda_1 = \phi_1\alpha$, $\lambda_2 = \phi_1\beta$ and $\lambda_3 = \phi_2\alpha$, and a wave function describing the situation would be $\lambda_1(1)\lambda_2(2)\lambda_3(3)$. This function, however, is not antisymmetric; if we interchanged electrons 1 and 2 we would not get the negative of it but the new function

$$\lambda_1(2)\lambda_2(1)\lambda_3(3) = \lambda_2(1)\lambda_1(2)\lambda_3(3)$$

† For another account of the material covered in this section, see Chap. XIX of Ref. 8, or Sec. 12-5 of Ref. 34.

This tells us that the combination

$$\lambda_1(1)\lambda_2(2)\lambda_3(3) - \lambda_2(1)\lambda_1(2)\lambda_3(3)$$

would be antisymmetric for 1-2 interchange. But it is still not satisfactory, because 1-3 interchange takes it into still a different function

$$\lambda_3(1)\lambda_2(2)\lambda_1(3) - \lambda_3(1)\lambda_1(2)\lambda_2(3)$$

This gives us

$$\lambda_1(1)\lambda_2(2)\lambda_3(3) + \lambda_3(1)\lambda_1(2)\lambda_2(3) - \lambda_2(1)\lambda_1(2)\lambda_3(3) - \lambda_3(1)\lambda_2(2)\lambda_1(3)$$

as having the correct behavior with regard to both 1-2 and 1-3 interchange. But, finally, we also need antisymmetry for 2-3 interchange, giving us, with the introduction of the numerical factor for convenience,

$$\begin{aligned}\Delta = \frac{1}{\sqrt{6}}[&\lambda_1(1)\lambda_2(2)\lambda_3(3) + \lambda_3(1)\lambda_1(2)\lambda_2(3) + \lambda_2(1)\lambda_3(2)\lambda_1(3) \\ &- \lambda_2(1)\lambda_1(2)\lambda_3(3) - \lambda_3(1)\lambda_2(2)\lambda_1(3) - \lambda_1(1)\lambda_3(2)\lambda_2(3)]\end{aligned} \tag{5-3}$$

This function satisfies the Pauli principle; it is the type with which we must learn to deal. It will be observed that it is by no means a simple product of space and spin parts.

Most fortunately, a compact and familiar notation exists for functions like Eq. (5-3); Eq. (5-3) is no more no less than a determinant,

$$\Delta = \frac{1}{\sqrt{6}}\begin{vmatrix} \lambda_1(1) & \lambda_2(1) & \lambda_3(1) \\ \lambda_1(2) & \lambda_2(2) & \lambda_3(2) \\ \lambda_1(3) & \lambda_2(3) & \lambda_3(3) \end{vmatrix} \tag{5-4}$$

Alternatively, to introduce a shorthand notation due to Craig, we could simply write $\Delta = (\phi_1\bar{\phi}_1\phi_2)$, in which no bar implies spin α, a bar implies spin β, and the parentheses denote formation of the determinant and multiplication by the factor $1/\sqrt{6} = 1/(3!)^{\frac{1}{2}}$.

More generally, we define *Slater determinants* to be the antisymmetric functions

$$\Delta = \frac{1}{\sqrt{n!}}\begin{vmatrix} \lambda_1(1) & \lambda_2(1) & \cdots & \lambda_n(1) \\ \lambda_1(2) & \lambda_2(2) & \cdots & \lambda_n(2) \\ \vdots & & & \\ \lambda_1(n) & \lambda_2(n) & \cdots & \lambda_n(n) \end{vmatrix} \tag{5-5}$$

Equivalently, to put down explicitly the definition of a determinant, we may write

$$\Delta = \mathcal{A}\,[\lambda_1(1)\lambda_2(2)\ldots\lambda_n(n)] \tag{5-6}$$

$$= \frac{1}{\sqrt{n!}}\sum_P (-1)^P P[\lambda_1(1)\lambda_2(2)\ldots\lambda_n(n)] \tag{5-7}$$

where the antisymmetrization operator $\mathcal{A}$ is defined by this equation, the summation is over all $n!$ distinct permutations P of the electrons among themselves, and $(-1)^P$ is $+1$ if the permutation entails an even number of pair interchanges, -1 if it involves an odd number. We note that antisymmetry of Δ follows from the theorem that interchange of two rows of a determinant changes its sign.†

Now it is possible to express any exact or approximate solution of Schrödinger's equation with the Hamiltonian operator of Eq. (5-1) linearly in terms of Slater determinants of order n built from a complete set of one-electron spin orbitals λ_i,

$$\Phi(1,2,\ldots,n) = \sum_I C_I \Delta_I \tag{5-8}$$

Here the C_I are coefficients, and the Δ_I are determinants like Eq. (5-6), differing in the particular spin orbitals they contain. Any function of this form satisfies the Pauli principle, since each term in it does, and every function satisfying the Pauli principle can be expressed in this form.

Since Eq. (5-8) is of the linear form of Eq. (2-5), we may use the linear variational method to determine the coefficients C_I. This requires the computation of two sets of integrals, those of Eqs. (2-7) and (2-8), or, in the present notation,

$$S_{IJ} = \int \Delta_I^* \Delta_J \, d\tau(1)\, d\tau(2)\ldots d\tau(n) \tag{5-9}$$

and

$$H_{IJ} = \int \Delta_I^* \mathcal{H}_e \Delta_J \, d\tau(1)\, d\tau(2)\ldots d\tau(n) \tag{5-10}$$

Using Eq. (5-1), these last may be broken up into two pieces,

$$H_{IJ} = I_{IJ} + G_{IJ} \tag{5-11}$$

† The old form of the exclusion principle also follows: No two electrons can have the same set of quantum numbers. For a determinant in which two columns are identical is identically zero—an unacceptable form for a wave function.

where

$$I_{IJ} = \int \Delta_I^* \sum_{\zeta} \mathcal{H}_N(\zeta) \Delta_J \, d\tau(1)\, d\tau(2) \ldots d\tau(n) \tag{5-12}$$

and

$$G_{IJ} = \int \Delta_I^* \sum_{\zeta < \eta} (1/r_{\zeta\eta}) \Delta_J \, d\tau(1)\, d\tau(2) \ldots d\tau(n) \tag{5-13}$$

A formal problem that we might hope to solve once and for all is the reduction of the integrals S_{IJ}, I_{IJ}, and G_{IJ} over any two given Slater determinants Δ_I and Δ_J to integrals involving the spin orbitals λ from which these determinants are built.

The entire mathematics of this problem is much simplified if we assume at the outset that we are dealing with space orbitals and spin orbitals that are orthonormal:

$$\int \lambda_i^* \lambda_j \, d\tau = \delta_{ij} \tag{5-14}$$

$$\int \phi_i^* \phi_j \, dv = \delta_{ij} \tag{5-15}$$

This restriction is not one which can detract from the accuracy of the description of Eq. (5-8), since orthonormalizing the orbitals in the Δ_I only changes them by multiplicative constants.

In our evaluation of the integrals for given Δ_I and Δ_J, it will be convenient to distinguish a number of cases, based on the number of orbitals that differ in Δ_I and Δ_J. To get a feeling for what we mean by this, consider the three Slater determinants

$$\Delta_1 = (\phi_1\bar{\phi}_1\phi_2) \qquad \Delta_2 = (\phi_1\phi_2\bar{\phi}_1) \qquad \Delta_3 = (\phi_1\bar{\phi}_1\phi_3) \tag{5-16}$$

Here Δ_2 looks at first glance as if it differed from Δ_1 in two places, Δ_3 from Δ_1 in one place. However, Δ_2 can be transformed by a simple interchange of the last two columns into Δ_1, so that, in fact, $\Delta_2 = -\Delta_1$; Δ_2 and Δ_1 differ only by the constant multiplicative factor -1. In order to rule out this type of trivial difference, we assume that, by interchanges of columns, Δ_I and Δ_J have already been put into *maximum coincidence* with each other, when compared column by column as above.† We may then distinguish four cases:

†In actual calculations on an electronic computer, one needs to include the step skipped here: the explicit transformation of each pair of determinants into maximum coincidence with each other.

Case 1: Δ_I and Δ_J are identical.

Case 2: Δ_I and Δ_J differ in one spin orbital, with λ_m entering Δ_I where λ_p enters Δ_J.

Case 3: Δ_I and Δ_J differ in two spin orbitals, λ_m and λ_n entering Δ_I where λ_p and λ_q enter Δ_j.

Case 4: Δ_I and Δ_J differ in three or more spin orbitals.

The formula for S_{IJ} is straightforward to derive, in fact,

$$S_{IJ} = \delta_{IJ} = \begin{Bmatrix} 1 \text{ if } \Delta_I \equiv \Delta_J & \text{(Case 1)} \\ 0 \text{ otherwise} & \text{(Cases 2, 3, 4)} \end{Bmatrix} \tag{5-17}$$

This follows immediately upon substitution of formulas such as Eq. (5-7) into Eq. (5-9) and use of Eq. (5-14); every term in the double summation is zero unless there is a complete coincidence of orbitals between $P[\lambda_{I1}(1)\lambda_{I2}(2)\ldots]$ and $Q[\lambda_{J1}(1)\lambda_{J2}(2)\ldots]$; thus there are n! distinct permutations $Q = P$ that give identical contributions to the integral (1/n!) in Case 1, 0 otherwise.

For the integral I_{IJ} we may write, from Eqs. (5-7) and (5-12)

$$\begin{aligned} I_{IJ} &= \frac{1}{n!}\int \sum_P (-1)^P P[\lambda_{I1}(1)\lambda_{I2}(2)\ldots]^* \sum_\zeta \mathcal{H}_N(\zeta) \sum_Q (-1)^Q \\ &\quad \times Q[\lambda_{J1}(1)\lambda_{J2}(2)\ldots]\, d\tau(1)\, d\tau(2)\ldots \\ &= \int [\lambda_{I1}(1)\lambda_{I2}(2)\ldots]^* \sum_\zeta \mathcal{H}_N(\zeta) \sum_Q (-1)^Q \times Q[\lambda_{J1}(1)\lambda_{J2}(2)\ldots]\, d\tau(1)\, d\tau(2)\ldots \\ &= \int [\lambda_{I1}(1)\lambda_{I2}(2)\ldots]^* \sum_\zeta \mathcal{H}_N(\zeta)[\lambda_{J1}(1)\lambda_{J2}(2)\ldots]\, d\tau(1)\, d\tau(2)\ldots \end{aligned} \tag{5-18}$$

The second line follows from the fact that each of the permutations P merely affects the labeling of the variables of integration. (Formally, one can apply to each term the inverse of the permutation P, which does not change

$$\sum_\zeta \mathcal{H}_N(\zeta)$$

or even

$$\sum_Q (-1)^Q\, Q[\lambda_{J1}(1)\,\lambda_{J2}(2)\ldots]$$

since the former is symmetrical and the latter is the sum over all permutations already.) The third line follows from the fact that

$$\sum_{\zeta} \mathcal{H}_N(\zeta)$$

is a sum of one-electron operators; any nontrivial permutation Q produces two noncoincidences of spin orbitals, one of which integrates to zero by Eq. (5-14). Introducing the notations

$$I'_{ii} = I'_i = \int \lambda_i^*(1)\mathcal{H}_N(1)\lambda_i(1)\, d\tau(1) \tag{5-19}$$

$$I'_{ij} = \int \lambda_i^*(1)\mathcal{H}_N(1)\lambda_j(1)\, d\tau(1) \tag{5-20}$$

we then obtain immediately

$$I_{IJ} = \begin{Bmatrix} \sum I'_i \text{ for Case 1} \\ I'_{mp} \text{ for Case 2} \\ 0 \text{ for Cases 3 and 4} \end{Bmatrix} \tag{5-21}$$

where the summation in Case 1 is over all the occupied spin orbitals in $\Delta_I \equiv \Delta_J$.

For the electron-repulsion terms, the reduction proceeds similarly, although now of all the permutations Q we must retain for each term $(1/r_{\zeta\eta})$ the permutation that interchanges electrons ζ and η:

$$\begin{aligned} G_{IJ} &= \int [\lambda_{I1}(1)\lambda_{I2}(2)\ldots]^* \left[\sum_{\zeta<\eta} (1/r_{\zeta\eta})\right] \sum_Q (-1)^Q Q[\lambda_{J1}(1)\lambda_{J2}(2)\ldots] \\ &\times d\tau(1)\, d\tau(2)\ldots = \int [\lambda_{I1}(1)\lambda_{I2}(2)\ldots\lambda_{I\zeta}(\zeta)\lambda_{I\eta}(\eta)\ldots]^* \sum_{\zeta<\eta} \{(1/r_{\zeta\eta}) \\ &\times [\lambda_{J1}(1)\lambda_{J2}(2)\ldots\lambda_{J\zeta}(\zeta)\lambda_{J\eta}(\eta)\ldots - \lambda_{J1}(1)\lambda_{J2}(2)\ldots \\ &\times \lambda_{J\zeta}(\eta)\lambda_{J\eta}(\zeta)\ldots]\}\, d\tau(1)\, d\tau(2)\ldots\, d\tau(\zeta)\, d\tau(\eta)\ldots \end{aligned} \tag{5-22}$$

This gives different answers for each of Cases 1, 2, 3, and 4. To introduce several new notations at once, we let

$$[ik|j\ell]' = (ij|k\ell)' = \iint \lambda_i^*(1)\lambda_k^*(2)(1/r_{12})\lambda_j(1)\lambda_\ell(2)\, d\tau(1)\, d\tau(2) \tag{5-23}$$

$$J'_{ij} = [ij|ij]' = (ii|jj)' = \iint \lambda_i^*(1)\lambda_j^*(2)(1/r_{12})\lambda_i(1)\lambda_j(2)\, d\tau(1)\, d\tau(2) \tag{5-24}$$

$$K'_{ij} = [ij|ji]' = (ij|ji)' = \iint \lambda_i^*(1)\lambda_j^*(2)(1/r_{12})\lambda_j(1)\lambda_i(2)\, d\tau(1)\, d\tau(2) \tag{5-25}$$

Then we find

$$G_{IJ} = \begin{cases} \sum_{i<i'} (J'_{ii'} - K'_{ii'}) \text{ for Case 1} \\ \sum_{i \neq m} [(ii|mp)' - (ip|mi)'] \text{ for Case 2} \\ (mp|nq)' - (mq|np)' \text{ for Case 3} \\ 0 \text{ for Case 4} \end{cases} \tag{5-26}$$

The double summation in Case 1 is over all spin orbitals occupied in $\Delta_I \equiv \Delta_J$; the single summation in Case 2 excludes the orbital λ_m in Δ_I and λ_p in Δ_J.

It is not difficult to make a further reduction, to integrals over space coordinates only. We define, for space orbitals ϕ_i, ϕ_j, ϕ_k, ϕ_ℓ,

$$I_{ij} = \int \phi_i^*(1)\mathcal{H}_N(1)\phi_j(1)\, dv(1) \qquad I_i = I_{ii} \tag{5-27}$$

$$(ij|k\ell) = \iint \phi_i^*(1)\phi_k^*(2)(1/r_{12})\phi_j(1)\phi_\ell(2)\, dv(1)\, dv(2) \tag{5-28}$$

$$J_{ij} = (ii|jj) \qquad K_{ij} = (ij|ji) \tag{5-29}$$

Then we have

$$I'_i = I_i \qquad I'_{ij} = \begin{cases} I_{ij}, \text{ if } \lambda_i \text{ and } \lambda_j \text{ have the same spin} \\ 0, \text{ if } \lambda_i \text{ and } \lambda_j \text{ have opposite spin} \end{cases} \tag{5-30}$$

$$(ij|k\ell)' = \begin{cases} (ij|k\ell), \text{ if } \lambda_i \text{ has the same spin as } \lambda_j \\ \qquad \text{and } \lambda_k \text{ has the same spin as } \lambda_\ell \\ 0, \text{ otherwise} \end{cases} \tag{5-31}$$

$$J'_{ij} = J_{ij} \qquad K'_{ij} = \begin{cases} K_{ij}, \text{ if } \lambda_i \text{ and } \lambda_j \text{ have the same spin} \\ 0, \text{ if } \lambda_i \text{ and } \lambda_j \text{ have opposite spin} \end{cases} \tag{5-32}$$

In each particular application, one can thus write down the matrix elements S_{IJ} and H_{IJ} once the determinantal functions Δ_I and Δ_J are specified

The most important special case is that of a single determinant representing a closed shell, say

$$\Delta_N = (\phi_1\bar{\phi}_1\phi_2\bar{\phi}_2\ldots\phi_\nu\bar{\phi}_\nu) \tag{5-33}$$

where $\nu = n/2$. What would be the expectation value of the energy? We use the first of Eqs. (5-21) and (5-26), and Eqs. (5-30) and (5-32), obtaining

$$E_N = \sum_i I'_i + \sum_{i<i'} (J'_{ij} - K'_{ij}) \tag{5-34}$$

$$= 2\sum_i I_i + \sum_{i<j} (4J_{ij} - 2K_{ij}) + \sum_i J_{ii} \tag{5-35}$$

Alternatively,

$$E_N = 2\sum_i I_i + \sum_{ij} (2J_{ij} - K_{ij}) \tag{5-36}$$

The sums are over occupied spin orbitals in Eq. (5-34), over occupied space orbitals in Eqs. (5-35) and (5-36). In going from Eq. (5-35) to Eq. (5-36), we have made use of the identity

$$J_{ii} = K_{ii} \tag{5-37}$$

The most convenient expression is Eq. (5-36), in which the sums over i and j are not subject to the restriction $i < j$; equivalently, we may write

$$E_N = \sum_i (I_i + \epsilon_i) \tag{5-38}$$

where

$$\epsilon_i = I_i + \sum_j (2J_{ij} - K_{ij}) \tag{5-39}$$

A physical interpretation of these quantities ϵ_i will be provided in Sec. 6.

To conclude this section, let us further illustrate the application of the formulas that we have obtained by considering the case of a configuration $(\phi_1)^2(\phi_2)^2\ldots(\phi_{\nu-1})^2\phi_\nu\phi_{\nu+1}$, in which two electrons occupy two orbitals outside a closed inner core. There are four determinants associated with this situation,

$$\begin{aligned}
\Delta_1 &= (\phi_1\bar{\phi}_1\phi_2\bar{\phi}_2\ldots\phi_{\nu-1}\bar{\phi}_{\nu-1}\phi_\nu\phi_{\nu+1}) \\
\Delta_2 &= (\phi_1\bar{\phi}_1\phi_2\bar{\phi}_2\ldots\phi_{\nu-1}\bar{\phi}_{\nu-1}\bar{\phi}_\nu\bar{\phi}_{\nu+1}) \\
\Delta_3 &= (\phi_1\bar{\phi}_1\phi_2\bar{\phi}_2\ldots\phi_{\nu-1}\bar{\phi}_{\nu-1}\phi_\nu\bar{\phi}_{\nu+1}) \\
\Delta_4 &= (\phi_1\bar{\phi}_1\phi_2\bar{\phi}_2\ldots\phi_{\nu-1}\bar{\phi}_{\nu-1}\bar{\phi}_\nu\phi_{\nu+1})
\end{aligned} \tag{5-40}$$

To get approximate wave functions for the states to which this configuration gives rise, we must mix Δ_1 to Δ_4 linearly; hence we need matrix elements

S_{IJ} and H_{IJ}. For the first, we have $S_{IJ} = \delta_{IJ}$ from Eq. (5-17). For the second we find readily, referring answers where appropriate to Eq. (5-36),

$$H_{11} = H_{22} = E_N + (I_{\nu+1} - I_\nu) + (J_{\nu,\nu+1} - K_{\nu,\nu+1}) - J_{\nu\nu} + \sum_{i=1}^{\nu-1} (2J_{i,\nu+1} - K_{i,\nu+1}) - \sum_{i=1}^{\nu-1} (2J_{i\nu} - K_{i\nu}) \tag{5-41}$$

$$H_{33} = H_{44} = E_N + (I_{\nu+1} - I_\nu) + J_{\nu,\nu+1} - J_{\nu\nu} + \sum_{i=1}^{\nu-1} (2J_{i,\nu+1} - K_{i,\nu+1}) - \sum_{i=1}^{\nu-1} (2J_{i\nu} - K_{i\nu}) = H_{11} + K_{\nu,\nu+1} \tag{5-42}$$

$$\left\{\begin{aligned} &H_{12} = H_{13} = H_{14} = H_{23} = H_{24} = 0 \\ &H_{34} = -K_{\nu,\nu+1} \end{aligned}\right\} \tag{5-43}$$

The secular equation thus factors into two 1×1 equations and one 2×2, and the solution of the latter is obtainable at inspection because the interacting states are degenerate. We obtain three functions Δ_1, Δ_2, and $\Delta_3 + \Delta_4$, that have the same energy

$$E_T = H_{11} \tag{5-44}$$

and one function $\Delta_3 - \Delta_4$, which has the energy

$$E_V = H_{11} + 2K_{\nu,\nu+1} \tag{5-45}$$

where H_{11} is given by Eq. (5-41). Alternatively, we could write

$$E_T = E_N + (\epsilon_{\nu+1} - \epsilon_\nu) - J_{\nu,\nu+1} \tag{5-46}$$

and

$$E_V = E_N + (\epsilon_{\nu+1} - \epsilon_\nu) - J_{\nu,\nu+1} + 2K_{\nu,\nu+1} \tag{5-47}$$

where $\epsilon_{\nu+1}$ and ϵ_ν are defined as having the values they would have for the "unexcited" configuration, as given by Eq. (5-39). These formulas are very useful in certain applications.

This last calculation, of course, represents the resolution of spin degeneracies, giving functions that are eigenfunctions of S^2 and S_z. The three degenerate functions having the energy of Eq. (5-46) are the $S_z = -1$, 0, and +1 components of a *triplet state* having $S^2 = 1$; the function having the energy of Eq. (5-47) is a *singlet state* with $S_z = 0$ and $S^2 = 0$. As will generally happen, the resolution automatically comes out of the secular equation for the problem. Special apparatus for resolving the spin degeneracies need not be employed, although such apparatus becomes indispensable for sufficiently complex cases.

6 THE SCF AND LCAO-SCF METHODS

We might ask the question: Given an electronic system of an even number of electrons, how could we find the *best* single determinantal wave function for it of the form of Eq. (5-33)? In principle, this is a straightforward problem; we need only compute E_N from Eq. (5-36) for successive sets of orthonormal trial orbitals ϕ_i until a minimum value for E_N is found. This defines the Hartree-Fock or *self-consistent-field* (SCF) method.[33,58]

Actually, it is no mean task to carry out such a calculation. To see what is involved, let us derive the general equations of the method. We want to minimize

$$E_N = 2\sum_i I_i + \sum_{ij}(2J_{ij} - K_{ij})$$

subject to the conditions $S_{ij} = \int \phi_i^* \phi_j \, dv = \delta_{ij}$ with respect to the ϕ_i. To do this, we may apply Lagrange's method of undetermined multipliers, requiring that the quantity

$$E' = E_N - 2\sum_{ij} \epsilon_{ij} S_{ij}$$

be a minimum, where the ϵ_{ij} are constants. That is, we require

$$0 = \delta E' = 2\sum_i \delta I_i + \sum_{ij}(2\delta J_{ij} - \delta K_{ij} - 2\epsilon_{ij}\delta S_{ij}) \tag{6-1}$$

where the δ's represent virtual variations induced by virtual variations in the ϕ_i. Thus, assuming for simplicity that all orbitals are real,

$$\begin{aligned} \delta I_i &= \int \delta\phi_i \mathcal{H}_N \phi_i \, dv + \int \phi_i \mathcal{H}_N \delta\phi_i \, dv = 2\int \delta\phi_i \mathcal{H}_N \phi_i \, dv \\ \delta S_{ij} &= \int \delta\phi_i \phi_j \, dv + \int \delta\phi_j \phi_i \, dv \end{aligned} \tag{6-2}$$

Similarly, if we write

$$J_{ij} = \iint \phi_i^2(1)(1/r_{12})\phi_j^2(2)\, dv(1)\, dv(2) = \int \phi_i(1) J_j(1)\phi_i(1)\, dv(1)$$
$$= \int \phi_j(2) J_i(2)\phi_j(2)\, dv(2) \qquad (6\text{-}3)$$

and

$$K_{ij} = \iint \phi_i(1)\phi_j(1)(1/r_{12})\phi_i(2)\phi_j(2)\, dv(1)\, dv(2) = \int \phi_i(1) K_j(1)\phi_i(1)\, dv(1)$$
$$= \int \phi_j(2) K_i(2)\phi_j(2)\, dv(2) \qquad (6\text{-}4)$$

where the coulomb operators J_j, J_i, and the exchange operators K_j, K_i, are defined by these equations; we then have

$$\delta J_{ij} = 2\int \delta\phi_i J_j \phi_i\, dv + 2\int \delta\phi_j J_i \phi_j\, dv$$
$$\delta K_{ij} = 2\int \delta\phi_i K_j \phi_i\, dv + 2\int \delta\phi_j K_i \phi_j\, dv \qquad (6\text{-}5)$$

and Eq. (6-1) gives

$$0 = \sum_i \int \delta\phi_i \left[4\mathcal{H}_N \phi_i + \sum_j (8J_j\phi_i - 4K_j\phi_i - 4\epsilon_{ij}\phi_j) \right] \qquad (6\text{-}6)$$

Since the $\delta\phi_i$ are arbitrary, the coefficients of each must vanish identically, viz.,

$$\left\{ \mathcal{H}_N(1) + \sum_j [2J_j(1) - K_j(1)] \right\} \phi_i(1) = \sum_j \epsilon_{ij}\phi_j(1) \qquad (6\text{-}7)$$

These are the Hartree-Fock integro-differential equations for the problem.

Equations (6-7) are coupled, in two ways. In the first place, on the right side we have a linear combination of all the occupied orbitals entering. Fortunately, this coupling can be removed by use of a certain arbitrariness in the initial determinant $\Phi_N = (\phi_1\bar{\phi}_1\phi_2\bar{\phi}_2\ldots)$. Namely, the orbitals can be subjected to an arbitrary linear transformation without affecting the physical significance of Φ_N (such a transformation only multiplies the determinant by a constant), and this transformation can be chosen so as to bring the ϵ_{ij} matrix to diagonal form

$$\epsilon_{ij} = \delta_{ij}\epsilon_i \qquad (6\text{-}8)$$

Assuming that this transformation has been made, Eq. (6-7) becomes more simply

$$F(1)\phi_i(1) = \epsilon_i\phi_i(1) \qquad (6\text{-}9)$$

where

$$F(1) = \mathcal{H}_N(1) + \sum_j [2J_j(1) - K_j(1)] \tag{6-10}$$

The solutions of Eq. (6-9) can be shown to have the orthogonality and other nice properties usually associated with solutions of a one-particle Schrödinger equation.[58] However, in spite of Eq. (6-10), the equations are not of a simple linear form. The operator F depends on *all* the occupied orbitals ϕ_i, through the dependence of the operators J_j and K_j on the orbital ϕ_j. This means that the operator F is not known until the equations are solved!

An iterative "self-consistent" procedure is therefore required for solution. We guess some ϕ_i, determine F, solve Eq. (6-9), and compare the ϕ_i obtained with those guessed, and repeat, until no further changes in the ϕ_i are found. Such procedures can be carried out for atoms[33]; they are not, however, truly practicable for molecules.

If we multiply Eq. (6-9) on the left by $\phi_i(1)$ and integrate, we immediately recover our previous Eq. (5-39) for the quantity ϵ_i. Hence Eq. (5-39), and Eq. (5-38), hold for the *orbital energies* of Eq. (6-9); we note from Eq. (5-38) that *the total energy is not a sum of orbital energies*. It is true, however, that each ϵ_i is an approximation to an ionization potential; if we compare Eq. (5-38) with a corresponding formula for the energy of a single determinant differing from Φ_N in the absence of one electron from ϕ_i, we obtain

$$\epsilon_i = -\mathcal{I}_i \tag{6-11}$$

where $\mathcal{I}_i$ is the ionization potential of the molecule for removal of an electron from the orbital ϕ_i. This important formula is known as *Koopmans' theorem*.

When the molecular state is not well represented by a single determinant, the corresponding treatment breaks down at the stage in which the ϵ_{ij} matrix is diagonalized [between Eqs. (6-7) and (6-8)]; the generalizations necessary for important special classes of such states have recently been described by Roothaan and Huzinaga.[59] Alternative schemes include the method proposed by Amos and Hall.[60]

For molecules, instead of the SCF method, the LCAO-SCF method is ordinarily employed, in which the ϕ_i are taken to be linear combinations of some starting atomic orbitals,

$$\phi_i = \sum_q C_{iq}\chi_q \tag{6-12}$$

where the χ_q are the atomic orbitals. If enough χ_q are included, this will introduce no error, but usually one uses a restricted set of χ_q and so incurs error—this, then, is an *LCAO approximation*.

If we insert Eq. (6-12) in Eq. (6-9), multiply on the left by χ_p, and integrate, we obtain†

$$\sum_q C_{iq}(F_{pq} - S_{pq}\epsilon) = 0 \tag{6-13}$$

where, in the notations of the previous section,

$$F_{pq} = \int \chi_p^* F \chi_q \, dv = I_{pq} + \sum_j [2(pq|jj) - (pj|jq)] \tag{6-14}$$

and

$$S_{pq} = \int \chi_p^* \chi_q \, dv \tag{6-15}$$

Equations (6-13) are simultaneous equations for the unknown C_{iq}; a nontrivial solution exists if

$$|F_{pq} - S_{pq}\epsilon| = 0 \tag{6-16}$$

This *secular equation* determines the orbital energies ϵ_i; Eqs. (6-13) determine the corresponding coefficients.

The starting atomic orbitals χ_q being presumed known, our carrying through the LCAO-SCF method requires computation of basic integrals of two kinds,

$$I_{pq} = \int \chi_p^*(1) \mathcal{H}_N(1) \chi_q(1) \, dv(1) \tag{6-17}$$

and

$$(pq|rs) = \iint \chi_p^*(1)\chi_q(1)(1/r_{12})\chi_r^*(2)\chi_s(2) \, dv(1) \, dv(2) \tag{6-18}$$

Equations (6-13) then can be solved by iteration: Guess the C_{iq}, compute the F_{pq} from Eq. (6-14), solve Eq. (6-16), determine the C_{iq} from Eq. (6-13), compare, and repeat.

We note immediately from the results of Sec. 5 that the integrals of Eqs. (6-17) and (6-18) are also what are needed to do an extensive configuration-interaction calculation including many more determinants than one, which can far transcend a single determinant in accuracy. This makes the LCAO-SCF procedure an optional step if one is planning a full configuration-interaction treatment with a given basic set of atomic orbitals.

The LCAO and SCF wave functions do have certain properties that make them uniquely suitable as approximate eigenfunctions, however. Equation (6-11) is one; Eq. (6-8) another. More explicitly, the latter equation may be rewritten

---

†For a more rigorous derivation, see Ref. 58.

$$\int \phi_i^* F \phi_j \, dv = \delta_{ij}\epsilon_i \qquad (6\text{-}19)$$

This gives rise to *Brillouin's theorem*: In a configuration-interaction calculation, using determinants built from SCF orbitals, all matrix elements connecting the ground configuration and singly excited configurations are zero. An important consequence, discussed in detail by Cohen and Dalgarno,[61] is that molecular properties that are expectation values of one-electron operators (for example, the dipole moment) are well approximated using SCF functions.

7 SURVEY OF PURELY THEORETICAL CALCULATIONS ON SMALL MOLECULES

Progress toward accurate wave functions for small molecules, built from atomic orbitals, thus depends in the first instance, and in the last instance, on our ability to evaluate integrals I_{pq} and $(pq|rs)$ for atomic orbitals in molecules. This problem, so simply stated, is one of consummate difficulty.

From the illustrations that have already been given, it is clear that not only the integrals involving 1s, 2s, and 2p orbitals are required, but also those involving orbitals of much-higher-quantum numbers. Furthermore, in a polyatomic molecule, the electronic-repulsion integrals may involve orbitals on as many as four different centers.

In 1960 Allen and Karo published a useful and complete survey[62] of calculations that had been made up to that time; they summarized the methods employed and results obtained in about 80 calculations on molecules with three or more electrons. Slater orbitals on the individual atoms have most frequently been employed, but we must also discuss calculations using elliptical coordinates, calculations using Gaussian-type orbitals, and calculations using orbitals on one center only.

As regards integrals for Slater orbitals, generally available machine subroutines for computing the most general of them are in the offing. One must be patient in waiting for them, however. A 1951 conference promised them shortly[63]; in 1958 there was an announcement concerning some of them.[64] But, in 1962, a letter appeared in the *Communications* column of the *Journal of Chemical Physics* describing a new method for obtaining the worst of them, which *ought* to work.[65] At the present time, in fact, computer routines for two-center integrals involving 1s, 2s, and 2p orbitals are routinely available in several laboratories, and routines for two-center integrals for 3p, 3d, etc. are about to become available. Three- and four-center integrals are much harder to come by, although Boys is systematically producing them.[66]

Recent and current publications from the University of Chicago typify the work that is now being done with the LCAO-SCF scheme and Slater orbitals. Ransil and Fraga have produced a mass of calculations on all the first-row diatomics using a restricted basis consisting of 1s, 2s, and 2p orbitals only.[67] These will be of much value in the assessment of the LCAO method in its simplest form,[68] and, indeed, it seems that many physical properties can be well approximated with this scheme. Equilibrium distances for ground and excited states appear to be predicted particularly well.

A variant of the simple LCAO-SCF method, which always has had great appeal for some, is to use as the atomic orbitals not Slater orbitals but atomic Hartree-Fock SCF orbitals, and this does seem to improve the results when a restricted basis of orbitals is used.[69] One problem inherent in such an approach is the neglect of orbital distortion, which necessarily accompanies molecular formation.[70]

More accurate LCAO-SCF calculations, with an extended Slater-atomic-orbital basis, also are being produced by the Chicago group. These include a calculation by Richardson on N_2, in which two instead of one of each of the orbitals 2s, $2p_x$, $2p_y$, and $2p_z$ were employed on each atom,[71] and a calculation on HF by Clementi, who brought in 3s, 3p, and 3d orbitals as well.[72] In Table 4, Clementi's calculations are compared with the simpler ones of Ransil, with some by Karo and Allen in which Hartree-Fock atomic orbitals were used,[69]

TABLE 4
LCAO-SCF Calculations on HF

Calculation	Ref.	E, au[a]	Δ, ev[c]	μ, Debye[d]
Slater orbitals 1s,2s,2p; effective charges from Slater rules	67(II)	− 99.48	28.5	0.88
Slater orbitals 1s,2s,2p; effective charges varied to give best atomic descriptions	67(II)	− 99.49	28.1	1.12
Slater orbitals 1s,2s,2p; effective charges varied to give best molecular energy	67(II)	− 99.54	26.9	1.44
Hartree-Fock atomic orbitals 1s, 2s, 2p	69	− 99.96	15.3	1.99
Slater orbitals, enlarged basis	73	− 99.99	14.7	1.96
Slater orbitals; enlarged basis including $2p\sigma$ orbitals on H and 3s, 3p, $3d\sigma$, $3d\pi$ on F	72	−100.06[b]	12.7	1.98
Experimental values	67(I)	−100.53	0	1.73

[a]Total energy, including nuclear repulsion, at the observed or predicted internuclear distance.

[b]In Ref. 72 it is estimated that this is 0.004 au short of the true SCF energy. We may infer a correlation energy of about 0.49 au or 13 ev (uncorrected for relativity).

[c]Absolute error in energy.

[d]Dipole moment.

and with some by Nesbet.[73] In Clementi's calculation convergence has been reached for the energy, but an error remains, as it must for any Hartree-Fock function. In addition the dipole moment has not yet reached a stable value.

Using a four-center integral program written by McLean,[74] McLean and Clementi have reported[74,75] LCAO-SCF calculations on the linear polyatomics C_2H_2, CO_2, C_3, C_4, C_2N_2, HCN, HF_2^-, and COS. These probably represent the most-advanced LCAO-SCF calculations yet carried out.

Among other LCAO-SCF calculations, we may mention Kaplan's 1957 calculation on NH_3,[76] which was far ahead of its time, and calculations by Nesbet and collaborators on N_2[77] and CO.[78] In his papers, Nesbet analyzes very carefully the behavior of molecular correlation energy as a function of internuclear distance, a subtle but important problem.

Boys also has reported LCAO-SCF calculations,[79] but he prefers to proceed directly to the configuration-interaction level.[80] With Shavitt, he has produced the best potential surface so far available for the famous $H_2 + H$ exchange reaction.[66,81] Or, more recent, his calculations on the electronic states of CH_2 and their geometries are of much interest.[82] These are summarized in Table 5.

TABLE 5
Configuration-Interaction Calculations on C, CH, and CH_2[a]

Species	State	Calculated (exptl.) total energy, au	Calculated (exptl.) geometrical parameters, au[b]
C	^3P	$-37.668(-37.841)$	
	^1D	$-37.594(-37.795)$	
CH	$^2\Pi$	$-38.254(-38.468)$	$r_{CH} = 2.26\ (2.12)$
	$^2\Sigma^-$	$-38.120(-38.350)$	$r_{CH} = 2.45\ (2.24)$
CH_2	$^3B_1$	-38.904	$r_{CH} = 2.11$, $\angle HCH = 129°$
	$^1A_1$	-38.865	$r_{CH} = 2.21$, $\angle HCH = 90°$
	$^1B_1$	-38.808	$r_{CH} = 2.11$, $\angle HCH = 132°$

[a]From Ref. 82. These calculations assume that the wave function for each state is a linear combination of the many Slater determinants of the appropriate symmetry, which can be constructed from two 1s-type, one 2s-type, and one each of $2p_x$-, $2p_y$-, $2p_z$-type Slater orbitals on C, plus one 1s-type orbital on H.

[b]The predictions for CH_2 agree qualitatively with what is known experimentally about this species.

It is not the particular calculation that is so important here but the method, which is general and transcends the SCF method in accuracy. Other configuration-interaction calculations have been summarized by Allen and Karo[62]; presumably many more of them are now in process around the world.

Elliptical coordinates for diatomics unquestionably have great value. Harris recently has initiated new studies on this subject,[83] and a definitive study of LiH has been carried out by Ebbing.[84] I suspect there will be a great deal published along these lines in the future. There is the disadvantage that the extension to polyatomics may be hopeless to attempt.

Gaussian functions, orbitals with $\exp(-\alpha r^2)$ dependence instead of $\exp(-\zeta r)$, were proposed as basis functions about a decade ago by Boys and by McWeeny. Results obtained[85] by Nesbet using Gaussians on the methane molecule were discouraging, but a resurgence of their use has recently begun.[86] The convenience of Gaussians is in integral evaluation; presaging their revival is the fact that the most recent proposal on three-center integrals entails expansions of Slater orbitals in terms of Gaussians.[65,87] The cost is that very many basis functions must be employed, but the spectacular success of Krauss in a very new calculation on methane[88] signals that it is worthwhile.

Expansions in Gaussians, in fact, have much in common with expansions in Slater (or other) orbitals at one atom only, which we shall now consider. A Gaussian has the wrong behavior at $r = 0$: It is smooth there, whereas a Slater or hydrogen-like orbital has a cusp; similarly, cusps at nuclei cannot be neatly reproduced if harmonic expansions about other points are employed.

One-center expansions for the methane molecule have given what I think are some exciting, suggestive results[89-91]; those of two sets of authors are summarized in Table 6. Saturno and Parr[89] constructed a wave function from Slater-type orbitals s, s', p_x, p_y, p_z, d_{yz}, d_{xz}, d_{xy}, f_{xyz}, f' (three functions), and g (three functions), with the n and ζ parameters for each orbital regarded as variational parameters. The specific form chosen was the linear combination [compare Eq. (4-24)]

$$\Phi = C_1(s^2s'^2p^6) + C_2(s^2s'^2p^5d) + C_3(s^2s'fp^6) + C_4(s^2s'^2p^5f) + C_5(s^2s'^2p^5g) \tag{7-1}$$

The first term is the neon-like single determinant $(s\bar{s}s'\bar{s}'p_x\bar{p}_xp_y\bar{p}_yp_z\bar{p}_z)$, the second term is the sum of the six determinants arising from replacement of a p orbital by an appropriate d orbital, the third term is the sum of the two determinants corresponding to replacement of s' with f_{xyz}, and so on. Albasiny and Cooper used the same spherical harmonics, but determined the radial factors numerically so as to give the best possible single determinant of the form

$$\Phi = (\phi_1\bar{\phi}_1\phi_2\bar{\phi}_2\phi_3\bar{\phi}_3\phi_4\bar{\phi}_4\phi_5\bar{\phi}_5) \tag{7-2}$$

where each ϕ is expanded in terms of these harmonics.[90] This last is a Hartree-Fock calculation done by an expansion in harmonics. Equation (7-1), in principle, might give a better result but, in practice, seems not to differ.

It can be seen that there is very good agreement between the two calculations. This confirms that the radial functions $r^{n-1}\exp(-\zeta r)$ are handy for calculations of this kind, and it has encouraged us to continue working along

TABLE 6
One-Center Wave Functions for the Normal Methane Molecule

Term type	Energy increment, au		Corresponding Ne increment, au	
	Saturno-Parr[a]	Albasiny-Cooper[b]	Slater orbitals[c]	Hartree-Fock
$(s^2s'^2p^6)$	−39.50	−39.53	−128.29	−128.55[d]
$(s^2s'^2p^5d)$	−0.16	} − 0.37	0	0
$(s^2s'fp^6)$	−0.06		0	0
$(s^2s'^2p^5f')$	−0.04		0	0
$(s^2s'^2p^5g)$	−0.08		0	0
Total computed energy	−39.84	−39.90	−128.29	−128.55
Experimental energy[a]	−40.52		−129.02	
Relativistic correction[a]	−0.01		−0.14	
Net error	0.67	0.61	0.59	0.33

[a]Reference 89, as corrected in Ref. 56. Slater orbitals.
[b]Reference 90. Numerical radial functions; actual form of wave function was Eq. (7-2) of text, not Eq. (7-1) (see text).
[c]Reference 92.
[d]References 37 or 38.

these same lines. In our laboratory, and also elsewhere,[91] much work is now in process or is planned in which variational calculations on ground and excited (and vibrating) states of molecules of the general type AH_n are carried out by the one-center expansion method.

The correlation energy for CH_4 inferred from these calculations is $\leqq 0.62$ au or 17 ev uncorrected for relativity, $\leqq 0.61$ au or 16 ev corrected for relativity, which may be compared with the correlation energy of Ne, which is 0.47 au or 13 ev uncorrected, 0.33 au or 9 ev corrected for relativity.[89,90] Krauss' more accurate calculation for methane[88] gives a correlation energy 0.34 au or 9 ev corrected for relativity, in good agreement with the neon value.

The predicted electronic-charge distribution can be compared with that in neon, and this is most interesting to do.[92,93] For the equilibrium tetrahedral configuration, we may expand the one-electron density in terms of the totally symmetric tetrahedral harmonics $T_\ell(\theta,\phi)$, which are appropriate combinations of the surface harmonics of the same ℓ value. Namely,

$$4\pi\rho(r,\theta,\phi) = \sum_{\ell = 0,3\ldots}^{\infty} A_\ell(r) T_\ell(\theta,\phi) \tag{7-3}$$

The functions $A_\ell(r)$ uniquely determine the density; the first several of them are shown in Figs. 1 and 2. $A_0(r)$ has the neon-like shape we would expect; the higher $A_\ell(r)$ confer shape upon the electron distribution near the nuclei. The electric multipole moments of the electron distribution can be computed directly from the $A_\ell(r)$; the fact that the $\ell = 1$ and $\ell = 2$ terms are missing from Eq. (7-3) is in accordance with the fact that methane has no dipole or quadrupole moment. The computed octupole moment agrees with the experimental implications about this moment.[93]

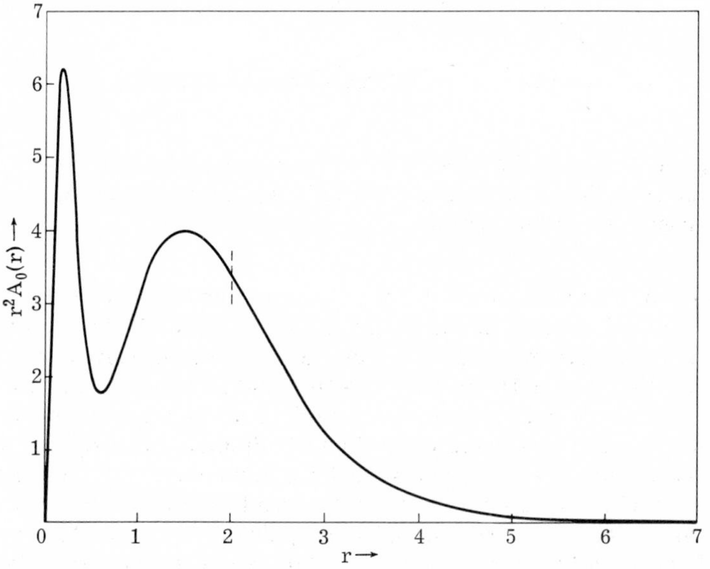

Figure 1. The spherically symmetric part of the electron density in methane [see Eq. (7-3) of text]. Atomic units. The hydrogen atoms are at r = 2.

In detail, we would expect wave functions determined in this way to be pretty good everywhere except right at the hydrogen nuclei.[94] If we plot a graph of the electron density, the result bears this out: There is a concentration of charge in the CH-bond regions, as we would expect, but too much depletion (relative to the separate neutral atoms) in the vicinity of the protons. However, we might expect to be able to invent special devices to remedy this sort of defect in a wave function, a problem on which research is now going on in our laboratory.

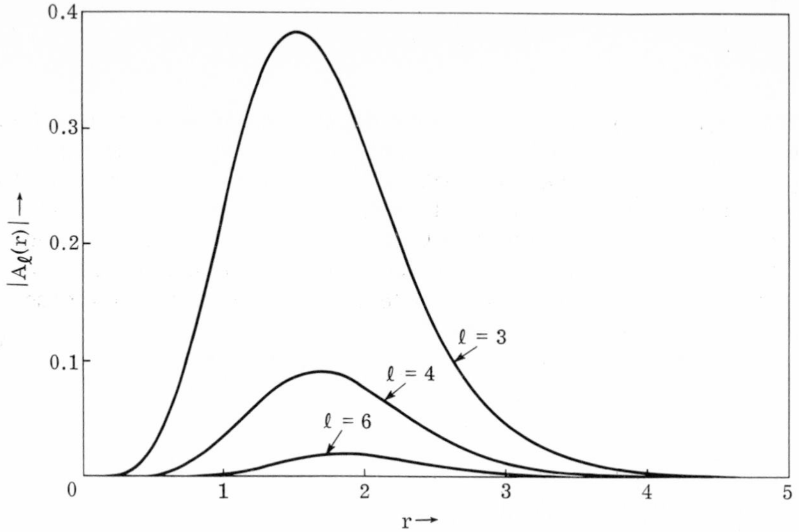

Figure 2. The radial distribution functions $A_\ell(r)$ for methane [see Eq. (7-3) of text]. A_3 and A_6 are positive; A_4 is negative. Atomic units.

Calculations of this kind would seem to bear on the validity of the classical quantum-mechanical concept of the united atom. In spite of what has been said above, the electron distribution in CH_4, and the electronic energy, are not nearly so much like that in Ne as they are like that in another pseudoatomic entity that I like to call the methane *atom puff*, in which a carbon nucleus of charge 6 is surrounded at a distance R (the CH distance in methane) by a uniformly charged surface of charge 4, and ten electrons. The first term in Eq. (7-1) is very close to the Hartree-Fock wave function for the methane puff, the other terms being perturbations induced by deviations from full-spherical symmetry of the actual proton distribution. We are now striving to develop the whole perturbation calculus of molecules AH_n viewed in this way.

Accurate quantum-mechanical calculations of many physical properties of many small molecules thus are imminent.

III. Planar Unsaturated Molecules

8 THE PI-ELECTRON APPROXIMATION

From the early days of quantum chemistry, a vast amount of theoretical work has been performed on unsaturated and conjugated hydrocarbon molecules and molecules simply related to them. Aromatic systems have been subjected to countless studies, and much success has accrued in rationalizing and correlating aromatic properties.

Just as the chemistry of these species affects, in large measure, only the multiple bonds, so the theory has devolved about a simple model in which the unsaturation or pi electrons alone are treated. In ethylene one has an underlying planar structure

which can be neatly described using sp^2 hybrids on the carbons and s orbitals on the hydrogens; this leaves for the last bond, between the carbons, two electrons and one p_z orbital on each carbon (taking the z axis to be perpendicular to the molecular plane). This is the *pi bond*; these are the *pi orbitals*; we have two *pi electrons*. In benzene we have 6 pi electrons, in naphthalene 10, and so on.

In the conventional theories, the pi electrons are treated apart from the rest; it is supposed that somehow the effects of the others, the *sigma electrons*, can be lumped into the Hamiltonian for the pi electrons. One takes a pi-electron Hamiltonian

$$\mathcal{H}_\pi(1,2,\ldots n_\pi) = \sum_{\mu=1}^{n_\pi} \mathcal{H}_{\text{core}}(\mu) + \frac{1}{2} \sum_{\mu,\nu=1}^{n_\pi}{}' \, (1/r_{\mu\nu}) \qquad (8\text{-}1)$$

and seeks pi-electron wave functions (Π), which are antisymmetric with respect to exchange of any two of the n_π pi electrons and which minimize the quantity

$$E_\pi = \int (\Pi)^* \mathcal{H}_\pi (\Pi)\, d\tau \Big/ \int (\Pi)^* (\Pi)\, d\tau \qquad (8\text{-}2)$$

In the less sophisticated of the theories, further assumptions are made regarding the pi-electron-repulsion terms $(1/r_{\mu\nu})$, as, for example, by ignoring them altogether. For the moment we concern ourselves with the validity of the use of Eq. (8-1) as it stands.

The problem is that Eq. (8-1) is far from the correct Hamiltonian for the problem [Eq. (5-1)]; for benzene, the true $\mathcal{H}$ involves 42 electrons, not just six. We seem to have thrown away all semblance of rigor when we write Eq. (8-1).

In fact we have not. As we shall now show, it is quite likely that Eq. (8-1) is a good, purely theoretical equation; in any case we can rigorously state the conditions under which Eqs. (8-1) and (8-2) provide a valid procedure for determining molecular properties.[95]

We start by setting down a set of *sigma-pi separability conditions*, which may or may not be satisfied by an actual, exact wave function for an actual molecular state. We suppose that we have a molecule containing n electrons, n_π of which, for one reason or another, we should like to call "pi," n_σ, "sigma," with $n = n_\sigma + n_\pi$. A total wave function Ψ is said to satisfy the sigma-pi separability conditions if:

A. The wave function $\Psi(1,2,\ldots,n)$ can be written in the form

$$\Psi = [(\Sigma)(\Pi)] \qquad (8\text{-}3)$$

where $(\Sigma) = [\Sigma(1,2,\ldots,n_\sigma)]$ is an antisymmetric function in the space and spin coordinates of electrons $1,2,\ldots,n_\sigma$, which describes the "sigma" part of the electronic structure; $(\Pi) = [\Pi(n_\sigma + 1, n_\sigma + 2, \ldots, n_\sigma + n_\pi)]$ is an antisymmetric function in the coordinates of electrons $n_\sigma + 1, n_\sigma + 2, \ldots, n_\sigma + n_\pi$, which describes the "pi" part of the electronic structure; and the outer square brackets denote antisymmetrization with respect to exchange of electrons $1,2,\ldots,n_\sigma$ with electrons $n_\sigma + 1, n_\sigma + 2, \ldots, n_\sigma + n_\pi$:

$$[(\Sigma)(\Pi)] = [(n_\sigma + n_\pi)!/n_\sigma! n_\pi!]^{-\frac{1}{2}} \sum_{P_{\sigma\pi}} (-1)^{P_{\sigma\pi}} P_{\sigma\pi}[(\Sigma)(\Pi)] \qquad (8\text{-}4)$$

Here the sum is over the $(n_\sigma + n_\pi)!/n_\sigma! n_\pi!$ distinct permutations of sigma with pi electrons; the constant is a normalizing factor.

B. The functions (Σ) and (Π) are each normalized to unity:

$$\int |(\Sigma)|^2\, d\tau_\sigma = \int |(\Pi)|^2\, d\tau_\pi = 1 \qquad (8\text{-}5)$$

C. The functions (Σ) and (Π), respectively, can be expanded in terms of orthonormal Slater determinants (Σ_k) and (Π_m) built from some orthonormal set of one-electron functions $\lambda_1, \lambda_2, \ldots$, with no spin orbital entering both some (Σ_k) and some (Π_m):

$$(\Sigma) = A_1(\Sigma_1) + A_2(\Sigma_2) + \cdots \tag{8-6}$$

$$(\Pi) = B_1(\Pi_1) + B_2(\Pi_2) + \cdots \tag{8-7}$$

We term the orbitals that enter the (Σ_k) the sigma orbitals, those that enter the (Π_m) the pi orbitals.[96]

The *pi-electron approximation* may now be defined as the approximation in which the wave functions for some set of molecular states satisfy the sigma-pi separability conditions A, B, and C, *with the same sigma wave function* (Σ) *for all states in the set.*

From the separability conditions, it follows that the total function Ψ is normalized. Various other consequences can be proved,[95] the most important of which is the following:

Theorem: For a wave function that satisfies the sigma-pi separability conditions, for a molecule with the Hamiltonian operator of Eq. (5-1), the expectation value of the electronic energy, Eq. (2-11), may be written in the form

$$E_e = E_\sigma^0 + E_\pi \tag{8-8}$$

where

$$E_\sigma^0 = \int (\Sigma)^* \mathcal{H}_\sigma^0 (\Sigma)\, d\tau_\sigma \tag{8-9}$$

$$E_\pi = \int (\Pi)^* \mathcal{H}_\pi (\Pi)\, d\tau_\pi \tag{8-10}$$

Here

$$\mathcal{H}_\sigma^0(1,2,\ldots,n_\sigma) = \sum_{\kappa=1}^{n_\sigma} \mathcal{H}_N(\kappa) + \frac{1}{2} \sum_{\kappa,\lambda=1}^{n_\sigma}{}' (1/r_{\kappa\lambda}) \tag{8-11}$$

and

$$\mathcal{H}_\pi(n_\sigma+1,\ldots,n_\sigma+n_\pi) = \sum_{\mu=n_\sigma+1}^{n_\sigma+n_\pi} \mathcal{H}_{core}(\mu) + \frac{1}{2} \sum_{\mu,\nu=n_\sigma+1}^{n_\sigma+n_\pi}{}' (1/r_{\mu\nu}) \tag{8-12}$$

where

$$\mathcal{H}_{core}(\mu) = \mathcal{H}_N(\mu) + J_\sigma(\mu) - K_\sigma(\mu) \tag{8-13}$$

The coulomb operator J_σ is defined by the formula

$$J_\sigma(\mu)(\Pi) = \int (\Sigma)^* \sum_\sigma (1/r_{\sigma\mu})(\Sigma)(\Pi)\, d\tau_\sigma \tag{8-14}$$

and the exchange operator K_σ by the formula

$$K_\sigma(\mu)(\Pi) = \int (\Sigma)^* \sum_\sigma \left[(1/r_{\sigma\mu})(\Sigma_{ex}^{\mu})(\Pi_{ex}^{\sigma})\right] d\tau_\sigma \tag{8-15}$$

in which $(\Sigma_{ex}^{\mu})(\Pi_{ex}^{\sigma})$ represents what is obtained from $(\Sigma)(\Pi)$ upon exchange of sigma electron σ for pi electron μ.

By the symmetry of the situation, there also is a resolution of the electronic energy of the form

$$E_e = E_\sigma + E_\pi^0 \tag{8-16}$$

where E_π^0 is obtained from (Π) using an $\mathcal{H}_\pi^0$ analogous to Eq. (8-11) and E_σ is obtained from (Σ) using an $\mathcal{H}_\sigma$ analogous to Eq. (8-12), namely,

$$\mathcal{H}_\sigma(1,2,\ldots,n_\sigma) = \sum_{\kappa=1}^{n_\sigma} \mathcal{H}_{peel}(\kappa) + \frac{1}{2} \sum_{\kappa,\lambda=1}^{n_\sigma}{}' (1/r_{\kappa\lambda}) \tag{8-17}$$

with

$$\mathcal{H}_{peel}(\kappa) = \mathcal{H}_N(\kappa) + J_\pi(\kappa) - K_\pi(\kappa) \tag{8-18}$$

With this partitioning of the energy, the sigma-pi interaction terms are all in E_σ, entering it through the terms $\mathcal{H}_{peel}$.

A justification for the usual procedure of applying the variational method to the pi wave function should now be clear. If we are willing to accept the same, fixed sigma description for a set of states, and total wave functions for the states which satisfy the separability conditions, that is, if we are willing to accept the pi-electron approximation as defined above, then the application of the variational method to Eq. (8-2) entails no error. For the term E_σ^0 in Eq. (8-8) will then be a constant, and the operator $\mathcal{H}_{core}(\mu)$ of Eq. (8-13) then is fixed.

An intriguing possibility is an iterative calculation of both (Σ) and (Π) in a description $[(\Sigma)(\Pi)]$: Guess (Σ), which fixes $\mathcal{H}_{core}$, determine (Π) by solving the pi variational problem, use this (Π) to fix $\mathcal{H}_{peel}$, determine (Σ) by solving the sigma variational problem, and repeat, until mutually consistent (Σ) and (Π) have been obtained. Calculations by this method have been carried out for the formaldehyde molecule by Parks and Parr.[97]

Ways to transcend systematically the pi-electron approximation can be readily fitted into this scheme.[95] For example, we might have for two distinct molecular states

$$\Psi_1 = [(\Sigma_1)(\Pi_1)] \quad \text{and} \quad \Psi_2 = [(\Sigma_2)(\Pi_2)] \tag{8-19}$$

with $(\Sigma_1) \neq (\Sigma_2)$. Then we would have the *pi-electron approximation with adjustable core*. Or, a particular state might require the superposition of two or more functions of the simple product type,

$$\Psi = C[(\Sigma)(\Pi)] + C'[(\Sigma')(\Pi')] + \cdots \tag{8-20}$$

This is a special form of configuration interaction, an important example of which is the interaction that provides the spin polarization required to account for the hyperfine structure in the electron-spin-resonance spectrum of an aromatic free radical[98]:

$$\Psi = C[(^1\Sigma)(^2\Pi)] + C'[(^3\Sigma)(^2\Pi)] + \cdots \tag{8-21}$$

A wave function of the form of Eq. (8-20) still does not have the most general possible form; it may be necessary to include terms in which the numbers of "sigma" and "pi" electrons are changed. An important problem for future investigation is the extent to which such configurations indeed are important. If they are important, the value of the pi-electron approximation will not ultimately turn out to be so great as if they are not (which is my own suspicion).

The type of "separation" argument and theorems that we have outlined here has other applications, as we shall see in a later section.

9 THE HÜCKEL METHOD VS. THE GOEPPERT-MAYER AND SKLAR METHOD

We may conclude from the foregoing that, if we proceed to do variational calculations with the pi-electron Hamiltonian of Eq. (8-1),

$$\mathcal{H}_\pi(1,2,\ldots,n_\pi) = \sum_\mu \mathcal{H}_{\text{core}}(\mu) + \frac{1}{2}\sum_{\mu\nu}{}' (1/r_{\mu\nu}) \tag{9-1}$$

we necessarily shall be neglecting correlation energy between sigma and pi electrons, and we shall be assuming that sigma parts of wave functions do not change from state to state. But these are not such extreme assumptions, and we can always correct for them by taking up some of the methods for transcending the pi-electron approximation that we have mentioned.

In the *Hückel method* for pi-electron calculations,[99,100] Eq. (9-1) is not employed, but the much simpler form

$$\mathcal{H}_\pi(1,2,\ldots,n_\pi) = \sum_\mu \mathcal{H}_{\text{eff}}(\mu) \tag{9-2}$$

is used, where $\mathcal{H}_{\text{eff}}(\mu)$ is some operator that incorporates the effects of the electron-repulsion terms in Eq. (9-1) in some average way. The Schrödinger equation $\mathcal{H}_\pi(\Pi) = E_\pi(\Pi)$ can then be immediately reduced to a series of one-electron equations. For, if we assume the product form $(\Pi) = \phi_1(1)\alpha(1)\phi_1(2)\beta(2)\cdots$, or indeed the antisymmetrization of this, we get differential equations for the ϕ_i:

$$\mathcal{H}_{eff}(\mu)\phi_i(\mu) = e_i\phi_i(\mu) \tag{9-3}$$

where, for the closed-shell case,

$$E_\pi = 2\sum_i e_i \tag{9-4}$$

the summation being over the distinct space orbitals, each of which accommodates two electrons.

A second assumption in the Hückel method is the LCAO approximation; it is supposed that

$$\phi_i = \sum_p C_{ip}\chi_p \tag{9-5}$$

where the χ_p are π atomic orbitals on the several atoms in the conjugated system (the 2p orbitals perpendicular to the molecular plane). Equations (9-3) and (9-5) define a linear variational problem; by Eqs. (2-6) to (2-9), the C_{ip} are solutions of the equations

$$\sum_p C_{ip}(H_{pq}^{eff} - S_{pq}e_i) = 0 \tag{9-6}$$

which has nontrivial solutions when the e_i are roots of the secular equation

$$\left|H_{pq}^{eff} - S_{pq}e\right| = 0 \tag{9-7}$$

The problem thus is to determine the matrix elements

$$H_{pq}^{eff} = \int \chi_p^*(1)\mathcal{H}_{eff}(1)\chi_q(1)\,dv(1) \tag{9-8}$$

and

$$S_{pq} = \int \chi_p^*(1)\chi_q(1)\,dv(1) \tag{9-9}$$

for given atomic orbitals χ_p.

The final and crucial assumptions in the Hückel method pertain to the evaluation of the integrals S_{pq} and H_{pq}^{eff}. The former often are computed for Slater orbitals, but more often they are ignored except when p is equal to q:

$$S_{pq} = \delta_{pq} \tag{9-10}$$

In fact, neighboring pi-overlap integrals in hydrocarbons are on the order of 0.3, so this assumption superficially is a bad one. However, it can be shown, by an argument similar to the one we shall be giving at the end of the next section, that this assumption leads to small error provided it is made in concert with the next assumptions.[101]

For the quantities H_{pq}^{eff} we distinguish the cases $p \neq q$ and $p = q$, and in the usual Hückel method regard the *coulomb integral*

$$\alpha_p = H_{pp}^{eff} = \int \chi_p^* \mathcal{H}_{eff}(1) \chi_p(1)\, dv(1) \tag{9-11}$$

as an empirical property of an atom, the *resonance integral*

$$\beta_{pq} = H_{pq}^{eff} = \int \chi_p(1) \mathcal{H}_{eff}(1) \chi_q(1)\, dv(1) \tag{9-12}$$

as an empirical property of a bond, and we set

$$\beta_{pq} = 0 \tag{9-13}$$

when p and q are not neighboring atoms. In this scheme, ethylene, benzene, and naphthalene are, for example, each two-parameter problems, requiring the values only of the carbon coulomb integral α_C and the carbon-carbon resonance integral β_{CC}; in pyridine there would also be an α_N, a β_{CN}, and possible changes in the α_C from one C to the next (due to "inductive" effects).

We need not outline the many applications that have been made of the Hückel method nor detail its successes, because the new books by Roberts and Streitwieser[99,100] do this very well. The Streitwieser treatment[100] is truly extraordinary. Especially fine is his Chapter 5 on heteroatoms, in which is given a table of best-compromise α and β values, for many molecules. The strong point of Roberts' book[99] is a set of 60 graded problems.

The disadvantages of the Hückel method are several. From the practical standpoint, the parameter values required to fit one property differ from those required to fit another, which should not be for a semiquantitative theory the internal mathematics of which is consistent, and it is impossible to describe with this independent-particle model the splittings of several electron volts that are found between singlet and triplet states arising from the same electron configuration. From the more theoretical standpoint, it just is not valid to write Eqs. (9-3) and (9-4). For although the Hartree-Fock operator of Eq. (6-9) might be interpreted as the $\mathcal{H}_{eff}$ of Eq. (9-3), in that case E_π would not be given by a sum of eigenvalues as in Eq. (9-4) but by Eq. (5-38):

$$E_\pi = 2 \sum_i \frac{1}{2}(\epsilon_i + I_i) \tag{9-14}$$

[The trouble with an equation like Eq. (9-4) is that it counts electronic repulsions twice.[102]] Against the theory from a purely theoretical viewpoint is its heavy use of empiricism; one really wants to compute molecular properties from scratch, so to speak.

A method that at first sight seems very much different indeed is the method of Goeppert-Mayer and Sklar.[8,103] Here the full pi-electron operator of Eq. (9-1) is employed, and the LCAO approximation of Eq. (9-5). Using proper theoretical formulas, LCAO-SCF,[104,105] and/or configuration-interaction,[106] calculations are carried through, in terms of integrals over the molecular orbitals ϕ_i, the integrals I_{ij} and $(ij|kl)$ of Eqs. (5-27) and (5-28), or, ultimately, in terms of the core and electron-repulsion integrals, over atomic $2p\pi$ orbitals, the integrals I_{pq} and $(pq|rs)$ of Eqs. (6-17) and (6-18). To obtain the I_{pq}, reasonable assumptions are made about $\mathcal{H}_{core}$; the $(pq|rs)$ are obtained by direct quadratures for Slater orbitals.[107]

Later we shall be giving a number of examples showing how the Goeppert-Mayer-Sklar method works: It does not work very well. Although singlet-triplet splits do appear, they tend to come out too big. The integrals are very difficult to compute, and there are very many of them—on the order of $N^4/8$ for a large molecule containing N pi orbitals! This "N^4 difficulty" simply halts any attempt to calculate molecules larger than, say, naphthalene by this method.

The purely theoretical delineation of $\mathcal{H}_{core}$ can be criticized. Treating it empirically admits of the strongest possible justification of the pi-electron approximation itself, whereas any actual evaluation requires some specific choice of sigma wave function, which inevitably means a guess.

Also against the Goeppert-Mayer-Sklar method is the more general argument that, if we want to predict data with such a simple model, we should incorporate at least some actual molecular data, to "calibrate" the theory.

Thus we seem to be caught in a dilemma. Wax empirical, never know the full theoretical basis, and give up the hope of accounting for excited-state properties in any more than a gross way. Or go purely theoretical and feel smug with the scheme, but bear much hard work, be content to treat small molecules, and also fail to account quantitatively for molecular properties.

10 SYNTHESIS OF THE HÜCKEL AND GOEPPERT-MAYER-SKLAR METHODS: EXTENDED HÜCKEL METHODS

The synthesis of the Hückel and Goeppert-Mayer-Sklar methods began, I would say, with two papers by Moffitt on the oxygen molecule.[108,109] This molecule has a rich electronic spectrum, and an elementary consideration of its orbital structure indicates that a pi-electron treatment of it would be appropriate. Moffitt accordingly set out to perform a Goeppert-Mayer-Sklar-type calculation. He obtained results in remarkable discord with experiment.[108]

This led Moffitt to invent (and test) a new method, called the *atoms-in-molecules method*.[109] This we shall consider in more detail in Sec. 17. Let it suffice here to state the key idea: Why not incorporate into molecular-orbital theory atomic-spectroscopic data, so that the various molecular-energy levels will at least come out correctly at infinite internuclear distance? This provided a direct challenge to the rather formal Goeppert-Mayer-Sklar method, which others soon took up.

Just what characteristics should we expect of a workable and useful theory of pi-electron systems? From what we have said, we might infer the following six:

1. Pi electrons should be treated apart from the rest; that is, the pi-electron approximation should be invoked.
2. Pi-electron wave functions should be composed from orbitals on the individual atoms.
3. Pi-electron repulsions should be included.
4. The treatment of pi-electron repulsions should be simplified.
5. Provision should be made for use of atomic data.
6. Empirical elements should be included.

Requirements 1 and 4 are necessary to make a method manageable; requirement 2 is an expression of our conviction that our elementary ideas about orbitals are valid; requirement 3 is necessary if we are going to treat spectra (how else can we separate singlet and triplet states?); statement 5, we shall see later, is what will allow us correctly to locate ionic- and covalent-molecular states on the energy scale relative to each other; requirement 6 will take care of the molecular core and the errors forced on us by the other requirements. The Hückel method satisfies 1 and 2 and 6, but goes so far in 4 that 3 is negated and 5 and 6 are ineffectual; the Goeppert-Mayer-Sklar method fails in 4, 5, and 6.

A theory has been evolving since 1953 that has all these characteristics,[110-112] a theory that has been called the *generalized Hückel method*[4] and *simplified complete LCAO-MO theory*.[113] The main features of this method as it was originally proposed (we shall discuss various modifications and extensions) are just those of the Goeppert-Mayer-Sklar method, except in the vital matter of integral evaluation.

For the various integrals, one proceeds according to the following prescription. The one-center core integrals are referred to atomic ionization potentials by elucidation of $\mathcal{H}_{\text{core}}$, in the manner of Goeppert-Mayer and Sklar.[103] This gives the formula

$$\alpha_p^{\text{core}} = -\mathcal{I}_p - \sum_{q \neq p} \gamma_{pq} - P_p = \alpha_p \tag{10-1}$$

where $\mathcal{I}_p$ is the ionization potential of an electron from atom p in its valence state, the quantity

$$\gamma_{pq} = (pp|qq) \tag{10-2}$$

is the coulomb-electronic repulsion between a pi electron in orbital χ_p and one in orbital χ_q, and the quantity

$$P_p = -\int \chi_p(1)\mathcal{H}^0_{\text{core}}(1)\chi_p(1)\,dv(1) \tag{10-3}$$

(called a *neutral penetration integral*) is the total (positive) attraction for an electron in χ_p for the rest of the *neutral* core.

The integrals S_{pq} and β_{pq} are treated as in the Hückel method:

$$S_{pq} = \delta_{pq} \tag{10-4}$$

$$\beta_{pq}^{\text{core}} = \left\{\begin{matrix}\text{empirical property of a bond} \\ \text{for p and q neighbors} \\ 0 \text{ otherwise}\end{matrix}\right\} \tag{10-5}$$

Equation (10-4) seems very drastic, but we shall subsequently see that it is not.

For the electronic-repulsion integrals $(pq|rs)$, one first makes the *zero-differential-overlap* assumption[114]

$$\chi_p(1)\chi_q(1)\,dv(1) = 0 \qquad \text{for} \qquad p \neq q \tag{10-6}$$

This immediately eliminates most of these integrals, leaving only the $\approx N^2/2$ of them of the form of Eq. (10-2). Again this seems drastic; again we shall subsequently see that it is not.

The integrals γ_{pq} for $p \neq q$ are computed from theoretical formulas or modified theoretical formulas of one kind or another, perhaps making use of empirical data, subject to the condition

$$\gamma_{pq} \rightarrow 1/R \qquad \text{for large } R = |\mathbf{r}_p - \mathbf{r}_q| \tag{10-7}$$

For $p = q$, a formula due to Pariser may be employed,[115]

$$\gamma_{pp} = \mathcal{I}_p - \mathcal{A}_p \tag{10-8}$$

where $\mathcal{A}_p$ is the orbital electron affinity of atom p.†

The rationalization of Eq. (10-8) is instructive and implies a good deal about the deficiencies in the usual orbital approaches. Pariser was led to this formula by an argument, deriving from Moffitt's work, on the energetics of a simple atomic charge-transfer process

$$\dot{C} + \dot{C} \rightarrow \ddot{C}^- + C^+ \tag{10-9}$$

This is the type of charge transfer that surely must be properly assessed in a molecule in order that orbital theories give reasonable answers, so let us see

† The ionization potential $\mathcal{I}_p$ here and that in Eq. (10-1) will not, in general, be for the same atomic valence state.

what ordinary theory would give for the energy change for this process. The electrons pictured are pi electrons; we suppose that the rest of the two-quantum electrons on each of the carbons are in sp^2-hybridized valence states.

According to the naive pi-electron theory at the Goeppert-Mayer and Sklar level, the energy of each of the electrons on the left is minus the valence-state ionization potential $-\mathcal{I}_C$. On the right we would have twice this $(-2\mathcal{I}_C)$ supplemented by the mutual repulsion of the two carbon pi electrons, $(cc|cc) = \gamma_{cc}$. Thus, ignoring core energy changes,

$$\Delta E_{theoret} = \gamma_{cc} \approx 16.93 \text{ ev} \qquad (10\text{-}10)$$

where the numerical value is for Slater $2p\pi$ orbitals with $Z = 3.18$.

This very energy change can be derived from atomic spectroscopic data (plus some theory on valence-state energies and how they relate to spectroscopic-state energies—itself an area of current research[116]). Namely, it is the valence-state ionization potential minus the valence-state electron affinity,

$$\Delta E_{exptl} = \mathcal{I}_C - \mathcal{A}_C = 11.54 - 0.46 = 11.08 \text{ ev} \qquad (10\text{-}11)$$

This value is very different from that in Eq. (10-10).

One way to resolve this dilemma is to note that the theoretical calculation clearly is wrong; it ignores changes in the sigma structure and kinetic energy and also correlation effects between the two pi electrons in C^-. But there is another way; set

$$\gamma_{cc} = \mathcal{I}_C - \mathcal{A}_C = 11.08 \text{ ev} \qquad (10\text{-}12)$$

and forge ahead, making sure that corresponding downward adjustments are made in $\gamma_{c_a c_b}$, and invoking the physical chemist's intuitive rule of smoothness. This is what was suggested,[111] and the idea has proved fruitful.

One can anticipate the consequences of changing this integral for aromatic systems. Simple molecular-orbital descriptions are going to be better than a Goeppert-Mayer-Sklar calculation would suggest, and configuration interaction less important. For, if we recall the discussion surrounding Eq. (4-10), the simple molecular-orbital description tends to emphasize ionic contributions, and these are enhanced by use of Eq. (10-12) in place of Eq. (10-10).

To complete our overview of the ideas involved in the generalized Hückel method, let us briefly discuss the rationalization of Eqs. (10-4) and (10-6) that can be given by invoking the idea of *orthogonalized atomic orbitals*.[117] The two-electron case should serve to illustrate what is involved,[118,119] so we reconsider the hydrogen molecule along the lines of Sec. 4, Eq. (4-6) and the following material, employing in place of the overlapping atomic orbitals $1s_A$ and $1s_B$ their symmetrically orthogonalized counterparts, the *Löwdin orbitals*,[117]

$$\lambda_A = \left[\frac{1}{2}(1+S)^{-\frac{1}{2}} + \frac{1}{2}(1-S)^{-\frac{1}{2}}\right](1s_A) + \left[\frac{1}{2}(1+S)^{-\frac{1}{2}} - \frac{1}{2}(1-S)^{-\frac{1}{2}}\right](1s_B)$$

$$\lambda_B = \left[\frac{1}{2}(1+S)^{-\frac{1}{2}} - \frac{1}{2}(1-S)^{-\frac{1}{2}}\right](1s_A) + \left[\frac{1}{2}(1+S)^{-\frac{1}{2}} + \frac{1}{2}(1-S)^{-\frac{1}{2}}\right](1s_B) \quad (10\text{-}13)$$

You may readily verify that λ_A and λ_B are orthonormal. In Fig. 3 the orbitals λ_A and λ_B are sketched together with $1s_A$ and $1s_B$. Notice that, near the atoms, λ_A is very like $1s_A$, λ_B like $1s_B$, but that in the bond region $\lambda_A\lambda_B$ is much smaller than $1s_A 1s_B$, and $\lambda_A\lambda_B$ integrates to zero over all space.

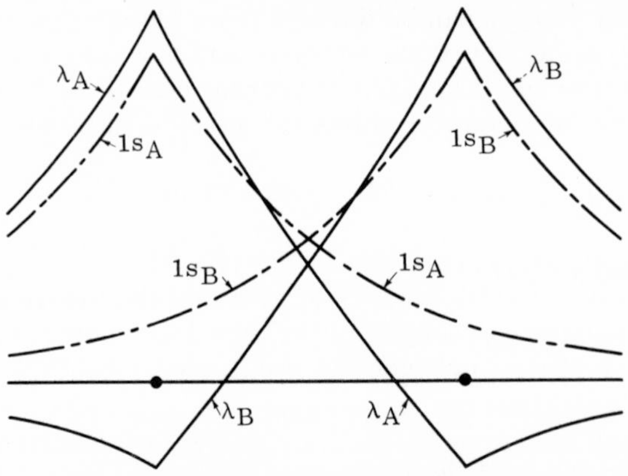

Figure 3. Orthogonalized atomic orbitals λ_A and λ_B in the hydrogen molecule, plotted along the internuclear axis. The protons are at the positions marked •. Effective charges in the original overlapping orbitals $1s_A$ and $1s_B$ are taken to be 1.193, the Weinbaum value.

We now set down orbital descriptions patterned after those in Sec. 4, but with λ_A and λ_B as the basic orbitals. If we label wave functions built from the λ by bars, we first have what we can call the $\overline{\text{VB}}$ scheme, which has been developed in detail and extensively applied by McWeeny[120,121]:

$$\overline{\Phi}_{\text{COVALENT}} = \lambda_A(1)\lambda_B(2) + \lambda_B(1)\lambda_A(2)$$
$$\overline{\Phi}_{\text{IONIC}} = \lambda_A(1)\lambda_A(2) + \lambda_B(1)\lambda_B(2) \quad (10\text{-}14)$$

$$\Phi_{\text{BETTER}} = \overline{C}\overline{\Phi}_{\text{COVALENT}} + \overline{D}\overline{\Phi}_{\text{IONIC}} \quad (10\text{-}15)$$

The final description of Eq. (10-15) is, of course, identical with the Weinbaum function of Eq. (4-10). However, the component functions $\overline{\Phi}_{\mathrm{COVALENT}}$ and $\overline{\Phi}_{\mathrm{IONIC}}$ are far from the analogous Φ_{COVALENT} and Φ_{IONIC} of Eqs. (4-8). Thus, although the $\overline{\mathrm{VB}}$ scheme has advantages over the VB scheme from the computational viewpoint, its components have lost their physical meaning. Indeed, Slater has shown that the function $\overline{\Phi}_{\mathrm{COVALENT}}$ completely fails to predict binding in the hydrogen molecule.[122] To ignore overlap in a simple valence-bond scheme is fatal.

But let us not despair before we have examined the molecular-orbital method. To continue in parallel with Sec. 4, we could write

$$\bar{\phi}(1) = \frac{1}{\sqrt{2}}[\lambda_A(1) + \lambda_B(1)]$$
$$\bar{\phi}'(1) = \frac{1}{\sqrt{2}}[\lambda_A(1) - \lambda_B(1)] \tag{10-16}$$

$$\overline{\Phi}_{\mathrm{MO}} = \bar{\phi}(1)\bar{\phi}(2)$$
$$\overline{\Phi}'_{\mathrm{MO}} = \bar{\phi}'(1)\bar{\phi}'(2) \tag{10-17}$$

$$\Phi_{\mathrm{BETTER}} = \overline{E}\,\overline{\Phi}_{\mathrm{MO}} + \overline{F}\,\overline{\Phi}'_{\mathrm{MO}} \tag{10-18}$$

In this, which we may label the $\overline{\mathrm{MO}}$ method, we again end up with the Weinbaum function. This time, however, we have a remarkable preservation of identity with the usual MO method at the intermediate stages. For, as can be immediately seen from Eq. (10-13), the basic building blocks have not changed at all,

$$\bar{\phi}(1) \equiv \phi(1) \qquad \bar{\phi}'(1) \equiv \phi'(1) \tag{10-19}$$

Hence

$$\overline{\Phi}_{\mathrm{MO}} \equiv \Phi_{\mathrm{MO}} \qquad \overline{\Phi}'_{\mathrm{MO}} \equiv \Phi'_{\mathrm{MO}} \qquad \overline{E} = E \qquad \overline{F} = F \tag{10-20}$$

That is to say, our ignoring overlap in the molecular-orbital scheme for this molecule brings in *no error whatsoever*, if all integrals are reinterpreted as being over orthogonalized atomic orbitals.

To be very specific, the energy formula of Eq. (4-20) may be accurately rewritten

$$\begin{aligned} E_{\mathrm{MO}} = 2W_H + \frac{1}{R} + \frac{1}{2}[(\lambda_a\lambda_a|\lambda_a\lambda_a) + (\lambda_a\lambda_a|\lambda_b\lambda_b) + 2(\lambda_a\lambda_b|\lambda_a\lambda_b) \\ + 4(\lambda_a\lambda_a|\lambda_a\lambda_b)] - 2[(a|\lambda_a\lambda_a) + (a|\lambda_a\lambda_b)] \end{aligned} \tag{10-21}$$

We further may expect, remembering Fig. 3, that

$$(\lambda_a\lambda_b|\lambda_a\lambda_b) \approx 0 \qquad (\lambda_a\lambda_a|\lambda_a\lambda_b) \approx 0 \tag{10-22}$$

so that

$$E_{MO} \approx 2W_H + \frac{1}{R} + \frac{1}{2}[(\lambda_a\lambda_a|\lambda_a\lambda_a) + (\lambda_a\lambda_a|\lambda_b\lambda_b)] - 2[(a|\lambda_a\lambda_a) + (a|\lambda_a\lambda_b)] \tag{10-23}$$

This is just the formula one gets using the zero-differential-overlap assumption of Eq. (10-6), with all integrals interpreted as over Löwdin orbitals. When one makes the zero-differential-overlap assumption, one is equating to zero electronic-repulsion integrals involving overlap distributions between distinct, orthogonalized atomic orbitals.

This argument, unfortunately, does not go through so neatly unless the molecular orbitals are determined by symmetry.[119] Nevertheless, we conclude that to ignore overlap and even differential overlap in a molecular-orbital scheme is not a bad procedure.

11 THE ETHYLENE MOLECULE

The conventional (although probably not the best) prototype for pi-electron systems is the ethylene molecule, with two pi electrons and two atomic $2p\pi$ orbitals available for the pi-bond formation.

Experimental facts about the molecule that we might hope to explain include its lowest pi-excited electronic-excitation energies, 4.6 ev for the triplet and 7.6 ev for the singlet, its first ionization potential at 10.5 ev, and a substantial barrier to cis-trans isomerizations in substituted ethylenes.

The Hückel theory for ethylene is very simple indeed. The secular equation is

$$\begin{vmatrix} \alpha - e & \beta \\ \beta & \alpha - e \end{vmatrix} = 0 \tag{11-1}$$

from which follow the one-electron energy levels

$$e_1 = \alpha + \beta \qquad e_2 = \alpha - \beta \tag{11-2}$$

and the molecular orbitals (including overlap)

$$\phi_1 = \frac{1}{\sqrt{2(1 + S)}}(a + b) \tag{11-3}$$

$$\phi_2 = \frac{1}{\sqrt{2(1 - S)}} (a - b) \tag{11-4}$$

where a and b are the two carbon $2p\pi$ atomic orbitals. The orbital ϕ_1 is bonding, the orbital ϕ_2 antibonding. In the molecular ground state N two electrons should be assigned to ϕ_1, giving the energy

$$E_N(C_2H_4) = 2\alpha + 2\beta \tag{11-5}$$

The first excited state will have one electron in each of ϕ_1 and ϕ_2:

$$E_{V \text{ or } T}(C_2H_4) = 2\alpha \tag{11-6}$$

With electronic repulsions neglected in this method, the singlet excited state V and the triplet excited state T will have the same energy; the excitation energy is

$$\Delta E(N \rightarrow T \text{ or } V) = -2\beta \tag{11-7}$$

The actual experimental separation between T and V is 3.0 ev, which this theory necessarily fails to predict. If we set the weighted average $[(4.6) + (7.6)]/2 = 6.1$ equal to -2β, we obtain $\beta = -3.0$ ev, as an empirical value that fits the spectra as well as possible.† How reasonable this is we may check by computing another property of this molecule or another molecule. Deferring the latter, we look at the ionization potential and electron affinity of ethylene itself. The same model gives

$$E(C_2H_4^+) = \alpha + \beta \tag{11-8}$$

and hence

$$\mathcal{J} = E(C_2H_4^+) - E_N(C_2H_4) = -\alpha - \beta \tag{11-9}$$

Similarly,

$$E(C_2H_4^-) = 3\alpha + \beta \tag{11-10}$$

and hence

$$\mathcal{A} = E_N(C_2H_4) - E(C_2H_4^-) = -\alpha + \beta \tag{11-11}$$

†Of course, we could take a value of β to fit the singlet state alone (or the triplet).

Using the experimental $\mathcal{I} = 10.5$ ev, Eq. (11-9) gives $\alpha = -10.5 + 3.0 = -7.5$ ev, so that Eq. (11-11) predicts $\mathcal{A} = 7.5 - 3.0 = 4.5$ ev. The electron affinity of ethylene is unknown; it may be positive but it is unlikely to be this large.

A theory including electron repulsion will presumably be better, so let us now look at the molecule from the Goeppert-Mayer-Sklar viewpoint.[123] The problem is to build up wave functions, including spins, from the molecular orbitals of Eqs. (11-3) and (11-4), and to compute energies from the Hamiltonian operator

$$\mathcal{H}_\pi(1,2) = \mathcal{H}_{\text{core}}(1) + \mathcal{H}_{\text{core}}(2) + (1/r_{12}) \qquad (11\text{-}12)$$

We have already set up the apparatus for doing this in Sec. 5, Eqs. (5-33) and following. The configurational wave functions are

$$\begin{aligned} &\Phi_1 = (\phi_1\bar{\phi}_1) \qquad \Phi_2 = (\phi_2\bar{\phi}_2) \\ &\Phi_V = 2^{-\frac{1}{2}}[(\phi_1\bar{\phi}_2) + (\phi_2\bar{\phi}_1)] \\ &\Phi_T = 2^{-\frac{1}{2}}[(\phi_1\bar{\phi}_2) - (\phi_2\bar{\phi}_1)] \end{aligned} \qquad (11\text{-}13)$$

The matrix elements for the linear variational function,

$$\Phi = C_1\Phi_1 + C_2\Phi_2 + C_V\Phi_V + C_T\Phi_T \qquad (11\text{-}14)$$

have the values

$$\begin{aligned} &H_{11} = 2I_1 + J_{11} \qquad H_{22} = 2I_2 + J_{22} \\ &H_{12} = K_{12} \\ &H_{VV} = I_1 + I_2 + J_{12} + K_{12} \\ &H_{TT} = I_1 + I_2 + J_{12} - K_{12} \\ &H_{1V} = H_{2V} = H_{1T} = H_{2T} = H_{VT} = 0 \end{aligned} \qquad (11\text{-}15)$$

where

$$\begin{aligned} I_1 &= \int \phi_1(1)\mathcal{H}_{\text{core}}(1)\phi_1(1)\,dv(1) \\ I_2 &= \int \phi_2(1)\mathcal{H}_{\text{core}}(1)\phi_2(1)\,dv(1) \\ J_{11} &= \iint \phi_1(1)\phi_1(1)(1/r_{12})\phi_1(2)\phi_1(2)\,dv(1)\,dv(2) \\ J_{22} &= \iint \phi_2(1)\phi_2(1)(1/r_{12})\phi_2(2)\phi_2(2)\,dv(1)\,dv(2) \\ J_{12} &= \iint \phi_1(1)\phi_1(1)(1/r_{12})\phi_2(2)\phi_2(2)\,dv(1)\,dv(2) \\ K_{12} &= \iint \phi_1(1)\phi_2(1)(1/r_{12})\phi_1(2)\phi_2(2)\,dv(1)\,dv(2) \end{aligned} \qquad (11\text{-}16)$$

That Φ_1 and Φ_2 do not interact with Φ_V and Φ_T follows from the fact that the former are symmetric, the latter antisymmetric, with respect to reflection in a plane bisecting the C—C bond. The secular equation thus factors into two 1×1's and a 2×2, giving the roots

$$E_V = H_{VV} = I_1 + I_2 + J_{12} + K_{12}$$
$$E_T = H_{TT} = I_1 + I_2 + J_{12} - K_{12} \tag{11-17}$$

and E_N and E_Z low and high roots of

$$\begin{vmatrix} H_{11} - E & K_{12} \\ K_{12} & H_{22} - E \end{vmatrix} = 0 \tag{11-18}$$

where H_{11} and H_{22} are given by Eqs. (11-15).

The problem of determining the energy levels is thus reduced to the problem of determining the electronic-repulsion integrals J_{11}, J_{22}, J_{12}, K_{12} and the core integrals I_1 and I_2 (or, alternatively, $2I_1$ and $I_2 - I_1$, the last only entering the excitation energies relative to the ground state). In terms of integrals over the atomic orbitals a and b, these are quickly seen† to be given by the formulas

$$I_1 = \frac{\alpha^{\text{core}} + \beta^{\text{core}}}{1 + S} \qquad I_2 = \frac{\alpha^{\text{core}} - \beta^{\text{core}}}{1 - S} \tag{11-19}$$

$$I_2 - I_1 = \frac{-2(\beta^{\text{core}} - S\alpha^{\text{core}})}{1 - S^2} \tag{11-20}$$

$$2J_{11} = \frac{(aa|aa) + (aa|bb) + 2(ab|ab) + 4(aa|ab)}{(1 + S)^2}$$
$$2J_{22} = \frac{(aa|aa) + (aa|bb) + 2(ab|ab) - 4(aa|ab)}{(1 - S)^2} \tag{11-21}$$

$$2J_{12} = \frac{(aa|aa) + (aa|bb) - 2(ab|ab)}{(1 - S^2)}$$
$$2K_{12} = \frac{(aa|aa) - (aa|bb)}{(1 - S^2)} \tag{11-22}$$

All that is left is the calculation of the integrals α^{core}, β^{core}, S, (aa|aa), (aa|bb), (ab|ab), and (aa|ab).

† This part of the problem is not so trivial for problems with many electrons!

Crawford and Parr[123] carried through the calculation "purely theoretically" using Slater 2pπ orbitals and the Goeppert-Mayer-Sklar prescription for $\mathcal{H}_{core}$. The results were qualitatively satisfactory, and further there was obtained a nice description of the effect on the levels of a twist of the molecule away from planarity. Some of the results for the planar configuration are displayed in Table 7; Table 8 gives numerical values for most atomic and all the molecular integrals that enter this calculation.

TABLE 7
Pi-Electron Energy Levels of Ethylene (in Electron Volts)

		Purely theoretical calculations			Simplified or semiempirical calculations		
State	Experimental	GMS method[a]	Murai[b]	Huzinaga[c]	Zero differential overlap (theoretical)[d]	Zero differential overlap (semiempirical)[e]	I'Haya[f]
N	0.0	0.0	0.0	0.0	0.0	0.0	0.0
T	4.6	3.1	4.6	4.5	3.3	4.6	3.7
V	7.6	11.5	11.2	7.3	11.0	7.6	7.1
1		1.3			1.1	0.2	0.3
N for $C_2H_4^+$	10.5[g]	11.9[i]	8.8	8.5	11.7	$-\alpha - 6.4$[j]	10.8
N for $C_2H_4^-$	$-\alpha$[h]	6.5[i]			5.8	$\alpha + 20.9$	6.0

[a]Reference 123, with Z = 3.18.
[b]Reference 124. Different Z values for different states.
[c]Reference 125. Different Z values for different states plus different Z values for bonding and antibonding molecular orbitals.
[d]Reference 110, slightly modified as described in text.
[e]Reference 111, slightly modified as described in text.
[f]Reference 126, first paper. Somewhat different values are reported in the second paper.
[g]Ionization potential of ethylene.
[h]Negative electron affinity of ethylene, experimentally unknown.
[i]Calculated as described in this text.
[j]The value $\alpha = -16.9$ ev will force a fit of the observed ionization potential, but it is not in accord with Eq. (10-1).

TABLE 8
Integrals Entering the Pi-Electron Treatment of Ethylene[a]

Integral	Slater orbitals[b]	Zero differential overlap, purely theoretical[c]	Zero differential overlap, semiempirical[d]	Löwdin orbitals[e]
S_{ab}	0.2772	0	0	0
(aa|aa)	16.93	16.93	11.08	17.29
(aa|bb)	9.26	9.26	8.08	8.98
(aa|ab)	3.58	0	0	−0.09
(ab|ab)	1.08	0	0	−0.12
I_1	−23.72[f]	−23.72	$\alpha + \beta$[g]	$\alpha^\lambda + \beta^\lambda = -23.72$[h]
$I_2 - I_1$	6.06	6.06	$-2\beta = 5.91$	$-2\beta^\lambda = 6.06$
J_{11}	13.08	13.09	9.58	13.08
J_{22}	13.44	13.09	9.58	13.44
J_{12}	13.01	13.09	9.58	13.01
K_{12}	4.16	3.84	1.50	4.16

[a]All values in ev.
[b]Reference 123, with $Z = 3.18$.
[c]Reference 110, slightly modified as described in text.
[d]Reference 111, slightly modified as described in text.
[e]Integrals calculated replacing a and b everywhere, respectively, by λ_A and λ_B, defined as in Eq. (10-13).
[f]This value assumes $-\mathcal{J} = -11.28$ ev in Eq. (10-1) and neglects the hydrogen atoms.
[g]The quantity α does not affect the excitation energies. See footnote j of Table 7.
[h]Superscripts λ denote integrals over Löwdin orbitals.

Several purely theoretical modifications of this calculation have been published.[8] We here mention only two, the one by Murai,[124] in which different effective charges were used in the pi atomic orbitals for the states N, T, and V, and a very recent one by Huzinaga,[125] in which in addition different charges were used in the bonding and antibonding molecular orbitals. These calculations are summarized in Table 7.

All these results are rather disappointing, the singlet-triplet split and ionization potential being hard to predict quantitatively and the calculations being unwieldy. We might hope for a simpler theory, and for a theory agreeing better with experiment.

The numbers in Table 8 themselves provide a clue as to how we might proceed: We should try to find a procedure whereby the clearly insignificant variations among the molecular integrals J_{11}, J_{22}, and J_{12} are caused to disappear. The zero-differential-overlap approximation of Eq. (10-6) will do the trick; if we employ it we obtain in place of Eqs. (10-6) the more simple

$$2J = 2J_{11} = 2J_{22} = 2J_{12} = (aa|aa) + (aa|bb) \qquad (11\text{-}23)$$

$$2K = 2K_{12} = (aa|aa) - (aa|bb) \qquad (11\text{-}24)$$

In this approximation we have

$$H_{22} - H_{11} = -4\beta \qquad (11\text{-}25)$$

so that the secular Eqs. (11-17) and (11-18) become

$$W_V = -2\beta + K \qquad W_T = -2\beta - K \qquad (11\text{-}26)$$

and W_N and W_Z low and high roots of

$$\begin{vmatrix} -W & K \\ K & -W - 4\beta \end{vmatrix} = 0 \qquad (11\text{-}27)$$

where $W = E - H_{11}$ is the energy relative to H_{11}, and the quantity β is defined by

$$-2\beta = I_2 - I_1 = \frac{-2(\beta^{\text{core}} - S\alpha^{\text{core}})}{1 - S^2} \qquad (11\text{-}28)$$

Results of doing the calculation in this way are shown in Tables 7 and 8. The results previously obtained are essentially duplicated with little effort.[110]

In this method of calculation, the quantity J does not even enter the excitation energies; they depend only on K and β. Thus we may use the experimental energies for the T and V states to determine empirical values of K and β, which gives $K = 1.50$ ev and $\beta = -2.96$ ev. If we then fix (aa|aa) at 11.1 ev by Pariser's argument [Eq. (10-12)], we obtain (aa|bb) = 8.1 ev, a little under the theoretical value for $2p\pi$ orbitals. This is the semiempirical zero-differential-overlap treatment, also summarized in Tables 7 and 8.[111]

The ionization potential and electron affinity can also be calculated in several ways, as shown in Tables 7 and 8. In order to get them right, I'Haya has used[126] a combination of theoretical and semiempirical reasoning, in which he takes cognizance of changes of pi-electron effective charges that accompany ionization; his results are included in Table 7. This particular complication should be less serious in larger conjugated systems than in ethylene, since the positive charge that results from ionization is spread over more atoms.†

Such modifications of the theory seem very drastic. We have tossed away some of the integrals, and we have changed the values of others. The value of the first is shown by the near equality of J, J_{11}, J_{22}, and J_{12} and of K and K_{12}; Table 7 shows that the truncation of the set of integrals has little effect. What we must have done in going from Eqs. (11-21) and (11-22) to Eqs. (11-23) and (11-24) was to make compensating errors in numerators and denominators.

The cancellation of errors can be viewed as a result of the remarkable accuracy of the *Mulliken approximation* to an overlap distribution,[127-129]

$$a(1)b(1) \approx \frac{S_{ab}}{2}[a(1)a(1) + b(1)b(1)] \tag{11-29}$$

If this is used to approximate the integrals (ab|ab) and (aa|ab) in Eqs. (11-21), overlap dependences of numerators and denominators cancel, and Eqs. (11-23) result; Eq. (11-24) comes more simply when S^2 is neglected compared with 1 in the denominator of Eq. (11-22).

Alternatively, we may see from the argument at the end of the last section that Eqs. (11-21) and (11-22) may be replaced without any error at all with a set of formulas in terms of integrals over Löwdin orthogonalized orbitals λ_A λ_B composed from a and b as in Eq. (10-13), namely,

$$\begin{aligned}
2J_{11} &= (\lambda_A\lambda_A|\lambda_A\lambda_A) + (\lambda_A\lambda_A|\lambda_B\lambda_B) + 2(\lambda_A\lambda_B|\lambda_A\lambda_B) + 4(\lambda_A\lambda_A|\lambda_A\lambda_B) \\
&\approx (\lambda_A\lambda_A|\lambda_A\lambda_A) + (\lambda_A\lambda_A|\lambda_B\lambda_B) \\
2J_{22} &= (\lambda_A\lambda_A|\lambda_A\lambda_A) + (\lambda_A\lambda_A|\lambda_B\lambda_B) + 2(\lambda_A\lambda_B|\lambda_A\lambda_B) - 4(\lambda_A\lambda_A|\lambda_A\lambda_B) \\
&\approx (\lambda_A\lambda_A|\lambda_A\lambda_A) + (\lambda_A\lambda_A|\lambda_B\lambda_B) \qquad\qquad (11\text{-}30) \\
2J_{12} &= (\lambda_A\lambda_A|\lambda_A\lambda_A) + (\lambda_A\lambda_A|\lambda_B\lambda_B) - 2(\lambda_A\lambda_B|\lambda_A\lambda_B) \\
&\approx (\lambda_A\lambda_A|\lambda_A\lambda_A) + (\lambda_A\lambda_A|\lambda_B\lambda_B) \\
2K_{12} &= (\lambda_A\lambda_A|\lambda_A\lambda_A) - (\lambda_A\lambda_A|\lambda_B\lambda_B)
\end{aligned}$$

The indicated approximate formulas are formally just our working Eqs. (11-23) and (11-24); that they are very good indeed may be seen from the numerical values of the integrals, listed in Table 8.

Further tampering with the formulas by changing the values of integrals is an even more subtle matter. The good results obtained suggest that there is

†It is for this reason that ethylene may not be such a good prototype for pi systems: it contains two ends, back to back, so to speak.

some validity to the Pariser argument; the failure of the purely theoretical treatment means that the pi-electron approximation is at fault, that the pi orbitals are not close to Slater $2p\pi$ orbitals, or that adequate provision has not been made for pi-electron correlations.

12 THE BENZENE MOLECULE

Saving the butadiene molecule for later consideration, we now consider the benzene molecule, the standard aromatic system.

Again we take the Hückel method first. There are six atomic $2p\pi$ orbitals, $\chi_0, \chi_1, \chi_2, \chi_3, \chi_4, \chi_5$, numbered consecutively around the ring, and six pi electrons; the molecular orbitals will be of the form

$$\phi_\ell = \sum_{p=0}^{5} C_{\ell p}\chi_p \tag{12-1}$$

where the $C_{\ell p}$ are solutions of the linear equations

$$\begin{aligned}
&C_{\ell 0}(\alpha - e) + C_{\ell 1}\beta + C_{\ell 5}\beta = 0\\
&C_{\ell 0}\beta + C_{\ell 1}(\alpha - e) + C_{\ell 2}\beta = 0\\
&C_{\ell 1}\beta + C_{\ell 2}(\alpha - e) + C_{\ell 3}\beta = 0\\
&C_{\ell 2}\beta + C_{\ell 3}(\alpha - e) + C_{\ell 4}\beta = 0\\
&C_{\ell 3}\beta + C_{\ell 4}(\alpha - e) + C_{\ell 5}\beta = 0\\
&C_{\ell 0}\beta + C_{\ell 4}\beta + C_{\ell 5}(\alpha - e) = 0
\end{aligned} \tag{12-2}$$

Nontrivial solutions are possible only when the energies e are solutions of the secular equation

$$\begin{vmatrix}
\alpha - e & \beta & 0 & 0 & 0 & \beta\\
\beta & \alpha - e & \beta & 0 & 0 & 0\\
0 & \beta & \alpha - e & \beta & 0 & 0\\
0 & 0 & \beta & \alpha - e & \beta & 0\\
0 & 0 & 0 & \beta & \alpha - e & \beta\\
\beta & 0 & 0 & 0 & \beta & \alpha - e
\end{vmatrix} = 0 \tag{12-3}$$

Evaluating the determinant by brute-force expansion, or otherwise, and factoring, we find

$$(\alpha + \beta - e)^2(\alpha - \beta - e)^2(\alpha + 2\beta - e)(\alpha - 2\beta - e) = 0 \qquad (12\text{-}4)$$

This gives the six roots, in order of decreasing energy,

$$\begin{aligned} e_3 &= \alpha - 2\beta \\ e_2 &= e_{-2} = \alpha - \beta \qquad \text{(degenerate level)} \\ e_1 &= e_{-1} = \alpha + \beta \qquad \text{(degenerate level)} \\ e_0 &= \alpha + 2\beta \end{aligned} \qquad (12\text{-}5)$$

These can be represented with a compact formula,

$$e_\ell = \alpha + 2\beta \cos(2\pi\ell/6) \qquad \ell = 0, \pm 1, \pm 2, 3 \qquad (12\text{-}6)$$

To obtain the corresponding coefficients, we substitute Eq. (12-6) into Eqs. (12-2), which gives, with the understanding that the index p is to be reduced modulo 6 ($p = 6$ is replaced by $p = 0$, $p = -1$ by $p = 5$, etc.),

$$C_{\ell p - 1} - 2C_{\ell p}\cos(2\pi\ell/6) + C_{\ell p + 1} = 0 \qquad p = 0,1,2,3,4,5 \qquad (12\text{-}7)$$

To solve for the $C_{\ell p}$, we try the substitution

$$C_{\ell p} = A_\ell (k_\ell)^p \qquad (12\text{-}8)$$

Then we get $k_\ell^2 - 2k_\ell \cos(2\pi\ell/6) + 1 = 0$, from which follows

$$k_\ell = \cos(2\pi\ell/6) \pm [\cos^2(2\pi\ell/6) - 1]^{\frac{1}{2}} = \cos(2\pi\ell/6) \pm i[\sin(2\pi\ell/6)] = \omega^{\pm\ell} \qquad (12\text{-}9)$$

where

$$\omega = \exp(2\pi i/6) \qquad (12\text{-}10)$$

Hence, finally, the molecular orbitals may be written

$$\phi_\ell = \frac{1}{(6\sigma_\ell)^{\frac{1}{2}}} \sum_{p=0}^{5} \omega^{\ell p} \chi_p \qquad (12\text{-}11)$$

where the factors σ_ℓ are normalizing constants. We note that these molecular orbitals have the property

$$\phi_\ell^* = \phi_{-\ell} \tag{12-12}$$

This implies that the degeneracy between ϕ_ℓ and $\phi_{-\ell}$ goes beyond the Hückel approximation. Indeed, the coefficients $\omega^{\ell p}$ are determined entirely by the hexagonal symmetry of the problem and can be derived by application of formal group theory.[130]

According to the Hückel theory, in the molecular ground state there would be two electrons in each of the orbitals ϕ_0, ϕ_1, and ϕ_{-1}, with total energy $6\alpha + 8\beta$. The first excited state would be highly degenerate, arising from excitations of one electron from ϕ_1 or ϕ_{-1} to ϕ_2 or ϕ_{-2}, with total energy $6\alpha + 6\beta$. The excitation energy then would be, for singlet and triplet states alike,

$$\Delta E(N \rightarrow T \text{ or } V) = -2\beta \tag{12-13}$$

This fails to account for the facts; experimentally there are excitations at 3.6, 4.7, 6.0, and 6.8 ev, the first level a triplet, the rest singlets, all these levels coming from this single excitation.

We accordingly turn to a theory including pi-electron repulsions, using the full six-electron pi Hamiltonian of the Goeppert-Mayer and Sklar method,

$$\mathcal{H}_\pi(1,2,\ldots,6) = \sum_{\mu=1}^{6} \mathcal{H}_{\text{core}}(\mu) + (1/2) \sum_{\mu,\nu=1}' (1/r_{\mu\nu}) \tag{12-14}$$

The LCAO scheme again provides an appropriate starting point, and so we again have the symmetry-determined molecular orbitals of Eq. (12-11) to work with. The problem is to construct various determinantal six-electron wave functions from these ϕ_ℓ, mix these linearly, and solve secular equations as appropriate. Different methods may be distinguished primarily by different integral-evaluation procedures.

The apparatus of Sec. 5 will suffice for our purposes provided the ϕ_ℓ are orthonormal. That they are, for suitable choice of the σ_ℓ, may be verified as follows: Making use of the facts that

$$\sum_{p=0}^{5} \omega^{Np} = 0 \quad \text{for} \quad N = 1,2,3,4,5 \tag{12-15}$$

and that the only distinct atomic orbital overlaps $S_{pq} = \int \chi_p^* \chi_q \, dv$ are

$$\begin{aligned} &S_{00} = S_{pp} = 1 \qquad S_{01} = S_{p,p+1} = S_{p,p-1} \\ &S_{02} = S_{p,p+2} = S_{p,p-2} \qquad S_{03} = S_{p,p+3} \end{aligned} \tag{12-16}$$

we have

$$S_{k\ell} = \int \phi_k^* \phi_\ell \, dv = \frac{1}{(36\sigma_k\sigma_\ell)^{\frac{1}{2}}} \sum_p \sum_q \omega^{-kp + \ell q} S_{pq}$$

$$= \frac{1}{(36\sigma_k\sigma_\ell)^{\frac{1}{2}}} \left[\sum_p \omega^{(-k+\ell)p}\right] \left[S_{00} + S_{01}(\omega^{\ell} + \omega^{-\ell}) + S_{02}(\omega^{2\ell} + \omega^{-2\ell}) \right.$$

$$\left. + S_{03}\,\omega^{3\ell}\right]$$

$$= \frac{\delta_{k1}}{\sigma_\ell}[1 + 2S_{01}\cos(2\pi\ell/6) + 2S_{02}\cos(4\pi\ell/6) + S_{03}\cos\pi\ell] \qquad (12\text{-}17)$$

Thus if we set

$$\sigma_\ell = 1 + 2S_{01}\cos(2\pi\ell/6) + 2S_{02}\cos(4\pi\ell/6) + S_{03}\cos\pi\ell \qquad (12\text{-}18)$$

the orbitals ϕ_ℓ are orthonormal.

Section 5 tells us that our numerical work will require the evaluation of two kinds of integrals, core integrals $I_{k\ell}$ and electron-repulsion integrals $(ij|k\ell)$, over the molecular orbitals. These are reducible to corresponding integrals I_{pq} and $(pq|rs)$ over the atomic orbitals χ_p, through the use of Eq. (12-11). For the core integrals we have, in analogy with Eq. (12-17),

$$I_{k\ell} = \int \phi_k^* \mathcal{H}_{\text{core}} \phi_\ell \, dv$$

$$= \frac{\delta_{k\ell}}{\sigma_\ell}[\alpha^{\text{core}} + 2\beta_{01}^{\text{core}}\cos(2\pi\ell/6) + 2\beta_{02}^{\text{core}}\cos(4\pi\ell/6)$$

$$+ \beta_{03}^{\text{core}}\cos\pi\ell] \qquad (12\text{-}19)$$

where we have set

$$\alpha^{\text{core}} = I_{pp} = \int \chi_p \mathcal{H}_{\text{core}} \chi_p \, dv$$

$$\beta_{0n}^{\text{core}} = I_{p,p+n} = \int \chi_p \mathcal{H}_{\text{core}} \chi_{p+n} \, dv \qquad (12\text{-}20)$$

Specific formulas for the nonzero $I_{k\ell}$ are

$$I_0 = I_{00} = \frac{\alpha^{\text{core}} + 2\beta_{01}^{\text{core}} + 2\beta_{02}^{\text{core}} + \beta_{03}^{\text{core}}}{1 + 2S_{01} + 2S_{02} + S_{03}}$$

$$I_1 = I_{11} = I_{-1-1} = \frac{\alpha^{\text{core}} + \beta_{01}^{\text{core}} - \beta_{02}^{\text{core}} - \beta_{03}^{\text{core}}}{1 + S_{01} - S_{02} - S_{03}}$$

$$I_2 = I_{22} = I_{-2-2} = \frac{\alpha^{\text{core}} - \beta_{01}^{\text{core}} + \beta_{02}^{\text{core}} - \beta_{03}^{\text{core}}}{1 - S_{01} + S_{02} - S_{03}} \tag{12-21}$$

$$I_3 = I_{33} = \frac{\alpha^{\text{core}} - 2\beta_{01}^{\text{core}} + 2\beta_{02}^{\text{core}} - \beta_{03}^{\text{core}}}{1 - 2S_{01} + 2S_{02} - S_{03}}$$

Evaluation of all possible $I_{k\ell}$ thus requires knowledge of four core integrals and three overlap integrals over atomic orbitals. Numerical values are given in Tables 9 and 10 for Slater orbitals of charge 3.18 and a Goeppert-Mayer-Sklar elucidation of $\mathcal{H}_{\text{core}}$, ignoring hydrogen atoms.[106]

With the electronic-repulsion integrals we meet for the first time a real "N^4 difficulty." A typical integral over molecular orbitals will be

$$(ij|k\ell) = \frac{1}{36(\sigma_i\sigma_j\sigma_k\sigma_\ell)^{\frac{1}{2}}} \sum_p \sum_q \sum_r \sum_s \omega^{-ip + jq - kr + \ell s}(pq|rs) \tag{12-22}$$

This is a sum of 1296 terms! It can be simplified, however, by collecting the coefficients of identical (pq|rs).[106] There are, in fact, just 30 distinct ones of these: γ_{00} = (00|00), γ_{01} = (00|11), γ_{02} = (00|22), γ_{03} = (00|33), (00|01), (00|12), (00|23), (00|02), (00|03), (00|13), (00|14), (00|15), (00|12), (01|02), (01|03), (01|04), (01|01), (01|13), (01|14), (01|15), (02|02), (02|03), (02|04), (02|13), (02|14), (02|15), (02|24), (02|25), (03|03), (03|14). Their values are given in Table 9; values of the 30 distinct $(ij|k\ell)$ integrals are given in Table 10.

The integrals (ij|kl) show a remarkable clustering, as indicated, into four distinct groups.[114,131] The ten in the J group cluster about an average of 8.61 ev, the six of them in the K_{01} group cluster about an average of 2.69, the ten in the K_{02} group cluster about their average of 1.35, and the four in the K_{03} group cluster about their average of 1.06 ev. Deviations from the means within each group being of doubtful significance, we might seek a way to smooth them out. The zero-differential-overlap assumption of Eq. (10-6) gives us just this.[114] According to it, Eq. (12-22) reduces to a twofold sum,

$$(ij|k\ell) = \frac{1}{36} \sum_p \sum_r \omega^{(j-i)p + (\ell - k)r} \gamma_{pr} \tag{12-23}$$

TABLE 9
Integrals over Atomic Orbitals for Benzene (in Electron Volts)

Integral	Slater orbitals[a]	Zero differential overlap: Purely theoretical[b]	Zero differential overlap: Uniformly charged spheres[b]	Zero differential overlap: Semi-empirical[c]	Löwdin orbitals[d]
S_{01}	0.2600	0	0	0	0
S_{02}	0.0389	0	0	0	0
S_{03}	0.0177	0	0	0	0
$\gamma_{00} = (00\|00)$	16.93	16.93	17.61	11.35	17.62
$\gamma_{01} = (00\|11)$	9.03	9.03	8.84	7.19	8.92
$\gamma_{02} = (00\|22)$	5.67	5.67	5.58	5.77	5.57
$\gamma_{03} = (00\|33)$	4.97	4.97	4.90	4.97	4.88
(00|01)	3.31	0	0	0	−0.12
(00|12)	1.87	0	0	0	−0.05
(00|23)	1.42	0	0	0	0.04
(01|01)	0.92	0	0	0	0.09
(01|05)	0.68	0	0	0	0.02
21 other electron repulsions	0.52 and lower values	0	0	0	All less than 0.1

[a]Reference 106. Slater orbitals, effective charge 3.18. The three- and four-center integrals were estimated.
[b]Reference 114.
[c]Determined from benzene electronic spectrum as described in present text. See also Refs. 111, 134, 135, and 181.
[d]Reference 121.

From this we have immediately, by an argument similar to the ones leading to Eqs. (12-17) and (12-19) above,

$$(ij|k\ell) = \begin{cases} \frac{1}{6}[\gamma_{00} + 2\gamma_{01}\cos(2\pi\mu/6) + 2\gamma_{02}\cos(4\pi\mu/6) + \gamma_{03}\cos\pi\mu] \\ \quad \text{if } j - i = k - \ell = \mu \text{ (modulo 6)} \\ 0 \text{ otherwise} \end{cases} \qquad (12\text{-}24)$$

TABLE 10
Integrals over Molecular Orbitals for Benzene (in Electron Volts)

		Zero differential overlap		
Integral[a]	Slater orbitals[a]	Purely theoretical[b]	Uniformly charged spheres[b]	Semiempirical[c]
$I_2 - I_1$	5.36	5.36	5.36	4.74
J group	8.63, 8.52, 8.50 8.55, 8.47, 8.52 8.52, 8.65, 8.79, 8.87; average 8.61	8.55	8.56	7.02
K_{01} group	2.58, 2.67, 2.87, 2.60, 2.63, 2.77; average 2.69	2.55	2.66	1.30
K_{02} group	1.30, 1.45, 1.34, 1.37, 1.33, 1.30, 1.30, 1.38, 1.34, 1.36; average 1.35	1.20	1.35	0.56
K_{03} group	0.93, 1.07, 1.01, 0.99; average 1.00	0.87	1.03	0.59

[a]Reference 106, where full identifications of all of the integrals are given.
[b]Reference 114.
[c]Determined from benzene spectrum as described in text.

This is to say that the only distinct electronic repulsions are the four integrals

$$\begin{aligned} J = K_{00} &= \frac{1}{6}(\gamma_{00} + 2\gamma_{01} + 2\gamma_{02} + \gamma_{03}) \\ K_{01} &= \frac{1}{6}(\gamma_{00} + \gamma_{01} - \gamma_{02} - \gamma_{03}) \\ K_{02} &= \frac{1}{6}(\gamma_{00} - \gamma_{01} - \gamma_{02} + \gamma_{03}) \\ K_{03} &= \frac{1}{6}(\gamma_{00} - 2\gamma_{01} + 2\gamma_{02} - \gamma_{03}) \end{aligned} \qquad (12\text{-}25)$$

All others are zero or equal to one of these, by Eq. (12-24). Numerical values of the integrals in this purely theoretical zero-differential-overlap prescription are included in Table 9.

Still a third a priori method for obtaining the electronic-repulsion integrals should be mentioned. As we have seen, the justification for zero differential overlap lies in the fact that reductions to the form of Eq. (12-23) are very accurate if the atomic orbitals are replaced by their localized orthogonalized counterparts. We can mimic this procedure if we replace our overlapping $2p\pi$ orbitals by classical electrostatic approximations to them which do not overlap: dumbbells made up of two uniformly charged spheres, each containing one-half an electronic charge, of such a size that neighboring dumbbells in benzene just touch.[114] Integral values obtained from this model are included in Tables 9 and 10, as are some of the corresponding values for Löwdin orbitals.[121] There is remarkable agreement between both sets of values and the values for the original, purely theoretical integrals, for all the relevant integrals over molecular orbitals. This lends confidence that a theory making use of Eq. (12-24) instead of Eq. (12-22) may be quite sound.

We are now prepared to compose wave functions and to derive energy formulas for the various states of the molecule.[119] The ground state is

$$N = (0\bar{0}1\bar{1}\text{-}1\text{-}\bar{1}) \tag{12-26}$$

which has an energy

$$E(N) = 2I_0 + 2I_1 + 2I_{-1} + J_{00} + J_{11} + J_{-1-1} + 4J_{01} + 4J_{0-1} + 4J_{1-1}$$
$$- 2K_{01} - 2K_{0-1} - 2K_{1-1} \tag{12-27}$$

Under the simplification of Eq. (12-24), which we assume henceforth,† all coulomb integrals are the same, and exchange integrals depend only on the difference of the indices, so that this formula becomes

$$E(N) = 2I_0 + 4I_1 + 15J - 4K_{01} - 2K_{02} \tag{12-28}$$

Similarly, the first excited states may be composed from the 16 determinants that can be obtained from Eq. (12-26) by replacement of 1 or −1 with 2 or −2. The analysis of Sec. 5 gives us the proper singlet (V) and triplet (T) functions in each case. Writing down only one of each, we have

$$\begin{aligned} V_{12} \text{ or } T_{12} &= 2^{-\frac{1}{2}}[(0\bar{0}1\bar{2}\text{-}1\text{-}\bar{1}) \pm (0\bar{0}2\bar{1}\text{-}1\text{-}\bar{1})] \\ V_{-1-2} \text{ or } T_{-1-2} &= 2^{-\frac{1}{2}}[(0\bar{0}1\bar{1}\text{-}1\text{-}\bar{2}) \pm (0\bar{0}1\bar{1}\text{-}2\text{-}\bar{1})] \\ V_{1-2} \text{ or } T_{1-2} &= 2^{-\frac{1}{2}}[(0\bar{0}1\text{-}\bar{2}\text{-}1\text{-}\bar{1}) \pm (0\bar{0}\text{-}2\bar{1}\text{-}1\text{-}\bar{1})] \\ V_{-12} \text{ or } T_{-12} &= 2^{-\frac{1}{2}}[(0\bar{0}1\bar{1}\text{-}1\bar{2}) \pm (0\bar{0}1\bar{1}2\text{-}\bar{1})] \end{aligned} \tag{12-29}$$

† Corresponding formulas without this simplification may be found in Ref. 103.

where the upper sign defines the singlet; the lower sign defines the triplet combination. The corresponding matrix elements of the energy can then be determined by the rules of Sec. 5, using in addition Eqs. (12-19) and (12-24). If we let $(V_i \| V_j)$, for example, stand for $\int V_i^* \mathcal{H} V_j \, dv$, we find all matrix elements between N and the functions of Eq. (12-29) to be zero. Further, the only interactions among the functions of Eq. (12-29) are between V_{1-2} and V_{-12} and between T_{1-2} and T_{-12}. The full formulas are:

$$\begin{aligned}(V_{12} \| V_{12}) \text{ or } (T_{12} \| T_{12}) &= 2I_0 + 3I_1 + I_2 + 15J - 3K_{01} - K_{1-1} - K_{02} \\ &\quad - K_{-12} \pm K_{-12} \\ &= 2I_0 + 3I_1 + I_2 + 15J - 3K_{01} - 2K_{02} - K_{03} \pm K_{01} \\ &= (V_{-1-2} \| V_{-1-2}) \quad \text{or} \quad (T_{-1-2} \| T_{-1-2})\end{aligned} \tag{12-30}$$

$$\begin{aligned}(V_{1-2} \| V_{1-2}) \text{ or } (T_{1-2} \| T_{1-2}) &= 2I_0 + 3I_1 + I_2 + 15J - 3K_{01} - K_{1-1} - K_{0-2} \\ &\quad - K_{12} \pm K_{1-2} \\ &= 2I_0 + 3I_1 + I_2 + 15J - 4K_{01} - 2K_{02} \pm K_{03} \\ &= (V_{-12} \| V_{-12}) \quad \text{or} \quad (T_{-12} \| T_{-12})\end{aligned} \tag{12-31}$$

$$\begin{aligned}(V_{1-2} \| V_{-12}) \text{ or } (T_{1-2} \| T_{-12}) &= (-21|-12) - (-22|-11) \pm (-21|-12) \\ &= K_{03} - K_{02} \pm K_{03}\end{aligned} \tag{12-32}$$

[The degeneracies manifest in Eqs. (12-30) and (12-31) are, of course, a consequence of the fact that V_{12} (T_{12}) and V_{-1-2} (T_{-1-2}) are complex conjugates of one another, and similarly V_{1-2} (T_{1-2}) and V_{-12} (T_{-12}).] If we have two normalized degenerate functions that interact, as do V_{1-2} (T_{1-2}) and V_{-12} (T_{-12}), the functions which are their normalized sum and difference do not, so that the 2×2 secular equation involving these last functions is immediately resolved if we take

$$\begin{aligned}V_{1-2}^{+} \text{ or } T_{1-2}^{+} &= 2^{-\frac{1}{2}}[(V_{1-2} \text{ or } T_{1-2}) + (V_{-12} \text{ or } T_{-12})] \\ V_{1-2}^{-} \text{ or } T_{1-2}^{-} &= i2^{-\frac{1}{2}}[(V_{1-2} \text{ or } T_{1-2}) - (V_{-12} \text{ or } T_{-12})]\end{aligned} \tag{12-33}$$

These functions have the energies, from Eqs. (12-31) and (12-32),

$$(V^{+}_{1-2}\|V^{+}_{1-2}) \text{ or } (T^{+}_{1-2}\|T^{+}_{1-2}) = 2I_0 + 3I_1 + I_2 + 15J - 4K_{01} - 2K_{02} \pm K_{03} + (K_{03} - K_{02} \pm K_{03}) \tag{12-34}$$

$$(V^{-}_{1-2}\|V^{-}_{1-2}) \text{ or } (T^{-}_{1-2}\|T^{-}_{1-2}) = 2I_0 + 3I_1 + I_2 + 15J - 4K_{01} - 2K_{02} \pm K_{03} + (K_{03} - K_{02} \pm K_{03}) \tag{12-35}$$

This achieves the solution of the problem of the linear mixing of all the determinants we have considered, as all interaction elements among the functions N, V_{12}, V_{-1-2}, V^{+}_{1-2}, V^{-}_{1-2}, T_{12}, T_{-1-2}, T^{+}_{1-2}, T^{-}_{1-2} are zero, and these functions are orthonormal. The factorization can be thought of as a consequence of the symmetry of the problem,[103] but explicit use of formal group theory is not necessary to bring it about.

The formulas for the excitation energies from the ground state are now readily obtained. Putting the usual group-theoretical notations in parentheses, we find

$$\begin{aligned}
&\left.\begin{aligned}\Delta E(N \rightarrow V_{12}) &= (I_2 - I_1) + 2K_{01} - K_{03}\\ \Delta E(N \rightarrow V_{-1-2}) &= (I_2 - I_1) + 2K_{01} - K_{03}\end{aligned}\right\}\ (E_{1u})\\
&\Delta E(N \rightarrow V^{+}_{1-2}) = (I_2 - I_1) - K_{02} + 3K_{03} \quad ({}^1B_{1u})\\
&\Delta E(N \rightarrow V^{-}_{1-2}) = (I_2 - I_1) + K_{02} - K_{03} \quad ({}^1B_{2u})\\
&\left.\begin{aligned}\Delta E(N \rightarrow T_{12}) &= (I_2 - I_1) - K_{03}\\ \Delta E(N \rightarrow T_{-1-2}) &= (I_2 - I_1) - K_{03}\end{aligned}\right\}\ ({}^3E_{1u})\\
&\Delta E(N \rightarrow T^{+}_{1-2}) = (I_2 - I_1) - K_{02} - K_{03} \quad ({}^3B_{1u})\\
&\Delta E(N \rightarrow T^{-}_{1-2}) = (I_2 - I_1) + K_{02} - K_{03} \quad ({}^3B_{2u})
\end{aligned} \tag{12-36}$$

According to this set of simplified formulas the excitation energies depend on four quantities only, $I_2 - I_1$, K_{01}, K_{02}, and K_{03}.

In Table 9 the various excitation energies as calculated in several different ways are presented and compared with experimental values. The original Goeppert-Mayer and Sklar calculation[103] was with theoretical values for all integrals, calculated for Slater orbitals with a certain elucidation of $\mathcal{H}_{core}$. The actual calculation made use of incorrect values for certain integrals[107,132] and inconsistently neglected others; when these factors were corrected, the results shown in the table were obtained.[133] They are not particularly good. In this calculation it should be noted that the zero-differential-overlap formulas of Eq. (12-36) were not used.

In a much more complicated calculation still,[106] Craig, Ross, and Parr sought to discover whether inclusion of interactions with the other one-electron excitations (configurations 0^21^2-13, etc.) and two-electron excitations (configurations $0^21^22^2$, etc.) would improve the agreement with experiment. These

TABLE 11
Pi-Electron Energy Levels of Benzene (in Electron Volts)

		Purely theoretical calc.		Simplified or semi-empirical calc.	
State[a]	Experimental	GMS method[b]	Configuration interaction[c]	Uniformly charged spheres[d]	Semi-empirical[e]
N	0.00	0.0	0.0	0.0	0.00
$^1E_{1u}$	6.76[f]	9.8	9.9	9.9	6.76
$^1B_{1u}$	5.96[f]	7.3	9.0	7.3	5.96
$^1B_{2u}$	4.71[f]	5.9	4.4	5.9	4.71
$^3E_{1u}$		4.4	4.7	4.5	4.16
$^3B_{1u}$	3.59[f]	3.1	4.1	3.2	3.59
$^3B_{2u}$		5.8	8.2	5.9	4.71
$^1E_{2g}$		10.9	7.7		8.18[g]
$^5A_{1g}$		6.1	5.9		
N for $C_6H_6^+$	9.52[h]	9.7			$-\alpha - 30.87$[i]
N for $C_6H_6^-$	$-\alpha$[j]	3.4			$\alpha + 42.04$

[a]For group-theoretical notations, see Refs. 103 and 106.
[b]Reference 103 as corrected in Ref. 133.
[c]Reference 106.
[d]Reference 110.
[e]Present text, but see also Refs. 111, 134, 136, and 181.
[f]As assigned in Ref. 134.
[g]Reference 135.
[h]Vertical ionization potential, value taken in Ref. 136. The ionization potential from Rydberg series is 9.24 ev, as determined by M. F. A. El-Sayed, M. Kasha, and Y. Tanaka, *J. Chem. Phys.*, **34**, 334 (1961).
[i]$\alpha = -40.39$ will fit the observed ionization potential, but this is not in accordance with Eq. (10-1). Note that this α is not the same as the α of Table 7 for ethylene.
[j]Negative electron affinity, experimentally unknown.

results are included in Table 11. Their main feature was the prediction of a low-lying $^1E_{2g}$ state, though the quintuplet at 5.9 ev might also be noted.

An alternative procedure is the use of the simplified Eqs. (12-36), with the same or slightly modified values for the integrals. As Table 11 shows, the calculation done this way[110] reproduces the more complicated calculation to good accuracy.

But this, we may argue,[111,134] does not use Eqs. (12-36) to their full power. We might use the experimental excitation energies to determine some or all the quantities $(I_2 - I_1)$, K_{01}, K_{02}, K_{03}. From the values we obtain, we may work back to elementary integrals over the atomic orbitals, obtaining empirical values for them. If these are in good accord with our previous arguments about integral values, we may then proceed confidently to calculate spectra of other aromatic molecules. (There are many planar unsaturated hydrocarbons, with much information about their electronic spectra, and we shall be able to test our theory amply.) In this spirit, we set (see Table 11)

$$\begin{aligned} 6.76 &= (I_2 - I_1) + 2K_{01} - K_{03} \\ 5.96 &= (I_2 - I_1) - K_{02} + 3K_{03} \\ 3.59 &= (I_2 - I_1) - K_{02} - K_{03} \\ 4.71 &= (I_2 - I_1) + K_{02} - K_{03} \end{aligned} \tag{12-37}$$

and obtain (in ev)

$$\begin{aligned} &I_2 - I_1 = 4.74 \\ &K_{01} = 1.30 \qquad K_{02} = 0.56 \qquad K_{03} = 0.59 \end{aligned} \tag{12-38}$$

For the integrals over atomic orbitals we then get, using Eqs. (12-21) and (12-25), neglecting β_{02}^{core}, β_{03}^{core}, S_{02}, and S_{03} (for simplicity), and setting γ_{03} equal to the theoretical value 4.97,

$$\begin{aligned} &\frac{\beta_{01}^{\text{core}} - S_{01}\alpha^{\text{core}}}{1 - S_{01}^2} = \beta = -2.37 \text{ ev} \\ &\gamma_{00} = 11.35 \qquad \gamma_{01} = 7.19 \qquad \gamma_{02} = 5.77 \qquad \gamma_{03} = 4.97 \text{ ev} \end{aligned} \tag{12-39}$$

All these values, which have been included in Table 9, are reasonable; their behavior is just what we have already anticipated in the argument of Secs. 10 and 11.

From these integral values we can proceed to predict the positions of the other low-lying excited electronic states of the molecule.[111,135] We might also hope to account for properties other than the spectra, for example, the pi ionization potential and electron affinity.[136] The positive ion will have a ground state $(\bar{0}0 1\bar{1}\text{-}1)$ and hence an energy

$$E(C_6H_6^+) = 2I_0 + 3I_1 + 10J - 3K_{01} - K_{02} \tag{12-40}$$

The negative ion will have the description $(\bar{0}01\bar{1}\text{-}1\text{-}\bar{1}2)$ and the energy

$$E(C_6H_6^-) = 2I_0 + 4I_1 + I_2 + 21J - 5K_{01} - 3K_{02} - K_{03} \tag{12-41}$$

Hence we have, by subtractions from Eq. (12-27),

$$\mathcal{I} = E(C_6H_6^+) - E(C_6H_6) = -I_1 - 5J + K_{01} + K_{02} \tag{12-42}$$

$$\begin{aligned} \mathcal{A} = E(C_6H_6) - E(C_6H_6^-) &= -I_2 - 6J + K_{01} + K_{02} + K_{03} \\ &= -I_1 - (I_2 - I_1) - 6J + K_{01} + K_{02} + K_{03} \end{aligned} \tag{12-43}$$

The ionization potential and electron affinity calculated from these formulas are given in Table 11. The purely theoretical results are not bad. Using integral values that fit the spectra, we can also use Eq. (12-42) to determine an I_1 value that fits the experimental $\mathcal{I}$ and then predict $\mathcal{A}$ from Eq. (12-43). The result is $\mathcal{A} = -1.6$ ev, a reasonable value.

Lykos[136] has extended the discussion to include the resonance energy[137] and anisotropy of the diamagnetic susceptibility,[138] and he has considered nonneighbor overlap and resonance integrals. The parameters he recommends do not differ substantially from those we have obtained.

13 ALTERNANT AND OTHER HYDROCARBONS

In this and the next section we shall confine our discussion mainly to the applications that have been made to conjugated systems of methods in which the pi electrons alone are considered, wave functions for the pi electrons are built from atomic $p\pi$ orbitals, pi-electron repulsions are included, the treatment of pi-electron repulsions is simplified by the use of the zero-differential-overlap assumption, and empirical elements are included. In Sec. 15 we shall consider certain other methods, and in Sec. 16 some speculations as to how one might proceed to obtain improved pi-electron theories will be indulged in. Reviews covering similar ground have been written by Pople[139] and by Longuet-Higgins.[140]

Planar-conjugated-hydrocarbon molecules, radicals, and ions form a beautiful class of molecules for detailed and extended quantum-chemical study. The Hückel method for them is well developed, their properties are well-known experimentally, and they are of much everyday concern in organic chemistry. The new techniques of electron spin resonance and nuclear magnetic resonance have provided new information about them which has demanded development of theory for its elucidation. The story of the theoretical developments in this area has been and continues to be an encouraging one.

To demonstrate immediately the level and scope of the success, we may refer to Pariser's treatment[134] of the polyacene series, benzene, naphthalene, anthracene, tetracene, and pentacene. For these molecules, Pariser computed the low-lying singlet and triplet excited-state energies, and the oscillator strengths for transitions to the singlet states from the ground state; for naphthalene he also computed the bond orders. The results were in good agreement with experiment, and experimental confirmations of some of his predictions have since been obtained.[141] A summary of the energy levels is given in Table 12.

TABLE 12

Pi-Electron Energy Levels of the Polyacenes (in Electron Volts)[a,b,c]

State		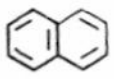	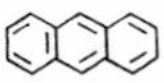	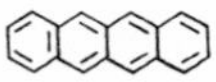	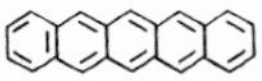
Singlets					
B^{+}_{2u}	6.6 } (6.8)	6.3(5.9)	5.3(5.5)	4.7(4.1)	4.1(3.8)
B^{+}_{3u}	6.6	5.9(5.7)	5.5(5.0)	5.1(4.6)	4.8(4.3)
B^{+}_{2u}	6.0(6.0)	4.5(4.5)	3.6(3.4)	3.1(2.9)	2.8(2.4)
B^{-}_{3u}	4.7(4.7)	4.0(4.0)	3.7(3.8)	3.6(3.6)	3.5(3.5)
Triplets					
B^{+}_{2u}	4.1 } (4.2)	4.2	3.6	3.2	2.7
B^{+}_{3u}	4.1	3.6(3.7)	3.5	3.5	3.5
B^{+}_{2u}	3.6(3.6)	2.2(2.5)	1.7(1.7)	1.1(1.2)	0.8
B^{-}_{3u}	4.7(4.9?)	4.0	3.7	3.6	3.5

[a]From Pariser, Ref. 134; numbers in parentheses are experimental values.

[b]For notations, see Ref. 134; the α, β, and p bands of Clar are the singlets labeled B^{-}_{3u}, B^{+}_{3u}, and B^{+}_{2u}, respectively (see text).

[c]Other states than those listed were considered in Ref. 134. Also computed were f values, which also come out in good agreement with experiment.

The procedures Pariser employed illustrate the decisions one must make, and the ambiguities one meets, in such calculations. A complete configuration-interaction calculation is not feasible, even granted electronic computers. The particular molecular orbitals one starts with are therefore important, and the amount of configuration interaction one includes becomes, in part, a matter of personal taste. Pariser started with the ordinary Hückel orbitals (which should reasonably approximate best LCAO-SCF molecular orbitals) and included interactions among all configurations that arise from excitations of one electron from the ground configuration to excited molecular orbitals. This should give a ground-state description about as accurate as the LCAO-SCF one (using a $2p\pi$ atomic orbital basis),[142] and a reasonable representation of the low-lying excited states. Pariser chose values of the parameters β, γ_{00}, γ_{01} to fit the benzene spectrum much as we did in the previous section, and values of γ_{02}, γ_{03}, etc., from theoretical formulas; the values he actually employed were $\beta = -2.371$, $\gamma_{00} = 10.959$, $\gamma_{01} = 6.895$, $\gamma_{02} = 5.682$, $\gamma_{03} = 4.978$ ev, etc. He further made an assumption that makes all the polyacene spectra independent of the values of the quantities $\mathcal{J}_p$ and P_p; namely, he presumed that the relation,

$$\mathcal{J}_p + P_p = \text{constant} \tag{13-1}$$

holds for all carbon pi orbitals in these systems. As we shall discuss later in more detail, this is the analog in the improved theory of the assumption, α = constant, which characterizes carbon atoms in hydrocarbons in the original Hückel method. An assumption that the penetration terms are the same for all carbon atoms in naphthalene, for example, is clearly not strictly valid; that such an assumption gives results which agree so well with experiment is pleasing.

With these good results steeling us, let us now pause to consider the butadiene molecule, which is simple enough to allow much testing of alternative procedures and yet complex enough to prefigure complicated hydrocarbons without high symmetry. The Goeppert-Mayer-Sklar calculation at the simple LCAO-SCF level had been performed in 1950.[104] Extensions to include configuration interaction have been carried out by Pullman,[143] Nesbet,[144] and Fain and Matsen.[145] Semiempirical calculations of the kind discussed here have been performed by Pariser and Parr,[111] Pople,[112] Nesbet,[144] Pullman and Berthod,[146] Hall,[147] Mori,[148] and others, but the most definitive study is due to Moser.[149] Table 13 summarizes some of the results.

The theoretical LCAO-SCF orbitals for the *trans* form of the molecule are, with the atomic orbitals lettered consecutively,[104]

$$\begin{aligned}
\phi_1 &= 0.354(\chi_a + \chi_d) + 0.469(\chi_b + \chi_c) \\
\phi_2 &= 0.508(\chi_a - \chi_d) + 0.423(\chi_b - \chi_c) \\
\phi_3 &= 0.645(\chi_a + \chi_d) - 0.470(\chi_b + \chi_c) \\
\phi_4 &= 0.534(\chi_a - \chi_d) - 0.727(\chi_b - \chi_c)
\end{aligned} \tag{13-2}$$

TABLE 13
The Electronic Spectrum of *trans*-Butadiene[a]

Quantity	Experiment	1[b]	2[c]	3[d]	4[e]	5[f]	6[g]	7[h]
$^1A_{1g} \rightarrow {}^1B_{1u}$ transition energy (ev)	6.0	6.5	6.4	6.2	5.9	6.4	8.1	9.6
f number (for above transition)	0.53	0.51	0.51	0.51	0.47	0.93	1.1	0.44
$^1A_{1g} \rightarrow {}^1A_{2g}$ transition energy (ev)	7.2	7.3	6.3	7.9	7.7	7.7	10.1	7.1

[a]After Moser, Ref. 149.
[b]Full configuration interaction, empirical integral values.
[c]Restricted configuration interaction, empirical integral values.
[d]Configuration interaction among one-electron jumps only, starting from molecular orbitals of Eq. (13-3) of this text, empirical integral values.
[e]No configuration interaction, molecular orbitals of Eq. (13-3), empirical integral values. Method of Ref. 111.
[f]No configuration interaction, molecular orbitals like those of Eq. (13-2) of this text, empirical integral values.
[g]No configuration interaction, molecular orbitals of Eq. (13-2) of text, theoretical integral values from Ref. 104.
[h]Restricted configuration interaction, theoretical integral values.

These have zero, one, two and three nodes, respectively, and are given in order of increasing energy. From a consideration of the nodes alone one sees that these orbitals could have been expected to have the approximate forms

$$\begin{aligned} \phi_1 &= C_1[(\chi_a + \chi_d) + (\chi_b + \chi_c)] \\ \phi_2 &= C_2[(\chi_a - \chi_d) + (\chi_b - \chi_c)] \\ \phi_3 &= C_3[(\chi_a + \chi_d) - (\chi_b + \chi_c)] \\ \phi_4 &= C_4[(\chi_a - \chi_d) - (\chi_b - \chi_c)] \end{aligned} \qquad (13\text{-}3)$$

Realizing this, Pariser and Parr did their first calculations using these simpler orbitals. Moser compares this procedure with a calculation starting with orbitals like those of Eq. (13-2). With full configuration interaction (column 1 of Table 13) the results, of course, are identical; with limited configuration interaction there will be some difference, and the first set gives slightly better results (column 2 vs. column 3). As Table 13 shows, generally good agreement with experimental data on the molecule is obtained with the semiempirical scheme invoking either little or much configuration interaction, whereas the Goeppert-Mayer and Sklar method is less satisfactory (columns 6 and 7). But as the table also shows, no unique "best" way to do the calculation emerges.

For this molecule there is good evidence validating the zero-differential-overlap approximation. The coefficients of Eq. (13-2) make the orbitals orthonormal with the nonorthogonality between atomic orbitals included. If they are renormalized with the assumption of orthogonality among the atomic orbitals, the first two orbitals become

$$\begin{aligned} \phi_1 &= 0.421(\chi_a + \chi_d) + 0.569(\chi_b + \chi_c) \\ \phi_2 &= 0.559(\chi_a - \chi_d) + 0.433(\chi_b - \chi_c) \end{aligned} \tag{13-4}$$

It is noteworthy, as Peradejordi has pointed out,[150] that, if the whole LCAO-SCF procedure is repeated assuming zero-differential overlap but retaining theoretical values for all integrals not made zero thereby, the orbitals that result are simply

$$\begin{aligned} \phi_1 &= 0.426(\chi_a + \chi_d) + 0.564(\chi_b + \chi_c) \\ \phi_2 &= 0.544(\chi_a - \chi_d) + 0.452(\chi_b - \chi_c) \end{aligned} \tag{13-5}$$

which differ very little from those of Eq. (13-4). This demonstrates that the zero-differential-overlap assumption, in this case in which symmetry does not fix the molecular orbitals, does not alter the coefficients very much. Independent indication that this assumption is not bad for this molecule is provided by some calculations of the basic integrals by Hall.[147] Transformed to a certain localized orthogonalized set of orbitals, not exactly the Löwdin orbitals but close to them, the 28 distinct electron-repulsion integrals are changed as shown in Table 14. It is seen that those which are annihilated by the zero-differential-overlap assumption are transformed nearly to zero by this change of orbital basis.

To take a rather different type of molecule, in Table 15 are summarized some calculations by Pariser on azulene.[151] Like naphthalene, azulene has 10 pi orbitals and 10 pi electrons, but it has five- and seven-membered rings, and the experimental properties of azulene and naphthalene are quite different. Agreement between calculated and observed spectra is good, and again some confirmation of the theory came later.[152] The calculated pi dipole moment 1.9 D cannot be equated to the observed total moment 1.0 D, because of sigma contributions to this moment, but this value is much more reasonable than the value 6.4 D, which is given by the simple Hückel method. Julg also has reported a calculation on this molecule.[153]

Of all these molecules, only azulene is not at least quite close to what has been termed an *alternant hydrocarbon*. An alternant hydrocarbon in the first instance must be one of the planar conjugated systems of the type we have

TABLE 14
Electron-Repulsion Integrals for *trans*-Butadiene (in Electron Volts)

Integral	Slater orbitals[a]	Hall orbitals[b]
(aa|aa)	16.93	17.26
(bb|bb)	16.93	17.56
(aa|bb)	9.24	9.03
(bb|cc)	8.69	8.63
(aa|cc)	5.52	5.48
(aa|dd)	3.83	3.78
(aa|ab)	3.61	−0.38
(bb|bc)	2.93	−0.09
(ab|ab)	1.09	0.23
20 others	Various values	All <0.13

[a]Reference 104. Z = 3.18.
[b]Reference 147. These are localized orthogonal orbitals similar to those of Löwdin.

been describing, *with no odd-membered rings*. In the Hückel method, one further requires a common α value for all carbons, a common neighbor β value, zero nonneighbor β's, and ignores overlap. If we include electron repulsion but make the zero-differential-overlap approximation, common neighboring β values, zero nonneighboring β values, Eq. (13-1), and common γ_{pp} values must all be assumed. For alternant hydrocarbons in the Hückel method, Coulson and Longuet-Higgins and others have established a series of remarkable theorems; the generalizations to include electron repulsion are due to Pople, Pariser, Lefebvre, McLachlan, and others.

An alternant hydrocarbon may be *even* or *odd*, according as it has an even or an odd number of $2p\pi$ orbitals; it may be a neutral molecule, a radical, a positive ion, or a negative ion. The theorems have to do with the one-electron Hartree-Fock orbital-energy schemes, the total energies for ground and excited states, the forms of the molecular orbitals, the charge and spin densities, and other properties, for some or all such species. In our discussion we shall at first consider the case of an even alternant having an even number of pi electrons, with a closed-shell ground state.

The starting point for the analysis is the LCAO-SCF scheme of Roothaan,[58,59] our Eqs. (6-12) to (6-18). According to this, the one-electron Hartree-Fock

TABLE 15
Electronic Spectra and Structure of Azulene[a]

Electronic state	Excitation energy, ev		f number	
	Calculated[b]	Observed	Calculated	Observed
$^1A_1$ (ground)[c]	0	0		
$^1B_{1\perp}$	1.7	1.8	0.016	0.009
$^1A_{1\parallel}$	3.1	3.5	0.002	0.08
$^1B_{1\perp}$	4.1	4.1	0.116	?
$^1A_{1\parallel}$	4.7	4.5	1.243	1.10
$^1B_{1\perp}$	5.6	5.2	0.365	0.38

[a]Reference 151. Bond orders and charge densities were also computed for all states.
[b]Calculated dipole moment of pi electrons 1.88 D (observed total moment 1.0 D).
[c]Excited $^3B_1$ states are predicted at 1.5, 3.5, 4.1, 4.9, and 5.4 ev, experimental evidence (Ware, Ref. 152) indicating that the lowest triplet indeed lies below the lowest excited singlet.

energies ϵ_i are the roots of Eq. (6-16), with the matrix elements F_{pq} given by Eq. (6-14). Thus we have, in the zero-differential-overlap approximation, noting that we must now employ $\mathcal{H}_{core}$ in place of $\mathcal{H}_N$, and assuming all quantities to be real,[112,154]

$$\begin{aligned} F_{pp} &= I_{pp} + \sum_j [2(pp|jj) - (pj|pj)] \\ &= I_{pp} + \sum_j \sum_r \sum_s C_{jr}C_{js}[2(pp|rs) - (pr|ps)] \\ &= I_{pp} + \sum_j \sum_r C_{jr}C_{jr}[2(pp|rr) - (pr|pr)] \\ &= \alpha_p^{core} + \sum_r p_{rr}[\gamma_{pr} - (1/2)\gamma_{pp}] \end{aligned} \tag{13-6}$$

where

$$p_{rr} = 2\sum_j C_{jr}C_{jr} \tag{13-7}$$

is the pi *charge density* on atom r in the ground state. (The sum over j is over the occupied molecular orbitals; the factor 2 is present because each orbital is doubly occupied in the ground state.) Similarly,

$$F_{pq} = I_{pq} + \sum_j [2(pq|jj) - (pj|qj)] = \beta_{pq}^{core} - [(1/2)p_{pq}\gamma_{pq}] \tag{13-8}$$

where

$$p_{pq} = 2\sum_j C_{jp}C_{jq} \tag{13-9}$$

is the *bond order* for the p-q bond in the molecule. Equation (13-6) may be further reduced using Eq. (10-1), giving

$$F_{pp} = -\mathcal{I}_p - P_p + \sum_{r \neq p}{}' (p_{rr} - 1)\gamma_{pr} + (1/2)p_{pp}\gamma_{pp} \tag{13-10}$$

The molecular-orbital coefficients then are solutions of the equations

$$\sum_p C_{ip}(F_{pq} - \delta_{pq}\epsilon_i) = 0 \tag{13-11}$$

which requires that the orbital energies ϵ_i be solutions of

$$\left| F_{pq} - \delta_{pq}\epsilon \right| = 0 \tag{13-12}$$

Total energies for ground and excited states follow from the formulas of Sec. 5, for example, Eqs. (5-38) to (5-47).

The key theorem is that first proved by Pople,[112]

$$p_{rr} = 1 \tag{13-13}$$

for all atoms, both in ground and excited states, so that, from Eq. (13-10),

$$F_{pp} = -\mathcal{I}_p - P_p + (1/2)\gamma_{pp} = \text{constant} \tag{13-14}$$

for all atoms. This is enough to insure the validity of the theorem Coulson and Rushbrooke had earlier proved for the Hückel theory,[155] the so-called *pairing theorem*. The roots ϵ_i of the Eqs. (13-12) are symmetrically disposed about their mean F_{pp}, as sketched in Fig. 4. The corresponding molecular orbitals also are paired in a certain way. As a consequence of there being no odd-membered rings, alternant atoms may be labeled with "stars," so that the atoms may be divided into two sets, the "starred" and the "unstarred,"

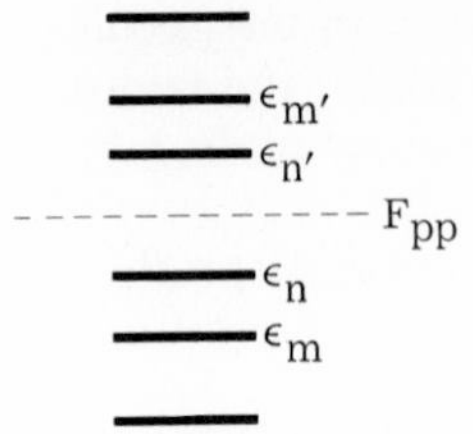

Figure 4. One-electron energy-level scheme for an even alternant hydrocarbon.

with no two atoms of the same set neighbors. If the bonding molecular orbital ϕ_n, with energy $\epsilon_n = F_{pp} - (F_{pp} - \epsilon_n)$ is written

$$\phi_n = \sum_{\substack{\text{starred}\\ \text{atoms}}} C_{np}\chi_p + \sum_{\substack{\text{unstarred}\\ \text{atoms}}} C_{np}\chi_p \tag{13-15}$$

then the antibonding molecular orbital $\phi_{n'}$, with energy $\epsilon_{n'} = F_{pp} + (F_{pp} - \epsilon_n)$, may be taken to have the form

$$\phi_{n'} = \sum_{\substack{\text{starred}\\ \text{atoms}}} C_{np}\chi_p - \sum_{\substack{\text{unstarred}\\ \text{atoms}}} C_{np}\chi_p \tag{13-16}$$

with the coefficients C_{np} the same as those in ϕ_n, except for the signs of those associated with the unstarred set of atoms.

For a molecule with the levels occupied up to ϵ_n, according to the self-consistent field theory,[33,58] ionization will require an energy $\mathcal{I} = -\epsilon_n$, whereas gain of an electron will confer an extra stability $\mathcal{A} = -\epsilon_{n'}$. Hence

$$\mathcal{I} + \mathcal{A} = -\epsilon_n - \epsilon_{n'} = -2F_{pp} = 2\mathcal{I}_p + 2P_p - \gamma_{pp} = \text{constant} \tag{13-17}$$

This theorem was first proved by Hush and Pople[156]; it appears to be moderately well satisfied for alternant hydrocarbons all the way up to graphite, with the constant given a value of about 9.5 ev.[156-160] (However, if the Pariser relation, Eq. (10-8), is inserted in this formula, the result is

$$\mathcal{I} + \mathcal{A} = \mathcal{I}_p + \mathcal{A}_p + 2P_p \tag{13-18}$$

which gives too high values for $\mathcal{I} + \mathcal{A}$ if $\mathcal{I}_C + \mathcal{A}_C$ is set equal to its value for carbon, 11.54 + 0.46 = 12.0 ev, and P_C is assumed to be positive.) By an extension of the argument,[161] Hush has predicted the ionization potential of the benzene negative ion to be 16.9 ev, in good agreement with the inferred experimental value of 17.2 ev.

The electronic spectra of alternants show some remarkable regularities.[140] These have been accounted for in the quantitative calculations of Pariser,[134] or in the elegant, simple, qualitative discussion of Moffitt[162] deriving from the arguments of Platt,[163] or in a modified Hückel discussion of Dewar and Longuet-Higgins.[164] Perhaps the most lucid discussion of the main features is, however, due to Pople.[165] He showed that the one-electron degeneracies (see Fig. 4)

$$\epsilon_{m'} - \epsilon_n = \epsilon_{n'} - \epsilon_m \tag{13-19}$$

carry over to the corresponding many-electron excitation energies. To obtain his result, we need only apply Eqs. (5-46) and (5-47) to the excitation processes $n \to m'$ and $m \to n'$, and use the pairing property of Eqs. (13-15) and (13-16). The result is, in the notation of the previous section,

$$E(V_{nm'}) = E(V_{mn'}) \quad \text{and} \quad E(T_{nm'}) = E(T_{mn'}) \tag{13-20}$$

The states $V_{nn'}$ and $T_{nn'}$ also will be important; they are at lower energies; the states $V_{mm'}$ and $T_{mm'}$ will be at higher energies. This gives the predicted energy levels shown on the left side of Fig. 5. A further result is that the transition moments from N to $V_{nm'}$ and $V_{mn'}$ are equal.

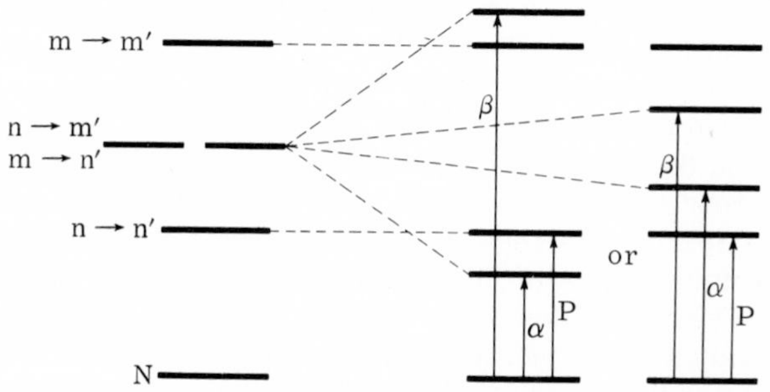

Figure 5. Many-electron energy levels for alternant hydrocarbons. On the left are the levels before electron repulsion is taken into account. To the right are the levels after electronic repulsion is considered; first, for a case for which the effect is relatively large (e.g., benzene), and then for a case for which the effect is small (e.g., pentacene).

This picture, which is essentially the Hückel one, would not account for the experimental facts. The incorporation of electron repulsion will, however. The degenerate states $V_{nm'}$ and $V_{mn'}$, and $T_{nm'}$ and $T_{mn'}$, are split by electron repulsion [by an amount $(\phi_n\phi_{n'}|\phi_{m'}\phi_m) \pm (\phi_n\phi_m|\phi_{m'}\phi_{n'})$ for the singlet and triplet, respectively], giving what Pariser calls + states at higher energy, $V_{nm'} + V_{mn'}$ and $T_{nm'} + T_{mn'}$, and corresponding $-$ states at lower energy, $V_{nm'} - V_{mn'}$ and $T_{nm'} - T_{mn'}$, the transition to the + singlet state from the ground state being strongly allowed, to the $-$ singlet state essentially forbidden. This gives the situation pictured on the right of Fig. 5, agreeing very well with experiments. In benzene, the splitting is so large as to bring the $-$ component of the $n \rightarrow m'$, $m \rightarrow n'$ state below the $n \rightarrow n'$ state, but in anthracene is not so large as to effect this inversion. The $n \rightarrow n'$ transition is the p band of Clar,[166] relatively weak in intensity, the $-$ component of the $n \rightarrow m'$, $m \rightarrow n'$ transition is the α band of Clar, weak in intensity, and the + component of the $n \rightarrow m'$, $m \rightarrow n'$ transition is the β band of Clar, and is very strong.

McLachlan has given some good, very general proofs of the pairing relations,[167] and he and Weijland[168] have shown that the electronic excitations of the positive and negative ions derived from a neutral even alternant should be very close to the same, and the spin densities for the ground states of these species (important for understanding electron spin resonance spectra) should be similar. For the theory of odd-alternant radicals and ions, the early basic theoretical work is by Brickstock and Pople,[169] Longuet-Higgins and Pople,[170] and Lefebvre.[142]

Further quantitative calculations accord well with these ideas for neutral molecules,[171-181] and quantitative applications to spectra of hydrocarbon radicals and mono- and di-, positive and negative ions are about equally successful.[182-194] We conclude that the molecular-orbital method applied this way accounts for and correctly predicts alternant hydrocarbon spectra.

For the hydrocarbon ground states,[112,134,151,169,172,176,178,195-214] special attention has been given the bond order-bond length question for the more common species, resonance energies, and spin distributions for the unusual species. Observed bond lengths seem to correlate better with bond orders computed in this manner than with Hückel bond orders.[196] The large resonance energy of carbonium cations is accounted for.[169,197] Molecules all the way from C_2[179] to infinitely long polyenes[203,209,210] to graphite[201] have been subjected to calculations of this type. A discussion of the $4n + 2$ rule for aromaticity has been given,[205] and forces between pi systems have been considered.[209,211] And results obtained recently for spin distributions are encouraging.[193,212-214]

Acetylene and its higher homologues have been treated by Serre,[215] and the effects of nonplanarity on a conjugated double-bond system has been discussed by several authors.[123,185] Additional calculations on nonalternants are multiplying.[174-176,181,216-219]

In a very recent comprehensive study,[181] Hummel and Ruedenberg have predicted the electronic spectra of a total of 38 alternant and nonalternant hydrocarbons by methods that are related to those we have described here. Figure 6, taken from their paper, illustrates their results. They are in remarkable agreement with experiment for the alternants, fair agreement for the nonalternants.

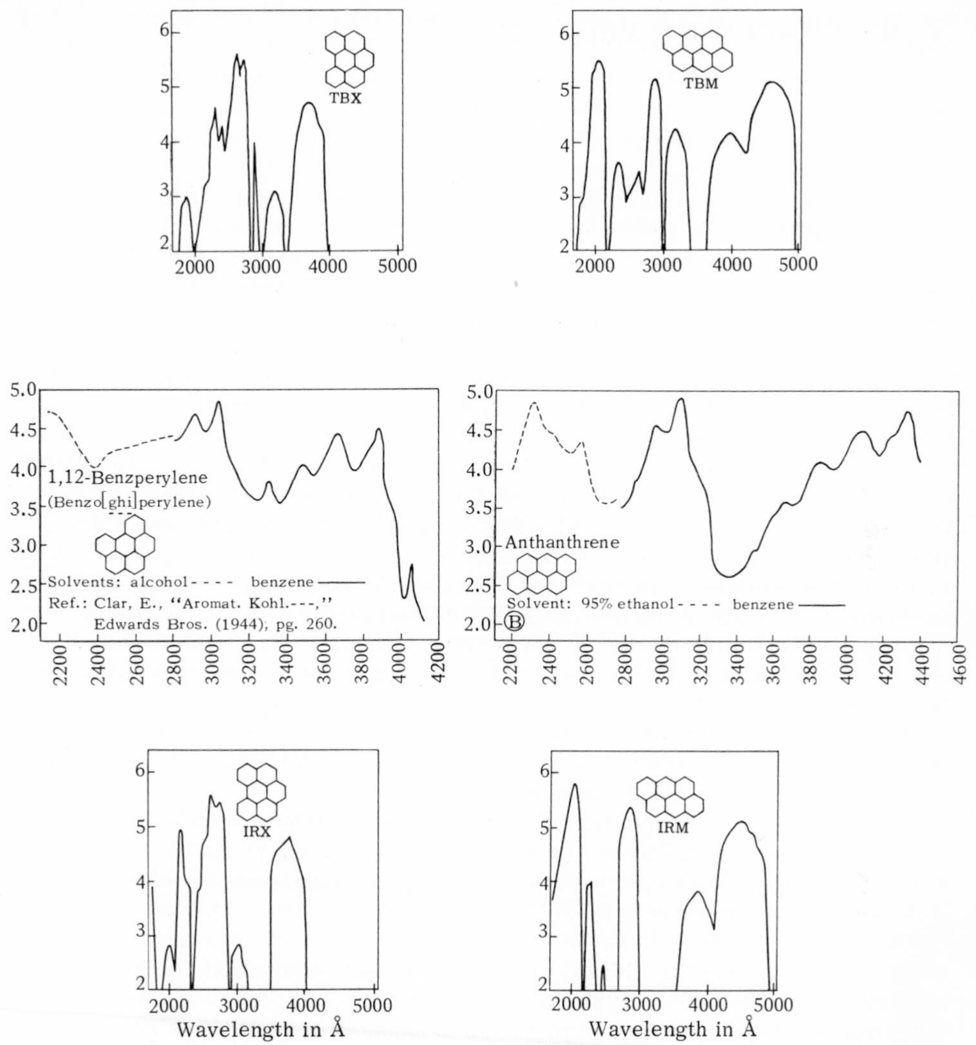

Figure 6. Theoretical and experimental ultraviolet spectra for the isomers benzperylene and anthanthrene, from Hummel and Ruedenberg.[181] Experimental spectra are in the center; above and below are theoretical spectra calculated by two different approximations. The intensity ordinate is the decimal logarithm of the extinction coefficient. Whereas the experimental spectra contain vibronic structure, the theoretical spectra simulate a smooth broadening in accordance with the calculated oscillator strengths.

14 NONHYDROCARBON MOLECULES

The heteronuclear aromatic conjugated systems offer problems no different in principle from those presented by hydrocarbons. Again, there is a wealth of data for correlation and prediction, and, again, theories can be built by explicitly considering only the pi electrons.

There are, however, certain very substantial difficulties attendant the heteromolecule problem. In the first place, it necessarily involves many theoretical parameters—the W_p, P_p for all the atoms p and the β_{pq}, γ_{pq} for all the atom pairs pq in the molecule. This means that we cannot expect to be able to test any theory, by prediction, until we have done considerable work on many molecules, in which we test our suppositions about the parameters by suitable correlations of known data. We must be systematic and patient in this endeavor.

As important is the fact that the validity of almost any approximate theory can be expected to depend on the degree of heteropolarity in the molecules we treat. In our treatment of hydrocarbons, we have shown that the blasé neglect of differential overlap leads to little error. To summarize the previous discussion, this can be thought of as a result of a fortunate smallness of electronic-repulsion integrals involving overlap distributions between orthogonalized atomic orbitals on two centers, or, alternatively, as a result of the remarkable reliability of the Mulliken approximation Eq. (11-29) for atomic-orbital overlap distributions.[129] We have no assurance that such assumptions can be carried over to the general case; indeed, of course, we must anticipate that they cannot.

A final point is that the σ-π separation itself may possibly be more nearly valid for the essentially homopolar case of hydrocarbons than for the general case. It probably is not the assumption of separability $\Psi = [(\Sigma)(\Pi)]$ that breaks down, but rather the assumption of constant sigma structure from state to state.[97] That is to say, intramolecular-charge transfers in the pi-electron system will be accompanied by adjustments in the sigma-electron core.

It was with an awareness of such difficulties that it was recognized early in the development of the Hückel method that the nonhydrocarbon molecules most suitable for treatment by Hückel-like methods were those that could be viewed as minor perturbations of hydrocarbons. For them, quantum-mechanical perturbation techniques may be employed, and *changes* of properties relative to parent hydrocarbons can be computed. Thus we have red or blue *shifts* of spectral lines on aromatic substitution, dipole moments produced when they were not present in the parent, *relative* basicities, and so on. I would refer you to Streitwieser's book for an account of these matters from the Hückel point of view.[100]

With methods including electron repulsion, the situation is much the same; most work has been done on systems more or less close to hydrocarbons in their electronic structure. To illustrate what is involved, let us consider the very simple case of two pi electrons in two nonequivalent pi orbitals—what we call *ethylene-like molecules*.[220] Examples would include any substituted ethylene (if mesomeric effects are neglected) or formaldehyde.

The analysis may be patterned after Eqs. (11-12) et seq. and Eqs. (11-23) et seq., still starting (and this is the trick, which will be the better the closer we are to a true homopolar situation) from the LCAO combinations appropriate for the full ethylene symmetry,

$$\phi_1 = \frac{1}{\sqrt{2}}(a + b) \qquad \phi_2 = \frac{1}{\sqrt{2}}(a - b) \tag{14-1}$$

Then we have, to put the equations down concisely in the zero-differential-overlap approximation,†

$$\mathcal{H} = \mathcal{H}_{core}(1) + \mathcal{H}_{core}(2) + (1/r_{12}) \tag{14-2}$$

$$\begin{gathered}\Phi = C_1\Phi_1 + C_2\Phi_2 + C_V\Phi_V + C_T\Phi_T \qquad \Phi_1 = (\phi_1\bar{\phi}_1) \qquad \Phi_2 = (\phi_2\bar{\phi}_2) \\ \Phi_V = 2^{-1/2}[(\phi_1\bar{\phi}_2) + (\phi_2\bar{\phi}_1)] \qquad \Phi_T = 2^{-1/2}[(\phi_1\bar{\phi}_2) - (\phi_2\bar{\phi}_1)]\end{gathered} \tag{14-3}$$

$$\begin{aligned}H_{11} &= 2I_1 + J = \alpha_a + \alpha_b + 2\beta + J \\ H_{22} &= 2I_2 + J = \alpha_a + \alpha_b - 2\beta + J \\ H_{VV} &= I_1 + I_2 + J + K = \alpha_a + \alpha_b + J + K \\ H_{TT} &= I_1 + I_2 + J - K = \alpha_a + \alpha_b + J - K \\ H_{1T} &= H_{2T} = H_{VT} = 0 \qquad H_{12} = K \\ H_{1V} &= H_{2V} = 2^{1/2}[I_{12} + (11|12)] = 2^{-1/2}[\alpha_a + (1/2)\gamma_{aa} - \alpha_b - (1/2)\gamma_{bb}] \\ J &= (1/4)(\gamma_{aa} + \gamma_{bb} + 2\gamma_{ab}) \\ K &= (1/4)(\gamma_{aa} + \gamma_{bb} - 2\gamma_{ab})\end{aligned} \tag{14-4}$$

Further, from Eq. (10-1)

$$\alpha_a = -(\mathcal{I}_a + P_a + \gamma_{ab}) \qquad \alpha_b = -(\mathcal{I}_b + P_b + \gamma_{ab}) \tag{14-5}$$

If therefore we define

$$\begin{gathered}y_a = \mathcal{I}_a - (1/2)\gamma_{aa} + P_a \qquad y_b = \mathcal{I}_b - (1/2)\gamma_{bb} + P_b \\ Y = y_a - y_b\end{gathered} \tag{14-6}$$

† The precise interpretation of each of the atomic-orbital integrals in these equations, including α_a, α_b, and β, is that it is an over orthogonalized atomic orbital.

we obtain

$$H_{1V} = H_{2V} = -2^{-1/2} Y \tag{14-7}$$

This, of course, is the matrix element that is zero in ethylene itself—the measure of heteropolarity of the bond. The secular equation for the singlet states thus reads, with $W = E - H_{11}$,

$$\begin{vmatrix} -W & K & -2^{-\frac{1}{2}}Y \\ K & -W - 4\beta & -2^{-\frac{1}{2}}Y \\ -2^{-\frac{1}{2}}Y & -2^{-\frac{1}{2}}Y & -W - 2\beta + K \end{vmatrix} = 0 \tag{14-8}$$

whereas the triplet-state energy is

$$W_T = -2\beta - K \tag{14-9}$$

If we set $Y = 0$, we recover our previous Eqs. (11-26) and (11-27).

How do the excitation energies as obtained from Eqs. (14-8) and (14-9) compare with those obtained from Eqs. (11-26) and (11-27)? If Y is zero as, for example, in tetramethyl ethylene, the solution is formally the same as in ethylene itself, and, at first glance, we predict no change in excitation energies. This is wrong, however: A change in any one or several of the quantities β, γ_{aa}, or γ_{ab} may occur, and such changes are going to affect the energies. If Y is not zero, we get an additional effect, depression of the ground state and elevation of the first excited singlet state. This in itself produces a shift to the blue of the $N \rightarrow V$ transition, but it is quite possible for the first effect to constitute a shift to the red that outweighs the effect of Y. And mesomeric effects of substituents have been neglected entirely in this treatment. These results are typical: Several effects are operative, all of which must be unraveled in treating a particular case.

To continue the analysis, let us see what we would predict for the dipole moment of the two pi electrons by this scheme. Supposing for simplicity that $\int a(1)x(1)a(1)\,dv(1) = -(1/2)R$, $\int b(1)x(1)b(1)\,dv(1) = +(1/2)R$, and $\int a(1)x(1)b(1)\,dv(1) = 0$, and that we may neglect the contribution of Φ_2, we obtain

$$\mu_\pi = e\bar{x} = e\iint \Phi_N[x(1) + x(2)]\Phi_N\,dv(1)\,dv(2) \tag{14-10}$$

$$\approx e(C_1^2 + C_V^2)[((1/2)R) + (-(1/2)R)] + 2C_1C_V\,2^{-\frac{1}{2}}[((1/2)R) - (-(1/2)R)]$$

$$= 2^{\frac{1}{2}}C_1C_V eR = 2^{\frac{1}{2}}C_1^2(C_V/C_1)eR \approx 2^{\frac{1}{2}}(C_V/C_1)eR \approx Y/(E_V - E_N)$$

The pi dipole moment is thus proportional to Y; we may regard Y as an *electronegativity difference*, and y_a and y_b as defined by Eq. (14-6) as effective *orbital electronegativities*. The reasonableness of our entire analysis follows immediately if we insert Pariser's Eq. (10-8) into Eq. (14-6), for we then get

$$y_a = \frac{\mathcal{I}_a + \mathcal{A}_a}{2} + P_a \tag{14-11}$$

which is just Mulliken's definition of absolute electronegativity[221] corrected by a penetration term! We shall come back to the electronegativity concept in a later section.

A corresponding analysis of *benzene-like molecules* can be given, and there emerges a perspicuous scheme for handling inductive effects on the spectra of these molecules.[119,222-225] The important work of Petruska is related.[226]

More generally, some quite elegant and useful theoretical perturbation techniques for handling the change from a parent hydrocarbon to a heteromolecule have been worked out by various authors.[223,224,227,228]

Many actual calculations have been carried out on unsaturated heteromolecules using extended Hückel methods (few comparable molecules have been treated with the Goeppert-Mayer-Sklar scheme[229]). Pariser and Parr performed calculations on the nitrogen heterocyclic analogs of benzene,[111] and Parks and Parr on formaldehyde.[97] Using parameters from the latter work, Sidman considered two other molecules containing the carbonyl group, glyoxal and *p*-benzoquinone.[230] His conclusions typify those of other authors:

> By a judicious choice of parameters and integrals it is possible to describe semiquantitatively the π-electron ionization potentials, $n \rightarrow \pi$ and $\pi \rightarrow \pi$ electron transition energies, and π-electronic contribution to the dipole moment of formaldehyde, glyoxal, and *p*-benzoquinone.

Recent work on ketones by McClelland[231] continues in this optimistic tone.

The molecules that have been studied have been quite diverse. Thus McGlynn and Simpson have considered dye ions of the general formula

$$Me_2N - (CH{=}CH)_{n-1} - CH = N^+ - Me_2$$

finding that[232]

> The results correspond to experiment, not only with respect to pattern, but also in many cases with respect to calculated transition energies.

The extreme is represented by a calculation[233] by Grabe on electronic energy levels and electron distribution in reduced and oxidized forms of diphosphopyridine nucleotide and of flavine, which also gave results that the author considers encouraging, or some very recent calculations[234] by Sappenfield and

Kreevoy on the oxygen and sulfur heteromolecules furan, thiophene, and 1,4-dithiadiene. The latter authors state

> It is possible to reproduce the spectra, dipole moments, resonance energies and reactivities of these molecules with a small number of adjusted parameters all of which have reasonable values.

We thus may feel generally heartened.

Of singular interest is a definitive study of the aniline molecule by Fischer-Hjalmars.[235] Also worthy of special study is a series of papers by McWeeny and Peacock.[199,236-240] They have given procedures for the formal calculation of the molecular orbitals,[199,236] and applied these to the benzene nitrogen heterocycles[237,239] and other molecules.[240] McWeeny's comparative study of different methods applied to the pyridine and pyrazine molecules is of considerable methodic importance.[237] The recent paper by Amos and Hall derives from this work; it, too, is instructive.[241]

Mataga, Mataga, Nishimoto, and Fujishiro have carried out calculations on these same molecules and some others.[242-245] The way these authors handle the coulomb integrals γ_{pq} is interesting and unique. For a homopolar case they take, with R the p-q distance,

$$\gamma_{pq} = \frac{1}{R + a_p} \tag{14-12}$$

$$\gamma_{pp} = \frac{1}{a_p} = \mathcal{I}_p - \mathcal{A}_p \tag{14-13}$$

For a heteropolar case they take arithmetic means of the appropriate homopolar formulas. Equation (14-12) is a simple interpolation formula between the Pariser one-center formula of Eq. (14-13) and the correct large distance Pople formula $1/R$. If expanded in inverse powers of R, it contains terms in $1/R^2$, $1/R^3$, and so on. It can be argued that the quadratic term should be missing,[119] because an undistorted atomic $2p\pi$ orbital has no dipole moment, but perhaps inclusion of such a term is an acceptable way to include some polarization of the π atomic orbitals on molecule formation.

R. D. Brown and collaborators have given special attention to what is clearly a most important problem—how the parameters change, especially the quantities $\mathcal{I}_p$ (or W_p or α_p) and γ_{pp}, when there is a big pile-up of charge on one atom in a molecule, as may occur in a highly heteropolar case. After some early, more-routine calculations on heteromolecules,[246-248] they have invented[249] and widely applied[218,249] a special "variable electronegativity" method for applying corrections for this effect.

Anno and collaborators have performed theoretical calculations on *p*-benzoquinone,[250] formaldehyde,[251] and the nitrogen-containing heterocyclic molecules,[251,252] trying to include $n \rightarrow \pi$ transitions in the theory. This last is nontrivial to do and, of course, takes us out of the realm of pi-electron problems. To indicate the sort of results one gets (not always spectacularly good) with this sort of calculation on this sort of molecule, in Table 16 are summarized Anno's calculations on the pyridine-singlet excited-electronic levels.[252]

TABLE 16
Low Singlet-Excited States of Pyridine (in Electron Volts)[a]

Excitation	Calculated energy	Experimental energy
$n \to \pi^*$	4.31	4.31
$\pi \to \pi^*$	4.32	4.75
$n \to \pi^*$	5.04	4.52
$\pi \to \pi^*$	5.81	6.41
$\pi \to \pi^*$	7.58	7.23
$\pi \to \pi^*$	7.69	

[a]From Anno, Ref. 252.
[b]The excitations labeled $n \to \pi^*$ involve lone pair electrons, the others the pi electrons.

Paoloni and Dewar have reported calculations on s-tetrazine and melamine,[253,254] and Paoloni has used similar techniques in some calculations on the hydrogen bond.[255] A calculation similar to the one Fumi and Parr performed on O_2[118] has been carried out for O_2^+.[256]

The other applications to heteromolecules of this type of theory are numerous;[225,257-272] they cover topics from ferrocene[257] through hyperconjugation.[259] Some of the papers described in earlier sections, with special reference to their contributions to method, also contain applications to particular heteromolecules; for example, the papers from the English school ordinarily are well documented with examples. Of the additional contributions on method, we might single out for mention Longuet-Higgins and Murrell's discussion of the interaction of two conjugated systems,[273] and Fukui's discussions of reactivity indices in theories including electron repulsion.[274]

Typically in these calculations, electronic-excitation energies agree with experimental values to, say, 0.1 to 0.5 ev, the several levels being sufficiently spaced apart and different in their transition moments with the ground state to permit the theory to aid in the assignments of observed bands. Effects of molecular perturbations on ionization potentials generally come out right, as do the red or blue shifts of transitions. Bond lengths correlate reasonably well with computed bond orders, and dipole moments make more sense than those calculated by the Hückel method. To be sure, the theoretical parameters employed at times are highly arbitrary, but the results that have been obtained both agree with experiment and survive theoretical scrutiny well enough that one is encouraged to proceed both with further applications and with theoretical studies designed to improve the theoretical basis.

15 OTHER PI-ELECTRON METHODS

In this section, we shall describe a number of minor variations of the theoretical methods we have been discussing, and several unique new methods which derive in part from these methods. In addition, we shall make some remarks about recent work with the more traditional methods.

We have mentioned Brown's variable-electronegativity method,[249] which goes beyond the original, generalized-Hückel methods by providing corrections for local accumulations of charges in heteropolar systems. Hoyland and Goodman,[208,275] in part following I'Haya,[126] have had success recently with a similar procedure designed to correct the parameters for disruptions of electronic structure such as accompany ionization. In the work on such effects in formaldehyde,[97] Parks and Parr had ignored the changes in sigma-electron effective charges that accompany ionization and had concentrated on charge shifts in the sigma structure; it is clear from Hoyland and Goodman's work that the two effects are of comparable importance.

The semiempirical method[276] of Goodman and Shull should also be mentioned. This adheres more to the Hückel formalism, interpreting the matrix elements in the Hückel method as over the Hartree-Fock operators F instead of over the bare-nuclear operators $\mathcal{H}_{core}$. As we shall discuss further in Sec. 16, there are important unsolved questions about what the best quantities to regard as semiempirical are, but Eq. (13-8) shows that the choice between the F_{pq} and the β_{pq}^{core} is a nontrivial one; experience and theory both favor the latter.

Ruedenberg has published a useful comprehensive series of studies[277] of many of the facets of pi-electron theory. Starting from no assumption whatsoever but sigma-pi separability, he examines all the parameters that enter under various simplifying assumptions. He prefers the Mulliken assumption of Eq. (11-29) to the outright neglect of differential overlap of Eq. (10-6), but, since the latter can be obtained from the former by setting $S = 0$ in the final formulas, much of his analysis applies as well to zero-differential-overlap methods. For the benzene case, de Heer and Pauncz also have shown that a very simple scheme can be obtained with the Mulliken approximation if it is applied uniformly to all electronic-repulsion integrals.[278]

To turn to less-drastic suggestions regarding generalized-Hückel methods, we have already mentioned the neat, simple method Nishimoto and Mataga suggest for evaluation of the two-center electron-repulsion integrals γ_{pq}.[242] I have suggested use of multipole expansion formulas for these.[119] Ooshika[202] and Companion and Ellison[279] recommend on the other hand formulas like

$$\gamma_{pq} = [1 - \exp(-KR)]/R \tag{15-1}$$

This form, like Mataga's, can be made to satisfy Eqs. (10-7) and (10-8). As another suggestion along similar lines, we may mention Kon's proposal[280] that the quantities β_{pq} be assumed inversely proportional to the sixth power of the distance between atoms p and q.

Longuet-Higgins and Salem have gone so far as to retain only the integrals γ_{pp} and γ_{pq} for p and q neighbors.[281] If triplet states are not considered, this gives a reasonably good fit of spectroscopic data. As Murrell and Salem have shown,[282] the assumption is not as bad as it first appears because the *differences* of electronic repulsions are really what enter the formulas. We shall return to this question in Sec. 16.

The one-center integrals γ_{pp} have been the subject of considerable discussion.[283-287] If we view them as quantities that must be determined from atomic data, just how to best carry out their evaluation is a mean problem; one must identify the correct state (including state of ionization) of the atom everywhere such an integral appears, and suitably correct for the inadequacies of the simple orbital description, without violating the virial theorem.[287] At the present stage of development of the theory, I am inclined to think that it is better to view these integrals as empirical properties of the pi orbitals in a molecule; from this point of view the problem becomes one of secondary importance.

A purely theoretical series of studies by Kolos[288] has furnished insight on the question of why the semiempirical values for the γ_{pq} integrals in pi-electron theory are so much lower than the values for Slater orbitals. If we assume pi-electron correlations are the cause, we may argue that, given two pi electrons with opposite spins in the same molecular orbital in a hydrocarbon, for example, their repulsion when on the same atom should not be as high as 16.9 ev because they will like to dodge each other. We can produce this effect by introducing into the pi-electron wave function $\phi_1\bar{\phi}_1$ describing such a pair a multiplicative factor r_{12}, and Kolos has done calculations on ethylene and benzene with such a modified Goeppert-Mayer-Sklar scheme. The improved agreement with experiment is remarkable, and one would like to be able to include correctly such factors in systematic calculations on many molecules. Unfortunately, this does not appear to be feasible computationally. Even the calculations of Kolos suffer from some apparent nonorthogonality difficulties, and the generalizations to more complex systems than benzene are unwieldy without simplifying assumptions.

Julg has set out on a similar track, with some success; in what he calls the "méthode LCAO améliorée," he has semiempiricized a Kolos-like scheme, in which a general function $f(r_{12})$ is used as the multiplicative factor.[289-291] He has treated singlet-excitation energies, ionization potentials, and electron distributions, in a number of molecules. He prefers not to discuss triplet states, for which Kolos suggested omission of factors r_{12}, since electrons with the same spin are kept well apart by the Pauli principle. Some of Julg's argument is difficult to follow, in particular his claim that, if ϕ_1 and ϕ_2 are orthogonal, then ϕ_1 and $f^2\phi_2$ are also. His final result, however, certainly is suggestive; he finds that the effect of the factors f can be incorporated by replacing the pi-electron repulsion terms $1/r_{\mu\nu}$ in the Hamiltonian with $f^2(r_{\mu\nu})/r_{\mu\nu}$.[289] This would imply an effective microscopic dielectric constant for the pi-electron motions, a concept that might well be investigated further. To this end, a *physical* assumption that would define a model leading to Julg's result might be made; this might be the assumption that the one-electron density is unaffected by correlation.

A not unrelated method is the one Dewar has named the "split-p method," in which the two ("upper" and "lower") lobes of an atomic $2p\pi$ orbital are used in place of just one.[292-298] When one electron is in the upper lobe and the other in the lower lobe in a Slater $2p\pi$ orbital with charge 3.18, their mutual repulsion is just 11.0 ev,[293,295] very close to the empirical value for this integral we obtained in Sec. 12; and, indeed, the whole γ_{pq} curve between an upper lobe on atom p and a lower lobe on atom q falls almost on top of the empirical values.[295] This coincidence is remarkable indeed, and it has led Dewar to develop an entire theory emphasizing this "up-down" or "vertical" correlation effect.[294,296]

For ethylene,[294] we can put one pi electron in an upper molecular orbital ϕ_1^u or ϕ_2^u, the other in a lower molecular orbital ϕ_1^ℓ or ϕ_2^ℓ, taking as the space part of the ground-state description $\phi_1^u(1)\phi_1^\ell(2) + \phi_1^\ell(1)\phi_1^u(2)$. Equivalently, Dewar shows that just one factor suffices; including spin, one can merely employ $\phi_1^u(1)\alpha(1)\phi_1^\ell(2)\beta(2)$. Generalizing, for benzene he puts three electrons, with spin α, above the ring, three electrons, with spin β, below the ring, and so on. This is great fun, and the numerical results are good.[296]

There is one apparent difficulty with this procedure, and another real one.[295,297,298] Apparently, we shall meet trouble when we come to compute kinetic energies, because an integral

$$T_{fg} = -(1/2)\int f \nabla^2 g \, dv \qquad (15\text{-}2)$$

involves an undefined integrand if g is a function like an individual pi lobe which has a discontinuous derivative. When such a trouble occurs, it usually[299] can be circumvented[293,295,300] by employing an alternative form

$$T_{fg} = +(1/2)\int \nabla f \cdot \nabla g \, dv \qquad (15\text{-}3)$$

As Dewar recognized, the need for this equation does not arise in the pure pi-electron treatments with the individual pi lobes, because Eq. (15-2) causes no difficulty if the divergence of $\nabla^2 g$ occurs at a place where f vanishes strongly.

On the other hand, wave functions built from the split-p functions are not orthogonal to sigma orbitals,[295,297] so that, in the calculations with the split-p method, one is employing a simplified model in which the sigma-pi separability conditions are not satisfied. Saturno, Joy, and Snyder have recently demonstrated that a proper consideration of the nonorthogonality weakens Dewar's results.[298]

In this rundown of methods we must consider a number of others. The *valence-bond method* remains valuable, especially for handling certain problems in spin resonance spectra.[301] Valence-bond techniques have gained power in recent years, both from the molecular integrals that have become available and from the methods that have been developed by McWeeny[120] and others[302-305] for handling the nonorthogonality difficulties. The resonance-force theory of Simpson is conceptually related.[304] The so-called *atoms-in-molecules method*, which we shall be discussing in Sec. 17, is intimately related to the valence-bond method. Applications of atoms-in-molecules methods to unsaturated systems are still appearing,[306,307] but in this context these methods are not fully satisfactory.

The *free-electron model*[308] remains important and useful. In its refinement to include electronic repulsions,[309-311] it becomes almost indistinguishable from the LCAO-molecular-orbital theory, as was decisively shown by Ruedenberg and Ham in 1956.[309] (In the simple version of this model, electronic repulsion is ignored; that this is intolerable in a quantitative theory of aromatic properties follows for the same reasons that neglect of electron repulsion in the Hückel method produces large quantitative errors.) Recent work by Olszewski on the free-electron theory makes use of an elegant Green's function technique,[311] and Labhart's attempt to include deformations in a sigma core may also be noted.[312] Three-dimensional free-electron network models of solids have recently been developed.[313]

Finally, we should discuss the *alternant molecular-orbital method* of Löwdin.[314] This is a clever device for obtaining most of the "side-wise" or "horizontal" correlation in an alternant hydrocarbon. Where Dewar puts one electron in an upper lobe when the other is in a lower lobe, Löwdin puts one electron on one atom when the other is on a neighboring atom—"different orbitals for different spins." Here, the basic idea may be illustrated by considering the two-electron case of the hydrogen (or ethylene) molecule. If, in place of the usual molecular-orbital description (excluding spin) $\Phi = \phi(1)\phi(2)$, we take a description of the form

$$\Phi(1,2) = \phi(1)\phi'(2) + \phi'(1)\phi(2) \tag{15-4}$$

we certainly can get a better result. Thus, in place of the usual choice $\phi = a + b$, where a and b are the two atomic orbitals, we can take

$$\phi = a + \lambda b \qquad \phi' = b + \lambda a \tag{15-5}$$

where λ is a parameter. We then obtain

$$\Phi(1,2) = (1 + \lambda^2)[a(1)b(2) + b(1)a(2)] + 2\lambda[a(1)a(2) + b(1)b(2)] \tag{15-6}$$

This is just the best covalent-ionic wave function of Weinbaum, if λ is suitably chosen—nothing very new or surprising. The generalization to an alternant hydrocarbon, however, is of interest. The traditional description of a closed-shell ground state of an even alternant has a series of bonding molecular orbitals doubly occupied in pairs, these orbitals having the form of Eq. (13-15): $\Phi_N = (\phi_1\bar{\phi}_1\phi_2\bar{\phi}_2\cdots)$. The correlation within an electron pair presumably being much more important than between pairs, we take a typical pair description $\phi_n\bar{\phi}_n$ here and replace it with $\psi_n\bar{\psi}_{n'}$, in which

$$\begin{aligned}\psi_n &= A_n\phi_n + B_n\phi_{n'} = (A_n + B_n) \sum_{\substack{\text{starred}\\ \text{atoms}}} C_{np}\chi_p + (A_n - B_n) \sum_{\substack{\text{unstarred}\\ \text{atoms}}} C_{np}\chi_p \\ \psi_{n'} &= A_n\phi_n - B_n\phi_{n'} = (A_n - B_n) \sum_{\substack{\text{starred}\\ \text{atoms}}} C_{np}\chi_p + (A_n + B_n) \sum_{\substack{\text{unstarred}\\ \text{atoms}}} C_{np}\chi_p\end{aligned} \tag{15-7}$$

where $\phi_{n'}$ is the antibonding orbital of Eq. (13-16), paired with ϕ_n. By varying A_n/B_n, the terms ψ_n and $\psi_{n'}$ can be caused to separate the two electrons onto the starred and unstarred atoms; a modified function

$$\Phi'_N = (\psi_1\bar{\psi}_{1'}\psi_2\bar{\psi}_{2'}\cdots) \tag{15-8}$$

may thus be presumed to include a considerable fraction of the total horizontal-correlation energy if the parameters A_n/B_n are suitably chosen. A complication is that the single determinant of Eq. (15-8) is not, in general, an eigenfunction of the total spin. The singlet component of this function can be extracted by application of a suitable projection operator, however,[314] which gives for the ground-state eigenfunction in the alternant molecular orbital method

$$^1\Phi_N = \mathcal{O}_{00}(\psi_1\bar{\psi}_{1'}\psi_2\bar{\psi}_{2'}\cdots) \tag{15-9}$$

Configuration interaction in the Goeppert-Mayer-Sklar method for benzene gives a ground-state correlation energy of 2.7 ev. Of this, 2.4 ev can be obtained with the alternant-molecular-orbital method using a common parameter A_n/B_n for the three occupied molecular orbitals.[315] All of it (indeed 2.8 ev!)

can be obtained if one A_n/B_n is used for the orbital ϕ_0, another for the orbitals ϕ_1 and ϕ_{-1}.[316] De Heer has also done the alternant-molecular-orbital calculation for benzene using the semiempirical integral values of Pariser; again the full horizontal correlation energy is obtained.[316]

Extensions of the alternant-molecular-orbital calculations to the general alternant or other molecules will be difficult, but they are being attempted.[317] The spin densities in odd alternants apparently can be computed with good accuracy by this method.[318]

16 DISCUSSION

From the successful applications of pi-electron theory, we should not conclude that the theory has reached a refined or satisfactory state. There is too much vagueness in the assumptions, there are too many ambiguities in the procedures, and authors do not agree on many points.

Rather, we should be encouraged to seek further improvements, both through carefully contrived calculations on particular molecules and through study of the basic theoretical framework. In the ultimate theory, every parameter that enters must have a value that can be rationalized by a purely theoretical argument, and no quantity that is neglected can have a value such that its inclusion would vitiate agreement with experiment.

It is not clear that there can ever be found an ultimate theory for pi systems that is simple. If one wants to be pessimistic, one may merely quote the 0.5-ev or so errors commonplace in the heteropolar applications we have described. I prefer the optimistic view that these errors probably can be reduced by an order of magnitude through careful studies of the basic methods, and subsequent modifications of them.

Of course, the sense in which sigma-pi separability and the pi-electron approximation will survive refinements in the theory is restricted. Separability will be valid for only certain properties, for certain (probably the planar) molecules, and to only a certain accuracy. We have already seen that adjustment of the sigma structure in going from neutral to ionized states may be significant,[275] and that sigma-pi configuration interaction must sometimes be invoked to account for the proton fine structure in electron-spin-resonance spectra.[98] To give another example, according to Karplus and Fraenkel[319] the C^{13} hyperfine interactions in electron-spin-resonance spectra ''provide an excellent semi-quantitative estimate of the validity of separating pi and sigma wave functions in the ground electronic states of pi-electron systems.''

Further development of theory of complex unsaturated molecules should depend more and more on accurate theory of small molecules. The latter theory has progressed to the point that some simple pi-electron systems can be treated quite precisely, and there is no substitute for the exact checking out of a separability or other semiempirical postulate against the exact solution of a problem. An additional reason for leaning on theory to verify theory is provided by the inherent, many-parameter nature of the heteromolecule problem.

It thus would appear to be imperative to initiate systematic, purely theoretical studies of some model pi-electron systems, such as the valence state of the carbon atom itself, the methyl radical, ethylene, and acetylene.[320] Accurate reproduction of experimental properties of these molecules will be of interest. But, just as important, one will want to see how well one can do with separated sigma-pi descriptions built from atomic orbitals, which can be carried over to larger molecules.

If the approximate validity of the sigma-pi separability can be upheld, it will be most important to examine the pi-electron descriptions in two stages. First, one should attempt to ascertain how good Slater atomic $2p\pi$ orbitals are as a basis for LCAO-SCF pi-electron wave functions. In principle, we know that the basis should be enlarged, to include $3p\pi$, $3d\pi$, and higher orbitals. Some studies of $3p\pi$ and $3d\pi$ mixing have already been carried out.[321-323] These should be extended, with special emphasis on the question: Given an accurate LCAO-SCF wave function, when the molecular orbitals are transformed to a localized orthogonal basis, what do the localized orbitals look like? (For instance, what are the values for the one-center electronic-repulsion integrals γ_{pp}?)

Second, the correlation energy for pi electrons must be studied. Thanks to the recent work of Dewar with his split-p orbital method on the one hand,[296] and the renewed emphasis on the alternant-molecular-orbital method on the other,[316,317] we now see clearly the point at issue: Is it vertical (up-down) correlation that is important, or horizontal correlation, or both? Dewar's own calculations are too simplified to settle this, and, anyway, he is daring to put most of the burden on the vertical correlation. Some more general calculations on some model pi-electron system could settle the question very easily.[298] In particular, I wonder whether it would not be a good idea to do some calculations incorporating the $3d\sigma$ orbitals. For, combinations $2p\pi + 3d\sigma$ and $2p\pi - 3d\sigma$ would be very much like Dewar's upper- and lower-lobe functions, and would not suffer from the nonorthogonality difficulty with respect to inner shells. This would mean that, for ethylene, for example, the relative importance of horizontal and vertical correlations would be measured by the coefficients B and C in the expansion

$$\Phi(1,2) = A(2p\pi_a + 2p\pi_b)^2 + B(2p\pi_a - 2p\pi_b)^2 + C(3d\sigma_a + 3d\sigma_b)^2 \qquad (16\text{-}1)$$

Here, we may note that the effective charge in the $3d\sigma$ orbitals may be chosen to make that orbital big where $2p\pi_a$ and $2p\pi_b$ are big, without violating orthogonality to inner shells. This type of adjustment of 3s orbitals would not be possible, which probably makes them less important.[324]

The large problem of the best quantum-mechanical description of the sigma-pi separability itself must be kept open. One should examine the relative merits of the sigma-pi description of a double bond and the "banana-bond" description recently favored by Pauling.[325] If we let $\sigma = \sigma_a + \sigma_b$ where

σ_a and σ_b are the bonding sp^2 orbitals on atoms A and B, pointing toward each other, and $\pi = \pi_a + \pi_b$, then the descriptions

$$\Phi(1,2,3,4) = (\sigma\bar{\sigma}\pi\bar{\pi}) \qquad \text{and} \qquad \Phi(1,2,3,4) = (b_u\bar{b}_u b_\ell \bar{b}_\ell) \tag{16-2}$$

are completely equivalent, where $b_u = \sigma + \pi$ and $b_\ell = \sigma - \pi$, since the two determinants differ only by a linear transformation among rows or columns. The question is, which description stands up best when higher-order effects are brought in.

Very recent research by Sinanoğlu is of relevance for the separability problem; his work will be discussed in Sec. 19. Sigma-pi-interaction effects need to be studied in detail and at length. These, Sinanoğlu treats quite explicitly.

The problem of the pi-electron repulsions is by no means solved either. The zero-differential-overlap method that works so well for hydrocarbons does so by virtue of their fortunate uniform charge distributions. At least for alternant hydrocarbons the zero-differential-overlap approximation is a very good one. As a molecule becomes heteropolar, this approximation naturally breaks down.[326] The Mulliken approximation probably holds over a wider range, but in my opinion a best-compromise (simple and yet reasonably accurate) method for treating electron repulsions in heteropolar systems has not yet been found.

On the other hand, the electron-repulsion problem probably is not as severe as most of the recent work and our own discussion would make it seem. Central in the calculations have been the pi-electron bare-nuclear operators $\mathcal{H}_{core}$ in the pi-electron operator

$$\mathcal{H}_\pi(1,2,\ldots,n) = \sum_\mu \mathcal{H}_{core}(\mu) + \sum_{\mu<\nu} (1/r_{\mu\nu}) \tag{16-3}$$

This partitioning of the Hamiltonian brings the pi-electron repulsions into full view. However, bare nuclei are not present in actual molecules, and (as has already been pointed out) electron repulsions do not appear alone in energy formulas, but as differences. It seems desirable to recast the general theory in a form that acknowledges this, which has been done by Del Re and Parr.[327] Although the electron repulsions do not appear in the final formulas in an especially simple form, they do appear as differences, and the operators that in the recast theory appear in place of the operators $\mathcal{H}_{core}$ are not so drastically different as are the operators $\mathcal{H}_{core}$ from the fields a single pi electron feels in one of these molecules. Revision of extended Hückel methods along these lines will return these methods closer to the Hückel method and will add to the justification[158,328-330] of the Hückel method as a good first approximation.

This brings us to what I believe is one of the weaker facets of current pi-electron theories, treatment of matrix elements of the operators $\mathcal{H}_{core}$ as the basic semiempirical parameters. For a single molecule this can do no harm. But to transfer the matrix elements β_{pq}^{core}, and especially the elements α_{p}^{core}, from molecule to molecule surely is somewhat dangerous,[136] especially for hetero systems. So basic studies of *transferability of parameters* are much needed. This problem also has been discussed by Del Re and Parr.[327]

As for the over-all structure of the theory, I wonder whether the role of the overlap integrals should not be made more dominant. The familiar β proportional to S is not right, but Ruedenberg's result[331]

$$\beta \propto S(1 - S) \tag{16-4}$$

may be quite sufficient. Electron repulsions relate to overlap integrals, atomic multipole moments and atomic spectroscopic data through Mulliken's approximation,[127] Pariser's formula for one-center repulsions,[115] and multipole expansion formulas for two-center repulsions,[119] so one might build a whole theory just from atomic data and overlap integrals.

One of the advantages of zero-differential overlap over the Mulliken approximation is that it allows the preservation of the Coulson-Rushbrooke theorem on uniform charge densities in alternant hydrocarbons. Are the atomic charge densities in naphthalene actually close to uniform? How should we best plan to handle penetration integrals in such problems?[231]

Two other problems in pi-electron theory have to do with the interpretation of muclear-magnetic and electron-spin resonance spectra. Orbital theories of the proton and C^{13} chemical shifts in nuclear-magnetic resonance spectra of aromatic hydrocarbons are notably lacking; one should try to develop such theories. The proton hyperfine splittings of electron-spin resonance spectra are better understood. Sigma-pi configuration interaction in a CH bond in an aromatic radical produces some density of the odd electron at the proton, proportional to the odd pi-electron spin density at the carbon; the latter can be discussed with orbital theories of the pi-electron structure itself. However, it seems artificial to single out the neighboring carbon atom in this way. Perhaps an orbital discussion of whole molecule, including sigma-pi configuration interaction, would eliminate discrepancies among predictions of spin densities by rival schemes for computing them.[332]

To summarize, there now are available reasonably well-tested theories of the electronic structure of planar unsaturated molecules. Their degree of complexity requires the use (without overly taxing the power) of modern electronic computers: "...Hückel calculations by electronic computer are marginally justifiable, and should soon be replaced as a standard form of m.o. calculation."[333] Systematic further application of these methods are in order, but fundamental studies of the methods themselves are equally desirable.

IV. Three Approaches to the Many-Electron Correlation Problem

17 THE METHOD OF ATOMS IN MOLECULES

In what we have said up to now, we have generally supposed that, whenever we are faced with the problem of constructing a molecular wave function, we can do it by starting from some large set of one-electron orbitals, by composing many Slater determinants from them, and by then linearly mixing enough of these determinants to achieve any desired accuracy.

This prescription is, in principle, adequate and it corresponds to the way most calculations actually are done. However it ignores the possibility that there may exist useful general analyses of the correlation problem. In this part of these lectures we shall consider three such approaches, the method of atoms in molecules (and its variants), the theory of separated electron pairs, and the many-electron theory of Sinanoğlu. In a molecule the correlations among valence electrons may be easier to compute than the correlations among inner-shell electrons; in the present section we shall examine the possibility of taking the latter from what we know about unbound atoms. To emphasize another feature, we know that in a molecule the most important correlations are between two electrons in the same space orbital with opposite spins; in Sec. 18 we shall develop the hypothesis that only such correlations are important. The analysis in Sec. 19 will be more general. Throughout, the terminology and manipulations will not be dissimilar to those in the discussion of sigma-pi separability in Sec. 8; that separability may be usefully thought of as an example of a separation of electrons into two groups, each described by a complicated wave function, albeit the complete wave function is a simple antisymmetrized product of the pieces.[334]

The basic plan in the *atoms-in-molecules method*, as invented by Moffitt[109] and modified by Arai[335] and Hurley,[336] is to separate intra-atomic and inter-atomic correlation effects, to extract estimates of the former from atomic spectroscopic data, and to calculate the latter from some orbital theory.[8,39] To enable us to carry out this separation, we need to separate the matrix elements of the molecular Hamiltonian into intra-atomic and interatomic pieces; that is the key to these methods.

For simplicity and preciseness, let us consider a diatomic molecule AB. An exact description of its electronic structure at any definite internuclear distance can be obtained by superposition of enough *composite functions* for the atom pair

$$\Phi_{ij} = [\Phi_{Ai}\Phi_{Bj}] = \Phi_k \tag{17-1}$$

where the Φ_{Ai} and Φ_{Bj} are a complete set of antisymmetrized orthonormal eigenfunctions (including continuum functions) for atoms A and B

$$\begin{aligned} \mathcal{H}_A\Phi_{Ai} &= W_{Ai}\Phi_{Ai} \\ \mathcal{H}_B\Phi_{Bj} &= W_{Bj}\Phi_{Bj} \end{aligned} \tag{17-2}$$

and the brackets antisymmetrize the product with respect to interchange of electrons (say, $1,2,\ldots,n_A$) on atom A and electrons on atom B (say, $n_A + 1,\ldots, n_A + n_B$). Indeed, if we write the AB function in the form

$$\Phi = \sum_{ij} C_{ij}\Phi_{ij} = \sum_{k} C_k\Phi_k \tag{17-3}$$

the problem of determining Φ, once the Φ_{ij} are chosen, is a linear variational problem for determination of the C_{ij}. Improvement of convergence in Eq. (17-3) can be achieved by including ionic as well as covalent structures; that this produces, in principle, an over-completeness in the basis (in the limit of an infinite number of structures of covalent and ionic type) is not a practical impediment.

The secular equation takes the form

$$|H_{k\ell} - M_{k\ell}W| = 0 \tag{17-4}$$

where W is the electronic energy to be determined, the overlap-matrix elements $M_{k\ell}$ are given by

$$M_{k\ell} = \int \Phi_k^*\Phi_\ell \, d\tau \tag{17-5}$$

and the Hamiltonian operator matrix elements are given by

$$H_{k\ell} = \int \Phi_k^*\mathcal{H}\Phi_\ell \, d\tau \tag{17-6}$$

where

$$\mathcal{H} = \sum_{\zeta=1}^{n_A+n_B} [T(\zeta) + U_A(\zeta) + U_B(\zeta)] + \sum_{\zeta<\eta} (1/r_{\zeta\eta}) \tag{17-7}$$

The matrix elements $M_{k\ell}$ reduce to $\delta_{k\ell}$ when the interatomic distance is infinity, otherwise they depend on the overlap between the distributions on atoms A and B; given the eigenfunctions Φ_{Ai} and Φ_{Bj} their computation is straightforward.

To calculate $H_{k\ell}$, with $\Phi_k = [\Phi_{Aki}\Phi_{Bkj}]$ and $\Phi_\ell = [\Phi_{A\ell i}\Phi_{B\ell j}]$, we make use of the facts that the partial antisymmetrization operator [ ] commutes with $\mathcal{H}$ and that many of the components of $\mathcal{H}$ differ trivially in the naming of the variables. Thus

$$\begin{aligned} H_{k\ell} &= \int [\Phi_{Aki}\Phi_{Bkj}]^* \mathcal{H} [\Phi_{A\ell i}\Phi_{B\ell j}]\, d\tau \\ &= \left[\frac{(n_A+n_B)!}{n_A!n_B!}\right]^{\frac{1}{2}} \int [\Phi_{Aki}\Phi_{Bkj}]^* \mathcal{H}\, \Phi_{A\ell i}\Phi_{B\ell j}\, d\tau \end{aligned} \tag{17-8}$$

At this stage we may pick $\mathcal{H}_A$ and $\mathcal{H}_B$ out of $\mathcal{H}$:

$$\begin{aligned} \mathcal{H} = {} & \sum_{\zeta=1}^{n_A} [T(\zeta) + U_A(\zeta)] + \sum_{\zeta<\eta\leqq n_A} (1/r_{\zeta\eta}) + \sum_{\zeta=n_A+1}^{n_A+n_B} [T(\zeta) + U_B(\zeta)] \\ & + \sum_{\zeta>\eta\geqq n_A} (1/r_{\zeta\eta}) + \sum_{\substack{\zeta\leqq n_A \\ \eta>n_A}} [U_B(\zeta) + U_A(\zeta) + (1/r_{\zeta\eta})] = \mathcal{H}_A + \mathcal{H}_B + \mathcal{V} \end{aligned} \tag{17-9}$$

Eq. (17-8) thus gives, using Eq. (17-2),

$$H_{k\ell} = M_{k\ell}W_\ell + V_{k\ell} \tag{17-10}$$

where the quantity $V_{k\ell}$ is the matrix element of the *interaction operator* $\mathcal{V}$ and Φ_k and Φ_ℓ and the quantity

$$W_\ell = W_{A\ell} + W_{B\ell} \tag{17-11}$$

is the atom-pair energy when A is in its eigenstate $\Phi_{A\ell i}$ and B is in its eigenstate $\Phi_{B\ell j}$.

From the Hermitian property of $\mathcal{H}$ we could also write

$$H_{k\ell} = H^*_{\ell k} = (M_{\ell k}W_k + V_{\ell k})^* = W_k M_{k\ell} + V^*_{\ell k} \tag{17-12}$$

Or, taking the average of Eqs. (17-10) and (17-12),

$$H_{k\ell} = (1/2)(M_{k\ell}W_\ell + W_k M_{k\ell}) + (1/2)(V_{k\ell} + V_{\ell k}^*) \tag{17-13}$$

This equation is at the root of atoms-in-molecules methods; it refers the quantities $H_{k\ell}$ to the eigenvalues W_ℓ and W_k for the separated-atom states. The term involving the interaction operators vanishes for infinite interatomic distance, and $M_{k\ell}$ becomes the diagonal unit matrix there.

If sufficient terms are included in Eq. (17-3) and the matrix elements of the secular Eq. (17-4) are exactly computed from Eq. (17-13) and exact atomic eigenfunctions, the exact molecular eigenfunction will be obtained. The quantities W_k and W_ℓ in that case could be computed from the atomic wave functions or taken from tables of atomic spectroscopic data, the only difference being that relativistic corrections are automatically incorporated in the latter method. Suppose, however, that exact atomic eigenfunctions were not available. If we used tables of data to obtain W_k and W_ℓ, we could still get them right. Perhaps we can estimate the other quantities in Eq. (17-13) using orbital approximations to the atomic eigenfunctions. If molecule formation is a relatively small perturbation on atoms (which total energies certainly indicate it is), we may expect good accuracy by this method.

Let us denote a quantity computed using orbital wave functions with a tilde; thus $\widetilde{M}_{k\ell}$ implies this overlap element is computed using orbital approximations for Φ_k and Φ_ℓ, $\widetilde{\Phi}_k$ and $\widetilde{\Phi}_\ell$. One method of computation on molecules involves the approximations

$$M_{k\ell} \approx \widetilde{M}_{k\ell} \tag{17-14}$$

$$H_{k\ell} \approx (1/2)(\widetilde{M}_{k\ell}W_\ell + W_k\widetilde{M}_{k\ell}) + (1/2(\widetilde{V}_{k\ell} + \widetilde{V}_{\ell k}^*) \tag{17-15}$$

This method was suggested by Moffitt, but it has not been used frequently because of the relative difficulty of dealing with the quantities $\widetilde{V}_{k\ell}$. However, Ellison has recently taken up calculations with these equations.[337]

A second method proposed by Moffitt is much easier to apply. In this, the quantities $V_{k\ell}$ are eliminated by referring them back to the orbitally computed $\widetilde{H}_{k\ell}$:

$$(1/2)(V_{k\ell} + V_{\ell k}^*) \approx \widetilde{H}_{k\ell} - (1/2)(\widetilde{M}_{k\ell}\widetilde{W}_\ell + \widetilde{W}_k\widetilde{M}_{k\ell}) \tag{17-16}$$

Assuming Eq. (17-14) once more, Eqs. (17-13), (17-14), and (17-16) then give

$$H_{k\ell} \approx \widetilde{H}_{k\ell} + (1/2)[\widetilde{M}_{k\ell}(W_\ell - \widetilde{W}_\ell) + (W_k - \widetilde{W}_k)\widetilde{M}_{k\ell}] \tag{17-17}$$

This is easy to employ: One computes $\widetilde{H}_{k\ell}$ by the usual orbital methods (for example, McWeeny's valence-bond scheme) and corrects them as indicated. The W_k and W_ℓ are obtained from spectroscopic data (or exact wave functions); the $\widetilde{W}_k$ and $\widetilde{W}_\ell$ are orbital estimates for W_k and W_ℓ obtained by inspecting the asymptotic behavior (as interatomic distance approaches infinity) of the matrix elements $\widetilde{H}_{k\ell}$.

The first applications of Eq. (17-17) were made by Moffitt on the oxygen molecule; his results were promising.[108] He then proceeded to do calculations on pi-electron systems[338-340]; with these[306,307,340,341] or other simple molecules[342-346] the successes were not so spectacular. We already have seen, however, that the method directly influenced the development of semiempirical theories of complex molecules.

Pauncz,[347] Scherr,[348], and Hurley[349] examined the application of this method to the hydrogen molecule in some detail, and uncovered a basic fault in the manner in which the calculations were being done. For H_2 the expansion may reasonably be composed of one covalent structure, $\Phi_1 = S_A(1)S_B(2) + S_B(1)S_A(2)$, and one ionic structure, $\Phi_2 \approx S_A(1)S_A(2) + S_B(1)S_B(2)$. If $Z = 1$ orbitals are used throughout, a good binding energy, 4.9 ev, is obtained from the prescription of Eq. (17-17). However, the details of the energy calculation (for example, the per cent of ionic versus covalent character) do not make sense. And most important, as the description of the ionic state H^- is improved, the situation alters greatly. Indeed, if an accurate H^- wave function is employed, the binding energy becomes just 3.2 ev,[347] not even as good as the original ionic-covalent-mixing calculation of Weinbaum. It is recalled that the 1s orbitals in Weinbaum's treatment have effective charges of 1.19 in both ionic and covalent parts. Values appropriate for the free atoms and ions, 1.00 and 0.69, respectively, simply do not produce good convergence in the expansion of Eq. (17-3). It is not that the approximation of Eq. (17-17) produces large errors; in fact it is quite a good approximation. Rather, the basis functions chosen for expansion of the wave function are not favorable for a fast convergence.

We could discard the method, or we could try to preserve the atoms-in-molecules idea in some modified form. This last has been done by Arai, in his *method of deformed atoms in molecules*,[335] and by Hurley, in his *method of intra-atomic correlation corrections*.[336] Both methods attempt to take advantage of the following three factors:

1. Orbital calculations on molecules—the calculation of the matrix elements $\widetilde{H}_{k\ell}$ of Eq. (17-17)—are easier to perform, simply because of integral difficulties, if a given atomic orbital may be given the same effective charge in covalent and ionic structures alike. (For example, $Z = 1$, or $Z = 1.19$, in the 1s orbitals in H_2, give a much easier computational scheme than $Z = 1$ in the covalent structure, $Z = 0.69$ in the ionic structure.)

2. The convergence of the expansion, Eq. (17-3), for the molecular wave function may indeed be improved by taking equal effective charges for ionic and covalent states, as evidenced by the comparison we have already quoted between the Weinbaum and atoms-in-molecules calculation for H_2.

3. The correlation energy between two electrons in a pair is remarkably unchanged by a change of scale (although not the type) of the wave function for that pair.

The third factor is one to which we shall be returning in both of the next sections of these lectures: to elucidate its limitations is an important area for present and future research. Arai and Hurley themselves leaned heavily on evidence compiled by Arai and Onishi,[350] according to whom, for example, the $(1s)^2$ correlation energy varies only from 1.1 ev in He to about 2.0 ev in O^{6+}; the correlation energy between the p electrons in the ^3P states of the species Be through O^{4+} varies only between about 0.3 ev and 0.4 ev.

Arai explicitly introduced deformation factors to change atomic eigenfunctions to functions more appropriate for the molecular calculations. He did this precisely, in a way that, in principle, can be handled without introduction of approximations or errors and that allows for deformation of shape as well as scale in each orbital.[351] Of course he had to deform only the *space* parts of the atomic wave function. This required the use of the representations of many-electron wave functions as sums of products of space and spin parts, a special procedure that has not been much used except by the Japanese school. (See, however, the recent work of Harris.[83]) The final formulas are somewhat complicated, but the whole procedure can be programmed for an electronic computer without prohibitive difficulty.[352] Applications of this method have not been widespread,[353,354] but the results in Li_2 definitely are encouraging.[354] It might be of interest to examine a simplified form of this method, in which each atomic wave function is deformed by a uniform scaling of all orbitals in it.

The method of Hurley[336] has been systematically derived by Arai.[351] It can be given a simple intuitive derivation as follows: In Eq. (17-17), the orbitals used in the calculation of $\tilde{H}_{k\ell}$, $\tilde{M}_{k\ell}$, and $\tilde{W}_\ell$ are presumed to be those that would give a good representation of the atomic states. Suppose we wanted to improve the convergence of the expansion of Eq. (17-3) by changing the orbital effective charges. We might presume, in the light of factor 3 above, that this would not affect the atomic correlation energies, so in Eq. (17-17) we leave $W_\ell - \tilde{W}_\ell$ and $W_k - \tilde{W}_k$ unchanged. But we should recompute $\tilde{H}_{k\ell}$ and $\tilde{M}_{k\ell}$ to assess properly the interatomic effects of deformation. Labeling matrix elements computed with this revised orbital basis with double tildes, we obtain in this way the working formula of the method of intra-atomic correlation corrections

$$H_{k\ell} \approx \tilde{\tilde{H}}_{k\ell} + (1/2)[\tilde{\tilde{M}}_{k\ell}(W_\ell - \tilde{W}_\ell) + (W_k - \tilde{W}_k)\tilde{\tilde{M}}_{k\ell}] \qquad (17\text{-}18)$$

The results of calculations with this scheme are generally very good[336,355-364]; some of them are summarized in Table 17.

In Eq. (17-18) the $\tilde{W}_\ell$ and $\tilde{W}_k$ are calculated so as to give the best possible orbital approximations to W_ℓ and W_k, the $\tilde{\tilde{H}}_{k\ell}$ and $\tilde{\tilde{M}}_{k\ell}$ are calculated with orbital parameters chosen to speed the convergence of Eq. (17-3). The computations can be done in either a molecular-orbital or valence-bond framework, although suitable care must be taken when transformations are made from one of these bases to the other. The orthogonalized valence-bond method of McWeeny[120] comes in handy, as do suitable analyses of atomic valence states.[116,358]

TABLE 17
Some Calculations by Hurley's Method of Intra-Atomic Correlation Corrections

Molecule	Quantity computed[a]	Computed (experimental)[a,b]	Ref.
H_2	D	4.72(4.74)[c]	336
LiH	D	2.09(2.59)	358
	μ	6.65(5.88)	358
BH	D	2.72(3.15)[d]	359
CH	D	2.94(3.65)[d]	359
NH	D	3.21(3.9)[d]	359
OH	D	4.00(4.58)[d]	359
OH^-	$\mathcal{I}$	2.0(1.8)	363
HF	$\mathcal{I}$	16.5(15.8 or 16.0)	359
	D	5.59(6.08)[d]	359
	μ	2.35(1.91)	359
HeH^+	D	1.77(~1.9)	357
Li_2	D	1.05(0.96)[e]	354
N_2	D	9.18 ± 0.5(9.91)	356
CO	D	11.0 ± 0.5(11.24)	360

[a]Dissociation energies D and ionization potential $\mathcal{I}$ in ev, dipole moments μ in D.
[b]Computed values of D should, according to Hurley, be *lower* bounds for the actual values.
[c]The energy agrees with experiment within 0.05 ev over the range R = 1 to R = $4a_0$.
[d]Many excitation energies of these species also have been successfully computed. See Ref. 359, second and third papers.
[e]Method of deformed atoms in molecules of Arai.

Corresponding theoretical methods have been proposed in which one refers the molecular situation to the situation in the united atom,[365] but the disruption in going from united atom to molecule is so great[89] that I do not believe that this method can be very potent. One can even construct a theory that averages the united-atom and separated-atom reference points[366]; this is clever but leads to unmanageable equations.

Much work on simple and complex molecules always has used, and always will use, atoms-in-molecules ideas in some measure.[367] Whether or not one chooses to use atoms-in-molecules methods for actual calculations, I believe that, whenever one talks of ionic and covalent structures in resonance and such matters, one should have the atoms-in-molecules theoretical framework in mind. Thus I am not concerned that the ionic and covalent structures for H_2 are so highly nonorthogonal (overlap 0.95 at the equilibrium distance).[368] That is their nature, and to invent new orthogonalized analogues of them[369] will destroy this nature.[120,122]

In his informal summary of the 1959 Boulder Conference on Molecular Quantum Mechanics,[15] Professor C. A. Coulson speaks of the method of atoms in molecules:

> It is not true to say that in the last week we have killed the theory of atoms in molecules, but it is true to say that it has been very seriously wounded.

If he was referring to the original method of Moffitt,[109] I would agree, but if we extend the term "atoms-in-molecules method" to include the method of intra-atomic correlation corrections and the method of deformed atoms in molecules, then I would not be so pessimistic. In his paper in the same conference proceedings, Arai[351] relates the several atoms-in-molecules methods to each other and to exact theory, and shows that, in principle, his method can be made exact. Hurley's paper[360] is just a calculation, but a calculation that demands attention. He computes the dissociation energy of the carbon monoxide molecule, the most difficult type of property to compute from quantum mechanics, and obtains 11.00 ± 0.5 ev. Until the heat of sublimation of carbon was settled, experimental spectroscopic data admitted three values, 11.24, 9.74, and 9.28 ev; Hurley's calculation agrees only with the first, and that is the one the heat of sublimation of carbon requires! It seems to me that he has well documented his 1956 conclusion[355]:

> The present method of calculation is capable of yielding the binding energy of diatomic molecules to an accuracy closer than 5% (about 0.5 ev).

If we discard atoms in molecules, then, in my opinion, we should leave intra-atomic correlation corrections in their place.

18 THE THEORY OF SEPARATED ELECTRON PAIRS

An electron pair in a molecule is a complex entity and is ill described by a simple orbital description, because correlation between two electrons moving in the same region of space with opposite spins is substantial and difficult to describe accurately. On the other hand, there are many indications that correlations between pairs of electrons are not so important: Given one pair of electrons, in one part of space, another pair of electrons necessarily will be concentrated in another part of space, and correlation effects between the pairs are not so great. Quantitative evidence bearing on the relative magnitudes of intra-pair and interpair correlations unfortunately is scanty, but it is fast accumulating; we shall review it at the end of this section. In any case, it is important to have available a theory of many-electron systems that admits complex descriptions of many pairs of electrons, but restricts interpair interactions to be averaged out in a Hartree-Fock sense.

Such a molecular description was first proposed by Hurley, Lennard-Jones, and Pople.[370] The theory has been further discussed and extended by Slater,[371] Parks and Parr,[372] McWeeny,[373] Arai,[96] Löwdin,[96] Kapuy,[374] and Allen and Shull[375]; applications of the equations obtained have been made by Parks and Parr,[97] Karplus and Grant,[376] McWeeny and Ohno,[377] Barfield and Grant,[378] and Allen and Shull.[379] Sinanoğlu has frequently commented upon this theory—his arguments will be the subject of our next section.

Following Parks and Parr,[372] we first define a case of *separated electron pairs* as a situation in which a molecular wave function Λ satisfies the following three *separability conditions for electron pairs*:

A. The wave function $\Lambda(1,2,\ldots,2n)$ (we assume an even number of electrons for simplicity) may be written as an antisymmetrized product of two-electron antisymmetrized pair wave functions or *geminals*[375] $\Lambda_A(1,2)$, $\Lambda_B(3,4),\ldots,$ $\Lambda_M(2n-1,2n)$:

$$\Lambda = [\Lambda_A \Lambda_B \cdots \Lambda_M] \tag{18-1}$$

Here the square brackets indicate antisymmetrization with respect to permutations P_{IJ} of electrons between pairs:

$$[\Lambda_A \Lambda_B \cdots] = [(2n)!/2^n]^{-\frac{1}{2}} \sum_{P_{IJ}} (-1)^{P_{IJ}} P_{IJ}(\Lambda_A \Lambda_B \cdots) \tag{18-2}$$

B. The geminals Λ_I are well-behaved and normalized to unity:

$$\iint |\Lambda_I(1,2)|^2 \, d\tau_1 \, d\tau_2 = 1 \tag{18-3}$$

C. Distinct geminals Λ_I and Λ_J satisfy the generalized strong orthogonality condition

$$\iint \Lambda_I^*(1,2) \Lambda_J(1,4) \, d\tau_1 = 0 \qquad \text{for} \qquad I \neq J \tag{18-4}$$

These conditions are formally very similar to the sigma-pi separability conditions of Sec. 8; indeed, a general discussion can be given that has both sigma-pi separability and electron-pair separability as special cases.[334]

As consequences of these conditions, we have the normalization of the total wave function,

$$\iint \cdots \int |\Lambda|^2 \, d\tau_1 \, d\tau_2 \cdots d\tau_{2n} = 1 \tag{18-5}$$

and the weaker orthogonality condition,

$$\iint \Lambda_I^*(1,2)\Lambda_J(1,2)\, d\tau_1\, d\tau_2 = 0 \qquad \text{for} \qquad I \neq J \tag{18-6}$$

We also have the not-so-trivial result[96] that there must exist some set of orthonormal one-electron orbitals $\lambda A1, \lambda A2 \ldots; \lambda B1, \lambda B2, \ldots; \ldots;$ such that Λ_I can be linearly expressed in terms of Slater determinants built from the orbitals λIi, the orbitals entering the description of each geminal being distinct from those entering the description of every other geminal. This last could be postulated and Eq. (18-4) derived as a consequence[372]; the advantage of taking Eq. (18-4) as basic is that then there is no mention at all of one-electron orbitals in the defining equations for separated pairs.

It is of considerable interest to examine methods for systematically relaxing Eq. (18-4), by stages, because, insofar as an actual molecule will only approximately obey the conditions for pair separability, an improved accuracy necessarily could be obtained thereby. One might proceed by allowing first one, then two, then three, etc., orbitals to enter both some Λ_I and some Λ_J.[372] Kapuy suggests another method, in which strict orthogonalities are replaced with approximate ones.[374] And it is in large part to the orthogonality condition that Sinanoğlu directs his attention.

The total electronic energy can be obtained from Eq. (18-1) and the electronic Hamiltonian

$$\mathcal{H}_e = \sum_\zeta \mathcal{H}_N(\zeta) + \frac{1}{2} \sum_{\zeta\eta}{}' (1/r_{\zeta\eta}) \tag{18-7}$$

where

$$\begin{aligned} \mathcal{H}_N(\zeta) &= T(\zeta) + U_N(\zeta) \\ U_N(\zeta) &= -\sum_\alpha (Z_\alpha / r_{\zeta\alpha}) \end{aligned} \tag{18-8}$$

The result is†

$$E_\Lambda = \sum_I I_I + (1/2) \sum_{I \neq J} (J_{IJ} - K_{IJ}) \tag{18-9}$$

where I_I is the pair or geminal I energy as if other pairs were absent,

$$I_I = \iint \Lambda_I^*(1,2)[\mathcal{H}_N(1) + \mathcal{H}_N(2) + (1/r_{12})]\Lambda_I(1,2)\, d\tau_1\, d\tau_2 \tag{18-10}$$

The quantities J_{IJ} and K_{IJ} are coulomb and exchange electronic-repulsion interactions between geminal I and geminal J,

†Note continuing analogies with Secs. 5 and 8.

$$J_{IJ} = \iiiint \Lambda_I^*(1,2)\Lambda_J^*(3,4)[(1/r_{13}) + (1/r_{14}) + (1/r_{23}) + (1/r_{24})]$$
$$\times \Lambda_I(1,2)\Lambda_J(3,4)\, d\tau_1\, d\tau_2\, d\tau_3\, d\tau_4 \qquad (18\text{-}11)$$

$$K_{IJ} = \iiiint \Lambda_I^*(1,2)\Lambda_J^*(3,4)[(1/r_{13})\Lambda_I(3,2)\Lambda_J(1,4) + (1/r_{14})\Lambda_I(4,2)\Lambda_J(3,1)$$
$$+ (1/r_{23})\Lambda_I(1,3)\Lambda_J(2,4) + (1/r_{24})\Lambda_I(1,4)\Lambda_J(3,2)]\, d\tau_1\, d\tau_2\, d\tau_3\, d\tau_4$$
$$(18\text{-}12)$$

It is important to note that

$$J_{II} \neq K_{II} \qquad (18\text{-}13)$$

which contrasts with the corresponding result for one-electron functions, the *equality* of Eq. (5-37).

Equation (18-9) is an additive partition of the electronic energy. If we define the geminal energy E_I by the formula

$$E_I = I_I + \sum_{J \neq I} (J_{IJ} - K_{IJ}) \qquad (18\text{-}14)$$

we can rewrite Eq. (18-9) in the form of a subtractive partition

$$E_\Lambda = \sum_I E_I - (1/2) \sum_{I \neq J} (J_{IJ} - K_{IJ}) \qquad (18\text{-}15)$$

or as a median partition

$$E_\Lambda = \sum_I (1/2)(E_I + I_I) \qquad (18\text{-}16)$$

This last formally gives the electronic energy as a sum of geminal contributions.

For actual calculations, none of the above forms for E_Λ is as convenient as another form, in which one geminal is singled out from the rest. Letting this be geminal K, described by Λ_K, we may write E_Λ in the form

$$E_\Lambda = E^0_{\Lambda - K} + E_K \qquad (18\text{-}17)$$

Here $E^0_{\Lambda - K}$ is the energy of all the pairs but K, computed as if pair K were absent, viz.

$$E^0_{\Lambda - K} = \sum_{I \neq K} I_I + (1/2) \sum_{\substack{I \neq J \\ I,J \neq K}} (J_{IJ} - K_{IJ}) \qquad (18\text{-}18)$$

The quantity E_K is the pair K energy, including all its interactions with other pairs, as given by Eq. (18-14), or

$$E_K = \iint \Lambda_K^*(1,2)\mathcal{H}_K(1,2)\Lambda_K(1,2)\, d\tau_1\, d\tau_2 \tag{18-19}$$

where

$$\mathcal{H}_K(1,2) = \mathcal{H}_N(1) + \mathcal{H}_N(2) + (1/r_{12}) + G_{\Lambda - K}(1) + G_{\Lambda - K}(2) \tag{18-20}$$

in which the coulomb-exchange operators $G_{\Lambda - K}$ are defined by

$$G_{\Lambda - K}(1) = \sum_{I \neq K} G_I(1) = \sum_{I \neq K} [J_I(1) - K_I(1)] \tag{18-21}$$

$$J_I(1)f(1) = \iint \Lambda_I^*(3,4)[(1/r_{13}) + (1/r_{14})]\Lambda_I(3,4)f(1)\, d\tau_3\, d\tau_4 \tag{18-22}$$

$$K_I(1)f(1) = \iint \Lambda_I^*(3,4)[(1/r_{13})\Lambda_I(1,4)f(3) + (1/r_{14})\Lambda_I(3,1)f(4)]\, d\tau_3\, d\tau_4 \tag{18-23}$$

The operators $G_{\Lambda - K}$ thus are functions of the other-pair wave functions Λ_I; they are fixed if those wave functions are fixed.

To determine actually the best separated-pair function for a molecule, one might hope to find a general self-consistent-field technique for obtaining the pair functions. One can indeed, by patterning the argument after the one-electron case,[58] find differential equations of the form

$$F_I\Lambda_I = \sum_J E_{IJ}\Lambda_J \tag{18-24}$$

satisfied by the geminals Λ_I. The only trouble is that the operator F_I depends on I; because of Eq. (18-13), one cannot remove the condition $J \neq I$ on the summation in Eq. (18-9). Actual calculations are most conveniently done with Eq. (18-17). If we guess all pair functions but one, say the K-th, the determination of that one is a two-electron problem defined by the Hamiltonian of Eq. (18-20); after one is determined, we can proceed to the next pair, and iterate. An illustration of this technique is provided by the six-electron calculation by Parks and Parr on the formaldehyde molecule, in which three electron pairs were explicitly treated, the two in the C=O bond and one in the pi-lone pair on the oxygen atom.[97]

Equation (18-16) provides only an apparent proof of additivity of bond energies, because it does not contain the nuclear-nuclear repulsions, which are big and nonadditive. Parks and Parr,[372] following Slater,[371] attempted to analyze the total energy into components and found an approximate additivity relation for homopolar systems. Allen and Shull have recently found a more satisfactory analysis of the additivity question.[375] There is a theorem[30]† that, if a molecular trial function $\Phi(1,2,\ldots,2n)$ is minimized with respect to a scale factor in all coordinates, at the predicted equilibrium configuration for the molecule,

$$\overline{E}_{total} = -\overline{T} = +(1/2)\overline{V} \tag{18-25}$$

where the bars indicate expectation values. Therefore, it may be pertinent to assume, in addition to the conditions A, B, and C above, the additional condition:

D. The wave function $\Lambda(1,2,\ldots,2n)$ is the best wave function of the class of functions which differ from it only in a scale factor for all coordinates, for the molecule in its equilibrium nuclear configuration as predicted assuming its electronic structure is accurately described by a wave function of this class.

When this and the other separability conditions are satisfied, we shall have, for the fixed-nuclei configuration,

$$\overline{E}_{total} = -\overline{T}_{total} = -\overline{T}_{el} = -\sum_{I} \overline{T}_{I} \tag{18-26}$$

where

$$T_I = \iint \Lambda_I^*(1,2)[-(1/2)\nabla^2(1) - (1/2)\nabla^2(2)]\Lambda_I(1,2)\, d\tau_1\, d\tau_2 \tag{18-27}$$

is the electronic kinetic energy for the I geminal. This result shows that, if indeed we can accurately describe a molecule with a wave function satisfying conditions A through D, the total energy will be a sum of pair energies, and each pair energy is a function of that pair wave function only.

Additivity of bond energies would thus appear to be established, in the dual sense required for it to have operational utility.[375] Not only is there a formal additivity, but also the energy contribution is transferable from molecule to molecule if the pair wave function does not change in going from molecule to molecule. The "if" here is a big one, of course, and the result depends on the separability conditions, but I think that one should at least record a certain pleasure from the fact that additivity falls so neatly out of this analysis.

Parks and Parr introduced what was called the *best-orbital description* of an electron pair.[372] This was a pair function [cf. Eqs. (14-1) et seq.] of the form

$$\Phi_K = C_{K1}\Phi_{K1} + C_{K2}\Phi_{K2} + C_{KV}\Phi_{KV} \tag{18-28}$$

† The proof is straightforward. If for $\Phi = \Phi(r_\mu, R_\alpha)$, $\overline{E} = \overline{T}_1 + \overline{V}_1(R_\alpha)$, then, for $\Phi' = \Phi(\zeta r_\mu, \zeta R_\alpha)$, $\overline{E} = \zeta^2\overline{T}_1 + \zeta\overline{V}_1(\zeta R_\alpha)$. Hence, if $\partial E/\partial R_\alpha = 0$ for all α, $\partial E/\partial\zeta = 0$ gives $\zeta_{best} = -\overline{V}_1(\zeta_{best} R_\alpha)/2\overline{T}_1$ and $\overline{E}_{best} = -\overline{V}_1^2/4\overline{T}_1 = -\overline{T}_{best} = (1/2)\overline{V}_{best}$.

where

$$\Phi_{K1} = (\phi_{K1}\bar{\phi}_{K1}) \qquad \Phi_{K2} = (\phi_{K2}\bar{\phi}_{K2})$$
$$\Phi_{KV} = 2^{-\frac{1}{2}}[(\phi_{K1}\bar{\phi}_{K2}) + (\phi_{K2}\bar{\phi}_{K1})] \tag{18-29}$$

and

$$\phi_{K1} = \frac{1}{\sqrt{2}}(a_K + b_K) \qquad \phi_{K2} = \frac{1}{\sqrt{2}}(a_K - b_K) \tag{18-30}$$

and the pair K atomic orbitals a_K and b_K are presumed orthogonal to those entering the descriptions of the other pairs. The determination of the coefficients C_K then becomes a two-electron linear-variation problem of the form we have considered several times already, the only formal difference between this case and the one considered in Sec. 14 being that the former Eq. (14-2) is replaced with the present Eq. (18-20), containing the effect of other pairs on pair K through the operators $G_{\Lambda - K}$. A secular equation such as Eq. (14-8) results, with the difference that, in place of the previous α_a, α_b, β_{ab}, there enter the new quantities α_{Ka}, α_{Kb}, β_{Kab}:

$$\alpha_{Ka} = \int a_K(1)\left[\mathcal{H}_N(1) + \sum_{I \neq K} G_I(1)\right]a_K(1)\,dv(1) \tag{18-31}$$

$$\beta_{Kab} = \int a_K(1)\left[\mathcal{H}_N(1) + \sum_{I \neq K} G_I(1)\right]b_K(1)\,dv(1) \tag{18-32}$$

We shall not give further details of the analysis here, except to quote the most interesting results. Under approximations like the Mulliken approximation of Eq. (11-29), just in the terms involving the other-pair operators G_I, we find that

$$\beta_{Kab} = \beta_{Nab} = \int a_K(1)\mathcal{H}_N(1)b_K(1)\,dv(1) \tag{18-33}$$

That is, the resonance integrals are independent of the other-pair electronic distributions. Further, in place of the formula of Eq. (14-11), for the effective orbital a_K electronegativity we obtain the formula

$$y_{Ka} = \frac{\mathcal{I}_{Ka} + \mathcal{A}_{Ka}}{2} + P_{Ka} + \sum_{I \neq K} Q_I(\zeta_{KaIa} - \zeta_{KaIb}) \tag{18-34}$$

where

$$Q_I = \frac{\sqrt{2}\, C_{IV}(C_{I1} + C_{I2})}{(1 - S_{IaIb})^{\frac{1}{2}}} \tag{18-35}$$

is a pair-I polarity parameter [to which the pair-I electric moment is proportional in the sense of Eq. (14-10)] and

$$\zeta_{pq} = (pp|qq) - (1/2)(pq|pq) \tag{18-36}$$

is a coulomb-exchange interaction between orbital p and orbital q. Equation (18-34) gives the effect of charge transfers in one bond on the effective electronegativities determining charge transfer effects in another bond; in the absence of charge transfer in geminal I in this approximation there is no effect of geminal I on the electronic distribution in geminal K.

This type of analysis was used by Parks and Parr for formaldehyde.[97] They were pleased to find the effects of charge transfer in the C=O sigma bond not too important for determining the pi structure in the C=O bond. This calculation was of an approximate nature, however, and quite sensitive to the integrals of Eq. (18-36) so one must wait for highly accurate calculations on a molecule such as this before deciding how important this type of interaction really is.

The further analysis that McWeeny has made of separated-pair descriptions, using density-matrix techniques, is elegant.[373] He and Kapuy[374] have also treated configuration interaction among several terms of the form of Eq. (18-1), which can lead to the exact molecular wave function.

There are three studies that are important for assessing whether atoms and molecules can be accurately described with separated-electron-pair descriptions, obeying the strong orthogonality condition of Eq. (18-4). These are the study of H_2O by McWeeny and Ohno,[377] a study of Be by Allen and Shull,[379] and the very recent calculation on LiH by Ebbing.[84]

For the water molecule at its equilibrium configuration, McWeeny and Ohno[377] found an energy of −2061.0 ev by the LCAO-SCF method, which improved to −2062.1 on inclusion of configuration interaction. With a separated-pair description, the separated pairs being dealt with one at a time, much as was done by Parks and Parr for formaldehyde, they obtained −2061.3 ev. They concluded:

> ...a mental separation of the electrons into different groups is sometimes well justified and...it is then much more profitable to improve the wave function *within* each group (e.g., by configuration interaction involving the orbitals of that group) than to refine the whole wave function by admitting inter-group mixing.

Unfortunately their atomic orbital basis set was not large.

For the Be atom, Allen and Shull[379] have found a separated-electron-pair description that has an overlap of 0.99989 with the complicated configuration-interaction function of Watson,[36] compared with a corresponding value of

0.95758 for the Hartree-Fock function. For LiH, Ebbing[84] states that more work is necessary but that indications are that a model based on separated electron pairs would be adequate. We agree that there is need for further work, but we conclude that separated-pair descriptions hold considerable promise.[380]

19 THE MANY-ELECTRON THEORY OF SINANOĞLU

We now are prepared to discuss the recent many-electron theory of Sinanoğlu.[381-387] This is an adaptation to molecules of some ideas and techniques that have proved useful in solid-state and nuclear many-body theory,[388] and it appears to have much potential.

Sinanoğlu's theory is designed to identify the physical factors governing electron correlation in atoms and molecules, without any approximations whatever, to provide perspicuous and useful schemes for characterization and calculation of correlation effects to any degree of accuracy, and to provide understanding of why the traditional orbital pictures and semiempirical methods have transcendent validity.

These, of course, are not new goals, and other recent work employs similar mathematics. The separated-electron-pair theory of the previous section meets at least some of the need, and Szász has been developing many-electron theory along somewhat similar lines.[389] Sinanoğlu's theory appears to be unique in its emphasis on the Hartree-Fock method as the best starting point[382,384]; and it seems to be rather effective in justifying the orbital picture with a minimum of auxiliary assumptions.[383,386,387]

To begin, Sinanoğlu takes the Hartree-Fock wave function of a molecule as the first approximation to the accurate description of it. In this wave function, the electronic repulsions are taken into account in a sensibly averaged way. The presumption is that corrections to this description will be small, but that is not all that favors this starting point. Further theoretical arguments can be given, which we shall come to later. And it has been known for a long time that charge distributions are remarkably well reproduced by Hartree-Fock wave functions.[33]

If we consider for simplicity the ground state[390] for a system of an even number of electrons, and if the Hartree-Fock function is given by

$$\Phi_0 = \mathcal{A}(\lambda_1(1)\lambda_2(2)\cdots\lambda_N(N)) = (12\cdots N) \tag{19-1}$$

$$\int |\Phi_0|^2 d\tau = 1 \tag{19-2}$$

then the exact wave function may be written

$$\Psi = \Phi_0 + \chi \tag{19-3}$$

where

$$\int \Phi_0^* \chi \, d\tau = 0 \tag{19-4}$$

and

$$\int |\Psi|^2 d\tau = 1 + \int |\chi|^2 d\tau \tag{19-5}$$

We may suppose the Hartree-Fock function Φ_0 itself is known. (Certainly the molecular Hartree-Fock problem may be regarded as solved by the LCAO-SCF procedures we have described earlier.) The function χ is a correction function that incorporates correlation effects; our problem may be thought of as the determination of the function χ in such a way as to minimize the total electronic energy of Eq. (2-11), subject to the orthogonality condition of Eq. (19-4).

We may refer the energy to the Hartree-Fock energy, given by Eqs. (5-34) and (5-38),

$$E_{HF} = \int \Phi_0^* \mathcal{H} \Phi_0 \, d\tau = \sum_i \epsilon_i - \sum_{i>j} (J'_{ij} - K'_{ij}) \tag{19-6}$$

Here the coulomb integrals J'_{ij}, exchange integrals K'_{ij}, and Hartree-Fock orbital energies ϵ_i have the meanings previously defined; the sums are over the distinct spin orbitals occupied in Φ_0. From Eq. (6-9) we have $\mathcal{F}(1)\lambda_i(1) = \epsilon_i \lambda_i(1)$, or

$$e_i(1)\lambda_i(1) = 0 \tag{19-7}$$

where

$$e_i(1) = \mathcal{F}(1) - \epsilon_i \tag{19-8}$$

Hence the exact total energy is given by

$$E = \int \Psi^* \mathcal{H} \Psi \, d\tau \Big/ \int |\Psi|^2 d\tau = E_{HF} + \int \Psi^* (\mathcal{H} - E_{HF}) \Psi \, d\tau \Big/ \int |\Psi|^2 d\tau$$

$$= E_{HF} + \left[\frac{2\int \Phi_0^* (\mathcal{H} - E_{HF}) \chi \, d\tau + \int \chi^* (\mathcal{H} - E_{HF}) \chi \, d\tau}{1 + \int |\chi|^2 d\tau} \right] \tag{19-9}$$

Or,

$$E - E_{HF} = \frac{2\int \Phi_0^* \left[\sum_{i>j} m_{ij} \right] \chi \, d\tau + \int \chi^* \left[\sum_i e_i + \sum_{i>j} m_{ij} \right] \chi \, d\tau}{1 + \int |\chi|^2 d\tau} \tag{19-10}$$

where

$$m_{ij} = (1/r_{ij}) + J'_{ij} - K'_{ij} - G'_i(j) - G'_j(i) \qquad (19\text{-}11)$$

in which the operators $G'_i(j)$ are the coulomb-exchange operators of Eq. (6-10):

$$G'_i(j) = J'_i(j) - K'_i(j) \qquad (19\text{-}12)$$

That is, $G'_i(j)$ is the coulomb-exchange operator of spin orbital i acting on electron j; $G'_j(i)$ the operator for spin orbital j acting on electron i. The quantity on the right side of Eq. (19-10) is the correlation energy. The operators m_{ij} may be called *fluctuation potentials*.

Given the Hartree-Fock function Φ_0, the operators e_i and m_{ij} that enter the correlation energy are fixed, so the determination of χ to minimize E is a variational problem involving only one-electron and two-electron operators. Various approximate methods for determining χ, and hence $E - E_{HF}$, can be generated if we minimize different portions of Eq. (19-10); hopefully, we may seek to pick out the most significant portions by more detailed consideration of this formula.

Without any approximation, we can write the exact correction function as the sum of N terms, as follows†:

$$\chi = \mathcal{A}\left\{(1\ 2\ 3\ldots N)\left[\sum_{i=1}^{N} \frac{\hat{f}_i}{(i)} + \frac{1}{\sqrt{2!}}\sum_{i>j}^{N} \frac{\hat{u}'_{ij}}{(ij)} + \frac{1}{\sqrt{3!}}\sum_{ijk}^{N} \frac{\hat{U}'_{ijk}}{(ijk)} + \cdots + \frac{1}{\sqrt{N!}}\frac{\hat{U}'_{1\,2\,3\ldots N}}{(1\ 2\ 3\ldots N)}\right]\right\} \qquad (19\text{-}13)$$

Here the successive terms represent, in configuration-interaction language, the collections of one-electron-jump, two-electron-jump, ..., N-electron-jump Slater determinants that enter the exact χ when expanded in terms of such determinants, obtained by excitation from the occupied orbitals in Φ_0 to other orbitals in the complete set of orbitals that are solutions of the Hartree-Fock equation. The successive functions $\hat{f}_i$, $\hat{u}'_{ij}$, $\hat{U}'_{ijk}$, etc., are functions F of the coordinates of one, two, three, etc., electrons. The carets indicate that they are all orthogonal to the original orbitals λ_i in the sense

$$\int F^*(1,2,3\ldots)\lambda_i(1)\,d\tau(1) = 0 \qquad (19\text{-}14)$$

Furthermore, they may be taken to be antisymmetric with respect to interchange of any two electrons (this removes redundancies that otherwise would be present in the configuration-interaction expansion).

† Sinanoğlu is not consistent in his notations for, and definitions of, the various correlation functions in his several papers; ours are a selection of his.

If we were to insert the full Eq. (19-13) in Eq. (19-10) and minimize, we would obtain exact equations for obtaining the $\hat{f}_i$, $\hat{u}'_{ij}$, etc. These are coupled equations of a most unwieldy sort, and actually are not much of an advance over the many-electron Schrödinger equation itself. (Beware of transformations of equations from one unsoluble form to another!) Further progress requires a special analysis of the various terms in Eq. (19-13).

The terms $\hat{f}_i$ may be expected to be very small and of negligible importance. If we omitted the other terms, they would not enter, because Φ_0 already is the best single determinant, which does not mix with one-electron jumps derived from it [the Brillouin theorm of Eq. (6-19)]. When two-electron jumps are included, the one-electron jumps may come in, but only indirectly through their interactions with these two-electron jumps. In the language of perturbation theory,[391] the first-order wave function contains the two-electron jumps but not the one-electron jumps; since the first-order wave function determines the energy to third order, the functions $\hat{f}_i$ do not affect the energy except in the fourth and higher orders. That charge densities are given so well by the Hartree-Fock functions also supports this view. Accordingly we anticipate that the assumption

$$\hat{f}_i = 0 \qquad \text{for all } i \tag{19-15}$$

will lead to very little errors in wave functions, probably less than 0.01 ev errors in energies, and small errors in most other molecular properties.[61]

Each of the quantities $\hat{u}'_{ij}$, $\hat{U}'_{ijk}$, etc., may be decomposed into a sum of terms, the antisymmetrized sum of all possible products of previous terms plus a new term, in what is called a *cluster expansion*.[384,387,388] Namely,

$$\begin{aligned}
\hat{u}'_{ij} &= \mathcal{A}_2(\hat{f}_i\hat{f}_j) + \hat{u}_{ij} \\
\hat{U}'_{ijk} &= \mathcal{A}_3(\hat{f}_i\hat{f}_j\hat{f}_k + \hat{f}_i\hat{u}_{jk}/\sqrt{2} + \cdots) + \hat{U}_{ijk} \\
\hat{U}'_{ijk\ell} &= \mathcal{A}_4(\hat{f}_i\hat{f}_j\hat{f}_k\hat{f}_\ell + \hat{f}_i\hat{f}_j\hat{u}_{k\ell}/\sqrt{2} + \hat{f}_i\hat{U}_{jk\ell}/\sqrt{6} + \hat{u}_{ij}\hat{u}_{k\ell}/2 + \cdots) + \hat{U}_{ijk\ell} \\
&\cdots\cdot
\end{aligned} \tag{19-16}$$

Here the operator $\mathcal{A}_n$ is the normalized n-electron antisymmetrizer. All except the last terms in each of these formulas represent *unlinked clusters* of n electrons; the last terms represent *linked clusters*.

The linked cluster of two electrons, represented by $\hat{u}_{ij}$ in the first of Eqs. (19-16), is of penultimate importance; it defines the correlation function for an electron pair. The linked clusters of three or more electrons are of negligible importance, however, because of the relatively short range of the fluctuation potentials m_{ij} (Sinanoğlu discusses this short-range nature of the m_{ij} at some length[384]; the point is that whereas $1/r_{ij}$ is long range, $(1/r_{ij}) - G_i'(j) - G_j'(i)$ dies off much faster with distance between the electrons, for electron configurations of importance.) In other words, a linked cluster corresponds to all the electrons being together at the same time, and such simultaneous "collisions" of three or more electrons in a molecule rarely occur. For, given two electrons in some region of space, a third electron will always have the same spin as one of them and will be kept away from that region by the Pauli principle.

These considerations lead us to suppose that linked clusters of three or more electrons can be ignored:

$$\hat{U}_{ijk} = \hat{U}_{ijk\ell} = \cdots = 0 \tag{19-17}$$

Inserting these formulas and Eq. (19-15) into Eq. (19-16), and using Eq. (19-13), we now obtain the basic unlinked-cluster expansion of the correlation function,[384]

$$\chi = \mathcal{A}\left\{(123\ldots N)\left[\frac{1}{\sqrt{2}}\sum_{i>j}\frac{\hat{u}_{ij}}{(ij)} + \frac{1}{2}\sum_{\substack{i>j\\ i,j\neq k,\ell}}\sum_{k>\ell}\frac{\hat{u}_{ij}\hat{u}_{k\ell}}{(ijk\ell)} + \cdots\right]\right\} \tag{19-18}$$

Our problem is thereby reduced to finding the correlation functions $\hat{u}_{ij}$ for every pair of electrons, or, equivalently, for every two of the original Hartree-Fock molecular orbitals occupied in the ground state.

The determination of the $\hat{u}_{ij}$ and the correlation energy can be carried out in various ways.[385] In many cases it is probably sufficient to find the $\hat{u}_{ij}$ by second-order perturbation theory[382] and to put the resulting functions into Eq. (19-10) to get the correlation energy. This is tantamount to minimizing only the numerator of Eq. (19-10) and including the denominator as an afterthought. There results a differential equation for the pair function $\hat{u}_{ij}$,

$$(e_i + e_j)\hat{u}_{ij} + \hat{m}_{ij}\mathcal{A}_2(ij) = 0 \tag{19-19}$$

where $\widehat{m_{ij}\mathcal{A}_2(ij)}$ connotes what one obtains from $m_{ij}\mathcal{A}_2(ij)$ upon orthogonalizing it to all the λ_i in the sense of Eq. (19-14). More-accurate differential equations than this have also been given by Sinanoğlu[385]; this one shows the main features and should provide good accuracy.

The correlation-energy formula that one obtains by inserting Eq. (19-18) into Eq. (19-10) involves what can be called the *pair-correlation energies*

$$\tilde{\epsilon}_{ij} = 2\int \mathcal{A}_2(ij)^* m_{ij}\hat{u}_{ij}\, d\tau + \int \hat{u}_{ij}^*(e_i + e_j + m_{ij})\hat{u}_{ij}\, d\tau \tag{19-20}$$

and the normalizing factors

$$D_{ij} = 1 + \sum_{k,\ell \neq i,j} \int |u_{k\ell}|^2 d\tau \qquad (19\text{-}21)$$

and

$$D = 1 + \sum_{i>j} \int |u_{ij}|^2 d\tau \qquad (19\text{-}22)$$

Indeed, *if we neglect certain three-electron correlation terms* (which can be computed if one wishes), we find

$$E - E_{HF} = \sum_{i>j} \tilde{\epsilon}_{ij}(D_{ij}/D) \approx \sum_{i>j} \tilde{\epsilon}_{ij} \qquad (19\text{-}23)$$

The correlation energy is thus reduced to a sum of pair-correlation energies, each calculable by solution of a two-electron problem.

The differential Eq. (19-19) is elegant, but its form is deceptively simple. To solve it requires the full apparatus of first-order perturbation theory—expansions in complete sets of functions, the diagram techniques of modern many-body theory, or the like. No solutions for an actual case have yet been found.

Watson's accurate configuration-interaction wave function for the $(1s)^2(2s)^2$ ground state of the Be atom[36] has been analyzed by Sinanoğlu.[384,385] The error produced in the correlation energy by the assumption of Eq. (19-17) is only one part in seventy-five, just 0.001 ev. The neglect of the three-electron correlation terms in Eq. (19-23) gives errors that are entirely negligible. As for the the D_{ij} and D in Eq. (19-23), their values are $D = 1.0905$, $D_{1s1s} = 1.0886$, $D_{2s2s} = 1.0017$, $D_{1s\alpha 2s\alpha} = 1.0000$, $D_{1s\alpha 2s\beta} = 1.0001$. Sinanoğlu does not quote values for the individual $\tilde{\epsilon}_{ij}$, but we may infer from the work of Allen and Shull[379] that the $\tilde{\epsilon}_{1s2s}$ are negligible.

Much work must be done in order to confirm the utility of this analysis and establish numerical methods for its application. It is already clear, however, that it provides a lucid breakdown of the correlation effects in molecules. Sinanoğlu himself has discussed the implications for the theory of core polarization,[381] bond energies,[386,387] separate treatment of core and valence electrons in a molecule,[384,385] the sigma-pi separability question,[383,385] intramolecular forces,[386] the theory of finite nuclei,[385] and other problems. His conclusions are uniformly optimistic that orbital pictures can be preserved in more accurate descriptions of molecular wave functions.

In a recent paper, Stanton[392] has used Sinanoğlu's analysis and the Hellmann-Feynman theorem to derive a formula for the dependence of the correlation energy on an arbitrary parameter in the molecular Hamiltonian. From this formula Stanton shows that, as a function of bond distances, the Hartree-Fock and exact potential-energy surfaces should be close to parallel, and that the change of correlation energy on change of nuclear charge should be small.

There are several differences between this theory and the theory of separated electron pairs described in the previous section. This theory, in the first place, is considerably more general, dealing with all the $N(N-1)/2$ pairs of electrons in a molecule, not just $N/2$ distinct groups of two electrons each. If it turns out, as the evidence for Be[379] and LiH[84] seems to indicate it may (see the end of Sec. 18), that separated pair descriptions will suffice, that will be fine.

The orthogonality condition in this theory, Eq. (19-14), is different from the orthogonality condition in the theory of separated electron pairs, Eq. (18-4). McWeeny[393] and Sinanoğlu[382] correctly point out that the latter condition prevents incorporation of r_{12} coordinates into the wave functions for the separate pairs. On the other hand, I cannot understand Sinanoğlu's statement that separated pair functions "violate the exclusion principle."[382] And I am not so sure that, when one has two or more pairs, r_{12} coordinates remain appropriate for describing correlation. To be sure, one needs factors like $1 + cr_{12}$ when electrons 1 and 2 are close, in the regions of space where they are likely to be found. But use of r_{12} when r_{12} is, say, $4a_0$ for describing correlation between two 1s electrons in a shell of Bohr radius, say, $1a_0$ is clearly an artifact that one may be able to do without. The successful Allen-Shull analysis of the beryllium atom wave function into strongly orthogonal parts[379] suggests that one should not too quickly give up the separated-electron-pair description.

Similar remarks apply to sigma-pi separability conditions. The conditions given in Sec. 8 certainly are *sufficient* to validate the separate treatment of sigma and pi electrons that is employed in the semiempirical theories; admittedly they may not be *necessary*. Sinanoğlu has also stated some sufficient conditions, Eqs. (19-15) and (19-17), plus the assumption inherent in Eq. (19-23); they too may not be accurately satisfied, although I do suspect that they are less stringent than those we gave.

It ought to be interesting to try to develop from this theory, by further analysis or simplification, a means for handling electron correlations in molecules through use of effective dielectric constants for electron-electron repulsions. In any case, the work of Sinanoğlu certainly is a refreshing development on the quantum-chemical scene.

V. Conclusion

20 SUMMARY

What I have been saying in these notes can be said in a word: Accurate descriptions of the electronic structure of molecules are upon us.[394] What this means for each chemist, he himself should decide, but many old ambiguities are certainly disappearing, and many old questions can now be precisely answered.

We have indicated that descriptions of small molecules are being generated to good accuracy in several laboratories, with improvement to high accuracy a technical problem that is being met.[80] We have described how the theory of the breakdown of large molecules into smaller components is concurrently being developed, so that the small-molecule breakthrough is having immediate effect on the theory of large organic molecules. Most important, I hope we have destroyed the fallacy that the large molecule is forever inaccessible to accurate treatment because it contains too many electrons. To state the counterargument: In a molecule there are never more than a few electrons in one region of space much of the time. We must be prepared to deal with two, or three, or four electrons (which we now are), but then the difficulty goes up approximately as the number of groups of two, or three, or four, not as some high power of that number.

The form in which the results are being generated—computer output—seems strange and incomprehensible. But here, too, I hope we have destroyed a fallacy. It has been said that an accurate molecular wave function would be useless, because to report it would require tables stacking to the moon. But to "use" a wave function only means to determine some observable from it, which a computer can do internally, and to "report" a wave function only requires stating values for a limited number of parameters. On the high-speed computations themselves, I can do no better than to quote Professor J. C. Slater[395]:

> Before leaving the subject of computing, it is worth while outlining our views as to the philosophy of large-scale machine computations. Many theoretical physicists have a great prejudice against such computations. We do not hold to this view. Every theorist approves of the use of power series expansions. One must realize, however, that this is merely one method of approximation to a function, and often not a very suitable one. Expansion in various types of basis functions is much more flexible, and most of our work is carried out with a great variety of such basis sets. We do not feel that this is in any sense less desirable than finding the coefficients of a power series expansion. Furthermore, it is a misconception to think, as many persons do, that it is only for numerical calculation that the digital computers are required. A very large amount of our use of these machines is in the form of algebraic manipulation, combining terms, carrying out operations of logic which could be done in principle without the machine, but which in practice are so complicated and tedious that they become practically impossible by hand. We believe very firmly that the use of digital computers opens up a new era in applied mathematics, quite different from past practice, and that these new methods are required very specifically in wave mechanics, on account of the great inherent difficulty of this science.

This is not to say that qualitative interpretations are not meaningful, far from it, but that they must be developed to fit the improving quantitative descriptions. I recall someone stating a few years ago that he thought the outstanding unsolved problem in valence theory was the nature of the chemical bond in LiH. On March 1 of 1962 there was published in *The Journal of Chemical Physics* a very good wave function for LiH,[84] a superposition of no less than 53 configurations, built from elliptical coordinate orbitals. One may not enjoy trying to understand such a construct as this, but there may be no alternative.

The quantum theory of valence, even as it was defined at the beginning of these lectures, is a much broader subject and more concerned with experimental chemistry than the coverage provided in these lectures would imply. Fundamental topics that have been neglected include relativistic effects,[396] solution of the Schrödinger equation by other than variational methods,[397] natural orbital expansions of wave functions,[398] the double quartet theory,[399] electrostatic models,[400] special electron-density functions,[401] the Hellmann-Feynman theorem,[402] ligand-field theory,[403] and vibronic-electronic interaction.[404] A multitude of applications have been slighted, from donor-acceptor complexes[405] to chemisorption[406] to biology.[407] Reaction rates, the *ultima Thule* in the world of theoretical chemists, have hardly been touched.[408] And new experiments, revealing much new information, have been entirely ignored.[409] The field is a growing as well as a dynamic one; little of it has been covered here.

21 THE FUTURE

I hasten to admit that the foregoing puts in the present tense developments that are taking years to come to fruition; I use this tense to emphasize my conviction that the successes I describe are within the grasp of the present generation. Of course, not everyone should strive to become a computer expert, but a surprising number of people are moving in that direction, and those who do not can profit by following the activities of those who do.

For the practicing organic or inorganic chemist, physical chemist or spectroscopist, or for the biologist, each with his ever-increasing store of experimental knowledge about molecules and their behavior, the tools of molecular quantum mechanics ought to be increasingly useful. As quantum chemistry develops, purely theoretical calculations will become a standard method for accurate determination of properties of small molecules, and semiempirical methods will be tested and sharpened up, becoming less arbitrary and more accurate.[410] The cost at times will seem dear, for any theoretical concept that is applicable to small molecules must stand its trial in that context. If it holds up quantitatively, fine, but if it does not, it will have to be discarded.

The interesting research problems in this field are many and varied. My own present favorites have to do with one-center expansion techniques,[411] pi-electron systems,[327,412] magnetic properties,[413] and electron correlation,[414] but you may take your choice from all those I have described and countless others. In any case, I am confident that over the years ahead, and with your efforts, quantum theory will find very extensive and bountiful applications in chemistry.

References

1. R. S. Mulliken, What Are the Electrons Really Doing in Molecules? *The Vortex*, Cal. Sec. of Am. Chem. Soc., Spring, 1960.
2. C. A. Coulson, *Valence*, Oxford University Press, London, 2nd ed., 1961.
3. J. H. Van Vleck and A. Sherman, The Quantum Theory of Valence, *Revs. Mod. Phys.*, **7**, 167-228 (1935).
4. R. G. Parr and F. O. Ellison, The Quantum Theory of Valence, *Ann. Rev. Phys. Chem.*, **6**, 171-192 (1955), and other reviews on quantum theory in volumes 1-12 of *Ann. Rev. Phys. Chem.*
5. G. G. Hall, Application of Quantum Mechanics in Theoretical Chemistry, *Repts. Progr. in Phys.* **22**, 1-32 (1959).
6. L. Pauling and E. B. Wilson, Jr., *Introduction to Quantum Mechanics*, McGraw-Hill, New York, 1935.
7. H. Eyring, J. Walter, and G. E. Kimball, *Quantum Chemistry*, Wiley, New York, 1944.
8. R. Daudel, R. Lefebvre, and C. Moser, *Quantum Chemistry Methods and Applications*, Interscience, New York, 1959.
9. M. Karplus, Weak Interactions in Molecular Quantum Mechanics, *Revs. Mod. Phys.*, **32**, 455-460 (1960). The several additional small terms in the true Hamiltonian are responsible for many spectroscopically observable phenomena but only 10^{-4} ev or less of the total energy.
10. A. Fröman, Relativistic Corrections in Many-Electron Systems, *Revs. Mod. Phys.*, **32**, 317-321 (1960). Relativistic effects on energy increase with increasing atomic number, as about its fourth power, reaching about 1 kcal/mole for the 1s electrons in phosphorus.
11. H. Shull and P. O. Löwdin, Variation Theorem for Excited States, *Phys. Rev.*, **110**, 1466-1467 (1958).

12. L. Pauling, *Nature of the Chemical Bond*, Cornell University Press, Ithaca, N.Y., 3rd ed., 1960.
13. G. Wheland, *Resonance in Organic Chemistry*, Wiley, New York, 1955.
14. A. Fröman, Isotope Effects and Electronic Energy in Molecules, *J. Chem. Phys.* **36**, 1490-1495 (1962); D. W. Jepsen and J. O. Hirschfelder, Calculation of the Coupling Terms Neglected in Performing the Born-Oppenheimer Separation for the Hydrogen Molecule Ion, *J. Chem. Phys.*, **32**, 1323-1335 (1960). Errors due to the Born-Oppenheimer approximation may be as much as 1 kcal/mole in unfavorable cases.
15. C. A. Coulson, Present State of Molecular Structure Calculations, *Revs. Mod. Phys.*, **32**, 170-177 (1960).
16. H. A. Bethe and E. E. Salpeter, *Quantum Mechanics of One- and Two-Electron Atoms*, Academic, New York, 1957.
17. C. L. Pekeris, Ground State of Two-Electron Atoms, *Phys. Rev.*, **112**, 1649-1658 (1958); 1^1S and 2^3S States of Helium, *Phys. Rev.*, **115**, 1217-1221 (1959).
18. See, however, L. Szász, Über die Berechnung der Korrelationsenergie der Atomelektronen, *Z. Naturforsch.*, **15a**, 909-926 (1960); On the Evaluation of Integrals Occuring in the Theory of the Correlated Electronic Wave Functions, *J. Chem. Phys.*, **35**, 1072-1076 (1961).
19. R. G. Parr and H. W. Joy, Why Not Use Slater Orbitals of Nonintegral Principal Quantum Number? *J. Chem. Phys.*, **26**, 424 (1957); see also O. G. Ludwig and R. G. Parr, On the Introduction of Arbitrary Angular Peakedness into Atomic Orbitals, *J. Chem. Phys.*, **35**, 754-755 (1961).
20. C. C. J. Roothaan, L. M. Sachs, and A. W. Weiss, Analytical Self-Consistent Field Functions for the Atomic Configurations $1s^2$, $1s^22s$, and $1s^22s^2$, *Revs. Mod. Phys.*, **32**, 186-194 (1960).
21. J. N. Silverman, O. Platas, and F. A. Matsen, Simple Configuration-Interaction Wave Functions. I. Two-Electron Ions: A Numerical Study, *J. Chem. Phys.*, **32**, 1402-1406 (1960).
22. For a modification of the Eckart treatment, which represents "in-out" correlation in a more clear-cut way, see L. C. Snyder and R. G. Parr, Extraordinary Basic Functions in Valence Theory, *J. Chem. Phys.*, **34**, 1661-1665 (1961). These authors employ a wave function of the form $A \exp(-Z_< r_< - Z_> r_>)$, obtaining an energy of −2.873 au.
23. H. Shull and P. O. Löwdin, Superposition of Configurations and Natural Spin Orbitals, Applications to the He Problem, *J. Chem. Phys.*, **30**, 617-626 (1959).
24. J. E. Lennard-Jones and J. A. Pople, The Spatial Correlation of Electrons in Atoms and Molecules: I. Helium and Similar Two-Electron Systems in Their Ground States, *Phil. Mag.*, **43**, 581-591 (1952).
25. G. R. Taylor and R. G. Parr, Superposition of Configurations: The Helium Atom, *Proc. Natl. Acad. Sci. U.S.*, **38**, 154-160 (1952)(included in this volume).
26. L. C. Snyder, Helium Atom Wave Functions from Slater Orbitals of Nonintegral Principal Quantum Number, *J. Chem. Phys.*, **33**, 1711-1712 (1960).

27. R. K. Nesbet and R. E. Watson, Approximate Wave Functions for the Ground State of Helium, *Phys. Rev.*, **110**, 1073-1076 (1958); see also Ref. 23, and D. H. Tycko, L. H. Thomas, and K. M. King, Numerical Calculation of the Wave Functions and Energies of the 1^1S and 2^3S States of Helium, *Phys. Rev.*, **109**, 369-374 (1958).
28. A. W. Weiss, Configuration Interaction in Simple Atomic Systems, *Phys. Rev.*, **122**, 1826-1836 (1961).
29. T. Arai and P. G. Lykos, Correlation Energy and the One-Center Coulomb Repulsion Integral, *J. Chem. Phys.*, **38**, 1447-1448 (1963).
30. For example, see the lucid account by P. O. Löwdin, Scaling Problem, Virial Theorem, and Connected Relations in Quantum Mechanics, *Mol. Spectr.*, **3**, 46-66 (1959); for generalizations and extensions, see J. O. Hirschfelder and C. A. Coulson, Hypervirial Theorems Applied to Molecular Quantum Mechanics, *J. Chem. Phys.*, **36**, 941-946 (1962); A. C. Hurley, Virial Theorem for Polyatomic Molecules, *J. Chem. Phys.*, **37**, 449-450 (1962).
31. P. O. Löwdin, Correlation Problem in Many-Electron Quantum Mechanics. I. Review of Different Approaches and Discussion of Some Current Ideas, *Advan. Chem. Phys.*, **2**, 207-323 (1959); H. Yoshizumi, Correlation Problem in Many-Electron Quantum Mechanics. II. Bibliographical Survey of the Historical Developments with Comments, *Advan. Chem. Phys.*, **2**, 323-367 (1959).
32. E. U. Condon and G. H. Shortley, *The Theory of Atomic Spectra*, Cambridge University Press, Cambridge, 1951.
33. D. R. Hartree, *The Calculation of Atomic Structures*, Wiley, New York, 1957.
34. J. C. Slater, *Quantum Theory of Atomic Structure*, McGraw-Hill, New York, 1960, Vols. I and II.
35. J. S. Griffith, *The Theory of Transition Metal Ions*, Cambridge University Press, Cambridge, 1961.
36. R. E. Watson, Approximate Wave Functions for Atomic Be, *Phys. Rev.*, **119**, 170-177 (1960).
37. W. E. Donath, Atomic Wave Functions for the Ground States of Na^+, Ne, and F^-, *J. Chem. Phys.*, **35**, 817-820 (1961); L. M. Sachs, Analytical Hartree-Fock Self-Consistent Field Wave Functions for Some $1s^2 2s^2 2p^6$ Configurations, *Phys. Rev.*, **124**, 1283-1289 (1961).
38. E. Clementi, C. C. J. Roothaan, and M. Yoshimine, Accurate Analytical Self-Consistent Field Functions for Atoms. II. Lowest Configurations of the Neutral First Row Atoms, *Phys. Rev.*, **127**, 1618-1620 (1962); E. Clementi, Analytical Self-Consistent Field Functions for Positive Ions, *J. Chem. Phys.*, **38**, 996-1008 (1963).
39. M. Kotani, K. Ohno, and K. Kayama, Quantum Mechanics of Electronic Structure of Simple Molecules, *Handbuch der Physik*, **37/2** (1961), pp. 1-172; J. C. Slater, *Quantum Theory of Molecules and Solids, Volume 1, Electronic Structure of Molecules*, McGraw-Hill, New York, 1963. The book by Slater contains a very fine bibliography.

40. R. F. Wallis and H. M. Hulburt, Approximation of Molecular Orbitals in Diatomic Molecules by Diatomic Orbitals, *J. Chem. Phys.*, **22**, 774-781 (1954).
41. Recent examples include the following: K. M. Howell and H. Shull, Single-Center Expansions for One-Electron Systems. H_2^+, *J. Chem. Phys.*, **30**, 627-633 (1959); M. Geller and O. G. Ludwig, On the Use of Nonintegral Exponents in Elliptical Coordinate Wave Functions, with Special Reference to the Hydrogen Molecule-Ion, *J. Chem. Phys.*, **36**, 1442-1444 (1962); M. Geller, Two-Center Nonintegral, Slater-Orbital Calculations: Integral Formulation and Application to the Hydrogen Molecule-Ion, *J. Chem. Phys.*, **36**, 2424-2428 (1962); T. J. Houser, P. G. Lykos, and E. L. Mehler, One-Center Wave Function for the Hydrogen Molecule-Ion, *J. Chem. Phys.*, **38**, 583-586 (1963); H. O. Pritchard and F. H. Sumner, Complete Set Expansions for Molecular Wave Functions, *J. Phys. Chem.*, **65**, 641-645 (1961).
42. R. S. Mulliken, quoted by C. A. Coulson in Ref. 15.
43. A. D. McLean, A. Weiss, and M. Yoshimine, Configuration Interaction in the Hydrogen Molecule—the Ground State, *Revs. Mod. Phys.*, **32**, 211-218 (1960).
44. H. M. James and A. S. Coolidge, The Ground State of the Hydrogen Molecule, *J. Chem. Phys.*, **1**, 825-835 (1933).
45. W. Kolos and C. C. J. Roothaan, Accurate Electronic Wave Functions for the H_2 Molecule, *Revs. Mod. Phys.*, **32**, 219-232 (1960).
46. F. E. Harris, Molecular Orbitals for the Ground State of the H_2 Molecule, *J. Chem. Phys.*, **27**, 812-813 (1957).
47. E. R. Davidson, First Excited $^1\Sigma_g^+$ State of the Hydrogen Molecule, *J. Chem. Phys.*, **35**, 1189-1202 (1961).
48. W. Heitler and F. London, Wechselwirking Neutraler Atome und Homöopolare Binding nach der Quantenmechanik, *Z. Physik*, **44**, 455-472 (1927).
49. For further generalizations still in orbital form, see, for example, H. Shull and D. D. Ebbing, Floating Wave Functions for H_2^+ and H_2, *J. Chem. Phys.*, **28**, 866-870 (1958), or R. L. Miller and P. G. Lykos, Use of Distorted Atomic Orbitals in Molecular Wave Functions, *J. Chem. Phys.*, **35**, 1147-1148 (1961).
50. S. Weinbaum, The Normal State of the Hydrogen Molecule, *J. Chem. Phys.*, **1**, 593-596 (1933); see also S. L. Altmann and N. V. Cohan, On the Screening Constants in the Hydrogen Molecule, *Trans. Faraday Soc.*, **50**, 1151-1158 (1954).
51. For evaluation of the integrals entering Eq. (4-15), see, for example, Appendix 4 of K. S. Pitzer, *Quantum Chemistry*, Prentice-Hall, Englewood Cliffs, N.J., 1953.
52. J. N. Murrell, Construction of Hybrid Orbitals, *J. Chem. Phys.*, **32**, 767-770 (1960); T. L. Gilbert and P. G. Lykos, Maximum-Overlap Directed-Hybrid Orbitals, *J. Chem. Phys.*, **34**, 2199-2200 (1961); P. G. Lykos and H. N. Schmeising, Maximum-Overlap Atomic and Molecular Orbitals,

J. Chem. Phys., **35**, 288-293 (1961); A. Golebiewski, Construction of Approximate Best-Hybrid Orbitals, *Trans. Faraday Soc.*, **57**, 1849-1853 (1961); M. Randić, Quadricovalent Maximum Overlap Hybrid Orbitals, *J. Chem. Phys.*, **36**, 3278-3282 (1962).

53. K. Ruedenberg, The Physical Nature of the Chemical Bond, *Revs. Mod. Phys.* **34**, 326-376 (1962).
54. J. R. Hoyland and R. G. Parr, Magnetic Properties of Molecules from One-Center Wave Functions. Theory and Application to the Hydrogen Molecule, *J. Chem. Phys.*, **38**, 2991-2998 (1963).
55. H. W. Joy and R. G. Parr, A One-Center Wave Function for the Hydrogen Molecule, *J. Chem. Phys.*, **28**, 448-453 (1958).
56. D. M. Bishop, Improved One-Center Wave Functions for the Hydrogen and Methane Molecules, *Mol. Phys.*, **6**, 305-315 (1963).
57. S. Hagstrom and H. Shull, Single-Center Wave Function for the Hydrogen Molecule, *J. Chem. Phys.*, **30**, 1314-1322 (1959).
58. C. C. J. Roothaan, New Developments in Molecular Orbital Theory, *Revs. Mod. Phys.*, **23**, 69-89 (1951) (included in this volume).
59. C. C. J. Roothaan, Self-Consistent Field Theory for Open Shells of Electron Systems, *Revs. Mod. Phys.*, **32**, 179-185 (1960); S. Huzinaga, Application of Roothaan's Self-Consistent Field Theory, *Phys. Rev.*, **120**, 866-871 (1960); Analytical Methods in Hartree-Fock Self-Consistent Field Theory, *Phys. Rev.*, **122**, 131-138 (1961).
60. A. T. Amos and G. G. Hall, Single Determinant Wave Functions, *Proc. Roy. Soc. (London)*, **A263**, 483-493 (1961).
61. M. Cohen and A. Dalgarno, Stationary Properties of the Hartree-Fock Approximation, *Proc. Phys. Soc. (London)*, **77**, 748-750 (1961); see also J. Goodisman and W. Klemperer, On Errors in Hartree-Fock Calculations, *J. Chem. Phys.*, **38**, 721-725 (1963).
62. L. C. Allen and A. M. Karo, Basis Functions for Ab Initio Calculations, *Revs. Mod. Phys.*, **32**, 275-285 (1960) (included in this volume); see also L. C. Allen and A. M. Karo, Electronic Structure of Simple Molecules, *J. Phys. Chem.*, **66**, 2329-2331 (1962).
63. R. G. Parr and B. L. Crawford, Jr., National Academy of Sciences Conference on Quantum-Mechanical Methods in Valence Theory, *Proc. Natl. Acad. Sci. U.S.*, **38**, 547-553 (1952).
64. C. C. J. Roothaan, Evaluation of Molecular Integrals by Digital Computer, *J. Chem. Phys.*, **28**, 982-983 (1958); see also F. J. Corbato, On the Computation of Auxiliary Functions for Two-Center Integrals by Means of a High-Speed Computer, *J. Chem. Phys.*, **24**, 452-453 (1956).
65. I. Shavitt and M. Karplus, Multicenter Integrals in Molecular Quantum Mechanics, *J. Chem. Phys.*, **36**, 550-551 (1962).
66. S. F. Boys, G. B. Cook, C. M. Reeves, and I. Shavitt, Automatic Fundamental Calculations of Molecular Structure, *Nature*, **178**, 1207-1209 (1956).
67. B. J. Ransil, Studies in Molecular Structure. I. Scope and Summary of the Diatomic Molecule Program, *Revs. Mod. Phys.*, **32**, 239-244 (1960); Studies in Molecular Structure. II. LCAO-MO-SCF Wave Functions for

Selected First-Row Diatomic Molecules, *Revs. Mod. Phys.*, **32**, 245-254 (1960); S. Fraga and B. J. Ransil, Studies in Molecular Structure. III. Population Analyses for Selected First-Row Diatomic Molecules, *J. Chem. Phys.*, **34**, 727-742 (1961); B. J. Ransil, Studies in Molecular Structure. IV. Potential Curve for the Interaction of Two Helium Atoms in Single-Configuration LCAO-MO-SCF Approximation, *J. Chem. Phys.*, **34**, 2109-2118 (1961); S. Fraga and B. J. Ransil, Studies in Molecular Structure. V. Computed Spectroscopic Constants for Selected Diatomic Molecules of the First Row, *J. Chem. Phys.*, **35**, 669-678 (1961); Studies in Molecular Structure. VI. Potential Curve for the Interaction of Two Hydrogen Atoms in the LCAO-MO-SCF Approximations, *J. Chem. Phys.*, **35**, 1967-1977 (1961); Studies in Molecular Structure. VII. Limited Configuration Interaction for Selected First-Row Diatomics, *J. Chem. Phys.*, **36**, 1127-1142 (1962); Studies in Molecular Structure. VIII. He_2^{++} in the LCAO-MO-SCF Approximations, *J. Chem. Phys.*, **37**, 1112-1119 (1962).

68. R. S. Mulliken, Criteria for the Construction of Good Self-Consistent Field Molecular Orbital Wave Functions, and the Significance of LCAO-MO Population Analysis, *J. Chem. Phys.*, **36**, 3428-3439 (1962).
69. A. M. Karo and L. C. Allen, LCAO Wave Functions for Hydrogen Fluoride with Hartree-Fock Atomic Orbitals, *J. Chem. Phys.*, **31**, 968-977 (1959).
70. M. Geller, A. A. Frost, and P. G. Lykos, Distortion of Atomic Orbitals in Molecular Orbitals. I. Polarization of the Hydrogen Atom in H_2^+, *J. Chem. Phys.*, **36**, 2693-2698 (1962); R. L. Miller and P. G. Lykos, Distortion of Atomic Orbitals in Molecular Orbitals. II. Charge Shift and Charge Deformation of the Hydrogen Atom in H_2^+, *J. Chem. Phys.*, **37**, 993-1000 (1962).
71. J. W. Richardson, Double-ζ SCF-MO Calculation of the Ground and Some Excited States of N_2, *J. Chem. Phys.*, **35**, 1829-1839 (1961).
72. E. Clementi, SCF-MO Wave Functions for the Hydrogen Fluoride Molecule, *J. Chem. Phys.*, **36**, 33-44 (1962).
73. R. K. Nesbet, Approximate Hartree-Fock Calculations for the Hydrogen Fluoride Molecule, *J. Chem. Phys.*, **36**, 1518-1533 (1962).
74. A. D. McLean, LCAO-MO-SCF Ground State Calculations on C_2H_2 and CO_2, *J. Chem. Phys.*, **32**, 1595-1597 (1960).
75. E. Clementi and A. D. McLean, SCF-LCAO-MO Wave Function for the $^1\Sigma_g^+$ Ground State of C_3, *J. Chem. Phys.*, **36**, 45-47 (1962); E. Clementi, Electronic States in the C_4 Molecule, *J. Am. Chem. Soc.*, **83**, 4501-4505 (1961); E. Clementi and A. D. McLean, A Computation on the Ground State Wave Function for the C_2N_2 Molecule, *J. Chem. Phys.*, **36**, 563-564 (1962); A. D. McLean, Structure of the Ground State of HCN, *J. Chem. Phys.*, **37**, 627-630 (1962); E. Clementi and A. D. McLean, SCF-LCAO-MO Wave Functions for the Bifluoride Ion, *J. Chem. Phys.*, **36**, 745-749 (1962); E. Clementi, Ground State SCF-LCAO-MO Wave Function for the Carbonyl Sulfide Molecule, *J. Chem. Phys.*, **36**, 750-752 (1962).
76. H. Kaplan, Study of the Electronic Ground State of the Ammonia Molecule, *J. Chem. Phys.*, **26**, 1704-1713 (1957).

77. R. K. Nesbet, Molecular Model of the Heisenberg Exchange Interaction, *Phys. Rev.*, **122**, 1497-1508 (1961).
78. H. Lefebvre-Brion, C. M. Moser, and R. K. Nesbet, A Calculation of the Potential Energy Curves for Some Electronic States of Carbon Monoxide, *J. Chem. Phys.*, **34**, 1950-1957 (1961).
79. J. M. Foster and S. F. Boys, A Quantum Variational Calculation for HCHO, *Revs. Mod. Phys.*, **32**, 303-304 (1960).
80. S. F. Boys and G. B. Cook, Mathematical Problems in the Complete Quantum Predictions of Chemical Phenomena, *Revs. Mod. Phys.*, **32**, 285-295 (1960) (included in this volume).
81. I. Shavitt, A Calculation of the Rates of the Ortho-Para Conversions and Isotope Exchanges in Hydrogen, *J. Chem. Phys.*, **31**, 1359-1367 (1959).
82. J. M. Foster and S. F. Boys, Quantum Variational Calculations for a Range of CH_2 Configurations, *Revs. Mod. Phys.*, **32**, 305-307 (1960). The LCAO-SCF dipole moment is 1.1 D, vs. the experimental 2.3 D.
83. F. E. Harris, Molecular Orbital Studies of Diatomic Molecules. I. Method of Computation for Single Configurations of Heteronuclear Systems, *J. Chem. Phys.*, **32**, 3-18 (1960); H. S. Taylor and F. E. Harris, Molecular Orbital Studies of Diatomic Molecules. II. Method of Computation for Multi-Configurations of Heteronuclear and Homonuclear Systems, *Mol. Phys.*, **6**, 183-192 (1963); F. E. Harris and H. S. Taylor, A Quantum Mechanical Study of the LiH Molecule in the Ground State, *Physica*, in press.
84. D. D. Ebbing, Configuration Interaction Study of the Lithium Hydride Molecule, *J. Chem. Phys.*, **36**, 1361-1370 (1962).
85. R. K. Nesbet, Ground State Electronic Wave Function of Methane, *J. Chem. Phys.*, **32**, 1114-1122 (1960).
86. S. F. Boys, The Integral Formulae for the Variational Solution of the Molecular Many-Electron Wave Equation in Terms of Gaussian Functions with Direct Electronic Correlation, *Proc. Roy. Soc. (London)*, **A258**, 402-411 (1960); R. Singer, The Use of Gaussian (Exponential Quadratic) Wave Functions in Molecular Problems. I. General Formulae for the Evaluation of Integrals, *Proc. Roy. Soc. (London)*, **A258**, 412-420 (1960); The Use of Gaussian (Exponential Quadratic) Wave Functions in Molecular Problems. II. Wave Functions for the Ground States of the Hydrogen Atom and of the Hydrogen Molecule, *Proc. Roy. Soc. (London)*, **A258**, 421-430 (1960); M. Krauss, Use of Gaussian Orbitals for Atoms-in-Molecule Calculations, *J. Chem. Phys.*, **34**, 692-693 (1961); L. C. Allen, Gaussian Orbitals for Many-Electron Molecular Wave Functions, *J. Chem. Phys.*, **37**, 200-201 (1962); J. C. Browne and R. D. Poshusta, Quantum-Mechanical Integrals over Gaussian Atomic Orbitals, *J. Chem. Phys.*, **36**, 1933-1937 (1962).
87. Compare R. G. Parr, 1s Orbitals as Base Functions for Molecular Calculations, *J. Chem. Phys.*, **26**, 428 (1957), and G. E. Kimball and J. G. Trulio, Quantum Mechanics of the H_3 Complex, *J. Chem. Phys.*, **28**, 493-497 (1958), where it is pointed out that any molecular function can be ex-

pressed as a combination of an infinite number of 1s functions distributed continuously through space.

88. M. Krauss, Hartree-Fock Approximation of CH_4, *J. Chem. Phys.*, **38**, 564-565 (1963).
89. A. F. Saturno and R. G. Parr, A One-Center Wave Function for the Methane Molecule, *J. Chem. Phys.*, **33**, 22-27 (1960). For some minor corrections, see Ref. 56.
90. E. L. Albasiny and J. R. A. Cooper, A One-Center SCF Wave Function for the Methane Molecule, *Mol. Phys.*, **4**, 353-368 (1961).
91. R. Moccia, One-Center Expansion Self-Consistent-Field Molecular Orbital Electronic Wave Functions for XH_n Molecules, *J. Chem. Phys.*, **37**, 910-911 (1962).
92. A. F. Saturno and R. G. Parr, Improved Simple Analytical Wave Functions for Atoms, *J. Chem. Phys.*, **29**, 490-493 (1958).
93. A. G. Turner, A. F. Saturno, P. Hauk, and R. G. Parr, Description of the Distribution of Electrons in the Methane Molecule, *J. Chem. Phys.*, in press. A preliminary report may be found in R. G. Parr, Recent Advances in Quantum Chemistry, *Sci. Rept. Ist. Super. Sanita,* **1**, 551-559 (1961).
94. M. Cohen and C. A. Coulson, Single-Centre Expansions for the Hydrogen Molecule Ion, *Proc. Cambridge Phil. Soc.*, **57**, 96-106 (1961); M. Cohen, Single-Centre Expansions for the Hydrogen Molecular Ion. II., *Proc. Cambridge Phil. Soc.*, **58**, 130-135 (1962).
95. P. G. Lykos and R. G. Parr, On the Pi-Electron Approximation and Its Possible Refinement, *J. Chem. Phys.*, **24**, 1166-1173; **25**, 1301 (1956) (included in this volume).
96. One may replace condition C with an assumption of a generalized orthogonality between (Σ) and (Π); see Ref. 95, and also T. Arai, Theorem on Separability of Electron Pairs, *J. Chem. Phys.*, **33**, 95-98 (1960), and P. O. Löwdin, Note on the Separability Theorem for Electron Pairs, *J. Chem. Phys.*, **35**, 78-81 (1961).
97. J. M. Parks and R. G. Parr, Theory of Electronic Excitation and Reorganization in the Formaldehyde Molecule, *J. Chem. Phys.*, **32**, 1657-1681 (1960).
98. Page 1171 of Ref. 95; H. M. McConnell, Indirect Hyperfine Interactions in the Paramagnetic Resonance Spectra of Aromatic Free Radicals, *J. Chem. Phys.*, **24**, 764-766 (1956); A. D. McLachlan, H. H. Dearman, and R. Lefebvre, Theory of Hyperfine Interactions in Aromatic Radicals, *J. Chem. Phys.*, **33**, 65-70 (1960).
99. J. D. Roberts, *Notes on Molecular Orbital Calculations*, Benjamin, New York, 1961.
100. A. Streitwieser, Jr., *Molecular Orbital Theory for Organic Chemists*, Wiley, New York, 1961.
101. For a recent discussion of nonorthogonality in the Hückel method, see

G. Del Re, On the Non-Orthogonality Problem in the Semi-Empirical MO-LCAO Method, *Nuovo Cimento*, **17**, 644-664 (1960).

102. R. G. Parr, On LCAO Molecular Orbital Schemes and Theoretical Resonance Energies, *J. Chem. Phys.*, **19**, 799-800 (1951).
103. M. Goeppert-Mayer and A. L. Sklar, Calculations of the Lower Excited Levels of Benzene, *J. Chem. Phys.*, **6**, 645-652 (1938) (included in this volume).
104. R. G. Parr and R. S. Mulliken, LCAO Self-Consistent Field Calculation of the π-Electron Levels of *cis*- and *trans*-1,3-Butadiene, *J. Chem. Phys.*, **18**, 1338-1346 (1950) (included in this volume).
105. R. G. Parr and G. R. Taylor, LCAO Self-Consistent Field Calculation of the Twisting Frequency and π-Electron Energy Levels of Allene, *J. Chem. Phys.*, **19**, 497-501 (1951).
106. R. G. Parr, D. P. Craig, and I. G. Ross, Molecular Orbital Calculations of the Lower Excited Levels of Benzene, Configuration Interaction Included, *J. Chem. Phys.*, **18**, 1561-1563 (1950) (included in this volume); F. A. Gray, I. G. Ross, and J. Yates, Refined Antisymmetric Molecular-Orbital Calculations of the Energy Levels of Benzene and Hexamethylbenzene, *Australian J. Chem.*, **12**, 347-355 (1959).
107. R. G. Parr and B. L. Crawford, Jr., On Certain Integrals Useful in Molecular Orbital Calculations, *J. Chem. Phys.*, **16**, 1049-1056 (1948); H. J. Kopineck, Austausch- und andere Zweizentrenintegrale mit 2s- und 2p-Funktionen, *Z. Naturforsch.*, **5a**, 420-431 (1950), Zweizentrenintegrale mit 2s- und 2p-Funktionen II, *Z. Naturforsch.*, **6a**, 177-183 (1951); now, subroutines are usually written for computing the various integrals on a digital computer.
108. W. Moffitt, The Electronic Structure of the Oxygen Molecule, *Proc. Roy. Soc. (London)*, **A210**, 224-245 (1951).
109. W. Moffitt, Atoms in Molecules and Crystals, *Proc. Roy. Soc. (London)*, **A210**, 245-268 (1951).
110. R. Pariser and R. G. Parr, A Semi-Empirical Theory of the Electronic Spectra and Electronic Structure of Complex Unsaturated Molecules. I, *J. Chem. Phys.*, **21**, 466-471 (1953) (included in this volume).
111. R. Pariser and R. G. Parr, A Semi-Empirical Theory of the Electronic Spectra and Electronic Structure of Complex Unsaturated Molecules. II, *J. Chem. Phys.*, **21**, 767-776 (1953) (included in this volume).
112. J. A. Pople, Electron Interaction in Unsaturated Hydrocarbons, *Trans. Faraday Soc.*, **49**, 1375-1385 (1953) (included in this volume).
113. Name used in abstracts and oral presentations of the material in Refs. 110 and 111 in papers at the Ohio State Spectroscopy Symposium, June, 1952.
114. R. G. Parr, A Method for Estimating Electronic Repulsion Integrals over LCAO MO's in Complex Unsaturated Molecules, *J. Chem. Phys.*, **20**, 1499 (1952) (included in this volume).

115. R. Pariser, An Improvement in the π-Electron Approximation in LCAO-MO Theory, *J. Chem. Phys.*, **21**, 568-569 (1953) (included in this volume).
116. For example, A. L. Companion, and F. O. Ellison, Calculation of Atomic Valence State Energies, *J. Chem. Phys.*, **28**, 1-8 (1958); F. O. Ellison, Calculation of Atomic Valence State Energies of B^-, C, and N^+ in BH_n^-, CH_n and NH_n^+, n = 1 to 4, *J. Chem. Phys.*, **36**, 3107-3112 (1962); U. Öpik, Mean Energies of Hybridized Valence States, *Mol. Phys.*, **4**, 505-508 (1961).
117. P. O. Löwdin, On the Non-Orthogonality Problem Connected with the Use of Atomic Wave Functions in the Theory of Molecules and Crystals, *J. Chem. Phys.*, **18**, 365-375 (1950).
118. F. G. Fumi and R. G. Parr, Electronic States of Diatomic Molecules: The Oxygen Molecule, *J. Chem. Phys.*, **21**, 1864-1868 (1953).
119. R. G. Parr, Three Remarks on Molecular Orbital Theory of Complex Molecules, *J. Chem. Phys.*, **33**, 1184-1199 (1960) (included in this volume).
120. R. McWeeny, The Valence-Bond Theory of Molecular Structure. I. Orbital Theories and the Valence-Bond Method, *Proc. Roy. Soc. (London)*, **A223**, 63-79 (1954); The Valence-Bond Theory of Molecular Structure. II. Reformulation of the Theory, *Proc. Roy. Soc. (London)*, **A223**, 306-323 (1954).
121. R. McWeeny, The Valence-Bond Theory of Molecular Structure. III. Cyclobutadiene and Benzene, *Proc. Roy. Soc. (London)*, **A227**, 288-312 (1955).
122. J. C. Slater, Note on Orthogonal Atomic Orbitals, *J. Chem. Phys.*, **19**, 220-223 (1951).
123. R. G. Parr and B. L. Crawford, Jr., Molecular Orbital Calculations of Vibrational Force Constants. I. Ethylene, *J. Chem. Phys.*, **16**, 526-532 (1948); see also R. S. Mulliken and C. C. J. Roothaan, The Twisting Frequency and the Barrier Height for Free Rotation in Ethylene, *Chem. Rev.*, **41**, 219-231 (1947).
124. T. Murai, Electronic States of Ethylene Molecule, *Progr. Theoret. Phys. (Kyoto)*, **7**, 345-352 (1952).
125. S. Huzinaga, Variational Calculation of Ethylene, *J. Chem. Phys.*, **36**, 453-457 (1962).
126. Y. I'Haya, A Semi-Empirical Theory of the Electronic Structure of Ethylene, with Particular Reference to the Ionization Potential, *Mol. Phys.*, **3**, 513-519 (1960); A Further Study of the Electronic Structure and Spectrum of Ethylene, *Mol. Phys.*, **3**, 521-531 (1960).
127. R. S. Mulliken, Quelques aspects de la théorie des orbitales moléculaires, *J. Chim. Phys.*, **46**, 497-542, 675-713 (1949); this remarkable paper contains a wealth of good material, anticipating later work in many ways.
128. K. Ruedenberg, On the Three- and Four-Center Integrals in Molecular Quantum Mechanics, *J. Chem. Phys.*, **19**, 1433-1434 (1951).

129. A. L. Companion and R. G. Parr, Remark on the Mulliken Approximation for Two-Center Electron Distributions, *J. Chem. Phys.*, **35**, 2268-2269 (1961).
130. See, for example, pp. 256ff of Ref. 7.
131. See footnote 9 of Ref. 106, first paper.
132. B. L. Crawford, Jr., and R. G. Parr, Molecular Orbital Calculations of Vibrational Force Constants. II. The Ring-Twisting Constants of Benzene, *J. Chem. Phys.*, **17**, 726-733 (1949).
133. C. C. J. Roothaan and R. G. Parr, Calculations of the Lower Excited Levels of Benzene, *J. Chem. Phys.*, **17**, 1001 (1949); see also Ref. 127.
134. R. Pariser, Theory of the Electronic Spectra and Structure of the Polyacenes and of Alternant Hydrocarbons, *J. Chem. Phys.*, **24**, 250-268 (1956) (included in this volume).
135. J. N. Murrell and K. L. McEwen, Importance of Doubly Excited Configurations in the Interpretation of Electronic Spectra, *J. Chem. Phys.*, **25**, 1143-1149 (1956).
136. P. G. Lykos, On the Parameters Used in Semiempirical Molecular Orbital Theory for Conjugated Hydrocarbons, *J. Chem. Phys.*, **35**, 1249-1255 (1961); The Present Status of π-Electron Calculations, *J. Phys. Chem.*, **66**, 2324-2329 (1962).
137. R. S. Mulliken and R. G. Parr, LCAO Molecular Orbital Computation of Resonance Energies of Benzene and Butadiene, with General Analysis of Theoretical Versus Thermochemical Resonance Energies, *J. Chem. Phys.*, **19**, 1271-1278 (1951).
138. P. G. Lykos and R. G. Parr, On the Diamagnetic Anisotropy of Benzene, *J. Chem. Phys.*, **28**, 361 (1958).
139. J. A. Pople, Application of Self-Consistent Molecular Orbital Methods to π-Electrons, *J. Phys. Chem.*, **61**, 6-10 (1957).
140. H. C. Longuet-Higgins, Recent Developments in Molecular Orbital Theory, *Advan. Chem. Phys.*, **1**, 239-265 (1958).
141. For example, J. W. Sidman, Electronic and Vibrational States of Anthracene, *J. Chem. Phys.*, **25**, 115-121 (1956); Electronic and Vibrational States of Tetracene (Naphthacene), *J. Chem. Phys.*, **25**, 122-124 (1956); M. R. Padhye, S. P. McGlynn, and M. Kasha, Lowest Triplet State of Anthracene, *J. Chem. Phys.*, **24**, 588-594 (1956); G. B. Porter and M. W. Windsor, The Triplet State in Fluid Media, *Proc. Roy. Soc. (London)*, **A245**, 238-258 (1958).
142. Indeed, the actual SCF molecular orbitals can be obtained by iterating this procedure of guessing the orbitals, occupied and unoccupied, for the ground state, mixing the ground state with all "one-electron jumps" obtainable from it, redetermining the molecular orbitals, and repeating, until there results a ground configuration that gives no mixing with singly-excited configurations, which property characterizes the SCF function. See H. Brion, R. Lefebvre, and C. M. Moser, Alternative Method for Calculating SCF Orbitals, *J. Chem. Phys.*, **23**, 1972 (1955),

R. Lefebvre and C. M. Moser, L'interaction de configuration comme méthode de calcul des orbitales moléculaires du champ self-consistent. I. États à couches complètes. Cas des hydrocarbures conjugés alternants pairs, *J. Chim. Phys.*, **53**, 393-399 (1956), and R. Lefebvre, L'interaction de configuration comme méthode de calcul des orbitales moléculaires du champ self-consistent. II. État fondamental d'un système à un nombre impair d'électrons, *J. Chim. Phys.*, **54**, 168-174 (1957).

143. A. Pullman, L'interaction des configurations dans un butadiène self-consistent, *J. Chim. Phys.*, **51**, 188-196 (1954).

144. R. K. Nesbet, Excited Electronic States of 1,3-Butadiene, *Proc. Roy. Soc. (London)*, **A230**, 322-330 (1955).

145. J. Fain and F. A. Matsen, Complete π-Electron Treatment of the Butadiene Molecule and Ion, *J. Chem. Phys.*, **26**, 376-379 (1957).

146. A. Pullman and H. Berthod, L'influence de la correction des integrales monocentriques sur les caractéristiques d'un butadiène calculé par la méthode du champ moléculaire self-consistent, *Compt. Rend.*, **239**, 812-814 (1954).

147. G. G. Hall, The Electronic Structure of *trans*-Butadiene Calculated by the Standard Excited State Method, *Trans. Faraday Soc.*, **50**, 773-779 (1954).

148. Y. Mori, On the Electronic Structures of Butadiene, *Bull. Chem. Soc. Japan*, **28**, 291-295 (1955).

149. C. M. Moser, Calculations on the Electronic Spectra of *trans*-Butadiene by a Semi-Empirical Molecular-Orbital Approximation, *J. Chem. Soc.*, **1954**, 3455-3461.

150. F. Peradejordi, Sur l'approximation de Pariser et Parr, *Compt. Rend.*, **243**, 276-278 (1956).

151. R. Pariser, Electronic Spectrum and Structure of Azulene, *J. Chem. Phys.*, **25**, 1112-1116 (1956) (included in this volume).

152. J. W. Sidman and D. S. McClure, Electronic and Vibrational States of Azulene, *J. Chem. Phys.*, **24**, 757-763 (1956); W. R. Ware, Location of the Lowest Triplet Level in Azulene, *J. Chem. Phys.*, **37**, 923-924 (1962).

153. A. Julg, Étude de l'azulène par la méthode du champ moléculaire self-consistent, *J. Chim. Phys.*, **52**, 377-381 (1955).

154. H. Kon, A. Semi-Empirical Approach to the SCF Molecular Orbitals, *Bull. Chem. Soc. Japan*, **28**, 275-280 (1955) (included in this volume).

155. C. A. Coulson and G. S. Rushbrooke, The Method of Molecular Orbitals, *Proc. Cambridge Phil. Soc.*, **36**, 193-200 (1940).

156. N. S. Hush and J. A. Pople, Ionization Potentials and Electron Affinities of Conjugated Hydrocarbon Molecules and Radicals, *Trans. Faraday Soc.*, **51**, 600-605 (1955) (included in this volume).

157. F. A. Matsen, Electron Affinities, Methyl Affinities, and Ionization Energies of Condensed Ring Aromatic Hydrocarbons, *J. Chem. Phys.*, **24**, 602-606 (1956).

158. R. M. Hedges and F. A. Matsen, Antisymmetrized Hückel Orbital Calcu-

lations of Ionization Potentials and Electron Affinities of Some Aromatic Hydrocarbons, *J. Chem. Phys.*, **28**, 950-953 (1958).

159. W. I. J. Aalbersberg and E. L. Mackor, The Polarographic Reduction of Aromatic Hydrocarbon Positive Ions and Proton Complexes, *Trans. Faraday Soc.*, **56**, 1351-1356 (1960).

160. A. G. Harrison and F. P. Lossing, Free Radicals by Mass Spectrometry. XVIII. The Ionization Potentials of Hydrocarbon Radicals and the Resonance Energies of Radicals and Carbonium Ions, *J. Am. Chem. Soc.*, **82**, 1052-1054 (1960).

161. N. S. Hush, Successive Ionization Potentials of Unsaturated Hydrocarbons, *J. Chem. Phys.*, **27**, 612-613 (1957).

162. W. Moffitt, The Electronic Spectra of Cata-Condensed Hydrocarbons, *J. Chem. Phys.*, **22**, 320-333 (1954) (included in this volume).

163. J. R. Platt, Classification of Spectra of Cata-Condensed Hydrocarbons, *J. Chem. Phys.*, **17**, 484-495 (1949).

164. M. J. S. Dewar and H. C. Longuet-Higgins, The Electronic Spectra of Aromatic Molecules. I. Benzenoid Hydrocarbons, *Proc. Phys. Soc. (London)*, **A67**, 795-804 (1954).

165. J. A. Pople, The Electronic Spectra of Aromatic Molecules. II. A Theoretical Treatment of Excited States of Alternant Hydrocarbon Molecules Based on Self-Consistent Molecular Orbitals, *Proc. Phys. Soc.* (*London*), **A68**, 81-89 (1955) (included in this volume).

166. E. Clar, *Aromatische Kohlenwasserstoffe*, Springer-Verlag, Berlin, 1941.

167. A. D. McLachlan, The Pairing of Electronic States in Alternant Hydrocarbons, *Mol. Phys.*, **2**, 271-284 (1959) (included in this volume); Electrons and Holes in Alternant Hydrocarbons, *Mol. Phys.*, **4**, 49-56 (1961).

168. W. P. Weijland, Thesis, Free University, Amsterdam, 1958; G. J. Hoijtink, Excitations électroniques des ions monopositifs et mononégatifs des hydrocarbures alternants, Colloque International sur le Calcul des Fonctions d'Onde Moléculaires, *C.N.R.S.* (Paris) **1958**, 239-246.

169. A. Brickstock and J. A. Pople, Resonance Energies and Charge Distributions of Unsaturated Hydrocarbon Radicals and Ions, *Trans. Faraday Soc.*, **50**, 901-911 (1954) (included in this volume).

170. H. C. Longuet-Higgins and J. A. Pople, The Electronic Spectra of Aromatic Molecules. IV. Excited States of Odd Alternant Hydrocarbon Radicals and Ions, *Proc. Phys., Soc. (London)*, **A68**, 591-600 (1955) (included in this volume).

171. R. Lefebvre and C. M. Moser, Lowest Singlet Excited Levels of Naphthalene. II., *J. Chem. Phys.*, **23**, 754-755 (1955); The Lowest Singlet Excited Levels of Naphthalene. I. A Semi-Empirical Calculation, *J. Chem. Soc.*, **1956**, 1557-1563; The Lowest Singlet Excited Levels of Naphthalene. II. Restricted Calculations, *J. Chem. Soc.*, **1956**, 2734-2739.

172. P. G. Lykos, Ph.D. Thesis, Carnegie Institute of Technology, Pittsburgh, 1954.

173. P. Schiess and A. Pullman, Recherches théoriques sur le cyclooctatetraene, *J. Chim. Phys.*, **53**, 101-105 (1956).
174. K. L. McEwen and H. C. Longuet-Higgins, Electronic Spectra of Cyclo-Octatetraene, Tetraphenylene, and s-Dibenzcyclo-Octatetraene, *J. Chem. Phys.*, **24**, 771-776 (1956).
175. R. B. Hermann, The Ultraviolet Spectrum of Bicycloheptadiene, *J. Org. Chem.*, **27**, 441-442 (1962).
176. W. L. Allinger, Aromatic and Pseudoaromatic Non-Benzenoid Systems. IV. Cyclooctatetraene, *J. Org. Chem.*, **27**, 443-447 (1962).
177. K. Iguchi, The Lower Excited States and the Phosphorescent State of Diphenyl. I., *J. Phys. Soc. Japan*, **12**, 1250-1255 (1957).
178. N. Mataga, K. Nishimoto, and S. Mataga, Remarks on the Molecular Calculation of Naphthalene and Anthracene, *Bull. Chem. Soc. Japan*, **32**, 395-399 (1959).
179. E. Clementi and K. S. Pitzer, Low Excited States in C_2, *J. Chem. Phys.*, **32**, 656-662 (1960).
180. C. F. Wilcox, Jr., The Ultraviolet Spectrum of Triptycene, *J. Chem. Phys.*, **33**, 1874-1875 (1960); C. F. Wilcox, Jr., S. Winstein, and W. G. McMillan, Neighboring Carbon and Hydrogen. XXXIV. Interaction of Non-conjugated Chromophores, *J. Am. Chem. Soc.*, **82**, 5450-5454 (1960).
181. R. L. Hummel and K. Ruedenberg, Electronic Spectra of Catacondensed and Pericondensed Aromatic Hydrocarbons, *J. Phys. Chem.*, **66**, 2334-2359 (1962).
182. H. Brion and R. Lefebvre, L'interaction de configuration comme méthode de calcul des orbitales moléculaires self-consistentes. III. États électroniques de quelques hydrocarbures radicalaires; l'allyle, le pentadiènyle et le benzyle, *J. Chim. Phys.*, **54**, 363-368 (1957).
183. J. N. Murrell and H. C. Longuet-Higgins, Electronic Spectrum of the Cycloheptatrienyl (Tropylium) Ion, *J. Chem. Phys.*, **23**, 2347-2348 (1955).
184. H. C. Longuet-Higgins and K. L. McEwen, Electronic Spectra of Cyclic Aromatic Hydrocarbon Radicals and Ions, *J. Chem. Phys.*, **26**, 719-723 (1957).
185. J. N. Murrell, Electronic Spectra of the Triarylmethyl Radicals, *J. Chem. Phys.*, **26**, 1738-1741 (1957).
186. N. S. Hush and J. R. Rowlands, Electronic Spectra of Hydrocarbon Anions, *J. Chem. Phys.*, **25**, 1076-1077 (1956).
187. Y. Mori, Doublet States of Benzyl Radical, *J. Chem. Phys.*, **24**, 1253 (1956); Electronic Structure of Benzyl Radical, *Bull. Chem. Soc. Japan*, **34**, 1031-1035 (1961); The Effect of Electron Transfer in the Electronic Structure of Benzyl Radical, *Bull. Chem. Soc. Japan*, **34**, 1035-1040 (1961).
188. A. A. V. Stuart and E. L. Mackor, Electronic Spectra of Carbonium Ions, *J. Chem. Phys.*, **27**, 826-827 (1957).
189. P. Balk, S. de Bruijn, and G. J. Hoijtink, Electronic Spectra of Alternant Hydrocarbon Mononegative Ions, *Rec. Trav. Chim.*, **76**, 907-918 (1957).

190. P. Balk, S. de Bruijn, and G. J. Hoijtink, Electronic Spectra of Alternant Hydrocarbon Di-Negative Ions, *Mol. Phys.*, **1**, 151-156 (1958).
191. G. J. Hoijtink, Correlations between the Electronic Spectra of Alternant Hydrocarbon Molecules and Their Mono- and Di-Valent Ions. I. Benzene, Coronene, and Triphenylene, *Mol. Phys.*, **2**, 85-95 (1959); G. J. Hoijtink, N. H. Velthorst, and P. J. Zandstra, Correlations between the Electronic Spectra of Alternant Hydrocarbon Molecules and Their Mono- and Di-Valent Ions. II. Hydrocarbons with Symmetry D_{2h}, *Mol. Phys.*, **3**, 533-546 (1960).
192. J. P. Colpa, C. MacLean, and E. L. Mackor, Ions of Odd Alternant Systems. Proton Complexes of Aromatic Hydrocarbons, *Tetrahedron,* **19**, Suppl. 2, 65-88 (1963).
193. A. T. Amos, Calculations on the Ions and Lowest π Triplet States of Some Conjugated Hydrocarbons, *Mol. Phys.*, **5**, 91-104 (1962) (included in this volume).
194. A. D. McLachlan, Spin Density and Spin Correlation in Triplet States, *Mol. Phys.*, **5**, 51-62 (1962).
195. H. O. Pritchard and F. H. Sumner, The Application of Electronic Digital Computers to Molecular Orbital Problems. I. The Calculation of Bond Lengths in Aromatic Hydrocarbons, *Proc. Roy. Soc. (London)*, **A226**, 128-140 (1954); The Calculation of Bond Lengths in Naphthalene and Anthracene, *Trans. Faraday Soc.*, **51**, 457-462 (1955).
196. G. G. Hall, The Bond Orders of Alternant Hydrocarbon Molecules, *Proc. Roy. Soc. (London)*, **A229**, 251-259 (1955); The Bond Orders of Some Conjugated Hydrocarbon Molecules, *Trans. Faraday Soc.*, **53**, 573-581 (1957).
197. S. F. Mason, The Ionic Dissociation and Reactivity of Some Arylmethyl Chlorides, *J. Chem. Soc.*, **1958**, 808-817.
198. C. M. Moser, Sur les coefficients LCAO du naphtalène obtenus par une approximation semi-empirique de la méthode du champ self-consistent, *J. Chim. Phys.*, **52**, 24-33 (1955).
199. R. McWeeny, The Density Matrix in Self-Consistent Field Theory. II. Applications in the Molecular Orbital Theory of Conjugated Systems, *Proc. Roy. Soc. (London)*, **A237**, 355-371 (1956).
200. T. E. Peacock, The π-Electronic Structure and Properties of Naphthalene, *J. Chem. Soc.*, **1959**, 3241-3244.
201. T. E. Peacock and R. McWeeny, A Self-Consistent Calculation of the Graphite π Bond, *Proc. Phys. Soc. (London)*, **74**, 385-394 (1959); T. E. Peacock, The π-Electron Properties of Graphite, *J. Chim. Phys.*, **57**, 844-847 (1960); The Effective Number of Electrons in the π Bond of Graphite, *Proc. Phys. Soc. (London)*, **77**, 1214-1215 (1961).
202. Y. Ooshika, A Semi-Empirical Theory of the Conjugated Systems. I. General Formulation, *J. Phys. Soc. Japan*, **12**, 1238-1245 (1957).
203. Y. Ooshika, A Semi-Empirical Theory of the Conjugated Systems. II. Bond Alternation in Conjugated Chains, *J. Phys. Soc. Japan*, **12**, 1246-1250 (1957).

204. F. Combet-Farnoux and G. Berthier, Electronic Structure of Conjugated Monocyclic Hydrocarbons, *Compt. Rend.*, **248**, 688-690 (1959).
205. K. Fukui, A. Imamura, T. Yonezawa, and C. Nagata, A Quantum-Mechanical Approach to the Theory of Aromaticity, *Bull. Chem. Soc. Japan*, **33**, 1591-1599 (1960).
206. M. Randić, Comment on the Difference between the Bond Orders Calculated by SCF MO and Simple MO Method, *J. Chem. Phys.*, **34**, 693-694 (1961).
207. O. W. Adams and P. G. Lykos, Open- and Closed-Shell SCF Method for Conjugated Systems, *J. Chem. Phys.*, **34**, 1444-1445 (1961).
208. J. R. Hoyland and L. Goodman, Open-Shell Wave Functions for Conjugated Hydrocarbons, *J. Chem. Phys.*, **34**, 1446-1447 (1961).
209. H. C. Longuet-Higgins and L. Salem, The Forces between Polyatomic Molecules. I. Long-Range Forces, *Proc. Roy. Soc. (London)*, **A259**, 433-441 (1961).
210. J. A. Pople and S. H. Walmsley, Electronic States of Long Polyenes with Alternating Bond Lengths, *Trans. Faraday Soc.*, **58**, 441-448 (1962).
211. R. K. Nesbet, Interaction of Two Ethylene Molecules, *Mol. Phys.*, **5**, 63-69 (1962).
212. G. J. Hoijtink, Electron Spin Densities in Alternant Hydrocarbon Mononegative and Mono-Positive Ions and in Odd Alternant Hydrocarbon Radicals, *Mol. Phys.*, **1**, 157-162 (1958).
213. A. D. McLachlan, Self-Consistent Field Theory of the Electron-Spin Distribution in π-Electron Radicals, *Mol. Phys.*, **3**, 233-252 (1960).
214. G. J. Hoijtink, J. Townsend, and S. I. Weissman, Spin Density in Pyrene Negative Ion, *J. Chem. Phys.*, **34**, 507-508 (1961).
215. J. Serre, Recherches théoriques sur les composes acétylèniques. III. Les transitions spectrales de l'acétylène et de ses homologues superieurs, *J. Chim. Phys.*, **52**, 331-338 (1955).
216. A. Julg and B. Pullman, Recherches complémentaires sur la structure du fulvène et de l'heptafulvène. Incorporation du procédé de Pariser et Parr dans la méthode du champ moléculaire self-consistent, *J. Chim. Phys.*, **52**, 481-485 (1955).
217. H. Kon, Simplified SCF Calculation for Fulvene, *J. Chem. Phys.*, **23**, 1176-1177 (1955).
218. R. D. Brown and M. L. Heffernan, The Variable Electronegativity Method. VI. Azulene, *Australian J. Chem.*, **13**, 38-48 (1960).
219. A. J. Silvestri, L. Goodman, and J. A. Dixon, Molecular Diagrams of Some Nonbenzenoid Aromatic Hydrocarbons, *J. Chem. Phys.*, **36**, 148-151 (1962).
220. R. G. Parr and R. Pariser, On the Electronic Structure and Electronic Spectra of Ethylene-Like Molecules, *J. Chem. Phys.*, **23**, 711-725 (1955).
221. R. S. Mulliken, A New Electroaffinity Scale: Together with Data on Valence States and on Valence Ionization Potentials and Electron Affinities, *J. Chem. Phys.*, **2**, 782-793 (1934).

222. J. S. Griffith, Group Theory and Aromatic Molecules, *J. Chem. Phys.*, **35**, 1901-1902 (1961).
223. J. N. Murrell and H. C. Longuet-Higgins, The Electronic Spectra of Aromatic Molecules. III. The Effect of Inductive Substituents, *Proc. Phys. Soc. (London)*, **A68**, 329-339 (1955).
224. J. N. Murrell, The Electronic Spectra of Aromatic Molecules. VI. The Mesomeric Effect, *Proc. Phys. Soc. (London)*, **A68**, 969-975 (1955).
225. J. N. Murrell, The π-Electron Spectra of the Benzene N-Heterocycles, *Mol. Phys.*, **1**, 384-390 (1958).
226. J. Petruska, Changes in the Electronic Transitions of Aromatic Hydrocarbons on Chemical Substitution. I. Perturbation Theory for Substituted Cyclic Polyenes, *J. Chem. Phys.*, **34**, 1111-1120 (1961); Changes in the Electronic Transitions of Aromatic Hydrocarbons on Chemical Substitution. II. Application of Perturbation Theory to Substituted-Benzene Spectra, *J. Chem. Phys.*, **34**, 1120-1136 (1961).
227. J. N. Murrell, The Electronic Spectra of Substituted Aromatic Hydrocarbons, *Tetrahedron*, **19**, Suppl. 2, 277-286 (1963).
228. J. A. Pople, Molecular Orbital Perturbation Theory. I. A Perturbation Method Based on Self-Consistent Orbitals, *Proc. Roy. Soc. (London)*, **A233**, 233-241 (1956); J. A. Pople and P. Schofield, Molecular Orbital Perturbation Theory. II. Charge Displacement and Stabilization in Conjugated Molecules, *Proc. Roy. Soc. (London)*, **A233**, 241-247 (1956).
229. For example, K. Iguchi, π-Electronic Structure of the HCN Molecule, *J. Chem. Phys.*, **23**, 1983-1988 (1955).
230. J. W. Sidman, Electronic Spectra and Structure of the Carbonyl Group, *J. Chem. Phys.*, **27**, 429-435 (1957).
231. B. J. McClelland, π-Electron Distribution in Some Ketones, *Trans. Faraday Soc.*, **57**, 2073-2080 (1961).
232. S. P. McGlynn and W. T. Simpson, Application of the Pariser and Parr Method to Dye Ions with Amidinium Resonance, *J. Chem. Phys.*, **28**, 297-300 (1958).
233. B. Grabe, Calculation of Energy Levels and Electron Distribution in Reduced and Oxidized Forms of Diphosphopyridine Nucleotide and of Flavine, *Arkiv Fysik*, **17**, 97-111 (1960).
234. D. S. Sappenfield and M. M. Kreevoy, The Electronic Structure of Oxygen and Sulfur Heterocyclics, *Tetrahedron*, **19**, Suppl. 2, 157-171 (1963).
235. I. Fischer-Hjalmars, Different MO Approximations Applied to Aniline, *Arkiv Fysik*, **21**, 123-143 (1962) (included in this volume).
236. T. E. Peacock, An Approximation Method for Self-Consistent Charges and Bond Orders, *Trans. Faraday Soc.*, **53**, 1042-1045 (1957).
237. R. McWeeny, Electronic Absorption Spectra of Heterocyclic Systems. I. A Comparison of Theoretical Methods: Pyridine and Pyrazine, *Proc. Phys. Soc. (London)*, **A70**, 593-604 (1957).
238. T. E. Peacock, Electronic Absorption Spectra of Heterocyclic Systems. II. Applications to Some Two-Ring Nitrogen Heterocyclics, *Proc. Phys. Soc. (London)*, **A70**, 654-660 (1957).

239. R. McWeeny and T. E. Peacock, The Electronic Structure and Spectra of Some Nitrogen Heterobenzenes, *Proc. Phys. Soc. (London)*, **A70**, 41-50 (1957); T. E. Peacock, Electronic Structure and Spectrum of s-Triazine, *Nature*, **179**, 684-685 (1957).
240. T. E. Peacock, A Molecular-Orbital Calculation of the Ultraviolet Absorption Spectra of 1:5- and 1:8-Naphthyridine, *J. Chem. Soc.*, **1959**, 2308-2310; A Molecular Orbital Calculation of the Ultraviolet Absorption Spectrum of the Quinolizinium Cation, *J. Chem. Soc.*, **1959**, 3645-3646; The Effect of Bond Length Variations in Molecular Orbital Calculations of π-Electron Spectra—Aniline, *Mol. Phys.*, **3**, 453-456 (1960); The Electronic Structure and Spectrum of Nitrobenzene, *Proc. Phys. Soc. (London)*, **78**, 460-463 (1961); T. E. Peacock and P. T. Wilkinson, The Electronic Structure and Spectrum of Benzonitrile, *Proc. Phys. Soc. (London)*, **79**, 105-109 (1962).
241. A. T. Amos and G. G. Hall, Ground-State Properties of Some Heterocyclics, *Mol. Phys.*, **4**, 25-31 (1961).
242. K. Nishimoto and N. Mataga, Electronic Structure and Spectra of Some Nitrogen Heterocycles, *Z. Physik. Chem. (Frankfurt)*, **12**, 335-338 (1957); **13**, 140-157 (1957).
243. N. Mataga, Electronic Structure and Spectra of s-Tetrazine, *Bull. Chem. Soc. Japan*, **31**, 453-458 (1958); Electronic Spectra of Quinoline and Isoquinoline and the Mechanism of Fluorescence Quenching in these Molecules, *Bull. Chem. Soc. Japan*, **31**, 459-462 (1958); Electronic Spectra of Acridine and Phenazine, *Bull. Chem. Soc. Japan*, **31**, 463-467 (1958).
244. K. Nishimoto and R. Fujishiro, Electronic Structure of Phenol. *Bull. Chem. Soc. Japan*, **31**, 1036-1040 (1958); A Convenient Method for the Calculation of the π-Electronic Structures of Aromatic Derivatives, *Bull. Chem. Soc. Japan*, **32**, 699-702 (1959); Electronic Spectra of Naphthols, *J. Chem. Phys.*, **36**, 3494-3495 (1962); A Semi-Empirical Theory of the π-Electronic Spectra of Aromatic Derivatives, *Bull. Chem. Soc. Japan*, **35**, 905-910 (1962).
245. S. Mataga and N. Mataga, Protonation Effects on the Electronic Spectra of Pyrazine, *Bull. Chem. Soc. Japan*, **32**, 511-513 (1959); Effects of Protonation on the Electronic Structure and Spectra of Nitrogen Heterocycles, *Bull. Chem. Soc. Japan*, **32**, 521-525 (1959); N. Mataga and S. Mataga, On the Intramolecular Charge-Transfer Spectra and Structure of Isomeric Aminopyridines, *Bull. Chem. Soc. Japan*, **32**, 600-603 (1959).
246. R. D. Brown and A. Penfold, Comparison of SCFMO and ASMOCI Calculations of Electron Densities, *J. Chem. Phys.*, **24**, 1259-1260 (1956).
247. R. D. Brown and A. Penfold, The Molecular-Orbital Parameters for Conjugated Nitrogen Atoms, *Trans. Faraday Soc.*, **53**, 397-402 (1957).
248. R. D. Brown and M. L. Heffernan, The π Electron Distribution in Pyridine and the Molecular Orbital Parameters for Nitrogen, *Australian J. Chem.*, **10**, 211-217 (1957).
249. R. D. Brown and M. L. Heffernan, Study of Formaldehyde by a "Self-

Consistent Electronegativity'' Molecular-Orbital Method, *Trans. Faraday Soc.*, **54**, 757-764 (1958); The "Variable Electronegativity" Method. II. Pyrrole, *Australian J. Chem.*, **12**, 319-329 (1959); The "Variable Electronegativity" Method. III. The Pyrrole Anion and Electronegativity Reversal, *Australian J. Chem.*, **12**, 330-334 (1959); The Variable Electronegativity Method. IV. Glyoxaline, Its Cation and Anion, *Australian J. Chem.*, **12**, 543-553 (1959); The Variable Electronegativity Method. V. Pyridine, the Pyridinium Cation, and the Evaluation of Core-Attraction Integrals, *Australian J. Chem.*, **12**, 554-568 (1959); The Variable Electronegativity Method. VII. Pyrazole, Its Anion and Cation, *Australian J. Chem.*, **13**, 49-57 (1960).

250. T. Anno, I. Matubara, and A. Sadô, Electronic States of Para-Benzoquinone. I. Calculation of the Energy Levels by a Semi-Empirical Molecular Orbital Method Neglecting Configuration Interaction, *Bull. Chem. Soc. Japan*, **30**, 168-177 (1957); T. Anno, A. Sadô, and I. Matubara, Electronic States of Para-Benzoquinone. II. Calculation of the Energy Levels by a Semiempirical Molecular Orbital Method Including Configuration Interaction, *J. Chem. Phys.*, **26**, 967-968 (1957).

251. T. Anno and A. Sadô, Calculation on the Electronic States of the Formaldehyde Molecule by a Semiempirical Molecular Orbital Method, *J. Chem. Phys.*, **26**, 1759-1760 (1957); T. Anno, Semiempirical Calculation on the Electronic Structure of the Nitrogen-Containing Heterocyclic Molecules. I. General Theory, *J. Chem. Phys.*, **29**, 1161-1169 (1958); T. Anno and A. Sadô, Semiempirical Calculation on the Electronic Structure of the Nitrogen-Containing Heterocyclic Molecules. II Electronic Structure of Pyrazine with Particular Reference to Its n-π Transition, *J. Chem. Phys.*, **29**, 1170-1173 (1958); Semiempirical Calculation on the Electronic Structure of the Nitrogen-Containing Heterocyclic Molecules. III. Lower Triplet Levels of Pyrazine, *J. Chem. Phys.*, **32**, 619-620 (1960).

252. T. Anno, Semiempirical Calculation on the Electronic Structure of the Nitrogen-Containing Heterocyclic Molecules. IV. Electronic Structure of Pyridine, *J. Chem. Phys.*, **32**, 867-871 (1960).

253. L. Paoloni, Electronic Structure of s Tetrazine, *J. Chem. Phys.*, **25**, 1277 (1956); Studio della struttura elettronica della tetrazine simmetrica e della p-diamminotetrazina con il metodo degli orbitali molecolari antisimmetrizzati (ASMO), *Gazz. Chim. Ital.*, **87**, 313-328 (1957).

254. M. J. S. Dewar and L. Paoloni, The Electronic Structure of Melamine, *Trans. Faraday Soc.*, **53**, 261-271 (1957).

255. L. Paoloni, Nature of the Hydrogen Bond, *J. Chem. Phys.*, **30**, 1045-1058 (1959).

256. T. Bassani, E. Montaldi, and F. G. Fumi, Electronic States of Diatomic Molecules: the O_2^+ Molecular Ion, *Nuovo Cimento*, **4**, 893-901 (1956).

257. M. Yamazaki, Electronic Structure of Ferrocene, *J. Chem. Phys.*, **24**, 1260-1261 (1956).

258. M. Okuda, Electronic Structures and Electronic Spectra of p-Quinoid Compounds, *J. Chem. Phys.*, **25**, 1083-1084 (1956).

259. T. Morita, Hyperconjugation in the Semiempirical ASMO Method, *J. Chem. Phys.*, **27**, 1442 (1957); Self-Consistent Field Molecular Orbital Treatment of Benzenium Ion for a Simplified Model of Hyperconjugation, *Bull. Chem. Soc. Japan*, **33**, 1486-1492 (1960).
260. S. Carrà, S. Polezzo, and M. Simonetta, Momenti elettrici e distanze interatomiche delle azine, *Rend. Accad. Nazl. Lincei*, **23**, 428-433 (1957); G. Favini and S. Carrà, Struttura eletronica e velocità di reazione in derivati della piridina, *Gazz. Chim. Ital.*, **87**, 1367-1376 (1957); S. Carrà and S. Polezzo, Richerche sulla struttura eletronica nel pirrolo, *Gazz. Chim. Ital.*, **88**, 1103-1108 (1958).
261. M. Simonetta, G. Favini, and S. Carrà, A Molecular Orbital Treatment of the Vinyl Chloride Molecule, *Mol. Phys.*, **1**, 181-188 (1958).
262. S. Maeda, Some Studies of the Inductive Effect, *Bull. Chem. Soc. Japan*, **31**, 260-267 (1958).
263. H. Baba and S. Suzuki, Electronic Structure and Spectrum of Acetanilide, *J. Chem. Phys.*, **32**, 1706-1713 (1960).
264. D. W. Davies, Self-Consistent Molecular Orbital Calculations on π-Electron Systems. Part 1-The Electronic Spectrum of Borazine, *Trans. Faraday Soc.*, **56**, 1713-1718 (1960).
265. J. C. Patel and S. Basu, Electronic Spectra of Borazine, *Naturwissenschaften*, **47**, 302-303 (1960).
266. S. Nagakura, Intramolecular Charge-Transfer Absorption Spectra of Formamide and Acrolein, *Mol. Phys.*, **3**, 105-113 (1960); Ultra-Violet Absorption Spectra and π-Electron Structures of Nitromethane and the Nitromethyl Anion, *Mol. Phys.*, **3**, 152-162 (1960).
267. K. L. McEwen, Electronic Structures and Spectra of Nitromethane and Nitrogen Dioxide, *J. Chem. Phys.*, **32**, 1801-1814 (1960); Electronic Structures and Spectra of Some Nitrogen-Oxygen Compounds, *J. Chem. Phys.*, **34**, 547-555 (1961).
268. J. Serre, On the Electronic Structures of NO_2 and its Plane Dimer N_2O_4, *Mol. Phys.*, **4**, 269-270 (1961); R. Le Goff and J. Serre, Structures électroniques de NO_2 et de N_2O_4, *Theoret. Chim. Acta (Berl.)*, **1**, 66-82 (1962).
269. K. Inuzuka, Calculation on the Electronic States of the Acrolein Molecule by the Semi-Empirical Molecular Orbital Method, *Bull. Chem. Soc. Japan*, **34**, 6-8 (1961); π-Electronic Structure of Cinnamaldehyde, *Bull. Chem. Soc. Japan*, **34**, 1557-1560 (1961).
270. S. Bratož and S. Besnainou, Influence of the Molecular Environment on the Carbonyl Frequency-Electronic Calculation, *J. Chem. Phys.*, **34**, 1142-1148 (1961).
271. M. Klessinger and W. Lüttke, UV-Spektren und Konstellation α,β-ungesättigter Carbonylverbindungen, *Z. Elektrochem.*, **65**, 707 (1961).
272. J. E. Bloor and F. Peradejordi, Self-Consistent Field Molecular Orbital Calculations for Mono- and Disubstituted Benzenes, *Theoret. Chim. Acta. (Berl.)* **1**, 83-85 (1962).
273. H. C. Longuet-Higgins and J. N. Murrell, The Electronic Spectra of

Aromatic Molecules. V. The Interaction of Two Conjugated Systems, *Proc. Phys. Soc. (London)*, **A68**, 601-611 (1955).

274. K. Fukui, K. Morokuma, and T. Yonezawa, LCAO SCF Calculation on Anthracene and Reactivity Indices in SCF Method, *Bull. Chem. Soc. Japan*, **32**, 853-857 (1959); Localization Energy with Electronic Interaction, *Bull. Chem. Soc. Japan*, **32**, 1015-1019 (1959); see also R. K. Nesbet, Sur les relations entre les ênergies de localisation et les constantes de vitesse des rêactions de substitution, *J. Chim. Phys.*, **59**, 750-753 (1962).

275. J. R. Hoyland and L. Goodman, A Modification of Koopmans' Theorem for Conjugated Hydrocarbons, *J. Chem. Phys.*, **33**, 946-947 (1960); Charge Distributions in Positive Ions and Ionization Energies of Conjugated Hydrocarbons, *J. Chem. Phys.*, **36**, 12-20 (1962); Charge Distribution in Negative Ions and the Electron Affinities of Conjugated Hydrocarbons, *J. Chem. Phys.*, **36**, 21-24 (1962).

276. L. Goodman and H. Shull, Molecular Calculations. III. A Modification of the Naive Semiempirical MO Method, *J. Chem. Phys.*, **23**, 33-43 (1955).

277. K. Ruedenberg, Quantum Mechanics of Mobile Electrons in Conjugated Bond Systems. I. General Analysis in the Tight-Binding Formulation, *J. Chem. Phys.*, **34**, 1861-1877 (1961) (included in this volume); Quantum Mechanics of Mobile Electrons in Conjugated Bond Systems. II. Augmented Tight-Binding Formulation, *J. Chem. Phys.*, **34**, 1878-1883 (1961); Quantum Mechanics of Mobile Electrons in Conjugated Bond Systems. III. Topological Matrix as Generatrix of Bond Orders, *J. Chem. Phys.*, **34**, 1884-1891 (1961); Quantum Mechanics of Mobile Electrons in Conjugated Bond Systems. IV. Integral Evaluation, *J. Chem. Phys.*, **34**, 1892-1896 (1961); K. Ruedenberg and E. M. Layton, Jr., Quantum Mechanics of Mobile Electrons in Conjugated Bond Systems. V. Empirical Determination of Integrals between Carbon Atomic Orbitals from Experimental Data on Benzene, *J. Chem. Phys.*, **34**, 1897-1907 (1961); K. Ruedenberg, Quantum Mechanics of Mobile Electrons in Conjugated Bond Systems. VI. Theoretical Evaluation of Energy Contributions, *J. Chem. Phys.*, **34**, 1907-1913 (1961).

278. J. de Heer and R. Pauncz, Molecular Electronic Integrals for Cyclic Systems, *J. Mol. Spectr.*, **5**, 326-333 (1960); see also N. Bouman, Calculations of the Lower Excited Energy Levels of the Cyclic Polyenes, Radicals, and Ions, *J. Chem. Phys.*, **35**, 1661-1664 (1961).

279. A. L. Companion and F. O. Ellison, Calculation of the Dissociation Energy of NH by a Semiempirical Interpolative Method, *J. Chem. Phys.*, **32**, 1132-1133 (1960).

280. H. Kon, A Semi-Empirical Approach to the SCF Molecular Orbitals, *Bull. Chem. Soc. Japan*, **28**, 275-280 (1955) (included in this volume).

281. H. C. Longuet-Higgins and L. Salem, The Alternation of Bond Lengths in Large Conjugated Molecules, *Proc. Roy. Soc. (London)*, **A257**, 445-456 (1960).

282. J. N. Murrell and L. Salem, Energies of Excited Electronic States as Calculated with the Zero Differential Overlap Approximation, *J. Chem. Phys.*, **34**, 1914-1915 (1961).

283. L. Paoloni, Coulomb Repulsion Integrals (pp | pp) and Bonding Power of an Atom in a Given Valence State, *Nuovo Cimento*, **4**, 410-417 (1956).
284. R. D. Brown, Evaluation of Coulomb Repulsion Integrals from Spectroscopic Data, *Mol. Phys.*, **1**, 304-306 (1958).
285. A. Julg, Nouveau procédé de calcul semi-théorique des intégrales coulombiennes mono et dicentriques, *J. Chim. Phys.*, **55**, 413-418 (1958); Nouveau procédé de calcul semi-théorique des intégrales électroniques (suite), *J. Chim. Phys.*, **56**, 235-239 (1959).
286. C. Bessis and O. Chalvet, Sur la méthode de Pariser et Parr. L'obtention rapide des intégrales coulombiennes, *Compt. Rend.*, **251**, 2712-2714 (1960).
287. F. O. Ellison, Approximating Two-Electron Atomic Energies using Scaled Eigenfunctions: Semi-Empirical Coulomb Repulsion Integrals, *J. Chem. Phys.*, **37**, 1414-1417 (1962). See also F. O. Ellison and N. T. Huff, A New Method for Determining Semi-Empirical One-Center Coulomb Repulsion Integrals, *J. Chem. Phys.*, **38**, 2444-2447 (1963).
288. W. Kolos, Excitation Energies of Ethylene, *J. Chem. Phys.*, **27**, 591-592 (1957); Excitation Energies of Benzene, *J. Chem. Phys.*, **27**, 592 (1957); Electron Correlation in Molecules. I. The Ethylene Molecule, *Acta Phys. Polon.*, **16**, 257-266 (1957); Electron Correlation in Molecules. II. The Benzene Molecule, *Acta Phys. Polon.*, **16**, 267-278 (1957); On the One-Centre Interaction Integrals in the Molecular Orbital Method, *Acta Phys. Polon.*, **16**, 299-301 (1957).
289. A. Julg, Traitement L.C.A.O. amélioré des molécules conjuguées. I. Théorie générale. Application aux hydrocarbures, *J. Chim. Phys.*, **57**, 19-30 (1960); A. Julg and M. Bonnet, Traitement L.C.A.O. amélioré des molécules conjuguées. II. Application aux molécules contenant des héteroatoms: Exemple du groupement carbonyle, *J. Chim. Phys.*, **57**, 434-438 (1960).
290. A. Julg and P. Francois, Structure électronique de l'hexatriène (méthode L.C.A.O. améliorée), *J. Chim. Phys.*, **57**, 63 (1960); P. Francois and A. Julg, Structure électronique du fulvene: étude par la méthode L.C.A.O. améliorée, *J. Chim. Phys.*, **57**, 490-491 (1960); A. Julg and P. Carles, Structure électronique de l'ion iminium (méthode des combinaison linéaires d'orbitales atomiques améliorée), *Compt. Rend.*, **251**, 1782-1783 (1961); A. Julg and J. C. Donadini, Structure électronique du *trans*-et due *cis*-glyoxal (méthode des combinaisons linéaires des orbitales atomiques améliorée), *Compt. Rend.*, **252**, 1798-1799 (1961); A. Julg and M. Bonnet, Structure électronique de l'ion phénate (méthode L.C.A.O. améliorée), *J. Chim. Phys.*, **59**, 194 (1962); A. Julg and P. Francois, Structure électronique de l'azulene et du fulvène (méthode L.C.A.O. améliorée), *J. Chim. Phys.*, **59**, 339-341 (1962); A. Julg, P. Francois, and R. Mourre, Recherches sur la structure électronique du naphthalène par la méthode L.C.A.O. améliorée, *J. Chim. Phys.*, **59**, 363-366 (1962); A. Julg, Étude théorique du spectre d'absorption de l'ion tropylium,

J. Chim. Phys., **59**, 367-368 (1962); A. Julg and P. Francois, Recherches théoriques sur le déplacement des bandes d'absorption des hydrocarbures conjugués causé par des substituants saturés, *Compt. Rend.*, **254**, 3547-3548 (1962).
291. A. Julg, Un perfectionnement de la théorie des orbitales moléculaires: la méthode L.C.A.O. améliorée, *Tetrahedron*, **19**, Suppl. 2, 25-42 (1963).
292. M. J. S. Dewar and C. E. Wulfman, Pi-Electron Correlation in the Polyenes, *J. Chem. Phys.*, **29**, 158-161 (1958).
293. L. C. Snyder and R. G. Parr, Some Extraordinary Functions for Improving Calculations of Electronic Energies, *J. Chem. Phys.*, **28**, 1250-1251 (1958).
294. M. J. S. Dewar and N. L. Hojvat, The SPO (Split-p-Orbital) Method and Its Application to Ethylene, *J. Chem. Phys.*, **34**, 1232-1236 (1961).
295. L. C. Snyder and R. G. Parr, Extraordinary Basis Functions in Valence Theory, *J. Chem. Phys.*, **34**, 1661-1665 (1961); L. C. Snyder, One-Center Integrals of Extraordinary Functions, *J. Chem. Phys.*, **37**, 2986-2989 (1962).
296. M. J. S. Dewar and N. L. Hojvat, The s.p-o. (Split p-Orbital) Method. II. Further Definition and Application to Acetylene, *Proc. Roy. Soc. (London)*, **A264**, 431-444 (1961); M. J. S. Dewar and N. L. Sabelli, The Split p-Orbital (s.p.o.) Method. III. Relationship to Other M. O. Treatments and Application to Benzene, Butadiene, and Naphthalene, *J. Phys. Chem.* **66**, 2310-2316 (1962).
297. J. S. Griffith, Critique of the Method of the Split p-Orbital, *J. Chem. Phys.*, **36**, 1689 (1962); M. J. S. Dewar, The SPO Method; Reply to Dr. J. S. Griffith, *J. Chem. Phys.*, **36**, 1689-1690 (1962).
298. A. F. Saturno, H. W. Joy, and L. C. Snyder, Computations to Evaluate Dewar's Split p-Orbital (SPO) Method, *J. Chem. Phys.*, **38**, 2494-2499 (1963).
299. For an exception, see Ref. 41, second listing.
300. J. O. Hirschfelder and G. V. Nazaroff, Applicability of Approximate Quantum-Mechanical Wave Functions Having Discontinuities in their First Derivatives, *J. Chem. Phys.*, **34**, 1666-1670 (1961).
301. A. D. McLachlan, Hyperconjugation in the Electron Resonance Spectra of Free Radicals, *Mol. Phys.*, **1**, 233-240 (1958); T. H. Brown, D. H. Anderson, and H. S. Gutowsky, Spin Densities in Organic Free Radicals, *J. Chem. Phys.*, **33**, 720-726 (1960); H. H. Dearman and H. M. McConnell, Spin Densities in Several Odd Alternant Radicals, *J. Chem. Phys.*, **33**, 1877-1878 (1960); J. C. Schug, T. H. Brown, and M. Karplus, Spin Resonance Spectra of Substituted Aromatic Ions; Superposition Model, *J. Chem. Phys.*, **37**, 330-339 (1962).
302. W. T. Simpson, Modification of the Vector Model to Include a First-Order Nonorthogonality Correction, *J. Chem. Phys.*, **25**, 1124-1127 (1956).
303. C. Zauli, The Study of π-Electron States by the Valence-Bond Method, *J. Chem. Soc.*, **1960**, 2204-2209; A. Mangini and C. Zauli, Calculation of Some π-Electron States in Furan, Thiophen, and the Parent Hydrocarbon

Compound Using Valence-Bond Approximation, *J. Chem. Soc.*, **1960**, 2210-2217.
304. W. T. Simpson, Resonance Force Theory of Carotenoid Pigments, *J. Am. Chem. Soc.*, **77**, 6164-6168 (1955); M. R. Robin and W. T. Simpson, Assignment of Electronic Transitions in Azo Dye Prototypes, *J. Chem. Phys.*, **36**, 580-588 (1962).
305. W. T. Simpson, *Theories of Electrons in Molecules*, Prentice-Hall, Englewood Cliffs, N.J., 1962.
306. R. S. Berry, Conjugation and Polar Effects in Butadiene, *J. Chem. Phys.*, **30**, 936-941 (1959).
307. M. Sender and G. Berthier, Recherches théoriques sur des composés oxygénés. II. Le calcul des transitions électroniques du groupement carbonyle, *J. Chim. Phys.*, **56**, 946-954 (1959).
308. For example, K. Ruedenberg and R. G. Parr, A Mobile Electron Model for Aromatic Molecules, *J. Chem. Phys.*, **19**, 1268-1270 (1951).
309. N. S. Ham and K. Ruedenberg, Electron Interaction in the Free-Electron Network Model for Conjugated Systems. I. Theory, *J. Chem. Phys.*, **25**, 1-13 (1956); **29**, 237 (1958) (included in this volume); N. S. Ham and K. Ruedenberg, Electron Interaction in the Free-Electron Network Model for Conjugated Systems. II. Spectra of Aromatic Hydrocarbons, *J. Chem. Phys.*, **25**, 13-26 (1956).
310. N. S. Ham, Electronic Interaction in the Free-Electron Network Model for Conjugated Systems. III. Spectra of Hydrocarbons Other than Even Alternants, *J. Chem. Phys.*, **32**, 1445-1448 (1960).
311. S. Olszewski, Electron Interaction in the Free-Electron Model for Non-Branched Conjugated Systems, *Acta Phys. Polon.*, **14**, 419-431 (1955); Interaction Energy of Electronic Charges in a Very Thin Tube, *Nature*, **179**, 1296 (1957); On the Free-Electron Theory of Absorption Spectra of Some Linear Conjugated Systems, *Acta Phys. Polon.*, **16**, 211-276 (1957); Nuclear Charge Effect on the Free-Electron Model Energy States, *Acta Phys. Polon.*, **18**, 107-120 (1959); On the Coulomb and Exchange Operators in the Free-Electron Model, *Acta Phys. Polon.*, **18**, 121-132 (1959); Simplified Self-Consistent Field Equations with Correlations, *Phys. Rev.*, **121**, 42-45 (1961).
312. H. Labhart, FE Theory Including an Elastic σ Skeleton. I. Spectra and Bond Lengths in Long Polyenes, *J. Chem. Phys.*, **27**, 957-962 (1957); FE Theory Including an Elastic σ Skeleton. II. Changes of Molecule Dimensions due to Optical Excitation, *J. Chem. Phys.*, **27**, 963-965 (1957).
313. For example, J. A. Hoerni, Application of the Free-Electron Theory to Three-Dimensional Networks, *J. Chem. Phys.*, **34**, 508-513 (1961).
314. P. O. Löwdin, Quantum Theory of Many-Particle Systems. III. Extension of the Hartree-Fock Scheme to Include Degenerate Systems and Correlation Effects, *Phys. Rev.*, **97**, 1509-1520 (1955).
315. H. Yoshizumi and T. Itoh, Applications of the Alternant Molecular Orbital Method to Six- and Four-Electron Systems, *J. Chem. Phys.*, **23**, 412-413 (1955); T. Itoh and H. Yoshizumi, Application of the Alternant Orbital Method to Benzene, *J. Phys. Soc. Japan*, **10**, 201-207 (1955).

316. J. de Heer, A Refined Alternant Molecular Orbital Treatment of the Ground State of Benzene, *J. Phys. Chem.*, **66**, 2288-2293 (1962).
317. R. Pauncz, J. de Heer, and P. O. Löwdin, Studies on the Alternant Molecular Orbital Method. I. General Energy Expression for an Alternant System with Closed-Shell Structure. II. Application to Cyclic Systems, *J. Chem. Phys.*, **36**, 2247-2265 (1962); J. de Heer, Studies on the Alternant Molecular Orbital Method. III. A Many-Parameter Energy Expression for Systems with Closed-Shell Structure, *J. Chem. Phys.*, **37**, 2080-2083 (1962); R. Pauncz, Studies on the Alternant Molecular Orbital Method. IV. Generalization of the Method to States with Different Multiplicities, *J. Chem. Phys.*, **37**, 2739-2747 (1962); R. Pauncz, The Application of the Alternant Molecular Orbital Method to Aromatic Compounds, *Tetrahedron*, **19**, Suppl. 2, 43-50 (1963).
318. R. Lefebvre, H. H. Dearman, and H. M. McConnell, Spin Densities in Odd Alternant Hydrocarbon Radicals, *J. Chem. Phys.*, **32**, 176-181 (1960); H. H. Dearman and R. Lefebvre, Method of Alternant Orbitals for Allyl, *J. Chem. Phys.*, **34**, 72-73 (1961).
319. M. Karplus and G. K. Fraenkel, Theoretical Interpretation of Carbon-13 Hyperfine Interactions in Electron Spin Resonance Spectra, *J. Chem. Phys.*, **35**, 1312-1323 (1961).
320. For a first such model calculation on atoms, see E. T. Stewart, Partial Variational Calculations on π-Electron Systems: An Atomic Analogue, *Proc. Phys. Soc. (London)*, **75**, 138-141 (1960); for two such calculations on molecules, see H. Berthod, Étude de l'éthylène par la méthode du champ moléculaire self-consistent, *Compt. Rend.*, **249**, 1354-1355 (1959), and E. T. Stewart, The Scale Parameters in Non-Empirical Molecular-Orbital Calculations on σ-π Systems, *Proc. Phys. Soc. (London)*, **75**, 220-227 (1960).
321. J. Jacobs, The Effect of $3p\pi$ Electrons: Energy Levels of Ethylene, *Proc. Phys. Soc. (London)*, **A68**, 72-78 (1955).
322. K. Iguchi, The Lower Excited States and the Phosphorescent State of Diphenyl. II. Scheme of Modification of MO, *J. Phys. Soc. Japan*, **13**, 1186-1189 (1958). This paper considers $3p\pi$ mixing.
323. O. Sovers and W. Kauzmann, d-Hybridization of the Pi Bond in the $2p\pi_u$ State of H_2^+, *J. Chem. Phys.*, **35**, 652-655 (1961); Role of d-Hybridization in the Pi Molecular Orbitals of Unsaturated Hydrocarbons, *J. Chem. Phys.*, **38**, 813-824 (1963).
324. But see J. Higuchi, Electronic Structures of the Methyl Radical: Effect of 3s Atomic Orbital of Carbon, *J. Chem. Phys.*, **28**, 527-531 (1958); Isotropic Proton Hyperfine Interaction in the Methyl Radical, *J. Chem. Phys.*, **32**, 52-55 (1960).
325. L. Pauling, Kekulé and the Chemical Bond, *Theoret. Org. Chem., Papers Kekulé Symp., London*, **1958**, 1-8 (1959); see also pp. 137-138 of Ref. 12.
326. C. A. Coulson and L. J. Schaad, On the Approximation of Zero Differential Overlap, *J. Chem. Phys.*, **35**, 294-297 (1961).
327. G. Del Re and R. G. Parr, Toward an Improved Pi-Electron Theory,

Revs. Mod. Phys., **35**, 604-611 (1963); see also Ref. 277, 281, and 282.

328. W. T. Simpson, Formal Hückel Theory, *J. Chem. Phys.*, **28**, 972-974 (1958); W. D. Jones, Hückel Theory: An Effective Hamiltonian, *J. Chem. Phys.*, **31**, 1317-1319 (1959); see also Ref. 305.
329. H. Gotz and E. Heilbronner, Notiz über die Berechnung des längstwelligen π-π^*-Uberganges nach dem Verfahren von E. Hückel, *Helv. Chim. Acta*, **44**, 1365-1373 (1961).
330. J. Koutecký, J. Paldus, and R. Zahradník, Calculation of p-Band Positions of Aromatic Polycyclic Hydrocarbons by Limited Configuration Interaction Method, *J. Chem. Phys.*, **36**, 3129-3134 (1962).
331. K. Ruedenberg and E. L. Mehler, unpublished work. These authors relate Eq. (16-4) to the "interference" between atomic orbitals.
332. For example, J. C. Schug, T. H. Brown, and M. Karplus, Theory of the Spin and Charge Distribution in Aromatic Ion Radicals; Application to the Naphthalene Negative Ion, *J. Chem. Phys.*, **35**, 1873-1883 (1961).
333. H. H. Greenwood and T. H. J. Hayward, Properties of the Self-Consistent Field Treatment of Conjugated Molecules, *Mol. Phys.*, **3**, 495-509 (1960).
334. R. G. Parr, F. O. Ellison, and P. G. Lykos, Generalized Antisymmetrized Product Wave Functions for Atoms and Molecules, *J. Chem. Phys.*, **24**, 1106 (1956); for some misprints in this paper, see footnote 5 in Ref. 372.
335. T. Arai, New Approach to the Quantum-Mechanical Analysis of the Electronic Structures of Molecules. The Method of Deformed Atoms in Molecules, *J. Chem. Phys.*, **26**, 435-450 (1957).
336. A. C. Hurley, On the Method of Atoms in Molecules. II: An Intra-Atomic Correlation Correction, *Proc. Phys. Soc. (London)*, **A69**, 49-56 (1956).
337. F. O. Ellison, Some Applications of Semi-Empirical Valence Bond Theory to Small Molecules, *J. Phys. Chem.*, **66**, 2294-2299 (1962).
338. W. Moffitt and J. Scanlan, Some Calculations on the Ethylene Molecule, *Proc. Roy. Soc. (London)*, **A218**, 464-486 (1953).
339. W. Moffitt, The Electronic Structure of Conjugated Hydrocarbons, *Proc. Roy. Soc. (London)*, **A218**, 486-506 (1953).
340. W. Moffitt and J. Scanlan, Calculation of the Lower Excited Electronic Energy Levels of Cyclobutadiene and Benzene, *Proc. Roy. Soc. (London)*, **A220**, 530-541 (1953).
341. A. Pullman and H. Berthod, L'étude du butadiène par la méthode des atomes dans les molécules, *J. Chim. Phys.*, **52**, 771-774 (1955); R. S. Berry, Pi-Electron Structure of Butadiene, *J. Chem. Phys.*, **26**, 1660-1664 (1957).
342. D. Kastler, Théorie quantique de la molécule HF, *J. Chim. Phys.*, **50**, 556-572 (1953).
343. A. Rahman, Excitation Energies of Li_2-Molecule, *Physica*, **20**, 623-632 (1954).
344. R. Fieschi, Electronic States of Diatomic Molecules: The Lithium Molecule, *Nuovo Cimento*, **6**, 197-203 (1957).
345. K. Ohno, On the Electronic Structure of the BH Molecule, *J. Chem. Phys.*, **26**, 1754-1755 (1957).

346. K. Hijikata, Energy Levels of F_2 and F_2^+, *Revs. Mod. Phys.*, **32**, 445-446 (1960).
347. R. Pauncz, Investigation of a New Quantum-Mechanical Method of Approximation, *Acta Phys. Acad. Sci. Hung.*, **4**, 237-253 (1954).
348. C. W. Scherr, On the Use of Atomic Term Values in Molecular Wave Functions, *J. Chem. Phys.*, **22**, 149-150 (1954).
349. A. C. Hurley, On the Method of Atoms in Molecules, *Proc. Phys. Soc. (London)*, **A68**, 149-155 (1955); see also A. Batana and N. V. Cohan, On the Application of Two Simple Approaches of "Atoms in Molecules," *Proc. Phys. Soc. (London)*, **79**, 279-283 (1962).
350. T. Arai and T. Onishi, Correlation Energies in Atoms and Electron Affinities, *J. Chem. Phys.*, **26**, 70-74 (1957).
351. T. Arai, General Analysis of Various Methods of Atoms in Molecules, *Revs. Mod. Phys.*, **32**, 370-400 (1960).
352. T. Arai, Automatic Computation of Electronic Energies of Diatomic Molecules, *J. Phys. Soc. Japan*, **18**, 718-732 (1963).
353. T. Arai, Application of the Method of Deformed Atoms in Molecules to the Hydrogen Molecule, *J. Chem. Phys.*, **26**, 451-454 (1957).
354. T. Arai and M. Sakamoto, Application of the Method of Deformed Atoms in Molecules to the Li_2 Molecule, *J. Chem. Phys.*, **28**, 32-48 (1958); I. Mannari and T. Arai, Nuclear quadrupole coupling in the Li_2 Molecule, *J. Chem. Phys.*, **28**, 28-31 (1958).
355. A. C. Hurley, On the Method of Atoms in Molecules. III. The Ground State of Hydrogen Fluoride, *Proc. Phys. Soc. (London)*, **A69**, 301-309 (1956).
356. A. C. Hurley, The Binding Energy of the Nitrogen Molecule, *Proc. Phys. Soc. (London)*, **A69**, 767-776 (1956).
357. A. C. Hurley, On the Binding Energy of the Helium Hydride Ion, *Proc. Phys. Soc. (London)*, **A69**, 868-870 (1956).
358. A. C. Hurley, Role of Atomic Valence States in Molecular Energy Calculations, *J. Chem. Phys.*, **28**, 532-542 (1958).
359. A. C. Hurley, Electronic Structure of the First Row Hydrides BH, CH, NH, OH, and FH. I. Ground States, *Proc. Roy. Soc. (London)*, **A248**, 119-135 (1958); The Electronic Structure of the First Row Hydrides BH, CH, NH, OH, and FH. II. Excited States, *Proc. Roy. Soc. (London)*, **A249**, 402-413 (1959); Electronic Structure of the First Row Hydrides. III. Predissociation by Rotation in the $A^1\Pi$ State and the Dissociation Energy of BH, *Proc. Roy. Soc. (London)*, **A261**, 237-245 (1961).
360. A. C. Hurley, Electronic Structure and Binding Energy of Carbon Monoxide, *Revs. Mod. Phys.*, **32**, 400-411 (1960) (included in this volume).
361. A. C. Hurley and V. W. Maslen, Potential Curves for Doubly Positive Diatomic Ions, *J. Chem. Phys.*, **34**, 1919-1925 (1961).
362. M. Krauss and J. F. Wehner, Correlation Correction Study of CH, NH, and OH, *J. Chem. Phys.*, **29**, 1287-1297 (1958).
363. M. Krauss and B. J. Ransil, Some Intra-Atomic Correlation Correction

Studies, *J. Chem. Phys.*, **33**, 840-842 (1960); see also the paper by Krauss listed in Ref. 86.

364. E. T. Stewart "Atoms in Molecules." A Simple Approach, *Proc. Phys. Soc. (London)*, **75**, 402-411 (1960).

365. W. Bingel, A New Method for the Calculation of Electron Terms of Molecules, *Z. Naturforsch.*, **12a**, 59-70 (1957); C. E. Wulfman, Semiquantitative United Atom Treatment and the Shape of Triatomic Molecules, *J. Chem. Phys.*, **31**, 381-386 (1959); C. E. Reid, Electronic Energy of HF as a Power Series in the Internuclear Distance, *J. Chem. Phys.*, **36**, 1263-1264 (1962).

366. H. Preuss, The "Methods of Atoms in Molecules," *Z. Naturforsch.*, **12a**, 599-603 (1957); Method of Atom Association, *Z. Naturforsch.*, **13a**, 364-385 (1958).

367. For example, much of the new pi-electron theory is described earlier in these notes, or the following papers on simple molecules: J. T. Vanderslice, E. A. Mason, and E. R. Lippincott, Interactions between Ground-State Nitrogen Atoms and Molecules. The N-N, N-N_2, and N_2-N_2 Interactions, *J. Chem. Phys.*, **30**, 129-136 (1959); J. T. Vanderslice, E. A. Mason, and W. G. Maisch, Interactions between Oxygen and Nitrogen: O-N, O-N_2, and O_2-N_2, *J. Chem. Phys.*, **31**, 738-746 (1959); Interactions between Ground-State Oxygen Atoms and Molecules: O-O and O_2-O_2, *J. Chem. Phys.*, **32**, 515-524 (1960); J. T. Vanderslice and E. A. Mason, Interaction Energies for the H-H_2 and H_2-H_2 System, *J. Chem. Phys.*, **33**, 492-494 (1960); S. M. Read, J. T. Vanderslice, and F. Jenč, Potential Curves for BeH^+ and CH^+, *J. Chem. Phys.*, **37**, 205-206 (1962); F. O. Ellison, Semiempirical Valence Bond Calculations of Electronic Energies of CH, CH_2, CH_3, and CH_4, *J. Chem. Phys.*, **36**, 3112-3122 (1962); P. C. H. Jordan and H. C. Longuet-Higgins, The Lower Electronic Levels of the Radicals CH, CH_2, CH_3, NH, NH_2, BH, BH_2, and BH_3, *Mol. Phys.*, **5**, 121-138 (1962).

368. J. Braunstein and W. T. Simpson, Overlaps of Trial Functions for the Hydrogen Molecule. II. Covalent and Ionic Character of H_2, *J. Chem. Phys.*, **23**, 176-178 (1955).

369. H. Shull, The Nature of the Two-Electron Chemical Bond. I. The Homopolar Case, *J. Am. Chem. Soc.*, **82**, 1287-1295 (1960); The Nature of the Two-Electron Chemical Bond. II. The Heteropolar Case, *J. Phys. Chem.*, **66**, 2320-2324 (1962).

370. A. C. Hurley, J. E. Lennard-Jones, and J. A. Pople, The Molecular Orbital Theory of Chemical Valency. XVI. A Theory of Paired-Electrons in Polyatomic Molecules, *Proc. Roy. Soc. (London)*, **A220**, 446-455 (1953).

371. J. C. Slater, *Quart. Progr. Rept., No. 16*, Solid-State and Molecular Theory Group, Massachusetts Institute of Technology, Cambridge, April 15, 1955, pp. 5ff.

372. J. M. Parks and R. G. Parr, Theory of Separated Electron Pairs, *J. Chem. Phys.*, **28**, 335-345 (1958) (included in this volume).

373. R. McWeeny, The Density Matrix in Many-Electron Quantum Mechanics. I. Generalized Product Functions. Factorization and Physical Interpretation of the Density Matrices, *Proc. Roy. Soc. (London)*, **A253**, 242-259 (1960) (included in this volume); R. McWeeny and Y. Mizuno, The Density Matrix in Many-Electron Quantum Mechanics. II. Separation of Space and Spin Variables; Spin Coupling Problems, *Proc. Roy. Soc. (London)*, **A259**, 554-577 (1961); R. McWeeny, Some Recent Advances in Density Matrix Theory, *Revs. Mod. Phys.*, **32**, 335-369 (1960).

374. E. Kapuy, Calculation of the Energy Expression in Case of a Wave Function Built from Two-Electron Orbits, *Acta Phys. Acad. Sci. Hung.*, **9**, 237-239 (1958); Density Matrices for Wave Functions Built up from Non-Orthogonal Two-Electron Orbits, *Acta Phys. Acad. Sci. Hung.*, **10**, 125-127 (1959); An Exact Derivation of Orthogonal Two-Electron Orbitals, *Acta. Phys. Acad. Sci. Hung.*, **12**, 185-187 (1960); Configuration Interaction for Wave Functions Built up from Orthogonal Two-Electron Orbitals, *Acta Phys. Acad. Sci. Hung.*, **12**, 351-357 (1960); Derivation of Approximate Two-Electron Orbitals, *Acta Phys. Acad. Sci. Hung.*, **11**, 409-415 (1960); Configuration Interaction for Wave Functions Constructed from Orthogonal Many-Electron Group Orbitals, *Acta Phys. Acad. Sci. Hung.*, **13**, 345-352 (1961); Derivation of "Almost" Orthogonal Two-Electron Orbitals, *Acta Phys. Acad. Sci. Hung.*, **13**, 461-468 (1961).

375. T. L. Allen and H. Shull, The Chemical Bond in Molecular Quantum Mechanics, *J. Chem. Phys.*, **35**, 1644-1651 (1961) (included in this volume).

376. M. Karplus and D. M. Grant, A Criterion for Orbital Hybridization and Charge Distribution in Chemical Bonds, *Proc. Natl. Acad. Sci. U.S.*, **45**, 1269-1273 (1959).

377. R. McWeeny and K. A. Ohno, A Quantum-Mechanical Study of the Water Molecule, *Proc. Roy. Soc. (London)*, **A255**, 367-381 (1960).

378. M. Barfield and D. M. Grant, Valence-Bond Calculation of Geminal Spin-Spin Coupling Constants in Substituted Methanes, *J. Chem. Phys.*, **36**, 2054-2059 (1962).

379. T. L. Allen and H. Shull, Electron Pairs in the Beryllium Atom, *J. Phys. Chem.*, **66**, 2281-2283 (1962).

380. Calculations on beryllium and four-electron ions, by R. McWeeny and B. T. Sutcliffe, published in 1963, strengthen this optimistic view.

381. O. Sinanoğlu, Inter- and Intra-Atomic Correlation Energies and Theory of Core Polarization, *J. Chem. Phys.*, **33**, 1212-1226 (1960); O. Sinanoğlu and E. M. Mortensen, Core Polarization in Li_2, *J. Chem. Phys.*, **34**, 1078-1079 (1961).

382. O. Sinanoğlu, Perturbation Theory of Many-Electron Atoms and Molecules, *Phys. Rev.*, **122**, 493-499 (1961); Theory of Electron Correlation in Atoms and Molecules, *Proc. Roy. Soc. (London)*, **A260**, 379-392 (1961); On the Reduction of Many Electron Problems by Perturbation Theory, *J. Chem. Phys.*, **36**, 564-565 (1962).

383. O. Sinanoğlu, Many Electron Theory of Atoms and Molecules, *Proc. Natl. Acad. Sci. U.S.*, **47**, 1217-1226 (1961) (included in this volume).
384. O. Sinanoğlu, Many Electron Theory of Atoms and Molecules. I. Shells, Electron Pairs vs. Many-Electron Correlations, *J. Chem. Phys.*, **36**, 706-717 (1962).
385. O. Sinanoğlu, Many Electron Theory of Atoms and Molecules. II., *J. Chem. Phys.*, **36**, 3198-3208 (1962).
386. O. Sinanoğlu, Bonds and Intra-Molecular Forces, *J. Chem. Phys.*, **37**, 191-192 (1962).
387. O. Sinanoğlu, Some Aspects of the Quantum Theory of Atoms, Molecules, and Their Interactions, *J. Phys. Chem.*, **66**, 2283-2287 (1962).
388. D. Pines, *The Many-Body Problem*, Benjamin, New York, 1961, Many of the important papers are reprinted in this volume. See also R. Brout, Variational Methods and the Nuclear Many-Body Problem, *Phys. Rev.*, **111**, 1324-1333 (1958).
389. L. Szász, Atomic Many-Body Problem. I. General Theory of Correlated Wave Functions, *Phys. Rev.*, **126**, 169-181 (1962); Single Substitution Configurations, *J. Chem. Phys.*, **37**, 193-194 (1962).
390. But, see O. Sinanoğlu, Variation-Perturbation Method for Excited States, *Phys. Rev.*, **122**, 491-492 (1961).
391. O. Sinanoğlu, Relation of Perturbation Theory to Variation Method, *J. Chem. Phys.*, **34**, 1237-1240 (1961).
392. R. E. Stanton, Hellmann-Feynman Theorem and Correlation Energies, *J. Chem. Phys.*, **36**, 1298-1300 (1962).
393. R. McWeeny, On the Non-Orthogonality Problem for Interacting Electronic Systems, *Preprint No. 59*, Quantum Chemistry Group for Research in Atomic, Molecular and Solid-State Theory, Uppsala University, Uppsala, Sweden, January 15, 1961. See also Y. Ohrn and R. McWeeny, Justification of the One-Body Model for an Electron outside a "Core" with Applications to Lithium and Sodium, *Preprint No. 60*, same group, February 15, 1961.
394. C. C. J. Roothaan and R. S. Mulliken, Broken Bottlenecks and the Future of Molecular Quantum Mechanics, *Proc. Natl. Acad. Sci. U.S.*, **45**, 394-398 (1959).
395. J. C. Slater, *Quart. Progr. Rept. No. 43*, Solid-State and Molecular Theory Group, Massachusetts Institute of Technology, Cambridge, January 15, 1962, pp 8-9.
396. For typical recent papers see Ref. 10, and W. N. Asaad, Relativistic K Electron Wave Functions by the Variational Principle, *Proc. Phys. Soc. (London)*, **76**, 641-649 (1960); I. P. Grant, Relativistic Self-Consistent Fields, *Proc. Roy. Soc. (London)*, **A262**, 555-576 (1961); J. Ladik, The Ground State of the Hydrogen Molecule on the Basis of Relativistic Quantum Mechanics with the Aid of the Wang Wave Function, *Acta Phys. Acad. Sci. Hung.*, **13**, 124-136 (1961).
397. A. A. Frost, R. E. Kellogg, B. M. Gimarc, and J. D. Scargle, Least-

Squares Local-Energy Method for Molecular Energy Calculations Using Gauss Quadrature Points, *J. Chem. Phys.*, **35**, 827-831 (1961); R. E. Knight and C. W. Scherr, Helium Atom: A Fifth-Order Wavefunction, *J. Chem. Phys.*, **37**, 2503-2504 (1962).

398. E. R. Davidson, Natural Expansions of Exact Wave Functions. I. Method, *J. Chem. Phys.*, **37**, 577-581 (1962); E. R. Davidson and L. L. Jones, Natural Expansions of Exact Wavefunctions. II. The Hydrogen-Molecule Ground State, *J. Chem. Phys.*, **37**, 2966-2971 (1962).

399. J. W. Linnett, A. Modification of the Lewis-Langmuir Octet Rule, *J. Am. Chem. Soc.*, **83**, 2643-2653 (1961).

400. J. R. Platt, The Chemical Bond and the Distribution of Electrons in Molecules, *Handbuch der Physik*, **37/2** (1961), pp. 173-281; G. G. Hall and D. Rees, Scaling of the Platt Electrostatic Model of Diatomic Hydrides, *Mol. Phys.*, **5**, 279-284 (1962); see also C. E. Wulfman, Approximate Electronic Energy Surfaces from Cuspless Wave Functions, *J. Chem. Phys.*, **33**, 1567-1576 (1960).

401. E. B. Wilson, Jr., Four-Dimensional Electron Density Function, *J. Chem. Phys.*, **36**, 2232-2233 (1962); A. A. Frost, Three-Dimensional Electron Density Function, *J. Chem. Phys.*, **37**, 1147-1148 (1962).

402. L. Salem and E. B. Wilson, Jr., Reliability of the Hellmann-Feynman Theorem for Approximate Charge Densities, *J. Chem. Phys.*, **36**, 3421-3427 (1962); C. A. Coulson and A. C. Hurley, Comment on "Hellmann-Feynman Wave Functions," *J. Chem. Phys.*, **37**, 448-449 (1962).

403. J. Ballhausen, *Introduction to Ligand Field Theory*, McGraw-Hill, New York, 1962.

404. A. D. Liehr, Quantum Theory: An Essay on Higher-Order Vibronic Interactions, *Ann. Rev. Phys. Chem.*, **13**, 41-76 (1962); L. C. Snyder, A Simple Molecular Orbital Study of Aromatic Molecules and Ions Having Orbitally Degenerate Ground States, *J. Phys. Chem.*, **66**, 2299-2306 (1962).

405. R. S. Mulliken and W. B. Person, Donor-Acceptor Complexes, *Ann. Rev. Phys. Chem.*, **13**, 107-126 (1962).

406. J. Koutecký, A Contribution to the Molecular-Orbital Theory of Chemisorption, *Trans. Faraday Soc.*, **54**, 1038-1052 (1958).

407. A. Pullman and B. Pullman, Aspects de la structure électronique des acides nucléiques, *J. Chim. Phys.*, **58**, 904-913 (1961).

408. W. R. Thorsson, Quantum-Mechanical Transition-Complex Theory of Rearrangement Collisions, *J. Chem. Phys.*, **37**, 433-445 (1962).

409. For example, W. A. Yager, E. Wasserman, and R. M. R. Cramer, ESR Observation of $\Delta m = 1$ Transitions of Triplet States in Glasses, *J. Chem. Phys.*, **37**, 1148-1149 (1962); H. H. Claassen, H. Selig, and J. G. Malm, Xenon Tetrafluoride, *J. Am. Chem. Soc.*, **84**, 3593 (1962); A. Kuppermann and L. M. Raff, Determination of Electronic Energy Levels of Molecules by Low-Energy Electron Impact Spectroscopy, *J. Chem. Phys.*, **37**, 2497-2498 (1962).

410. M. Kasha, Commentary on the Scheme of the Semi-Empirical Molecular Orbital Calculation, *J. Chim. Phys.*, **58**, 914-915 (1961).
411. For example, J. R. Hoyland and F. W. Lampe, Single-Center Single-Determinant Calculation of the Relative Energies of CH_3^+, CH_3, CH_4, and CH_5^+. The Proton Affinity of Methane, *J. Chem. Phys.*, **37**, 1066-1068 (1962); D. M. Bishop, J. R. Hoyland, and R. G. Parr, Simple One-Center Calculation of Breathing Force Constants and Equilibrium Internuclear Distances for NH_3, H_2O, and HF, *Mol. Phys.*, **6**, 467-476 (1963); or M. Karplus and R. G. Parr, Approach to the Internal Rotation Problem, *J. Chem. Phys.*, **38**, 1547-1552 (1963), where some one-center ideas are applied to the problem of the origin of the barrier to internal rotation about single bonds.
412. G. Giacometti and G. Rigatti, Considerazioni sullo spettro elettronico del "Barilene," *Ricera Scientifica*, **30**, 1061-1064 (1960); J. Koutecký and J. Paldus, Quantum Chemical Study of Transannular Interaction. I. Model of (n,n) Paracyclophanes not Considering the Benzene Ring Distortion, *Collection Czechoslov. Chem. Commun.*, **27**, 599-618 (1962); J. Paldus and J. Koutecký, Quantum Chemical Study of Transannular Interaction. II. Interaction of Two Double Bonds in the Molecules of Germacrol and Bicyclo-[1,2,2]-Heptadiene-(2,5) and Interaction of Three Double Bonds in the Molecule of Barrelene, *Collection Czechoslov. Chem. Commun.*, **27**, 2139-2151 (1962).
413. L. C. Snyder and R. G. Parr, Problems in Perturbation Theory Calculation of Diamagnetic Susceptibility and Nuclear Magnetic Shielding in Molecules. Illustration with the Hydrogen Atom, *J. Chem. Phys.*, **34**, 837-842 (1961); A. Dalgarno, Perturbation Theory Calculations, *J. Chem. Phys.*, **35**, 1898 (1961); R. G. Parr and L. C. Snyder, Perturbation Theory Calculations, *J. Chem. Phys.*, **35**, 1898-1899 (1961); see also Ref. 54, and M. Karplus and H. J. Kolker, Magnetic Susceptibility of Diatomic Molecules, *J. Chem. Phys.*, **38**, 1263-1275 (1963).
414. C. Edmiston, Relation of Sinanoğlu's Theory of "Exact Pairs" to the First Iteration, beyond SCF, in Separated-Pair Theory, *J. Chem. Phys.*, **39**, 2394-2395 (1963); J. O. Hirschfelder, Removal of Electron-Electron Poles from Many-Electron Hamiltonians, *J. Chem. Phys.*, **39**, 3145-3146 (1963); M. Krauss and A. W. Weiss, Pair Correlations in Closed-Shell Systems, *J. Chem. Phys.*, **40**, 80-85 (1964).

Reprints

Reprinted from REVIEWS OF MODERN PHYSICS, Vol. 23, No. 2, pp. 69–89, April, 1951
Printed in U. S. A.

New Developments in Molecular Orbital Theory*†

C. C. J. ROOTHAAN
Department of Physics, University of Chicago, Chicago, Illinois

INTRODUCTION

FOR dealing with the problems of molecular quantum mechanics, two methods of approximation have been developed which are capable of handling many-electron systems. The Heitler-London-Pauling-Slater or valence bond (*VB*) method[1–3] originated from a chemical point of view. The atoms are considered as the material from which the molecule is built; accordingly, the molecular wave function is constructed from the wave functions of the individual atoms. The Hund-Mulliken or molecular orbital (*MO*) method[4] is an extension of the Bohr theory of electron configurations from atoms to molecules. Each electron is assigned to a one-electron wave function or molecular orbital, which is the quantum-mechanical analog of an electron orbit. Each of the two fundamentally so different approaches has its merits; so that chemical valence finds a more natural place in the *VB* method, whereas the *MO* method is simpler in describing the processes of excitation and ionization. However, when the two methods are carried through to their ultimately possible refinements, they lead to the same molecular wave function; from a mathematical point of view, they differ only in taking a different starting point as a first approximation.

It is the purpose of this paper to build a rigorous mathematical framework for the *MO* method. Much attention has been devoted to developing an unambiguous and consistent notation system, and to keeping it as simple as possible. We shall be concerned only with the electronic part of the molecular wave functions. For the processes of excitation and ionization the nuclei are considered to be kept in fixed positions; our calculations therefore apply to vertical excitation and ionization. The magnetic effects due to the spins and the orbital motions of the electrons will be neglected throughout this paper.

I. GENERAL CONSIDERATIONS

The basic concept of the *MO* method is to find approximate electronic wave functions for a molecule by assigning to each electron a one-electron wave function which in general extends over the whole molecule.

The simplest procedure is as follows: give each electron a wave function depending on the space coordinates of that electron only, called a ***molecular orbital*** (*MO*):

$$\varphi_i^\mu = \varphi_i(x^\mu, y^\mu, z^\mu), \tag{1}$$

where x^μ, y^μ, z^μ, or simply the superscript μ, stands for the coordinates of the μth electron; the subscript i labels the different *MO*'s.

The total N-electron wave function is now built up as a product of such *MO*'s; it has, however, to be borne in mind that the Pauli principle allows each *MO* to be occupied by not more than two electrons, that is, a particular *MO* φ_i may occur not more than twice in the product wave function.

The more refined procedure requires that we give each electron a wave function which in addition to the space coordinates also contains the spin coordinates of that electron, and which will be called a ***molecular spinorbital*** (*MSO*). Since we shall neglect magnetic effects, each *MSO* factors into a *MO* and a spin function:

$$\psi_\kappa^\mu = \psi_\kappa(x^\mu, y^\mu, z^\mu, s^\mu) = \varphi_{i(\kappa)}(x^\mu, y^\mu, z^\mu)\eta_\kappa(s^\mu) = \varphi_{i(\kappa)}{}^\mu\eta_\kappa{}^\mu, \tag{2}$$

where the superscript μ again stands for the (in this case space and spin) coordinates of the μth electron; and the subscripts κ and i label the different *MSO*'s and

* Part of a thesis, submitted to the Department of Physics of the University of Chicago, in partial fulfillment of the requirements for the degree of Ph.D.

† This work was assisted by the ONR under Task Order IX of Contract N6ori with the University of Chicago.

[1] W. Heitler and F. London, Z. Physik **44**, 455 (1927).

[2] L. Pauling and E. B. Wilson, *Introduction to Quantum Mechanics* (McGraw-Hill Book Company, Inc., New York, 1935), pp. 340–380.

[3] Eyring, Walter, and Kimball, *Quantum Chemistry* (John Wiley and Sons, Inc., New York, 1944), Chapters XII and XIII.

[4] F. Hund, Z. Physik **51**, 759 (1928); **73**, 1 (1931); etc.; R. S. Mulliken, Phys. Rev. **32**, 186 (1928); **32**, 761 (1928); **41**, 49 (1932); etc.

MO's, respectively. Since the same *MO*, when connected with different spin factors, may occur in different *MSO*'s, the labelings κ and i can in general not be identified. The spin factors can usually be taken to be

$$\eta_\kappa{}^\mu = \begin{cases} \alpha^\mu \\ \beta^\mu \end{cases}, \tag{3}$$

although occasionally it may be useful to use more general spin functions of the type

$$\eta_\kappa{}^\mu = c_{\kappa\alpha}\alpha^\mu + c_{\kappa\beta}\beta^\mu, \tag{4}$$

with

$$\bar{c}_{\kappa\alpha}c_{\kappa\alpha} + \bar{c}_{\kappa\beta}c_{\kappa\beta} = 1. \tag{5}$$

The total N-electron wave function is now built up as an *antisymmetrized product of MSO's* (*AP*):[5,6]

$$\Phi = (N!)^{\frac{1}{2}}\psi_1{}^{[1}\psi_2{}^2\cdots\psi_N{}^{N]} = (N!)^{-\frac{1}{2}}\begin{vmatrix} \psi_1{}^1 & \psi_2{}^1 & \cdots & \psi_N{}^1 \\ \psi_1{}^2 & \psi_2{}^2 & \cdots & \psi_N{}^2 \\ \cdots & \cdots & \cdots & \cdots \\ \psi_1{}^N & \psi_2{}^N & \cdots & \psi_N{}^N \end{vmatrix}. \tag{6}$$

The operation of "alternation,"[7] indicated by $[1\,2\cdots N]$, is defined by: take all the permutations of the sequence $1\,2\cdots N$, give the even ones a plus sign, the odd ones a minus sign, add them together and divide by their total number, $N!$.

We mention now two important rules which the operation of "alternation" obeys. The first one states that for an *AP* it makes no difference whether the alternation is carried out over the superscripts, the subscripts, or both:

$$\psi_1{}^{[1}\psi_2{}^2\cdots\psi_N{}^{N]} = \psi_{[1}{}^1\psi_2{}^2\cdots\psi_{N]}{}^N = \psi_{[1}{}^{[1}\psi_2{}^2\cdots\psi_{N]}{}^{N]}. \tag{7}$$

The proof of Eq. (7) is elementary, and will be omitted here. The second rule states that when $\mathfrak{M}$ is any operator which acts symmetrically on the superscripts of an *AP* (that is, which acts symmetrically on all the N electrons), then

$$\begin{aligned} &\int \bar{\psi}'_1{}^{[1}\bar{\psi}'_2{}^2\cdots\bar{\psi}'_N{}^{N]}\mathfrak{M}\psi_1{}^{[1}\psi_2{}^2\cdots\psi_N{}^{N]}d\tau \\ &\qquad = \int \bar{\psi}'_1{}^1\bar{\psi}'_2{}^2\cdots\bar{\psi}'_N{}^N\mathfrak{M}\psi_1{}^{[1}\psi_2{}^2\cdots\psi_N{}^{N]}d\tau \\ &\qquad = \int \bar{\psi}'_1{}^{[1}\bar{\psi}'_2{}^2\cdots\bar{\psi}'_N{}^{N]}\mathfrak{M}\psi_1{}^1\psi_2{}^2\cdots\psi_N{}^N d\tau, \end{aligned} \tag{8}$$

where $d\tau$ is the volume element of all configuration space, including the spins; $\psi_1, \psi_2, \cdots, \psi_N$ and $\psi'_1, \psi'_2, \cdots, \psi'_N$ can be any two sets of *MSO*'s. The proof of Eq. (8) can be found in most textbooks on quantum mechanics.[8]

A wave function of the type (6) has several interesting properties. We note first that all the *MSO*'s must be linearly independent, since otherwise the determinant vanishes identically. In particular, no two *MSO*'s can be the same; or, only two *MO*'s can be the same, namely, when the corresponding *MSO*'s have opposite spins. Therefore, the Pauli principle in the form given above is automatically satisfied.

It is often useful to collect the set of *MSO*'s ψ_κ in a row vector $\boldsymbol{\psi}$:[9]

$$\boldsymbol{\psi} = (\psi_1\,\psi_2\,\cdots\,\psi_N). \tag{9}$$

Let us subject the *MSO*'s ψ_κ to a linear transformation

$$\psi'_\kappa = \sum_\lambda \psi_\lambda A_{\lambda\kappa}, \tag{10}$$

or

$$\boldsymbol{\psi}' = \boldsymbol{\psi}\mathbf{A}, \tag{10'}$$

where $\mathbf{A}$ is a nonsingular $N\times N$ matrix. If we designate the *AP*'s built from $\boldsymbol{\psi}$ and $\boldsymbol{\psi}'$ by Φ and Φ', respectively, then

$$\Phi' = \Phi\ \mathrm{Det}(\mathbf{A}). \tag{11}$$

The proof of Eq. (11) is elementary and will be omitted here.

From Eq. (11) it is obvious that Φ' represents the same physical situation as Φ. Since the *MSO*'s ψ_κ are linearly independent, we can always choose the transformation matrix $\mathbf{A}$ such that the transformed *MSO*'s ψ'_κ form an orthonormal set (one way of achieving this is Schmidt's orthogonalization process).[10] Hence we may as well assume that our initial *MSO*'s are orthonormal, that is

$$\int \bar{\psi}_\kappa\psi_\lambda d\tau = \delta_{\kappa\lambda}, \tag{12}$$

where $d\tau$ is the one-electron volume element including spin. *We shall assume throughout this paper that Eq. (12) holds.*

[5] M. Goeppert-Mayer and A. L. Sklar, J. Chem. Phys. **6**, 645 (1938).

[6] M. Goeppert-Mayer and A. L. Sklar wrote down that part of the benzene wave function involving the six carbon π-electrons only, and antisymmetrized it. In the present paper we consider antisymmetrized wave functions involving *all* the electrons of the molecule.

[7] J. A. Schouten and D. Struik, *Einführung in die neueren Methoden der Differentialgeometrie* (P. Noordhoff, Groningen, 1935), Vol. I, p. 15.

[8] See, for instance, reference 3, p. 144.

[9] The reason for writing the set of *MSO*'s in a row vector rather than a column vector is the following. The wave functions ψ_κ are geometrical objects, which, under transformations, have the same properties as base vectors; e.g., the $2px$, $2py$, $2pz$ functions for an atom behave like the unit vectors $\mathbf{i}, \mathbf{j}, \mathbf{k}$. Since it is customary to write the components v_1, v_2, v_3 of an arbitrary vector $\mathbf{v}$ as a column vector, it follows that $\mathbf{i}, \mathbf{j}, \mathbf{k}$ should be written as a row vector, so that

$$\mathbf{v} = \mathbf{i}v_1 + \mathbf{j}v_2 + \mathbf{k}v_3 = (\mathbf{i}\,\mathbf{j}\,\mathbf{k})\begin{pmatrix} v_1 \\ v_2 \\ v_3 \end{pmatrix}.$$

[10] Schmidt's orthogonalization process is usually formulated for real functions. See for instance R. Courant and D. Hilbert, *Methoden der mathematischen Physik* (1931), Vol. I, p. 41. The generalization to the case of complex functions causes hardly any complication.

It follows then that in a given *AP* the *MSO*'s are determined except for a *unitary* transformation among themselves; for orthonormality of the *MSO*'s is preserved under a linear transformation if and only if the transformation is unitary. The transformation of the *AP*, Eq. (11), now reduces to multiplication by a phase factor, since the determinant of a unitary matrix is a number of modulus unity. The freedom which here still remains in the choice of the *MSO*'s will be used later (Secs. II and III).

Equation (12) also has the important implication that the *AP* given by (6) is now normalized, that is,

$$\int \bar{\Phi}\Phi d\tau = 1. \tag{13}$$

Equation (13) is easily proved by use of Eqs. (7) and (8). The totally symmetrical operator $\mathfrak{M}$ of Eq. (8) is here the identity operator. We have

$$\int \bar{\Phi}\Phi d\tau = N!\int \bar{\psi}_1{}^{[1}\bar{\psi}_2{}^2\cdots\bar{\psi}_N{}^{N]}\psi_1{}^{[1}\psi_2{}^2\cdots\psi_N{}^{N]}d\tau$$

$$= N!\int \bar{\psi}_1{}^1\bar{\psi}_2{}^2\cdots\bar{\psi}_N{}^N\psi_{[1}{}^1\psi_2{}^2\cdots\psi_{N]}{}^N d\tau.$$

In the last expression, only the first permutation, which leaves all the subscripts unchanged, gives a contribution; the other terms vanish because of Eq. (12). The first permutation appears with a factor $1/N!$, so that

$$\int \bar{\Phi}\Phi d\tau = \int \bar{\psi}_1{}^1\psi_1{}^1 d\tau^1 \int \bar{\psi}_2{}^2\psi_2{}^2 d\tau^2 \cdots \int \bar{\psi}_N{}^N\psi_N{}^N d\tau^N = 1,$$

each integral being unity because of Eq. (12).

When an electronic state is represented by the normalized wave function Φ, its electronic energy is given by

$$E = \int \bar{\Phi}\mathcal{H}\Phi d\tau, \tag{14}$$

where the *total hamiltonian operator* $\mathcal{H}$ is defined by

$$\mathcal{H} = \sum_{\mu} H^{\mu} + \tfrac{1}{2}e^2 \sum_{\mu\neq\nu} \frac{1}{r^{\mu\nu}};^{11} \tag{15}$$

H^{μ} is the hamiltonian operator for the μth electron moving in the field of the nuclei alone; this operator is linear and hermitian;[12] $r^{\mu\nu}$ is the distance between the μth and the νth electron.

An important concept in molecular orbital theory, as in the theory of atomic structure, is that of *electron shells*. An electron shell is defined as a set of *MSO*'s, in which (1) every *MO* occurs twice, namely, once with either spin, and (2) if there is degeneracy on account of the molecular symmetry, the *MO*'s in the shell form a complete degenerate set. Accordingly, a *closed-shell structure* refers to an *AP* which is made up of complete electron shells. Unlike atoms, most molecules in the *MO* method have a closed-shell structure in the ground state, the most notable exception being O_2; that is, there exists an *AP* of closed-shell type which is a reasonably good approximation to the exact wave function of the ground state; but only in so far as this approximation is reasonably good does it make sense to speak of a closed-shell structure. A more detailed discussion of electron-shells and closed-shell structure will be given in Sec. V.

For a closed-shell structure, the *MSO*'s are given by

$$\psi_{2i-1} = \varphi_i\alpha, \quad \psi_{2i} = \varphi_i\beta, \tag{16}$$

where the *MO*'s may be grouped in complete degenerate sets. We introduce for the *MO*'s and spin functions also a matrix notation:

$$\left.\begin{aligned} \boldsymbol{\phi} &= (\varphi_1\ \varphi_2 \cdots \varphi_n),\\ \mathbf{n} &= (\alpha\ \beta), \end{aligned}\right\} \tag{17}$$

so that we may write the row vector $\boldsymbol{\psi}$ representing the set of closed-shell *MSO*'s as the direct product[13] of $\boldsymbol{\phi}$ and $\mathbf{n}$:

$$\boldsymbol{\psi} = \boldsymbol{\phi}\times\mathbf{n}. \tag{16$'$}$$

If we apply Eq. (12) to the *MSO*'s ψ_{2i} and ψ_{2j} (or ψ_{2i-1} and ψ_{2j-1}), we can integrate over the spin factors, and obtain

$$\int \bar{\varphi}_i\varphi_j dv = \delta_{ij}, \tag{18}$$

so that the *MO*'s which make up a closed shell also form an orthonormal set.

The $2n$-electron *AP* for the closed-shell is now given by

$$\Phi = [(2n)!]^{\frac{1}{2}}(\varphi_1\alpha)^{[1}(\varphi_1\beta)^2\cdots(\varphi_n\alpha)^{2n-1}(\varphi_n\beta)^{2n]}. \tag{19}$$

Substituting this wave function into the expression for the energy (14), and using methods similar to those used for the proof of Eq. (13), we find for the energy of a

---

[11] The summation over μ runs from 1 to N; in the double summation, μ and ν run from 1 to N independently, except for the restriction $\mu\neq\nu$.

[12] An operator M is linear if

$$M(c\varphi + c'\varphi') = cM\varphi + c'M\varphi',$$

where φ and φ' are any two functions, and c and c' any two constants. The operator M is hermitian if

$$\int \bar{\varphi}M\varphi dv = \int \varphi\bar{M}\bar{\varphi}dv,$$

for any function φ. This is equivalent to the requirement

$$\int \bar{\varphi}'M\varphi dv = \int \varphi\bar{M}\bar{\varphi}'dv,$$

for any two functions φ and φ'.

[13] For the definition and properties of the direct product of matrices, see E. Wigner, *Gruppentheorie und ihre Anwendungen auf die Atomspektren* (Friedrich Vieweg and Sohn, Braunsweig, 1931), p. 19.

closed-shell AP

$$E=2\sum_i H_i+\sum_{ij}(2J_{ij}-K_{ij}),^{14} \tag{20}$$

where the *nuclear-field orbital energies* H_i, the *coulomb integrals* J_{ij}, and the *exchange integrals* K_{ij} are defined by

$$H_i=\bar{H}_i=\int \bar{\varphi}_i H\varphi_i dv, \tag{21}$$

$$\left.\begin{aligned} J_{ij}=J_{ji}=\bar{J}_{ij}=\bar{J}_{ji}=e^2\int\frac{\bar{\varphi}_i^{\mu}\bar{\varphi}_j^{\nu}\varphi_i^{\mu}\varphi_j^{\nu}}{r^{\mu\nu}}dv^{\mu\nu},\\ K_{ij}=K_{ji}=\bar{K}_{ij}=\bar{K}_{ji}=e^2\int\frac{\bar{\varphi}_i^{\mu}\bar{\varphi}_j^{\nu}\varphi_j^{\mu}\varphi_i^{\nu}}{r^{\mu\nu}}dv^{\mu\nu}.\end{aligned}\right\} \tag{22}$$

From Eqs. (22) it is clear that

$$K_{ii}=J_{ii}. \tag{23}$$

For later purposes it is useful to define the *coulomb operator* J_i and the *exchange operator* K_i by means of

$$\left.\begin{aligned} J_i^{\mu}\varphi^{\mu}=e^2\left(\int\frac{\bar{\varphi}_i^{\nu}\varphi_i^{\nu}}{r^{\mu\nu}}dv^{\nu}\right)\varphi^{\mu},\\ K_i^{\mu}\varphi^{\mu}=e^2\left(\int\frac{\bar{\varphi}_i^{\nu}\varphi^{\nu}}{r^{\mu\nu}}dv^{\nu}\right)\varphi_i^{\mu}.\end{aligned}\right\} \tag{24}$$

These operators are linear and hermitian.[12] J_i is just the potential energy operator which would arise from an electron distributed in space with a density $|\varphi_i|^2$; K_i, however, has no classical analog.

The coulomb and exchange integrals J_{ij} and K_{ij} can be expressed as one-electron integrals, making use of the coulomb and exchange operators J_i and K_i, namely:

$$\left.\begin{aligned} J_{ij}=\int\bar{\varphi}_iJ_j\varphi_i dv=\int\bar{\varphi}_jJ_i\varphi_j dv,\\ K_{ij}=\int\bar{\varphi}_iK_j\varphi_i dv=\int\bar{\varphi}_jK_i\varphi_j dv.\end{aligned}\right\} \tag{25}$$

In Appendix I the following useful relation is proved:

$$0\leqslant K_{ij}\leqslant J_{ij}\leqslant\tfrac{1}{2}(J_{ii}+J_{jj}); \tag{26}$$

the first equality sign holds if and only if φ_i and φ_j do not penetrate each other; the second one if and only if $\varphi_i=\varphi_j$; the third one if and only if $|\varphi_i|=|\varphi_j|$.

Equations (20), (21), and (22) will be the starting point for the theory to be developed in the next two sections. It is to be noted that the expression for the total electronic energy in terms of integrals over *MO*'s, Eq. (20), was derived on the basis that the *MO*'s form an orthonormal set. If non-orthonormal *MO*'s were used, a much more complicated expression for the total electronic energy would result; and a physical interpretation along the lines of footnote 14 would not apply in that case.

II. THE HARTREE-FOCK SELF-CONSISTENT FIELD METHOD FOR A CLOSED-SHELL GROUND-STATE[15]

We consider an AP which represents a closed-shell ground state; this AP is built up from n *MO*'s each of which may extend over the whole molecule. When looking for a good set of *MO*'s, one may of course find that there are a number among them each of which is concentrated mainly around a particular atom; such orbitals form the *inner shells* of the molecule, and do not play an essential role in the chemical binding. It is to be expected that these inner-shell *MO*'s are very nearly equal to the inner-shell atomic orbitals (*AO*'s) of the corresponding free atoms. This question will be discussed in more detail at the end of Sec. III.

We ask now for the best AP, that is, the AP for which the energy reaches its absolute minimum. We then have to minimize the expression (20) by varying the *MO*'s within the limits permitted by the requirement that they form an orthonormal set, as expressed by Eq. (18).

When each MO φ_i is varied by an infinitesimal amount $\delta\varphi_i$, the variation of the energy becomes

$$\begin{aligned}\delta E&=2\sum_i\delta H_i+\sum_{ij}(2\delta J_{ij}-\delta K_{ij})\\ &=2\sum_i\int(\delta\bar{\varphi}_i)H\varphi_i dv+\sum_{ij}\left\{\int(\delta\bar{\varphi}_i)(2J_j-K_j)\varphi_i dv\right.\\ &\quad\left.+\int(\delta\bar{\varphi}_j)(2J_i-K_i)\varphi_j dv\right\}+2\sum_i\int\bar{\varphi}_iH(\delta\varphi_i)dv\\ &\quad+\sum_{ij}\left\{\int\bar{\varphi}_i(2J_j-K_j)(\delta\varphi_i)dv\right.\\ &\quad\left.+\int\bar{\varphi}_j(2J_i-K_i)(\delta\varphi_j)dv\right\}.\end{aligned}$$

For each of the two expressions in curly brackets, the second term gives, after complete summation over i and j, the same result as the first term. If we also make use of the hermitian property of the operators H, J_i, K_i,

[14] The summations have to be taken over all the *MO*'s of the closed-shell ground state, that is, from 1 to n; in the double sum, the two summations have to be carried out independently. It is well known that Eq. (20) permits the following physical interpretation. The first sum represents the energy of all the electrons in the field of the nuclei alone (each *MO* is doubly occupied, hence the factor 2). The second sum represents the electronic interactions. The repulsion energy which one would expect classically between the four electrons in φ_i and φ_j, with probability densities $|\varphi_i|^2$ and $|\varphi_j|^2$, is $4J_{ij}+J_{ii}+J_{jj}$. This explains all the coulomb integrals in Eq. (20) except one J_{ii} for every i; but these cancel against the K_{ii}'s according to Eq. (23). The remaining exchange integrals K_{ij} for $i\neq j$ have no classical analog; they represent additional interactions between all the pairs of electrons with parallel spins.

[15] The treatment of Fock's equations presented in this chapter is an elaboration of the treatment given by F. Seitz, *The Modern Theory of Solids* (McGraw-Hill Book Company, Inc., New York, 1940), Chapters VI and VII, where also references to original papers can be found.

we may write

$$\delta E=2\sum_i\int(\delta\bar{\varphi}_i)\{H+\sum_j(2J_j-K_j)\}\varphi_i dv$$

$$+2\sum_i\int(\delta\varphi_i)\{\bar{H}+\sum_j(2\bar{J}_j-\bar{K}_j)\}\bar{\varphi}_i dv. \quad (27)$$

The *MO*'s φ_i always have to conform to the orthonormality conditions (18); the resulting restrictions on the variations $\delta\varphi_i$, obtained by varying (18), are as follows:

$$\int(\delta\bar{\varphi}_i)\varphi_j dv+\int(\delta\varphi_j)\bar{\varphi}_i dv=0. \quad (28)$$

In order that E may reach its absolute minimum, it is necessary, although not sufficient, that $\delta E=0$ for any choice of the $\delta\varphi_i$'s in (27) which is compatible with the restrictions (28). The standard mathematical technique to solve this problem is the method of the lagrangian multipliers:[16] multiply each Eq. (28) by a factor, to be determined later, called a lagrangian multiplier, and add them all to δE, to give, say, $\delta E'$. The problem of finding the conditions for $\delta E=0$ for any choice of the $\delta\varphi_i$'s compatible with (28) now becomes the problem of finding the conditions for $\delta E'=0$ for any choice of the $\delta\varphi_i$'s without restrictions, and at the same time of giving suitable values to the lagrangian multipliers. The conditions for $\delta E'=0$ are that in the integrands the coefficient of each individual $\delta\bar{\varphi}_i$ and $\delta\varphi_i$ vanishes.

We multiply each Eq. (28) by the lagrangian multiplier $-2\epsilon_{ji}$ and add the resulting equations together; we obtain

$$-2\sum_{ij}\epsilon_{ji}\int(\delta\bar{\varphi}_i)\varphi_j dv-2\sum_{ij}\epsilon_{ji}\int(\delta\varphi_j)\bar{\varphi}_i dv=0,$$

which can be written in the form

$$-2\sum_{ij}\epsilon_{ji}\int(\delta\bar{\varphi}_i)\varphi_j dv-2\sum_{ij}\epsilon_{ij}\int(\delta\varphi_i)\bar{\varphi}_j dv=0. \quad (29)$$

This we add now to δE of Eq. (27), and obtain

$$\delta E'=2\sum_i\int(\delta\bar{\varphi}_i)\times[\{H+\sum_j(2J_j-K_j)\}\varphi_i-\sum_j\varphi_j\epsilon_{ji}]dv$$

$$+2\sum_i\int(\delta\varphi_i)\times[\{\bar{H}+\sum_j(2\bar{J}_j-\bar{K}_j)\}\bar{\varphi}_i-\sum_j\bar{\varphi}_j\epsilon_{ij}]dv. \quad (30)$$

[16] For the method of lagrangian multipliers in the case of real functions see reference 10, pp. 140, 190. The generalization to the case of complex functions is obtained by considering each auxiliary condition and its conjugate complex as two independent auxiliary conditions; after their elimination by means of the lagrangian multipliers, the variation of every function and its conjugate complex are independent variations.

The conditions for $\delta E'=0$ are now given by

$$\left.\begin{aligned}\{H+\sum_j(2J_j-K_j)\}\varphi_i&=\sum_j\varphi_j\epsilon_{ji},\\ \{\bar{H}+\sum_j(2\bar{J}_j-\bar{K}_j)\}\bar{\varphi}_i&=\sum_j\bar{\varphi}_j\epsilon_{ij}.\end{aligned}\right\} \quad (31)$$

We show now that the lagrangian multipliers must be the elements of an hermitian matrix. Taking the complex conjugate of the second one of Eqs. (31), and subtracting it from the first one, we obtain

$$\sum_j\varphi_j(\epsilon_{ji}-\bar{\epsilon}_{ij})=0;$$

since the *MO*'s φ_j are linearly independent, it follows that

$$\epsilon_{ji}=\bar{\epsilon}_{ij}, \quad (32)$$

that is, the matrix $\boldsymbol{\epsilon}$ of which ϵ_{ij} are the elements is hermitian. A consequence of this is that the two Eqs. (31) become equivalent (each others conjugate complex).

We define now the *total electron interaction operator* G and the *Hartree-Fock hamiltonian operator* F by

$$G=\sum_i(2J_i-K_i), \quad (33)$$

$$F=H+G. \quad (34)$$

The Eqs. (31) which the best *MO*'s have to satisfy can now be written

$$F\varphi_i=\sum_j\varphi_j\epsilon_{ji}, \quad (35)$$

or, in matrix notation

$$F\boldsymbol{\phi}=\boldsymbol{\phi\epsilon}. \quad (35')$$

We now subject the set of *MO*'s $\boldsymbol{\phi}$ to a transformation by means of a unitary matrix $\mathbf{U}$ to give the new set $\boldsymbol{\phi}'$:

$$\boldsymbol{\phi}'=\boldsymbol{\phi}\mathbf{U}, \quad (36)$$

with

$$\mathbf{U}^*\mathbf{U}=\mathbf{E}.^{17} \quad (37)$$

If we also define the transformed matrix $\boldsymbol{\epsilon}'$ by

$$\boldsymbol{\epsilon}'=\mathbf{U}^*\boldsymbol{\epsilon}\mathbf{U}, \quad (38)$$

it follows from Eqs. (35'), (36), (37), and (38) that

$$F\boldsymbol{\phi}'=\boldsymbol{\phi}'\boldsymbol{\epsilon}'. \quad (39)$$

We note that Eq. (39) does not yet have the exact same form as Eq. (35'). Namely, the operator F, which is defined in terms of the *MO*'s φ_i (via G), operates in Eq. (35') on these *same MO*'s; this is not the case in Eq. (39). However, if we construct the operator F' which is defined in terms of the *MO*'s φ'_i just like F

[17] We write $\bar{\mathbf{U}}$ for the complex conjugate, $\mathbf{U}^\dagger$ for the transpose, and $\mathbf{U}^*$ for the hermitian conjugate of the matrix $\mathbf{U}$. The symbol $\mathbf{E}$ is used for the unit matrix.

was defined in terms of φ_i, we can show that $F'=F$. We have, namely,

$$\sum_i \bar{\varphi}'^{\mu}_i \varphi'^{\nu}_i = \sum_{jk} \bar{\varphi}_j^{\mu} \varphi_k^{\nu} \sum_i \bar{U}_{ji} U_{ki}$$

$$= \sum_{jk} \bar{\varphi}_j^{\mu} \varphi_k^{\nu} \delta_{jk} = \sum_j \bar{\varphi}_j^{\mu} \varphi_j^{\nu};$$

from this equality it follows easily that

$$\sum_i J'_i = \sum_i J_i, \quad \sum_i K'_i = \sum_i K_i,$$

hence also $G'=G$ and

$$F'=F. \tag{40}$$

As a result, we may rewrite Eq. (39) as

$$F'\boldsymbol{\phi}'=\boldsymbol{\phi}'\boldsymbol{\varepsilon}'. \tag{41}$$

We see thus that if the "best" *MO*'s φ_i are subjected to a unitary transformation, then the set of transformed *MO*'s φ'_i satisfies a set of equations of exactly the same form as did the *MO*'s φ_i. This result was to be expected. For the two sets of *MO*'s both give rise to the same $2n$-electron wave function (except for a phase factor); hence each of these two sets furnishes a set of "best" *MO*'s.

The explicit transformation of the *AP* Φ into Φ' is found as follows. From the two sets of *MO*'s $\boldsymbol{\phi}$ and $\boldsymbol{\phi}'$ we construct the two sets of *MSO*'s $\boldsymbol{\psi}$ and $\boldsymbol{\psi}'$ according to Eq. (16′):

$$\boldsymbol{\psi}=\boldsymbol{\phi}\times\mathbf{n}, \quad \boldsymbol{\psi}'=\boldsymbol{\phi}'\times\mathbf{n};$$

the transformation matrix for the *MSO*'s follows from

$$\boldsymbol{\psi}'=(\boldsymbol{\phi}\mathbf{U})\times\mathbf{n}=(\boldsymbol{\phi}\mathbf{U})\times(\mathbf{nE})=(\boldsymbol{\phi}\times\mathbf{n})(\mathbf{U}\times\mathbf{E})=\boldsymbol{\psi}(\mathbf{U}\times\mathbf{E}).$$

For the *AP* follows then according to Eq. (11):

$$\Phi'=\Phi \operatorname{Det}(\mathbf{U}\times\mathbf{E})=\Phi \operatorname{Det}^2(\mathbf{U}).^{18} \tag{42}$$

Since the matrix $\boldsymbol{\varepsilon}$ is hermitian, there exists a unitary matrix $\mathbf{U}$ so that $\boldsymbol{\varepsilon}'=\mathbf{U}^*\boldsymbol{\varepsilon}\mathbf{U}$ is a diagonal matrix with real diagonal elements. It is therefore no loss of generality if we assume that our set of "best" *MO*'s satisfies the simpler equations

$$F\varphi_i=\epsilon_i\varphi_i. \tag{43}$$

The set of Eqs. (43) is the most commonly known form of Fock's equations; they state that the *MO*'s which give the best *AP* are all eigenfunctions of the same hermitian operator F, which in turn is defined in terms of these *MO*'s.

Let us assume for the moment that we know the solutions of Fock's equations; that is, that we know a set of n *MO*'s which are eigenfunctions of the operator F calculated with this set. F being thus known, let us consider the equation

$$F\varphi=\epsilon\varphi. \tag{44}$$

Equation (44) is the eigenvalue problem of the hermitian operator F.

It is well known that the following statements hold for an hermitian operator:

(1) All the eigenvalues are real.

(2) Eigenfunctions belonging to different eigenvalues are mutually orthogonal.

(3) Any eigenfunction belonging to a particular eigenvalue is expressible as a linear combination of a number, say p, of linearly independent eigenfunctions; conversely, any linear combinations of these p functions is an eigenfunction. The number p is called the degree of degeneracy of the eigenvalue.

(4) The p linearly independent eigenfunctions belonging to a particular eigenvalue can always be chosen so as to form an orthonormal set; this set is determined except for a unitary transformation of these p functions among themselves (this reduces, in the case $p=1$, to multiplication by a phase factor).

(5) After orthonormalization has been carried out for every eigenvalue, all the eigenfunctions of the operator form together an orthonormal set.

Among the solutions ϵ, φ of Eq. (44) there will be, of course, the set ϵ_i, φ_i, $i=1, 2, \cdots, n$, which satisfied Eqs. (43). The n eigenvalues ϵ_i must evidently be the n *lowest* eigenvalues of the operator F, for if we did not take the n lowest eigenvalues, we would actually be solving Fock's equations for an excited state. This result is not surprising, for Fock's equations were obtained as necessary, but not sufficient, conditions that the energy may reach its absolute minimum. The n functions φ_i we shall call *ground-state orbitals*. The remaining eigenfunctions of F[19] we shall call excited orbitals; in order to avoid confusion, we shall label them with the indices a, b running up from $n+1$, $n+2, \cdots$; the labels i, j, k, l will be reserved exclusively for the ground-state orbitals. If we do not want to specify whether we refer to ground-state orbitals or excited orbitals, we shall use the labels f, g. The eigenvalues ϵ_f (that is, ϵ_i and ϵ_a) we shall call *Hartree-Fock orbital energies*.

The general procedure for solving Fock's equations is one of trial and error. One assumes a set of φ_i's, calculates the operator G (hence F), solves Eq. (44) for the n lowest eigenvalues, and compares the resulting φ_i's with the assumed ones. Guided by this comparison, a new set of φ_i's is chosen and the procedure is repeated. This process is then repeated until the assumed and

[18] Note that the dimensions of $\mathbf{U}$ and $\mathbf{E}$ are n and 2, respectively. If $\mathbf{A}^{(m)}$ and $\mathbf{B}^{(n)}$ are $m\times m$ and $n\times n$ matrices, then $\operatorname{Det}(\mathbf{A}^{(m)}\times\mathbf{B}^{(n)})=\operatorname{Det}^n(\mathbf{A}^{(m)})\operatorname{Det}^m(\mathbf{B}^{(n)})$; applying this to the present case, we obtain $\operatorname{Det}(\mathbf{U}\times\mathbf{E})=\operatorname{Det}^2(\mathbf{U})\operatorname{Det}^n(\mathbf{E})=\operatorname{Det}^2(\mathbf{U})$.

[19] Whether F has any eigenfunctions aside from the φ_i's, and if so, how many, is a question which is open to some doubt. Namely, if F operates on a function φ_i, it represents a $2n-1$ electron field; this is due to the fact that the operators J_i and K_i become equal when they operate on φ_i, as can be seen from Eqs. (24). However, if F operates on any function φ which is orthogonal to all the φ_i's, then F represents approximately a $2n$-electron field. This can be seen by observing that such a function φ cannot penetrate the closed-shell orbitals φ_i very much (φ has to be orthogonal to *all* the φ_i's); hence, the exchange operators K_i become in this case small compared with the coulomb operators J_i. The operators $2\Sigma_i J_i$ just represent the potential energy arising from the charge distribution of the closed shell. Such a function φ therefore roughly represents an *extra* electron moving at the outside of the molecule. It is known that negative ions do not exist for every molecule, and if so, only in a limited number of states. Therefore, it will depend upon the particular molecule whether F has any eigenfunctions aside from the φ_i's.

calculated φ_i's agree. This method for solving Fock's equations is called the Hartree-Fock *self-consistent field* (*SCF*) method.

III. THE *LCAO* SELF-CONSISTENT FIELD METHOD FOR A CLOSED-SHELL GROUND STATE

For atoms, the problem of solving Fock's equations is greatly simplified by the central symmetry. For molecules, because of the absence of central symmetry, the situation is less fortunate; solving Fock's equations for molecules is such a difficult mathematical problem that it is at present out of the question except perhaps for the simplest cases. We therefore have to use approximations to the best *MO*'s. In most *MO* treatments, the inner-shell electrons of the molecule are represented by free-atom *atomic orbitals* (*AO*'s); for each of the valence-shell *MO*'s one takes then a *linear combination of atomic orbitals* (*LCAO*). We generalize this procedure by representing *all* the electrons of the molecule by *LCAO MO*'s, as given by

$$\varphi_i=\sum_p \chi_p C_{pi}, \tag{45}$$

where the χ_p's are normalized *AO*'s, that is,

$$\int \bar{\chi}_p \chi_p dv=1. \tag{46}$$

It is useful to introduce the following matrix notation:

$$\left.\begin{aligned} \chi&=(\chi_1 \quad \chi_2 \quad \cdots \quad \chi_m), \\ \mathbf{c}_i&=\begin{bmatrix} C_{1i} \\ C_{2i} \\ \cdot \\ \cdot \\ \cdot \\ C_{mi} \end{bmatrix}, \\ \mathbf{C}&=\begin{bmatrix} C_{11} & C_{12} & \cdots & C_{1n} \\ C_{21} & C_{22} & \cdots & C_{2n} \\ \cdot & \cdot & \cdot & \cdot \\ C_{m1} & C_{m2} & \cdots & C_{mn} \end{bmatrix}. \end{aligned}\right\} \tag{47}$$

We may write then for Eq. (45)

$$\varphi_i=\chi\mathbf{c}_i \tag{45'}$$

and also

$$\boldsymbol{\phi}=\chi\mathbf{C}. \tag{45''}$$

Equation (45′) is useful if we consider a particular *MO* φ_i, and Eq. (45″) is useful if we consider the whole set of *MO*'s φ_i.

Note that the first index on C_{pi} refers to the *AO*'s and the second one to the *MO*'s. These two labelings have to be clearly distinguished. As general indices we shall use for the *MO*'s, as before, i, j, k, l; and for the *AO*'s p, q, r, s. As can be seen from (47), we denote the total number of *MO*'s and *AO*'s by n and m, respectively. Since we have to construct n linearly independent *MO*'s from m *AO*'s, we must have $m \geqslant n$.

An *AP* built from *LCAO MO*'s is obviously a less good approximation to the exact wave function than the *AP* built from the Hartree-Fock *MO*'s, since the latter one is the best possible *AP*. In order that an *LCAO AP* be not too bad, the *LCAO MO*'s should resemble the Hartree-Fock *MO*'s rather well. Whether this can be achieved depends on the choice of the *AO*'s from which the *MO*'s are to be built. In the past, mostly Slater-type *AO*'s have been used; for the screening constants, usually those values were taken which give the best results for the isolated atoms. It has been pointed out by several investigators[5,20] that these values might not give the best results for the *MO*'s. It is also quite possible that atomic Hartree-Fock orbitals will give considerably better results than Slater orbitals. These questions are far from settled, but will not be pursued any further here.

In the previous section we asked for the *best MO's* for a closed-shell ground state. In this section we shall ask for the *best LCAO MO's* for a closed-shell ground state, considering the *AO*'s as given functions. Apparently then, our problem is to find that set of coefficients C_{pi} for which the energy of the corresponding *AP* reaches its absolute minimum.

In the mathematical treatment of this problem it is useful to define for every one-electron operator M the corresponding matrix elements M_{pq} evaluated with the set of *AO*'s, and the matrix $\mathbf{M}$ which collects all the matrix elements M_{pq}:

$$\left.\begin{aligned} M_{pq}&=\int \bar{\chi}_p M \chi_q dv, \\ \mathbf{M}&=\begin{bmatrix} M_{11} & M_{12} & \cdots & M_{1m} \\ M_{21} & M_{22} & \cdots & M_{2m} \\ \cdot & \cdot & \cdot & \cdot \\ M_{m1} & M_{m2} & \cdots & M_{mm} \end{bmatrix}. \end{aligned}\right\} \tag{48}$$

If the operator M is hermitian,[12] then it is easy to show that the matrix $\mathbf{M}$ is also hermitian, that is, $\bar{M}_{pq}=M_{qp}$ or $\mathbf{M}^*=\mathbf{M}$. Corresponding to the (hermitian) operators H, J_i, K_i, G, and F we shall make use of the (hermitian) matrices $\mathbf{H}$, $\mathbf{J}_i$, $\mathbf{K}_i$, $\mathbf{G}$, and $\mathbf{F}$. The operators J_i, K_i, G, and F were defined in terms of the *MO*'s φ_i. In the previous section we assumed implicitly that they were defined in terms of the *best MO's*. Here we shall assume that they are defined in terms of the *best LCAO MO's*. There is one more (hermitian) matrix which will play a role in the following discussion, namely the matrix $\mathbf{S}$ the elements of which are the

[20] C. A. Coulson, Trans. Faraday Soc. **33**, 1479 (1937); R. S. Mulliken, J. Chem. Phys. **8**, 241 (1940).

overlap integrals

$$S_{pq}=\int \bar{\chi}_p\chi_q dv; \tag{49}$$

obviously, the matrix **S** corresponds to the identity operator. Equation (46) states that the diagonal elements of **S** are unity.

The usefulness of the matrix notation (48) is obvious from the following equation:

$$\int \bar{\varphi}_i M \varphi_j dv = \mathbf{c}^*{}_i \mathbf{M} \mathbf{c}_j.^{21} \tag{50}$$

Equation (50) follows easily by substituting for $\bar{\varphi}_i$ and φ_j in the integral the expression (45).

Again we may assume without loss of generality that the *LCAO MO*'s form an orthonormal set, for if they did not, we could subject them to a linear transformation which would make them orthonormal; after this transformation, they would still be *LCAO MO*'s. We shall assume then that the *LCAO MO*'s satisfy Eq. (18); in view of Eqs. (49) and (50) this leads to

$$\int \bar{\varphi}_i\varphi_j dv = \mathbf{c}^*{}_i\mathbf{S}\mathbf{c}_j=\delta_{ij}. \tag{51}$$

Similarly, we find from Eqs. (21), (25), and (50)

$$H_i=\mathbf{c}^*{}_i\mathbf{H}\mathbf{c}_i, \tag{52}$$

$$\left.\begin{aligned} J_{ij}&=\mathbf{c}^*{}_i\mathbf{J}_j\mathbf{c}_i=\mathbf{c}^*{}_j\mathbf{J}_i\mathbf{c}_j,\\ K_{ij}&=\mathbf{c}^*{}_i\mathbf{K}_j\mathbf{c}_i=\mathbf{c}^*{}_j\mathbf{K}_i\mathbf{c}_j.\end{aligned}\right\} \tag{53}$$

In order to determine the best *LCAO MO*'s we carry out a variational treatment analogous to that of the previous section. We vary the vectors $\mathbf{c}_i$ by infinitesimal amounts $\delta\mathbf{c}_i$ (that is, the coefficients C_{pi} are varied by the amounts δC_{pi}) and find for the variation of the energy

$$\begin{aligned}\delta E&=2\sum_i \delta H_i+\sum_{ij}(2\delta J_{ij}-\delta K_{ij})\\ &=2\sum_i(\delta\mathbf{c}^*{}_i)\mathbf{H}\mathbf{c}_i+\sum_{ij}\{(\delta\mathbf{c}^*{}_i)(2\mathbf{J}_j-\mathbf{K}_j)\mathbf{c}_i\\ &\quad+(\delta\mathbf{c}^*{}_j)(2\mathbf{J}_i-\mathbf{K}_i)\mathbf{c}_j\}+2\sum_i\mathbf{c}^*{}_i\mathbf{H}(\delta\mathbf{c}_i)\\ &\quad+\sum_{ij}\{\mathbf{c}^*{}_i(2\mathbf{J}_j-\mathbf{K}_j)(\delta\mathbf{c}_i)+\mathbf{c}^*{}_j(2\mathbf{J}_i-\mathbf{K}_i)(\delta\mathbf{c}_j)\};\end{aligned}$$

this expression we simplify, using methods similar to those of the previous section, to

$$\begin{aligned}\delta E&=2\sum_i(\delta\mathbf{c}^*{}_i)\{\mathbf{H}+\sum_j(2\mathbf{J}_j-\mathbf{K}_j)\}\mathbf{c}_i\\ &\quad+2\sum_i(\delta\mathbf{c}\dagger_i)\{\bar{\mathbf{H}}+\sum_j(2\bar{\mathbf{J}}_j-\bar{\mathbf{K}}_j)\}\bar{\mathbf{c}}_i,\end{aligned}$$

or

$$\delta E=2\sum_i(\delta\mathbf{c}^*{}_i)\mathbf{F}\mathbf{c}_i+2\sum_i(\delta\mathbf{c}\dagger_i)\bar{\mathbf{F}}\bar{\mathbf{c}}_i. \tag{54}$$

The restricting conditions for the $\delta\mathbf{c}_i$'s which result from the orthonormality of the *MO*'s are obtained by varying Eq. (51):

$$(\delta\mathbf{c}^*{}_i)\mathbf{S}\mathbf{c}_j+\mathbf{c}^*{}_i\mathbf{S}(\delta\mathbf{c}_j)=0,$$

or

$$(\delta\mathbf{c}^*{}_i)\mathbf{S}\mathbf{c}_j+(\delta\mathbf{c}\dagger_j)\bar{\mathbf{S}}\bar{\mathbf{c}}_i=0. \tag{55}$$

We multiply the restricting conditions (55) by the lagrangian multipliers $-2\epsilon_{ji}$ and add them together:

$$-2\sum_{ij}(\delta\mathbf{c}^*{}_i)\mathbf{S}\mathbf{c}_j\epsilon_{ji}-2\sum_{ij}(\delta\mathbf{c}\dagger_j)\bar{\mathbf{S}}\bar{\mathbf{c}}_i\epsilon_{ji}=0,$$

or

$$-2\sum_{ij}(\delta\mathbf{c}^*{}_i)\mathbf{S}\mathbf{c}_j\epsilon_{ji}-2\sum_{ij}(\delta\mathbf{c}\dagger_i)\bar{\mathbf{S}}\bar{\mathbf{c}}_j\epsilon_{ij}=0. \tag{56}$$

Adding (56) to the variation of the energy (54), we obtain

$$\begin{aligned}\delta E'&=2\sum_i(\delta\mathbf{c}^*{}_i)(\mathbf{F}\mathbf{c}_i-\sum_j\mathbf{S}\mathbf{c}_j\epsilon_{ji})\\ &\quad+2\sum_i(\delta\mathbf{c}\dagger_i)(\bar{\mathbf{F}}\bar{\mathbf{c}}_i-\sum_j\bar{\mathbf{S}}\bar{\mathbf{c}}_j\epsilon_{ij}).\end{aligned} \tag{57}$$

The condition for $\delta E'=0$ for any choice of the vectors $\delta\mathbf{c}_i$ and $\delta\bar{\mathbf{c}}_i$, or $\delta\mathbf{c}\dagger_i$ and $\delta\mathbf{c}^*{}_i$, are given by

$$\left.\begin{aligned}\mathbf{F}\mathbf{c}_i&=\sum_j\mathbf{S}\mathbf{c}_j\epsilon_{ji},\\ \bar{\mathbf{F}}\bar{\mathbf{c}}_i&=\sum_j\bar{\mathbf{S}}\bar{\mathbf{c}}_j\epsilon_{ij}.\end{aligned}\right\} \tag{58}$$

In the same way as in the previous section it follows that the ϵ_{ij}'s are the elements of an hermitian matrix $\boldsymbol{\varepsilon}$; the two equations (58) then become equivalent. We may write then for Eqs. (58)

$$\mathbf{FC}=\mathbf{SC}\boldsymbol{\varepsilon}. \tag{58'}$$

Again we may assume without loss of generality that $\boldsymbol{\varepsilon}$ is a diagonal matrix with real diagonal elements ϵ_i; Eq. (58′) then reduces to

$$\mathbf{F}\mathbf{c}_i=\epsilon_i\mathbf{S}\mathbf{c}_i. \tag{59}$$

Let us assume for the moment that the Eqs. (59) have been solved, that is, that we have found a set of n vectors $\mathbf{c}_i$ satisfying Eqs. (59), where the matrix **F** in turn is calculated from this set.

Now regarding **F** as a given matrix, that is, assuming **F** to be expressed explicitly in terms of the solutions of Eqs. (59), we consider the equation

$$\mathbf{F}\mathbf{c}=\epsilon\mathbf{S}\mathbf{c},\quad\text{or}\quad(\mathbf{F}-\epsilon\mathbf{S})\mathbf{c}=0. \tag{60}$$

[21] Note that $\mathbf{c}^*{}_i$ is the *row* vector $(\bar{C}_{1i}\,\bar{C}_{2i}\cdots\bar{C}_{mi})$; see also footnote 17.

In Eq. (60), **F** and **S** are given matrices, and **c** and ϵ are to be found. Equation (60) is a generalization of the eigenvalue equation for an hermitian matrix; Eq. (60) becomes identical with the latter if **S** is replaced by the unit matrix. It is convenient to use the standard terminology of eigenvalues and eigenvectors for the solutions of Eq. (60); however, these eigenvalues and eigenvectors depend on both matrices **F** and **S**.

In Appendix II it is shown that all the important statements about the eigenvalues and eigenvectors of an hermitian matrix still hold with slight modifications for the eigenvalues and eigenvectors of Eq. (60), namely:

(1) The eigenvalues of Eq. (60) are the roots of the secular equation

$$\mathrm{Det}(\mathbf{F}-\epsilon\mathbf{S})=0; \qquad (61)$$

this equation is always of the mth degree in ϵ (**F** and **S** are $m\times m$ matrices), and all its m roots are real.

(2) Eigenvectors belonging to different eigenvalues are mutually orthogonal.[22]

(3) Any eigenvector belonging to a p-fold root of Eq. (61) is expressible as a linear combination of p linearly independent eigenvectors; conversely, any linear combination of these p independent vectors is an eigenvector. The number p is called the degree of degeneracy of the eigenvalue.

(4) The p linearly independent eigenvectors belonging to a p-fold degenerate eigenvalue can always be chosen so as to form an orthonormal set;[22] this set is determined except for a unitary transformation of these p vectors among themselves (this reduces, in the case of $p=1$, to multiplication by a phase factor).

(5) After orthonormalization has been carried out for every eigenvalue, all the m eigenvectors form together an orthonormal set.

Among the solutions ϵ, **c** of Eq. (60) there will of course be the set ϵ_i, $\mathbf{c}_i$, $i=1, 2, \cdots, n$, which satisfied Eqs. (59). The n eigenvectors $\mathbf{c}_i$ must belong to the n lowest eigenvalues of Eq. (60), since otherwise we would be dealing with an excited state. The n eigenvectors $\mathbf{c}_i$ represent the n ground-state orbitals; the remaining eigenvectors $\mathbf{c}_{n+1}, \cdots, \mathbf{c}_m$ represent excited orbitals. As in the Hartree-Fock method, we label the ground-state orbitals with the indices $i, j, k, l=1, 2, \cdots, n$; the excited orbitals with $a, b=n+1, n+2, \cdots, m$; and either ground state or excited orbitals with $f, g=1, 2, \cdots, m$. We shall call the eigenvalues of Eq. (60) *LCAO orbital energies*.

The general procedure for solving Eqs. (59) is one of trial and error. One assumes a set of vectors $\mathbf{c}_i$, calculates the matrix **G** (hence **F**), solves (60) and (61) for the n lowest eigenvalues, and compares the resulting $\mathbf{c}_i$'s with the assumed ones. Guided by this comparison, a new set of $\mathbf{c}_i$'s is chosen and the outlined procedure repeated. This process is then continued until the assumed and calculated $\mathbf{c}_i$'s agree. Because of the great similarity with the Hartree-Fock self-consistent field method, we shall call this procedure the *LCAO self-consistent field method.*

[22] Ordinarily, orthogonality of the vectors $\mathbf{c}_i$ and $\mathbf{c}_j$ is expressed by $\mathbf{c}^*_i\mathbf{c}_j=0$. However, in the present case we define $\mathbf{c}_i$ and $\mathbf{c}_j$ to be orthogonal if $\mathbf{c}^*_i\mathbf{S}\mathbf{c}_j=0$. Another way of saying this is that **S** is the metric fundamental tensor in the space subtended by the vectors $\mathbf{c}_i$.

The Hartree-Fock and *LCAO* self-consistent field methods have been developed above along analogous lines and yielded analogous results. The most important difference between the two methods from a practical point of view is the amount of labor required for carrying out the numerical calculations; the *LCAO* method is usually feasible and rather straightforward, whereas the Hartree-Fock method is a very complicated mathematical problem.

For the set of *AO*'s from which the *MO*'s are to be constructed, we take all the *AO*'s of the corresponding free atoms that are occupied in their ground states, and those unoccupied ones which differ little in energy from the occupied ones. This means for the elements in the first row of the periodic table the 1*s*, 2*s*, and 2*p AO*'s. The 1*s AO*'s are then commonly called the *inner shell AO*'s. We assume that the *AO*'s on the same atom are orthonormal; this involves no loss of generality, since they can always first be orthogonalized.

We now expect that the matrices **S** and **F** have approximately the following block form

inner sh. atom *a*	0	0	0
0	inner sh. atom *b*	0	0
0	0	valence sh. atom *a*	interaction val. sh. *a* and *b*
0	0	interaction val. sh. *a* and *b*	valence sh. atom *b*

for a diatomic molecule; the generalization to the case of a polyatomic molecule is obvious. Then the linear equation (60) and the corresponding secular equation (61) break down into inner shell equations, one for each atom, and a valence shell equation involving all the atoms of the molecule. The inner shell equations should be nearly identical with the corresponding equations for the free atoms; then the *MO*'s and orbital energies of the *molecular* inner shells are practically identical with those of the *atomic* inner shells. There is one exception to this, namely, when there is degeneracy among the inner shell *AO*'s of the different atoms, which is to be expected in case the molecule has symmetry. Then the very small interaction between degenerate *AO*'s which is always present is sufficient to make the correct *MO*'s quite different from single atom *AO*'s although the *MO* energies are still practically identical with the *AO* energies. So, for instance, in N_2, if $1s$ and $1s'$ are the two inner shell *AO*'s of the two nitrogen atoms, the correct inner shell *MO*'s which can be built from these are $2^{-\frac{1}{2}}(1s+1s')$ and $2^{-\frac{1}{2}}(1s-1s')$; and in the more general case of a polyatomic molecule the inner shell *MO*'s are obtained by a unitary transformation of the inner shell *AO*'s. Since in the molecule *all* the inner shell *MO*'s will be occupied, we can subject these *MO*'s to a unitary transformation by which we obtain back the inner shell *AO*'s; the total *AP* wave function then undergoes a transformation of the type (42), i.e., remains unchanged. Hence it makes no difference in the total wave function whether the inner shell electrons are assigned to the *MO*'s or *AO*'s.

Frequently, Eqs. (60) and (61) can be reduced to still smaller blocks by using the molecular symmetry if present. These matters will be discussed in detail in Sec. VI.

We finally note that in all important problems of molecule formation the number of valence *AO*'s always exceeds the number of *LCAO MO*'s that is necessary for the ground state *AP*: $m \geqslant n$. This guarantees that Eqs. (60) and (61) have always more eigenvectors and eigenvalues than are required for the ground-state *AP*; consequently, by solving the ground-state problem we obtain always a number of "excited orbitals."

IV. IONIZATION AND EXCITATION ENERGIES

For the calculation of molecular ionization and excitation energies, we have to set up approximate wave functions for the ionized or excited states. In the two preceding sections, we obtained a fairly simple theoretical framework for the following reasons:

(1) We restricted ourselves to a single *AP* of the closed-shell type.
(2) In the process of minimizing the energy, the *AP* was not subjected to any auxiliary condition (keeping the *MO*'s orthonormal was no restriction on the *AP*).

For ionized and excited states, however, matters are more complicated because:

(1) Most ionized and excited states in which we are interested do not have a closed-shell structure.
(2) For an excited state, the approximate wave function must be kept orthogonal to the wave functions of all the states of lower energy, which is a rather unpleasant auxiliary condition when minimizing the energy. This difficulty disappears, however, if the excited state under consideration is the lowest state of its symmetry species, since the required orthogonality is then automatically achieved by permitting only functions of the correct symmetry species in the variational process.
(3) For many excited states a single *AP* is inadequate, and we have to use a *linear combination of AP's* (*LCAP*), or, in the case of a degenerate state, a set of several *LCAP*'s; this also complicates the procedure of minimizing the energy in an unpleasant way.

These mathematical complications, aside from making a treatment analogous to that of the previous sections rather cumbersome, necessitate in practically every type of case a special treatment. We shall therefore develop a less accurate but much simpler method, which can be used as an extension of both the Hartree-Fock and the *LCAO* method.

The basic idea of this procedure is that for an ionized or excited state we do not set up and solve the appropriate variational problem by which all the *MO*'s have to be determined for that particular state, but we make use of the *MO*'s which were found from the variational problem for the ground state.

The wave function of an ionized state is now obtained by omitting one (or several) of the *MO*'s from the ground-state *AP*.[23]

The wave function for the ground state is given by

$$ {}^1\Phi_0 = [(2n)!]^{-\frac{1}{2}} |(\varphi_1\alpha)^{(1)}(\varphi_1\beta)^{(2)}\cdots(\varphi_n\alpha)^{(2n-1)}(\varphi_n\beta)^{(2n)}|. \quad (19) $$

We shall use the shorthand notation

$$ {}^1\Phi_0 = (\varphi_1\alpha)(\varphi_1\beta)\cdots(\varphi_n\alpha)(\varphi_n\beta). \quad (62) $$

The left superscript on Φ refers to the multiplicity (that is, degree of spin degeneracy) of the electronic state; a closed-shell ground state is of course a singlet. The subscript 0 refers to the ground state.

The energy of the ground state is given by

$$ E({}^1\Phi_0) = 2\sum_i H_i + \sum_{ij} (2J_{ij} - K_{ij}). \quad (20) $$

Let us consider the singly ionized state obtained by removing either of the two electrons occupying the *MO* φ_i, and let us first assume that φ_i does not belong to a degenerate set. The wave functions for this ionized state are in our approximation

$$ {}^2\Phi_i = (\varphi_1\alpha)(\varphi_1\beta)\cdots(\varphi_{i-1}\alpha)(\varphi_{i-1}\beta) \times \begin{Bmatrix} (\varphi_i\alpha) \\ (\varphi_i\beta) \end{Bmatrix} (\varphi_{i+1}\alpha)(\varphi_{i+1}\beta)\cdots(\varphi_n\alpha)(\varphi_n\beta). \quad (63) $$

This state is a doublet, the two wave functions (63) having the energy[24]

$$ \begin{aligned} E({}^2\Phi_i) &= 2\sum_{j\neq i} H_j + H_i + \sum_{j,k\neq i} (2J_{jk} - K_{jk}) \\ &\quad + \sum_{j\neq i} (2J_{ij} - K_{ij}) = 2\sum_j H_j \\ &\quad + \sum_{jk} (2J_{jk} - K_{jk}) - H_i - \sum_j (2J_{ij} - K_{ij}) \\ &= E({}^1\Phi_0) - H_i - \sum_j (2J_{ij} - K_{ij}). \end{aligned} $$

Hence, in this approximation, the energy required for removing one of the electrons occupying φ_i is given by

$$ E({}^2\Phi_i) - E({}^1\Phi_0) = -H_i - \sum_j (2J_{ij} - K_{ij}). \quad (64) $$

Equation (64) can be written in a more convenient form. Namely, in the Hartree-Fock method (see Eqs. (21), (25), (33), and (43)) we have

$$ \begin{aligned} H_i + \sum_j (2J_{ji} - K_{ji}) &= \int \bar{\varphi}_i \{H + \sum_j (2J_j - K_j)\} \varphi_i dv \\ &= \int \bar{\varphi}_i F \varphi_i dv = \epsilon_i \int \bar{\varphi}_i \varphi_i dv = \epsilon_i. \end{aligned} $$

---

[23] The procedure of using the ground state *MO*'s gives rather good approximations for singly ionized states; see reference 25. For multiple ionization the approximation is expected to become progressively worse.

[24] This expression can easily be found by an argument analogous to that of footnote 14.

Similarly, in the *LCAO* method (see Eqs. (52), (53), and (59)) we have

$$H_i+\sum_j (2J_{ji}-K_{ji})=\mathbf{c}^*{}_i\{\mathbf{H}+\sum_j (2\mathbf{J}_j-\mathbf{K}_j)\}\mathbf{c}_i$$
$$=\mathbf{c}^*{}_i\mathbf{F}\mathbf{c}_i=\epsilon_i\mathbf{c}^*{}_i\mathbf{S}\mathbf{c}_i=\epsilon_i.$$

Hence in both the Hartree-Fock and *LCAO* method Eq. (64) reduces to

$$E(^2\Phi_i)-E(^1\Phi_0)=-\epsilon_i. \tag{65}$$

In Eq. (65), if $^1\Phi_0$ and $^2\Phi_i$ are built from Hartree-Fock *MO*'s, then ϵ_i is the Hartree-Fock orbital energy of φ_i; if $^1\Phi_0$ and $^2\Phi_i$ are built from *LCAO MO*'s, then ϵ_i is the *LCAO* orbital energy.

If $^1\Phi_0$ and $^2\Phi_i$ (Hartree-Fock or *LCAO*) are reasonable approximations to the exact wave functions of the corresponding electronic states, then the $-\epsilon_i$'s should give reasonable approximations to experimental ionization potentials; this justifies the name "orbital energy" for ϵ_i.

It is remarkable that the ionization potentials calculated by means of (65) are in closer agreement with experiment than those obtained by solving the variational problems for the energies of the ground state and the ionized state separately, and subtracting. The explanation for this was given by Mulliken.[25]

If in the ground-state *AP* the orbitals $\varphi_i, \cdots, \varphi_{i+p-1}$ form a p-fold degenerate set, then we can construct p pairs of wave functions of the type (63), corresponding to removal of an electron from any one of the *MO*'s $\varphi_i, \cdots, \varphi_{i+p-1}$. These wave functions all have the same energy. The ionized state therefore has, apart from spin duplicity, the same degeneracy as the orbitals $\varphi_i\cdots$, φ_{i+p-1}.

Ionized states obtained by removing two or more electrons can be treated in a fashion analogous to that for singly ionized states. The treatment, however, is more complicated. Since these states are also less important from an experimental point of view, we shall not develop the theory for them.

For the lowest excited states, approximate wave functions are obtained by replacing one *MSO* of the ground-state *AP* by a new *MSO*, which has to be orthogonal to all the ground-state *MSO*'s, in particular to the one which it replaces. Let us first assume that an electron is excited from φ_i to φ_a, and that neither φ_i nor φ_a is a member of a degenerate set. Then, corresponding to the different possibilities with respect to the spin functions, we have to consider simultaneously the four wave functions

$$(\varphi_1\alpha)(\varphi_1\beta)\cdots(\varphi_{i-1}\alpha)(\varphi_{i-1}\beta)\begin{Bmatrix}(\varphi_i\alpha)(\varphi_a\alpha)\\(\varphi_i\alpha)(\varphi_a\beta)\\(\varphi_i\beta)(\varphi_a\alpha)\\(\varphi_i\beta)(\varphi_a\beta)\end{Bmatrix}$$
$$\times(\varphi_{i+1}\alpha)(\varphi_{i+1}\beta)\cdots(\varphi_n\alpha)(\varphi_n\beta).$$

These four wave functions have to be considered on an equal footing; hence we should be prepared if necessary to take four new linear combinations of these four. Indeed, it is well known that they give rise to a singlet and a triplet state for which the correct linear combinations are given by

$$\left.\begin{aligned}
{}^1\Phi_{ia}&=(\varphi_1\alpha)\cdots(\varphi_{i-1}\beta)\\
&\quad\times\frac{1}{\sqrt{2}}\{(\varphi_i\alpha)(\varphi_a\beta)-(\varphi_i\beta)(\varphi_a\alpha)\}\\
&\quad\times(\varphi_{i+1}\alpha)\cdots(\varphi_n\beta),\\
{}^3\Phi_{ia}&=(\varphi_1\alpha)\cdots(\varphi_{i-1}\beta)\\
&\quad\times\begin{Bmatrix}(\varphi_i\alpha)(\varphi_a\alpha)\\ \frac{1}{\sqrt{2}}\{(\varphi_i\alpha)(\varphi_a\beta)+(\varphi_i\beta)(\varphi_a\alpha)\}\\(\varphi_i\beta)(\varphi_a\beta)\end{Bmatrix}\\
&\quad\times(\varphi_{i+1}\alpha)\cdots(\varphi_n\beta).
\end{aligned}\right\} \tag{66}$$

The three triplet wave functions have, of course, the same energy, since we neglect spin-orbit coupling throughout this paper; the triplet energy ordinarily is below the singlet energy (Hund's rule; see Eq. (67)). We note that in (66) the singlet wave function and one of the triplet wave functions are *LCAP*'s whereas the two other triplet wave functions are still *AP*'s.

In the case that *either* φ_i *or* φ_a is a member of a p-fold degenerate set, then there are p sets of wave functions of the type (66); all the singlets have the same energy, and the same holds for the triplets.

If *both* φ_i *and* φ_a belong to a degenerate set, then the wave functions of the type (66) are in general no longer good approximations to the exact wave functions. In this case wave functions of the relatively simple type (66) do not belong to particular symmetry species. We have then to form suitable linear combinations of wave functions of the type (66); there will result various *LCAP*'s of different symmetry species and different energies. An interesting example of this case is provided by the lowest excited states of benzene.[5]

This last case, where it is impossible to set up wave functions of correct symmetry of the type (66), is a special case of the frequently occurring phenomenon of *configurational mixing*. Namely, if there are two or more sets of wave functions of the type (66) which belong to the same symmetry species and whose energies lie fairly close together, then in general no such single set is acceptable; but an acceptable wave function can then be formed as a linear combination from these various sets. Such an acceptable *LCAP* consists then of a mixture of different orbital excitations, that is, a mixture of different configurations.

We now turn to the question of how an excited *MO* φ_a is to be determined. If we want to find the best wave function for the excitation from one particular *MO* φ_i to

[25] R. S. Mulliken, J. chim. phys. **46**, 497 (1949).

an excited MO φ_a, then we have to minimize the average energy of the singlet and triplet states given by (66). However, if we want to use the *same* MO φ_a to describe excitations from different MO's φ_i, then we have to minimize the average energy of all the singlets and triplets which are under consideration. It is obvious then that we obtain different equations for determining φ_a according to what use we want to make of φ_a. In addition, such equations for φ_a are rather complicated. It therefore seems hardly worth while to develop the theory for the most general cases.

However, in the $LCAO$ treatment of molecules of considerable symmetry the excited MO's are often uniquely determined by the symmetry and/or the required orthogonality of the excited MO to the ground-state MO's. In these cases the excited MO's are identical with the excited MO's which are found from the linear equations (60); the latter satisfy the requirements just mentioned of symmetry (see Sec. VI) and orthognality (see Sec. III). It seems likely that in those cases where the symmetry and orthogonality requirements do not uniquely determine the excited MO's, the excited MO's found from Eqs. (60) may still be acceptable for describing actual excitation processes.

The energies of the singlet and triplet states given by the wave functions (66) are[26]

$$E(^{1,3}\Phi_{ia}) = 2\sum_{j\neq i} H_j + H_i + H_a + \sum_{j,k\neq i} (2J_{jk} - K_{jk})$$
$$+\sum_{j\neq i} (2J_{ij} - K_{ij}) + \sum_{j\neq i} (2J_{ja} - K_{ja}) + J_{ia} \pm K_{ia},$$

where the plus sign holds for the singlet, and the minus sign for the triplet. This expression reduces to

$$E(^{1,3}\Phi_{ia}) = \sum_j H_j + \sum_{jk} (2J_{jk} - K_{jk}) - H_i$$
$$-\sum_j (2J_{ij} - K_{ij}) + H_a + \sum_j (2J_{ja} - K_{ja})$$
$$-(J_{ia} - K_{ia}) \pm K_{ia},$$

where the summations now are to be taken over all the ground-state MO's. Comparing this result with Eq. (20), we find for the excitation energy

$$E(^{1,3}\Phi_{ia}) - E(^1\Phi_0) = H_a + \sum_j (2J_{ja} - K_{ja})$$
$$-H_i - \sum_j (2J_{ij} - K_{ij}) - (J_{ia} - K_{ia}) \pm K_{ia}. \quad (67)$$

If we apply this result now to the $LCAO$ treatment of a case where φ_a is obtained from Eqs. (60), we obtain

$$E(^{1,3}\Phi_{ia}) - E(^1\Phi_0) = \epsilon_a - \epsilon_i - (J_{ia} - K_{ia}) \pm K_{ia}. \quad (68)$$

It is to be noted that the average excitation energy of the singlet and triplet is not what one would expect offhand, namely, $\epsilon_a - \epsilon_i$. The reason for this is that ϵ_i and ϵ_a are both eigenvalues of the self-consistent field $LCAO$ hamiltonian of the ground state; for the excited state the quantity ϵ_a can therefore not be expected to have the same meaning as the orbital energies ϵ_i of the ground-state MO's.[27]

[26] The case where both φ_i and φ_a are degenerate is here to be excluded.

V. THE USE OF MOLECULAR SYMMETRY IN THE HARTREE-FOCK TREATMENT OF A CLOSED-SHELL GROUND STATE[28]

When a molecule has symmetry, group theory provides a powerful means of simplifying the problem of finding the exact electronic wave functions. From the fact that the total hamiltonian operator $\mathcal{H}$ is invariant under any operation of the symmetry group of the molecule, it follows that the exact wave function(s) of a particular electronic state belong(s) to an irreducible representation of that symmetry group (or, in the very improbable case of accidental degeneracy, that the wave functions can always be chosen in sets so that each set belongs to an irreducible representation).[28] The wave functions of the various states can then be classified according to the *symmetry species* (irreducible representations) to which they belong.

It would be gratifying if it could be shown that for a molecule the best Hartree-Fock AP or the best $LCAO$ AP also necessarily belongs to a particular symmetry species.

That this is by no means obvious is known from self-consistent field calculations on atoms. Namely, in the Hartree-Fock method for many non-closed-shell atoms, and also in the older Hartree method (orbital product wave function instead of AP), the field for the individual electrons is not always spherically symmetrical. As a result, the self-consistent field AO's, and consequently also, the total wave functions, do not belong to irreducible representations of the group of rotations and reflections around the center of symmetry. Therefore, in most applications in the past the Hartree and Hartree-Fock methods have been modified so as to give the best AO's which do belong to irreducible representations.

In this section we shall prove the following facts for the Hartree-Fock method of a *closed-shell ground state;* these are equally valid for atoms using AO's and for molecules using MO's:

(1) The AP built from Hartree-Fock MO's in the manner described in Sec. II is a singlet and is totally symmetrical; that is, it belongs to the identical representation of both the spin and symmetry groups.
(2) The Hartree-Fock MO's used may be grouped in sets such that each set belongs to an irreducible representation of the symmetry group.
(3) The Hartree-Fock MO's can always be chosen real.

[27] The ϵ_a as defined here is called an "unacceptable" ϵ by Mulliken; he defines our $\epsilon_a - J_{ia} + K_{ia}$ as the orbital energy—see reference 25.

[28] The methods used in this capter follow closely those of E. Wigner, reference 13, especially Chapters XI and XII.

In Sec. I we have made implicit use of some of these facts; namely, in the definition of electron shells and of a closed-shell ground state, we assumed that degeneracy can occur for the *MO*'s, usually as a result of molecular symmetry. We therefore have to give a new definition of a closed-shell ground state which does not involve molecular symmetry.

We now define a molecule with a closed-shell ground state as a molecule for which there exists, aside from an arbitrary phase factor, only one *AP* which makes the energy reach its absolute minimum.

The first conclusion which can be drawn from this definition is that each *MO* in the closed-shell *AP* occurs twice, once with either spin function. For if this were not the case, then we could obtain by changing spin functions one or several other *AP*'s for which the energy would also reach its absolute minimum. An *AP* representing a closed-shell ground state therefore has the form (19).

Next we show that the *AP* belongs to a one-dimensional representation of the symmetry group. Let $f(\mathbf{r})$ be any function of $\mathbf{r}$, the radius vector of the point (x, y, z). We subject $\mathbf{r}$ to the transformation

$$\mathbf{r} \rightarrow \mathbf{r}' \equiv \mathcal{R}\mathbf{r}, \tag{69}$$

where $\mathcal{R}$ is the operator symbolizing the transformation. The transformed function $f'(\mathbf{r})$, or $\mathcal{R}f(\mathbf{r})$,[29] we define by means of

$$f'(\mathbf{r}') = f(\mathbf{r}), \tag{70}$$

which expresses that the function $f'(\mathbf{r})$, evaluated at the transformed point $\mathbf{r}'$, has the same numerical value as the function $f(\mathbf{r})$ at the untransformed point $\mathbf{r}$. Using the operator notation, we can write for Eq. (70)

$$\mathcal{R}f(\mathcal{R}\mathbf{r}) = f(\mathbf{r}),$$

or, if the operator $\mathcal{R}$ has an inverse,

$$\mathcal{R}f(\mathbf{r}) = f(\mathcal{R}^{-1}\mathbf{r}). \tag{71}$$

Equation (71) defines the function $\mathcal{R}f$ in terms of the function f.

It is easily established that the operator $\mathcal{R}$ is linear, that is

$$\mathcal{R}(af+bg) = a(\mathcal{R}f)+b(\mathcal{R}g), \tag{72}$$

and that

$$\mathcal{R}(fg) = (\mathcal{R}f)(\mathcal{R}g), \tag{73}$$

where f and g are any functions, and a and b any constants. The correctness of Eqs. (72) and (73) is easily seen by applying the definition (70) to both sides of the equations.

Let $\Phi(\mathbf{r})$ be the normalized *AP* representing the closed-shell ground state, where $\mathbf{r}$ now stands as an abbreviation for all the space coordinates of the $2n$ electrons; then

$$\int \bar{\Phi}(\mathbf{r})\Phi(\mathbf{r})d\tau = 1, \tag{74}$$

$$\int \bar{\Phi}(\mathbf{r})\mathcal{H}\Phi(\mathbf{r})d\tau = E_{\min} \tag{75}$$

Now let $\mathcal{R}$ be any operation of the symmetry group of the molecule; this is expressed by[28]

$$\mathcal{H}\mathcal{R} = \mathcal{R}\mathcal{H}. \tag{76}$$

Performing in Eqs. (74) and (75) the operation $\mathcal{R}^{-1}$ under the integral signs on the *integration variables* obviously does not change the values of these integrals. Since $\mathcal{R}^{-1}$ effects an orthogonal transformation on the coordinates of the electrons, the volume element $d\tau$ remains unchanged. Hence we find

$$1 = \int \bar{\Phi}(\mathcal{R}^{-1}\mathbf{r})\Phi(\mathcal{R}^{-1}\mathbf{r})d\tau = \int \overline{\mathcal{R}\Phi}(\mathbf{r})\mathcal{R}\Phi(\mathbf{r})d\tau,$$

$$E_{\min} = \int \bar{\Phi}(\mathcal{R}^{-1}\mathbf{r})\mathcal{H}\Phi(\mathcal{R}^{-1}\mathbf{r})d\tau$$

$$= \int \overline{\mathcal{R}\Phi}(\mathbf{r})\mathcal{R}\mathcal{H}\Phi(\mathbf{r})d\tau = \int \overline{\mathcal{R}\Phi}(\mathbf{r})\mathcal{H}\mathcal{R}\Phi(\mathbf{r})d\tau.$$[30]

We see thus that the transformed wave function $\mathcal{R}\Phi$ is also normalized and minimizes the energy. *Since it was assumed that there is only one AP which minimizes the energy*, $\mathcal{R}\Phi$ can differ from Φ only by a phase factor:

$$\mathcal{R}\Phi = c_{\mathcal{R}}\Phi, \quad \bar{c}_{\mathcal{R}}c_{\mathcal{R}} = 1. \tag{77}$$

For any two successive operations of the group we have

$$c_{\mathcal{S}\mathcal{R}}\Phi = \mathcal{S}\mathcal{R}\Phi = \mathcal{S}c_{\mathcal{R}}\Phi = c_{\mathcal{R}}\mathcal{S}\Phi = c_{\mathcal{R}}c_{\mathcal{S}}\Phi = c_{\mathcal{S}}c_{\mathcal{R}}\Phi,$$

where the third equality sign holds because of (72). we now have the result

$$c_{\mathcal{S}\mathcal{R}} = c_{\mathcal{S}}c_{\mathcal{R}}; \tag{78}$$

so that the numbers $c_{\mathcal{R}}$ furnish a one-dimensional representation of the symmetry group. We shall see presently that this representation has to be the identical representation, that is, $c_{\mathcal{R}} = 1$ for every $\mathcal{R}$.

We show now that the Hartree-Fock *MO*'s furnish a representation of the symmetry group. Writing out Eq. (77) in terms of *MO*'s, and using Eqs. (72) and (73), we obtain

$$(\mathcal{R}\varphi_1\alpha)^{[1}\cdots(\mathcal{R}\varphi_n\alpha)^{n}(\mathcal{R}\varphi_1\beta)^{n+1}\cdots(\mathcal{R}\varphi_n\beta)^{2n]}$$
$$= c_{\mathcal{R}}(\varphi_1\alpha)^{[1}\cdots(\varphi_n\alpha)^{n}(\varphi_1\beta)^{n+1}\cdots(\varphi_n\beta)^{2n]}. \tag{79}$$

Now the orthonormal set of functions φ_i, $i=1, 2, \cdots, n$ can always be supplemented by additional func-

[29] Note that $\mathcal{R}f$ is used as the symbol for a function of $\mathbf{r}$ just as f is used.

[30] Note that $\mathcal{H}\Phi$ is treated as *one* function symbol like $\mathcal{R}\Phi$. Then from (71) and (76) follows $\mathcal{H}\Phi(\mathcal{R}^{-1}\mathbf{r}) = \mathcal{R}\mathcal{H}\Phi(\mathbf{r}) = \mathcal{H}\mathcal{R}\Phi(\mathbf{r})$.

tions φ_a, $a=n+1, n+2, \cdots$ in such a way that the set φ_f, $f=1, 2, \cdots, n, n+1, n+2, \cdots$ is a complete orthonormal set. Then any one-electron function can be developed in terms of this set. We develop the function $\mathcal{R}\varphi_i$:

$$\mathcal{R}\varphi_i=\sum_{f=1}^{\infty} \varphi_f U_{fi}, \quad i=1, 2, \cdots, n, \tag{80}$$

where the coefficients U_{fi} are to be determined. Inserting (80) into the left side of Eq. (79), we obtain

$$\sum_{f_1\cdots f_{2n}} U_{f_11}\cdots U_{f_nn}U_{f_{n+1}1}\cdots U_{f_{2n}n}(\varphi_{f_1}\alpha)^{[1}\cdots(\varphi_{f_n}\alpha)^n(\varphi_{f_{n+1}}\beta)^{n+1}\cdots(\varphi_{f_{2n}}\beta)^{2n]}$$
$$=c_{\mathcal{R}}(\varphi_1\alpha)^{[1}\cdots(\varphi_n\alpha)^n(\varphi_1\beta)^{n+1}\cdots(\varphi_n\beta)^{2n]}. \tag{81}$$

Equation (81) must be an identity. The left side is seen to be a sum over AP's, while the right side is a single AP. The AP's which represent different spin-orbital configurations are all linearly independent. Hence, upon expansion of the summation in the left side of Eq. (81), we can put the coefficient of the ground-state AP equal to $c_{\mathcal{R}}$, whereas the coefficients of all the other configurations have to vanish. The ground-state AP occurs whenever $f_1, \cdots, f_n$, and $f_{n+1}, \cdots, f_{2n}$ are permutations of $1, \cdots, n$. It is easily seen that the coefficients of all these terms add up to

$$\begin{vmatrix} U_{11} & \cdots & U_{1n} \\ \cdot & \cdot & \cdot \\ \cdot & \cdot & \cdot \\ U_{n1} & \cdots & U_{nn} \end{vmatrix}^2.$$

Similarly, for the configuration

$$(\varphi_1\alpha)^{[1}\cdots(\varphi_{i-1}\alpha)^{i-1}(\varphi_a\alpha)^i(\varphi_{i+1}\alpha)^{i+1}\cdots(\varphi_n\alpha)^n(\varphi_1\beta)^{n+1}\cdots(\varphi_n\beta)^{2n]},$$

where $a>n$, the coefficient is found to be

$$\begin{vmatrix} U_{11} & \cdots & U_{1n} \\ \cdot & \cdot & \cdot \\ U_{i-1,1} & \cdots & U_{i-1,n} \\ U_{a1} & \cdots & U_{an} \\ U_{i+1,1} & \cdots & U_{i+1,n} \\ \cdot & \cdot & \cdot \\ U_{n1} & \cdots & U_{nn} \end{vmatrix} \times \begin{vmatrix} U_{11} & \cdots & U_{1n} \\ \cdot & \cdot & \cdot \\ \cdot & \cdot & \cdot \\ \cdot & \cdot & \cdot \\ U_{n1} & \cdots & U_{nn} \end{vmatrix}.$$

Hence, we find

$$\mathrm{Det}^2(\mathbf{U})=c_{\mathcal{R}}, \tag{82}$$

$$\mathrm{Det}(\mathbf{U})\sum_{j=1}^{n} U_{aj}\,\mathrm{cofactor}(U_{ij})=0, \tag{83}$$

where $\mathbf{U}$ is an abbreviation for the matrix

$$\begin{pmatrix} U_{11} & \cdots & U_{1n} \\ \cdot & \cdot & \cdot \\ \cdot & \cdot & \cdot \\ U_{n1} & \cdots & U_{nn} \end{pmatrix}.$$

We multiply Eq. (83) by U_{ik}, and sum over i; the result is

$$0=\mathrm{Det}(\mathbf{U})\sum_{i,j=1}^{n} U_{ik}U_{aj}\,\mathrm{cofactor}(U_{ij})$$
$$=\mathrm{Det}(\mathbf{U})\sum_{j=1}^{n} U_{aj}\sum_{i=1}^{n} U_{ik}\,\mathrm{cofactor}(U_{ij})$$
$$=\mathrm{Det}^2(\mathbf{U})\sum_{j=1}^{n} U_{aj}\delta_{kj}=\mathrm{Det}^2(\mathbf{U})U_{ak}=c_{\mathcal{R}}U_{ak};$$

and since $c_{\mathcal{R}}\neq 0$,

$$U_{ai}=0 \quad \text{for} \quad i=1, \cdots, n, \quad a=n+1, \cdots. \tag{84}$$

Inserting Eq. (84) into Eq. (80), we see that under the operation $\mathcal{R}$ the MO's transform among themselves:

$$\mathcal{R}\varphi_i=\sum_{j=1}^{n} \varphi_j U_{ji}, \tag{85}$$

or, in matrix notation

$$\mathcal{R}\boldsymbol{\phi}=\boldsymbol{\phi}\mathbf{U}. \tag{85'}$$

We show now that the matrix $\mathbf{U}$ is unitary. The MO's φ_i are normalized:

$$\int \bar{\varphi}_i\varphi_j dv=\delta_{ij}.$$

The same holds for the transformed MO's $\mathcal{R}\varphi_i$. Transforming the integration variables $\mathbf{r}\rightarrow\mathcal{R}^{-1}\mathbf{r}$ we find that the MO's $\mathcal{R}\varphi_i$ are also orthonormal:

$$\int \overline{\mathcal{R}\varphi_i}\mathcal{R}\varphi_j dv=\delta_{ij}. \tag{86}$$

Inserting (85) into (86), we obtain

$$\sum_{kl} \bar{U}_{ki}U_{lj}\int \bar{\varphi}_k\varphi_l dv=\sum_{kl} \bar{U}_{ki}U_{lj}\delta_{kl}=\sum_{k} \bar{U}_{ki}U_{kj}=\delta_{ij},$$

or

$$\mathbf{U}^*\mathbf{U}=\mathbf{E}; \tag{87}$$

that is, the matrix $\mathbf{U}$ is unitary.

The matrices $\mathbf{U}$ furnish a representation of the symmetry group. Namely,

$$\boldsymbol{\phi}\mathbf{U}_{\mathcal{S}\mathcal{R}}=\mathcal{S}\mathcal{R}\boldsymbol{\phi}=\mathcal{S}(\boldsymbol{\phi}\mathbf{U}_{\mathcal{R}})=(\mathcal{S}\boldsymbol{\phi})\mathbf{U}_{\mathcal{R}}=\boldsymbol{\phi}\mathbf{U}_{\mathcal{S}}\mathbf{U}_{\mathcal{R}},$$

or

$$\mathbf{U}_{\mathcal{S}\mathcal{R}}=\mathbf{U}_{\mathcal{S}}\mathbf{U}_{\mathcal{R}}. \tag{88}$$

In Sec. II it was shown that the Hartree-Fock operator F is invariant if the *MO*'s are subjected to a unitary transformation. The Hartree-Fock *MO*'s then have to be eigenfunctions of a totally symmetrical operator; therefore, we can apply what was said about exact wave functions in the first paragraph of this section, namely, that they can always be grouped in sets, each set belonging to an irreducible representation.

We show now that the *MO*'s can always be chosen real. This follows from the fact that $\mathcal{H}$ is a real operator. Namely, if Φ is the closed-shell *AP* which minimizes the energy, then the same is true for $\bar{\Phi}$; and since it was assumed that there is only one such *AP* aside from an arbitrary phase factor, $\bar{\Phi}=c\Phi$. The operation of taking the complex conjugate can therefore be considered as another symmetry operation; it is easily seen that this operation satisfies Eqs. (72) and (73). Using the same type of argument as before for the transformed *MO*'s, we find

$$\bar{\boldsymbol{\phi}}=\boldsymbol{\phi}\mathbf{U}, \tag{89}$$

where the matrix $\mathbf{U}$ is unitary. Taking the complex conjugate and the inverse of Eq. (89), we obtain

$$\boldsymbol{\phi}=\bar{\boldsymbol{\phi}}\bar{\mathbf{U}},\quad \boldsymbol{\phi}=\bar{\boldsymbol{\phi}}\mathbf{U}^*,$$

hence, $\bar{\mathbf{U}}=\mathbf{U}^*$, or

$$\mathbf{U}=\mathbf{U}^\dagger, \tag{90}$$

that is, the matrix $\mathbf{U}$ is, aside from being unitary, also symmetrical.

In Appendix III it is shown that if a unitary matrix is also symmetrical, then it can always be written as the square of another symmetrical unitary matrix. Hence there exists a matrix $\mathbf{V}$ so that

$$\mathbf{U}=\mathbf{V}^2,\quad \mathbf{V}^*\mathbf{V}=\mathbf{E},\quad \mathbf{V}=\mathbf{V}^\dagger. \tag{91}$$

Using this result in Eq. (89), we get

$$\bar{\boldsymbol{\phi}}=\boldsymbol{\phi}\mathbf{V}^2,$$

and

$$\boldsymbol{\phi}\mathbf{V}=\bar{\boldsymbol{\phi}}\mathbf{V}^*=\overline{(\boldsymbol{\phi}\mathbf{V}^\dagger)}=\overline{(\boldsymbol{\phi}\mathbf{V})};$$

so that the new set of *MO*'s defined by

$$\boldsymbol{\phi}'=\boldsymbol{\phi}\mathbf{V} \tag{92}$$

is real:

$$\bar{\boldsymbol{\phi}}'=\boldsymbol{\phi}. \tag{93}$$

Finally, we show that Φ is totally symmetrical. We can choose the *MO*'s all real. Subjecting them to a molecular symmetry operation, there result again real orbitals, since the arguments of the *MO*'s have been subjected to a real orthogonal transformation. Therefore, the transformation matrices $\mathbf{U}_{\mathcal{R}}$ are all real orthogonal matrices, hence

$$\mathrm{Det}(\mathbf{U}_{\mathcal{R}})=\pm 1. \tag{94}$$

From Eq. (82) it follows then that

$$c_{\mathcal{R}}=\mathrm{Det}^2(U_{\mathcal{R}})=1. \tag{95}$$

It is to be noted that it is not always possible to choose the *MO*'s so that they belong to irreducible representations and are at the same time real. This is the case if the symmetry group of the molecule is C_n, S_n, C_{nh}, $n>2$, or T, T_h. These groups have some irreducible representations which are necessarily complex. In that case we can obtain *MO*'s which are all real and occur in sets, each set belonging either to a real irreducible representation or to a reducible representation which consists of two irreducible conjugate complex representations.

VI. THE USE OF MOLECULAR SYMMETRY IN THE *LCAO* PROCEDURE

In the previous section we defined a molecule with a closed-shell ground state as a molecule for which there exists, aside from a phase factor, only one *AP* built from Hartree-Fock *MO*'s which minimizes the energy.

The *LCAO* procedure, developed in Sec. III, was founded on the expectation that it is possible to approximate the best *MO*'s reasonably well by *LCAO MO*'s; whether this can be achieved or not depends to a considerable extent upon the choice of the *AO*'s from which the *LCAO MO*'s are to be built. If the *LCAO* method works at all, we expect it to give the same qualitative features as the Hartree-Fock method. In particular, if for a particular molecule there is only one Hartree-Fock *AP* which minimizes the energy, we also expect there to be only one *LCAO AP* which minimizes the energy. Starting from this assumption, we can derive for a molecule with a *closed-shell ground state* the following statements:

(1) The *LCAO AP* which minimizes the energy is necessarily a singlet and is totally symmetrical with respect to the symmetry group of the molecule.

(2) The best *LCAO MO*'s can be chosen so that they belong in sets to irreducible representations of the symmetry group of the molecule.

(3) The best *LCAO MO*'s can all be chosen real.

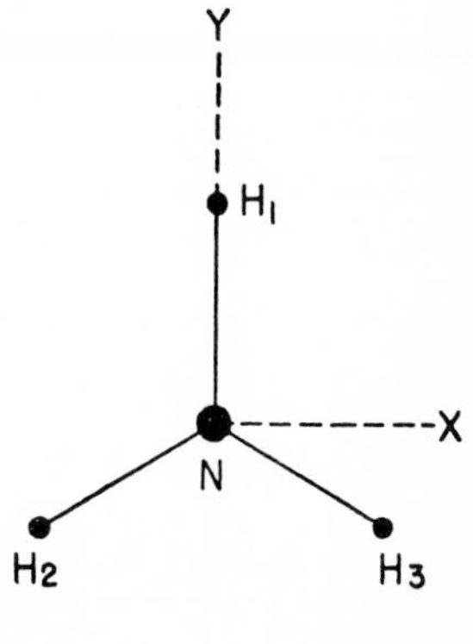

FIG. 1. The NH_3 molecule. The origin is taken at the N nucleus. The three H atoms are located in a plane below and parallel to the *XY*-plane.

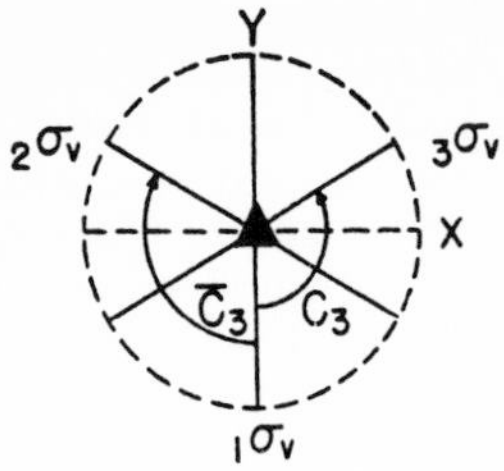

FIG. 2. The symmetry elements of C_{3v}.

The proof is analogous to that for the Hartree-Fock case discussed in the preceding section.

In a symmetrical molecule, there are in general sets of equivalent atoms, that is, of atoms which can be transformed into each other by applying a symmetry operation. So, for instance, in benzene the six carbon atoms form a set of equivalent atoms, and so do the six hydrogen atoms. The set of *AO*'s from which the *LCAO MO*'s are to be built must contain like *AO*'s on equivalent atoms. Thus in the NH_3 molecule (see Fig. 1) we use for the three hydrogen atoms three 1*s* *AO*'s which are identical analytical functions in the local coordinate systems centered in the respective hydrogen atoms. For the nitrogen atom, we use the 1*s*, 2*s*, 2*pz*, 2*px*, and 2*py* *AO*'s.

If we perform a group operation $\mathcal{R}$ on the set of *AO*'s χ_p, then the set of transformed *AO*'s $\mathcal{R}\chi_p$ is a permutation of the original set χ_p, followed in general by a spatial orthogonal transformation on some subsets. In our example of NH_3, for a rotation by 120°, the three hydrogen 1*s* *AO*'s undergo a cyclic permutation; the nitrogen 1*s*, 2*s*, and 2*pz* *AO*'s remain unchanged; and the pair 2*px*, 2*py* undergoes a rotation by 120°. In general, it is clear that the set $\mathcal{R}\boldsymbol{\chi}$ is a unitary transformation of the set $\boldsymbol{\chi}$:

$$\mathcal{R}\boldsymbol{\chi} = \boldsymbol{\chi}\mathbf{A}_{\mathcal{R}} \tag{96}$$

where $\mathbf{A}_{\mathcal{R}}$ is a unitary matrix. Using the same method which established Eq. (88), we find that the matrices $\mathbf{A}_{\mathcal{R}}$ furnish a representation of the symmetry group, namely,

$$\mathbf{A}_{\mathcal{S}\mathcal{R}} = \mathbf{A}_{\mathcal{S}}\mathbf{A}_{\mathcal{R}}. \tag{97}$$

The representation $\mathbf{A}_{\mathcal{R}}$ will in general be reducible. Since it is a unitary representation, it can be reduced by means of a suitable unitary matrix $\mathbf{U}$. Then in the equivalent representation $\mathbf{B}_{\mathcal{R}}$ given by

$$\mathbf{B}_{\mathcal{R}} = \mathbf{U}^*\mathbf{A}_{\mathcal{R}}\mathbf{U} \tag{98}$$

every matrix $\mathbf{B}_{\mathcal{R}}$ appears as a step matrix:

$$\mathbf{B}_{\mathcal{R}} = \begin{bmatrix} \mathbf{B}_{\mathcal{R}}^{(1)} & \mathbf{0} & \cdots & \mathbf{0} \\ \mathbf{0} & \mathbf{B}_{\mathcal{R}}^{(2)} & \cdots & \mathbf{0} \\ \cdot & \cdot & \cdot & \cdot \\ \mathbf{0} & \mathbf{0} & \cdots & \mathbf{B}_{\mathcal{R}}^{(s)} \end{bmatrix}, \tag{99}$$

where the steps $\mathbf{B}_{\mathcal{R}}^{(1)}, \mathbf{B}_{\mathcal{R}}^{(2)}, \cdots, \mathbf{B}_{\mathcal{R}}^{(s)}$ are square matrices, and furnish irreducible representations. In general, among these irreducible representations there will occur equivalent ones; if that is the case, then we can always choose the matrix $\mathbf{U}$ so that the equivalent ones are identical and appear adjacently; we shall hereafter assume this to be done.

To illustrate the representations $\mathbf{A}_{\mathcal{R}}$ and $\mathbf{B}_{\mathcal{R}}$, let us again consider NH_3. The symmetry group is C_{3v}; the symmetry elements and their notation are shown in Fig. 2. The irreducible representations are listed in Table I. The generating elements of the group C_{3v} are C_3 and ${}_1\sigma_v$; hence it is sufficient to consider the matrices $\mathbf{A}_{\mathcal{R}}$ and $\mathbf{B}_{\mathcal{R}}$ for $\mathcal{R} = C_3$ and $\mathcal{R} = {}_1\sigma_v$.

We number the *AO*'s as follows: $1sN = \chi_1$, $1sH_1 = \chi_2$, $1sH_2 = \chi_3$, $1sH_3 = \chi_4$, $2sN = \chi_5$, $2pzN = \chi_6$, $2pxN = \chi_7$, $2pyN = \chi_8$. The transformation matrices $\mathbf{A}_{\mathcal{R}}$ for $\mathcal{R} = C_3$ and $\mathcal{R} = {}_1\sigma_v$ are found as follows:

$$C_3(\chi_1\,\chi_2\,\chi_3\,\chi_4\,\chi_5\,\chi_6\,\chi_7\,\chi_8)$$

$$= (\chi_1\,\chi_3\,\chi_4\,\chi_2\,\chi_5\,\chi_6\; -\tfrac{1}{2}\chi_7 + \tfrac{1}{2}\sqrt{3}\chi_8\; -\tfrac{1}{2}\sqrt{3}\chi_7 - \tfrac{1}{2}\chi_8)$$

$$= (\chi_1\,\chi_2\,\chi_3\,\chi_4\,\chi_5\,\chi_6\,\chi_7\,\chi_8)$$

$$\times \begin{bmatrix} 1 & 0 & 0 & 0 & 0 & 0 & 0 & 0 \\ 0 & 0 & 0 & 1 & 0 & 0 & 0 & 0 \\ 0 & 1 & 0 & 0 & 0 & 0 & 0 & 0 \\ 0 & 0 & 1 & 0 & 0 & 0 & 0 & 0 \\ 0 & 0 & 0 & 0 & 1 & 0 & 0 & 0 \\ 0 & 0 & 0 & 0 & 0 & 1 & 0 & 0 \\ 0 & 0 & 0 & 0 & 0 & 0 & -\tfrac{1}{2} & -\tfrac{1}{2}\sqrt{3} \\ 0 & 0 & 0 & 0 & 0 & 0 & \tfrac{1}{2}\sqrt{3} & -\tfrac{1}{2} \end{bmatrix},$$

TABLE I. The irreducible representations of C_{3v}.

C_{3v}	E	C_3	$\bar{C}_3$	${}_1\sigma_v$	${}_2\sigma_v$	${}_3\sigma_v$
A_1	1	1	1	1	1	1
A_2	1	1	1	−1	−1	−1
E	$\begin{pmatrix} 1 & 0 \\ 0 & 1 \end{pmatrix}$	$\begin{pmatrix} -\frac{1}{2} & -\frac{1}{2}\sqrt{3} \\ \frac{1}{2}\sqrt{3} & -\frac{1}{2} \end{pmatrix}$	$\begin{pmatrix} -\frac{1}{2} & \frac{1}{2}\sqrt{3} \\ -\frac{1}{2}\sqrt{3} & -\frac{1}{2} \end{pmatrix}$	$\begin{pmatrix} -1 & 0 \\ 0 & 1 \end{pmatrix}$	$\begin{pmatrix} \frac{1}{2} & -\frac{1}{2}\sqrt{3} \\ -\frac{1}{2}\sqrt{3} & -\frac{1}{2} \end{pmatrix}$	$\begin{pmatrix} \frac{1}{2} & \frac{1}{2}\sqrt{3} \\ \frac{1}{2}\sqrt{3} & -\frac{1}{2} \end{pmatrix}$

$${}_1\sigma_v(\chi_1\,\chi_2\,\chi_3\,\chi_4\,\chi_5\,\chi_6\,\chi_7\,\chi_8)=(\chi_1\,\chi_2\,\chi_4\,\chi_3\,\chi_5\,\chi_6\,-\chi_7\,\chi_8)$$

$$=(\chi_1\,\chi_2\,\chi_3\,\chi_4\,\chi_5\,\chi_6\,\chi_7\,\chi_8)\begin{pmatrix}1&0&0&0&0&0&0&0\\0&1&0&0&0&0&0&0\\0&0&0&1&0&0&0&0\\0&0&1&0&0&0&0&0\\0&0&0&0&1&0&0&0\\0&0&0&0&0&1&0&0\\0&0&0&0&0&0&-1&0\\0&0&0&0&0&0&0&1\end{pmatrix}.$$

The two matrices are $\mathbf{A}_{C_3}$ and $\mathbf{A}_{1\sigma_v}$, respectively.

We now wish to completely reduce the representation $\mathbf{A}_{\mathcal{R}}$. This reduction is achieved by means of the following transformation matrix:

$$\mathbf{U}=\begin{pmatrix}1&0&0&0&0&0&0&0\\0&3^{-\frac{1}{2}}&0&0&0&2\cdot3^{-\frac{1}{2}}&0&0\\0&3^{-\frac{1}{2}}&0&0&-2^{-\frac{1}{2}}&-6^{-\frac{1}{2}}&0&0\\0&3^{-\frac{1}{2}}&0&0&2^{-\frac{1}{2}}&-6^{-\frac{1}{2}}&0&0\\0&0&1&0&0&0&0&0\\0&0&0&1&0&0&0&0\\0&0&0&0&0&0&1&0\\0&0&0&0&0&0&0&1\end{pmatrix},$$

for if we use this $\mathbf{U}$ in Eqs. (98), we find

$$\mathbf{B}_{C_3}=\mathbf{U}^*\mathbf{A}_{C_3}\mathbf{U}$$

$$=\begin{pmatrix}1&0&0&0&0&0&0&0\\0&1&0&0&0&0&0&0\\0&0&1&0&0&0&0&0\\0&0&0&1&0&0&0&0\\0&0&0&0&-\frac{1}{2}&-\frac{1}{2}\surd3&0&0\\0&0&0&0&\frac{1}{2}\surd3&-\frac{1}{2}&0&0\\0&0&0&0&0&0&-\frac{1}{2}&-\frac{1}{2}\surd3\\0&0&0&0&0&0&\frac{1}{2}\surd3&-\frac{1}{2}\end{pmatrix}$$

$$\mathbf{B}_{1\sigma_v}=\mathbf{U}^*\mathbf{A}_{1\sigma_v}\mathbf{U}=\begin{pmatrix}1&0&0&0&0&0&0&0\\0&1&0&0&0&0&0&0\\0&0&1&0&0&0&0&0\\0&0&0&1&0&0&0&0\\0&0&0&0&-1&0&0&0\\0&0&0&0&0&1&0&0\\0&0&0&0&0&0&-1&0\\0&0&0&0&0&0&0&1\end{pmatrix}$$

Referring to Table I, it is seen that the representation $\mathbf{B}_{\mathcal{R}}$ consists of four times A_1 and twice E.

We return now to the general theory. From Eqs. (96) and (97) it is easily established that the symmetry orbitals σ_p defined by

$$\sigma_p=\sum_q \chi_q U_{qp}, \tag{100}$$

or

$$\boldsymbol{\sigma}=\chi\mathbf{U} \tag{100'}$$

transform under the operations $\mathcal{R}$ according to the representation $\mathbf{B}_{\mathcal{R}}$:

$$\mathcal{R}\boldsymbol{\sigma}=\boldsymbol{\sigma}\mathbf{B}_{\mathcal{R}}. \tag{101}$$

Since $\mathbf{B}_{\mathcal{R}}$ is in completely reduced form, the symmetry orbitals appear in sets such that each set belongs to an irreducible representation or symmetry species.

In our example the symmetry orbitals are

$$(\sigma_1\,\sigma_2\,\sigma_3\,\sigma_4\,\sigma_5\,\sigma_6\,\sigma_7\,\sigma_8)=(\chi_1\,\chi_2\,\chi_3\,\chi_4\,\chi_5\,\chi_6\,\chi_7\,\chi_8)\mathbf{U}$$
$$=(\chi_1\;3^{-\frac{1}{2}}(\chi_2+\chi_3+\chi_4)\;\chi_5\;\chi_6\;2^{-\frac{1}{2}}(-\chi_3+\chi_4)\;6^{-\frac{1}{2}}(2\chi_2-\chi_3-\chi_4)\;\chi_7\;\chi_8),$$

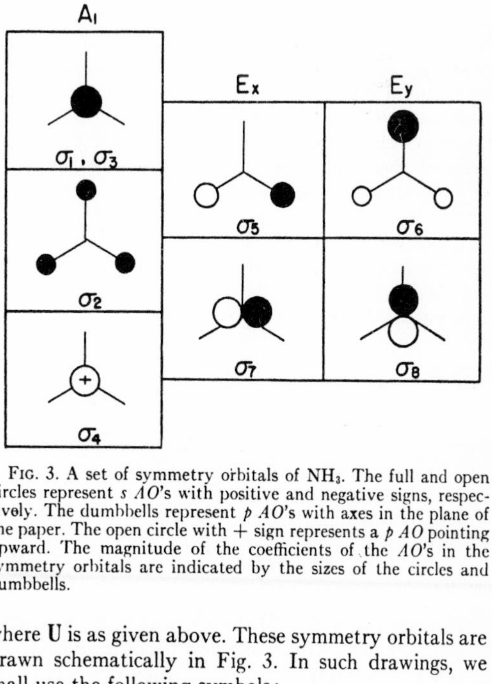

FIG. 3. A set of symmetry orbitals of NH_3. The full and open circles represent s AO's with positive and negative signs, respectively. The dumbbells represent p AO's with axes in the plane of the paper. The open circle with + sign represents a p AO pointing upward. The magnitude of the coefficients of the AO's in the symmetry orbitals are indicated by the sizes of the circles and dumbbells.

where $\mathbf{U}$ is as given above. These symmetry orbitals are drawn schematically in Fig. 3. In such drawings, we shall use the following symbols:

- ● s AO, positive;
- ○ s AO, negative;
- ○● p AO, with axis in the plane of the paper, positive part at the right;
- ⊕ p AO, with axis perpendicular to the plane of the paper, positive above this plane;
- ⊖ p AO, with axis perpendicular to the plane of the paper, negative above this plane.

The magnitude of the coefficient with which an *AO* enters a symmetry orbital will be indicated by the size of the symbol.

The choice of the symmetry orbitals is in general not unique. First, there is freedom in choosing the explicit forms of the degenerate representations. In C_{3v} we chose the doubly degenerate representation so as to be the explicit transformation of the base vectors $(\mathbf{i}\,\mathbf{j})$ along the X and Y axes. Secondly, if the same irreducible representation occurs more than once in $\mathbf{B}_{\mathcal{R}}$, then any linear combination of the symmetry orbitals of that species is still a symmetry orbital of that species. Hence, we can replace the set belonging to a particular species by any linear transformation of that set. In NH_3 we can thus replace the set σ_1, σ_2, σ_3, σ_4 by any linear transformation of this set, and similarly the set σ_5, σ_7, provided we subject σ_6, σ_8 to the same transformation.

In order to obtain the symmetry orbitals in a nearly unique manner, we shall use the following procedure. First, we pick the degenerate representations in a convenient manner, preferably in real form. Then we arrange the natural *AO*'s (no hybrids) in sets of equivalent *AO*'s; these are the smallest possible sets which transform within themselves under the symmetry operations. Finally, we construct then from each set of equivalent *AO*'s a set of symmetry orbitals. This procedure is unique, except for the choice of the explicit forms of the degenerate representations, and except for an arbitrary phase factor for each symmetry orbital (or, in the case of degeneracy, a common phase factor for all the members of the degenerate set). This method has been followed in our construction of the symmetry orbitals of NH_3.

Just as we defined the matrix elements

$$M_{pq}=\int \bar{\chi}_p M \chi_q dv$$

corresponding to the operator M, we can now define the corresponding matrix elements $M^\sigma{}_{pq}$ evaluated with the symmetry orbitals:

$$M^\sigma{}_{pq}=\int \bar{\sigma}_p M \sigma_q dv; \tag{102}$$

we shall use the symbol $\mathbf{M}^\sigma$ for the matrix the elements of which are $M^\sigma{}_{pq}$. It is easily seen that the matrices $\mathbf{M}$ and $\mathbf{M}^\sigma$ are connected by

$$\mathbf{M}^\sigma=\mathbf{U}^*\mathbf{M}\mathbf{U}, \tag{103}$$

where $\mathbf{U}$ is the matrix which forms the symmetry orbitals from the *AO*'s (see Eq. (100′)). Similarly, we define the vectors $\mathbf{c}^\sigma{}_f$ by means of

$$\mathbf{c}^\sigma{}_f=\mathbf{U}^*\mathbf{c}_f, \tag{104}$$

so that the *MO*'s φ_f can be expressed either in the *AO*'s χ or the symmetry orbitals $\boldsymbol{\sigma}$:

$$\varphi_f=\boldsymbol{\chi}\mathbf{c}_f=\boldsymbol{\sigma}\mathbf{c}^\sigma{}_f. \tag{105}$$

The linear equations (60) and the secular equation (61) can now be transformed into

$$\mathbf{F}^\sigma\mathbf{c}^\sigma=\epsilon\mathbf{S}^\sigma\mathbf{c}^\sigma, \tag{106}$$

$$\mathrm{Det}(\mathbf{F}^\sigma-\epsilon\mathbf{S}^\sigma)=0, \tag{107}$$

where $\mathbf{F}^\sigma$ and $\mathbf{S}^\sigma$ are defined by means of (102) or (103).

Now let the irreducible representations or symmetry species of the symmetry group of the molecule be $\Gamma^{(1)}$, $\Gamma^{(2)}$, $\cdots$, $\Gamma^{(\pi)}$, $\cdots$. The symmetry orbitals belong in sets to these representations. We relabel the symmetry orbitals accordingly with triple indices: $\sigma_{\alpha\pi\kappa}$. The index π indicates that $\sigma_{\alpha\pi\kappa}$ belongs to $\Gamma^{(\pi)}$. If there are several sets of symmetry orbitals belonging to $\Gamma^{(\pi)}$, then we number these sets: 1, 2, $\cdots$, α, $\cdots$; $\sigma_{\alpha\pi\kappa}$ is a member of the αth set of species $\Gamma^{(\pi)}$. Finally, if $\Gamma^{(\pi)}$ is a p-fold degenerate representation, then a set of symmetry orbitals of this species transforms under group operations like the base vectors of a p-dimensional vector space: $\mathbf{e}^{(1)}$, $\mathbf{e}^{(2)}$, $\cdots$, $\mathbf{e}^{(p)}$; the index κ indicates that $\sigma_{\alpha\pi\kappa}$ behaves like $\mathbf{e}^{(\kappa)}$.[31]

The following statement is a well-known result from group theory:[32] If M is a totally symmetrical operator, then

$$\left.\begin{aligned}&\int \bar{\sigma}_{\alpha\pi\kappa}M\sigma_{\beta\rho\lambda}dv=0, \quad \text{unless } \pi=\rho \text{ and } \kappa=\lambda;\\ &\quad\text{if this is the case, then}\\ &\int \bar{\sigma}_{\alpha\pi\kappa}M\sigma_{\beta\pi\kappa}dv=\int \bar{\sigma}_{\alpha\pi\mu}M\sigma_{\beta\pi\mu}dv\\ &\quad\text{for any } \kappa \text{ and } \mu.\end{aligned}\right\} \tag{108}$$

If we take for M the identity operator or the operator F, then theorem (108) is seen to apply to the elements of $\mathbf{S}^\sigma$ and $\mathbf{F}^\sigma$. Writing out Eqs. (106) and (107) according to the triple indices, we have

$$\sum_{\beta\rho\lambda}(F^\sigma{}_{\alpha\pi\kappa,\beta\rho\lambda}-\epsilon S^\sigma{}_{\alpha\pi\kappa,\beta\rho\lambda})c_{\beta\rho\lambda}=0, \tag{106′}$$

$$\mathrm{Det}(F^\sigma{}_{\alpha\pi\kappa,\beta\rho\lambda}-\epsilon S^\sigma{}_{\alpha\pi\kappa,\beta\rho\lambda})=0; \tag{107′}$$

these equations reduce, because of (108), to

$$\sum_{\beta}(F^\sigma{}_{\alpha\pi,\beta\pi}-\epsilon S^\sigma{}_{\alpha\pi,\beta\pi})c_{\beta\pi\kappa}=0 \tag{106″}$$

$$\mathrm{Det}(F^\sigma{}_{\alpha\pi,\beta\pi}-\epsilon S^\sigma{}_{\alpha\pi,\beta\pi})=0. \tag{107″}$$

[31] A special case of these triple indices is encountered in the customary notation for *AO*'s: (n, l, m). Here the quantum number l indicates the irreducible representation; the quantum number m labels the different members in the same irreducible representation; and the quantum number n is an index to distinguish between *AO*'s which cannot be distinguished any more by symmetry characteristics.

[32] See reference 13, p. 124.

There is a set of this type for each symmetry species $\Gamma^{(\pi)}$; if $\Gamma^{(\pi)}$ is p-fold degenerate, then we get the same set p times, once for each value of the index κ, which we omitted accordingly.

The multiple indices which we used to formulate these general results are somewhat cumbersome in practical cases. In explicit calculations it is usually simpler to use the simple numbering of the symmetry orbitals.

In our example of NH_3 the equations (107) and (108) are a set of 4×4 for the A_1 orbitals, and two identical sets of 2×2 for the E orbitals.

APPENDIX I‡

If $\rho(x, y, z)$ is any continuous electrostatic charge distribution, which may be positive, negative, or partially positive and partially negative, and which vanishes sufficiently strongly at infinity, then the total energy of this charge distribution is given by

$$\int \frac{\rho^\mu \rho^\nu}{r^{\mu\nu}} dv^{\mu\nu} = \frac{1}{8\pi}\int E^2 dv \geqslant 0,$$

where $\rho^\mu = \rho(x^\mu, y^\mu, z^\mu)$, $\operatorname{div}\mathbf{E} = 4\pi\rho$; the equal sign holding if and only if $\rho = 0$ for all values of x, y, z.

Now let $\rho = e^2(\bar{\varphi}_i\varphi_i - \bar{\varphi}_j\varphi_j)$; then

$$0 \leqslant e^2 \int \frac{(\bar{\varphi}_i\varphi_i - \bar{\varphi}_j\varphi_j)^\mu (\bar{\varphi}_i\varphi_i - \bar{\varphi}_j\varphi_j)^\nu}{r^{\mu\nu}} dv^{\mu\nu} = J_{ii} + J_{jj} - 2J_{ij},$$

or

$$J_{ij} \leqslant \tfrac{1}{2}(J_{ii} + J_{jj}),$$

the equal sign holding if and only if $\bar{\varphi}_i\varphi_i = \bar{\varphi}_j\varphi_j$, or $|\varphi_i| = |\varphi_j|$. This establishes the third relation expressed in (26).

Next let $\varphi_i = \xi_i + i\eta_i$, $\varphi_j = \xi_j + i\eta_j$, where ξ and η are real. Then

$$K_{ij} = e^2 \int \frac{(\xi_i - i\eta_i)^\mu (\xi_j - i\eta_j)^\nu (\xi_j + i\eta_j)^\mu (\xi_i + i\eta_i)^\nu}{r^{\mu\nu}} dv^{\mu\nu}$$

$$= e^2 \int \frac{\{\xi_i\xi_j + \eta_i\eta_j + i(\xi_i\eta_j - \eta_i\xi_j)\}^\mu \{\xi_i\xi_j + \eta_i\eta_j - i(\xi_i\eta_j - \eta_i\xi_j)\}^\nu}{r^{\mu\nu}} dv^{\mu\nu} = \int \frac{(\rho_1 + i\rho_2)^\mu (\rho_1 - i\rho_2)^\nu}{r^{\mu\nu}} dv^{\mu\nu},$$

where $\rho_1 = e^2(\xi_i\xi_j + \eta_i\eta_j)$, $\rho_2 = e^2(\xi_i\eta_j - \eta_i\xi_j)$. Hence

$$K_{ij} = \int \frac{\rho_1{}^\mu \rho_1{}^\nu}{r^{\mu\nu}} dv^{\mu\nu} + \int \frac{\rho_2{}^\mu \rho_2{}^\nu}{r^{\mu\nu}} dv^{\mu\nu} \geqslant 0,$$

the equal sign holding if and only if

$$\rho_1 = 0, \quad \rho_2 = 0,$$

or

$$\xi_i\xi_j + \eta_i\eta_j = 0, \quad \xi_i\eta_j - \eta_i\xi_j = 0.$$

Multiplying the second one of these equations by i, and adding the results to the first one, we obtain

$$\bar{\varphi}_i\varphi_j = 0;$$

hence for any point in space either $\varphi_i = 0$ or $\varphi_j = 0$, that is, φ_i and φ_j do not penetrate each other. This establishes the first relation expressed in (26).

Finally,

$$0 \leqslant \frac{e^2}{2}\int \frac{|\varphi_i{}^\mu \varphi_j{}^\nu - \varphi_j{}^\mu \varphi_i{}^\nu|^2}{r^{\mu\nu}} dv^{\mu\nu}$$

$$= \frac{e^2}{2}\int \frac{(\bar{\varphi}_i{}^\mu \bar{\varphi}_j{}^\nu - \bar{\varphi}_j{}^\mu \bar{\varphi}_i{}^\nu)(\varphi_i{}^\mu \varphi_j{}^\nu - \varphi_j{}^\mu \varphi_i{}^\nu)}{r^{\mu\nu}} dv^{\mu\nu} = J_{ij} - K_{ij},$$

the equal sign holding if and only if

$$\varphi_i{}^\mu \varphi_j{}^\nu = \varphi_j{}^\mu \varphi_i{}^\nu, \quad \text{or} \quad \varphi_i{}^\mu/\varphi_j{}^\mu = \varphi_i{}^\nu/\varphi_j{}^\nu;$$

the left- and right-hand side of this equation are functions of different arguments, hence equal to a constant, or $\varphi_i = c\varphi_j$. Since the *MO*'s φ_i and φ_j occur in the same *AP*, this linear dependence implies identity, $\varphi_i = \varphi_j$. This establishes the second relation expressed in (26).

APPENDIX II

The necessary and sufficient condition that there is a nonvanishing vector $\mathbf{c}$ satisfying

$$(\mathbf{F} - \epsilon\mathbf{S})\mathbf{c} = 0$$

is given by the secular equation

$$\operatorname{Det}(\mathbf{F} - \epsilon\mathbf{S}) = 0.$$

This equation is of the mth degree in ϵ, where m is the dimension of the matrices $\mathbf{F}$ and $\mathbf{S}$; the coefficient of ϵ^m is $(-1)^m \operatorname{Det}(\mathbf{S})$. We show first that this coefficient cannot vanish. The necessary and sufficient condition for $\operatorname{Det}(\mathbf{S}) = 0$ is a linear dependence of the columns (or rows) of $\mathbf{S}$:

$$\sum_q S_{pq} c_q = 0,$$

the trivial case $c_1 = c_2 = \cdots = c_m = 0$ being excluded. Such a linear dependence, however, leads to a contradiction; namely, multiply the last equation by $\bar{c}_p$ and sum over p:

$$\sum_{pq} \bar{c}_p S_{pq} c_q = 0, \quad \text{or} \quad \int \overline{\left(\sum_p c_p\chi_p\right)}\left(\sum_q c_q\chi_q\right) dv = 0$$

‡ The author is indebted to Professor K. F. Herzfeld for valuable advice on the proofs in this appendix.

from which we conclude

$$\sum_p c_p \chi_p = 0,$$

which is clearly an impossibility, since the *AO*'s are linearly independent. Therefore, Det(S)$\neq 0$, and the secular equation is always of the mth degree in ϵ. As a consequence, the secular equation has always m roots ϵ_f, $f=1, 2, \cdots, m$, provided we count multiple roots as often as their multiplicity.

We show now that all the roots ϵ_f are real. For a root ϵ_f there exists at least one nonvanishing vector $\mathbf{c}_f$ so that

$$\mathbf{F}\mathbf{c}_f = \epsilon_f \mathbf{S}\mathbf{c}_f, \quad \mathbf{c}^*_f\mathbf{F} = \bar{\epsilon}_f \mathbf{c}^*_f\mathbf{S},$$

the second equation being the hermitian conjugate of the first one. Multiplying the first equation from the left by $\mathbf{c}^*_f$ and the second one from the right by $\mathbf{c}_f$, there results

$$\mathbf{c}^*_f\mathbf{F}\mathbf{c}_f = \epsilon_f \mathbf{c}^*_f\mathbf{S}\mathbf{c}_f = \bar{\epsilon}_f \mathbf{c}^*_f\mathbf{S}\mathbf{c}_f.$$

Now $\mathbf{c}^*_f\mathbf{S}\mathbf{c}_f \neq 0$, since otherwise the *AO*'s χ_p would be linearly dependent. Hence

$$\bar{\epsilon}_f = \epsilon_f.$$

Next we show that if $\epsilon_f \neq \epsilon_g$, eigenvectors corresponding to ϵ_f and ϵ_g are mutually orthogonal in the sense that $\mathbf{S}$ is the metric fundamental tensor: $\mathbf{c}^*_g\mathbf{S}\mathbf{c}_f=0$. Namely,

$$\mathbf{F}\mathbf{c}_f = \epsilon_f \mathbf{S}\mathbf{c}_f, \quad \mathbf{F}\mathbf{c}_g = \epsilon_g \mathbf{S}\mathbf{c}_g.$$

Taking the hermitian conjugate of the second one of these equations, and observing that ϵ_g is real, we obtain

$$\mathbf{F}\mathbf{c}_f = \epsilon_f \mathbf{S}\mathbf{c}_f, \quad \mathbf{c}^*_g\mathbf{F} = \epsilon_g \mathbf{c}^*_g\mathbf{S}.$$

Multiplying the first equation from the left by $\mathbf{c}^*_g$ and the second one from the right by $\mathbf{c}_f$, there results

$$\mathbf{c}^*_g\mathbf{F}\mathbf{c}_f = \epsilon_f \mathbf{c}^*_g\mathbf{S}\mathbf{c}_f = \epsilon_g \mathbf{c}^*_g\mathbf{S}\mathbf{c}_f;$$

and since $\epsilon_f \neq \epsilon_g$, we conclude that

$$\mathbf{c}^*_g\mathbf{S}\mathbf{c}_f = 0.$$

Assuming now that the eigenvalues ϵ_f are all distinct, it follows that there are at least m eigenvectors $\mathbf{c}_f$ which are mutually orthogonal. It is no loss of generality if we assume the vectors $\mathbf{c}_f$ to be also normalized; they form then an orthonormal set, that is,

$$\mathbf{c}^*_g\mathbf{S}\mathbf{c}_f = \delta_{gf}.$$

This relation implies that the vectors $\mathbf{c}_f$ are linearly independent, for a relation

$$\sum_f \alpha_f \mathbf{c}_f = 0$$

gives upon multiplication by $\mathbf{c}^*_g\mathbf{S}$ from the left

$$\sum_f \alpha_f \mathbf{c}^*_g\mathbf{S}\mathbf{c}_f = \sum_f \alpha_f \delta_{gf} = \alpha_g = 0.$$

Since there can be at most m m-dimensional vectors in an orthonormal set, there are exactly m vectors $\mathbf{c}_f$, one for each eigenvalue ϵ_f, which are determined except for an arbitrary phase factor.

Finally, we have to show that if the secular equation has one or several multiple roots, then for each root there can be found as many linearly independent eigenvectors as the multiplicity of the root, which can be chosen so as to form an orthonormal set. The validity of these statements is easily established in the following way. If the matrices $\mathbf{F}$ and $\mathbf{S}$ are such that their eigenvalue problem furnishes multiple eigenvalues, then $\mathbf{F}$ and $\mathbf{S}$ can be obtained from matrices $\mathbf{F}'$ and $\mathbf{S}'$ for which this is not the case by changing $\mathbf{F}'$ and $\mathbf{S}'$ continuously. In this continuous process, eigenvalues and eigenvectors also change continuously (except for the phase factors of the latter), and the set of eigenvectors remains orthonormal throughout this process. In this way the existence of an orthonormal set of m eigenvectors has been established for the degenerate case. This set is not unique, however; namely, if there are p linearly independent eigenvectors belonging to a p-fold eigenvalue, then any linear combination of these vectors is also an eigenvector belonging to that eigenvalue. Restricting these p eigenvectors to be orthonormal, they are therefore determined except for a unitary transformation among themselves.

APPENDIX III

A unitary matrix $\mathbf{U}$ can be transformed into a diagonal matrix $\mathbf{D}$ by means of another unitary matrix $\mathbf{W}$

$$\mathbf{W}^*\mathbf{U}\mathbf{W} = \mathbf{D}.$$

If the diagonal elements of $\mathbf{D}$ are not all distinct, then we can always choose the matrix $\mathbf{W}$ such that equal diagonal elements appear adjacently; we assume this to be the case. Then $\mathbf{D}$ has the form

$$\begin{pmatrix} d_1\mathbf{E}_1 & \mathbf{0} & \cdots & \mathbf{0} \\ \mathbf{0} & d_2\mathbf{E}_2 & \cdots & \mathbf{0} \\ \cdot & \cdot & \cdot & \cdot \\ \mathbf{0} & \mathbf{0} & \cdots & d_p\mathbf{E}_p \end{pmatrix},$$

where $d_1, d_2, \cdots, d_p$ are all distinct, and $\mathbf{E}_1, \mathbf{E}_2, \cdots, \mathbf{E}_p$ are unit matrices of the appropriate dimensions. The numbers $d_1, d_2, \cdots, d_p$ are all of modulus unity, since they are the eigenvalues of the unitary matrix $\mathbf{U}$.

Now let the unitary matrix $\mathbf{U}$ be also symmetrical: $\mathbf{U}\dagger = \mathbf{U}$. Then

$$(\mathbf{WDW^*})\dagger = \mathbf{WDW^*},$$

or

$$\bar{\mathbf{W}}\mathbf{DW}\dagger = \mathbf{WDW^*}.$$

Multiplying this equation from the left by $\mathbf{W}\dagger$ and from the right by $\mathbf{W}$, there results

$$\mathbf{DS} = \mathbf{SD}, \quad \text{where} \quad \mathbf{S} = \mathbf{W}\dagger\mathbf{W}.$$

We write the matrix $\mathbf{S}$ in block form according to the structure of $\mathbf{D}$:

$$\begin{pmatrix} \mathbf{S}_1 & \mathbf{S}_{12} & \cdots & \mathbf{S}_{1p} \\ \mathbf{S}_{21} & \mathbf{S}_2 & \cdots & \mathbf{S}_{2p} \\ \cdot & \cdot & \cdot & \cdot \\ \mathbf{S}_{p1} & \mathbf{S}_{p2} & \cdots & \mathbf{S}_p \end{pmatrix}.$$

We have then from $\mathbf{DS} = \mathbf{SD}$:

$$\begin{pmatrix} d_1\mathbf{S}_1 & d_1\mathbf{S}_{12} & \cdots & d_1\mathbf{S}_{1p} \\ d_2\mathbf{S}_{21} & d_2\mathbf{S}_2 & \cdots & d_2\mathbf{S}_{2p} \\ \cdot & \cdot & \cdot & \cdot \\ d_p\mathbf{S}_{p1} & d_p\mathbf{S}_{p2} & \cdots & d_p\mathbf{S}_p \end{pmatrix} = \begin{pmatrix} d_1\mathbf{S}_1 & d_2\mathbf{S}_{12} & \cdots & d_p\mathbf{S}_{1p} \\ d_1\mathbf{S}_{21} & d_2\mathbf{S}_2 & \cdots & d_p\mathbf{S}_{2p} \\ \cdot & \cdot & \cdot & \cdot \\ d_1\mathbf{S}_{p1} & d_2\mathbf{S}_{p2} & \cdots & d_p\mathbf{S}_p \end{pmatrix};$$

hence for $\alpha \neq \beta$: $(d_\alpha - d_\beta)\mathbf{S}_{\alpha\beta} = \mathbf{0}$, and since $d_\alpha \neq d_\beta$, $\mathbf{S}_{\alpha\beta} = \mathbf{0}$. It follows that $\mathbf{S}$ is a step matrix:

$$\begin{pmatrix} \mathbf{S}_1 & \mathbf{0} & \cdots & \mathbf{0} \\ \mathbf{0} & \mathbf{S}_2 & \cdots & \mathbf{0} \\ \cdot & \cdot & \cdot & \cdot \\ \mathbf{0} & \mathbf{0} & \cdots & \mathbf{S}_p \end{pmatrix},$$

where $\mathbf{S}_1, \mathbf{S}_2, \cdots, \mathbf{S}_p$ are square matrices which have the same dimensions as $\mathbf{E}_1, \mathbf{E}_2, \cdots, \mathbf{E}_p$. With the matrix $\mathbf{S}$ now commutes any matrix of the type

$$\begin{pmatrix} c_1\mathbf{E}_1 & 0 & \cdots & 0 \\ 0 & c_2\mathbf{E}_2 & \cdots & 0 \\ \cdot & \cdot & \cdot & \cdot \\ 0 & 0 & \cdots & c_p\mathbf{E}_p \end{pmatrix},$$

where $c_1, c_2, \cdots, c_p$ are arbitrary numbers; in particular, $\mathbf{S}$ commutes with the matrix $\mathbf{D}^{\frac{1}{2}}$, defined by

$$\mathbf{D}^{\frac{1}{2}} = \begin{pmatrix} (d_1)^{\frac{1}{2}}\mathbf{E}_1 & 0 & \cdots & 0 \\ 0 & (d_2)^{\frac{1}{2}}\mathbf{E}_2 & \cdots & 0 \\ \cdot & \cdot & \cdot & \cdot \\ 0 & 0 & \cdots & (d_p)^{\frac{1}{2}}\mathbf{E}_p \end{pmatrix}.$$

This matrix is unitary, since $(d_1)^{\frac{1}{2}}, (d_2)^{\frac{1}{2}}, \cdots, (d_p)^{\frac{1}{2}}$ are numbers of modulus unity. From $\mathbf{D}^{\frac{1}{2}}\mathbf{S} = \mathbf{S}\mathbf{D}^{\frac{1}{2}}$ follows

$$\mathbf{D}^{\frac{1}{2}}\mathbf{W}\dagger\mathbf{W} = \mathbf{W}\dagger\mathbf{W}\mathbf{D}^{\frac{1}{2}}.$$

Multiplication from the left by $\bar{\mathbf{W}}$ and from the right by $\mathbf{W^*}$ gives

$$\bar{\mathbf{W}}\mathbf{D}^{\frac{1}{2}}\mathbf{W}\dagger = \mathbf{W}\mathbf{D}^{\frac{1}{2}}\mathbf{W^*},$$

or

$$(\mathbf{W}\mathbf{D}^{\frac{1}{2}}\mathbf{W^*})\dagger = \mathbf{W}\mathbf{D}^{\frac{1}{2}}\mathbf{W^*}.$$

Hence the unitary matrix V defined by

$$\mathbf{V} = \mathbf{W}\mathbf{D}^{\frac{1}{2}}\mathbf{W^*}$$

is symmetric:

$$\mathbf{V}\dagger = \mathbf{V},$$

and

$$\mathbf{U} = \mathbf{WDW^*} = \mathbf{W}\mathbf{D}^{\frac{1}{2}}\mathbf{D}^{\frac{1}{2}}\mathbf{W^*} = \mathbf{W}\mathbf{D}^{\frac{1}{2}}\mathbf{W^*}\mathbf{W}\mathbf{D}^{\frac{1}{2}}\mathbf{W^*} = \mathbf{V}^2.$$

ACKNOWLEDGMENT

The author expresses his indebtedness to Professor R. S. Mulliken, who sponsored this research, for many stimulating discussions and suggestions.

Reprinted from the Proceedings of the NATIONAL ACADEMY OF SCIENCES,
Vol. 38, No. 3, pp. 154–60. March, 1952

*SUPERPOSITION OF CONFIGURATIONS: THE HELIUM ATOM**

BY G. RUSSELL TAYLOR† AND ROBERT G. PARR

DEPARTMENT OF CHEMISTRY, CARNEGIE INSTITUTE OF TECHNOLOGY, PITTSBURGH, PENNSYLVANIA

Communicated by R. S. Mulliken, January 7, 1952

Introduction.—A very nearly exact approximation to the ground state wave function for the helium atom was obtained by Hylleraas in 1930.[1] His approximation is so accurate that calculation of the ground state wave function and energy for helium no longer remains an interesting problem *per se*, but the extension of his method beyond two-electron problems is quite hopeless.[2] The work reported in the present paper therefore was undertaken as a step in the development of a systematic, practical procedure for obtaining an accurate wave function for any atom or molecule.

The quantitative shortcomings of the methods that have been most commonly applied to many-electron systems heretofore, the Hartree-Fock method for atoms and molecules and the valence bond and molecular orbital methods for molecules, are becoming more apparent with each new application. There has resulted an increased use of wave functions involving configuration interaction.[3, 4] Wave functions of any desired accuracy in principle can be obtained by the superposition of a sufficiently large number of configurations,[5] but if the method is to be of practical value the number of configurations required should be small; i.e., the configurations should be chosen with discretion. Present knowledge regarding configuration interaction effects is very meager, however, so that inspiration now serves in place of discretion. Prospects of progress have been termed melancholy,[6] but melancholy or not there appears to be no other road. At the beginning lies the simplest non-trivial example, the helium atom.

In the problem of the helium atom the number of simplifying assumptions is a minimum, the required integrals can be evaluated to any desired accuracy without prohibitive effort, and accurate experimental data are available for evaluation of results. Furthermore the relative simplicity of the system permits the variational determination of the best effective charges to be used in one-electron functions, which is not feasible for most more complex systems. Simplicity, of course, has as its concomitant disadvantage the loss of generality. Nevertheless, conclusions reached for the helium atom can be used as a guide in further exploratory investigations of successively more complex systems, which might have as their goal the formulation of a set (probably a large set, accompanied by massive tables of definite integrals) of empirical rules whereby an accurate configuration interaction wave function for any atom or molecule would be obtainable with a minimum of trial and error effort.

Approximate Ground State Wave Functions and Energies.—We seek a normalized approximate wave function for the ground state of helium which has the form

$$\Psi = \sum_j a_j \Psi_j, \tag{1}$$

where the Ψ_j are normalized antisymmetrized product wave functions (AP's) for various configurations. The best set of coefficients a_j is determined by minimization of the energy $E = \int \Psi^* H \Psi dv$, where H is the Hamiltonian operator for the helium atom neglecting spin-orbit interaction and relativistic effects and assuming infinite mass for the nucleus, namely,

$$H = -\nabla_1^2 - \nabla_2^2 - 4/r_1 - 4/r_2 + 2/r_{12}, \tag{2}$$

where the unit of energy is the atomic unit $e^2/2a_0 = 13.603$ e.v. The best coefficients satisfy the equations

$$\sum_j a_j (H_{ij} - S_{ij}E) = 0, \qquad i = 1, 2, \ldots, \tag{3}$$

and the corresponding best energy E is the lowest root of the secular equation

$$|H_{ij} - S_{ij}E| = 0, \tag{4}$$

where

$$H_{ij} = \int \Psi_i^* H \Psi_j dv \qquad \text{and} \qquad S_{ij} = \int \Psi_i^* \Psi_j dv. \tag{5}$$

The one-electron functions used in the construction of the AP's are taken as products of the form

$$(i) = (n_i l_i m_i)^{Z_{n_i}}(\eta_i), \quad (6)$$

where $(n_i l_i m_i)^{Z_{n_i}}$ is the hydrogen-like atomic orbital of total quantum number n_i, azimuthal quantum number l_i, magnetic quantum number m_i and effective charge Z_{n_i}, and (η_i) is a spin function (either α or β).

A *configuration* of an atom is defined by the specification of the total and azimuthal quantum numbers for each electron in the system. Belonging to a given configuration there are in general many different AP's corresponding to the many possible assignments of magnetic and spin quantum numbers. We could in equation (1) include all the AP's for each configuration which we wish to superpose and proceed to solve equation (4) by brute force. Since we are neglecting spin-orbit interactions, however, we know in advance that the secular equation may be factored into a product of independent equations, each factor of which involves interactions only between those *LS* vector-coupled functions belonging to the several configurations which have the same eigenvalues for L^2, S^2, L_z, S_z.[7] Thus in the *LS* coupling scheme the ^1S ground state wave function for helium, Ψ, is a superposition of ^1S wave functions, Φ_j, belonging to the several configurations:

$$\Psi = \sum_j b_j \Phi_j. \quad (7)$$

The Φ_j for a given configuration are linear combinations of the Ψ_j for that configuration; the procedure for obtaining the former from the latter is well known.[7]

Let us designate the ^1S vector coupled function belonging to the configuration $(1s)^{Z_1}(1s)^{Z_1'}$ by $\Phi(1s^{Z_1}, 1s^{Z_1'})$, that belonging to the configuration $(2p)^{Z_2}(2p)^{Z_2'}$ by $\Phi(2p^{Z_2}, 2p^{Z_2'})$, etc. The approximate wave functions for the ground state of the helium atom which we have investigated may then be written as follows:

$$\Psi_A = \sum_{n_1=1}^{3} \sum_{n_2=1}^{3} A_{n_1n_2}\Phi(n_1s^Z, n_2s^Z), \quad (8)$$

$$\Psi_B = B_1\Phi(1s^{Z_1}, 1s^{Z_1}) + B_2\Phi(2p^{Z_2}, 2p^{Z_2}) + B_3\Phi(3d^{Z_3}, 3d^{Z_3}) + B_4\Phi(4f^{Z_4}, 4f^{Z_4}), \quad (9)$$

$$\Phi_C = C_1\Phi(1s^{Z_1}, 1s^{Z_1'}) + C_2\Phi(2p^{Z_2}, 2p^{Z_2}) + C_3\Phi(3d^{Z_3}, 3d^{Z_3}) + C_4\Phi(4f^{Z_4}, 4f^{Z_4}). \quad (10)$$

Table 1 gives numerical results of variational calculations using these functions. For a given function, one assumes values for the effective charges, computes the matrix elements H_{ij} and S_{ij} (this requires only well-known procedures[7]), solves equation (4) for the energy E, and repeats with new values for the effective charges until a minimum E is obtained.

Discussion.—A single AP (e.g., function A-1 of Table 1) can be a solution of the wave equation for an atom only if the r_{ij} terms in the Hamiltonian operator are neglected or replaced by a spherically symmetric potential function. The principal difficulty with such wave functions is that they allow the electrons to move independently of one another; hence, in general, the functions are not small, as they should be, when the electrons are close together. One says that the wave function does not *correlate* the motion of the electrons, and the difference between the correct ground-

TABLE 1

VARIATION FUNCTIONS FOR THE NORMAL HELIUM ATOM

FUNCTION[a]	CONFIGURATIONS SUPERPOSED	PARAMETER VALUES	$-E_{calc.}$ (ATOMIC UNITS[e])	$E_{calc.} - E_{exptl.}$[f, g] (ATOMIC UNITS[e])
A-1 = B-1[b]	$(1s)^2$	$Z = 1.6875$	5.69531	0.1113
A-2	$(1s)^2, (1s2s)$	$Z = 1.757$	5.7085	0.0981
A-3	$(1s)^2, (1s2s), (1s3s)$	$Z = 1.777$	5.7117	0.0949
A-4	$(1s)^2, (1s2s), (2s)^2$	$Z = 1.78$	5.7095	0.0971
A-5	$(1s)^2, (1s2s), (1s3s), (2s)^2, (2s3s), (3s)^2$	$Z = 1.764$	5.7148	0.0918
B-2	$(1s)^2, (2p)^2$	$Z_1 = 1.6896, Z_2 = 3Z_1$	5.73870	0.0679
B-3	$(1s)^2, (2p)^2, (3d)^2$	Z_1 and Z_2 as above, $Z_3 = 6Z_1$	5.742867	0.0637
B-4	$(1s)^2, (2p)^2, (3d)^2, (4f)^2$	Z_1, Z_2, Z_3 as above, $Z_4 = 12Z_1$	5.743770	0.0628
C-1[c]	$(1s1s')$	$Z_1 = 1.19, Z_1' = 1.835Z_1$	5.751316	0.0552
C-2	$(1s1s'), (2p)^2$	Z_1 and Z_1' as above, $Z_2 = 4.16Z_1$	5.790369	0.0162
C-3	$(1s1s'), (2p)^2, (3d)^2$	Z_1, Z_1', Z_2 as above, $Z_3 = 9.5Z_1$	5.794033	0.0125
C-4	$(1s1s'), (2p)^2, (3d)^2, (4f)^2$	Z_1, Z_1', Z_2, Z_3 as above, $Z_4 = 16.0Z_1$	5.79486	0.0117
Hartree-Fock[d]	...	...	5.734	0.073

[a] Functions labeled A, B, C are of the types Ψ_A, Ψ_B, Ψ_C of equations (8), (9) and (10), respectively.

[b] Kellner, G. W., *Z. Physik*, **44**, 91 (1927).

[c] Eckart, C., *Phys. Rev.*, **36**, 878 (1930).

[d] Bethe, H., *Handbuch der Physik*, Vol. XXIV/1, p. 324.

[e] One atomic unit = $e^2/2a_0$ = 13.603 e.v. More strictly the values of $E_{calc.}$ should be interpreted as in units of $e^2/2a_{He}$, where $a_{He}/a_0 = 0.999863$, which corrects for the finite mass of the nucleus.

[f] $E_{exptl.} = -5.80656e^2/2a_0$—see Paschen, F., *Sitzber. preuss. Akad. Wiss.*, 1929, p. 662.

[g] These values are calculated assuming those in the previous column are in units of $e^2/2a_0$. Strictly the correction indicated in note *e* should be applied, which increases all $E_{calc.}$-$E_{exptl.}$ values by 0.0008.

state energy of a system and that calculated with the best function of this type (the Hartree-Fock function) is called the *correlation energy*. Thus the correlation energy for the helium atom is 0.073 atomic unit or 0.99 e.-v. (cf. Table 1).

There are essentially two ways (other than explicit introduction of r_{12} in the wave function) in which electron correlation can be brought into an analytical wave function for helium: either the electrons may be separated into concentric spherical shells or the wave function may be given angular dependence (e.g., one electron may be concentrated along the x axis and one along the y axis). In Table 1, all functions in set A and function C-1 fall in the first category, all functions in set B in the second category, and functions C-2, C-3 and C-4 in both categories. Set A separates the electrons into the concentric so-called K, L and M shells, as the same effective charge is used in each of the hydrogen-like orbitals $1s$, $2s$, $3s$. Essentially the same effect is achieved in C-1 through variation of the charges in $1s$ orbitals. It might appear as though such an effect

TABLE 2

EFFECTIVE CHARGES: BEST VALUES VERSUS VALUES DETERMINED BY CRITERION OF MAXIMUM OVERLAP[a]

		Z_1[e]	Z_1'	Z_2	Z_3	Z_4
Function B-4[b]	Best[d]	1.6896	...	$3Z_1$	$6Z_1$	$12Z_1$
	Max. overlap	1.6875	...	$(10/3)Z_1$	$7Z_1$	$12Z_1$
Function C-4[c]	Best	1.19	$1.835Z_1$	$4.16Z_1$	$9.5Z_1$	$16.0Z_1$
	Max. overlap	1.19	$1.835Z_1$	$4.57Z_1$	$9.6Z_1$	$16.6Z_1$

[a] Criterion of maximum overlap: to determine the effective charge for a given high energy configuration wave function, maximize the three-dimensional overlap of the radial part of this function with the wave function for the lowest energy configuration.

[b] See equation (9) and table 1.

[c] See equation (10) and table 1.

[d] Variation of the effective charges was not carried out as precisely with the B functions as with the C functions.

[e] Best and maximum overlap Z_1 values in the case of the B function differ because the former is an adjusted best value for the four-term function B-4 while the latter is the best value for the one-term function B-1. Adjustment does not give appreciable improvement in the case of the C function.

is also operative in the B set of functions, but there it is minor. For although hydrogen-like orbitals for K, L, M and N shells are used, the effective charges are varied, and the best values as given in Table 1 result in almost maximum overlap of the radial portions of the higher energy configuration wave functions with the $1s^2$ wave function (see below). Both effects are operative in the functions C-2, C-3 and C-4. Here $(1s^{Z_1}, 1s^{Z_1'})$ separates the electrons into two shells, and the angular correlation is obtained from $2p^2$, $3d^2$ and $4f^2$ configurations, where again the radial portions of the higher energy functions have almost maximum overlap with the lower energy function.

In Table 2 the variationally determined effective charges for the higher energy configurations in the type B and C functions are compared with values determined by a maximum overlap criterion. The agreement is striking, particularly in view of the fact that the calculated energies are not very sensitive to small changes in the parameters near their best values.[8]

The angular and radial correlation effects are almost independent of each other. Thus, the improvement resulting from superposition of $2p^2$, $3d^2$ and $4f^2$ configurations is about the same in both B and C sets of functions, even though the radial correlation obtained with B-1 and C-1 are very different (zero in the former case). Successive improvements from introduction of angular factors in the two cases are, in atomic units, 0.0434, 0.0042, 0.0009 for set B and 0.0390, 0.0037 and 0.0008 for set C. On this basis the angular correlation appears to account for about the fraction 0.045/0.073 or 62% of the total correlation energy, radial correlation for about 38%. The best function in Table 1, C-4, contains the fraction 0.0643/0.073 or 88% of the total correlation energy, about 64% of the radial correlation energy, and about 97% of the angular correlation energy. For this function, $C_1:C_2:C_3:C_4::1000:-60:-12:-4$.

Summary.—The wave function for the ground state of the helium atom is approximated by a superposition of vector-coupled ^1S functions for the configurations $(1s^{Z_1}, 1s^{Z_1'})$, $(2p^{Z_2})^2$, $(3d^{Z_3})^2$, $(4d^{Z_4})^2$, where the one-electron functions are hydrogen-like orbitals with the indicated charges. The best calculated energy, 5.79486 $e^2/2a_0$ (experimental value: 5.80656 $e^2/2a_0$), obtained with $Z_1 = 1.19$, $Z_1' = 1.835Z_1$, $Z_2 = 4.16Z_1$, $Z_3 = 9.5Z_1$, $Z_4 = 16.0Z_1$, contains 88% of the total correlation energy (Hartree-Fock energy-experimental energy).

Comparison with similar calculations putting $Z_1 = Z_1'$ suggests that total electronic correlation energy in an atom may be considered as a sum of radial and angular correlation energies. *Radial correlation energy* is tentatively defined as the difference between the Hartree-Fock energy and the energy calculated using the best superposition of all configurations obtainable from a complete set of purely radial one-electron functions (e.g., all *ns* hydrogen-like functions), and *angular correlation energy* is defined as the difference between total and radial correlation energies. The calculations then indicate that the correlation energy in the helium atom is about 62% angular and 38% radial, and that the best wave function obtained contains 97% of the angular and 64% of the radial correlation.

In attempting to regain radial correlation (separate electrons into concentric shells) weakly overlapping shells are found to effect little improvement; hence the use of the complete subset of *ns* functions with only one charge would be a slowly convergent process. Similarly in regaining angular correlation, maximizing the overlap of the *radial* factors of the high-energy angle-dependent terms in the wave function with the purely radial first term is found to yield almost optimum values for the charges.

* This paper was prepared in connection with a conference on "Quantum-Mechanical Methods in Valence Theory" held at Shelter Island, September 7–10, 1951, under the auspices of the NATIONAL ACADEMY OF SCIENCES (see "Summary of the Conference" in a subsequent issue of these PROCEEDINGS). The paper is based on part of a thesis submitted by G. Russell Taylor in partial fulfillment of the requirements for the degree of Doctor of Science, Carnegie Institute of Technology, 1951. The work was assisted in part by the Office of Naval Research, U. S. Navy, through Contract Nonr-493(00) with Carnegie Institute of Technology, in part by a grant from the Research Corporation. G. F. Hadley aided in the computations.

† DuPont Postgraduate Fellow, 1950–1951; Research Corporation Fellow, 1951. Present address: Mellon Institute of Industrial Research, Pittsburgh, Pennsylvania.

[1] Hylleraas, E., *Z. Physik*, **65**, 209 (1930).

[2] James, H. M., and Coolidge, A. S., *Phys. Rev.*, **49**, 688 (1936).

[3] For complex organic molecules, see, for example, Parr, Craig and Ross, *J. Chem. Phys.*, **18**, 1561 (1950) or Coulson, Craig and Jacobs, *Proc. Roy. Soc.*, **206A**, 297 (1951).

[4] For important developments in theory, clear statements of the general method of attack and a calculation on the beryllium atom, see Boys, S. F., *Proc. Roy. Soc.*, **200A**, 542 (1950); **201A**, 125 (1950).

[5] This has long been known and is implicit in statements of many authors, yet correct statements still crop up in the literature. Thus the LCAO molecular orbital method including configuration interaction is identical with the valence bond method including ionic structures, and as the number of AO's is increased both methods converge to the true wave function.

[6] Coulson, Craig and Jacobs, *op. cit.*

[7] Condon, E. U., and Shortley, G. H., *Theory of Atomic Spectra*, Cambridge University Press, Cambridge, 1935; Ufford, C. W., and Shortley, G. H., *Phys. Rev.*, **42**, 167 (1932).

[8] Only after the present work was complete, indeed only after this paragraph was written, was it noticed that S. F. Boys (*op. cit.*, paper II) had earlier also come to the conclusion that maximum overlap of radial functions gives maximum gain of angular correlation energy.

Reprinted from REVIEWS OF MODERN PHYSICS, Vol. 32, No. 2, 275–285, April, 1960
Printed in U. S. A.

Basis Functions for *Ab Initio* Calculations*

LELAND C. ALLEN†

Department of Physics, University of California, Berkeley 4, California

AND

ARNOLD M. KARO

Lawrence Radiation Laboratory, University of California, Livermore, California

I. INTRODUCTION

THIS article gives a compilation and basis function analysis of existing *ab initio* molecular eigenfunctions. Our review pertains to that body of the literature in which a direct solution of the Schrödinger equation is attempted, and especially that part which we believe offers the greatest opportunity for extension to the complicated molecules of chemical interest. The specific content of the article is frankly devoid of a connection with chemically significant problems. It is important for a future review to develop this connection, and it should be done in a more empirical framework than we have used.

By *ab initio* we imply: First, consideration of all the electrons simultaneously. Second, use of the exact nonrelativistic Hamiltonian (with fixed nuclei),

$$\mathcal{H}=-\tfrac{1}{2}\sum_{i}\nabla_i^2-\sum_{i,a}\frac{Z_a}{r_{ia}}+\sum_{i>j}\frac{1}{r_{ij}}+\sum_{a,b}\frac{Z_aZ_b}{r_{ab}}; \quad (1)$$

the indices i, j and a, b refer, respectively, to the electrons and to the nuclei with nuclear charges Z_a and Z_b. Third, an effort should have been made to evaluate all integrals rigorously. Thus, calculations are omitted in which the Mulliken integral approximations or electrostatic models have been used exclusively. These approximate schemes are valuable for many purposes, but present experience indicates that they are not sufficiently accurate to give consistent results in *ab initio* work. Some three- and four-center calculations are included, however, where such procedures were the only available means of obtaining certain integrals. While not imposed as a restriction on our listings, it is nevertheless true that all of the calculations have been carried out with nuclei fixed. In other words, no problems involving more than three particles in which vibronic interactions are important or where the mass of the negative particles is significant with respect to the nuclear masses (e.g., mesonic molecules) have been treated *ab initio*.

In addition to the preceding restrictions, we have limited the survey to molecular wave functions that involve more than two electrons and employ one-electron basis orbitals. Although two-electron problems comprise a large part of our detailed knowledge of electronic systems, a full treatment of this subject would be a review in itself, and the points we wish to bring out here become important primarily for molecules with more than two electrons. Actually the limitation to systems of more than two electrons essentially implies the use of one-electron basis orbitals, since only one or two quite specialized and apparently not readily generalizable calculations explicitly include r_{ij} in the wave function for more than two electrons.

In the mid-thirties a number of rigorous applications of quantum theory to simple molecular systems were made by several investigators, principally James, Coolidge, Knipp, and Coulson. However, it is not incorrect to state that the major effort in *ab initio* work dates from the Shelter Island Conference in 1951. At that conference there was a great deal of discussion on the evaluation of two-electron molecular integrals and considerable optimism for the early realization of extensive results, at least for the diatomic case. In the conference summary the question was asked, "Are Slater atomic orbitals really the best orbitals to use as a basis for molecular calculations?" The dearth of calculations made it impossible to discuss the question at that time; but now, at the Boulder Conference, sufficient data have been accumulated to give an answer. Nearly a decade has elapsed because only very recently have we had a rapid means for obtaining large numbers of integrals over the wide range of parameters required for practical basis function experimentation.

As in 1951, it is still true that the most rapid advances in the next year or two are to be expected in the diatomic case. This follows directly from the present existence of highly efficient digital computer programs for two-center integrals. These have been devised by Boys at Cambridge University, Nesbet at Boston University, Roothaan and co-workers at the University of Chicago, Switendick and Corbató at the Massachusetts Institute of Technology, and Harris at the University of California, Berkeley.[1] More than half of these have been written for commercial machines of which there are many copies. Besides the two-center

* This work was performed in part under the auspices of the U. S. Atomic Energy Commission.

† National Science Foundation Postdoctoral Fellow and staff member Materials Research Laboratory, OMRO, Watertown, Massachusetts.

[1] This work is reported at greater length elsewhere in this issue of *Reviews of Modern Physics*, and further discussion is inappropriate here.

integral programs, several of the groups have prepared programs such as the transformation of integrals to the SCF basis set and the Roothaan scheme, which are applicable to any molecular problem.

In undertaking the review just outlined, we would also like to call attention to the recent article by Kotani, Mizuno, Kayama, and Yoshizumi in the *Annual Review of Physical Chemistry* [9, 245 (1958)]. Their paper includes a discussion of semiempirical theories as well as *ab initio* work and thus has a greater breadth than we have attempted. It is certainly the reference which is most pertinent and closely related to our survey.

II. METHODS OF CONSTRUCTING MOLECULAR WAVE FUNCTIONS

(a) Non-AO Methods

The construction of non-AO wave functions has proceeded along two lines. Both methods essentially attempt to exploit more fully spatial geometry in special classes of molecules than would be possible in a strict AO treatment.

The first of these is the use of an elliptical coordinate system, and the most extensive effort along this line has been made by Harris and Taylor on small diatomic molecules. In addition to the use of natural coordinates, Harris seeks to minimize the number of required configurations by relaxing the constraints that the orbitals be orthogonal and filled in pairs. This technique, coupled with computer programs for varying the nonlinear parameters automatically, is very likely the most efficient scheme for diatomic molecules with from three to six or eight electrons. For larger diatomic molecules the greater importance of the atomic singularities and the rapidly increasing complexity introduced by the relaxation of the orbital constraints appear to limit the usefulness of the method.

The other non-AO proposal has been for the use of a single coordinate origin for all basis functions. Because of high symmetry and light surrounding atoms, molecules like the central hydrides are especially suited to this scheme. A good example is the encouraging work of Saturno and Parr[2] on CH_4. Another illustration is Allen's calculation of HF. Because this molecule is also a hydride and has a large positive dipole moment, the fluorine center was chosen as the coordinate origin. The principal idea behind one-center treatments is that the simplicity of having only one-center integrals to evaluate more than compensates for a larger basis set and higher l values. The use of a single coordinate origin seems justified for cases such as those cited in the foregoing or for various arrangements of two or three hydrogen atoms, but it is difficult to imagine a widespread generalization of this technique.

[2] Saturno and Parr have employed nonintegral principal quantum numbers in their single exponential basis functions.

Finally, Bingel (1)[3] recently has given the expansion of the molecular wave function in terms of the eigenfunctions of the united atom. For small separations the expansion depends on the internuclear distances, the united-atom charge density and its radial gradient at the origin. Although no calculations have yet been reported, this approach may prove to be a valuable adjunct to LCAO calculations at small internuclear distances. (In their review Kotani et al. use the term "united-atom orbitals" to refer to the type of basis functions mentioned both in this paragraph and the one preceding.)

(b) AO Methods

The valence bond and the LCAO molecular orbital schemes are the two general methods which form a natural framework for the use of AO's. In the valence bond method, as supplemented by configuration interaction (CI), the molecular wave function is expanded as a number of determinantal functions, each of which corresponds to a molecular system built up from definite states of the free atoms. The linear coefficients of this set of determinantal functions are obtained by energy minimization. When relatively few configurations can give a good result, this is an efficient method and is the procedure most used in early work.

On the other hand, the molecular orbital method is an approach to a molecular Hartree-Fock solution. In practice, the Roothaan procedure is the most useful technique for constructing the molecular orbital solution. The molecular orbitals are expanded as a finite set of specified basis functions with energy-determined linear coefficients, and when expressed in matrix form, this scheme is ideally suited for use with digital computers. Experience has shown that the molecular orbital state determined in this manner gives moderately good results for molecules at their equilibrium separations. This fact, together with the computational advantages of the Roothaan scheme, has led to the recent ascendancy of this procedure over all others for constructing molecular wave functions. (The notation, SCF LCAO-MO, has now become standardized for this type of calculation.) As is well known, configurations arising from one- and two-orbital substitutions in this single molecular-orbital determinant must be added to make the treatment equivalent to the valence bond method described in the preceding paragraph.

Assuming that one is able to carry out the necessary integrations, the central problem becomes the choice of AO's. By far the largest number of existing calculations have employed single exponential AO's. (Mulliken has introduced at the conference the designation and abbreviation, Slater Type Orbital—STO.) Except for symmetry considerations, basis orbital choice is then reduced to a specification of the three nonlinear param-

[3] References are listed in the Bibliography at the end of the article.

eters, n, a, and l, in $r^n e^{-ar} Y_l^{|m|}(\theta,\varphi)$. Rules for obtaining these have been given by Slater (2), Pauling (3), Zener (4), Roothaan (5), Duncanson and Coulson (6), and Morse, Young, and Haurwitz (7). The lists given by Duncanson and Coulson, and Morse et al. are slightly more complicated than the others; e.g., the 2s function is constructed from two exponentials with the parameters of the second term differing somewhat from those for the 1s function. The results of our survey appear to indicate, however, that all of these various rules for choosing nonlinear parameters lead to almost the same total molecular energies.

In addition to STO's, Gaussian and Hartree-Fock AO's have been used for a few molecules, and a detailed comparison is given in later sections.

(c) Configuration Interaction

Many of the calculations we have tabulated include a limited configuration interaction. The results uniformly show a small energy lowering of the order of 1 ev, and this slow convergence has led to much discouragement concerning the utility of the configuration interaction method. Typical of current work is the limited CI treatment of HF. Six excited MO configurations are formed by allowing promotion of all but the 1σ electrons into the more energetic 4σ MO. (The two-electron integral problem is so severe that, in general, only those configurations have been considered whose Hamiltonian matrix elements may be formed from the same integrals over the original basis functions needed for the single lowest configuration.) This can give only very limited freedom in describing electron correlation, and in the HF example, at least some type of δ and φ MO's should be available for CI.

Fortunately, almost all of the problems in configuration interaction can be investigated by resorting to free-atom calculations. Some of the most thorough work has been performed by Boys on Be, F^-, Ne, and Na^+ (8, 9). Considerable insight has also been gained from such a simple system as helium, and this serves as a good example. Taylor and Parr (10), Green et al. (11), Löwdin and Shull (12, 13), Holøien (14), and Nesbet and Watson (15), have all made studies on He with methods applicable to molecules with more than two electrons. The last calculation considered ten single exponential basis functions (with l values from 0 to 3) formed into 20 configurations. The choice of nonlinear parameters was the principal problem, and the significant result was that all functions should have the same radial maxima. This is in sharp contrast to the successive spreading out of the maxima with higher l values, or with increase in the number of radial nodes, which is characteristic of solutions for the central-field problem.

A new scheme for picking configuration-interaction orbital parameters has been suggested by Boys. He introduces "exclusive orbitals" and "oscillator orbitals," defined by externally imposed auxiliary conditions, that may lead to a more rapid convergence of the configuration interaction. Boys has also described some "correlation functions" through which he hopes to make a separate calculation for part of the correlation energy. These functions may contain explicit dependence on r_{ij}, but they are also functions for which the necessary integrals may be computed readily.[1]

III. TABULATION OF *AB INITIO* CALCULATIONS

Table I (16–74) lists the calculations that we have found in the literature, technical reports, and through private communication. There are approximately eighty calculations, three-fourths of which are for diatomic molecules. The structure of the table reflects the emphasis on basis orbitals and our belief that this is the central problem around which future development will take place. Our table lacks completeness for three-electron systems. There are so many of these that only a representative sampling of more recent work has been included.

(a) Other Computed Molecular Quantities

The total molecular energy and the dipole moment, both especially characteristic of the molecular wave function, have been tabulated in separate columns. Quadrupole moments, ionization potentials, polarizabilities, quadrupole coupling constants, etc., are all listed in a single column because so few results are available. The *Annual Review of Physical Chemistry* article by Kotani et al. and a paper by Karplus[1] survey values computed for these quantities. For example, rather good agreement with experiment is obtained for the $\langle r^2 \rangle$ part of the magnetic susceptibility of H_2O by using a molecular-orbital wave function with STO's, while the same type of wave function yields poor results for quadrupole coupling constants in O_2 and NO.

(b) Binding Energies

Present calculations are limited to atoms from the first row of the periodic table, and to a crude first approximation, they yield simply a fixed percentage (~99 to 99.5) of the total observed energy. Binding energies, however, for nearly all molecules are much less than 0.5% of the total energies, and it is possible to compute almost any value through a choice of basis functions that yield a relatively poor free-atom energy. The few calculations that obtain a total molecular energy lower than the *experimental* separated-atom energies are restricted to the class of small molecules with small total energies. For these reasons, binding-energy results have been relegated to the "other quantities computed" column.

(c) Approximate Calculations

As stated in the Introduction, we have omitted from the tabulation all calculations deviating appreciably

TABLE I. Compilation and summary of *ab initio* calculations.

Molecule	Reference	Method	Basis functions[a]	No. of configurations in CI	% total energy (single determinant)	% total energy (single determinant +CI)[b]	Dipole moment (debyes)[b,c]	Other computed molecular quantities[b]	Remarks
H_3	16	SCF LCAO-MO	STO (S)	···	93.03	···	···	D_e =1.17 (4.47) ev E_{act} =1.81 (0.43) ev r_e =2.0 a.u.	Linear nuclear configuration. H_3 approximated from SCF procedure for H_3^-.
H_3	17	LCAO-MO	STO (V)	21–35	···	98.14 (21)	···	D_e =3.48 (4.47) ev (21) r_e =1.779 a.u. (21) E_{act} =0.65 (0.43) ev (21)	Nine nuclear configurations.
H_3	18	LCAO-MO	STO (V)	20	···	97.39 (20)	···	r_e =1.93 a.u. (20) D_e =3.14 (4.47) ev (20)	Five 1*s* hydrogenlike orbitals with centers equally spaced on line of nuclei.
H_3	19	SCF LCAO-MO	STO (V)	3	···	95.95 (3)	···	r_e =1.84 a.u. (3) D_e =2.49 (4.47) ev (3)	Variable shifting parameter used.
He – He	20	SCF LCAO-MO	STO (S)	···	···	···	···	*I* (He) =24.39 (24.58) ev $E_{van\ d.\ Waals}$ =5.82 $\times 10^{-4}$ (9.25 $\times 10^{-4}$) ev	He_2^+ potential curve obtained with D_e =2.07 (2.5) ev, r_e =2.27 (2.06) a.u.
He – He	21	VB	Elliptic (V)	2	···	···	···	···	Complete variation of orbital parameters. Experimental and calculated values differ by 24 ev.
H_2+H_2	22	SCF LCAO-MO	STO (S)	···	···	···	···	···	Rectangular nuclear configuration found unstable.
H_3^-	23	VB	STO (S)	2	···	···	···	D_e =1.78 ev (2) r_e =2.25 a.u. (2)	Linear symmetrical configuration. Many-center integral approximations are compared.
H_4	24	LCAO-MO	STO (S)	6	···	···	···	D_e =0.44 ev (1) D_e =2.26 ev (6)	Linear nuclear configuration; complex stable w.r.t. 4H and unstable w.r.t. $2H_2$.
		SCF LCAO-MO	STO (S)	1	···	···	···	D_e =1.49 ev (1)	
H_4	25	SCF LCAO-MO	STO (S)	···	···	···	···	D_e =2.11 ev r_e =2.1 a.u.	Four linear nuclear configurations; complex stable w.r.t. 4H and unstable w.r.t. $2H_2$.
LiH	26	Variational	STO (S) + Elliptic	11	···	98.90 (11)	···	D_e =1.82 (2.52) ev (11)	STO's for Li 1*s* electrons. Valence electrons treated by James-Coolidge type expansion with r_{12} terms omitted.
LiH	27	VB	STO (S)	20	98.37	98.85 (20)	−6.04 (6)	E_1-E_0 =3.18 (3.66) ev (6) *I* =7.52 ev	Four sets of orbital exponential parameters.
LiH	28	VB	STO (DC)	6	···	98.86 (6)	−6.31 (6)	D_e =1.66 (2.52) ev (6)	
LiH	29	Variational	STO (S) + Elliptic	10	···	98.90 (10)	−5.57 (10)	···	Orbital parameter variation; r_{12} terms omitted.
LiH	30	VB	STO (S)	10	···	98.93 (6)	−5.61 (6)	···	Four sets of orbital exponential parameters. $2p_\sigma$ on hydrogen introduces hydrogen atom polarization.
LiH	31	SCF LCAO-MO	STO (V)	···	98.75	···	−5.92	D_e =1.41 (2.52) ev	Complete variation of orbital exponential parameters.
LiH	32	VB	Hartree-Fock	6	98.61	99.03 (6)	−6.05 (6)	D_e =1.62 (2.52) ev (6) r_e =3.24 (3.01) a.u. (6) ω_e =1212 (1406) cm^{-1} (6) T_e =2.66 (3.286) ev (6)	Nine internuclear distances; excited Σ^+ state evaluated.
LiH	33	SCF LCAO-MO	Hartree-Fock	6	98.83	99.03 (6)	−6.05 (6)	Equivalent to preceding calculation	Equivalent to preceding calculation.
LiH[d]	21	VB	Elliptic (V)	4	99.19	99.61 (4)	···	D_e =1.30 (2.52) ev (1) D_e =2.21 (2.52) ev (4)	Complete variation of orbital parameters.

[a] A further classification of the STO's is given in parenthesis: (S), orbital exponents adopted with or without modification from Slater's rules (2); (V), orbital exponents in the molecule determined by energy minimization; (DC), orbital exponents tabulated by Duncanson and Coulson (6); (MYH), orbital exponents tabulated by Morse, Young, and Haurwitz (7); (R), orbital exponents tabulated by Roothaan (5).
[b] Following the computed number, the experimental value and the number of configurations in the CI are given in parentheses. Where possible, computed values are given for the experimental internuclear distance.
[c] The sign of the dipole moment is relative to the heavier atom taken to be at the origin of coordinates.
[d] Evaluated at 3.2 a.u.
[e] Evaluated at 5.63 a.u.
[f] Evaluated at 5 a.u.
[g] Evaluated at 6.01 a.u.
[h] Corrected by R. K. Nesbet (cf. reference 58).
[i] *f* terms included.
[j] Evaluated at $r=\infty$.
[k] Apex atom positive.

TABLE I.—*Continued.*

Molecule	Reference	Method	Basis functions[a]	No. of configurations in CI	% total energy (single determinant)	% total energy (single determinant +CI)[b]	Dipole moment (debyes)[b,c]	Other computed molecular quantities[b]	Remarks
BeH^+	27	VB	STO (S)	10	···	98.98 (10)	···	$E_1-E_0=5.22$ (5.40) ev (6)	Two sets of orbital exponential parameters.
BeH	34	SCF LCAO-MO	STO (S)	···	99.41	···	···	$D_e=2.75$ (2.22) ev $r_e=2.51$ (2.54) a.u. $I=8.43$ (8.1) ev	Four internuclear distances. Be 1*s* not mixed in forming MO's.
Li_2^+[e]	35	VB	STO (S)	···	···	···	···	$D_e=0.304$ (1.30) ev	
		Variational	STO (S) + Elliptic	8	···	···	···	$D_e=0.49$ (1.30) ev (1) $D_e=1.24$ (1.30) ev (8)	STO's for Li 1*s*. Valence electrons treated by James-Coolidge type expansion with r_{12} terms omitted.
Li_2	36, 37	VB	STO (S)	2	99.00[g]	99.00(2)	···	$D_e=0.27$ (1.05) ev (2) $r_e=6.01$ (5.049) a.u. $q'=0.0040$ a.u.	Integrals evaluated in polar or elliptical coordinates. Three internuclear distances. Orbital variations for 2*s*.
		Variational	STO (S) + Elliptic	18	···	99.11 (18)	···	$D_e=0.51$ (1.05) ev (18) $q'=-0.0030$ a.u. (18)	STO's for Li 1*s* electrons. Valence electrons treated by James-Coolidge type expansion with r_{12} terms omitted.
Li_2[f]	38	LCAO-MO	STO (S)	···	98.82	···	···	$D_e=-0.3$ (1.05) ev	Li 1*s* not mixed in forming MO's; orbital exponential parameters varied.
Li_2	39	SCF LCAO-MO	STO (MYH)	···	99.02	···	···	$D_e=0.33$ (1.05) ev $I=4.91$ ev $E_1-E_0=2.30$ (1.895) ev $Q(Li_2)=-0.17$ a.u.	
Li_2	40	LCAO-MO	STO (S)	8	98.88	99.11 (8)	···	$D_e=0.77$ (1.05) ev (8) $Q(Li_2)=19.46$ a.u. (8) $q'=0.0016$ a.u. (8)[e]	Three sets of orbital exponential parameters and three internuclear distances. Excited states obtained from ground state secular equation.
		SCF LCAO-MO	STO (S)	···	98.95	···	···	$D_e=0.124$(1.05) ev $Q(Li_2)=22.31$ a.u.	
Li_2	31	SCF LCAO-MO	STO (V)	···	98.98	···	···	$D_e=0.15$ (1.05) ev	Complete variation of orbital exponential parameters.
BH	41	SCF LCAO-MO	STO (S)	···	99.17	···	0.99	$D_e=1.80$ (3.14) ev	
BH	17	LCAO-MO	STO (S)	23	···	99.34 (23)	···	$D_e=1.50$ (3.14) ev (23) $r_e=2.33$ (2.33) a.u. (23)	Scale factor variation. Three internuclear distances.
BH	42	VB	STO (S)	13	99.11	99.36 (13)	···	$D_e=1.46$ (3.14) ev (1) $D_e=2.22$ (3.14) ev (13)	Hybridization introduced in single determinant calculation. Excited states evaluated.
BH	31	SCF LCAO-MO	STO (V)	···	99.21	···	1.58	$D_e=2.07$ (3.14) ev	Complete variation of orbital exponential parameters.
CH^+	43	SCF LCAO-MO	STO (S)	···	99.20	···	···	$D_e=0.9$ (3.77) ev	Excitation energies computed.
CH	43	SCF LCAO-MO	STO (S)	···	99.16	···	0.93	$D_e=1.2$ (3.64) ev $I=11.1$ (11.1) ev	Excitation energies computed.
CH	44	VB	STO (S) and Hartree-Fock	8	···	···	···	$D_e=2.51$ (3.64) ev (8) $\omega_e=3400$ (2900) cm^{-1} (8) $r_e=2.00$ (2.12) a.u. (8)	Five internuclear distances. Orthogonality between C 1*s* and H 1*s* assumed. C 1*s* not mixed in forming MO's. One-center integrals from Hartree-Fock AO's. Two-center integrals from Slater AO's. Excited states obtained from ground state secular equation.
		SCF LCAO-MO	STO (S) and Hartree-Fock	12	···	···	1.97 (1)	$D_e=2.27$ (3.64) ev $D_e=2.95$ (3.64) ev (12) $\omega_e=3100$ (2900) cm^{-1} (12) $r_e=2.06$ (2.12) a.u. (12) $I=12.7$ (11.1) ev	
Be_2	31	SCF LCAO-MO	STO (V)	···	···	···	···	···	Complete variation of orbital exponential parameters. Total energy computed.
NH	43	SCF LCAO-MO	STO (S)	···	99.14	···	0.90	$D_e=0.5$ (4.01)ev $I=11.8$ ev	Excitation energies computed.
NH	45	SCF LCAO-MO	STO (S) and Hartree-Fock	···	···	···	1.24	$D_e=1.40$ (4.01) ev	Cf. remarks for CH (reference 44). N 1*s* not mixed in forming MO's. Excited states obtained from ground state secular equation.
NH	46	SCF LCAO-MO	STO (S)	···	99.16	···	0.91	$D_e=0.50$ (4.01) ev	Separate SCF calculation for *d* $^1\Sigma^+$ state. Other excited states obatined from ground state secular equation.
NH	31	SCF LCAO-MO	STO (V)	···	···	···	2.01	···	Complete variation of orbital exponential parameters. Total energy computed.

TABLE I.—*Continued.*

Molecule	Reference	Method	Basis functions[a]	No. of configurations in CI	% total energy (single determinant)	% total energy (single determinant +CI)[b]	Dipole moment (debyes)[b,c]	Other computed molecular quantities[b]	Remarks
OH	47	VB	Hartree-Fock	10	99.24	99.40 (10)	2.29 (3)	D_e =1.04 (4.58) ev (10)	
		SCF LCAO-MO	Hartree-Fock	6	99.39	99.41 (6)	2.66 (1)	D_e =1.25 (4.58) ev (6)	Three internuclear distances.
OH	43	SCF LCAO-MO	STO (S)	···	99.06	···	0.92	D_e =0.8 (4.58) ev I =10.8 (13.16) ev	Excitation energies computed.
NH_2	45	SCF LCAO-MO	STO (S) and Hartree-Fock	···	···	···	1.9	D_e =4.2 ev I =14.16 (11.05) ev Equil. bond angle =105°	Cf. remarks for NH (reference 45). Variation w.r.t. bond angle. Two-electron three-center integrals approximated.
CH_3	58	SCF LCAO-MO	Approx SCF AO's	···	···	···	···	D_e =11.78 (12.7) ev I =12.04 (9.95) ev	Orthogonality between C 1*s* and H 1*s* assumed. C 1*s* not mixed in forming MO's. C 3*s* determined variationally. 3*s* exchange and two-electron three- and four-center integrals approximated. Excitation energies computed.
B_2	49	SCF LCAO-MO	STO (S)	···	99.10	···	···	D_e =0.17 (3.67) ev	Three internuclear distances. Excited states obtained from ground state ($^3\Sigma_g^-$) secular equation.
HF	50	VB	STO (S)	6	···	98.95 (2)	1.13 (1.74) (2)	D_e =1.03 (6.08) ev (2)	
		VB	STO (DC)	6	···	99.00 (6)	0.93 (1.74) (6)	D_e =1.96 (6.08) ev (6)	
HF	43	SCF LCAO-MO	STO (S)	···	98.95	···	0.87 (1.74)	D_e =1.1 (6.08) ev I =12.6 (15.77) ev	
HF	51	SCF LCAO-MO	STO (S)	7	98.96	98.99 (7)	0.69 (1.74) (7)	D_e =2.12 (6.08) ev (7) I =12.7 (15.77) ev I =15.5 (17.0) ev	
HF	52	SCF LCAO-MO	Hartree-Fock	7	99.44	99.46 (7)	1.84 (1.74) (7)	D_e =2.11 (6.08) ev (7) r_e =2.0 (1.7328) a.u. (7) I =17.31 (15.77) ev I =19.4 (17.0) ev	Five internuclear distances.
HF	31, 53	SCF LCAO-MO	STO (V)	···	99.01	···	1.49 (1.74)	D_e =2.42 (6.08) I =12.8 (15.77) ev I =16.2 (17.0) ev	Complete variation of orbital exponential parameters.
HF	54	One-center	STO (V)	···	99.42	···	2.28 (1.74)	D_e =1.59 (6.08) ev	*s*, *p*, and *d* orbitals on *F* center. *f* orbitals included in later calculation.
H_2O	55	SCF LCAO-MO	STO (S)	3	99.13_3	99.13_5 (3)	1.52 (1.84) (1)	D_e =7.7 (10.06) ev (1) I =11.79 (12.6) ev I =13.20 (14.5) ev I =18.55 (16.2) ev Equil. bond angle =120° (105°) (1)	Variation with respect to bond angle. Most three-center integrals approximated.
H_2O	17	LCAO-MO	STO (S)	30	···	99.08 (30)	···	D_e =5.81 (10.06) ev (30) r_e =1.95 (1.81) a.u. (30) Equil. bond angle =96° (105°) (30)	Seven nuclear configurations. Force constants computed.
NH_3	45	SCF LCAO-MO	STO (S) and Hartree-Fock	···	···	···	1.97 (1.46)	D_e =8.6 (12.47) ev I =13.14 (10.25) ev Equil. bond angle =108° (106.8°)	Cf. remarks for NH and NH_2 (reference 45). Two-electron three- and four-center integrals approximated. Barrier energy =0.4 (0.25) ev.
NH_3	56	SCF LCAO-MO	Hartree-Fock	13	99.43	99.46 (13)	1.82 (1.46)	D_e =10.3 (12.47) ev (13) I =14.0 (11.0) ev I =19.3 (17.0) ev	Two nuclear configurations. Barrier energy =3.97 (0.25) ev.
NH_3	57	SCF LCAO-MO	STO (S)	···	99.17	···	1.49 (1.46)	D_e =9.00 (12.47) ev I =9.94 (11.0) ev I =16.20 (17.0) ev	
NH_4^+	58	Variational spherical model	STO (V)	···	···	···	···	r_e =1.84 a.u.	Total energy computed.
CH_4	58	Variational spherical model	STO (V)	···	97.06	···	···	r_e =1.98 (2.041) a.u.	
CH_4	59	SCF MO spherical model	Hartree	···	97.43[h]	···	···	D_e = −5.44 (∼20) ev $\chi = -33.2\times10^{-6}$ (-12.2×10^{-6}) emu $\alpha = 7.6\times10^{-24}$ (2.5×10^{-24}) cm^3	Exchange neglected.
CH_4	60	SCF MO spherical model	Hartree-Fock	···	97.18	98.86[i]	···	···	*f* terms included for perturbation calculation.

TABLE I.—*Continued.*

Molecule	Reference	Method	Basis functions[a]	No. of configurations in CI	% total energy (single determinant)	% total energy (single determinant +CI)[b]	Dipole moment (debyes)[b,c]	Other computed molecular quantities[b]	Remarks
CH_4	61	One-center	STO (V); integer-*n* STO (V); non-integer-*n*	5 5	97.30 97.49	98.08 (5) 98.23 (5)	... ...	r_e = 1.93 (2.041) a.u. (5) r_e = 2.02 (2.041) a.u. (5)	Three internuclear distances. Force constants evaluated.
C_2	31	SCF LCAO-MO	STO (V)	...	...	...	...	...	Complete variation of orbital exponential parameters. Total energy computed.
LiF	31	SCF LCAO-MO	STO (R)	...	98.96	...	3.43	D_e = 0.58 (5.99) ev	
N_2	62, 63	SCF LCAO-MO	STO (S)	6	99.05	99.12 (6)	...	D_e = 1.20 (9.90) ev (1) D_e = 3.29 (9.90) ev (6) I = 14.82 (15.60) ev I = 15.77 (17.08) ev I = 19.88 (18.72) ev $Q(N_2) = -1.87$ ($\pm$1.11) a.u.	
N_2	31	SCF LCAO-MO	STO (V)	...	99.13	...	...	D_e = 2.61 (9.90) ev I = 15.11 (15.60) ev I = 14.84 (17.08) ev I = 19.42 (18.72) ev	Complete variation of orbital exponential parameters. Ionization potentials are not vertically corrected.
BF	31	SCF LCAO-MO	STO (S)	...	99.07	...	−2.16	D_e = 5.24 (4.39) ev	
CO	64	SCF LCAO-MO	STO (S)	...	99.27	...	−1.00 (−0.12)	D_e = 11.2 (11.11) ev I = 13.37 (14.01) ev I = 15.97 (16.58) ev I = 20.01 (19.70) ev	C 1*s* and O 1*s* not mixed in forming MO's.
CO	31	SCF LCAO-MO	STO (S)	...	99.09	...	−0.73 (−0.12)	D_e = 5.38 (11.11) ev I = 13.08 (14.01) ev I = 15.87 (16.58) ev I = 19.93 (19.70) ev	Ionization potentials are not vertically corrected.
HCN	65	SCF LCAO-MO	STO (DC)	...	...	...	...	I = 17.3 (13.7) ev I = 26.4 (26.3) ev $Q(N^{14}) = 0.0071 \times 10^{-24}$ cm^2	C 1*s* and N 1*s* not mixed in forming MO's.
NO	66	SCF LCAO-MO	STO (S)	9	99.05	99.14 (9)	−0.50 ($\pm$0.16)	D_e = 1.7 (6.6) ev (9) I = 9.14 (9.25) ev (1)	Excitation energies computed.
O_2	67	LCAO-MO	Gaussian	9	...	...	...	D_e = 5.07 (5.18) ev (9) r_e = 2.26 (2.28) a.u. (9) ω_e = 1503 (1580) cm^{-1} (9)	Six internuclear distances. $^1\Sigma_g^+$ state calculated with twelve configurations.
O_2	68	LCAO-MO SCF LCAO-MO	STO (S) STO (S)	15 ...	99.07 99.12	99.19 (15) ...	... ...	D_e = 3.63 (5.18) ev $Q(O_2) = -1.53$ ($\lvert Q\rvert$ <0.82) a.u. D_e = 0.80 (5.18) ev $Q(O_2) = -1.76$ ($\lvert Q\rvert$ <0.82) a.u.	Excited states obtained from ground-state secular equation. Excitation energies computed.
Be_4	69	SCF LCAO-MO	STO (S)	...	99.22[j]	...	...	I = 8.30 (9.33) ev[j]	Four square planar nuclear configurations. Three- and four-center integral approximations are compared.
F_2	70	VB	STO (S+DC)	...	99.16	...	...	D_e = 7.62 (1.68) ev	Exchange interactions between *F* 1*s* on one atom and electrons of other atom are neglected. One-center integrals from Duncanson-Coulson AO's. Two-center integrals from Slater AO's. $^3\Sigma_u^+$ state calculated.
F_2	71	SCF LCAO-MO	STO (S)	6	99.10	99.14 (6)	...	D_e = −0.23 (1.68) ev (1) D_e = 1.96 (1.68) ev (6) $Q(F_2)$ = 0.169 a.u. I = 12.33 (15.7) ev I = 14.34 ev I = 15.96 ev	Excitation energies computed.
F_2	31	SCF LCAO-MO	STO (V)	...	99.10	...	...	D_e = −0.20 (1.68) ev I = 12.91 (15.7) ev I = 14.86 ev I = 16.54 ev	Complete variation of orbital exponential parameters. Ionization potentials are not vertically corrected.
SiH_4	72	SCF MO spherical model	Hartree	...	...	...	...	D_e = −9.52 ev r_e = 3.10 (2.80) a.u.	Exchange included. Total energy computed.
CO_2	73	SCF LCAO-MO	STO (S)	...	99.36	...	...	D_e = 21.46 (16.5) ev I = 11.5 (13.75) ev I = 17.9 (18.0) ev I = 18.8 (17.29) ev	1*s* orbitals not mixed in forming MO's. Many two- and three-center integrals approximated.
O_3	74	SCF LCAO-MO	Hartree-Fock	...	98.45	...	−0.25 (−0.55)[k]	D_e = 5.05 (6.20) ev	O 1*s* not mixed in forming MO's. Excited states obtained from ground-state secular equation. Excitation energies computed.

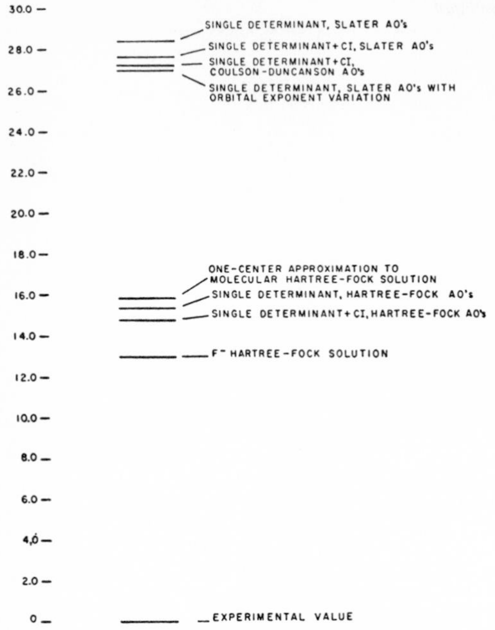

FIG. 1. Error in total energies (ev), $r_0 = 1.7328$ a.u.

from the *ab initio* prescription. But precisely what and how great departures may be made without causing a significant modification of results has by no means been sufficiently explored. Karo and Allen (51) and Ballinger (53) have investigated the accuracy requirements for the one- and two-electron integrals in HF. Ishiguro, Kayama, Kotani, and Mizuno (40) examined the validity of neglecting the overlap between the 1*s* orbital on one center and the 2*s*, 2*p* on the other for Li_2. They also made calculations with the 1*s* collapsed into the nuclear core. In general, Ishiguro et al. found that these approximations seriously affected the prediction of molecular quantities.

IV. DIATOMIC LCAO CALCULATIONS

Almost all of our *ab initio* experience derives from diatomic LCAO calculations, and thus we are best able to compare various types of basis orbitals for this class of wave functions. We have chosen hydrogen fluoride as an illustration because there are many existing wave functions for this molecule and because it is sufficiently complicated to possess the principal features of larger systems.

In Fig. 1 total energies at the equilibrium internuclear separation, 1.7328 a.u., are shown relative to the experimental molecular energy. (Data from 31, 50–54, 75.) All but one of the calculations have used the Roothaan procedure as a starting point. The exception is Kastler's valence bond treatment using Duncanson and Coulson basis orbitals. However, it can be shown that, for all practical purposes, the results are equivalent to a Roothaan calculation with limited CI. The striking feature of this figure is the clustering of results into two groups separated by about a rydberg. The upper group of calculations employ STO's; the lower group, Hartree-Fock AO's. It is apparently of relatively little consequence which rules are used for choosing the nonlinear parameters in the STO's. In fact, for the best of the upper calculations, there was a variation in the molecule of all the exponential parameters in the STO's. In these calculations, CI was carried out with the same configurations (or with the equivalent set of configurations using Duncanson and Coulson AO's) for both the Hartree-Fock AO's and for the various sets of STO's. The inclusion or deletion of this in no way affects the conclusions, since at the equilibrium separation these configurations contribute less than 1 ev for both types of orbitals. The wave functions employing Hartree-Fock orbitals also were carried through for larger internuclear distances; and in this region the CI makes a far larger contribution and is necessary to obtain a potential curve that exhibits even the qualitatively correct limiting behavior.

The one-rydberg decrease in the HF molecular energy is larger than would be expected to occur in many other molecules, and the explanation is simple: single exponential basis orbitals are notoriously poor for negative ions, and for fluorine they give a large electron affinity of the wrong sign, while Hartree-Fock solutions for F and F^- give the correct sign and close to the proper magnitude (75). The polar character of HF strongly brings out this shortcoming in the STO's.

There are three other molecules with LCAO wave functions made from both Hartree-Fock AO's and STO's: LiH, NH_3, and OH. Each of these yields a lower total energy for the Hartree-Fock AO's. Total energy differences range from 0.4 ev for LiH to 7 ev for OH.

The extensive work on HF allows us to make a reasonable estimate of the true *molecular* Hartree-Fock total energy. This has been done by making a plausible extrapolation of Allen's one-center calculation and by comparing with the F^- Hartree-Fock solution. (The F^- result is shown in Fig. 1 relative to its own experimental energy.) The conclusion is that the molecular Hartree-Fock total energy lies 2 to 3 ev below the single-determinant Hartree-Fock AO value. This is significant because this energy difference would appear directly in the binding energy and give a value close to that observed experimentally. It now seems possible and highly desirable to go beyond the LCAO approximation and seek true molecular Hartree-Fock solutions through the use of the Roothaan procedure. (Direct two-dimensional numerical integration of the Hartree-Fock differential equations for two centers is still out of reach for a ten-electron system such as HF.) Here again, choice of the nonlinear parameters in the finite basis set is the major problem. The work on HF (and also LiH, NH_3, and OH) points the way to a practical procedure: since most existing digital computer programs for two-electron integrals are written for STO basis functions, a good initial guess can be obtained from those nonlinear parameters corresponding to STO fits of the Hartree-Fock AO's. Very recently Nesbet (76) has essentially done this and more for HF. Besides those parameters that represent Hartree-Fock AO's, he has added *s* and *p* orbitals on the hydrogen center and two d_σ and two d_π basis functions on the fluorine center. The total molecular energy obtained from this calculation is -99.9847 a.u. and should be within 1 to 2 ev of the molecular Hartree-Fock value. There is another and very compelling reason for emphasis on a molecular Hartree-Fock solution: It is the best wave function we can obtain and still retain clear and straightforward interpretability in terms of simple one-electron orbitals.

So far our attention has been directed toward the total energy, but we would expect the dipole moment to show similar improvement when Hartree-Fock AO's are employed. Unfortunately, present results are inconclusive. Significantly better results are found for HF, but for NH_3, STO's seem to give an anomalously good answer. For LiH and OH, experimental values are lacking. Figure 2 is a plot of the dipole moment data for HF. In Allen's one-center approach to a molecular Hartree-Fock solution, all of the functions are located on the fluorine center, and since a finite series of terms is used to represent that part of the wave function centered at the hydrogen atom, there is a tendency to overweight the ionic character of the molecule. On the other hand, lack of sufficient flexibility in the molecular orbital LCAO wave function gives rise to an incorrect slope at small internuclear separations. In spite of these shortcomings, the wave functions based on Hartree-Fock AO's yield values superior to those using STO's. The really exciting result will be the μ versus r curve for a molecular Hartree-Fock solution (augmented by the usual limited configuration interaction). Pieceing together the various parts of the curves in Fig. 2 indicates that a high degree of quantitative accuracy might be achieved. In general, calculations directed toward exploring the effect of basis function choice are especially important for the dipole moment because of its sensitivity to any change in the basis-function parameters. Ballinger (53) has computed the charge distribution in HF for Slater parameter STO's and for those parameters which minimize the molecular energy. His graphs of the two charge distributions display the sensitive nature of the dipole moment. He concludes that simple ideas attempting to relate gross charges with μ are dangerous.

Our discussion in this section concerning the greater accuracy in total energies and dipole moments, obtained with an improved basis set, certainly indicates the desirability of correlating changes in the values of other

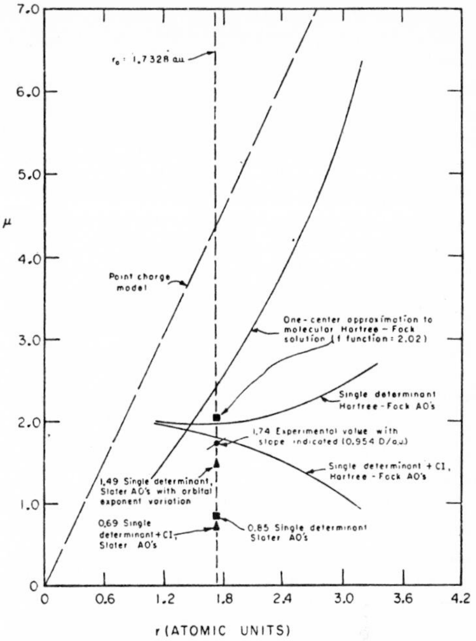

FIG. 2. Dipole moments (in debyes) for HF.

molecular quantities, such as quadrupole coupling constants, with modifications in the basis set.

V. MORE THAN TWO CENTERS

There are approximately twenty *ab initio* calculations for molecules with more than two atoms, but there is a decided dividing line between the existing diatomic and polyatomic wave functions. Confidence in the satisfactory evaluation of the many-center two-electron integrals is very much less than for the diatomic case, and it is clearly apparent that we are in major difficulty for three- and four-center two-electron integrals.

One line of attack being pursued is the formulation and improvement of integration methods for three and four centers with STO's. Three groups, each with different techniques, are actively working on the development of efficient digital computer programs: Boys at Cambridge University expresses the STO's in a series of Gaussians and then applies his analytic many-center Gaussian formulas; Barnett at the Massachusetts Institute of Technology in using his expansion about a single center; and Roothaan and co-workers at the University of Chicago utilize an expansion in elliptic coordinates, followed by a two-dimensional numerical integration.[1]

A second approach is to re-examine and modify the basis set. STO's form natural solutions to the central-field problem and are thus efficient for describing atomic singularities in molecular wave functions. Laguerre functions are also satisfactory in this regard, and some use has been made of them. However, in no case do these functions appear to have an overwhelming advantage over STO's, and there is every indication that three- and four-center integrals will be at least as hard to evaluate as for STO's. In general, any other analytic basis function type must pay a heavy price in the number of terms necessary to represent the wave function in the region around the nuclei. One suggestion (77) has been to use a mixed basis set composed of both Gaussians and exponentials. If the individual exponential functions, or a fixed linear combination of exponential and Gaussian terms, on one center do not overlap those on another, and if only Gaussians are used to represent the bonding part of the wave function, one can then obtain the benefit of the exponentials around the nuclei without the corresponding many-center integral problem. It can be shown that the exponential part may be transformed to a Gaussian form and the analytic many-center Gaussian integral formulas applied (78). This is done at the expense of a few more terms and a relatively simple numerical integration.

Another method which seems promising at the present time is based on the revival of Boys' 1950 proposal (78) for the use of an all-Gaussian basis set. During the intervening years a number of papers reported quite discouraging results with limited sets of Gaussian orbitals, and their use was largely abandoned. However, as we have shown in Sec. IV, it has become apparent that a more elaborate basis set, regardless of its analytic form, is required for many applications. Because of this, it appears quite possible that the larger number of Gaussians required, as compared to exponentials, may be offset by the very great simplification in evaluating the two-electron many-center integrals. Finally, basis functions in the form of plane waves may be added to the Gaussian functions with very little additional increase in the labor of computing the integrals. This additional flexibility in the basis set may prove valuable in conjugated molecules and other cases where some of the electrons are free to move throughout the system (79).

BIBLIOGRAPHY

1. W. A. Bingel, J. Chem. Phys. **30**, 1250 (1959).
2. J. C. Slater, Phys. Rev. **36**, 57 (1930).
3. L. Pauling, J. Am. Chem. Soc. **53**, 1367 (1931).
4. C. Zener, Phys. Rev. **36**, 51 (1930).
5. C. C. J. Roothaan, Laboratory of Molecular Structure and Spectra, University of Chicago, TR 1955 (October 1, 1954–September 30, 1955).
6. W. E. Duncanson and C. A. Coulson, Proc. Roy. Soc. Edinburgh **62**, 37 (1944).
7. P. M. Morse, L. A. Young, and E. S. Haurwitz, Phys. Rev. **48**, 948 (1935). Extended and corrected by A. Tubis, Phys. Rev. **102**, 1049 (1956).
8. S. F. Boys, Proc. Roy. Soc. (London) **A201**, 125 (1950).
9. M. J. M. Bernal and S. F. Boys, Phil. Trans. of Roy. Soc. London **A245**, 139 (1952).
10. G. R. Taylor and R. G. Parr, Proc. Natl. Acad. Sci. U. S. **38**, 154 (1952).
11. L. C. Green, M. N. Lewis, M. M. Mulder, C. W. Wyeth, and J. W. Woll, Jr., Phys. Rev. **93**, 273 (1954).
12. P.-O. Löwdin and H. Shull, Phys. Rev. **101**, 1730 (1955).
13. H. Shull and P.-O. Löwdin, J. Chem. Phys. **23**, 1362, 1565 (1955).
14. E. Holøien, Phys. Rev. **104**, 1301 (1956).
15. R. K. Nesbet and R. E. Watson, Phys. Rev. **110**, 1073 (1958).
16. V. Griffing and J. T. Vanderslice, J. Chem. Phys. **23**, 1039 (1955).
17. S. F. Boys, G. B. Cook, C. M. Reeves, and I. Shavitt, Nature **178**, 1207 (1956).
18. G. E. Kimball and J. G. Trulio, J. Chem. Phys. **28**, 493 (1958).
19. W. E. Meador, Jr., J. Chem. Phys. **29**, 1339 (1959).
20. V. Griffing and J. F. Wehner, J. Chem. Phys. **23**, 1024 (1955).
21. F. E. Harris and H. Taylor (private communication).
22. V. Griffing and A. Maček, J. Chem. Phys. **23**, 1029 (1955).
23. R. S. Barker, H. Eyring, D. A. Baker, and C. J. Thorne, J. Chem. Phys. **23**, 1381 (1955).
24. R. Taylor, Proc. Phys. Soc. (London) **A64**, 249 (1951).
25. V. Griffing and J. T. Vanderslice, J. Chem. Phys. **23**, 1035 (1955).
26. J. K. Knipp, J. Chem. Phys. **4**, 300 (1936).
27. J. Miller, R. H. Friedman, R. P. Hurst, and F. A. Matsen, J. Chem. Phys. **27**, 1385 (1957).
28. A. C. Hurley, J. Chem. Phys. **28**, 532 (1958).
29. F. T. Ormand and F. A. Matsen, J. Chem. Phys. **29**, 100 (1958).
30. O. Platas and F. A. Matsen, J. Chem. Phys. **29**, 965 (1958).
31. B. J. Ransil, Revs. Modern Phys. **32**, 245 (1960), this issue.
32. A. M. Karo and A. R. Olson, J. Chem. Phys. **30**, 1232 (1959).
33. A. M. Karo, J. Chem. Phys. **30**, 1241 (1959).
34. S. Aburto, R. Gallardo, and R. Muñoz, J. chim. phys. **56**, 563 (1959).
35. H. M. James, J. Chem. Phys. **3**, 9 (1935).
36. H. M. James, J. Chem. Phys. **2**, 794 (1934).
37. E. G. Harris and M. A. Melkanoff, Phys. Rev. **90**, 585 (1953).
38. C. A. Coulson and W. E. Duncanson, Proc. Roy. Soc. (London) **A181**, 378 (1943).
39. J. E. Faulkner, J. Chem. Phys. **27**, 369 (1957).
40. E. Ishiguro, K. Kayama, M. Kotani, and Y. Mizuno, J. Phys. Soc. Japan **12**, 1355 (1957).
41. R. C. Sahni, J. Chem. Phys. **25**, 332 (1956).
42. K. Ohno, J. Phys. Soc. Japan **12**, 938 (1957).
43. M. Krauss, J. Chem. Phys. **28**, 1021 (1958).
44. J. Higuchi, J. Chem. Phys. **22**, 1339 (1954).
45. J. Higuchi, J. Chem. Phys. **24**, 535 (1956).
46. M. E. Boyd, J. Chem. Phys. **29**, 108 (1958).
47. A. J. Freeman, J. Chem. Phys. **28**, 230 (1958).
48. J. Higuchi, J. Chem. Phys. **28**, 527 (1958).
49. A. A. Padgett and V. Griffing, J. Chem. Phys. **30**, 1286 (1959).
50. D. Kastler, J. chim. phys. **50**, 556 (1953).
51. A. M. Karo and L. C. Allen, J. Am. Chem. Soc. **80**, 4496 (1958).
52. A. M. Karo and L. C. Allen, J. Chem. Phys. **31**, 968 (1959).
53. R. A. Ballinger, Mol. Phys. **2**, 139 (1959).
54. L. C. Allen, Quart. Progr. Repts., Solid-State and Molecular Theory Group, Massachusetts Institute of Technology (April 15, 1956–January 15, 1958).
55. F. O. Ellison and H. Shull, J. Chem. Phys. **23**, 2348 (1955).
56. H. Kaplan, J. Chem. Phys. **26**, 1704 (1957).
57. A. B. F. Duncan, J. Chem. Phys. **27**, 423 (1957).
58. M. J. M. Bernal, Proc. Phys. Soc. (London) **A66**, 514 (1953).
59. R. A. Buckingham, H. S. W. Massey, and S. R. Tibbs, Proc. Roy. Soc. (London) **A178**, 119 (1941).
60. I. M. Mills, Mol. Phys. **1**, 99 (1958).
61. R. G. Parr and A. F. Saturno (private communication).
62. C. W. Scherr, J. Chem. Phys. **23**, 569 (1955).

63. A. C. Hurley, Proc. Phys. Soc. (London) **A69**, 767 (1956).
64. R. C. Sahni, Trans. Faraday Soc. **49**, 1246 (1953).
65. A. Bassompierre, Ann. phys. (Paris) **2**, 676 (1957).
66. H. Brion, C. Moser, and M. Yamazaki, J. Chem. Phys. **30**, 673 (1959).
67. A. Meckler, J. Chem. Phys. **21**, 1750 (1953).
68. M. Kotani, Y. Mizuno, K. Kayama, and E. Ishiguro, J. Phys. Soc. Japan **12**, 707 (1957).
69. R. D. Cloney and J. S. Dooling, J. Chem. Phys. **29**, 425 (1958).
70. C. R. Mueller, J. Chem. Phys. **21**, 1013 (1953).
71. J. Eve, Proc. Roy. Soc. (London) **A246**, 582 (1958).
72. C. Carter, Proc. Roy. Soc. (London) **A235**, 321 (1956).
73. J. F. Mulligan, J. Chem. Phys. **19**, 347 (1951).
74. I. Fischer-Hjalmars, Arkiv Fysik **11**, 529 (1957).
75. L. C. Allen, Quart. Progr. Repts., Solid-State and Molecular Theory Group, Massachusetts Institute of Technology (July 15, 1957 and October 15, 1957).
76. R. K. Nesbet (private communication).
77. L. C. Allen, J. Chem. Phys. **31**, 736 (1959).
78. S. F. Boys, Proc. Roy. Soc. (London) **A200**, 542 (1950).
79. L. C. Allen (submitted for publication).

Reprinted from REVIEWS OF MODERN PHYSICS, Vol. 32, No. 2, 285–295, April, 1960
Printed in U. S. A.

Mathematical Problems in the Complete Quantum Predictions of Chemical Phenomena

S. F. BOYS
Theoretical Chemistry Department, University of Cambridge, Cambridge, England

AND

G. B. COOK
Electronic Computing Laboratory, University of Leeds, Leeds, England

1. INTRODUCTION

AT present, there is only one main method which provides practical procedures for the accurate calculation of many-electron wave functions and energies. It is often referred to as the method of configurational interaction or, as we call it in this paper, the polydetor method. In using this term, we imply a general expansion of the wave function as a linear combination of Slater determinants constructed from orthonormal single electron functions, the coefficients in the expansion being determined by the Ritz variation method. Very few wave functions of this general type have been calculated, but the stage has now been reached where all the essential procedures of calculation have been programed for high-speed electronic computing machines in a fully automatic way, and many more results are to be expected.

The development of the theory given here depends on two explicit assumptions: first, the validity of Schrödinger's many-particle equation and the antisymmetry condition and, second, the sufficiency of the Born-Oppenheimer approximation in which nuclear and electronic motions are separated. The solutions are determined completely by these assumptions which are generally accepted as the basic laws for atomic and molecular structure.

It is convenient to regard the calculation of a wave function as consisting of eight distinct stages. The solutions of several of these stages have involved considerable mathematical difficulty, but each stage presents a definite problem for which the accuracy of the solution can be specified and the significance of which can be understood quite independently of the detailed method of solution. It appears certain that this multiplicity of stages and these difficulties have obscured the essentially systematic nature of the whole problem and have given the impression that there may be ambiguities where, in fact, there are none. The aim of this account is to discuss the mathematical nature of these various stages, pointing out the difficulties, and indicating techniques of solution known at present. Such an account should be useful in enabling those not working directly in this field to understand the complexities of the problem. However, more important, the scheme as given should simplify considerably future accounts of the details of solution of the different problems by enabling their relation to the whole problem to be shown.

Since this account was commenced, fully automatic solutions have been obtained for the stages not previously solved. This has made it possible to discuss with certainty the determinate nature of the whole calculation and of each stage in it. It is important to realize that the only element of choice involved in the calculation is at the stage in which the single electron functions are selected. Thereafter, the calculation is as determinate in principle as if the results for all possible selections were tabulated. The automatic solutions emphasize this beyond all doubt.

Before examining further details, let us consider pos-

TABLE I. Unit operations in polydetor calculations (complexities relative to a $2n \times 2n$ eigenvector problem).

Operation	Computation	Program
A. Basic expansion functions ($\eta = xe^{-\sigma r}$)	...	...
B. Single-electron integrals G, V, K	5	10
C. Electrostatic interaction integrals M	100	50
D. Choice of orthonormal functions and codetors	10	10
E. Assembly of G, V, K, and M matrices	3 to 15	20
F. Orthonormal transformation	10	2
G. Projective reduction	10	50
H. Eigenvector problem	8	2
I. Primary properties	5	5
J. Derivative properties (m arrangements)	$m\Sigma$ (A to I)	2
K. Primary induced properties	10	10
L. Interaction between q systems	$q^4\Sigma$ (A to H)	2

sible developments which could enable completely theoretical predictions to rival experimental measurements in several areas of chemical theory and, in certain cases, surpass them. Such a scheme can be represented as follows:

Limited polydetor variation calculation
+linear corrections for single electron functions
+linear corrections for "hypercorrelation."

To explain this scheme, it seems likely that the main framework of a fundamental quantitative calculation will consist of a polydetor variational calculation, the number and nature of the detors used being limited according to some theoretical criterion. In this calculation, it is hoped that the deviations of the initial single-electron functions from the "best" functions are sufficiently small so that corrections can be calculated according to some linear correction theory of a type completely different from the basic calculation. The limited variational calculation almost certainly would include a considerable amount of electronic correlation. The term "hypercorrelation" refers to correlation excluded at this stage, and it seems likely that a linear theory, having some similarities to perturbation theory, may be developed to calculate this hypercorrelation directly. Such a scheme may avoid the necessity of using the very large numbers of functions required in a full polydetor calculation to obtain sufficient accuracy but, in any case, the polydetor calculation remains as the basic calculation, and it is this that we now consider.

In Table I, brief headings are given for the division of a fundamental polydetor calculation into eight separate stages called $A, B, \ldots, H$. This is followed by four further stages, I, J, K, and L, which are considered to cover the predictions of all properties of arrangements of a finite number of atoms. The primary properties (I), which can be derived from the density kernel, are exemplified by the electronic density and the dipole moment. By "derivative" properties J, we mean those properties which can be calculated by examining the variation of a property of the system with different configurations of atomic nuclei. The simplest example is the calculation of force constants, but the most interesting is the calculation of potential energy barriers which control the rates of chemical reactions. It is shown later that induced properties K, such as polarizability and refractive index, can be fitted into the scheme. In L, we have written for completeness the interaction between two or more systems which, for the purposes of the present scheme, would be regarded as a single composite system.

The most important point of the table is that we consider all properties of molecules, atoms, and radicals to fall within a unified scheme and that the greatest part of any of the calculations is the basic polydetor calculation given by stages A to H.

In order to give most rapidly a sense of proportion about these problems, two columns of numbers have been included in the table. These are somewhat speculative and contain a considerable amount of subjective judgement; they are not to be regarded as numerically precise and they have been included to convey a useful idea of orders of magnitude. The first column measures the amount of computation necessary on an automatic computing machine. In order to make this independent of the particular machine, the figures are given in terms of the time taken to diagonalize a $2n \times 2n$ matrix, where n is the number of single-electron functions being used. These figures are based on actual machine programs with which we are familiar. Since these programs were constructed at very different stages of development, both of the general method and of automatic computers, the figures given have been modified to express our opinion in terms of current computer characteristics and the most recent developments in the mechanization of the complete calculation.

The figures in the second column, necessarily more subjective, are intended to provide some measure of the mathematical complexity of the particular stage and of the effort required to construct an automatic program for the stage, the figures again being relative to the diagonalization of a $2n \times 2n$ matrix.

The entry $m\Sigma(A \text{ to } I)$ opposite J is meant to indicate that derivative properties are just those for which m repetitions of the preceding stages A to I would be required, and hence the computation time is effectively multiplied by m. Further, the entry $q^4\Sigma(A \text{ to } H)$ is meant to show that, at present, for a composite system q times as large as a system treated before, the amount of computation increases as q^4. This appears as a severe limitation, but it need not be regarded as being in any sense permanent. In a following paper,[1] techniques where the increase is only linear in q will be discussed.

The sequence of mathematical stages in a polydetor calculation is examined systematically in Sec. 3. Of these stages, we single out for special discussion (Sec. 4)

[1] S. F. Boys, Revs. Modern Phys. 32, 296 (1960), this issue.

the projective reduction calculations by means of which the variational many-dimensional integrals are reduced to linear combinations of one- and two-electron integrals. This stage has been treated in particular problems in a manner dependent on physical considerations, but, in a general calculation, the mathematical difficulties become severe. For this reason, it has been considered worthwhile devoting a whole section (Sec. 2) to showing how projective reduction analysis occurs naturally in the variational solution of a simpler partial differential equation in many variables and how, in this simpler case, the projective reductions could be effected. It is shown that the calculation of the projective reduction coefficients could be carried out by a finite number of elementary operations. In practice, in quantum mechanical calculations, we use certain powerful analytical methods to obtain these coefficients; for example, in the case of atoms the most sophisticated use of vector coupling theory is made. It is most important to realize, however, that whatever detailed method is employed, essentially the same answer would be obtained. This exemplifies the fact that after stage A, the choice of the initial expansion functions, all stages of the calculation are fully determinate, no further physical assumptions being required and no ambiguities being present. This determinate nature has been emphasized recently by performing the whole of a polydetor calculation by automatic programs constructed for the EDSAC II in Cambridge, the starting point being simply a piece of tape with a coded form of the initial expansion functions punched on it.

We now proceed with a discussion of each of the stages listed in Table I, particular attention being devoted to projective reduction processes.

In order to appreciate the significance of the scheme as a whole, it is probably helpful to think in terms of particular problems which have been examined by the method and which show already that the possible applications are much wider than the investigation of stable molecules only. An exploration of the properties of the unknown CH_2 radical by Foster and Boys[2] can be taken as one example. For a reaction rate, one is limited to the simple case of the H_3 reaction examined by Shavitt and Boys,[3] although more complicated systems are being investigated at present.

2. ILLUSTRATION OF THE ESSENTIAL TECHNIQUE OF SOLUTION OF MANY-DIMENSIONAL WAVE EQUATIONS AND OCCURRENCE OF PROJECTIVE REDUCTION ANALYSIS

Converging quantum calculations for the properties of many-electron systems depend on the use of many-dimensional functions. For example, thirty space dimensions are required for the water molecule. An understanding of these calculations involves a familiarity with the construction, manipulation, and subsequent use of such functions. However, there is no necessity to attempt to visualize these functions physically since the many-dimensional character can be expressed solely in terms of coefficients and codes which specify, in a convenient form, the three-dimensional functions from which the many-dimensional functions are constructed.

In calculating the wave function by the variational polydetor method, only integrals of these many-dimensional functions are involved which factor into integrals of lower dimension. The wave function can be regarded solely as a mathematical intermediary from which numerical values of observable properties of the system can be calculated. In such calculations, integrals of the many-dimensional wave function are involved and these can be factorized in essentially the same way as those occurring in the calculation of the wave function itself.

Extremely complicated analysis does occur in quantum calculations (particularly for atoms and nuclei), but, from the logical point of view, this is not absolutely essential to the calculation. The value of this analysis is principally to reduce the amount of labor and the amount of data to be recorded at intermediate stages in the calculation. The same answer would be obtained by using simpler methods but in a much longer time. If this point can be realized, it may be very helpful in assessing the significance of different stages of reported calculations.

An understanding of this many-dimensional character is so important that this section is devoted to a mathematical treatment of a simpler problem which, however, exhibits many of the difficult features of a complete quantum calculation. Many-dimensional functions are not particular to quantum mechanics, and the method of solution of the given problem here is not without value in other physical situations. We have attempted to set out what might be called the product function variational method of solving a many-dimensional partial differential equation of eigenvalue type.

The problem which we examine here is one in which we suppose the value q_A of a property is given by the integral

$$q_A=\int d\tau\Psi^*Q_A\Psi, \tag{1}$$

where Q_A is a specified operator, and Ψ is the solution of the linear partial differential equation

$$D\Psi+W\Psi=0 \tag{2}$$

under certain given linear boundary conditions. In (2), W is an unknown real number (an eigenvalue) and D is an operator dependent, say, on coordinates x_1, x_2, $\cdots x_N$. The solution Ψ is therefore, in general, an N-dimensional function $\Psi=\Psi(x_1,x_2,\cdots x_N)$. Further, in (1), Q_A is an operator supposed dependent on N dimen-

[2] J. M. Foster and S. F. Boys, Revs. Modern Phys. **32**, 305 (1960), this issue.

[3] S. F. Boys, G. B. Cook, C. M. Reeves, and I. Shavitt, Nature **178**, 1207 (1956).

sions and the notation $\int d\tau$ is used to denote integration over the appropriate range of each of the variables $x_1, x_2, \cdots x_N$. To make the present situation more analogous to a quantum mechanical problem, we should consider values $q_A, q_B, q_C, \cdots$ to be given by operators $Q_A, Q_B, Q_C, \cdots$ from the same function Ψ by means of equations like (1), one for each property.

Unless Eq. (2) is separable with respect to the coordinates $x_1, x_2, \cdots x_N$, there is little likelihood of obtaining an explicit solution, and there is only one generally satisfactory approach. Consider an approximation to Ψ given by

$$\Psi=\sum_r Y_r\Phi_r, \tag{3}$$

where the Φ_r are suitable N-dimensional functions satisfying the boundary conditions of the problem and the Y_r are coefficients to be determined. The Φ_r can be constructed from a set $\{\phi_i(x)\}$ of one-dimensional functions which are orthonormal and complete so that

$$\int dx\phi_i^*\phi_j=\delta_{ij}, \tag{4}$$

and, for any continuous function $f(x)$, a linear combination $\sum_{i=0}^m c_i\phi_i(x)$ can be found which approximates more and more closely to $f(x)$ in a mean-square sense as m is increased. The Φ_r are taken to be serial products of the ϕ_i as follows:

$$\Phi_1=\phi_{11}(x_1)\phi_{21}(x_2)\phi_{31}(x_3)\cdots,$$
$$\Phi_r=\phi_{1r}(x_1)\phi_{2r}(x_2)\phi_{3r}(x_3)\cdots, \tag{5}$$

where ϕ_{kr} denotes the ϕ which is the kth factor of Φ_r. Each set ϕ_{kr} ($k=1, 2, \cdots N$) is a particular permutation of N of the original ϕ_i and the Φ_r ($r=1,2\cdots$) correspond to all such possible permutations. If the number of functions ϕ_i used is increased and all possible permutations are included in forming the Φ_r, the set of functions $\{\Phi_r\}$ so generated is complete in N dimensions in the limit, and the approximation (3) tends to Ψ in the mean-square sense. Considering, however, a finite number of terms in (3), the coefficients Y_r may be determined by the method of least squares in which the integral

$$I=\int d\tau[(D+W)\sum Y_r\Phi_r]^*[(D+W)\sum Y_s\Phi_s] \tag{6}$$

is minimized with respect to the Y_r. (This integral is always positive, and an exact solution would make it zero.) This minimization yields the set of equations

$$\sum_s Y_s\left\{\int d\tau(D\Phi_r)^*(D\Phi_s)+W\int d\tau\Phi_r^*D\Phi_s\right.$$
$$\left.+W\int d\tau(D\Phi_r)^*\Phi_s+W^2\int d\tau\Phi_r^*\Phi_s\right\}=0. \tag{7}$$

To emphasize the computational character of (7), we may write it as

$$\sum_s Y_s[(D^2)_{rs}+W(D_{rs}+D_{rs}^*)+W^2G_{rs}]=0, \tag{7'}$$

where Y_s and W are unknowns, and the other symbols are to be defined as equal to the quantities they replace in (7). These latter are integrals which can be evaluated numerically without any knowledge of the answer of the problem. If these values are inserted, then (7′) can be solved by computational procedures, which would be laborious without an electronic computer, but which could be performed by the systematic solution of sets of simultaneous equations. This is not discussed further, since when the Schrödinger Hamiltonian H replaces D there is an additional simplification which causes it only to be necessary to solve a standard eigenvector problem.

To obtain numerical values of the elements appearing in (7′), it would be necessary to evaluate the many-dimensional integrals in (7). Before discussing this, we may note that the evaluation of q_A requires the evaluation of similar integrals, for, if we substitute (3) into (1), dropping the suffix A, we obtain

$$q=\sum_{r,s} Y_r^*Y_s\int d\tau\Phi_r^*Q\Phi_s=\sum_{r,s} Y_r^*Y_sQ_{rs},\text{ say.} \tag{8}$$

The evaluation of such a double sum is trivial when once numerical values of the many-dimensional integrals have been found. To take a particular instance and to keep the problem close to the quantum problem, let us assume that an operator Q has the form

$$Q=\sum_{\alpha,\beta} U(x_\alpha,x_\beta), \tag{9}$$

where $U(x_\alpha,x_\beta)$ is an operator which depends only on the coordinates x_α and x_β. Then a typical many-dimensional integral Q_{rs} in (8) is a sum of terms of the form

$$\int d\tau\Phi_r^*U(x_1,x_2)\Phi_s$$
$$=\int\int dx_1dx_2\phi_{1r}^*(x_1)\phi_{2r}^*(x_2)U(x_1,x_2)$$
$$\times\phi_{1s}(x_1)\phi_{2s}(x_2)\int dx_3\phi_{3r}^*(x_3)\phi_{3s}(x_3)\cdots$$
$$=C\int\int dx_1dx_2\phi_{1r}^*(x_1)\phi_{2r}^*(x_2)$$
$$\times U(x_1,x_2)\phi_{1s}(x_1)\phi_{2s}(x_2). \tag{10}$$

The coefficient C is either 1 or 0 since all the integrals following the double integral in (10) are either 1 or 0 by (4). All the other terms of Q_{rs} are similar so that the final result is of the form

$$Q_{rs}=\sum_{i,j,k,l} C_{ijkl}\int\int dx_1dx_2\phi_i^*(x_1)\phi_j^*(x_2)\times U(x_1,x_2)\phi_k(x_1)\phi_l(x_2). \quad (11)$$

Hence the many-dimensional integrals all collapse to linear combinations of two-dimensional integrals with coefficients C_{ijkl} equal to 1 or 0. It is the evaluation of these coefficients of which there are such a large number which is called the projective reduction calculation. Now two-dimensional integrals can always be evaluated either analytically or numerically, and hence we see that all stages in the evaluation of q in Eq. (8) can be performed.

The key point of the method is now reached. Generally the operator D is of the same general type as Q and, in such a case, a reduction similar to that leading up to Eq. (11) can be made for all the integrals appearing in (7). Thus the coefficients in (7′) only depend on integrals of a few dimensions, and after these have been evaluated by one means or another, the Y_s are obtained by solving Eqs. (7′). Assuming this solution to have been obtained, the Y_s are then used in an equation such as (8) for the determination of the properties of the system. It should be noted that, in the analysis outlined in the foregoing, it was not necessary to attempt to visualize physically a many-dimensional function.

When the many-dimensional complexities of the problem have been thus reduced, it can nearly always be shown that, because of symmetry or for some other reason, there are relations between the Y_s coefficients. Suppose, as often occurs in practice, that Y_r $(r=1,\cdots m)$ are all multiples of Y_1 so that

$$Y_r=B_{1r}Y_1 \quad (r=1,\cdots m).$$

It then follows that the approximation (3) with M terms may be written

$$\sum_{r=1}^{M} Y_r\Phi_r=\sum_{r=1}^{m} Y_1B_{1r}\Phi_r+\sum_{r=m+1}^{M} Y_r\Phi_r$$

$$=Y_1\bar{\Phi}_1+\sum_{r=m+1}^{M} Y_r\Phi_r,$$

where

$$\bar{\Phi}_1=\sum_{r=1}^{m} B_{1r}\Phi_r.$$

Thus a composite function $\bar{\Phi}_1$ can be introduced and, assuming similar combinations can be made for other terms, the approximation can be written

$$\Psi=\sum_{r=1}^{M'} Y_r\bar{\Phi}_r, \quad (12)$$

where M' may be very much less than M, i.e., a shorter expansion can be considered. If now we use (12) as our approximation function, the equations for the Y_s are just as in (7) but in terms of functions $\bar{\Phi}_r$. Consider one of the integrals which would now be required:

$$\int d\tau\bar{\Phi}_r^*D\bar{\Phi}_s=\sum_{t,u} B_{rt}^*B_{su}\int d\tau\Phi_t^*D\Phi_u. \quad (13)$$

The effect of introducing the $\bar{\Phi}$'s is, on the one hand, to reduce the size of the set of Eqs. (7) and, on the other, to increase the complexity of the integrals. In practice, this is very worthwhile since the new integrals can nearly always be evaluated by deductions from the special theory which established the relations between the Y's. The whole analysis may be very complicated but, once established, the total evaluation of the integrals involves very much less work. In quantum mechanics, the formation of new expansion functions $\bar{\Phi}$ is carried out because of the antisymmetry principle. The formation of such linear combinations, however, need not stop at one stage since, for example, in a molecule, new expansion functions which may be designated $\bar{\Phi}_r^b$ could be formed from the $\bar{\Phi}$'s to satisfy symmetry requirements.

Let us consider now the special features of the many-dimensional wave equation not exhibited by the example we have been considering. This equation can be written

$$(H-W)\Psi=0, \quad (14)$$

where the Schrödinger Hamiltonian operator H is defined in Sec. 3. First, H is a self-adjoint operator, and a variational theorem can be applied to show that an expression of the form (3) leads to the eigenvalue problem

$$\sum_s Y_s[(\Phi_r|H|\Phi_s)-W(\Phi_r|\Phi_s)]=0 \quad (15)$$

(where the usual quantum mechanical bracket notation has been employed), rather than the set of Eqs. (7). Second, associated with each electron, there is a set of four variables (x, y, z, v), where v denotes the discrete spin coordinate taking the values $\pm\frac{1}{2}$ only. The Φ's are now constructed as serial products of single-electron functions $\phi_i(x,y,z,v)$ rather than the one-dimensional functions $\phi_i(x)$. Third, owing to the antisymmetry postulate, it can be shown that the Φ_r occur in particular linear combinations of the type indicated in the previous paragraph. Such linear combinations are called Slater determinants and, when the single-electron ϕ's from which they are constructed are orthonormal, it is convenient to call them "detors." There are frequently high degrees of symmetry in the system, and linear combinations of these detors, called "codetors," are formed and used as expansion functions.

The great theoretical complexity of many-electron wave function calculations is bound up with the determination of the C_{ijkl} coefficients for the integrals $(\Phi_r|H|\Phi_s)$ where Φ_r and Φ_s are codetors. In principle, these could all be calculated by expansion in terms of more primitive functions but, for atoms, very powerful theory is available. In the future, it appears as if the projective reduction formulas will be worked out automatically on high-speed machines by a procedure which is likely to be intermediate in complexity between the most refined analysis used by hand and the direct but very lengthy method of using the simplest expansion functions.

It is interesting to note that the C_{ijkl} coefficients do not depend on the numerical values of parameters contained in the functions ϕ_i. For example, these coefficients would not depend on the value of g in an orbital specified as e^{-gr}. This property may enable a considerable economy to be effected in practice. For example, the same coefficients could be used in calculations for different internuclear distances in a radical such as BH and also for isoelectronic systems such as CH^+ or BeH^-.

The preceding account is an attempt to show the essential characteristics of many-dimensional problems and how the solution of these involves basically a large number of comparatively simple algebraic steps. The way in which mathematical analysis can reduce the number of steps by a large factor at the expense of complexity in formulation and manipulation has been indicated. The addi ional complexities of wave-mechanical problems have been pointed out. In the next two sections, the stages A to L involved in complete quantum calculations are examined in detail.

3. SEQUENCE OF MATHEMATICAL STAGES IN VARIATIONAL CODETOR CALCULATIONS

To give particulars of the calculations which are necessary for the stages listed in Table I, we consider the case where the elementary expansion functions are of the type $\eta_r\alpha$ and $\eta_r\beta$, where

$$\eta_r = x^a y^b z^c r^d e^{-gr}. \tag{16}$$

a, b, c, and d are positive integers or zero, and g is a positive number. α and β denote usual normalized spin wave functions with the values unity for $v=\frac{1}{2}$ and $v=-\frac{1}{2}$, respectively, and zero otherwise. For atoms, such a set of functions centered on one origin, the nucleus, would be used but, for molecules, functions of this general type centered on each of the nuclei and possibly on other points would be taken.

The methods to be described are limited to the circumstances, where the Born-Oppenheimer separation is sufficiently accurate so that the wave function is calculated for all electrons but with the nuclei in assigned positions. The following variational assumption is taken to be valid for the functions used. Let η_r be a complete system of three-dimensional functions such that a linear combination can be found to approximate indefinitely closely to any given continuous quadratically integrable function by choosing n sufficiently large. Let $\Phi_s = \Phi_s(x_1,y_1,z_1,v_1,\cdots,x_N,y_N,z_N,v_N)$, $(s=1, 2, \cdots)$ denote all the independent antisymmetric N-electron functions which can be constructed from serial products of the $\eta_r\alpha$ and $\eta_r\beta$. Then, it is assumed that for each electronic state, there is a solution $\{Y_s\}$, W of the eigenvalue problem

$$\textstyle\sum_s Y_s[(\Phi_r|H|\Phi_s) - W(\Phi_r|\Phi_s)] = 0, \tag{17}$$

where H is the Hamiltonian given in Sec. 3B, which converges to the electronic energy and for which

$$q = \sum_{r,s} Y_r^* Y_s(\Phi_r|Q|\Phi_s) \tag{18}$$

converges to the value of a property given by an operator Q. This assumption is equivalent to the statement that $\sum_r Y_r\Phi_r$ converges to the wave function, but it emphasizes that the latter is essentially a means of predicting observables. Rigorous proofs have so far not been obtained for this variational assumption, but it has appeared to be completely satisfactory in the instances in which it has been applied in practice.

A. Basic Expansion Functions

The first point to note about the choice of these functions η_r $(r=1, 2, \cdots n)$ is that this is, in principle, only a matter of computational economics. If these functions can be specified so that as $n\rightarrow\infty$, they form a complete system, then the same answer would be obtained irrespective of the particular functions chosen. In practice, the amount of work increases so rapidly with n that it is important to attempt to make a good choice. The usual procedures can be classified as (a) choice from trials on simpler systems, (b) choice from trials on similar systems, (c) choice by trials on the system being examined. A number of calculations have been made according to (a) by using parameter values given by Slater for the simplest type of exponential wave functions for atoms, and there have been some attempts at finding the "best" values of such parameters for molecules. Boys has used two or more exponential functions instead of a single Slater function (e.g., e^{-4r} and e^{-3r} instead of $e^{-3.7r}$ for Be), and this has been extended to molecules. While the choice in any particular problem is rather an open question, there is fortunately no doubt about the criterion which tests the quality of the choice. Once the η functions have been chosen, the whole calculation through to the final energy W is fully determinate, and the best choice is that for which W is lowest. If it were not for the rapid increase in labor as n is increased, it would probably be better to increase n than vary the parameters in the η_r; at present, some compromise between these considerations is necessary.

B. Single-Electron Integrals

It is convenient to write the Schrödinger Hamiltonian for a general molecular system as

$$H=\sum_i K_i-\sum_{i,I} Z_I V_{iI}+\sum_{i>j} M_{ij}$$

$$=-\tfrac{1}{2}\sum_i\left(\frac{\partial^2}{\partial x_i^2}+\frac{\partial^2}{\partial y_i^2}+\frac{\partial^2}{\partial z_i^2}\right)-\sum_{i,I}\frac{Z_I}{r_{iI}}+\sum_{i>j}\frac{1}{r_{ij}}, \quad (19)$$

where corresponding terms define K, V, and M. The suffix i numbers the electrons, I the nuclei, and Z_I is the atomic number of the Ith nucleus. The single-electron integrals which arise when the problem is treated as in Sec. 2 are $(\eta_r|G|\eta_s)$, $(\eta_r|V_I|\eta_s)$, and $(\eta_r|-\tfrac{1}{2}\nabla^2|\eta_s)$, where the first of these types of integral are the overlap integrals, the symbol G having been introduced into the bracket for future reference. The V_I integrals which involve three different nuclei require, in general, a method of numerical evaluation which is a much simplified version of the method used for the electrostatic integrals described in Sec. 3C. All the other integrals can be expressed as explicit formulas, but the organization of the evaluation of these is tedious owing to the number of different cases.

C. Electrostatic Interaction Integrals

These are conveniently denoted by

$$(\eta_i\eta_j:\eta_k\eta_l)=(\eta_i\eta_k|M|\eta_j\eta_l)$$

$$=\int\int d\mathbf{r}_1 d\mathbf{r}_2 \eta_i^*(\mathbf{r}_1)\eta_j(\mathbf{r}_1)\eta_k^*(\mathbf{r}_2)\eta_l(\mathbf{r}_2)/r_{12}. \quad (20)$$

The evaluation of these integrals constitutes one of the two most formidable problems in molecular quantum calculations. However, they constitute a definite mathematical problem, and there are various though difficult ways of obtaining these integrals to any desired accuracy. If the expansion functions η_r are formulated in terms of Gauss functions rather than exponential functions, this stage is simplified to the evaluation of explicit formulas for all types of electrostatic integral.[4]

D. Choice of Orthonormal Functions and Codetors

In principle, the calculation of a wave function could be carried out in terms of the η_r functions, but it is very advantageous to take linear combinations of these functions defined by $\phi_r=\sum_i X_i^r\eta_i$, such that the ϕ's are orthonormal, i.e., $(\phi_r|\phi_s)=\delta_{rs}$. The calculation is lengthened by stage F below, but stage G is shortened by a factor of about $1/N^7$, the net result generally being a large economy in calculation. There are an infinite number of choices of the coefficients X_i^r. One possibility is the Schmidt method and this has been used in practice. In principle, from these orthonormal functions all possible detors of the form

$$\Phi=\mathfrak{A}\phi_1(\mathbf{r}_1)\mu_1(v_1)\phi_2(\mathbf{r}_2)\mu_2(v_2)\cdots\phi_N(\mathbf{r}_N)\mu_N(v_N) \quad (21)$$

are formed, where $\mathbf{r}$ has been used to denote (x, y, z) and μ denotes either the α or β spin wave function. $\mathfrak{A}$ is the antisymmetry operator defined by

$$\mathfrak{A}=\sum_u \sigma_u P_u,$$

where P_u is one of the $N!$ permutations of the suffixes $1,\cdots N$ and σ_u is 1 or -1 according as the permutation is even or odd.

It is nearly always possible to use linear combinations of detors to obtain a smaller eigenvector problem at the expense of mathematical complexity. This procedure depends on a group-theoretical analysis which is too extensive to be included here. The most feasible method is probably a compromise between the complexities of the most advanced theory and the heavy labor of the more direct approach.

In practice, it is found that, if the first detor or codetor is a reasonable approximation to the wave function, only a small proportion of the other possible Φ's have an appreciable effect on Ψ and W. This means that it is worthwhile making some special choice of the ϕ_r so that Φ_1 by itself is a reasonable approximation. This has been done in an intuitive way (see Boys[5]), but recently a first systematic way of making a good choice has been found and is described by Foster and Boys[2] in a subsequent paper. A dual system of orbitals, described as exclusive and oscillator, are defined in a way which suggests that only a small number of the Φ's appreciably affect the lowest energy level when this is a common type of singlet. Further investigations along these lines might be fruitful both in this and other circumstances. In the absence of other evidence, the contribution of each Φ to the lowering of the energy W should be estimated numerically. If the matrix H_{rs} is roughly diagonal, then the contribution of Φ_s is approximately

$$[(\Phi_1|H|\Phi_s)]^2/(\Phi_s|H|\Phi_s). \quad (22)$$

To conclude the discussion of this stage, it should be noted that, provided a full systematic calculation is made, these choices do not affect the final answer.

E. Assembly of the G, K, V, and M Matrices

This stage is not of fundamental mathematical significance but is often tedious and liable to error. It is concerned with sorting the G, V, K, and M integrals into the order required for the transformations at stage F. It is desirable to construct a fully automatic or semi-automatic scheme for generating these matrices. This has proved difficult on account of the considerable number of different procedures required for the various types of integral. Further, many elements of the matrix may be equal on account of symmetry and only one of these needs to be evaluated.

[4] S. F. Boys, Proc. Roy. Soc. (London) **A200**, 542 (1950).

[5] S. F. Boys, Proc. Roy. Soc. (London) **A217**, 136 (1953).

F. Orthonormal Transformation

The following integrals which are required, since the subsequent calculation is to be performed in terms of the orthonormal ϕ's, are obtained by the transformations shown. This is an extremely tedious desk calculation but is reasonably straightforward to program for an automatic computer:

$$(\phi_r\phi_s:\phi_t\phi_u)=\sum_{i,j,k,l}(X_i{}^rX_k{}^t)^*X_j{}^sX_l{}^u(\eta_i\eta_j:\eta_k\eta_l), \qquad (23)$$

$$(\phi_r|K-\sum_I Z_IV_I|\phi_s)=\sum_{i,j}X_i{}^{r*}X_j{}^s(\eta_i|K-\sum Z_IV_I|\eta_j). \qquad (24)$$

G. Projective Reduction Analysis

The object of the analysis is to find coefficients, designated B^{ij} and C^{ijkl} in the following, such that the many-dimensional integrals $(\Phi_r|H|\Phi_s)$, where Φ_r and Φ_s are codetors, are reduced to one- and two-electron integrals, numerical values of which are available from stages B, C, and F. Thus

$$(\Phi_r|H|\Phi_s)=\sum_{i,j}B_{rs}{}^{ij}(\phi_i|K-\sum_I Z_IV_I|\phi_j)+\sum_{i,j,k,l}C_{rs}{}^{ijkl}(\phi_i\phi_j:\phi_k\phi_l). \qquad (25)$$

The calculation of these coefficients can be performed several ways and at different levels of abstract theory. The most advanced theory normally gives the briefest calculation but is probably not worthwhile except for specialists in the field. Once the B and C coefficients are tabulated and checked, the details of the derivation are not important. A general method which suffices for any vector-coupled functions of atoms has been given by Boys,[6] and an automatic method for molecules will be reported by Boys and Reeves. The latter method is restricted in form, and further development of automatic schemes is being examined.

H. Eigenvector Problem

This is the last numerical step in the energy and wave function calculation. The former is the most important observable property, and the latter is the key intermediary to the prediction of other observable properties. The values of the integrals obtained from stage F are substituted into the projective reduction formulas from stage G to give the eigenvector problem

$$\sum_s Y_s[(\Phi_r|H|\Phi_s)-W(\Phi_r|\Phi_s)]=0, \qquad (26)$$

which is solved numerically for the values of Y_s and W. The simple interative method of solution given by Boys[7] has been found very satisfactory.

[6] S. F. Boys, Proc. Roy. Soc. (London) **A206**, 489 (1951); **207**, 181, 197 (1951).

[7] S. F. Boys, Proc. Roy. Soc. (London) **A201**, 125 (1950).

I. Prediction of Primary Properties

A number of properties such as electronic density, electric dipole moment, etc., are given by integrals of the form

$$q=(\Psi|\sum_i Q(\mathbf{r}_i)|\Psi), \qquad (24)$$

where Q is a specified single-electron operator. By using the wave function $\Psi=\sum_r Y_r\Phi_r$, we have

$$q=\sum_{r,s}Y_r{}^*Y_s(\Phi_r|\sum_i Q(\mathbf{r}_i)|\Phi_s)=\sum_{r,s,i,j}Y_r{}^*Y_sD_{rs}{}^{ij}(\phi_i|Q(\mathbf{r})|\phi_j)=\sum_{i,j}D^{ij}(\phi_i|Q(\mathbf{r})|\phi_j), \qquad (28)$$

where the integrals of the form $(\Phi_r|\sum_i Q(\mathbf{r}_i)|\Phi_s)$ are reduced by an analysis precisely similar to that for the single-electron operator occurring in the Hamiltonian. The D^{ij} coefficients can be calculated as shown and used to predict a number of particular properties by combination with various integrals of the type

$$(\phi_i|Q|\phi_j)=\sum_{r,s}X_i{}^{r*}X_j{}^s(\eta_r|Q|\eta_s), \qquad (29)$$

which are generally easily evaluated.

The D^{ij} are frequently called the density matrix, and particular properties of this have been demonstrated. However, the fundamental calculation is direct without any further consideration of these properties. Other properties such as radiation strengths, between two states Ψ_1 and Ψ_2 are given by

$$q=(\Psi_1|\sum_i Q(r_i)|\Psi_2).$$

The evaluation differs from the preceding only by the first set of Y_r being taken from Ψ_1 and the second set from Ψ_2.

J. Prediction of Derivative Properties

Several physical properties of molecules are given by the rate of change of a primary property with a change in the configuration of the positions of the nuclei. Thus, the rates of change of energy for small changes of positions are the force constants of a molecule and these determine the frequencies of the infrared vibrational spectra. Again, the rates of change of dipole moment give the intensities of these bands.

The present scheme provides a straightforward method of predicting such properties by repeating the evaluation of the property for a number of distortions of the nuclear configuration. In an extensive calculation, the variation of the property would be fitted by a polynomial in the displacements, and exact derivatives (symbolically $\partial q/\partial R$) or finite alterations (symbolicallv $\Delta q/\Delta R$) could be evaluated as desired.

It should be noted that, in using the word molecule in this section, any configuration of atomic nuclei is implied. Thus, in the prediction of chemical reaction rates, quantities of the form $\Delta q/\Delta R$ are particularly important.

K. Prediction of Primary Induced Properties

For the sake of completeness, the formula which predicts such induced properties as polarizability, magnetic susceptibility, etc., is given. In general, the rate of increase of some property q for unit increase in λ, where λF is some field applied to the system, is given by

$$-2\mathcal{R} \sum_{r,s,t,u,v} Y_r^* Y_v (\Phi_r|Q|\Phi_s)(H-WS)_{st}^{-1} \times(\delta_{tu}-Y_tY_u^*)(\Phi_u|F|\Phi_v), \quad (31)$$

where $\mathcal{R}$T denotes the real part of T. S denotes the matrix $S_{rs}=(\Phi_r|\Phi_s)$ and $(H-WS)^{-1}$ denotes the reciprocal matrix of $(H-WS)$. The reciprocal need not be calculated explicitly since quantities

$$X_s=E_t(H-WS)_{st}^{-1}Z_t$$

are given by the solution of

$$\sum_s(H-WS)_{rs}X_s=Z_t.$$

The preceding formula follows from perturbation theory, but no calculations for general atoms or molecules have yet been made. It seems certain that predictions will be made when fully automatic methods are in operation, but until then, the chief problem concerns the number of Φ's which must be included to obtain reasonable accuracy.

L. Interactions between Systems

This item has been included to make the list cover practically all physical phenomena which do not involve nuclear changes or macroscopic numbers of atoms. It merely indicates the obvious fact that the interaction of two or more systems can be predicted by calculations for the composite system. The direct labor of computation would increase as q^4 for a composite system q times as large as a system treated before, but there are some hopes of developing theories[1] to avoid this rapid increase.

COMMENT

It was most convenient to set out the calculation for electronic wave functions of molecules, although only small changes are necessary to convert this into the scheme for atomic or nuclear wave functions.

First, however, we consider what changes in molecular calculations occur if $\exp(-gr^2)$ is used in place of $\exp(-gr)$ in the expansion functions. The difficult stage C is simplified to the evaluation of explicit formulas and the labor is reduced by a factor of about 100. However, unless a much larger number of η functions is used, the accuracy is much diminished since the Gauss function is always a bad fit to an orbital while the exponential can be a good fit.

For atoms, stage D no longer presents a difficult obstacle and formulas for interaction integrals have been given by Boys.[7] Stage G becomes very abstract in practice but a completely general method appropriate to desk calculations has been given.[6] Stage J can be omitted, since there is no configuration of nuclei to be considered. Atomic calculations as a whole are much simpler.

In the nuclear case, the first difference to note is that at present, no Hamiltonian with two-particle interactions is known accurately. A number of possible forms of this type are known and these are complicated by the presence of spin interactions. For such a tentative H, a somewhat different problem has to be formulated at stage A to allow for the elimination of the center-of-mass motion. Expansion functions in which $\exp(-gr^2)$ replaces $\exp(-gr)$ are probably much more suitable and, for these, stage D would be laborious but not difficult. Because of spin interactions, stage G would become very complicated. A number of special cases have been analyzed in the literature, but no general method has been formulated yet.

4. PROBLEMS OF PROJECTIVE REDUCTION ANALYSIS

The essential problem is the calculation of the coefficients $C_{rs}{}^{ijkl}$ in the equation

$$M_{rs}=(\Phi_r|\sum_{i>j} M_{ij}|\Phi_s)=\sum_{i,j,k,l} C_{rs}{}^{ijkl}(\phi_i\phi_j:\phi_k\phi_l), \quad (32)$$

where Φ_r and Φ_s are codetors, together with the choice of the Φ's themselves so that the matrix M_{rs} contains as many zeros as possible and the calculation of the remaining C^{ijkl} is as simple as possible. The coefficients designated B^{ij} in the typical projective reduction formula given in G in the previous section can be derived from the C^{ijkl}. An ancillary problem of importance is the tabulation of the results, which, since the C's are independent of the ϕ's, can be used for repeated numerical calculations. Quite a considerable part of the latter problem is concerned with a description of the Φ_r themselves in terms of an unambiguous code; the need for this is pressing now that automatic methods are being considered. If this tabulation were possible, one piece of data could be used not only for different calculations but probably many times within the same calculation, since there are often elements M_{rs} which may be derived from each other by an interchange of ϕ's and others which could be described as degenerate cases of a particular key case.

Quite a large number of C coefficients have been reported in the literature for atoms and nuclei, but there has not been any general examination of the principles of the derivation and tabulation of these, particularly with reference to computing machines. The general procedure for atoms[6] is of a form requiring reference to previous tables and does not appear to be directly adaptable to machines. If these problems of mathematical analysis and of description and tabulation can be solved, presumably many man-years of work would be saved.

As an illustration of a possible method for automatic computing machines (but far too primitive for desk calculations), consider the case where the codetors are expanded explicitly as detors. Let

$$\Phi_r = \sum_i V_i^r \mathfrak{D}_i \tag{33}$$

so that

$$(\Phi_r | M | \Phi_s) = \sum_{a,b} V_a^{r*} V_b^s (\mathfrak{D}_a | M | \mathfrak{D}_b). \tag{34}$$

The rules for the evaluation of an integral $(\mathfrak{D}_a | M | \mathfrak{D}_b)$ are well known and simple. If the orbitals have been ordered to achieve maximum coincidence,

$$(\mathfrak{D}_a | M | \mathfrak{D}_b) = \sum_{i>j} Q_{ij} [(\phi_i^a \phi_i^b : \phi_j^a \phi_j^b) - (\phi_i^a \phi_j^b : \phi_j^a \phi_i^b)], \tag{35}$$

where $Q_{ij} = 1$ if $\phi_k^a = \phi_k^b$ ($k \neq i$ or j) and zero otherwise. Hence, all the difficult labor is in the determination of the V_i^r. Whether this can be done sufficiently simply for functions of given symmetry merits further investigation, but a great deal depends on the discovery of adequate coded descriptions of the functions.

5. RELATION OF THE HARTREE, FOCK, KOOPMANS AND ROOTHAAN METHODS TO THE POLYDETOR METHOD

The method associated with the names of these workers[8,9] is generally known as the self-consistent field method. In the framework of the present scheme it is possible to describe this as the approximation of using a single Φ and then adjusting some or all of the implicit parameters in this function to obtain a stationary value of the energy. This method cannot converge to the true solution of Schrödinger's equation. In the case of atoms, this introduction of a small finite error leads to a problem which can be solved efficiently by one-dimensional numerical integration. In the molecular case, however, most of the computation is concerned with the evaluation of molecular integrals (stages B and C) so that the self-consistent field calculation is comparable in computational effort with a polydetor calculation using the same η_r system. The real difference is that the answer is simpler to understand and that it is possible to perform the calculation without having to use the general theory of projective reduction (stage G).

The determination of the best single Φ can also be very useful as an intermediate in the clearest expression of a wave function in polydetor form, but then it can be regarded simply as an interesting step in the whole general calculation.

6. OTHER METHODS

In conclusion, it is important to state what other approaches to the general problem of finding the wave functions of many-electron systems have been made. None of these is at present applicable to a general molecule but, for one- and two-electron systems, they have given results of high accuracy for less labor than a polydetor calculation would involve. The outstanding examples are the wave functions for the helium atom determined by Hylleraas[10] and for the hydrogen molecule by James and Coolidge.[11] The methods employed in these calculations differ from those discussed here in that the functions used were not separable into orbitals, the interparticle distances being involved explicitly. Similar calculations have been attempted for nuclei using a Hamiltonian with two-body forces, but no general method is at present available.

7. DISCUSSION

The calculation of general many-electron wave functions for atoms and molecules by variational determinantal expansions has here been classified as consisting of eight distinct stages. From the wave function, it has been shown that it is possible to calculate any observable property by means of one or more of four further stages to an accuracy consistent with the assumption of the Born-Oppenheimer separation and with the omission of relativistic effects. It is generally known that, in principle, all molecular properties are calculable by such processes, but it is not always realized that these may be classified and reduced to so few different types of calculation.

It is considered that the classification provides a very useful mental picture of these complicated calculations and that this is particularly apposite now that it is possible to perform all the stages completely automatically by electronic computers. These different stages can all be specified as completely determinate calculations and, in fact, it is now possible to give tentative estimates of the effort involved in the programing and performance of these. The list in Table I appears to be the first explicit statement of this subdivision, but a limited number of calculations which are in accordance with this general scheme have already been reported. The earliest clear examples are probably the calculations for the Be, B, and C atoms by Boys,[5,7,12] although the calculation for the oxygen atom by Hartree and Swirles[13]

[8] T. Koopmans, Physica **1**, 104 (1953).
[9] C. C. J. Roothaan, Revs. Modern Phys. **23**, 69 (1951).
[10] E. Hylleraas, Z. Physik **54**, 347 (1929); **65**, 759 (1930).
[11] H. M. James and A. S. Coolidge, J. Chem. Phys. **1**, 825 (1933).
[12] S. F. Boys, Proc. Roy. Soc. (London) **A217**, 235 (1953).
[13] D. R. Hartree, W. Hartree, and B. Swirles, Phil. Trans. **A238**, 229 (1939).

combines a two-determinant treatment with a numerical integration process. For molecules, the calculations by Kastler[14] for HF and by Meckler[15] for O_2 are early examples.

Several of the stages involve considerable mathematical complexity, but it is the projective reduction processes which always appear to have caused the most intellectual difficulty. It is important to realize that, from the logical point of view, nearly all the complexities of this stage are not essential aspects of the quantum calculation. If the calculation were performed in a direct manner without the use of powerful theorems and relations (that is, by a variational expansion of simple determinants or, in the logical limit, of products), the same answer would be obtained but with much more computation. In particular, this is true for all the vector-coupling calculations for atoms and nuclei and, in fact, it may be shorter for those not performing series of calculations not to use the most advanced theory but to keep to simpler explicit expressions. At present, it is interesting to observe that there may be a return to simpler but somewhat more laborious methods in the future when automatic programs are constructed for all these problems. If the present analysis has shown how the projective reduction calculation can be separated from the actual quantum theory, with which it is so frequently mingled in the exposition of particular nonconvergent approximations, it will have served a useful purpose.

It is intended to report various mathematical and numerical methods for the efficient performance of the stages of Table I in the near future. It is also to be hoped that other contributions to the solutions of the more difficult of these stages may be developed. It is considered that the explanation of the significance of new developments may perhaps be made most briefly and informatively by a statement of the relation to the preceding classification.

[14] D. Kastler, J. chim. phys. **50**, 556 (1953).
[15] A. Meckler, J. Chem. Phys. **21**, 1750 (1953).

Reprinted from THE JOURNAL OF CHEMICAL PHYSICS, Vol. 24, No. 6, 1166–1173, June, 1956
Printed in U. S. A.

On the Pi-Electron Approximation and Its Possible Refinement*

PETER G. LYKOS† AND ROBERT G. PARR
Department of Chemistry, Carnegie Institute of Technology, Pittsburgh, Pennsylvania

(Received August 4, 1955)

The *pi-electron approximation* is defined to be the approximation in which the following two restrictions are imposed upon the total approximate electronic wave functions for some group of molecular states:

(I) The wave function for each state satisfies the *sigma-pi separability conditions:* (A) the wave function has the form $\Psi=[(\Sigma)(\Pi)]$, where (Σ) and (Π) are antisymmetrized functions describing the so-called sigma and pi electrons, respectively, and the outer brackets connote antisymmetrization with respect to sigma-pi exchange; (B) each of (Σ), (Π), and Ψ is normalized to unity; (C) each of (Σ), (Π), and Ψ is well-behaved.

(II) The sigma description is the same for all states.

Imposition of these restrictions is shown to be sufficient to validate the customary procedure in which the pi electrons in a molecule are treated apart from the rest.

A formula is given for the pi-electron Hamiltonian to be used when the pi-electron approximation is invoked. Present day pi-electron theories are examined, and lines for carrying out improved calculations are suggested. An iterative procedure is proposed for treating both sigma and pi electrons wherein first a sigma function is assumed (which defines a "core" in the field of which the pi electrons move), then a pi function is computed (which defines a "peel" in the field of which the sigma electrons move), then a new sigma function is computed, and so on.

Certain generalizations of the quantum-mechanical argument are made which give it wider applicability, and several illustrations are drawn from pi-electron theory and elsewhere.

I. INTRODUCTION

Is it correct or is it not correct to compute by quantum-mechanical methods the electronic spectrum and other properties of the benzene molecule treating the problem as a six-electron one? The present communication is intended to provide full quantum-mechanical discussion of this question.

Crudely stated, the pi-electron approximation is the approximation in which properties of a molecule like benzene are computed treating the pi electrons apart from the rest, the "sigma" electrons, which are considered only as part of the "core" in the potential field of which the pi electrons move. A pi-electron wave function of some particular form is taken, and conventional variational techniques are applied to it to determine the "best" wave function(s) of that form for a state (or states) of the molecule. Put mathematically (but still crudely), for a molecule presumed to have n_π pi electrons, one takes a pi-electron Hamiltonian operator of the form

$$\mathbf{H}_\pi(1,2,\cdots,n_\pi)=\sum_{\mu=1}^{n_\pi}\mathbf{H}_{\text{core}}(\mu)+\tfrac{1}{2}\sum_{\mu,\nu=1}^{n_\pi}{}'(e^2/r_{\mu\nu}),\quad(1)$$

one chooses some pi-electron wave function (Π) which is an antisymmetric function of the coordinates of the n_π pi electrons, and one minimizes the energy,

$$E_\pi=\int(\Pi)^*\mathbf{H}_\pi(\Pi)d\tau_\pi\Big/\int(\Pi)^*(\Pi)d\tau_\pi,\quad(2)$$

with respect to linear or other variational parameters in (Π). The n_σ sigma electrons are taken into account through appropriate elucidation of the terms $\mathbf{H}_{\text{core}}(\mu)$.

The trouble with this way of stating the pi-electron approximation is that it leaves the validity of the approximation in doubt and its meaning obscure. The true Hamiltonian is not given by Eq. (1), so that application of the variational method to the expression (2) requires justification.

Indeed, McWeeny[1] recently has shown that the pi-electron approximation as just stated will be valid for some set of states of a molecule if one is willing to accept a description of the sigma electrons, common for all states in the set, that they occupy in pairs (with opposite spins) some set of σ-type orbitals. This gives the conventional method of performing pi-electron calculations a firm basis in the variational theorem.

The present purpose is to elaborate McWeeny's result.

II. THE PI-ELECTRON APPROXIMATION

A new definition of the term "pi-electron approximation" will now be given. Later it will be shown that there is a well-defined variational procedure for computing wave functions within this approximation which is just the conventional pi-electron procedure as described above.

The definition will be couched in terms of certain possible properties of a total n-electron wave function which may be called the *sigma-pi separability conditions*. These are as follows:

(A) The total wave function $\Psi(1,2,\cdots,n)$ may be

* Sponsored by the Office of Ordnance Research, U. S. Army, supported in part by a grant from the National Science Foundation.

† Present address: Department of Chemistry, Illinois Institute of Technology, Technology Center, Chicago 16, Illinois.

[1] R. McWeeny, Proc. Roy. Soc. (London) A223, 306 (1954).

written in the form

$$\Psi=[(\Sigma)(\Pi)], \tag{3}$$

where $(\Sigma(1,2,\cdots,n_\sigma))$ is some antisymmetric function of the coordinates of electrons 1, 2, $\cdots$, n_σ, $(\Pi(n_\sigma+1, n_\sigma+2, \cdots, n))$ is some antisymmetric function of the coordinates of electrons $n_\sigma+1$, $n_\sigma+2$, $\cdots$, $n_\sigma+n_\pi=n$, and the outer brackets connote the normalized partial antisymmetrization operator which antisymmetrizes the product $(\Sigma)(\Pi)$ with respect to exchange of the "sigma" electrons 1, 2, $\cdots$, n_σ with the "pi" electrons $n_\sigma+1$, $n_\sigma+2$, $\cdots$, n:

$$[(\Sigma)(\Pi)]=[(n_\sigma+n_\pi)!/n_\sigma!n_\pi!]^{-\frac{1}{2}} \times\sum_{P_{\sigma\pi}}(-1)^{P_{\sigma\pi}}P_{\sigma\pi}[(\Sigma)(\Pi)]. \tag{4}$$

Here the summation is over all the $(n_\sigma+n_\pi)!/n_\sigma!n_\pi!$ distinct permutations $P_{\sigma\pi}$ of electrons 1, 2, $\cdots$, n_σ with electrons $n_\sigma+1$, $n_\sigma+2$, $\cdots$, n, and the factor $(-1)^{P_{\sigma\pi}}$ is $+1$ or -1 according as the permutation $P_{\sigma\pi}$ is even or odd.

(B) The functions Ψ, (Σ), and (Π) are *simultaneously* normalized to unity:

$$1=\int|\Psi|^2d\tau=\int|(\Sigma)|^2d\tau_\sigma=\int|(\Pi)|^2d\tau_\pi. \tag{5}$$

Here the first integration is over all coordinates (including spin) of all electrons, the second is over all coordinates of electrons 1, 2, $\cdots$, n_σ, and the third is over all coordinates of electrons $n_\sigma+1$, $n_\sigma+2$, $\cdots$, n.

(C) The functions (Σ), (Π), [and Ψ] are well behaved. In particular, (Σ) and (Π) may each be expanded in terms of orthonormal Slater determinants, built from some orthonormal set of one-electron functions λ_1, λ_2, $\cdots$ (molecular spin orbitals):

$$(\Sigma)=A_1(\Sigma_1)+A_2(\Sigma_2)+\cdots, \tag{6}$$

$$(\Pi)=B_1(\Pi_1)+B_2(\Pi_2)+\cdots, \tag{7}$$

$$\sum_k|A_k|^2=\sum_m|B_m|^2=1. \tag{8}$$

Here the (Σ_k) are Slater determinants of order n_σ built from the λ_i and the (Π_m) are Slater determinants of order n_π built from them.

An exact molecular wave function will, in general, not satisfy the sigma-pi separability conditions. But for some states of some molecules wave functions satisfying the conditions should provide good approximations. The ***pi-electron approximation*** may be defined as the approximation in which the approximate wave functions for some set of molecular states are assumed to satisfy the sigma-pi separability conditions A, B, and C, *with the same sigma-electron wave function* (Σ) *for all states in the set.*

III. FUNDAMENTAL THEOREMS

Consider a molecule with n electrons, having the total electronic Hamiltonian operator

$$\mathbf{H}(1,2,\cdots,n)=\sum_{\zeta=1}^{n}\mathbf{H}_N(\zeta)+\tfrac{1}{2}\sum_{\zeta,\eta=1}^{n}{}'(e^2/r_{\zeta\eta}), \tag{9}$$

where $\mathbf{H}_N(\zeta)$ is the operator describing the motion of electron ζ in the field of the bare nuclei, *viz.*,

$$\mathbf{H}_N(\zeta)=\mathbf{T}(\zeta)+\mathbf{U}_N(\zeta),\quad \mathbf{U}_N(\zeta)=-\sum_\alpha(Z_\alpha e^2/r_{\zeta\alpha}), \tag{10}$$

where $\mathbf{T}(\zeta)$ is the kinetic energy operator for electron ζ and $\mathbf{U}_N(\zeta)$ is the potential energy operator for its attraction for all the nuclei; Z_α is the charge on nucleus α in units of the electronic charge e. The theorems which follow then provide a convenient basis for discussion of the pi-electron and other approximations.

Theorem 1. For any approximate electronic wave function Ψ that satisfies the sigma-pi separability conditions A, B, and C of Sec. II, the expectation value for the total electronic energy,

$$E_{el}=\int\Psi^*\mathbf{H}\Psi d\tau\Big/\int\Psi^*\Psi d\tau, \tag{11}$$

may be written in the following form:

$$E_{el}=E_\sigma{}^0+E_\pi, \tag{12}$$

where

$$E_\sigma{}^0=\int(\Sigma)^*\mathbf{H}_\sigma{}^0(\Sigma)d\tau_\sigma\Big/\int(\Sigma)^*(\Sigma)d\tau_\sigma, \tag{13}$$

$$E_\pi=\int(\Pi)^*\mathbf{H}_\pi(\Pi)d\tau_\pi\Big/\int(\Pi)^*(\Pi)d\tau_\pi, \tag{14}$$

$$\mathbf{H}_\sigma{}^0(1,2,\cdots,n_\sigma)=\sum_{\kappa=1}^{n_\sigma}\mathbf{H}_N(\kappa)+\tfrac{1}{2}\sum_{\kappa,\lambda=1}^{n_\sigma}{}'(e^2/r_{\kappa\lambda}), \tag{15}$$

and

$$\mathbf{H}_\pi(n_\sigma+1, n_\sigma+2, \cdots, n_\sigma+n_\pi)$$

$$=\sum_{\mu=n_\sigma+1}^{n_\sigma+n_\pi}\mathbf{H}_{\text{core}}(\mu)+\tfrac{1}{2}\sum_{\mu,\nu=n_\sigma+1}^{n_\sigma+n_\pi}{}'(e^2/r_{\mu\nu}), \tag{16}$$

with

$$\mathbf{H}_{\text{core}}(\mu)\equiv\mathbf{H}_N(\mu)+\mathbf{G}_\sigma(\mu), \tag{17}$$

in which the Coulomb-exchange operator $\mathbf{G}_\sigma$ is defined by the formula

$$\mathbf{G}_\sigma(\mu)\equiv\mathbf{J}_\sigma(\mu)-\mathbf{K}_\sigma(\mu), \tag{18}$$

with

$$\mathbf{J}_\sigma(\mu)[(\Pi)]\equiv\int(\Sigma)^*[\sum_\sigma(e^2/r_{\sigma\mu})](\Sigma)(\Pi)d\tau_\sigma \tag{19}$$

and

$$\mathbf{K}_\sigma(\mu)[(\Pi)]\equiv\int(\Sigma)^*[\sum_\sigma(e^2/r_{\sigma\mu})](\Sigma_{ex}{}^\mu)(\Pi_{ex}{}^\sigma)d\tau_\sigma, \tag{20}$$

in which $(\Sigma_{ex}{}^{\mu})(\Pi_{ex}{}^{\sigma})$ represents what is obtained from $(\Sigma)(\Pi)$ upon exchange of sigma electron σ for pi electron μ.

Proof: In the formula

$$E_{el}=\int[(\Sigma)(\Pi)]^*\mathbf{H}[(\Sigma)(\Pi)]d\tau,$$

the first partial antisymmetrization operator can be removed in the usual way. Each of the $(n_\sigma+n_\pi)!/n_\sigma!n_\pi!$ permutations of sigma with pi electrons in Eq. (4) gives the same contribution to the integral, so that only one need be considered, the nil permutation. Thus

$$E_{el}=[(n_\sigma+n_\pi)!/n_\sigma!n_\pi!]^{\frac{1}{2}}\int(\Sigma)^*(\Pi)^*\mathbf{H}[(\Sigma)(\Pi)]d\tau.$$

Now the complete Hamiltonian operator of Eq. (9) may be written

$$\mathbf{H}=\mathbf{H}_\sigma{}^0+\mathbf{H}_\pi{}^0+\Sigma_{\sigma\pi}(e^2/r_{\sigma\pi}),$$

where $\mathbf{H}_\pi{}^0$ is defined like $\mathbf{H}_\sigma{}^0$ [see Eq. (24)]. Hence, with

$$N_{\sigma\pi}\equiv[(n_\sigma+n_\pi)!/n_\sigma!n_\pi!]^{\frac{1}{2}},$$

one obtains

$$E_{el}=\int(\Sigma)^*\mathbf{H}_\sigma{}^0\left\{N_{\sigma\pi}\int(\Pi)^*[(\Sigma)(\Pi)]d\tau_\pi\right\}d\tau_\sigma$$
$$+\int(\Pi)^*\mathbf{H}_\pi{}^0\left\{N_{\sigma\pi}\int(\Sigma)^*[(\Sigma)(\Pi)]d\tau_\sigma\right\}d\tau_\pi$$
$$+\int(\Pi)^*\left\{N_{\sigma\pi}\int(\Sigma)^*[\Sigma_{\sigma\pi}(e^2/r_{\sigma\pi})][(\Sigma)(\Pi)]d\tau_\sigma\right\}d\tau_\pi.$$

By Lemma 3 of the Appendix, the term in braces in the first integral is just (Σ), the term in braces in the second integral (Π); using Eq. (4) again, the third integral may be reduced as follows:

$$\int(\Pi)^*\left\{N_{\sigma\pi}\int(\Sigma)^*[\Sigma_{\sigma\pi}(e^2/r_{\sigma\pi})][(\Sigma)(\Pi)]d\tau_\sigma\right\}d\tau_\pi$$
$$=\int(\Sigma)^*(\Pi)^*\{\Sigma_{\sigma\mu}(e^2/r_{\sigma\mu})[(\Sigma)(\Pi)-(\Sigma_{ex}{}^{\mu})(\Pi_{ex}{}^{\sigma})$$
$$+(\text{other terms})]\}d\tau_\sigma d\tau_\pi$$
$$=\int(\Sigma)^*(\Pi)^*\{\Sigma_{\sigma\mu}(e^2/r_{\sigma\mu})[(\Sigma)(\Pi)-(\Sigma_{ex}{}^{\mu})(\Pi_{ex}{}^{\sigma})]\}d\tau_\sigma d\tau_\pi$$
$$=\int(\Pi)^*\Sigma_\mu[\mathbf{J}_\sigma(\mu)-\mathbf{K}_\sigma(\mu)](\Pi)d\tau_\pi.$$

The "other terms" give no contribution by virtue of Lemma 2 of the Appendix. Therefore

$$E_{el}=\int(\Sigma)^*\mathbf{H}_\sigma{}^0(\Sigma)d\tau_\sigma+\int(\Pi)^*\mathbf{H}_\pi{}^0(\Pi)d\tau_\pi$$
$$+\int(\Pi)^*[\Sigma_\mu\mathbf{G}_\sigma(\mu)](\Pi)d\tau_\pi$$
$$=E_\sigma{}^0+E_\pi,$$

where due cognizance has been taken of the fact that the normalization factors in the denominators of Eqs. (11), (13), and (14) are each unity.

Theorem 2. For any approximate electronic wave function Ψ that satisfies the sigma-pi separability conditions A, B, and C of Sec. II, the expectation value for the total electronic energy may be expressed in the form

$$E_{el}=E_\sigma+E_\pi{}^0, \tag{21}$$

where

$$E_\sigma=\int(\Sigma)^*\mathbf{H}_\sigma(\Sigma)d\tau_\sigma\bigg/\int(\Sigma)^*(\Sigma)d\tau_\sigma, \tag{22}$$

$$E_\pi{}^0=\int(\Pi)^*\mathbf{H}_\pi{}^0(\Pi)d\tau_\pi\bigg/\int(\Pi)^*(\Pi)d\tau_\pi, \tag{23}$$

$$\mathbf{H}_\pi{}^0(n_\sigma+1,\, n_\sigma+2,\cdots,n_\sigma+n_\pi)$$
$$=\sum_{\mu=n_\sigma+1}^{n_\sigma+n_\pi}H_N(\mu)+\tfrac{1}{2}\sum_{\mu,\,\nu=n_\sigma+1}^{n_\sigma+n_\pi}{}'(e^2/r_{\mu\nu}), \tag{24}$$

and

$$\mathbf{H}_\sigma(1,2,\cdots,n_\sigma)=\sum_{\kappa=1}^{n_\sigma}\mathbf{H}_{\text{peel}}(\kappa)+\tfrac{1}{2}\sum_{\kappa,\lambda=1}^{n_\sigma}{}'(e^2/r_{\kappa\lambda}), \tag{25}$$

with

$$\mathbf{H}_{\text{peel}}(\kappa)\equiv\mathbf{H}_N(\kappa)+\mathbf{G}_\pi(\kappa), \tag{26}$$

in which the Coulomb-exchange operator $\mathbf{G}_\pi$ is defined by the formula

$$\mathbf{G}_\pi(\kappa)\equiv\mathbf{J}_\pi(\kappa)-\mathbf{K}_\pi(\kappa), \tag{27}$$

with

$$\mathbf{J}_\pi(\kappa)[(\Sigma)]\equiv\int(\Pi)^*[\Sigma_\pi(e^2/r_{\kappa\pi})](\Sigma)(\Pi)d\tau_\pi. \tag{28}$$

and

$$\mathbf{K}_\pi(\kappa)[(\Sigma)]\equiv\int(\Pi)^*[\Sigma_\pi(e^2/r_{\kappa\pi})](\Sigma_{ex}{}^{\pi})(\Pi_{ex}{}^{\kappa})d\tau_\pi. \tag{29}$$

Proof: This theorem follows from Theorem 1 by formal symmetry. In the proof of Theorem 1 the orthogonality to each other of sigma and pi functions was employed, but no other sigma or pi properties. The roles of sigma and pi functions therefore may be interchanged, which gives Theorem 2.

Theorem 3. For any case in which the sigma wave function is a known linear combination of Slater determinants, say

$$(\Sigma)=A_1(\Sigma_1)+A_2(\Sigma_2)+\cdots+A_s(\Sigma_s), \tag{30}$$

the operator $\mathbf{G}_\sigma$ of Theorem 1 is given by the formula

$$\mathbf{G}_\sigma(\mu)=\sum_{k,l=1}^{s}A_k{}^*A_l\mathbf{G}_{kl}{}^\sigma(\mu). \tag{31}$$

The operators $\mathbf{G}_{kl}{}^\sigma$ in turn are expressible in terms of operators $\mathbf{J}_{\sigma\sigma'}$ and $\mathbf{K}_{\sigma\sigma'}$, defined by

$$\mathbf{J}_{\sigma\sigma'}(\mu)[\varphi(\mu)]\equiv\int\sigma^*(\nu)\sigma'(\nu)(e^2/r_{\mu\nu})\varphi(\mu)d\tau_\nu, \tag{32}$$

and

$$\mathbf{K}_{\sigma\sigma'}(\mu)[\varphi(\mu)]\equiv\int\sigma^*(\nu)\varphi(\nu)(e^2/r_{\mu\nu})\sigma'(\mu)d\tau_\nu, \tag{33}$$

where φ is an arbitrary one-electron function. In fact,

$$\mathbf{G}_{kl}{}^\sigma(\mu)=\Sigma_\sigma[\mathbf{J}_{\sigma\sigma}(\mu)-\mathbf{K}_{\sigma\sigma}(\mu)], \tag{34a}$$

$$\mathbf{G}_{kl}{}^\sigma(\mu)=(\pm1)[\mathbf{J}_{\sigma\sigma'}(\mu)-\mathbf{K}_{\sigma\sigma'}(\mu)], \tag{34b}$$

or

$$\mathbf{G}_{kl}{}^\sigma(\mu)=0, \tag{34c}$$

according as (a) $(\Sigma_k)\equiv(\Sigma_l)$, the sum being over all spin orbitals occupied in (Σ_k), (b) (Σ_k) can be transformed by an even $(+1)$ or odd (-1) number of column interchanges into a determinant differing from (Σ_l) in only one spin orbital, σ appearing in the transformed (Σ_k) where σ' appears in (Σ_l), or (c) neither (a) nor (b) applies.

Proof: Substitution of (3) into (19) and (20) yields (31) directly. Expansion of the determinantal functions (Σ_k) in terms of products of one-electron spin orbitals σ_i and application of the usual Slater-Condon reduction procedure then leads to Eqs. (34). In this reduction cognizance must be taken of the orthonormality of the one-electron orbitals, the fact that $e^2/r_{\sigma\mu}$ is a one-electron operator as regards sigma electrons, and the one-sigma-electron dependence of $(\mathrm{II}_{e\tau}{}^{\sigma})$.

Theorem 4. For any case in which the pi wave function is a known linear combination of Slater determinants, say

$$(\Pi)=B_1(\Pi_1)+B_2(\Pi_2)+\cdots+B_p(\Pi_p), \tag{35}$$

the operator $\mathbf{G}_\pi$ of Theorem 2 is given by the formula

$$\mathbf{G}_\pi(\kappa)=\sum_{m,n=1}^{p} B_m{}^*B_n\mathbf{G}_{mn}{}^{\pi}(\kappa). \tag{36}$$

The operators $\mathbf{G}_{mn}{}^{\pi}$ in turn are expressible in terms of operators $\mathbf{J}_{\pi\pi'}$ and $\mathbf{K}_{\pi\pi'}$, defined by

$$\mathbf{J}_{\pi\pi'}(\kappa)[\varphi(\kappa)]\equiv\int\pi^*(\lambda)\pi'(\lambda)(e^2/r_{\kappa\lambda})\varphi(\kappa)d\tau_\lambda \tag{37}$$

and

$$\mathbf{K}_{\pi\pi'}(\kappa)[\varphi(\kappa)]\equiv\int\pi^*(\lambda)\varphi(\lambda)(e^2/r_{\kappa\lambda})\pi'(\kappa)d\tau_\lambda, \tag{38}$$

where φ is an arbitrary one-electron function. In fact,

$$\mathbf{G}_{mn}{}^{\pi}(\kappa)=\textstyle\sum_\pi[\mathbf{J}_{\pi\pi}(\kappa)-\mathbf{K}_{\pi\pi}(\kappa)], \tag{39a}$$

$$\mathbf{G}_{mn}{}^{\pi}(\kappa)=(\pm1)[\mathbf{J}_{\pi\pi'}(\kappa)-\mathbf{K}_{\pi\pi'}(\kappa)], \tag{39b}$$

or

$$\mathbf{G}_{mn}{}^{\pi}(\kappa)=0, \tag{39c}$$

according as (a) $(\Pi_m)\equiv(\Pi_n)$, the sum being over all spin orbitals occupied in (Π_m), (b) (Π_m) can be transformed by an even $(+1)$ or odd (-1) number of column interchanges into a determinant differing from (Π_n) in only one spin orbital, π appearing in the transformed (Π_m) where π' appears in (Π_n), or (c) neither (a) nor (b) applies.

Proof: This theorem follows from Theorem 3 by formal symmetry.

IV. PROCEDURES INVOKING THE PI-ELECTRON APPROXIMATION

Conventional Methods

The conventional treatment of pi electrons apart from the rest (e.g., the treatment of benzene as a six-electron problem) now may be given justification: *Subject to the auxiliary restriction that the approximate wave functions for some set of molecular states satisfy the sigma-pi separability conditions of Sec. II, with the same sigma wave function for all states—that is, subject to the pi electron approximation—variational treatment of the* n_π*-electron pi wave function* (Π) *with the Hamiltonian operator* $\mathbf{H}_\pi$ *of Eq. (16) is equivalent to variational treatment of the n-electron total wave function* Ψ *with the Hamiltonian operator* **H** *of Eq. (9).*

This result follows from Theorem 1 and the definition of the pi-electron approximation. The only term in the total electronic energy E_{el} of Eq. (12) which depends on the pi function is E_π, so that minimization of E_{el} with respect to variational parameters in the pi function, subject to the restriction of a fixed sigma function, is equivalent to minimization of E_π. Furthermore, for a fixed sigma function, the operators $\mathbf{H}_{\mathrm{core}}$ are fixed, that is, $\mathbf{H}_\pi$ is fixed and well-defined.

As McWeeny has already pointed out,[1] the fact that the operators $\mathbf{H}_{\mathrm{core}}$ are fixed for a fixed sigma description has another important consequence: *Empirical methods for handling integrals involving* $\mathbf{H}_{\mathrm{core}}$, *since they ordinarily do not require specification of the precise form of the sigma wave function, may often be preferable to purely theoretical methods for handling these integrals, which require specification of the sigma function. For a given sigma description, the integrals in question always may be computed theoretically, but a particular chosen sigma description is unlikely to be the best.*

A Generalized Self-Consistent Field Treatment of Sigma and Pi Electrons

Just as the pi electrons may be regarded as moving in the field of a "core" (bare nuclei plus sigma electrons), so the sigma electrons may be regarded as moving in the field of a "peel" (bare nuclei plus **pi** electrons—term coined by PL). This affords the possibility of iterative treatment of the *n*-electron problem: *For the molecular state of interest, assume some reasonable sigma description* (Σ^0) *and obtain the best pi complement* (Π^1) *using Theorem 1 (and perhaps also Theorem 3). Then, with this pi description, use Theorem 2 (and perhaps also Theorem 4) to obtain a new, improved sigma function* (Σ^1). *With this sigma function, employ Theorem 1 again to get a second pi function* (Π^2), *and so on, continuing until self-consistency is attained.*

This procedure represents a generalization of the usual self-consistent procedure of Hartree and Fock.

The "Best" Pi-Electron Approximation

There is another point that should be made, although it is somewhat academic. The validity of the procedures that have been described for treating pi electrons apart from the sigma depends on the detailed orthogonality of the sigma and pi parts of the wave function (Lemma 2 of Appendix), but not on any property specifically connoted by the labels σ and π. Thus, in a description $\Psi=[(\Sigma)(\Pi)]$ of some state of a conjugated aromatic hydrocarbon, it ordinarily would be supposed that $4p\pi$ atomic orbitals would, if they appear in the wave function at all, appear in the pi part (Π), but this actually is not required for the sigma-pi separation to be valid; the $4p\pi$ orbital could appear in (Σ) provided only it did not also appear in (Π) (Lemma 1 of Appendix). So the question arises: does a particular orbital enter (Σ) or does it enter (Π). Or more generally: *Given a molecule presumed to have n_π pi electrons and n_σ sigma electrons, and a complete set of one-electron spin orbitals λ_i, what is the best partition of the λ_i into two sets, the σ_i and the π_j, such that the n_σ-electron sigma part of the molecular wave function $\Psi=[(\Sigma)(\Pi)]$ can be built from the σ_i, the n_π-electron pi part from the π_j?* The "best partition" presumably gives minimum energy; in principle it may be found in each case by trial and error.

From the general point of view it is immaterial just how many electrons in a given state of a given molecule are termed "sigma" and how many "pi." The number to be allocated to each class usually will be clear from chemical or physical evidence.

V. PROCEDURES TRANSCENDING THE PI-ELECTRON APPROXIMATION

A first way to transcend the pi-electron approximation is to remove the restriction that the sigma wave function be the same for all members of a set of molecular states. For a set of molecular states 1, 2, ⋯, whereas under the pi-electron approximation one would have

$$\Psi_1=[(\Sigma)(\Pi^1)],\quad \Psi_2=[(\Sigma)(\Pi^2)]\cdots, \tag{40}$$

where (Σ) is some average sigma function, one could as well take

$$\Psi_1=[(\Sigma^1)(\Pi^1)],\quad \Psi_2=[(\Sigma^2)(\Pi^2)]\cdots, \tag{41}$$

where (Σ^1) is the sigma function for state 1, (Σ^2) is the sigma function for state 2, and so on. These last wave functions are the more general, so they are better (give lower energies). Moreover, since the sigma-pi separability conditions are still satisfied by the individual functions, the sigma-pi separation goes through for each, and the theorems and formulas of Sec. III apply. An orthogonality difficulty may crop up here, however: For the functions of Eq. (41) to be regarded as approximations to exact eigenfunctions, it is desirable that they be mutually orthogonal; mutual orthogonality is easier to preserve when the sigma component is held constant than when it is allowed to vary from state to state.

A second way to transcend the pi-electron approximation is to remove the restriction that the wave functions be antisymmetrized *products*, while preserving the partition of orbitals into sigma and pi classes and the allocation of a fixed number of electrons to each. By Eqs. (3), (6), and (7), under the pi-electron approximation a wave function may be written

$$\Psi=[(\Sigma)(\Pi)]=\textstyle\sum_{km} A_k B_m[(\Sigma_k)(\Pi_m)]. \tag{42}$$

More generally, one could take a wave function of the form

$$\Psi=C_1[(\Sigma)(\Pi)]+C_2[(\Sigma')(\Pi')]+\cdots, \tag{43}$$

which amounts to taking a wave function of the form

$$\Psi=\textstyle\sum_{km} C_{km}[(\Sigma_k)(\Pi_m)], \tag{44}$$

where the coefficients C_{km} are *not factorizable.* Use of such a procedure, a sort of restricted configuration interaction, requires more general formulas than those of Sec. III; complete discussion will not be given here.

A final way to transcend the pi-electron approximation, which in fact can lead to exact molecular wave functions, is to remove the allocation and partition assumptions also, that is, to add to a function of the form (44) terms corresponding to different numbers of sigma and pi electrons:

$$\Psi=\textstyle\sum_{km} C_{km}[(\Sigma_k)(\Pi_m)] + \sum_{ln} C_{ln}{}^{\ddagger}[(\Sigma_l{}^{\ddagger})(\Pi_n{}^{\ddagger})]+\cdots. \tag{45}$$

Here $[(\Sigma_l{}^{\ddagger})(\Pi_n{}^{\ddagger})]$ denotes a typical determinant having a different number of electrons assigned to sigma and pi orbitals than are so assigned in each of the determinants $[(\Sigma_k)(\Pi_m)]$. Since this expansion takes in all possible Slater determinants of order n that can be constructed from the given complete set of one-electron functions, if carried far enough it becomes completely equivalent to the expansion,

$$\Psi=\textstyle\sum_t D_t(\Delta_t), \tag{46}$$

of the exact molecular wave function in terms of all the Slater determinants (Δ_t) of order n that can be built from the given one-electron functions.

The term *pi-electron approximation* refers to the procedure represented by Eq. (40). When different sigma functions are used for different states, as in Eq. (41), one may speak of the *pi-electron approximation with adjustable core*; when serveral factorized functions are mixed, as in Eq. (43), one may speak of *sigma-pi configuration interaction without sigma-pi interchange*; and when one proceeds to the completely general case of Eq. (45) one may speak of *sigma-pi configuration interaction including sigma-pi interchange.*

VI. ILLUSTRATIONS

Molecular Orbital Calculations on the Benzene Molecule

In the simple Hückel-type calculation on benzene,[2] the pi-electron approximation is employed, but the energy of a molecular state is taken as the sum of one-electron energies. While useful and suggestive, this procedure does not have a truly satisfactory basis in quantum-mechanical equations.[3]

The first molecular orbital calculation on benzene that employed antisymmetrized wave functions and a Hamiltonian operator of the proper form was the

[2] For example, Eyring, Walter, and Kimball, *Quantum Chemistry* (John Wiley and Sons, Inc., New York, 1944), pp. 254–257.

[3] R. G. Parr, J. Chem. Phys. **19**, 799 (1951); J. A. Pople, Trans. Faraday Soc. **49**, 1375 (1953).

calculation by Goeppert-Mayer and Sklar[4] of the low electronic excitation energies. These authors invoked the pi-electron approximation and constructed pi-electron wave functions from molecular orbitals taken as linear combinations of atomic orbitals. They evaluated all integrals theoretically, which made the calculation a "purely theoretical" one. Integrals involving $\mathbf{H}_{\text{core}}$ were obtained through a certain approximate description of the core which neglected sigma-pi exchange terms [terms arising from the operator $\mathbf{K}_\sigma$ of Eq. (18)].

Still operating within the purely theoretical framework laid down by Goeppert-Mayer and Sklar, Parr, Craig, and Ross[5] refined the pi wave functions by inclusion of considerable configuration interaction among excited pi configurations, that is, by a pi configuration interaction calculation within the pi-electron approximation.

Parr, Craig, and Ross still omitted sigma-pi exchange energies. These were appended by Niira.[6] Precise specification of the sigma wave function is required [see Eq. (20)]; Niira investigated two alternative sigma descriptions. His calculations could be reorganized with a resultant economy of equations by use of Theorems 1 and 3 in the foregoing.

No definitive theoretical molecular orbital calculations on benzene appear to have been made that include sigma-pi configuration interaction either with or without sigma-pi interchange. However, suggestive calculations without sigma-pi interchange have been made on ethylene by Altmann[7] and by Van Dranen,[8] detailed calculations including sigma-pi interchange have been made on acetylene by Ross,[9] and primitive calculations on benzene have been reported by Van Dranen.[8]

A semiempirical theory of benzene and related molecules recently advanced[10] probably represents an approximation to a rather complete calculation within the pi-electron approximation (i.e., including considerable pi configuration interaction) further improved by consideration of some sigma-pi configuration interaction. The core integral β met in that theory was taken to be empirical; this is justified, or at least rationalized, by the argument given in the third paragraph in Sec. IV in the foregoing. The adjustment downward from its theoretical value of the electronic repulsion integral called $(11|11)$ most likely embodies pi correlation effects (another name for pi configuration interaction effects)[11]; the corresponding downward adjustment of the integral $(11|22)$ presumably incorporates sigma polarization effects (sigma-pi configuration interaction effects).

Two Problems in Pi-Electron Theory

Use of a wave function of the form required for the validity of the simple sigma-pi separation procedure does not admit valence bonds between sigma and pi electrons. For a given singlet total wave function, the component sigma and pi parts would each be singlets:

$$^1\Psi=[(^1\Sigma)(^1\Pi)]. \tag{47}$$

But in general the actual wave function will contain contributions involving sigma-pi bonding. This has been considered from the valence bond standpoint by Altmann[7] and by Van Dranen[8]; from the present point of view one would write, after the manner of Eq. (43),

$$^1\Psi=A[(^1\Sigma)(^1\Pi)]+\sum_{ij}B_{ij}[(^3\Sigma_i)(^3\Pi_j)]+\cdots, \tag{48}$$

where the (nine-term) sum is over the three components of $(^3\Sigma)$ and the three components of $(^3\Pi)$. The correction terms endow each of the sigma and pi components of the molecular wave function with a certain amount of *partial diradical character*; that corresponding correction terms will be important in organic free radicals and other molecules with an odd number of electrons has already been inferred by Weissman[12] from paramagnetic resonance absorption measurements.

Another problem in pi-electron theory is the theoretical calculation of vertical ionization potentials of unsaturated molecules. The usual procedure has been to suppose that molecule and ion have wave functions of the forms

$$\Psi_M=[(\Sigma)(\Pi_M)] \quad \text{and} \quad \Psi_{M^+}=[(\Sigma)(\Pi_{M^+})]. \tag{49}$$

Put another way, the Hamiltonian operator $\mathbf{H}_{\text{core}}$ of Eq. (17) is supposed to be the same for molecule and ion. Now recent semiempirical calculations of ionization potentials using this assumption give values which are too high[13]; a possible explanation of this discrepancy will now be offered. In the atomic case the corresponding approximation gives good results (Hartree-Fock energy parameters agree well with observed ionization potentials), supposedly only because of the mutual cancellation of two opposing effects: the greater correlation energy in the atom (because of more electrons), and the reorganization of the electronic substructure of the atom upon ionization.[14] The correlation effect in the semiempirical molecular treatments in question is taken into account in the choice of integral values[10,11]; it therefore seems reasonable that adjustment of the

[4] M. Goeppert-Mayer and A. L. Sklar, J. Chem. Phys. **6**, 645 (1938).
[5] Parr, Craig, and Ross, J. Chem. Phys. **18**, 1561 (1950).
[6] K. Niira, J. Phys. Soc. Japan **8**, 630 (1953).
[7] S. L. Altmann, Proc. Roy. Soc. (London) **A210**, 327, 343 (1952).
[8] J. van Dranen, thesis, University of Amsterdam (1951).
[9] I. G. Ross, Trans. Faraday Soc. **48**, 973 (1952).
[10] R. Pariser and R. G. Parr, J. Chem. Phys. **21**, 466, 767 (1953). See also Sec. 6 of R. McWeeny, Proc. Roy. Soc. (London) **A227**, 288 (1955).
[11] R. Pariser, J. Chem. Phys. **21**, 568 (1953).
[12] S. I. Weissman, conversation with PGL.
[13] P. G. Lykos, Ph.D. thesis, Carnegie Institute of Technology (1954); R. G. Parr and R. Pariser, J. Chem. Phys. **23**, 711 (1955).
[14] For example, R. S. Mulliken, J. chim. phys. **46**, 497 (1949).

core should be brought in too. That is, one should pass to the pi-electron approximation with adjustable core:

$$\Psi_M = [(\Sigma_M)(\Pi_M)] \quad \text{and} \quad \Psi_{M^+} = [(\Sigma_{M^+})(\Pi_{M^+})]. \tag{50}$$

Further preferential stabilization of the ion may be expected from sigma-pi configuration interaction effects of the type admitted in Eq. (48): the main contribution to the doublet ground state of the ion has the form $[(^1\Sigma)(^2\Pi)]$, but in general functions of the form $[(^3\Sigma)(^2\Pi)]$ also will enter.

VII. GENERALIZATIONS

The entire argument up to this point has turned on the sigma-pi separability conditions of Sec. II. Satisfaction of these conditions signifies that a wave function is expressible as an antisymmetrized product of two mutually exclusive factors, one describing the sigma electrons, one describing the pi electrons. "Mutual exclusiveness" here means that when determinants built from some orthonomal set of one-electron functions are used to represent both sigma and pi factors, no one-electron function enters both (Lemma 1 of Appendix).

This summary of the situation should make it evident that the separation into *two* factors is not vital; there could as well be one, three, or more. And the "sigma," "pi" designations are incidental; what counts is mutual exclusiveness of the factors—orthogonality between one-electron orbitals entering their descriptions.

The theorems of Sec. III therefore may be generalized to the case of antisymmetrized products of any number of mutually exclusive factors. From the generalization one can derive, among other results, both the Hartree-Fock equations so basic in molecular orbital theory and the Hurley, Lennard-Jones and Pople formulation of valence bond theory.[15] And there is a nice application to the theory of chemical reactions: "Participant" electrons can be treated apart from the rest if the total molecular wave function is representable as an antisymmetrized product of two mutually exclusive factors, one for the participant electrons, one for the "dormant" ones, and the latter description remains constant. So in pi-electron systems the higher-energy pi electrons only, the "frontier electrons" of Fukui,[16] for some purposes may be treated separately from the rest of the electrons, both sigma and pi.

VIII. ACKNOWLEDGMENTS

The authors are pleased to thank Professor Frank O. Ellison and Mr. Joe M. Parks of this laboratory for helpful discussions. Even before this work was begun, Mr. Parks had initiated calculations on the formaldehyde molecule using an iterative procedure of the type suggested in Sec. IV.

Support of this research by the National Science Foundation and the Office of Ordnance Research, U. S. Army, is gratefully acknowledged.

APPENDIX

Lemma 1.—Given the sigma-pi separability conditions A, B, and C of Sec. II, no spin orbital λ_i can enter both some (Σ_k) and some (Π_m) in the expansions of Eqs. (6) or (7) or of Eqs. (30) and (35). The λ_i therefore can be divided into two classes, the "sigma orbitals" σ_i, and the "pi orbitals" π_j, the (Σ_k) being built from the σ_i, the (Π_m) being built from the π_j.

Proof: By the normalization conditions (5) and (8), one must have

$$\int |\Psi|^2 d\tau = \Sigma_k \Sigma_m |A_k|^2 |B_m|^2 = 1. \tag{a}$$

But by (3), (6), (7) and the linear nature of antisymmetrization operators,

$$\Psi = \Sigma_k \Sigma_m A_k B_m [(\Sigma_k)(\Pi_m)] = \Sigma_k \Sigma_m A_k B_m \Psi_{km},$$

where $\Psi_{km} = [(\Sigma_k)(\Pi_m)]$ is a normalized Slater determinant of order n built from the λ_i. Hence explicit calculation gives

$$\int |\Psi|^2 d\tau = \Sigma_k \Sigma_m \Sigma_l \Sigma_n A_k^* B_m^* A_l B_n \int \Psi_{km}^* \Psi_{ln} d\tau. \tag{b}$$

Now if some λ_i enters both (Σ_k) and (Π_m), $\Psi_{km} \equiv 0$. If no such case happens, then the orthonormality integrals that appear in (b) are zero unless $k=l$ and $m=n$, when they are unity, giving

$$\int |\Psi|^2 d\tau = \Sigma_k \Sigma_m \Sigma_l \Sigma_n A_k^* B_m^* A_l B_n \delta_{kl} \delta_{mn} = \Sigma_k \Sigma_m |A_k|^2 |B_m|^2. \tag{c}$$

This is in agreement with (a). If, on the other hand, some λ_i enters say $(\Sigma_{k'})$ and $(\Pi_{m'})$, the corresponding result will be

$$\int |\Psi|^2 d\tau = \Sigma_k \Sigma_m |A_k|^2 |B_m|^2 - |A_{k'}|^2 |B_{m'}|^2 = 1 - |A_{k'}|^2 |B_{m'}|^2. \tag{d}$$

This is not in agreement with (a), so that no λ_i can enter both some (Σ_k) and some (Π_m).

Lemma 2.—Given the sigma-pi separability conditions A, B, and C of Sec. II, the following *generalized orthogonality relations* hold:

$$\int (\Sigma)^* (\Sigma_{ex})(\Pi_{ex}) d\tau_{ex} = 0, \tag{A1}$$

$$\int (\Pi)^* (\Sigma_{ex})(\Pi_{ex}) d\tau_{ex} = 0. \tag{A2}$$

Here $(\Sigma_{ex})(\Pi_{ex})$ is the result of exchanging one or more sigma electrons with one or more pi electrons in the product $(\Sigma)(\Pi)$, the first integration is over the coordinates of one or more of the sigma electrons so exchanged,

[15] Hurley, Lennard-Jones, and Pople, Proc. Roy. Soc. (London) **A220**, 446 (1953); J. C. Slater, Quarterly Progr. Rept. No. 16 (Solid-State and Molecular Theory Group, Massachusetts Institure of Technology, April 15, 1955), p. 5.

[16] Fukui, Yonezawa, and Nagata, Bull. Chem. Soc. Japan **27**, 423 (1954).

and the second integration is over the coordinates of one or more of the pi electrons so exchanged.

Proof: If the expansions (6) and (7) for each of (Σ), (Σ_{ex}), and (Π_{ex}) are inserted in (A1), and every determinant that enters then is expanded in terms of products of spin orbitals, each resultant term in (A1) will be zero by virtue of the orthogonality of all orbitals σ_i in any (Σ_k) to all orbitals π_i in any (Π_m) (Lemma 1): each term will have a factor of the type $\int\sigma_i(\xi)^*\pi_j(\xi)d\tau_\xi=0$. Hence (A1) follows, and (A2) similarly.

Lemma 3.—Given the sigma-pi separability conditions A, B, and C of Sec. II, the following *reciprocity relations* hold:

$$(\Sigma)=[(n_\sigma+n_\pi)!/n_\sigma!n_\pi!]^{\frac{1}{2}}\int(\Pi)^*[(\Sigma)(\Pi)]d\tau_\pi, \quad \text{(A3)}$$

$$(\Pi)=[(n_\sigma+n_\pi)!/n_\sigma!n_\pi!]^{\frac{1}{2}}\int(\Sigma)^*[(\Sigma)(\Pi)]d\tau_\sigma. \quad \text{(A4)}$$

Proof: If the expansion (4) is inserted in the right side of (A3) or (A4), the first term gives the desired result by the normalization condition (5); the other terms contribute nothing by Lemma 2.

Reprinted from THE JOURNAL OF CHEMICAL PHYSICS,
Vol. 25, No. 6, 1301, December, 1956
Printed in U. S. A.

Erratum: On the Pi-Electron Approximation and Its Possible Refinement

[J. Chem. Phys. 24, 1166 (1956)]

PETER G. LYKOS AND ROBERT G. PARR
Department of Chemistry, Carnegie Institute of Technology, Pittsburgh, Pennsylvania

LEMMA 1 of the appendix does not follow from the sigma-pi separability conditions A, B, and C of Sec. II as claimed—step (d) in the proof is fallacious. The essence of Lemma 1 consequently must be *postulated*, as by modifying condition C to read as follows:

(C) The functions (Σ) and (Π), respectively, may be expanded in terms of orthonormal Slater determinants (Σ_k) and (Π_m) built from some orthonormal set of one-electron functions $\lambda_1, \lambda_2, \cdots$ (molecular spin orbitals):

$$(\Sigma)=A_1(\Sigma_1)+A_2(\Sigma_2)+\cdots, \quad (6)$$

$$(\Pi)=B_1(\Pi_1)+B_2(\Pi_2)+\cdots, \quad (7)$$

$$\Sigma_k|A_k|^2=\Sigma_m|B_m|^2=1, \quad (8)$$

where no spin orbital λ_i enters both some (Σ_k) and some (Π_m).

With this modification of condition C, condition B can be relaxed to exclude the normalization condition on the total wave function Ψ, which now can be proved from the other conditions.

RGP is indebted to Dr. Per-Olov Löwdin for a helpful discussion.

Printed in U. S. A.

Calculations of the Lower Excited Levels of Benzene

M. GOEPPERT-MAYER, *Department of Physics, The Johns Hopkins University, Baltimore, Maryland*

AND

A. L. SKLAR,* *Department of Physics, The Catholic University of America, Washington, D. C.*
(Received August 3, 1938)

The energy of the first excited levels of benzene is calculated by the method of antisymmetrized molecular orbitals. The results predict two weak bands, due to forbidden electronic transitions, at $\lambda=2500$ and $\lambda=2100$ and a strong band at $\lambda=1500$. No empirical data except the carbon-carbon distance in benzene were used.

IN a previous paper,[1] one of the authors calculated the excited electronic levels of some organic molecules, among them benzene, on the basis of the Heitler-London method of approximation. The same calculation is undertaken here for benzene with the method of antisymmetrized products of molecular orbitals.[2]

I. THE ORBITALS

Of the four valence electrons of each carbon atom those in the 2*s*-eigenfunctions and in the 2*p*-eigenfunctions whose node is normal to the plane of the benzene molecule give rise to sp^2 hybridized single bonds to neighboring carbon atoms and to the hydrogens. The angles between the three sp^2 hybridized wave functions determine the geometry of the benzene molecule. The remaining 6 electrons, one for each carbon, are in the $2p\pi$ atomic eigenfunctions whose node coincides with the plane of the benzene ring. These electrons are responsible for the aromatic properties of benzene and for the lower absorption bands.[1] We are here concerned with the different molecular states of these 6 electrons only.

The electrons shall be denoted by Greek letters ν, μ, 1, $\cdots$, 6. The different carbon atoms will be denoted by k. The $2p\pi$ eigenfunction of the kth carbon atom will be written $K(\nu)$; specifically $I(\nu)$, $\cdots$, $VI(\nu)$. They are all taken to be positive on the same side of the benzene plane.

The interaction between the 6 electrons is at first neglected. The potential H_0 acting on the electrons has then the symmetry of the benzene molecule and may be written as a sum of the contributions from each atom.

$$\mathrm{H}_0=\sum_K H_K. \tag{1}$$

Of the 6 K-functions the following 6 mutually orthogonal orbitals have to be formed[3]

$$\phi_l(\nu)=(6\sigma_l)^{-\frac{1}{2}}\sum_{k=1}^{6}\exp^{2\pi ilk/6}K(\nu),\quad \phi_l^*=\phi_{-l} \tag{2}$$

with $l=0, \pm 1, \pm 2, 3$. The coefficients $\sigma_l^{-\frac{1}{2}}$ take care of the normalization. If the overlapping integral $\int I(\nu)II(\nu)d\tau_\nu$ is neglected, all σ's become unity.

With this approximation, and neglecting of integrals over products of K's which are not neighbors, the energies of the orbitals are:

$$\epsilon_l=\int I(T+H_0)Id\tau + 2\cos(2\pi l/6)\int I(T+H^0)IId\tau, \tag{3}$$

where T is the kinetic energy. In section IV the energies will be evaluated more exactly.

It is seen that the energies of the orbitals increase with $|l|$ since $\int I(T+H^0)IId\tau$ is negative. The energy depends only on the absolute value $|l|$, showing that the levels with $|l|=1$ and $|l|=2$ are doubly degenerate.

---

* This work was supported by a grant from the Penrose Fund of the American Philosophical Society.

[1] A. L. Sklar, J. Chem. Phys. **5**, 669 (1937).

[2] R. S. Mulliken, J. Chem. Phys. **1**, 492 (1933); Phys. Rev. **32**, 186, 761 (1928); **33**, 730 (1929); **40**, 55, **41**, 49, 751; **43**, 279 (1932–3). J. E. Lennard-Jones, Trans. Faraday Soc. **25**, 668 (1929). G. Herzberg, Zeits. f. Physik **57**, 601 (1929).

[3] E. Hückel, Zeits. f. Physik **70**, 204 (1931).

The energy of the molecule is lowest if the orbitals ϕ_0, ϕ_1, ϕ_{-1} contain two electrons each. The eigenfunction of the ground state in this order oi approximation is the product

$$\psi_0=\phi_0(1)\phi_0(2)\phi_1(3)\phi_1(4)\phi_{-1}(5)\phi_{-1}(6). \quad (4)$$

The first excited level arises if one electron from the state $l=+1$ or $l=-1$ is lifted to $l=2$ or $l=-2$. Its energy above the ground state is $\epsilon_2-\epsilon_1$. To this level belong four different eigenfunctions:

$$\begin{aligned}
&\psi_1=\phi_0(1)\phi_0(2)\phi_{+1}(3)\phi_{+1}(4)\phi_{-1}(5)\phi_{+2}(6),\\
&\psi_2=\phi_0(1)\phi_0(2)\phi_{-1}(3)\phi_{-1}(4)\phi_{+1}(5)\phi_{-2}(6),\\
&\psi_3=\phi_0(1)\phi_0(2)\phi_{+1}(3)\phi_{+1}(4)\phi_{-1}(5)\phi_{-2}(6), \quad (5)\\
&\psi_4=\phi_0(1)\phi_0(2)\phi_{-1}(3)\phi_{-1}(4)\phi_{+1}(5)\phi_{+2}(6),\\
&\psi_1=\psi_2^*;\quad \psi_3=\psi_4^*.
\end{aligned}$$

II. Group Theoretical Considerations

The way in which this 4-fold level of the molecule as a whole splits up, due to electronic interaction, and the behavior of the resultant molecular states can be determined without calculation by the application of group theory. The potential H_0 has the symmetry of the benzene ring, which is transformed into itself by rotations and reflections forming the group D_{6h}. The group operations transform any orbital ϕ_l into a linear combination of orbitals of the same energy, with coefficients which are the matrix elements of an irreducible representation of the group. The same holds true for a state of the molecule as a whole. The interaction between the electrons cannot alter this; it is only capable of splitting up "accidental" degeneracies, namely to separate the energies of states belonging to different irreducible representations which happened to be energetically equal in the zeroth approximation.

We wish therefore to investigate which irreducible representations of the benzene group are contained in the reducible fourth order representation determined by the transformation properties of the functions (5).

From the group table[4] of D_{6h}, by the usual method of comparison of the characters, the irreducible representations of the one electron orbitals can be found immediately. They are

$$\phi_0\subset\Gamma_8(A_{2u});\quad \phi_1,\ \phi_{-1}\subset\Gamma_6(E_{1g});$$

$$\phi_2,\ \phi_{-2}\subset\Gamma_{11}(E_{2u});\quad \phi_3\subset\Gamma_4(B_{2g}),$$

where the symbols in brackets are the notation of Mulliken and Placzek.[5] Every closed shell transforms like the identical representation $\Gamma_1(A_{1g})$, that is, remains unchanged under the operations of the group. We find therefore for the eigenfunction of the ground state

$$\psi_0\subset\Gamma_1(A_{1g}).$$

The four eigenfunctions of the excited level transform like the products $\phi_{\pm1}$, $\phi_{\pm2}$, namely:

$$\psi_1\cdots\psi_4\subset\begin{matrix}\Gamma_6\times\Gamma_{11}=(\Gamma_9+\Gamma_{10}+\Gamma_{12})\\ E_{1g}\times E_{2u}=(B_{1u}+B_{2u}+E_{1u})\end{matrix}.$$

The excited level will therefore split up into two single states belonging to Γ_9 and Γ_{10}, and one doubly degenerate one belonging to the two-rowed representation Γ_{12}.

Transitions between an excited state and the ground state with emission or absorption of light occur only if the integral of at least one component of the electric moment P multiplied by the eigenfunctions of ground- and excited state does not vanish. This is the case if the integrand is completely symmetrical, or at least contains an additive part which has this property. In other words, an excited level will be active in combination with the ground state only if the direct product of its representation and the representation of P contains the identical representation Γ_1. The transformation properties of P are the following:

$$P_z \text{ (normal to benzene plane)} \subset \Gamma_8(A_{2u});$$
$$P_x,\ P_y \text{ (in the plane)} \subset \Gamma_{12}(E_{1u}).$$

None of the products of Γ_8 with Γ_9, Γ_{10} or Γ_{12} contains Γ_1 nor do the products of Γ_{12} with Γ_9 and Γ_{10}. Only $\Gamma_{12}\times\Gamma_{12}$ contains a totally symmetrical part, so that Γ_{12} is the only active level, and is capable of emitting light polarized in the benzene plane, that is, perpendicular bands.

[4] Bright Wilson, Phys. Rev. **45**, 706 (1934).

[5] Mulliken, Phys. Rev. **43**, 279 (1933).

Transitions from the states Γ_9 and Γ_{10} to the ground state are, however, possible with simultaneous emission or absorption of vibrational energy, for instance of one quantum of vibration frequency of symmetry $\Gamma_5(E_{2g})$ that is of a degenerate, Raman active vibration (frequencies ν_6, ν_7, ν_8, ν_9 in the notation of E. Bright Wilson); or in combination with emission or absorption of two quanta of any degenerate vibration. It is to be expected that these transitions are weak, since they would vanish completely if the eigenfunction of the total molecule could be expressed as a product of vibrational and electronic functions.

The linear combinations of the four product eigenfunctions ψ (5) which have the symmetries Γ_9, Γ_{10}, Γ_{12} respectively are:

$$\begin{aligned}\Gamma_9(B_{1u})\Psi&=2^{-\frac{1}{2}}(\psi_1+\psi_2),\\ \Gamma_{10}(B_{2u})\Psi&=2^{-\frac{1}{2}}(\psi_1-\psi_2),\\ \Gamma_{12}(E_{1u})&\begin{cases}\Psi_3=\psi_3,\\ \Psi_4=\psi_4.\end{cases}\end{aligned}\tag{6}$$

III. Electronic Interaction

The change of energy of the states due to the electronic interaction

$$H^1=\sum_{\substack{\nu=1\\ \mu<\nu}}^{6}\frac{e^2}{r_{\nu\mu}}\tag{7}$$

will now be calculated.

The molecular eigenfunctions of the ground state (4) and the excited states (6) must be multiplied by an appropriate spin function and made completely antisymmetrical with respect to the exchange of electrons. The two possible spin functions for the νth electron will be denoted by $\alpha(\nu)$, $\beta(\nu)$. If two electrons are in the same orbital, they must necessarily have opposite spins. For the ground state, therefore, the spin function

$$\chi_0=\alpha(1)\beta(2)\alpha(3)\beta(4)\alpha(5)\beta(6)\tag{8}$$

gives the most general result.

For the excited states two cases must be distinguished. The spins of electrons 5 and 6, the only ones which are unpaired, may be either opposite or parallel. In the first case, the spin function must be made antisymmetric in 5 and 6, namely

$$\chi_s=2^{-\frac{1}{2}}\alpha(1)\beta(2)\alpha(3)\beta(4)\times[\alpha(5)\beta(6)-\beta(5)\alpha(6)].\tag{9}$$

In the second case it must be symmetric in 5 and 6, which can be done in three different ways, corresponding to the three orientations of the sum of the spins in space, one of which is

$$\chi_t=\alpha(1)\beta(2)\alpha(3)\beta(4)\alpha(5)\alpha(6),\tag{10}$$

while the others contain $\beta(5)\beta(6)$ and

$$2^{-\frac{1}{2}}[\alpha(5)\beta(6)+\beta(5)\alpha(6)].$$

Since the perturbing potential H^1 (7) is spin independent, spin states (9) and (10) do not interact. We shall refer to the states described by eigenfunctions obtained with (9) as singlet states, to those obtained with the three spin functions symmetric in 5 and 6, of which (10) is one, as triplet states. The energy of the latter three is the same in this approximation. The magnetic interaction between spin and orbit may however, bring about a fine structure splitting.

The totally antisymmetric eigenfunctions are then obtained by performing all 6! permutations P of electrons on the product of spin and coordinate function, multiplying the result by -1 to the order (odd or even) of the permutation and adding. For instance, for the ground state

$$\mathbf{\Psi}_0=(6!)^{-\frac{1}{2}}\sum_P(-1)^P P\Psi_0\chi_0.$$

Since the molecular orbitals ϕ_l are *strictly* orthogonal, the average value of H^1 for any such function can be expressed without any approximation, since all integrals over products of functions in which more than two electrons are in different molecular orbitals are zero. The energy will contain Coulomb terms, of the form

$$\gamma_{ll'}=\int\int\frac{e^2}{r_{\nu\mu}}|\phi_l(\nu)|^2|\phi_{l'}(\mu)|^2d\tau_\nu d\tau_\mu\tag{11}$$

and exchange terms

$$\delta_{ll'}=\int\int\frac{e^2}{r_{\nu\mu}}\phi_l(\nu)\phi_{l'}(\mu)[\phi_l(\mu)\phi_{l'}(\nu)]^*d\tau_\nu d\tau_\mu.\tag{12}$$

Of the product eigenfunctions (4), ψ_3 and ψ_4 interact with none of the permutations of any other one, bearing out the fact that the eigenfunctions (6) are the correct ones. The interaction between ψ_1 and ψ_2 brings in two more integrals,

$$\xi=\int\int\frac{e^2}{r_{\nu\mu}}\phi_1(\nu)\phi_{-1}^*(\nu)\phi_2(\mu)\phi_{-2}^*(\mu)d\tau_\nu d\tau_\mu$$

$$=\int\int\frac{e^2}{r_{\nu\mu}}\phi_1^2(\nu)\phi_2^2(\mu)d\tau_\nu d\tau_\mu, \quad (13)$$

$$\eta=\int\int\frac{e^2}{r_{\nu\mu}}\phi_1(\nu)\phi_2(\nu)\phi_1(\mu)\phi_2(\mu)d\tau_\nu d\tau_\mu. \quad (14)$$

All integrals γ, δ, ξ, η are real.

The energies, including electronic interaction, are then for the ground state

$$E_0=2\epsilon_0+4\epsilon_1+\gamma_{00}+8\gamma_{01}+6\gamma_{11}-4\delta_{01}-2\delta_{1-1}, \quad (15)$$

where ϵ_0 and ϵ_1 are the energies of the orbitals (3).

For the excited singlet states, the energies are

$$E_{1s}=E^{(1)}+\delta_{-12}-\delta_{12}-\xi+2\eta, \quad {}^1\Gamma_9(B_{1u}),$$
$$E_{2s}=E^{(1)}+\delta_{-12}-\delta_{12}+\xi-2\eta, \quad {}^1\Gamma_{10}(B_{2u}), \quad (16)$$
$$E_{3s}=E^{(1)}-\delta_{-12}+\delta_{12}, \quad {}^1\Gamma_{12}(E_{1u}),$$

and for the triplet states

$$E_{1t}=E^{(1)}-\delta_{-12}-\delta_{12}-\xi, \quad {}^3\Gamma_9(B_{1u}),$$
$$E_{2t}=E^{(1)}-\delta_{-12}-\delta_{12}+\xi, \quad {}^3\Gamma_{10}(B_{2u}), \quad (17)$$
$$E_{3t}=E^{(1)}-\delta_{-12}-\delta_{12}, \quad {}^3\Gamma_{12}(E_{1u}),$$

where the term E^1 which all excited levels have in common is

$$E^{(1)}=2\epsilon_0+3\epsilon_1+\epsilon_2+\gamma_{00}+6\gamma_{01}+2\gamma_{02}$$
$$+3\gamma_{11}+3\gamma_{12}-3\delta_{01}-\delta_{02}-\delta_{1-1}. \quad (18)$$

The subscripts 1, 2, 3 correspond to those on the eigenfunctions (6).

IV. The Energies in Terms of Atomic Integrals

The next task is to express all the integrals γ, δ, ξ, η over molecular orbitals in terms of integrals over the atomic eigenfunctions $K(\nu)$ through the use of (2).

The normalization coefficients σ_l of the orbitals are first determined by the relation:

$$\sigma_l=\tfrac{1}{6}\int\sum_K\{K^2(\nu)+2\cos(2\pi l/6)K(\nu)(K+I)(\nu)$$
$$+2\cos(4\pi l/6)K(\nu)(K+II)(\nu)$$
$$+(-1)^lK(\nu)(K+III)(\nu)\}d\tau_\nu$$
$$=1+2\cos(2\pi l/6)\int I(\nu)II(\nu)d\tau_\nu$$
$$+2\cos(4\pi l/6)\int I(\nu)III(\nu)d\tau_\nu$$
$$+(-1)^l\int I(\nu)IV(\nu)d\tau_\nu.$$

The functions $K(\nu)$ are assumed to be normalized. If the "overlap integrals" between neighbors are denoted by s_1, between next to neighbors s_2 and between opposite places in the ring s_3, the above expression can be written

$$\sigma_l=1+2s_1\cos\frac{2\pi l}{6}+2s_2\cos\frac{4\pi l}{6}+(-1)^ls_3. \quad (19)$$

The integrals $\gamma_{ll'}$ and $\delta_{ll'}$ contain the terms $\sigma_l\cdot\sigma_{l'}$ in the denominator, the integrals ξ and η the term $\sigma_1\cdot\sigma_2$. The expansions of the orbital integrals contain molecular integrals of Coulomb type between electrons on the same and on different atoms,

$$A_K=\int\int\frac{e^2}{r_{\nu\mu}}I^2(\nu)\cdot(K+I)^2(\mu)d\tau_\nu d\tau_\mu, \quad (20)$$

secondly a mixed exchange and Coulomb integral the interaction between an electron on one atom with one that is shared between the same and the neighboring atom,

$$B=\int\int\frac{e^2}{r_{\nu\mu}}I^2(\nu)I(\mu)II(\mu)d\tau_\nu d\tau_\mu, \quad (21)$$

and finally the exchange integral between electrons on neighboring atoms

$$C=\int\int\frac{e^2}{r_{\nu\mu}}I(\nu)II(\nu)I(\mu)II(\mu)d\tau_\nu d\tau_\mu. \quad (22)$$

Interactions between electrons which are partially on atoms which are not nearest neighbors shall be neglected, except for the purely Coulomb terms (20). All integrals A, B, C, s_ν are positive.

In this nomenclature, formulae(16) and (17) for the energies of the excited states take the form

$$
\begin{aligned}
E_{1s}&=E^{(1)}+(1/6\sigma_1\sigma_2)\{\ \ A_0-6A_1+8A_2-3A_3+\ C\}, && {}^1\Gamma_9(B_{1u}),\\
E_{2s}&=E^{(1)}+(1/6\sigma_1\sigma_2)\{-A_0-2A_2\qquad\quad +3A_3+5C\}, && {}^1\Gamma_{10}(B_{2u}), \quad (23)\\
E_{3s}&=E^{(1)}+(1/6\sigma_1\sigma_2)\{\qquad\quad 3A_1-3A_2\qquad -3C\}, && {}^1\Gamma_{12}(E_{1u}),\\
E_{1t}&=E^{(1)}+(1/6\sigma_1\sigma_2)\{-3A_0+2A_1\qquad\ +\ A_3+\ C\}, && {}^3\Gamma_9(B_{1u}),\\
E_{2t}&=E^{(1)}+(1/6\sigma_1\sigma_2)\{-A_0\qquad\ -2A_2+3A_3-7C\}, && {}^3\Gamma_{10}(B_{2u}), \quad (24)\\
E_{3t}&=E^{(1)}+(1/6\sigma_1\sigma_2)\{-2A_0+\ A_1-\ A_2+2A_3-3C\}, && {}^3\Gamma_{12}(E_{1u}).
\end{aligned}
$$

The order of the singlet terms will be shown to be $E_{2s}<E_{1s}<E_{3s}$, that of the triplet states $E_{1t}<E_{3t}<E_{2t}$, with the triplet states lower than the singlets.

The common term $E^{(1)}$ (18) of the excited states, as well as the energy of the ground state E_0 (15) are too complicated, due to the different normalization factors, to be written down in the general form. We are, here, however, interested only in the height of the excited levels above the ground state, and therefore in $E^{(1)}-E_0$. Using the numerical values of s_1, s_2, s_3, and therefore of the normalization coefficients σ_0, σ_1, σ_2 (see Table I), we obtain

$$
\begin{aligned}
E^{(1)}-E_0&=\epsilon_2-\epsilon_1-2\gamma_{01}+2\gamma_{02}-3\gamma_{11}\\
&\quad+3\gamma_{12}+\delta_{01}-\delta_{02}+\delta_{1-1}\\
&=\epsilon_2-\epsilon_1+0.41A_0+0.81A_1+0.64A_2\\
&\quad+0.23A_3-1.15B-1.26C.
\end{aligned}
\qquad (25)
$$

Lastly, we are confronted with the calculation of the energies ϵ_l of the orbitals due to the potential of the benzene rings. An approximate form for these was given in (3). The complete

TABLE I.

$s_1=\int I(\nu)II(\nu)d\tau_\nu$	=	.26
$s_2=\int I(\nu)III(\nu)d\tau_\nu$	=	.04
$s_3=\int I(\nu)IV(\nu)d\tau_\nu$	=	.02
$A_0=\int\int e^2/r_{\nu\mu}I^2(\nu)I^2(\mu)d\tau_\nu d\tau_\mu$	=	16.82 volts
$A_1=\int\int e^2/r_{\nu\mu}I^2(\nu)II^2(\mu)d\tau_\nu d\tau_\mu$	=	8.78
$A_2=\int\int e^2/r_{\nu\mu}I^2(\nu)III^2(\mu)d\tau_\nu d\tau_\mu$	=	5.64
$A_3=\int\int e^2/r_{\nu\mu}I^2(\nu)IV^2(\mu)d\tau_\nu d\tau_\mu$	=	4.95
$B=\int\int e^2/r_{\nu\mu}I^2(\nu)I(\mu)II(\mu)d\tau_\nu d\tau_\mu$	=	4.47
$C=\int\int e^2/r_{\nu\mu}I(\nu)II(\nu)I(\mu)II(\mu)d\tau_\nu d\tau_\mu$	=	.87
$Q=-\int \mathbf{H}_I(\nu)II^2(\nu)d\tau_\nu$	=	.83
$R=-\int \mathbf{H}_I(\nu)I(\nu)II(\nu)d\tau_\nu$	=	1.89

$I(\nu)$, $II(\nu)$ designate $2p\pi$ carbon functions (32) around nuclei I, II, respectively, $\mathbf{H}$ is the potential of a neutral carbon atom (33).

expression is

$$\epsilon_l=\frac{1}{\sigma_l}\int I(\nu)(T+H_0)\{I(\nu)+2\cos(2\pi l/6)II(\nu)$$
$$+2\cos(4\pi l/6)III(\nu)+(-1)^l IV(\nu)\}d\tau_\nu. \qquad (26)$$

The effect of the hydrogen atoms will be neglected completely. In the expression

$$H_0=\sum_K H_K$$

the potential H_K is then simply the attraction of the carbon nucleus and the repulsion of the other five carbon electrons. Since $I(\nu)$ is supposed to be an atomic eigenfunction, the relation

$$(T+H_I(\nu))I(\nu)=W_{2p}I(\nu) \qquad (27)$$

holds, where W_{2p} is the energy of a $2p$ electron in a carbon atom in the valence state. This term occurs once in every one of the 4 terms of ϵ_l (26), with coefficients that add up to σ_l, precisely canceling the σ_l in the denominator. W_{2p} therefore drops out of the difference $\epsilon_2-\epsilon_1$ since its coefficient in each ϵ_l is independent of l.

In the potential H_K the two electrons of the inner shell of the carbon atom shall be treated as if they were located in the nucleus. $H_K(\nu)$ is then the electrostatic potential at the place ν of a nucleus of charge 4 plus one electron in each of the three $2sp\sigma$ hybridized wave functions, or, which is the same, of the nucleus and one electron each in a $2s$ and the two $2p\sigma$ eigenfunctions. The calculation of the new integrals can be simplified by noticing that H_K is the potential of a neutral carbon atom with one electron in the $2s$ and each of the three $2p$ functions, minus the potential of a $2p\pi$ electron. The potential of the neutral carbon atom, $\mathbf{H}_K$ is a spherically symmetrical attraction and we may write

$$H_K(\nu)=\mathbf{H}_K(\nu)-\int\frac{e^2}{r_{\nu\mu}}K^2(\mu)d\tau_\mu \quad (28)$$

If (27) and (28) are inserted into (26) the second part gives rise to integrals of the types A and B (20), (21), the first part to new integrals, namely the effect of one neutral carbon atom on an electron at another nucleus,

$$Q=-\int\mathbf{H}_I(\nu)II^2(\nu)d\tau_\nu \quad (29)$$

and the effect of the potential on an electron partially on the same and on the neighboring atom

$$R=-\int\mathbf{H}_I(\nu)I(\nu)II(\nu)d\tau_\nu. \quad (30)$$

The minus sign is introduced in order to make both Q and R positive. All terms involving $\mathbf{H}_K$ which arise from interactions of non-neighbors are small enough to be neglected. The difference of ϵ_2 and ϵ_1 is then

$$\epsilon_2-\epsilon_1=\frac{\sigma_1-\sigma_2}{\sigma_1\sigma_2}\{-2Q-2A_1-2A_2-A_3\}+\frac{\sigma_1+\sigma_2}{\sigma_1\sigma_2}\{R+B\} \quad (31)$$
$$=-1.12Q+2.22R-1.12A_1-1.12A_2-0.56A_3+2.22B.$$

If (31) is put into (25) we obtain the final result for the part of the energy common to all excited states above the ground state

$$E^{(1)}-E_0=-1.12Q+2.22R+0.41A_0-0.31A_1-0.48A_2-0.33A_3+1.07B-1.26C. \quad (32)$$

V. Numerical Values

The eigenfunctions used for the calculation of the numerical integrals are $2p\pi$ hydrogen like functions at the different nuclei,

$$K(r,\theta,\phi)=\left(\frac{z^5}{32\pi}\right)^{\frac{1}{2}} r\exp(-zr/2)\sin\theta\cos\phi. \quad (33)$$

The screening constant z was chosen to be $z=3.18$, a value which was obtained by Zener[6] on the basis of a variational calculation minimizing the energy of the ground state of one carbon atom. This screening constant is not necessarily the most advantageous one for our molecular calculation. Minimizing the energy of one carbon atom in its valence state would presumably give a more correct value for z.

The distance between carbon atoms is $r_0=1.39A$,[7] which leads to $zr_0=8.37$ in atomic units.

The numerical values of the integrals used are collected in Table I.

The overlap integrals s can be calculated in closed form.[8] A_0, the repulsion between two electrons on the same atom, was calculated for this paper. The Coulomb repulsions between electrons on different atoms, A_1, A_2, A_3, as well as the exchange integral C were taken from the tables of Bartlett.[9]

The integral B, the repulsion between one electron on one atom and one shared between the same and a neighboring atom was not to be found in the literature. The evaluation was complicated and details of the calculation will be published shortly by one of the authors and R. H. Lyddane.

The attraction of a neutral carbon atom, in the valence state for an electron is:

$$\mathbf{H}_I=-\frac{4e^2}{r_\nu}+\frac{1}{r_\nu}\int_0^{r_\nu}e^2\sigma(r)r^2dr+\int_{r_\nu}^{\infty}e^2\sigma(r)rdr, \quad (34)$$

where

$$\sigma(r)=4\pi\{|\psi_{2s}|^2+|\psi_{2px}|^2+|\psi_{2py}|^2+|\psi_{2pz}|^2\}. \quad (35)$$

r_ν signifies the distance of the electron from the nucleus of the carbon atom I.

Since

$$\int_0^\infty\sigma(r)r^2dr=4$$

(34) may be simplified to

$$\mathbf{H}_I=-\int_{r_\nu}^{\infty}\left(\frac{r}{r_\nu}-1\right)\sigma(r)rdr. \quad (36)$$

[6] Zener, Phys. Rev. **36**, 51 (1930).
[7] *Handbuch der Physik*, Vol. 24, No. 2, p. 143.
[8] *Handbuch der Physik*, Vol. 24, No. 1. p. 643.
[9] J. H. Bartlett, Phys. Rev. **37**, 507 (1931). In Bartlett's notation, $A=i_1+\frac{1}{2}i_7$ and $C=i_2+\frac{1}{2}i_8$.

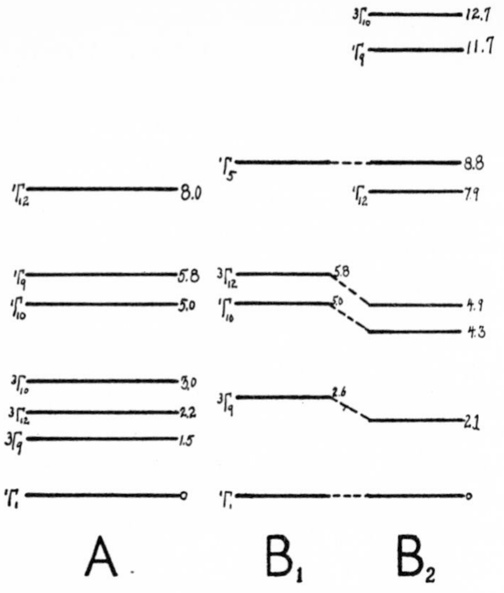

FIG. 1.

The effects of this potential of carbon atom I on an electron on the neighboring nucleus II, Q, as well as on an electron shared between atoms I and II, R, were calculated. Since the potential $\mathbf{H}_I$ decreases rapidly with distance, its effect on other than neighboring electrons was found to be completely negligible.

VI. Results

The levels calculated in this manner are shown in Fig. A. The numbers at the right of the lines give the energy in volts of the levels above the ground state. Since only the excitation of one electron from $l=1$ to $l=2$ has been considered, only the lowest levels are obtained. The next higher ones, however, arising from the excitation of one electron from $l=1$ to $l=3$, one electron from $l=0$ to $l=2$ or two electrons from $l=\pm 1$ to $l=\pm 2$ have different symmetry properties from any of those obtained here (for instance Γ_5) and therefore do not interact with the states considered.

Figures B_1 and B_2 show for comparison the level scheme obtained from the Heitler-London method of calculation.[1] Figure B_1 contains the levels as calculated from nonpolar terms, B_2 those obtained by the inclusion of some polar configurations. The contribution of the polar terms is somewhat uncertain since not all possible polar terms, but only the lowest ones, were considered, and since the energy depends on two parameters which can only be roughly determined empirically.[10]

The energy of the lowest singlet state, of symmetry ${}^1\Gamma_{10}$ agrees very well in the two methods. Experimentally, a band of oscillator strength $f=10^{-4}$ is observed at $\lambda=2600$A or energy about 4.7 volts. The small transition probability indicates that this band is due to a forbidden electronic transition. Analysis of the band structure shows that the observed vibrational progressions are in agreement with a symmetry character ${}^1\Gamma_{10}(B_{2u})$ for the excited electronic state.

Of the other singlet states, the energies of ${}^1\Gamma_{12}(E_{1u})$ agree well in both calculations. A glaring discrepancy occurs however in the position of the level ${}^1\Gamma_9$. In the Heitler-London calculation both ${}^1\Gamma_9$ and ${}^1\Gamma_{12}$ are purely polar terms. They are obtained in that method really as a second approximation, and it would not be surprising if the calculated energy would turn out to be too high. On the other hand, in the method of this paper, polar configurations enter with too large coefficients into all states, causing the polar states to be relatively too low, as will be discussed later. But the agreement for the level ${}^1\Gamma_{12}(E_{1u})$ must then be regarded as purely accidental.

The experimental evidence in the region of the far ultraviolet is not completely conclusive. The measurements of Henri[11] in solution, evaluated by Chako[12] show a band of oscillator strength one-tenth at about 2070A, or 6.0 ev. One must be inclined to attribute this to the electronic level ${}^1\Gamma_{12}$, since this is an allowed transition. On the other hand, the measurements of Carr and

[10] The two parameters are the difference between the Coulomb energy of a polar and a nonpolar state and the resonance integral $\int\psi_a(1)\psi_b(2)H\psi_a^*(1)\psi_a^*(2)$. Their values were estimated from the absorption frequency of pentene 2 (since cyclohexene has not been measured), and from the resonance of cyclohexene. States like  and 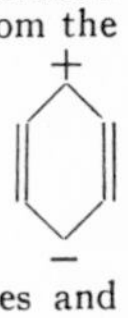 were omitted since they introduced new variables and complicated the determinant.

[11] V. Henri, J. de. Phys. **3**, 181 (1922).

[12] N. Chako, J. Chem. Phys. **2**, 644 (1934).

Stücklen[13] in the gas seem to indicate the presence of two bands at 2040A and 1850A, of 6.0 ev and 6.7 ev respectively, the band at longer wave-length being the weaker one. This would be in reasonable agreement with the calculations of this paper, which predict a state forbidden in combination with the ground state, therefore a weak band, at 5.8 ev, and an allowed band at 8.0 ev. Since in solution the 2600A band of benzene is considerably shifted to longer wave-length, it is conceivable that a strong band at 1850A might be shifted sufficiently in the liquid to mask a weak band at 2040A, which would correlate the experiments of Henri with the appearance of the bands in vapor.

The energy of the triplet states turns out to be uniformly lower in the molecular orbital than in the Heitler-London calculation. The best agreement is obtained for $^3\Gamma_9$, the worst for $^3\Gamma_{10}$. That the energy, calculated on the basis of molecular orbitals, is lower for the triplet states than the singlet states can be seen qualitatively. Since the eigenfunctions used are antisymmetrized they allow no more than two electrons of opposite spin to be simultaneously at one nucleus, but they allow this to happen very frequently. Terms corresponding to two electrons on one carbon atom give rise to a large repulsion and therefore an increase in the energy. Now in the triplet states, where four electrons have spin α, two spin β, this piling up of two electrons of opposite spin will not occur as often as in the singlet states, causing the calculated energy of the triplet states to be lower than that of the singlets. For the true electronic eigenfunctions two electrons will not accumulate as freely on one carbon atom, so that one must expect the true difference between the energies of the excited singlet and triplet states to be smaller than that calculated on the basis of molecular orbitals. In other words, the absolute value of the energies of all states computed on the basis of molecular orbitals are too high, but those of the singlet states more too high than those of the triplet states. Since we calculate the energies of all excited states above the ground state, which is a singlet state, it may be expected that the energies of the singlet states are more reliable than those of the triplet states.

[13] E. P. Carr and H. Stücklen, J. Chem. Phys. **6**, 55 (1938).

VII. Summary

The eigenfunctions used for the description of the states of the benzene molecule are built from products of molecular orbitals. They are made completely antisymmetric. The orbitals in turn are assumed to be linear combinations of the $2p\pi$ atomic eigenfunctions of the six carbon atoms. No assumptions other than these were made. The energy is obtained as a sum of integrals over atomic eigenfunctions. Except for the Coulomb term, interactions between electrons farther apart than on neighboring atoms were neglected. This approximation is not necessary, since the other occurring integrals can be estimated very easily. There exist, however, a great number of them, and the calculation of the coefficients with which they enter into the energy of the various levels becomes extremely tedious. We took into account the effect of quite a few of them and found that they tend to cancel. No other approximations were made and no empirical data were used, except the C-C distance in benzene.

The energies depend then on the form of the atomic eigenfunctions. The integrals which are most sensitive to a change in the screening constant are the overlapping integrals s, and they also enter rather critically into the energy. The screening constant used here was 3.18.

The authors wish to express their thanks to Professors K. F. Herzfeld and J. E. Mayer for their interest and for many valuable discussions.

Reprinted from THE JOURNAL OF CHEMICAL PHYSICS, Vol. 18, No. 10, 1338–1346, October, 1950
Printed in U. S. A.

LCAO Self-Consistent Field Calculation of the π-Electron Energy Levels of *cis*- and *trans*-1,3-Butadiene*

ROBERT G. PARR† AND ROBERT S. MULLIKEN
Department of Physics, University of Chicago, Chicago 37, Illinois

(Received June 6, 1950)

The π-electrons of the molecules *cis*- and *trans*-1,3-butadiene are treated by the method of antisymmetrized products of molecular orbitals, the molecular orbitals being taken as linear combinations of $2p\pi$-Slater atomic orbitals with effective charge 3.18. The *best* ground state *LCAO* molecular orbitals obtainable from these are found by application of a method recently proposed by Roothaan which is based on the variational theorem, and the π-electron energy of the ground state is calculated. Including a correction for nuclear repulsions, the *trans*- form is computed to be 0.12 ev more stable than the *cis*-form. Using the ground state orbitals to build up excited state wave functions, the energies of four singly excited singlet states and the corresponding triplet states are calculated, there resulting for the average of the lowest singlet and triplet states the excitation energy 5.4 ev for *cis*- and 5.7 ev for *trans*-, the experimental value for the lowest singlet state (probably for *trans*-) being 6.0 ev. The first ionization potential is computed to be 9.7 ev for both *cis*- and *trans*-, whereas the observed value is 9.1 ev. No extra-geometrical empirical data are used except in the calculation of ionization potentials, where the value −11.28 ev based on atomic spectroscopic data is used for the energy of a $2p\pi$-electron in a carbon atom in its valence state.

INTRODUCTION

RECENT calculations[1,2] have indicated that electronic excitation and ionization energies of unsaturated organic compounds can be computed with fair accuracy by the method of antisymmetrized products of molecular orbitals (in *LCAO* approximation) with the introduction of no extra-geometrical empirical factors. In most cases so far treated the molecular orbitals have been determined by symmetry considerations alone. In the present paper we consider a molecule (1,3-butadiene) where the orbitals can *not* be so de-

* This work was assisted in part by the ONR under Task Order IX of Contract N6ori-20 with the University of Chicago.

† Present address: Department of Chemistry, Carnegie Institute of Technology, Pittsburgh, Pennsylvania.

[1] For example, R. G. Parr and B. L. Crawford, Jr., J. Chem. Phys. **16**, 526 (1948); C. C. J. Roothaan and R. G. Parr, J. Chem. Phys. **17**, 1001 (1949).

[2] R. S. Mulliken, Parts II–III of "Report on molecular orbital theory," J. de Chim. Phys. **46**, 497 (1949)—see 1947–8 ONR Report of University of Chicago Physics Department Spectroscopic Laboratory for English version.

termined, and apply it to the *SCF* (self-consistent field) method which Roothaan[3] has developed for simultaneous determination of orbitals and energy.[4]

Roothaan's method could (and should) be used to treat butadiene as a full 30-electron problem, but this would require numerical values for certain integrals which are not yet available.[5] It is well known, however, and it has been assumed in the treatment of other molecules mentioned above, that the unsaturation electrons in conjugated molecules such as butadiene are responsible for the lowest frequency electronic transitions, and may be profitably studied apart from the rest. Accordingly, we shall treat butadiene as a four-electron problem, replacing the 26 more tightly bound electrons by an effective potential.

We shall carry the work for *cis*- and *trans*-butadiene along side by side. This will facilitate comparison of results on the two molecules at any stage, and will provide a means for detecting arithmetic errors which may crop up. The geometry we shall assume for the carbon skeletons $C_a-C_b-C_c-C_d$ of these molecules is based upon the electron diffraction results of Schomaker and Pauling:[6] skeletons planar, $C_a-C_b-C_c$ and $C_b-C_c-C_d$ angles 124°, C_a-C_b and C_c-C_d distances 1.35A, C_b-C_c distances 1.46A.

GROUND STATE ORBITALS AND ENERGY

We consider, then, four electrons moving in the field of the single-bonded, sp^2-hybridized, completely planar structure $H_2C-CH-CH-CH_2$ forming a core with charge +4, composed of a +1 charge on each carbon atom, but no charges on the hydrogen atoms. We take as "starting orbitals" for these electrons normalized $2p\pi$-Slater *AO*'s (atomic orbitals) χ_a, χ_b, χ_c, χ_d, on the four carbon atoms, and seek two orthonormal *MO*'s (molecular orbitals) ϕ_1, ϕ_2, which are linear combinations of these starting orbitals (*LCAO*):

$$\phi_i=\sum_p C_{ip}\chi_p; \tag{1}$$

and which minimize the energy

$$E_N=\int \Psi_N^*\mathbf{H}\Psi_N d\tau \tag{2}$$

calculated from the complete four-electron Hamiltonian operator **H** and the totally antisymmetric and normalized four-electron wave function

TABLE I. Integrals over the atomic orbitals χ_p.[a]

Integral	Value[d,e] *cis*-	Value[d,e] *trans*-	Integral	Value[d,e] *cis*-	Value[d,e] *trans*-
Overlap integrals			Coulomb-Exchange Integrals[f]		
S_{ab}	0.27854	0.27854	$aa \mid aa$	0.3914×Z	0.3914×Z
S_{bc}	0.23281	0.23281	$aa \mid bb$	0.2136	0.2136
S_{ac}	0.03371	0.03371	$bb \mid cc$	0.2010	0.2010
S_{ad}	0.01188	0.00218	$aa \mid cc$	0.1277	0.1277
Penetration			$aa \mid dd$	0.1083	0.0885
integrals[b]			$aa \mid ab$	0.0834	0.0834
$a:ab$	0.0527×Z	0.0527×Z	$bb \mid bc$	0.0678	0.0678
$b:bc$	0.0377	0.0377	$bb \mid cd$	0.0447	0.0447
$a:bb$	0.0228	0.0228	$aa \mid bc$	0.0384	0.0384
$b:cc$	0.0156	0.0156	$aa \mid cd$	0.0334	0.0291
$b:ac$	0.0070	0.0070	$aa \mid ac$	0.0069	0.0069
$a:ac$	0.0012	0.0012	$aa \mid bd$	0.0053	0.0043
$a:bc$	0.0008	0.0008	$bb \mid ac$	0.0107	0.0107
$b:cd$	0.0007	0.0007	$aa \mid ad$	0.0024	0.0004
$b:ad$	0.0003	0.0004	$bb \mid ad$	0.0026	0.0007
$a:cc$	0.0002	0.0002	$ab \mid ab$	0.0252	0.0252
$a:ad$	0.0002	0.0000	$bc \mid bc$	0.0169	0.0169
$a:bd$	0.0001	0.0000	$ab \mid bc$	0.0147	0.0147
$a:cd$	0.0000	0.0000	$ab \mid cd$	0.0110	0.0107
$a:dd$	0.0000	0.0000	$ab \mid ac$	0.0029	0.0029
Core			$ab \mid bd$	0.0019	0.0016
integrals[c]			$bc \mid ac$	0.0025	0.0025
$-I_{aa}$	0.4726×Z	0.4528×Z	$ab \mid ad$	0.0008	0.0001
$-I_{bb}$	0.5809	0.5809	$bc \mid ad$	0.0007	0.0002
$-I_{ab}$	0.2149	0.2106	$ac \mid ac$	0.0004	0.0004
$-I_{bc}$	0.1839	0.1839	$ac \mid bd$	0.0003	0.0002
$-I_{ac}$	0.0312	0.0301	$ac \mid ad$	0.0001	0.0000
$-I_{ad}$	0.0084	0.0026	$ad \mid ad$	0.0001	0.0000

[a] The χ_p are $2p\pi$-Slater *AO*'s—see Eq. (A1).
[b] $r:pq$ is an abbreviation for $(A_r:\chi_p\chi_q)$—see Eq. (A9).
[c] Energies given are relative to energy W_{2p} of a $2p\pi$-electron of a carbon atom in its valence state. ($W_{2p}=-11.28$ ev—see reference 2.)
[d] Overlap integrals are dimensionless; they are for Slater $2p\pi$-*AO*'s with $Z=3.18$ at distances indicated in text. The other integrals have dimensions of energy; their values are given in atomic units: 1 atomic unit = 13.602 ev.
[e] Values for all but the overlap integrals are the numerical entries in the table multiplied by Z (in the following, we use $Z=3.18$).
[f] $pr|qs$ is an abbreviation for $J_{pqrs}=(\chi_p\chi_r|\chi_q\chi_s)$—see Eq. (A2).

$$\Psi_N=\frac{1}{(4!)^{\frac{1}{2}}}\begin{vmatrix} (\phi_1\alpha)^1 & (\phi_1\beta)^1 & (\phi_2\alpha)^1 & (\phi_2\beta)^1 \\ (\phi_1\alpha)^2 & (\phi_1\beta)^2 & (\phi_2\alpha)^2 & (\phi_2\beta)^2 \\ (\phi_1\alpha)^3 & (\phi_1\beta)^3 & (\phi_2\alpha)^3 & (\phi_2\beta)^3 \\ (\phi_1\alpha)^4 & (\phi_1\beta)^4 & (\phi_2\alpha)^4 & (\phi_2\beta)^4 \end{vmatrix}. \tag{3}$$

Here α and β are the two possible (orthonormal) spin functions for an electron, and $(\phi_2\beta)^3$, for example, denotes the wave function of electron 3 in the molecular orbital ϕ_2 with the spin $-(1/2)(h/2\pi)$. E_N is the total ground state energy of the four π-electrons in the field of the core.

Writing H out in the form

$$\mathbf{H}=\sum_{\nu=1}^{4}(\mathbf{T}^\nu+\mathbf{U}_c^\nu)+(1/2)\sum_{\substack{\mu,\nu=1\\ \mu\neq\nu}}^{4}(e^2/r^{\mu\nu}), \tag{4}$$

where $\mathbf{T}^\nu$ is the kinetic energy of electron ν, $\mathbf{U}_c^\nu$ is the potential energy of electron ν in the $2p\pi$-electron-less framework, e is the electronic charge, and $r^{\mu\nu}$ is the distance between electrons μ and ν, and carrying out the

[3] C. C. J. Roothaan, Ph.D. thesis, University of Chicago (see 1948–9 ONR report for section on *LCAO SCF* method, 1949–50 ONR Report for section on application to benzene, including computation of ionization and excitation energy).
[4] See also R. S. Mulliken, "Report on molecular orbital theory," Part V, J. de Chim. Phys. **46**, 675 (1949)—see 1948–9 ONR Report for English version. A preliminary survey of the application of the present and other methods to 1,3-butadiene is given in Section 23 and Fig. 3.
[5] A systematic program for computation of integrals has been begun at the University of Chicago, but it may be several years before all of the integrals which enter *LCAO* computations on polyatomic molecules become available.
[6] V. Schomaker and L. Pauling, J. Am. Chem. Soc. **61**, 1769 (1939).

integration indicated in Eq. (2), one obtains[7]

$$E_N = 2I_1 + 2I_2 + J_{11} + J_{22} + 4J_{12} - 2K_{12}. \quad (5)$$

Here[8]

$$I_i = \int \phi_i^{*\nu}(\mathbf{T}^\nu + \mathbf{U}_c^\nu)\phi_i^\nu d\tau^\nu \quad (6)$$

$$J_{ij} = \int \phi_i^{*\nu}\phi_j^{*\mu}(e^2/r^{\mu\nu})\phi_i^\nu\phi_j^\mu d\tau^\nu d\tau^\mu, \quad (7)$$

and

$$K_{ij} = \int \phi_i^{*\nu}\phi_j^{*\mu}(e^2/r^{\mu\nu})\phi_i^\mu\phi_j^\nu d\tau^\nu d\tau^\mu, \quad (8)$$

are "core," "Coulomb," and "exchange" integrals, respectively, over the molecular orbitals ϕ_i or ϕ_i and ϕ_j. These integrals, and hence E_N, may be expressed in terms of integrals over the starting *AO*'s χ_p through the use of Eq. (1); the results are

$$I_i = \sum_{p,q} C_{ip}^* I_{pq} C_{iq}, \quad (9)$$

$$J_{ij} = \sum_{p,q,r,s} C_{ip}^* C_{jq}^* J_{pqrs} C_{ir} C_{js}, \quad (10)$$

and

$$K_{ij} = \sum_{p,q,r,s} C_{ip}^* C_{jq}^* J_{pqsr} C_{ir} C_{js}, \quad (11)$$

where

$$I_{pq} = \int \chi_p^{*\nu}(\mathbf{T}^\nu + \mathbf{U}_c^\nu)\chi_q^\nu d\tau^\nu \quad (12)$$

and

$$J_{pqrs} = \int \chi_p^{*\nu}\chi_q^{*\mu}(e^2/r^{\mu\nu})\chi_r^\nu\chi_s^\mu d\tau^\nu d\tau^\mu \quad (13)$$

are "core" and "Coulomb-exchange" integrals over the atomic orbitals χ_p.

Evaluation of the integrals I_{pq} and J_{pqrs} is discussed in the Appendix, and leads for the molecular dimensions we are assuming to the values given in Table I. With these values known, the only unknowns remaining in Eq. (5) for the energy E_N are the coefficients C_{ip} of Eqs. (1), (9)–(11), which must be assigned values such as to make E_N a minimum subject to orthonormalization of the ϕ_i, i.e., subject to

$$\int \phi_i^{*\nu}\phi_j^\nu d\tau^\nu = \sum_{p,q} C_{ip}^* S_{pq} C_{jq} = \begin{cases} 1 & \text{if } i=j \\ 0 & \text{if } i\neq j \end{cases}, \quad (14)$$

where

$$S_{pq} = \int \chi_p^{*\nu}\chi_q^\nu d\tau^\nu \quad (15)$$

is the "overlap" integral between χ_p and χ_q. The equations which the C_{ip} must in general satisfy have been derived by Roothaan;[3] in the present case they are the homogeneous set

$$\left.\begin{aligned} C_{ia}(L_{aa}-S_{aa}\epsilon_i)+C_{ib}(L_{ab}-S_{ab}\epsilon_i)+C_{ic}(L_{ac}-S_{ac}\epsilon_i)+C_{id}(L_{ad}-S_{ad}\epsilon_i)&=0\\ C_{ia}(L_{ba}-S_{ba}\epsilon_i)+C_{ib}(L_{bb}-S_{bb}\epsilon_i)+C_{ic}(L_{bc}-S_{bc}\epsilon_i)+C_{id}(L_{bd}-S_{bd}\epsilon_i)&=0\\ C_{ia}(L_{ca}-S_{ca}\epsilon_i)+C_{ib}(L_{cb}-S_{cb}\epsilon_i)+C_{ic}(L_{cc}-S_{cc}\epsilon_i)+C_{id}(L_{cd}-S_{cd}\epsilon_i)&=0\\ C_{ia}(L_{da}-S_{da}\epsilon_i)+C_{ib}(L_{db}-S_{db}\epsilon_i)+C_{ic}(L_{dc}-S_{dc}\epsilon_i)+C_{id}(L_{dd}-S_{dd}\epsilon_i)&=0 \end{aligned}\right\}. \quad (16)$$

Here the quantities L_{pq} are defined by

$$L_{pq} = I_{pq} + G_{pq}, \quad (17)$$

where the

$$G_{pq} = \sum_{i=1,2} \left[2\int \phi_i^{*\nu}\chi_p^{*\mu}(2/r^{\mu\nu})\phi_i^\nu\chi_q^\mu d\tau^\nu d\tau^\mu - \int \phi_i^{*\nu}\chi_p^{*\mu}(2/r^{\mu\nu})\phi_i^\mu\chi_q^\nu d\tau^\nu d\tau^\mu\right] \quad (18)$$

are components of the *LCAO SCF* Coulomb-exchange operator **G** for the problem. The ϵ_i are numbers which make non-trivial solutions for the C_{ip} possible; that is, the ϵ_i are solutions of the secular equation

$$\begin{vmatrix} L_{aa}-S_{aa}\epsilon & L_{ab}-S_{ab}\epsilon & L_{ac}-S_{ac}\epsilon & L_{ad}-S_{ad}\epsilon \\ L_{ba}-S_{ba}\epsilon & L_{bb}-S_{bb}\epsilon & L_{bc}-S_{bc}\epsilon & L_{bd}-S_{bd}\epsilon \\ L_{ca}-S_{ca}\epsilon & L_{cb}-S_{cb}\epsilon & L_{cc}-S_{cc}\epsilon & L_{cd}-S_{cd}\epsilon \\ L_{da}-S_{da}\epsilon & L_{db}-S_{db}\epsilon & L_{dc}-S_{dc}\epsilon & L_{dd}-S_{dd}\epsilon \end{vmatrix} = 0. \quad (19)$$

For given values of the L_{pq} and S_{pq}, there are four real roots of this equation.[3] Corresponding to each root there is a normalized molecular orbital ϕ_i, the coefficients C_{ip} in which can be found from Eqs. (14) and (16). The L_{pq} are not at first known, however, but depend upon the C_{ip} through the dependence of the G_{pq} on the occupied ϕ_i—see Eq. (18). A method of successive approximations must therefore be adopted. A set of C_{ip} values may be assumed, the G_{pq} calculated, the secular equation solved, and a new set of C_{ip} values found, and this process repeated until a "self-consistent" set of C_{ip} values is found. If the resulting orbitals are

[7] See, for example, B. L. Crawford, Jr. and R. G. Parr, J. Chem. Phys. **17**, 726 (1949), Eq. (26), or reference 2 or 3.

[8] $d\tau^\nu$ denotes the element of volume for electron ν, ϕ_i^* the complex conjugate of ϕ_i. All integrations are performed over all space.

denoted by ϕ_1, ϕ_2, ϕ_3, ϕ_4, in order of increasing energy (ϵ_i), ϕ_1 and ϕ_2 will be the ground state orbitals we are seeking, while ϕ_3 and ϕ_4 will represent some approximation to excited state orb tals (see infra).

Thus far, the fact that the χ_p are *atomic* orbitals has not been used—equations of precisely the same form would result if we began with *any* four independent orbitals. To take advantage of this fact, let us now begin again taking as starting orbitals the normalized[9] "symmetry orbitals"

$$\left\{\begin{array}{ll}\sigma_1=(1/N_1)(\chi_a+\chi_d), & N_1=1.42259 \text{ for } cis\text{-}, 1.41575 \text{ for } trans\text{-}\\ \sigma_2=(1/N_2)(\chi_b+\chi_c), & N_2=1.57023 \text{ for both } cis\text{- and } trans\text{-}\\ \sigma_3=(1/N_3)(\chi_b-\chi_c), & N_3=1.23870 \text{ for both } cis\text{- and } trans\text{-}\\ \sigma_4=(1/N_4)(\chi_a-\chi_d), & N_4=1.40577 \text{ for } cis\text{-}, 1.41267 \text{ for } trans\text{-}\end{array}\right\}. \quad (20)$$

Defining matrix elements S_{pq}^σ and L_{pq}^σ in terms of the σ_q in just the way S_{pq} and L_{pq} were defined in terms of the χ_p—see Eqs. (15), (17), and (18)—we then find that the secular equation becomes simply

$$\begin{vmatrix} L_{11}^\sigma-S_{11}^\sigma\epsilon & L_{12}^\sigma-S_{12}^\sigma\epsilon & 0 & 0\\ L_{21}^\sigma-S_{21}^\sigma\epsilon & L_{22}^\sigma-S_{22}^\sigma\epsilon & 0 & 0\\ 0 & 0 & L_{33}^\sigma-S_{33}^\sigma\epsilon & L_{34}^\sigma-S_{34}^\sigma\epsilon\\ 0 & 0 & L_{43}^\sigma-S_{43}^\sigma\epsilon & L_{44}^\sigma-S_{44}^\sigma\epsilon \end{vmatrix}=0 \quad (21)$$

since matrix elements between σ_1 or σ_2 and σ_3 or σ_4 vanish.[10] The *MO*'s ϕ_i may thus be written in the form

$$\left\{\begin{array}{ll}\phi_1=d_{11}\sigma_1+d_{12}\sigma_2 & \\ \phi_3=d_{31}\sigma_1+d_{32}\sigma_2 & \\ \phi_2= & d_{23}\sigma_3+d_{24}\sigma_4\\ \phi_4= & d_{43}\sigma_3+d_{44}\sigma_4\end{array}\right\}; \quad (22)$$

where the numbering of the ϕ's anticipates the order of the roots of Eq. (21) which will actually be found;[11] where the coefficients d_{iq} satisfy the normalization conditions

$$1=\sum_{p,q} d_{ip}{}^*S_{pq}{}^\sigma d_{iq}, \quad i=1, 2, 3, 4; \quad (23)$$

and where the ratios of the d_{iq} are equal to ratios of corresponding cofactors of the secular determinant in Eq. (21), that is,

$$\frac{d_{11}}{d_{12}}=-\frac{L_{12}^\sigma-S_{12}^\sigma\epsilon_1}{L_{11}^\sigma-S_{11}^\sigma\epsilon_1}, \quad \frac{d_{31}}{d_{32}}=-\frac{L_{12}^\sigma-S_{12}^\sigma\epsilon_3}{L_{11}^\sigma-S_{11}^\sigma\epsilon_3},$$
$$\frac{d_{23}}{d_{24}}=-\frac{L_{34}^\sigma-S_{34}^\sigma\epsilon_2}{L_{33}^\sigma-S_{33}^\sigma\epsilon_2}, \quad \frac{d_{43}}{d_{44}}=-\frac{L_{34}^\sigma-S_{34}^\sigma\epsilon_4}{L_{33}^\sigma-S_{33}^\sigma\epsilon_4}. \quad (24)$$

The d_{iq}, like the C_{ip}, require an iterative method of evaluation, but they are much easier to work with.

Table II lists values of the integrals S_{pq}^σ, I_{pq}^σ and J_{pqrs}^σ, determined from the integrals in Table I by direct insertion of Eq. (20) into the appropriate definitions.[12] From these basic integrals, the elements in the secular equation, Eq. (21), can be computed from any assumed set of values for the d_{iq}, through the use of the defining relations

$$L_{pq}^\sigma=I_{pq}^\sigma+G_{pq}^\sigma \quad (25)$$

and

$$G_{pq}^\sigma=\sum_{i=1,2}(2J_{i,\,pq}^\sigma-K_{i,\,pq}^\sigma), \quad (26)$$

TABLE II. Integrals over the symmetry orbitals σ_q.[a]

Integral	Value[c] *cis-*	Value[c] *trans-*	Integral	Value[c] *cis-*	Value[c] *trans-*
Overlap			22 44	7.306	7.319
integrals			33 44	7.438	7.445
S_{12}^σ	0.27957	0.28092	11 12	2.503	2.405
S_{34}^σ	0.28120	0.27983	22 21	3.829	2.843
Core			33 34	2.788	2.774
integrals[b]			44 43	2.594	2.504
$-I_{11}^\sigma$	20.561	19.655	11 34	2.602	2.504
$-I_{22}^\sigma$	26.834	26.834	22 34	2.718	2.705
$-I_{33}^\sigma$	22.383	22.383	33 12	2.809	2.823
$-I_{44}^\sigma$	20.320	19.516	44 12	2.493	2.408
$-I_{12}^\sigma$	9.531	9.367	12 12	0.806	0.782
$-I_{34}^\sigma$	9.126	8.923	13 13	0.343	0.363
Coulomb-exchange			14 14	6.124	6.551
integrals			23 23	4.354	4.354
11 11	10.762	10.368	24 24	0.289	0.318
22 22	12.770	12.770	34 34	0.779	0.754
33 33	13.044	13.044	13 14	1.188	1.275
44 44	10.860	10.389	23 24	0.856	0.852
11 22	7.363	7.350	13 23	0.881	0.885
11 33	7.475	7.468	14 24	1.011	1.109
11 44	10.805	10.379	12 34	0.789	0.767
22 33	12.773	12.773	13 24	0.314	0.336
			14 23	1.911	1.910

[a] The σ_q are defined in Eq. (20).
[b] See note c, Table I.
[c] Values for all but the overlap integrals are here in electron volts.

[9] The normalizing factors N_i are readily found from the overlap integrals S_{pq} given in Table I. For example, $N_2=[2(1+S_{bc})]^{\frac{1}{2}}=(2.46562)^{\frac{1}{2}}=1.57023$.

[10] This can be proved either by formal group theory or by direct computation making use of such equivalences as $S_{ab}=S_{cd}$.

[11] That the order of orbital energies is the one indicated can be seen by application of the classical criterion that energy increases with the number of nodes. As a rough approximation, the molecular orbitals for butadiene will be, in order of increasing energy,

$$\left\{\begin{array}{l}\phi_1\sim\chi_a+\chi_b+\chi_c+\chi_d\\ \phi_2\sim\chi_a+\chi_b-\chi_c-\chi_d\\ \phi_3\sim\chi_a-\chi_b-\chi_c+\chi_d\\ \phi_4\sim\chi_a-\chi_b+\chi_c-\chi_d\end{array}\right\}$$

and this is the order assumed in Eq. (22).

[12] For example,

$$I_{22}^\sigma=(1/N_2N_2)(I_{bb}+2I_{bc}+I_{cc})=(2/N_2N_2)(I_{bb}+I_{bc})$$
$$=-2(0.40558)(0.7648)Z=-0.62038Z \text{ atomic unit}$$
$$=-(0.62038)(3.18)(13.602)=-26.834 \text{ ev.}$$

where

$$J_{i,\,pq}{}^{\sigma}=\int \phi_i{}^{*\nu}\sigma_p{}^{*\mu}(2/r^{\mu\nu})\phi_i{}^{\nu}\sigma_q{}^{\mu}d\tau^{\nu}d\tau^{\mu}$$

$$=\sum_{r,\,s} d_{ir}{}^{*}J_{rpsq}{}^{\sigma}d_{is} \quad (27)$$

and

$$K_{i,\,pq}{}^{\sigma}=\int \phi_i{}^{*\nu}\sigma_p{}^{*\mu}(2/r^{\mu\nu})\phi_i{}^{\mu}\sigma_q{}^{\nu}d\tau^{\nu}d\tau^{\mu}$$

$$=\sum_{r,\,s} d_{ir}{}^{*}J_{rpqs}d_{is} \quad (28)$$

are Coulomb and exchange integrals intermediate in type between the $J_{ij}{}^{\sigma}$, $K_{ij}{}^{\sigma}$ and the $J_{pqrs}{}^{\sigma}$. This provides the starting point for solution of our problem. We assume a set of d_{iq} values, compute the L_{pq} by Eq. (25), solve Eq. (21) for the ϵ_i, solve Eqs. (23) and (24) for a new set of d_{iq} values, and repeat until self-consistency is attained. Table III gives details of the self-consistent solutions obtained in this way for *cis-* and *trans*-1,3-butadiene. Each of these solutions was found after about a dozen trials.[13, 14]

From Eqs. (20) and (22) and the d_{iq} values in Table III, we obtain four orthonormal molecular orbitals, as follows:

$$\left.\begin{array}{l}
\phi_1=\begin{Bmatrix}0.3484\\0.3540\end{Bmatrix}(\chi_a+\chi_d)+\begin{Bmatrix}0.4719\\0.4687\end{Bmatrix}(\chi_b+\chi_c)\\[2ex]
\phi_2=\begin{Bmatrix}0.5106\\0.5081\end{Bmatrix}(\chi_a-\chi_d)+\begin{Bmatrix}0.4222\\0.4229\end{Bmatrix}(\chi_b-\chi_c)\\[2ex]
\phi_3=\begin{Bmatrix}0.6439\\0.6452\end{Bmatrix}(\chi_a+\chi_d)-\begin{Bmatrix}0.4662\\0.4698\end{Bmatrix}(\chi_b+\chi_c)\\[2ex]
\phi_4=\begin{Bmatrix}0.5373\\0.5343\end{Bmatrix}(\chi_a-\chi_d)-\begin{Bmatrix}0.7276\\0.7268\end{Bmatrix}(\chi_b-\chi_c)
\end{array}\right\}\begin{Bmatrix}\text{upper values}\\ \textit{cis-}\\ \text{lower values}\\ \textit{trans-}\end{Bmatrix}. \quad (29)$$

These are listed in order of increasing energy; ϕ_1 and ϕ_2 are the best *LCAO SCF* ground state *MO*'s obtainable from Slater $2p\pi$-*AO*'s with $Z=3.18$.

We can now proceed to determine the ground state energy for the four π-electrons in the field of the core. This may be computed from Eq. (5), with [compare Eqs. (9) to (11)]

$$I_i=\sum_{p,\,q} d_{ip}{}^{*}I_{pq}{}^{\sigma}d_{iq}, \quad (30)$$

$$J_{ij}=\sum_{p,\,q,\,r,\,s} d_{ip}{}^{*}d_{jq}{}^{*}J_{pqrs}{}^{\sigma}d_{ir}d_{js}=\sum_{q,\,s} d_{jq}{}^{*}J_{i,\,qs}{}^{\sigma}d_{js}, \quad (31)$$

and

$$K_{ij}=\sum_{p,\,q,\,r,\,s} d_{ip}{}^{*}d_{jq}{}^{*}J_{pqsr}d_{ir}d_{js}=\sum_{q,\,s} d_{jq}{}^{*}K_{i,\,qs}{}^{\sigma}d_{js}. \quad (32)$$

TABLE III. Self-consistent molecular orbitals for the ground state.

	Cis-	*Trans-*		*Cis-*	*Trans-*
d_{11}/d_{12} assumed	0.6690	0.6810	2, 33	6.064	6.054
d_{23}/d_{24} assumed	0.7288	0.7298	2, 44	7.756	7.442
$(d_{12})^{-2}$	1.8216	1.8464	2, 34	5.185	5.134
$(d_{24})^{-2}$	1.9410	1.9411	Matrix elements $L_{pq}{}^{\sigma}$ [f,g]		
Coulomb integrals[a,b,c]			11	6.555	6.386
1, 11	8.525	8.359	22	2.291	2.297
1, 22	10.897	10.860	12	−5.490	−5.543
1, 12	2.760	2.721	33	9.245	9.215
1, 33	10.912	10.876	44	5.668	5.656
1, 44	8.497	8.347	34	−5.100	−5.111
1, 34	2.711	2.660	Orbital energies[f]		
2, 11	9.566	9.279			
2, 22	9.300	9.310	ϵ_1	−1.164	−1.241
2, 12	2.646	2.592	ϵ_2	1.620	1.599
2, 33	9.495	9.501	ϵ_3	14.090	14.050
2, 44	9.578	9.278	ϵ_4	17.689	17.639
2, 34	2.684	2.618	d_{11}/d_{12} found	0.6690	0.6811
Exchange integrals[a,d,e]			d_{23}/d_{24} found	0.7286	0.7299
1, 11	4.925	4.802	d_{11}	0.4957	0.5012
1, 22	9.286	9.210	d_{12}	0.7409	0.7359
1, 12	5.168	5.143	d_{31}	0.9160	0.9135
1, 33	3.122	3.102	d_{32}	−0.7320	−0.7376
1, 44	2.406	2.636	d_{23}	0.5230	0.5239
1, 34	1.579	1.610	d_{24}	0.7178	0.7177
2, 11	4.141	4.433	d_{43}	0.9013	0.9003
2, 22	1.983	1.999	d_{44}	−0.7554	−0.7548
2, 12	1.597	1.659			

[a] Values in electron volts.
[b] *i, pq* is abbreviated notation for $J_{i,pq}{}^{\sigma}$—see Eq. (27).
[c] Sample calculation: 1,11 (*cis-*) = (1/1.8216) [(1)(7.363) + 2(0.6690)(2.503) + $(0.6690)^2$(10.762)].
[d] *i, pq* is an abbreviation for $K_{i,pq}{}^{\sigma}$—see Eq. (28).
[e] Sample calculation: 1,11 (*cis-*) = (1/1.8216) [(1)(0.806) + 2(0.6690)(2.503) + $(0.6690)^2$(10.762)].
[f] Values in electron volts; energy zero W_{2p}—see Table I, Note c.
[g] *pq* is an abbreviation for $L_{pq}{}^{\sigma}$.

[13] The problem treated here is of course a particularly simple one. There are really only two parameters to be determined by minimization of the energy—the ratios of d_{11} to d_{12} and d_{23} to d_{24} (orthogonality and normalization conditions give all the coefficients once these two ratios are known). Further, the coupling between these parameters proves to be small, so that successive approximations to each converge more or less independently of the other.

[14] It does not appear to matter much what orbitals are assumed in the starting approximation. One can use orbitals obtained from a semi-empirical scheme, or orbitals obtained assuming completely localized bonds. The former are likely to be closer to the correct orbitals, but the latter have the advantages that they may be found without appeal to a different computational framework and that use of them permits the calculation of resonance energies with very little additional work. (This last will be discussed elsewhere.)

Equivalently, since according to Eqs. (9) to (18),[15]

$$\epsilon_i=\sum_{p,q} d_{ip}{}^*L_{pq}{}^\sigma d_{iq}=I_i+\sum_{j=1,2}(2J_{ij}-K_{ij}), \qquad (33)$$

one may use the formula

$$E_N=2\epsilon_1+2\epsilon_2-J_{11}-J_{22}-4J_{12}+2K_{12}. \qquad (34)$$

The result in either case is

$$E_N=\left\{\begin{matrix}4W_{2p}-49.78 \text{ ev for } cis\text{-}\\ 4W_{2p}-48.93 \text{ ev for } trans\text{-}\end{matrix}\right\}, \qquad (35)$$

where W_{2p} is the energy of a $2p\pi$-electron in a carbon atom in its valence state (−11.28 ev)..

EXCITED STATE ORBITALS AND ENERGIES

The π-electrons are presumably responsible for the lowest excited electronic states of butadiene. From the *MO* point of view these excited states may be thought of as the result of placing one or more of the electrons in π-*MO*'s other than the ground state orbitals ϕ_1 and ϕ_2 found above. Wave functions for such excited states cannot in general be written as single determinants, but once the excited state orbitals are known the excited state energies can be computed without much difficulty.

TABLE IV. Computed excitation energies of excited states, using *MO*'s given by Eq. (29).[a]

Energy		Excitation $\phi_1\to\phi_3$	$\phi_1\to\phi_3$	$\phi_2\to\phi_4$	$\phi_1\to\phi_4$
$\epsilon_j-\epsilon_i$	*Cis-*	12.470	15.254	16.069	18.853
	Trans-	12.451	15.291	16.040	18.880
J_{ij}	*Cis-*	9.461	9.291	9.524	10.021
	Trans-	9.315	9.218	9.429	9.956
K_{ij}	*Cis-*	2.395	2.178	2.292	1.759
	Trans-	2.551	2.087	2.169	1.828
$E_{V_{ij}}-E_N$	*Cis-*	7.799	10.319	11.129	12.350
	Trans-	8.238	10.247	10.949	12.580
$E_{T_{ij}}-E_N$	*Cis-*	3.009	5.963	6.545	8.832
	Trans-	3.136	6.073	6.611	8.924
$\bar{E}_{TV_{ij}}-E_N$[b]	*Cis-*	5.404	8.141	8.837	10.591
	Trans-	5.687	8.160	8.780	10.752

[a] All energies in electron volts.
[b] Mean of $E_{V_{ij}}-E_N$ and $E_{T_{ij}}-E_N$.

The simplest assumption we can make about the excited state orbitals is that they may be taken from the set ϕ_1, ϕ_2, ϕ_3, ϕ_4 found in our treatment of the ground state. This allows us to write down immediately approximate wave functions for excited states which are orthogonal to the ground state function of Eq. (3). For example, we may write, for the singlet excited state V_{23} resulting from excitation of an electron from ϕ_2 to ϕ_3, and for the $M_S=0$ component of the corresponding triplet state, T_{23},

$$\left.\begin{matrix}\Psi_{V_{23}}\\ \Psi_{T_{23}}\end{matrix}\right\}=\frac{1}{(2\cdot 4!)^{\frac{1}{2}}}\begin{vmatrix}(\phi_1\alpha)^1(\phi_1\beta)^1(\phi_2\alpha)^1(\phi_3\beta)^1\\ (\phi_1\alpha)^2(\phi_1\beta)^2(\phi_2\alpha)^2(\phi_3\beta)^2\\ (\phi_1\alpha)^3(\phi_1\beta)^3(\phi_2\alpha)^3(\phi_3\beta)^3\\ (\phi_1\alpha)^4(\phi_1\beta)^4(\phi_2\alpha)^4(\phi_3\beta)^4\end{vmatrix}\mp\frac{1}{(2\cdot 4!)^{\frac{1}{2}}}\begin{vmatrix}(\phi_1\alpha)^1(\phi_1\beta)^1(\phi_2\beta)^1(\phi_3\alpha)^1\\ (\phi_1\alpha)^2(\phi_1\beta)^2(\phi_2\beta)^2(\phi_3\alpha)^2\\ (\phi_1\alpha)^3(\phi_1\beta)^3(\phi_2\beta)^3(\phi_3\alpha)^3\\ (\phi_1\alpha)^4(\phi_1\beta)^4(\phi_2\beta)^4(\phi_3\alpha)^4\end{vmatrix} \qquad (36)$$

with the upper (−) sign for V_{23} and the lower (+) for the T_{23}. The energies $\int\Psi^*\mathbf{H}\Psi d\tau$ associated with each of these wave functions can be found by straightforward integration using Eq. (4) for **H**. The results are[16]

$$\left.\begin{matrix}E_{V_{23}}\\ E_{T_{23}}\end{matrix}\right\}=2I_1+I_2+I_3+J_{11}+2J_{12}+2J_{13}+J_{23}-K_{12}-K_{13}\pm K_{23}$$
$$=2\epsilon_1+\epsilon_2+\epsilon_3-J_{11}-J_{22}-4J_{12}-J_{23}+2K_{12}+K_{23}\pm K_{23} \qquad (37)$$

with $+K_{23}$ for V_{23} and $-K_{23}$ for T_{23}. Hence, employing Eqs. (5) and (34) for E_N, we find

$$\left.\begin{matrix}E_{V_{23}}-E_N\\ E_{T_{23}}-E_N\end{matrix}\right\}=I_3-I_2-J_{22}-2J_{12}+2J_{13}+J_{23}+K_{12}-K_{13}\pm K_{23}$$
$$=(\epsilon_3-\epsilon_2)-(J_{23}-K_{23})\pm K_{23}$$
$$=(\epsilon_3{}^{(2)}-\epsilon_2)\pm K_{23}. \qquad (38)$$

The last form of Eqs. (38), making use of the definition

$$\epsilon_3{}^{(2)}\equiv\epsilon_3-(J_{23}-K_{23}),$$

has been introduced to emphasize the fact that ϵ_3, although mathematically like ϵ_1 and ϵ_2 in being a root of the ground-state *SCF* Eq. (19), has a different physical significance. Physically, in states V_{23} and T_{23}, $\epsilon_3{}^{(2)}$ is much more closely an analog of ϵ_1 and ϵ_2 in representing a true orbital energy.[17] The superscript in $\epsilon_3{}^{(2)}$ indicates the presence of a "hole" in the ground state wave function, made by exciting a ϕ_2-electron. More generally, excitation of an electron from the $MO\phi_i$ to the $MO\phi_j$ gives rise to two excited states, one singlet and one triplet, with energies relative to the ground state given by

$$\left.\begin{matrix}E_{V_{ij}}-E_N\\ E_{T_{ij}}-E_N\end{matrix}\right\}=(\epsilon_j-\epsilon_i)-(J_{ij}-K_{ij})\pm K_{ij}$$
$$=(\epsilon_j{}^{(i)}-\epsilon_i)\pm K_{ij}. \qquad (39)$$

[15] More simply, see reference 2, Eq. (14),—"subtractive partition."

[16] For detailed derivations see reference 3, or references 2 and 4 with due regard for reference 17.

[17] See reference 4, Section 23 (where ϵ_3 and ϵ_4 for butadiene are called "unacceptable" ϵ's), and Eqs. (21) and (22) of reference 2, where the excited-orbital ϵ's called ϵ_{pV} and ϵ_{pT} are physically significant orbital energies of the type of $\epsilon_3{}^{(2)}$ or $\epsilon_j{}^{(i)}$ of Eqs. (38) and (39) above. The latter correspond to Eq. (17a) of reference 2,

TABLE V. *LCAO* parameters α_p and β_{pq}.

Parameter	Value (ev) *cis-*	*trans-*
α_a	-5.16	-5.26
α_b	-6.32	-6.33
β_{ab}	-7.01	-6.84
β_{bc}	-3.29	-3.27
β_{ac}	-1.03	-1.03
β_{ad}	$+0.44$	$+0.36$

Excitation energies computed from these formulas for *cis-* and *trans-*1,3-butadiene are given in Table IV.

One might think that a better approximation to excited state wave functions and energies could be obtained by taking only the orbitals for *unexcited* electrons from the ground state orbitals ϕ_1 and ϕ_2 of Eq. (29), and determining better orbitals for the excited electrons than ϕ_3 and ϕ_4 of Eq. (29). This idea, however, is incorrect, since the only orbitals orthogonal to ϕ_1 and ϕ_2 of Eq. (29) and of the desired *LCAO* form are just ϕ_3 and ϕ_4 of Eq. (29),[13] and it is a prerequisite of simple energy formulas such as Eq. (39) that the molecular orbitals be orthogonal.

Nevertheless, *best SCF* orbitals for use in an excited state wave function should minimize the energy of *that* state (subject to orthogonality of the total wave function to lower state wave functions), and not be derived from a *ground* state energy-minimizing secular equation, as the Eq. (29) orbitals are. This implies that (as a result of the altered self-consistency requirements) the coefficients in the best orbitals ϕ_1 and ϕ_2 will differ somewhat from their values for the like-designated ground-state orbitals in Eq. (29); concurrently, the coefficients in the best ϕ_3 or ϕ_4 will likewise differ from the values given in Eqs. (29).

The equations for the coefficients in such a treatment are no longer as simple as Eqs. (16), but presumably they can be handled without prohibitive difficulty. We will discuss the derivation of these equations and their application to butadiene in a later paper.[18,19] We shall there also examine the so-called "ionic Hamiltonian" method of Mulliken, which works directly with the quantities $\epsilon_j^{(i)}$ in Eq. (39).

DISCUSSION

In semi-empirical *LCAO* schemes for treating butadiene, a secular equation similar in form to Eq. (19) is usually considered, but excitation energies are approximated by differences in the roots ϵ_i alone. Our discussion above in connection with Eqs. (38) and (39), and the numerical values in Table IV, show that this is not a valid way to proceed from Eq. (19) theoretically, so that our secular determinant elements L_{pq} should not be associated directly with corresponding quantities determined semi-empirically.[20] More explicitly, one may define *LCAO* parameters

$$\alpha_p \equiv L_{pp} \tag{40}$$

and[21]

$$\beta_{pq} \equiv L_{pq} - (S_{pq}/2)(L_{pp}+L_{qq}), \tag{41}$$

and relate the L_{pq} to the L_{pq}^{σ} through the use of Eqs. (20). If [2,4] one assumes

$$W_{2p} = -11.28 \text{ ev}, \tag{42}$$

one then obtains the numerical values given in Table V, but these do not refer to the same thing as semi-empirical α_p- and β_{pq}-values do.[20] The Table V values may legitimately be compared with *theoretically* determined values for other molecules,[2,4] however, and are in fact in reasonable accord with them.[20,22]

One would not expect that the ground state orbitals given in Eqs. (29) would agree quantitatively with ones obtained semi-empirically, but the agreement is in fact fairly good; up to normalizing factors Lennard-Jones, for example, found[23]

$$\begin{aligned}\phi_1 &= 0.401(\chi_a+\chi_d)+0.582(\chi_b+\chi_c)\\ \phi_2 &= 0.582(\chi_a-\chi_d)+0.401(\chi_b-\chi_c)\end{aligned} \tag{43}$$

which are almost the same as our orbitals.

Theoretical first ionization potentials $\mathcal{I}_1$ for our molecules can be computed very easily from the results in Table III. According to Mulliken,[2]

$$\mathcal{I}_1 \sim -\epsilon_2. \tag{44}$$

Hence, from Table III and Eq. (42), we find

$$\mathcal{I}_1 \sim \begin{Bmatrix} -W_{2p}-1.620=9.66 \text{ ev for } cis- \\ -W_{2p}-1.599=9.68 \text{ ev for } trans- \end{Bmatrix}. \tag{45}$$

The experimental value (probably for *trans-*)[24] is

$$\mathcal{I}_1 \text{ (exper.)} = 9.0 \text{ ev}. \tag{46}$$

while Roothaan's ϵ's correspond to Eq. (17); Eqs. (17) and (17a) become identical for ground state ϵ's, but only for these.

[18] Just as the Roothaan *LCAO SCF* theory for a closed-shell ground state parallels the Hartree-Fock *SCF* theory for such a state, so a *LCAO SCF* theory for *T* and *V* states such as those represented by Eqs. (36) and (37) may be patterned after the corresponding Hartree-Fock theory. The latter has been given by D. R. Hartree and W. Hartree in an article on excited states of Be, Proc. Roy. Soc. **A154**, 588 (1936).

[19] Perhaps easier than separate minimization of *T* and *V* energies would be minimization of their center of gravity. The corresponding Hartree-Fock theory has been discussed by G. Shortley, Phys. Rev. **50**, 1072 (1936).

[20] See reference 4 for a discussion of the faults of the semi-empirical method, and for a discussion of the variously defined α's and β's, their meanings, their interconnections, and (see especially Table XVIII) their values in various molecules. The α's and β's in Table V are α^N's and β^N's in the notation of reference 4.

[21] See reference 2, Eq. (29).

[22] The most striking feature of our calculated β's is that non-neighbor β's are important, of our α's that α's on end and central atoms differ (cf. also reference 4, Tables XV and XVIII; and concluding section of reference 3 in 1949–50 ONR report).

[23] See. R. S. Mulliken, J. Chem. Phys. **7**, 121 (1939), Table II, for a summary of semi-empirically determined *LCAO*'s for 1, 3-butadiene, and references to the literature.

[24] R. S. Mulliken, Rev. Mod. Phys. **14**, 265 (1942), corrected for new values of fundamental constants.

The agreement is very encouraging, and is similar to agreements found in similar computations on other hydrocarbon molecules.[25]

At first sight, the ground state *electronic* energy values E_N of Eq. (35) would seem to predict *cis*- to be more stable than *trans*-1,3-butadiene by 0.85 ev. This interpretation is not justified, however, since the *total* energies (say W_N) of the two isomers include inter-nuclear repulsion terms which differ for *cis*- and *trans*-1,3-butadiene. These repulsion terms would appear as parts of the total energy W_N^c of the π-electron-less framework, giving

$$W_N = W_N^c + E_N \tag{47}$$

for the total energy of the neutral molecule. Although we do not know the W_N^c values, the *difference* between W_N^c for *cis*- and *trans*-forms can probably be obtained with little error by treating the core, for this purpose, as a system of four point charges $+e$ located at the centers of the four carbon atoms, and then taking

$$W_N(cis\text{-}) - W_N(trans\text{-}) = [W_N^c(cis\text{-}) - W_N^c(trans\text{-})] + [E_N(cis\text{-}) - E_N(trans\text{-})]. \tag{48}$$

It is readily seen that all the repulsion terms are the same for *cis*- and *trans*-, except for those between the end atoms *a* and *d*. With the geometrical model specified at the outset of this paper, the distance R_{ad} is 2.97A for *cis*- and 3.72A for *trans*-, giving 4.84 or 3.87 ev as the respective electrostatic repulsion energies. Taking the difference, and also using Eqs. (35) and (48), we have

$$W_N^c(cis\text{-}) - W_N^c(trans\text{-}) = +0.97;$$
$$E_N(cis\text{-}) - E_N(trans\text{-}) = -0.85;$$
$$W_N(cis\text{-}) - W_N(trans\text{-}) = +0.12.$$

Our prediction is then that the *trans*-form is more stable than the *cis*- by 0.12 ev. This result seems to be in agreement with the weight of experimental evidence.[24,26] It also agrees with a result obtained earlier by Mrs. C. A. Rieke and one of the writers in computations by the semiempirical *LCAO* method.[24]

So far as excitation energies are concerned, our results fall in line with those previously found for other molecules.[1,25] If the mean energy of any singlet and its corresponding triplet state is called $\bar{E}_{TV}$, then the theory [cf. Eq. (39) for butadiene] gives

$$\left.\begin{matrix} E_{V_{ij}} \\ E_{T_{ij}} \end{matrix}\right\} = \bar{E}_{TV_{ij}} \pm K_{ij}. \tag{49}$$

Just as in other cases where *LCAO* computations have been made (H_2, C_2H_4, C_6H_6), the computed singlet-triplet separations ($2K_{ij}$) are too large for butadiene, indicating that the *LCAO* method is unreliable for the computation of the K_{ij}'s, or else that other factors enter to modify Eq. (49).[27] But if, as in the other cases,[28] we use for butadiene the computed *mean* values $\bar{E}_{TV}$ (cf. last lines in Table IV) and replace K_{ij} by a reasonable estimated effective value [27] (say 0.5 ev), we obtain 5.9 and 6.2 ev for the lowest singlet excitation energies of the *cis*- and *trans*-forms, respectively, as compared with the observed value 6.0 ev.[24] The similarly obtained values 8.6 and 8.7 ev for the next lowest singlet excitation energy may be compared with the probable observed value[24] of 7.2 ev. It will be interesting to see the singlet-triplet splittings which result when T and V energies are separately minimized.[29]

There are several reasons why the numerical values we have obtained should not be regarded as final:

(1) Best orbitals and energies should really be determined by a method which includes inner shell electrons explicitly, i.e., by Roothaan's complete scheme.[3] This would incidentally remove the limitations imposed by our arbitrary assumption that the π-electron-less core consists of neutral hydrogen atoms and singly charged carbon atoms.

(2) The forms of the *AO*'s which are used in constructing the *LCAO MO*'s should themselves be determined by a variational procedure, at least for the valence *AO*'s. The Slater 2*p* *AO*'s with $Z=3.18$ which we have used might thus need to be strongly modified.[30]

(3) Approximations are necessary at the present time for the evaluations of three-center and penetration integrals (see Appendix) and orbitals and energies are sensitive to these values.

Our results should be at least semiquantitatively correct, however, and so may be regarded as a "go" sign for work with *LCAO SCF* methods on other molecules.[31]

APPENDIX: INTEGRALS

The integrals we need are overlap, Coulomb-exchange and core integrals involving the atomic orbitals χ_p, which we take in the form (in atomic units)

$$\chi_p^\nu = (Z^5/32\pi)^{\frac{1}{2}} z^\nu \exp(-Zr_p^\nu/2), \tag{A1}$$

where z^ν is the perpendicular distance of electron ν from the plane of the molecule, r_p^ν is the distance of that electron from the pth carbon nucleus, and the screening constant Z is taken to have the value 3.18. Numerical values are given in Table I.

Overlap integrals S_{pq} between the various χ's may be computed from well-known formulas.[32]

The Coulomb-exchange integrals J_{pqrs} which involve

---

[25] References 2 to 4; for a summary of values see reference 4, Table XIX.

[26] Aston, Szasz, Woolley, and Brickwedde, J. Chem. Phys. **14**, 67 (1946).

[27] Cf. reference 2, Eq. (22) and accompanying discussion.

[28] For comparison of computed and observed $\bar{E}_{TV}$ values for H_2, C_2H_4, and C_6H_6, see reference 4, Table XIX. For H_2, the true $E_V - E_T$ is known from accurate theoretical calculations; for C_2H_4 (reference 24) and for C_6H_6 [cf. Roothaan and Mulliken, J. Chem. Phys. **16**, 118 (1948)] approximate values are known from spectroscopic evidence.

[29] In the case of the Be atom, Hartree and Hartree (see reference 18) found a definite improvement when T and V energies were separately minimized. However, the improvement was not as large as would be needed in the present case.

[30] Note that the Slater 2*p* *AO*'s differ markedly from the best (*SCF*) *AO*'s of the free carbon atom [cf. e.g., Mulliken, Rieke, Orloff, and Orloff, J. Chem. Phys. **17**, 1248 (1949)].

[31] Cf. reference 4, Section 27, for some further general discussion.

[32] Cf. R. G. Parr and B. L. Crawford, Jr., J. Chem. Phys. **16**, 1049 (1948).

no more than two different χ's may be found by interpolation in a table of Parr and Crawford[32] (as slightly revised by Roothaan[33]); in a slight modification of their notation,

$$J_{pqrs} \equiv (\chi_p\chi_r | \chi_q\chi_s). \qquad \text{(A2)}$$

The J_{pqrs}'s which involve three or more different χ's must be estimated—we have used the approximation formula (due to Sklar[34])

$$(\chi_p\chi_r | \chi_q\chi_s) \sim S_{pr}S_{qs}(\chi_{p'}\chi_{p'} | \chi_{q'}\chi_{q'}), \qquad \text{(A3)}$$

where $\chi_{p'}$ is a Slater $2p\pi$-carbon *AO* taken as located midway between atoms p and r, $\chi_{q'}$ is a Slater $2p\pi$-*AO* located midway between atoms q and s, and S_{pr} and S_{qs} are overlap integrals between the indicated χ's.

Core integrals cannot be evaluated so accurately. According to Eq. (12), these are defined by

$$I_{pq} = \int \chi_p^{*\nu}(\mathbf{T}^\nu + \mathbf{U}_c^\nu)\chi_q^\nu d\tau^\nu, \qquad \text{(A4)}$$

where $\mathbf{T}^\nu$ is the kinetic energy operator for electron ν and $\mathbf{U}_c^\nu$ is the potential energy for electron ν in the field of the $2p\pi$-electron-less core. The difficulty lies in the $\mathbf{U}_c^\nu$ term. Following Goeppert-Mayer and Sklar,[35] we assume that the hydrogen atoms may be ignored, and write $\mathbf{U}_c^\nu$ as a sum of contributions from the four carbon atoms, each once ionized, giving

$$\mathbf{U}_c^\nu = \sum_{p=1}^{4} \mathbf{U}_p^\nu. \qquad \text{(A5)}$$

Here $\mathbf{U}_p^\nu$ is the potential of electron ν in the field of the pth carbon atom less its $2p\pi$-electron, and

$$\mathbf{U}_p^\nu = \mathbf{U}_p^{0\nu} - \int (e^2/r^{\mu\nu}) |\chi_p^\mu|^2 d\tau^\mu, \qquad \text{(A6)}$$

where $\mathbf{U}_p^{0\nu}$ is the potential of electron ν in the field of the *neutral* pth carbon atom, for which Goeppert-Mayer and Sklar have given an approximate expression. Using the relation

$$(\mathbf{T}^\nu + \mathbf{U}_p^\nu)\chi_p^\nu = W_{2p}\chi_p^\nu, \qquad \text{(A7)}$$

where W_{2p} is the energy of a $2p\pi$-electron in a carbon atom in its tetravalent valence state,[22] we then obtain, relative to W_{2p} as the zero of energy,

$$I_{pq} = -\sum_{r,\neq q} [(A_r : \chi_p\chi_q) + (\chi_p\chi_q | \chi_r\chi_r)], \qquad \text{(A8)}$$

where the quantities

$$(A_r : \chi_p\chi_q) = -\int \mathbf{U}_r^{0\nu}\chi_p^{*\nu}\chi_q^\nu d\tau^\nu \qquad \text{(A9)}$$

are "penetration integrals." Values for two-center penetration integrals based on Goeppert Mayer and Sklar's $\mathbf{U}_r^{0\nu}$ may be found in the paper of Parr and Crawford;[32] for three-center penetration integrals one may employ the formula

$$(A_r : \chi_p\chi_q) \sim S_{pq}(A_r : \chi_{p'}\chi_{p'}), \qquad \text{(A10)}$$

where $\chi_{p'}$ is a Slater $2p\pi$-*AO* located midway between atoms p and q.

---

[33] C. C. J. Roothaan (unpublished work)—see reference 5. Some of Parr and Crawford's Coulomb integrals are in error by a few units in the fourth decimal.

[34] A. L. Sklar, J. Chem. Phys. **7**, 984 (1939). For another useful but perhaps slightly less accurate formula, see Mulliken, reference 4, Eq. (154b).

[35] M. Goeppert-Mayer and A. L. Sklar, J. Chem. Phys. **6**, 645 (1938). See also reference 2 for further discussion, including an estimate of the effect of the H atoms in C_2H_4 and C_2H_2.

Reprinted from THE JOURNAL OF CHEMICAL PHYSICS, Vol. 18, No. 12, 1561-1563, December, 1950
Printed in U. S. A.

Molecular Orbital Calculations of the Lower Excited Electronic Levels of Benzene, Configuration Interaction Included

ROBERT G. PARR
Department of Chemistry, Carnegie Institute of Technology, Pittsburgh, Pennsylvania

AND

DAVID P. CRAIG AND IAN G. ROSS
Sir William Ramsay and Ralph Forster Laboratories, University College, London, England

(Received September 6, 1950)

The lower excited π-electron levels of benzene are calculated by the non-empirical method of antisymmetrized products of molecular orbitals (in LCAO approximation) including configuration interaction. All configurations arising from excitation of one or two electrons from the most stable configuration are considered, and all many-center integrals are retained. The results are in better agreement with experiment and valence-bond calculations than those obtained previously by Craig in a calculation neglecting many-center integrals. Configuration interaction is found to change the order of the ${}^1B_{1u}$ and ${}^1E_{2g}$ states but leave unchanged the order of the ${}^3B_{1u}$ and ${}^3B_{2u}$ states, in agreement with the assignments ${}^1A_{1g}-{}^3B_{1u}$ and ${}^1A_{1g}-{}^1E_{2g}$ for the experimental bands at 3.8 and 6.2 ev.

THE original calculation by Goeppert-Mayer and Sklar[1] of the lower excited levels of benzene by the method of antisymmetrized products of molecular orbitals has gone through several revisions[2–5] and one extension,[4] each step changing the numerical results considerably. In the present paper we report the results of repeating the calculation once more, including three-center and four-center integrals in the manner of London[2] and configuration interaction in the manner of Craig,[4] using revised values of two-center integrals as prescribed by Parr and Crawford.[6]

Our results are given in Table I. Details of the calculations will not be given, as these may be found in the papers of Goeppert-Mayer and Sklar[1] and Craig.[4] The computations, which are heavy, were carried through independently *ab initio* by RGP on the one hand, and DPC and IGR on the other.

The integrals over atomic orbitals upon which the results are based are set out in Table II. Two-center integrals were taken from the paper of Parr and Crawford.[6] Three- and four-center integrals however

[1] M. Goeppert-Mayer and A. L. Sklar, J. Chem. Phys. **6**, 645 (1938).
[2] A. London, J. Chem. Phys. **13**, 396 (1945).
[3] B. L. Crawford, Jr. and R. G. Parr, J. Chem. Phys. **17**, 726 (1949).
[4] D. P. Craig, J. Chem. Phys. **17**, 1358 (1949); Proc. Roy. Soc. **200**, 474 (1950).
[5] C. C. J. Roothaan and R. G. Parr, J. Chem. Phys. **17**, 1001 (1949).
[6] R. G. Parr and B. L. Crawford, Jr., J. Chem. Phys. **16**, 1049 (1948).

TABLE I. Electronic levels of benzene (ev).

Level	M.O.[c,d]	M.O. +configuration interaction (two-center integrals only)[e]	M.O. +configuration interaction (all integrals)	Valence bond[f]	Observed[g]
Singlets					
$A_{1g}(9)$[a]	0.0	0.0	0.0	0.0	0.0
$A_{2g}(3)$	11.1	—	12.5	—	—
$B_{1u}(6)$	7.3	4.5	9.0	—	—
$B_{2u}(5)$	5.9	2.0	4.4	4.7	4.9
$E_{1u}(11)$	9.8	6.2	9.9	7.9	7.0
$E_{2g}(11)$	10.9	—	7.7	6.6	6.2
Triplets					
$A_{1g}(4)$	13.6	—	14.9	—	—
$A_{2g}(7)$	11.1	—	11.8	—	—
$B_{1u}(5)$	3.1	—	4.1	—	3.8
$B_{2u}(4)$	5.8	—	8.2	—	—
$E_{1u}(12)$	4.4	—	4.7	—	—
$E_{2g}(9)$	8.3	—	6.4	—	—
Quintuplets[b]					
$A_{1g}(4)$	6.1	—	5.9	—	—
$E_{1u}(6)$	7.7	—	7.1	—	—

[a] The numbers of configuration wave functions used in the computations are given in parentheses.
[b] These results are based on *all* configurations. M.O.+configuration interaction (all integrals) results for $A_{2g}(2)$, $B_{1u}(3)$, $B_{2u}(2)$, $E_{2g}(6)$ quintuplet levels: 15.9, 19.8, 20.2, 9.6. The septuplet state ${}^7B_{1u}(1)$ falls at 11.2 ev.
[c] Method of antisymmetrized products of molecular orbitals (in LCAO approximation).
[d] This energy level scheme before configuration interaction is taken into account is a slight modification of that reported by Roothaan and Parr (reference 5). See also forthcoming publication of C. C. J. Roothaan.
[e] Reference 10.
[f] Reference 11.
[g] Assignment of reference 1 except for 6.2-ev band, for which see reference 11 and the text of the present paper.

TABLE II. Integrals over atomic orbitals.[a]

Integral[b]	Value (ev)[c]	Integral[e]	Value (ev)
11|11	16.930	1:22	0.856
11|22	9.027	1:33	0.013
11|33	5.668	1:44	0.003
11|44	4.968	1:12	1.887
11|12	3.313	1:13	0.109
11|13	0.376	1:14	0.037
11|14	0.160	1:23	0.039
11|23	1.870	1:24	0.006
11|24	0.280	1:25	0.015
11|25	0.160	1:26	0.318
11|26	0.524	1:34	0.002
11|34	1.421	1:35	0.002
11|35	0.251		
12|12	0.923[d]	S_{12}	0.25995
13|13	0.017[d]	S_{13}	0.03887
14|14	0.003[d]	S_{14}	0.01772
12|13	0.136		
12|14	0.046		
12|15	0.091		
12|16	0.677		
12|34	0.436		
12|35	0.073		
12|36	0.046		
12|45	0.383		
13|14	0.009		
13|15	0.015		
13|24	0.020		
13|25	0.009		
13|46	0.014		
14|25	0.005		

[a] The atomic orbitals employed are $2p\pi$-Slater orbitals with effective charge 3.18.
[b] $pq|rs$ is the Coulomb-exchange integral $\int \chi_p^*(1)\chi_r^*(2)(e^2/r_{12})\chi_q(1) \times\chi_s(2)d\tau(1)d\tau(2)$, where χ_p is the $2p\pi$-orbital on the pth carbon atom, and the carbon atoms are numbered consecutively around the ring.
[c] Conversion factor: 1 atomic unit = 13.602 ev.
[d] These values are derived from M. Kotani *et al.*, Proc. Phys.-Math. Soc. Japan **20**, Extra No. 1 (1938), as amended, *ibid.* **22**, Extra No. (1940). They were checked by the method of P. J. Wheatley and J. W. Linnett, Trans. Faraday Soc. **45**, 897 (1949), after changing the sign of the coefficient of H (6, 0), misprinted in that paper.
[e] $p:rs$ is the penetration integral $-\int \mathbf{U}_p(1)\chi_r^*(1)\chi_s(1)d\tau(1)$, where $\mathbf{U}_p(1)$ is the potential on electron 1 caused by a neutral pth carbon atom; S_{pq} is the overlap integral $\int \chi_p^*(1)\chi_q(1)d\tau(1)$.

were estimated by the method of Sklar.[7] This method applied to two-center integrals gives results generally higher than the correct ones. For example, 11|13 of Table I is 0.390 ev by Sklar's method instead of 0.376 ev, and 13|13 is 0.026 instead of 0.017 ev. An alternative approximation for these integrals is that of Mulliken,[8] which gives 0.439 and 0.017 ev, respectively, for 11|13 and 13|13. In these, and other similar cases, the success of the approximations perhaps varies too much to justify a choice between them; Sklar's method was therefore adopted to secure continuity with previous work.[5] It is certainly necessary to include these integrals because they have a considerable effect on the final results (compare columns 3 and 4 of Table I).

Integrals over molecular orbitals are expressible in terms of atomic integrals as indicated in the Appendix. Their values are set out in Table III. It is very striking that the Coulomb-exchange integrals cluster in four distinct groups. A similar (though then less striking) regularity was noted by London[2] and was shown by him to be a consequence of the approximation method for three- and four-center integrals. Exploitation of this would seem well worth while.[9]

Because the number of matrix elements increases so rapidly with increasing numbers of configurations it is important to keep the latter to a minimum. We included all the configurations obtained by excitation of one or two electrons from the lowest configuration, together with a few others which are associated with unusually large matrix components with the lowest states and are therefore important in spite of a high degree of excitation. A complete calculation (i.e., one including all configurations) of the singlet states using two-center integrals only[10] has shown that the configurations here neglected will have only a very small effect on the separations between the states. Our results should therefore represent a close approach to the best obtainable from the π-electron approximation.

In Table I our results are compared with experiment, with similar calculations excluding three- and four-

[7] A. L. Sklar, J. Chem. Phys. **7**, 984 (1939).
[8] R. S. Mulliken, J. de Chim. Phys. **46**, 497 (1949).
[9] One might, for example, assume constant values throughout each set and proceed semi-empirically, or one might seek atomic orbitals which render the approximate constancies exact.
[10] C. W. L. Bevan and D. P. Craig (to be published).

center integrals,[10] and with a previous valence-bond calculation by one of us.[11] The agreement with experiment is much improved by including three- and four-center integrals and is, for a non-empirical calculation, good. Some support is thereby lent to a proposed assignment[11] of the 6.2-ev band as an $^1A_{1g}-{}^1E_{2g}$ rather than an $^1A_{1g}-{}^1B_{1u}$ transition, and the possibility of inversion of the $^3B_{1u}$ and $^3B_{2u}$ states through configuration interaction is ruled out.[12]

RGP is indebted to J. G. Waltz and E. P. King for computational help and to the Research Corporation for a grant-in-aid. DPC is supported by a Turner and Newall Research Fellowship in the University of London and IGR by an Australian National University Scholarship. These awards are gratefully acknowledged.

APPENDIX. INTEGRALS OVER MOLECULAR ORBITALS

The molecular orbitals used in this work may be written in the form

$$\phi_j=(6N_j)^{-\frac{1}{2}}\sum_{p=1}^{6}\exp(2\pi ipj/6)\chi_p,\quad j=0,\pm1,\pm2,3,\tag{1}$$

where χ_p is the $2p\pi$-Slater atomic orbital on the pth carbon atom and N_j is a normalizing factor. The integrals over these orbitals which enter the calculations are the orbital energies

$$\epsilon_j=\int\phi_j^*(1)[\mathbf{U}_c(1)+\mathbf{T}(1)]\phi_j(1)d\tau(1)\tag{2}$$

and the Coulomb-exchange integrals

$$\zeta_{kl}{}^{ij}=\int\int\phi_i(1)\phi_j(1)(e^2/r_{12})\phi_k(2)\phi_l(2)d\tau(1)d\tau(2),\tag{3}$$

where $\mathbf{U}_c(1)$ is the mutual potential energy (operator) of electron 1 and the π-electronless $C_6H_6{}^{-6}$ core, $\mathbf{T}(1)$ is the kinetic energy operator for electron 1, e^2/r_{12} is the mutual potential energy (operator) of electrons 1 and 2, and integrations are over all space for the indicated electrons. The integrals

$$\gamma_{ij}=\zeta_{j-j}{}^{i-i},\quad \delta_{ij}=\zeta_{j-i}{}^{i-j};\tag{4}$$

and

$$\xi=\zeta_{22}{}^{11},\quad \eta=\zeta_{12}{}^{12};\tag{5}$$

are special cases of Eq. (3).

The basic integrals over atomic orbitals are

$$S_{pq}=\int\chi_p^*(1)\chi_q(1)d\tau(1),\tag{6}$$

$$(p:rs)=-\int\mathbf{U}_p(1)\chi_r^*(1)\chi_s(1)d\tau(1),\tag{7}$$

and

$$(pq|rs)=\int\int\chi_p^*(1)\chi_r^*(2)(e^2/r_{12})\chi_q(1)\chi_s(2)d\tau(1)d\tau(2),\tag{8}$$

where $\mathbf{U}_p(1)$ is the mutual potential energy (operator) of electron 1 and a neutral (assumed spherically symmetric) pth carbon atom.

Formulas for the integrals over molecular orbital in terms of integrals over atomic orbitals are as follows. First,

$$N_j=1+2S_{12}\cos(2\pi j/6)+2S_{13}\cos(4\pi j/6)+S_{14}\cos(\pi j).\tag{9}$$

Second,

$$N_j(\epsilon_j-W_{2p})=H_{11}+2H_{12}\cos(2\pi j/6)+2H_{13}\cos(4\pi j/6)+H_{14}\cos(\pi j),\tag{10}$$

where

$$H_{pq}=-\sum_{\substack{r=1\\r\neq q}}^{6}[(r:pq)+(pq|rr)]\tag{11}$$

and W_{2p} is the energy of a $2p\pi$-electron of a carbon atom in its valence state. Finally,

$$6(N_iN_jN_kN_l)^{\frac{1}{2}}\zeta_{kl}{}^{ij}=\text{linear combination of the 30 different integrals }(pq|rs)\equiv(1,1+u|1+v,1+w)=\sum C_{uvw}(1,1+u|1+v,1+w),\tag{12}$$

where

$$\begin{aligned}C_{uvw}=(s_i/8s_m)\{&2\cos[(2\pi/6)(iu+kv+lw)]\\&+2\cos[(2\pi/6)(iu+lv+kw)]+2\cos[(2\pi/6)(ju+kv+lw)]\\&+2\cos[(2\pi/6)(ju+lv+kw)]+2\cos[(2\pi/6)(ku+iv+jw)]\\&+2\cos[(2\pi/6)(ku+jv+iw)]+2\cos[(2\pi/6)(lu+iv+jw)]\\&+2\cos[(2\pi/6)(lu+jv+iw)]\},\end{aligned}\tag{13}$$

in which the "molecular symmetry number" s_m is 1 for integrals with no axis of symmetry (e.g., 12|35), 2 for integrals with an axis of symmetry in the plane of the molecule (e.g., 11|14) and 4 for integrals with an axis of symmetry perpendicular to the plane of the molecule (e.g., 11|44), and the "integral symmetry number" s_i is the number of distinct members in the set $pq|rs=pq|sr=qp|rs=qp|sr=rs|pq=rs|qp=sr|pq=sr|pq$ (e.g., s_i=8, 4, 2 for 12|35, 11|14, 11|44).

TABLE III. Integrals over molecular orbitals.[a]

Integral[b]	Value (ev)	Integral[b]	Value (ev)
γ_{00}	8.627	$\epsilon_2-\epsilon_1$	5.358
γ_{01}	8.522	$\epsilon_2-\epsilon_0$	8.290
γ_{02}	8.495	$\epsilon_3-\epsilon_1$	8.112
γ_{03}	8.554	$\epsilon_3-\epsilon_0$	11.044
γ_{11}	8.474		
γ_{12}	8.517	$\zeta_{1-2}{}^{10}$	2.601
γ_{13}	8.623	$\zeta_{23}{}^{10}$	2.633
γ_{22}	8.648	$\zeta_{13}{}^{20}$	1.299
γ_{23}	8.787	$\zeta_{22}{}^{20}$	1.302
γ_{33}	8.872	$\zeta_{11}{}^{-20}$	1.375
		$\zeta_{21}{}^{30}$	0.993
δ_{01}	2.584	$\zeta_{13}{}^{11}$	1.344
δ_{02}	1.304	$\zeta_{23}{}^{2-1}$	2.772
δ_{03}	0.934	$\zeta_{22}{}^{-13}$	1.362
δ_{1-1}	1.453		
δ_{12}	2.674	N_0	1.61536
δ_{1-2}	1.074	N_1	1.20336
δ_{13}	1.338	N_2	0.71890
δ_{2-2}	1.367	N_3	0.54012
δ_{23}	2.867		
ξ	1.328		
η	1.007		

[a] The molecular orbitals employed are $\phi_j=(6N_j)^{-\frac{1}{2}}\Sigma_{p=1}{}^6\exp(2\pi ipj/6)\chi_p$, where the N_j are normalizing factors.

[b] For definitions of the Coulomb-exchange integrals γ_{ij}, δ_{ij}, ξ, η, $\zeta_{kl}{}^{ij}$, and of the orbital energies ϵ_j, and for formulas for them in terms of integrals over atomic orbitals, see Appendix.

[11] D. P. Craig, Proc. Roy. Soc. **200**, 401 (1950).

[12] Compare D. P. Craig, J. Chem. Phys. **18**, 236 (1950).

Reprinted from THE JOURNAL OF CHEMICAL PHYSICS, Vol. 20, No. 9, 1499, September, 1952
Printed in U. S. A

A Method for Estimating Electronic Repulsion Integrals Over LCAO MO'S in Complex Unsaturated Molecules

ROBERT G. PARR
Department of Chemistry, Carnegie Institute of Technology, Pittsburgh, Pennsylvania
(Received July 1, 1952)

SUPPOSE that by some means one has obtained molecular orbitals ϕ_i as linear combinations of Slater $2p\pi$ atomic orbitals χ_p:

$$\phi_i=\sum_p C_{ip}\chi_p \tag{1}$$

and that one requires values for integrals over molecular orbitals of the form

$$(\phi_i\phi_j|\phi_k\phi_l)=\int\phi_i^*(1)\phi_j(1)(e^2/r_{12})\phi_k^*(2)\phi_l(2)dv. \tag{2}$$

Exact evaluation of these integrals is a tedious matter which requires prior knowledge of the numerical values of a large number of integrals over atomic orbitals.

To obtain approximate values for these integrals, one may first assume that

$$\chi_p\chi_q\equiv 0 \quad \text{for} \quad p\neq q \tag{3}$$

and renormalize the ϕ_i accordingly. One then obtains

$$(\phi_i\phi_j|\phi_k\phi_l)=\text{linear combination of integrals over atomic orbitals of the form } (\chi_p\chi_p|\chi_q\chi_q)\equiv(pp|qq). \tag{4}$$

The problem is thus formally reduced to the evaluation of a small number of integrals over atomic orbitals, all Coulomb integrals.

To obtain the integrals $(pp|qq)$, one may merely replace each $|\chi_p|^2e$ by a pair of tangent uniformly charged nonconducting spheres of *diameter*

$$R_p=(4.597/Z_p)\times 10^{-8}\text{ cm}, \tag{5}$$

where Z_p is the effective charge of the $2p\pi$ atomic orbital χ_p, and compute the Coulomb repulsive potential between $|\chi_p|^2e$ and $|\chi_q|^2e$ by classical electrostatic theory. This gives for the integral $(pp|pp)$ the correct value for $2p\pi$ Slater orbitals, namely,

$$(pp|pp)=5.3238\text{ ev}; \tag{6}$$

while for $(pp|qq)$ the result is

$$(pp|qq)=(14.395/r)\{(1/2)+(1/2)[1+(R/r)^2]^{-\frac{1}{2}}\}\text{ ev}, \tag{7}$$

where r is the distance between atoms p and q in A, provided that $R_p=R_q=R\leq r$. When $R_p\neq R_q$, the result for $(pp|qq)$ is slightly more complicated.

For benzene, if one takes $Z=3.18$ one obtains from Eq. (5) $R=1.45$A, which is greater than the distance between nearest neighbors, 1.39A. For simplicity one therefore takes $Z=3.307$, which gives $R=1.39$A. Application of Eqs. (6) and (7) then yields (atomic orbitals numbered consecutively around the ring): $(11|11)=17.61$, $(11|22)=8.84$, $(11|33)=5.58$, and $(11|44)=4.90$ ev. "True" values for these integrals, as given by Parr, Craig, and Ross,[1] are 16.93, 9.03, 5.67, and 4.97 ev, respectively.

Under the assumption of Eq. (3), there are only four distinct electronic repulsion integrals over molecular orbitals in benzene. Expanding these according to Eq. (4), one finds, in the notation of Parr, Craig, and Ross,

$$\left.\begin{aligned}6\gamma_{00}=6\gamma_{01}=\text{etc.}&=(11|11)+2(11|22)+2(11|33)+(11|44)\\6\delta_{01}=6\delta_{12}=\text{etc.}&=(11|11)+(11|22)-(11|33)-(11|44)\\6\delta_{02}=6\delta_{13}=\text{etc.}&=(11|11)-(11|22)-(11|33)+(11|44)\\6\delta_{03}=6\delta_{1-2}=\text{etc.}&=(11|11)-2(11|22)\\&\quad+2(11|33)-(11|44)\end{aligned}\right\}. \tag{8}$$

Using the numerical values above, one then obtains $\gamma_{00}=8.56$, $\delta_{01}=2.66$, $\delta_{02}=1.35$, and $\delta_{03}=1.03$ ev.

Parr, Craig, and Ross computed thirty different electronic repulsion integrals over molecular orbitals in benzene but found the values clustering in four distinct groups, average values within groups being 8.61, 2.69, 1.35, and 1.00 ev. The agreement between these average values and the values computed by the much shorter approximate method is very encouraging. The approximate method can be applied with some confidence to complex molecules containing heteroatoms, and the possibility of exact computation of electronic repulsion integrals through expansions of atomic orbitals in terms of step functions seems worth examining.

[1] Parr, Craig, and Ross, J. Chem. Phys. 18, 1561 (1950).

Reprinted from THE JOURNAL OF CHEMICAL PHYSICS, Vol. 21, No. 3, 568–569, March, 1953
Printed in U. S. A.

An Improvement in the π-Electron Approximation in LCAO MO Theory

RUDOLPH PARISER
Jackson Laboratory, E. I. du Pont de Nemours and Company, Wilmington, Delaware

(Received January 12, 1953)

As is usual in the π-electron approximation for complex unsaturated molecules, the total electronic energy is divided into two noninteracting parts: (1) the energy of the π-electrons, and (2) the energy of all other, or σ-electrons. The energy of the σ-electrons is consequently assumed to remain constant and independent of the charge distribution of the π-electrons. This is undoubtedly an unrealistic assumption. As is argued below, the effect of the σ-electrons can be approximately taken into account without any additional complication to the mathematics of the π-electron approximation, by changing the value of primarily one Coulomb repulsion integral.

The zero of energy is chosen to be the energy of the "core," which is obtained by removing the π-electrons from the molecule while holding the atoms in their original equilibrium positions. The σ-electrons are defined to have the energy which they would have in their valence state in a hypothetical molecule, where each atom is neutral with respect to π-electron polarization.

One now assumes that the energy of the σ-electrons is not affected in non-ionic valence bond resonance structures, but that it is affected in ionic resonance structures and particularly the energy of those σ-electrons which "belong" to the atom carrying a formal + or − sign. The occurrence of ionic structures in a neutral molecule in the LCAO MO treatment is determined by the occurrence of the Coulomb repulsion integral,

$$(11|11)=\int \chi_a(1)\chi_a(2)\frac{e^2}{r_{12}}\chi_a(1)\chi_a(2)dv_1dv_2. \tag{1}$$

The occurrence of this integral, giving the repulsive energy of two π-electrons on atom "a," implies that some other atom is deficient of its π-electron. The accompanying change of the σ-electron energy may thus conveniently be included by modifying the value of $(11|11)$.

To estimate $(11|11)$ for carbon, consider two neutral infinitely separated C atoms in their sp^2 valence states. By the π-electron approximation, their combined energy is expressed as $2Wp$, where Wp is the ionization potential of the $2p\pi$ electron. Now form the ions C^+ and C^- by ionizing one π-electron and placing it in the $2p\pi$ orbital of the other atom. The energy of the ions is, by the same theory, $2Wp+(11|11)$, so that the energy of forming the ion pair is just $(11|11)$. Experimentally this energy is given by the valence state ionization potential I of neutral carbon minus its electron affinity A. Thus,

$$(11|11)=I-A. \tag{2}$$

According to Mulliken,[1] $I=11.22$ ev and $A=0.69$ ev, making $(11|11)=10.53$ ev.

However, theoretical calculations for carbon using Slater orbitals give $(11|11)=16.93$ ev[2]. By Eq. (2), this implies an ionization potential of about 16 ev or a high negative electron affinity of about −6 ev, which values are inconsistent with the basic assumption that a carbon atom in a molecule behaves essentially as a free carbon atom in its valence state. Moffitt[3] has called attention to this basic discrepancy by showing that the usual MO theory does not give the correct assymptotic energies, as molecules are dissociated into atoms and ions. He has employed a method of correction (using ionization potentials and electron affinities) which is basically related to the method advocated above. As Moffitt points out, the discrepancy in the present case is due chiefly to the failure to consider the change in σ-electron energy when forming C^+ and C^- from 2C.

The question arises whether other interelectronic Coulomb repulsion integrals should also be modified in the π-electron approximation. The repulsion between two π-electrons on different atoms would be affected by the presence of a formal minus charge on one or both of the atoms. This effect, as well as correlation of the two π-electrons, would tend to lower the effective value of all Coulomb repulsion integrals with respect to values computed theoretically from Slater orbitals. The magnitude of the lowering is difficult to estimate precisely, but the correction should be considerably less than for $(11|11)$.

Detailed application of these ideas will be made in subsequent publications.

[1] R. S. Mulliken, J. Chem. Phys. **2**, 782 (1934).
[2] R. G. Parr and B. L. Crawford, Jr., J. Chem. Phys. **16**, 526 (1948).
[3] W. Moffitt, Proc. Roy. Soc. (London) **A210**, 224 (1951).

Reprinted from THE JOURNAL OF CHEMICAL PHYSICS, Vol. 21, No. 3, 466–471, March, 1953
Printed in U. S. A.

A Semi-Empirical Theory of the Electronic Spectra and Electronic Structure of Complex Unsaturated Molecules. I.*†

RUDOLPH PARISER, *Jackson Laboratory, E. I. du Pont de Nemours and Company, Wilmington, Delaware*

AND

ROBERT G. PARR, *Department of Chemistry, Carnegie Institute of Technology, Pittsburgh, Pennsylvania*

(Received September 4, 1952)

A semi-empirical theory is outlined which is designed for the correlation and prediction of the wavelengths and intensities of the first main visible or ultraviolet absorption bands and other properties of complex unsaturated molecules, and preliminary application of the theory is made to ethylene and benzene.

The theory is formulated in the language of the purely theoretical method of antisymmetrized products of molecular orbitals (in LCAO approximation), including configuration interaction, but departs from this theory in several essential respects. First, atomic orbital integrals involving the core Hamiltonian are expressed in terms of quantities which may be regarded as semi-empirical. Second, an approximation of zero differential overlap is employed, and an optional uniformly charged sphere representation of atomic π-orbitals is introduced, which greatly simplify the evaluation of electronic repulsion integrals and make applications to complex molecules containing heteroatoms relatively simple. Finally, although the theory starts from the π-electron approximation, in which the unsaturation electrons are treated apart from the rest, provision is included for the adjustment of the σ-electrons to the π-electron distribution in a way which does not complicate the mathematics.

Electronic energy levels in the theory are expressed in terms of ionization potentials of atoms, resonance integrals of bonds, Coulomb repulsion integrals between two π-electrons on the same atom and between two π-electrons on different atoms, and penetration integrals between π-electrons and neutral atoms. Preliminary applications to ethylene and benzene in which only the carbon-carbon resonance integral is treated as an empirical quantity show that the theory can reproduce the results of the purely theoretical method with very little labor. The reasonableness of considering all of the above quantities as semi-empirical is pointed out, however, and it is through a detailed examination and exploitation of this in the second paper of this series that correction for the inadequacies of the π-electron approximation is made and improved agreement with experiment is attained.

1. PREFACE

THIS paper is the first of a series presenting a new semi-empirical theory of the electronic spectra and structure of unsaturated molecules. Papers I and II present the main elements of the theory with primitive examples; later papers will emphasize applications to various molecules and series of molecules. The theory is primarily designed for the prediction of wavelength and intensity of the main visible or near ultraviolet electronic absorption bands of unsaturated organic molecules, but such topics as resonance energy, electron

* Contribution No. 128 from Jackson Laboratory, E. I. du Pont de Nemours and Company, Wilmington, Delaware.
† Presented at the Symposium on Molecular Structure and Spectroscopy, Ohio State University, June 9, 1952.

density, bond order, and dipole moment will receive some attention, and applications to certain saturated and certain inorganic molecules will also be considered.

The theory starts from the so-called π-electron approximation in which the unsaturation, or π, electrons of a molecule are treated apart from the rest, the latter being manifest only in the effective "core" in the field of which the former move. Wave functions for various states of the π-electrons are built from $2p$ atomic orbitals on the individual atoms, and energies of the various states are computed in a prescribed manner. The theory combines the advantages of the conventional semi-empirical LCAO MO method with the advantages of the conventional purely theoretical method of antisymmetrized products of molecular orbitals (in LCAO approximation), including configuration interaction.

The degree to which the semi-empirical LCAO MO method[1] can successfully correlate organic spectra has been examined by several authors.[2] The method is useful, but consideration of configuration interaction is essential for ultimate understanding of band positions and intensities. Configuration interaction is not quantitatively provided for in the conventional method, however, and furthermore, the method does not take proper cognizance of electronic interaction—it makes no distinction between singlet and multiplet states, for example. The present theory may be regarded as a quantitative prescription for inclusion of configuration interaction effects in a semi-empirical LCAO MO theory from which internal inconsistencies have been removed.

The method of antisymmetrized products of molecular orbitals (in LCAO approximation), including configuration interaction, as developed by Goeppert-Mayer and Sklar,[3] Craig,[4] and Roothaan,[5] and as discussed in detail by Mulliken,[6,7] provides a proper theoretical framework for a consistent theory. In its purely theoretical form this method is impractical, however; it lacks the empirical element which one must expect in a genuinely useful theory, and its mathematics is unwieldy—benzene is the most complex molecule on which the method has been fully tested,[8] and the organic chemist may reasonably expect more! The present theory incorporates an empirical element into the antisymmetrized product method. This by itself would not yield a wieldy method, but through the exploitation of a certain approximate property of atomic $2p$ orbitals in molecules a sweeping simplification of the mathematics is achieved which makes applications to complex molecules feasible.

2. THE TOTAL ENERGY OF AN ELECTRONIC STATE

For a molecule containing n π-electrons moving in the field of a core (in C_6H_6, for example, there are 6 π-electrons in the field of a $C_6H_6^{+6}$ core), the Hamiltonian operator will be expressed in the form[3]

$$\mathbf{H}=\mathbf{H}_{\text{core}}+\tfrac{1}{2}\sum_{ij}(e^2/r_{ij}), \tag{1}$$

where e^2/r_{ij} is the electrostatic repulsion between π-electrons i and j, and

$$\mathbf{H}_{\text{core}}=\sum_i \mathbf{H}_{\text{core}}(i), \tag{2}$$

where $\mathbf{H}_{\text{core}}(i)$ is the kinetic energy operator for electron i plus its potential energy operator in the field of the core:

$$\mathbf{H}_{\text{core}}(i)=\mathbf{T}(i)+\mathbf{U}_{\text{core}}(i). \tag{3}$$

Other than π-electrons are evinced only through the terms $\mathbf{U}_{\text{core}}(i)$. This is the so-called *π-electron approximation.*

Wave functions for the n-electron system will be constructed from normalized antisymmetrized product functions of the type

$$\Phi_\Lambda=\frac{1}{\sqrt{n!}}\begin{vmatrix}(\phi_1\alpha)^1 & (\phi_1\beta)^1 & (\phi_2\alpha)^1 & \cdots \\ (\phi_1\alpha)^2 & (\phi_1\beta)^2 & (\phi_2\alpha)^2 & \cdots \\ (\phi_1\alpha)^3 & (\phi_1\beta)^3 & (\phi_2\alpha)^3 & \cdots \\ \vdots & \vdots & \vdots & \vdots \end{vmatrix}, \tag{4}$$

where Λ is a running index characterizing the assignment of electrons to particular *molecular orbitals* ϕ_i with spin functions α or β; i.e., Λ is an index indicating the *spin-orbital configuration.*[6] The molecular orbitals (MO) ϕ_i will further be taken to be orthonormal linear combinations of atomic orbitals (AO) χ_p on the several nuclei:

$$\phi_i=\sum_p C_{ip}\chi_p. \tag{5}$$

This is the familiar LCAO *approximation.*

The expectation value for the energy of Φ_Λ, $\int\Phi_\Lambda{}^*\mathbf{H}\Phi_\Lambda dv$, is given by the formula:[6]

$$E_\Lambda=\sum_i I_i+\tfrac{1}{2}\sum_{ij}(J_{ij}-K_{ij}')$$

$$\text{(sums over occupied MO's in } \Phi_\Lambda), \tag{6}$$

where

$$I_i=\int\phi_i{}^*(1)\mathbf{H}_{\text{core}}(1)\phi_i(1)dv \tag{7}$$

[1] See, for example, Mulliken Rieke, and Brown, J. Am. Chem. Soc. **63**, 41 (1941), and R. S. Mulliken and C. A. Rieke, J. Am. Chem. Soc. **63**, 1770 (1941), where the semi-empirical LCAO MO method is described and applied in detail to the phenomenon of hyperconjugation.

[2] See, for example, J. R. Platt, J. Chem. Phys. **18**, 1168 (1950).

[3] M. Goeppert-Mayer and A. L. Sklar, J. Chem. Phys. **6**, 645 (1938).

[4] D. P. Craig, Proc. Roy. Soc. (London) **200**, 474 (1950).

[5] C. C. J. Roothaan, Revs. Modern Phys. **23**, 69 (1951).

[6] R. S. Mulliken, J. chim. phys. **46**, 497 (1949).

[7] R. S. Mulliken, J. chim. phys. **46**, 695 (1949).

[8] Parr, Craig, and Ross, J. Chem. Phys. **18**, 1561 (1950).

is the *core energy* for the MO ϕ_i,

$$J_{ij}=\int \phi_i^*(1)\phi_j^*(2)(e^2/r_{12})\phi_i(1)\phi_j(2)dv \qquad (8)$$

is the *Coulomb integral* between MO's ϕ_i and ϕ_j, and

$$K_{ij}=\int \phi_i^*(1)\phi_j^*(2)(e^2/r_{12})\phi_j(1)\phi_i(2)dv \qquad (9)$$

is the *exchange integral* between ϕ_i and ϕ_j, with $K_{ij}'=K_{ij}$ if ϕ_i and ϕ_j have the same spins in Φ_Λ, $K_{ij}'=0$ if ϕ_i and ϕ_j have different spins in Φ_Λ.

Now a single Φ_Λ may or may not be a good approximation to the total π-electron wave function Ψ_S for an actual electronic state S of the system. In cases for which a single Φ_Λ suffices, energies may be computed directly from Eq. (6); in cases for which a combination of several Φ_Λ is needed, a *configuration interaction* calculation needs to be performed by carrying out a linear variational calculation with the Φ_Λ as starting functions; i.e., by writing

$$\Psi_S=A_1\Phi_1+A_2\Phi_2+\cdots, \qquad (10)$$

determining the energy by solution of a *secular equation*

$$|H_{mn}-S_{mn}E|=0, \qquad (11)$$

and determining the coefficients A_m by solution of the simultaneous equations

$$\sum_m A_m[H_{mn}-S_{mn}E]=0, \quad n=1, 2, \cdots. \qquad (12)$$

The matrix elements,

$$S_{mn}=\int \Phi_m^*\Phi_n dv \qquad (13)$$

and

$$H_{mn}=\int \Phi_m^*\mathbf{H}\Phi_n dv, \qquad (14)$$

required for this calculation are readily derived; in particular, the H_{mn} always turns out to be expressible in terms of integrals which are generalizations of those appearing in Eqs. (7)–(9); namely, *core integrals*,

$$I_{ij}=\int \phi_i^*(1)\mathbf{H}_{\text{core}}(1)\phi_j(1)dv, \qquad (15)$$

and *electronic repulsion integrals*,

$$(ij|kl)=\int \phi_i^*(1)\phi_k^*(2)(e^2/r_{12})\phi_j(1)\phi_l(2)dv. \qquad (16)$$

Once one has chosen starting MO's and decided on the extent of configuration interaction to be taken into account, the determination of electronic energy levels is reduced to the problem of computing core integrals and electronic repulsion integrals. Methods for handling these two types of integrals are described in Secs. 3 and 4. The more subtle problems of choosing the initial MO's and deciding on the extent of configuration interaction are also considered in Sec. 3.

3. CORE INTEGRALS

Since according to Eqs. (5) and (15),

$$I_{ij}=\sum_p\sum_q C_{ip}^*C_{jq}H_{pq}^{\text{core}}, \qquad (17)$$

where

$$H_{pq}^{\text{core}}=\int \chi_p^*(1)\mathbf{H}_{\text{core}}(1)\chi_q(1)dv, \qquad (18)$$

it is sufficient for determination of the core integrals to know the LCAO coefficients C_{ip} and the AO matrix elements H_{pq}^{core}.

To determine the C_{ip}, one *might* set up a semi-empirical procedure of the conventional form,[1,9] using the linear variational method with some effective one-electron Hamiltonian operator $\mathbf{H}_{\text{eff}}(1)$ equal either to $\mathbf{H}_{\text{core}}(1)$ or to a self-consistent operator $\mathbf{F}(1)=\mathbf{H}_{\text{core}}(1)+\mathbf{G}(1)$, where $\mathbf{G}$ includes in the proper way[5] the effect of the other π-electrons on electron 1. One would then obtain simultaneous equations for the coefficients and for one-electron orbital energies of the form

$$\sum_p C_{ip}[H_{pq}^{\text{eff}}-S_{pq}e]=0$$

and

$$|H_{pq}^{\text{eff}}-S_{pq}e|=0, \quad \text{respectively.}$$

If $\mathbf{H}_{\text{eff}}=\mathbf{H}_{\text{core}}$ were used, the roots of the secular equation would be the diagonal elements $I_i\equiv I_{ii}$, and the off-diagonal I_{ij} would be zero; if $\mathbf{H}_{\text{eff}}=\mathbf{F}$ were used, the roots of the secular equation (for a closed-shell ground state) would be the self-consistent field energies.[5] In the former case one could proceed immediately to the use of the formulation of Sec. 2 for determination of total electronic energies, but one would have to be prepared to include a large amount of configuration interaction in order to compensate for the inadequacies of the MO's employed. The MO's used in the self-consistent case would be better, but one would be inextricably tied to a difficult and tedious iterative computational scheme.[10]

The point of view advocated here will be intermediate. Configuration interaction, sufficiently invoked, can correct in effect any error made in the choice of the LCAO coefficients. For this reason, any coefficients C_{ip} may be employed. One may therefore choose the coefficients arbitrarily, subject to the orthonormalization conditions. The closer the chosen MO's are to the

[9] R. G. Parr, J. Chem. Phys. 19, 799 (1951).

[10] See, for example, R. G. Parr and R. S. Mulliken, J. Chem. Phys. 18, 1338 (1950), where a self-consistent LCAO MO calculation on butadiene is carried out.

"best" or self-consistent field LCAO MO's, the less configuration interaction will have to be invoked. However, large deviations from self-consistent LCAO MO's brought on by ignorance or dictated by convenience may always be compensated through configuration interaction.

A procedure for obtaining the H_{pq}^{core} will now be outlined. Let

$$\alpha_p \equiv H_{pp}^{\text{core}} = \int \chi_p^*(1)\mathbf{H}_{\text{core}}(1)\chi_p(1)dv \tag{19}$$

and[11]

$$\beta_{pq} \equiv H_{pq}^{\text{core}} = \int \chi_p^*(1)\mathbf{H}_{\text{core}}(1)\chi_q(1)dv \tag{20}$$

and assume tentatively that

$$\beta_{pq} = 0 \text{ when } p \text{ and } q \text{ are non-neighbors.} \tag{21}$$

The *resonance integrals* β_{pq} may be shown by theoretical elucidation of H_{core} to depend on the type and length of the bond pq and the atoms p and q, but not sensibly on neighboring bonds or atoms.[12] Accordingly, they may be naturally carried from molecule to molecule and will be treated as basic empirical quantities.

The *Coulomb integrals* α_p, on the other hand, will depend on the bonding to atom p and the neighbors of atom p, and therefore are not appropriate for carry-over from molecule to molecule. They are better expressed in terms of more basic quantities, as follows: According to the argument of Goeppert-Mayer and Sklar,[3] the core Hamiltonian of Eq. (3) may be written as

$$\mathbf{H}_{\text{core}}(1) = \mathbf{T}(1) + \mathbf{U}_p(1) + \sum_{q\neq p} \mathbf{U}_q(1) + \sum_r \mathbf{U}_r^*(1), \tag{22}$$

where the atoms q are charged in the core (e.g., a carbon atom in benzene) and the atoms r are uncharged in the core (e.g., a hydrogen atom in benzene), and where the asterisk connotes a potential which is due to a *neutral* atom. Further,

$$\mathbf{U}_q(1) = \mathbf{U}_q^*(1) - \int \chi_q^*(2)\chi_q(2)(e^2/r_{12})dv_2. \tag{23}$$

If, therefore, the AO's χ_p are atomic eigenfunctions in the sense that

$$[\mathbf{T}(1) + \mathbf{U}_p(1)]\chi_p(1) = W_p\chi_p(1), \tag{24}$$

where W_p is an appropriate *atomic valence state ionization potential*, then Eqs. (19) and (22)–(24) yield

$$\alpha_p = W_p - \sum_{q\neq p} [(pp|qq) + (q:pp)] - \sum_r (r:pp), \tag{25}$$

where $(pp|qq)$ is the *Coulomb repulsion integral* between χ_p and χ_q [compare Eq. (16)] and $(q:pp)$ and $(r:pp)$ are *Coulomb penetration integrals* between χ_p and *neutral* atoms q and r:

$$(q:pp) = -\int \mathbf{U}_q^*(1)\chi_p^*(1)\chi_p(1)dv. \tag{26}$$

Equation (25) will be taken as the fundamental formula for determination of the atomic Coulomb integrals α_p from the empirical atomic ionization potentials W_p.

4. ELECTRONIC REPULSION INTEGRALS

The electronic repulsion integrals of Eq. (16) are of the form

$$(ij|kl) = \int \Omega_{ij}(1)(1/r_{12})\Omega_{kl}(2)dv, \tag{27}$$

with $\Omega_{ij}(1) = e\phi_i^*(1)\phi_j(1)$ and $\Omega_{kl}(2) = e\phi_k^*(2)\phi_l(2)$, and can be interpreted as classical electrostatic repulsions between the charge distribution Ω_{ij} and Ω_{kl}. To obtain approximate values for these integrals, one may make the assumption of *formal neglect of differential overlap*,

$$\chi_p^*\chi_q \equiv 0 \quad \text{for} \quad p \neq q, \tag{28}$$

and employ ϕ_i which are orthonormalized accordingly;[13] i.e., make

$$\sum_p C_{ip}^* C_{jp} = \delta_{ij}. \tag{29}$$

One then obtains

$$(ij|kl) = \text{linear combination of integrals over atomic orbitals of the form } (pp|qq). \tag{30}$$

The problem is thus reduced to the evaluation of a relatively small number of integrals over atomic orbitals, all of them being Coulomb repulsion integrals.

Formulas or tables for the integrals $(pp|qq)$ may be found in the literature.[14] Alternatively, the *uniformly charged sphere approximation* may be employed,[15,16] in

[11] Equation (20) is the *formal* definition of β_{pq} with which one works in conjunction with the formal neglect of overlap of Eq. (28). For theoretical purposes, β_{pq} is better thought of as defined by

$$\beta_{pq} = H_{pq}^{\text{core}} - (S_{pq}/2)(H_{pp}^{\text{core}} + H_{qq}^{\text{core}}), \tag{20a}$$

which takes more realistic account of the overlap integral

$S_{pq} = \int \chi_p^*(1)\chi_q(1)dv.$ (See references 1 and 6.)

[12] This may be shown to be true when β_{pq} is defined as in reference 11.

[13] One does not have to *orthogonalize* subject to formal neglect of differential overlap, but this appears to be the most natural and consistent procedure.

[14] Formulas for Coulomb repulsion integrals $(pp|qq)$, for Slater $2p\pi$ AO's, both for $Z_p = Z_q$ and $Z_p \neq Z_q$, are given by C. C. J. Roothaan, J. Chem. Phys. **19**, 1445 (1951). Numerical values for $Z_p \neq Z_q$ are not available in the literature, except for a few special cases. Numerical values for $Z_p = Z_q$ have been given by several authors; the best table now available is that of H. J. Kopineck, Z. Naturforsh. **5a**, 420 (1950).

[15] The uniformly charged sphere approximation seems to have been employed first by G. E. Kimball, who investigated such an approximation for $1s$ orbitals. See G. F. Neumark, Ph.D. thesis, Columbia University, 1951.

[16] For a preliminary discussion of the uniformly charged sphere approximation for $2p\pi$ orbitals, see R. G. Parr, J. Chem. Phys. **20**, 1499 (1952).

TABLE I. Electronic repulsion integrals in ethylene (ev).

Integral	Exact value[a]	Approximate value[b]
J_{11}	13.08	
J_{22}	13.44	13.09 or 13.58
J_{12}	13.01	
K_{12}	4.16	3.84 or 4.50

[a] Reference 18. These values are for Slater $2p\pi$ AO's with effective charge $Z=3.18$.
[b] Values in first column are calculated neglecting differential overlap; values in second column are calculated using uniformly charged sphere approximation. See text and reference 19.

which each $\chi_p{}^*\chi_p e$ is replaced by a pair of tangent uniformly charged nonconducting spheres of *diameter*

$$R_p=(4.597/Z_p)\times 10^{-8}\ \text{cm},^{17} \qquad (31)$$

where Z_p is the Slater effective nuclear charge for the $2p\pi$ atomic orbital χ_p, and the integrals $(pp|qq)$ are computed by means of classical electrostatic theory. A pronounced advantage of the uniformly charged sphere model is the relative ease with which heteroatoms may be handled.

5. PRIMITIVE APPLICATIONS TO ETHYLENE AND BENZENE

Tables I–IV give the results of application of the method outlined in Secs. 2–4 to ethylene and benzene. Results obtained by the much more tedious non-empirical antisymmetrized product method using Slater $2p\pi$ AO's are also displayed in the tables.[8,18] The two methods agree within the limits of precision in the nonempirical method. Agreement with experiment is another matter, which will be discussed briefly in Sec. 6 and in detail in paper II of this series.

The two π-electron LCAO MO's in ethylene are determined by symmetry. Neglecting overlap, they are

$$\left.\begin{aligned}\phi_1&=\frac{1}{\sqrt{2}}(\chi_1+\chi_2)\\ \phi_2&=\frac{1}{\sqrt{2}}(\chi_1-\chi_2)\end{aligned}\right\}, \qquad (32)$$

where χ_1 and χ_2 are $2p\pi$ AO's on carbons 1 and 2. The electronic repulsion integrals, when differential overlap is neglected, are therefore given by the simple formulas

$$\left.\begin{aligned}2J_{11}&=2J_{22}=2J_{12}=(11|11)+(11|22)\\ 2K_{12}&=(11|11)-(11|22)\end{aligned}\right\}. \qquad (33)$$

Table I gives purely theoretical values for these integrals,[18] values computed from Eq. (33) using exact values for the atomic Coulomb integrals (11|11) and (11|22), and values computed from Eq. (33) using uniformly charged sphere values for (11|11) and (11|22).[19]

Table II gives purely theoretical values for the π-electron energy levels of ethylene, values computed ignoring differential overlap, and values computed using the uniformly charged sphere approximation, a value of β being employed in the last two calculations which will make the "states" 1 and 2 have the same splitting as in the first calculation. Here states 1 and 2 arise from assignment of two electrons to the MO's ϕ_1 and ϕ_2, respectively. State N is the result of mixing states 1 and 2

TABLE II. Electronic energy levels of ethylene (ev).

State	Exact LCAO MO energy[a]	Approximate energy[b]	
$1(^1A_{1g})$	0.0	0.0	0.0
$2(^1A_{1g})$	12.5	12.5	12.5
$T(^3B_{1u})$	1.8	2.4	1.8
$V(^1B_{1u})$	10.2	10.1	10.8
Mean of T and V	6.0	6.2	6.2
$N(^1A_{1g})$	−1.3	−1.1	−1.4

[a] Reference 18. These values are for Slater $2p\pi$ AO's with effective charge $Z=3.18$.
[b] Values in first column are calculated neglecting differential overlap; values in second column are calculated using uniformly charged sphere approximation. See text and reference 19. $\beta=-3.125$ ev has been employed in each case.

to give the best approximation to the ground state obtainable from the AO's χ_1 and χ_2. States T and V are the triplet and singlet states arising from assignment of one electron to ϕ_1 and one electron to ϕ_2. The formulas for the energies of these various states have been given elsewhere,[18] and so will not be given here. The quantity α enters all the energies in the same additive way (note that the two carbon atoms in ethylene are equivalent) and, therefore, cancels when excitation energies are computed.

Neglecting overlap, the six π-electron LCAO MO's in benzene, as determined by symmetry, are[3]

$$\phi_l=\frac{1}{\sqrt{6}}\sum_{p=1}^{6}\omega^{lp}\chi_p,\quad l=0,\ \pm1,\ \pm2,\ 3; \qquad (34)$$

[17] This value for the diameter forces the integral $(pp|pp)$ to be in agreement with the value computed for Slater $2p\pi$ AO's, $(pp|pp)=0.1957\ (e^2/a_0)Z_p$. (See, for example, R. G. Parr and B. L. Crawford, Jr., J. Chem. Phys. **16**, 1049 (1948).) For the uniformly charged sphere model, with $\chi_p{}^2e$ replaced by two tangent uniformly charged spheres each of diameter R_p and carrying charge $e/2$, since the repulsive potential between one such sphere and itself is from classical electrostatics $(12/5R_p)$ for unit charge, $(pp|pp)=(e/2)^2|2(12/5R_p)+2(1/R_p)|=(17/10)\ (e^2/R_p)$. Hence, equating the two expressions for $(pp|pp)$, $R_p=(17/10)(a_0/0.1957Z_p)=(4.597/Z_p)\times10^{-8}$ cm.

[18] R. G. Parr and B. L. Crawford, Jr., J. Chem. Phys. **16**, 526 (1948).

[19] If one inserts the usual $Z_c=3.18$ in Eq. (31), one finds $R_c=1.45$A, which would cause spheres on neighboring carbon atoms to overlap in ethylene and benzene. The electrostatics can be handled in this case (see reference 15), but it is simpler and in more natural accord with Eq. (28) to contract the spheres enough that neighboring spheres are just tangent, which procedure has been used in computing Tables I–IV and which corresponds to $Z_c=3.40$ in ethylene and $Z_c=3.30$ in benzene.

where $\omega=\exp(2\pi i/6)$ and χ_p is the $2p\pi$ AO on carbon p. Without the formal neglect of differential overlap there are thirty different electronic repulsion integrals in benzene, the values of which cluster in four distinct groups.[20] With the assumption of formal neglect of differential overlap there are only four distinct integrals; namely,

$$\left.\begin{aligned} 6J_{00}=6J_{01} &=\text{etc.}=(11|11)+2(11|22)+2(11|33)+(11|44)\\ 6K_{01}=6K_{12} &=\text{etc.}=(11|11)+(11|22)-(11|33)-(11|44)\\ 6K_{02}=6K_{13} &=\text{etc.}=(11|11)-(11|22)-(11|33)+(11|44)\\ 6K_{03}=6K_{1-2} &=\text{etc.}=(11|11)-2(11|22)+2(11|33)-(11|44) \end{aligned}\right\}. \quad (35)$$

TABLE III. Electronic repulsion integrals in benzene (ev).

Integral	Exact value[a]	Approximate value[b]
J_{00} group	8.627, 8.522, 8.495, 8.554, 8.474, 8.517, 8.623, 8.648, 8.787, 8.872; average 8.61	8.56
K_{01} group	2.584, 2.674, 2.867, 2.601, 2.633, 2.772; average 2.69	2.66
K_{02} group	1.304, 1.453, 1.338, 1.367, 1.328, 1.299, 1.302, 1.375, 1.344, 1.362; average 1.35	1.35
K_{03} group	0.934, 1.074, 1.007, 0.993 average 1.00	1.03

[a] Reference 8. These values are for Slater $2p\pi$ AO's with effective charge $Z=3.18$.
[b] Calculated using uniformly charged sphere approximation. See text and reference 19.

In Table III purely theoretical values for these integrals[8] are compared with values computed from Eq. (35) and the uniformly charged sphere approximation.[21]

Table IV gives purely theoretical values for the π-electron energy levels of benzene[8] and values computed using the uniformly charged sphere approximation and a value of β chosen to make the energies of the first excited singlet state equal in the two calculations. Here interaction[22] has been taken into account between all configurations which arise from excitation of an electron from an MO ϕ_1 or ϕ_{-1} to an MO ϕ_2 or ϕ_{-2}. Formulas for the energies again may be found elsewhere,[3] and α again does not enter the excitation energies.

[20] See reference 8, especially footnote 9.
[21] Exact (reference 8) values for the atomic Coulomb integrals are $(11|11)=16.93$, $(11|22)=9.03$, $(11|33)=5.67$, $(11|44)=4.97$ ev; uniformly charged sphere approximation values (see footnote 19) are $(11|11)=17.61$, $(11|22)=8.84$, $(11|33)=5.58$, $(11|44)=4.90$ ev.
[22] This interaction can be handled by group theory, but this is a specialized technique not applicable to unsymmetrical molecules. Rather it appears preferable to handle the interaction by the configuration interaction technique of Sec. 2, which is completely general.

TABLE IV. Electronic energy levels of benzene (ev).

State	Exact LCAO MO energy[a]	Approximate energy[b]
$^1A_{1g}$	0.0	0.0
$^1B_{2u}$	5.9	5.9
$^1B_{1u}$	7.3	7.3
$^1E_{1u}$	9.8	9.9
$^3B_{2u}$	5.8	5.9
$^3B_{1u}$	3.1	3.2
$^3E_{1u}$	4.4	4.5

[a] Reference 8. These values are Slater $2p\pi$ AO's with effective charge $Z=3.18$.
[b] Calculated using uniformly charged sphere approximation, with $\beta=-2.790$ ev. See text and reference 19.

6. DISCUSSION

These results show that the present semi-empirical theory is capable of duplicating the results of the non-empirical antisymmetrized product method in cases where the latter has been applied, and with such a large reduction in labor that applications are now made possible to much more complex molecules than have heretofore been treated by an antisymmetrized product method.

How about agreement with experiment, however? Although the experimental data themselves are not unambigously understood, even in ethylene and benzene, enough is known to make one realize that the non-empirical method is not entirely satisfactory. The present theory, admittedly being semi-empirical, has a flexibility not inherent in the nonempirical method. The possibility of exploiting this flexibility will be investigated in the next paper of this series.

Quantities which enter the expressions for the electronic energy levels of a molecule in the present theory are of four types: (1) atomic ionization potentials, W_p; (2) bond resonance integrals, β_{pq}; (3) Coulomb repulsion integrals, $(pp|qq)$; (4) Coulomb penetration integrals, $(q:pp)$. In the preliminary calculations of Sec. 5 above, only the first two of these types were regarded as empirical. One might well ask whether empirical adjustment of the last two would also be worth while. In the next paper such an adjustment will indeed be carried out, and there will emerge both an improved fit of the theory with experiment and a natural correction for the inadequacies of the π-electron approximation.

Reprinted from THE JOURNAL OF CHEMICAL PHYSICS, Vol. 21, No. 5, 767–776, May, 1953
Printed in U. S. A.

A Semi-Empirical Theory of the Electronic Spectra and Electronic Structure of Complex Unsaturated Molecules. II*

RUDOLPH PARISER,
Jackson Laboratory, E. I. du Pont de Nemours and Company, Wilmington, Delaware

AND

ROBERT G. PARR,
Department of Chemistry, Carnegie Institute of Technology, Pittsburgh, Pennsylvania

(Received December 11, 1952)

The theory of electronic spectra and electronic structure, the elucidation of which was begun in the first paper of this series, is further developed and applied to ethylene, butadiene, benzene, pyridine, pyrimidine, pyrazine, and *s*-triazine.

A realistic and consistent LCAO-MO π-electron theory should allow the σ-electrons to adjust themselves to the instantaneous positions of the mobile π-electrons. This is accomplished in the theory by assignment of empirical values to the Coulomb electronic repulsion integrals and Coulomb penetration integrals which enter the formulas, these values being obtained in a prescribed way from valence state ionization potentials and electron affinities of atoms. Use of the empirical values in the molecular orbital theory reduces the magnitude of computed singlet-triplet splittings and the effects of configuration interaction without complicating the mathematics. From the valence-bond point of view, ionic structures may be said to be enhanced.

The applications to hydrocarbons and heteromolecules which are considered show that the theory can correlate known π-electron spectral wavelengths and intensities very successfully, which, together with the simple structure of the theory, signals that manifold applications of the theory are in order elsewhere.

1. INTRODUCTION

IN the first paper of this series,[1] hereafter denoted by I, the elements of a theory were presented for the determination of the electronic spectra and electronic structure of complex unsaturated molecules. In the present paper the theory is further expanded and applied to the calculation of some of the spectral properties of ethylene, benzene, butadiene, pyridine, pyrimidine, pyrazine, and *s*-triazine.

In I, results identical in effect with those of purely theoretical LCAO-MO π-electron calculations[2] on ethylene[3] and benzene[4] were obtained from the new theory with relatively little labor, indicating that the new theory can duplicate the results of the old while using a much simpler computational scheme. The present paper shifts the emphasis, duplication of *experimental* results now being taken as the primary desideratum. The guiding principle in molding the theory to give agreement with experiment has been that, to achieve this end, quantities conventionally regarded as purely theoretical may rightly be regarded as semi-empirical. As the shape of the mold emerged, it became apparent that no loss in rigor had actually been entailed, however. For, a re-examination of the assumptions of the purely theoretical LCAO-MO method (see below) shows that precisely such a semi-empirical evaluation of the basic quantities is what is called for by realistic consideration of the structure of the core which underlies the π-electrons in an unsaturated

* Presented at the Symposium on Molecular Structure and Spectroscopy, Ohio State University, June 9, 1952.

[1] R. Pariser and R. G. Parr, J. Chem. Phys. **21**, 466 (1953).

[2] The "purely theoretical LCAO-MO method" is the method of antisymmetrized products of molecular orbitals, in LCAO approximation, including configuration interaction, as developed by Goeppert-Mayer and Sklar, Craig and Roothaan. In this method all quantities which enter the formulas are computed theoretically in terms of a single parameter, the effective nuclear charge of an atom for a π-electron, taken as 3.18 for carbon. For detailed references, see reference 1.

[3] R. G. Parr and B. L. Crawford, Jr., J. Chem. Phys. **16**, 526 (1948).

[4] Parr, Craig, and Ross, J. Chem. Phys. **18**, 1561 (1950).

TABLE I. Theoretical and experimental electronic energy levels of ethylene and benzene (ev).

Molecule	State[a]	Theoretical LCAO MO energy[b]	Experimental energy
Ethylene	$N(^1A_{1g})$	0.0	0.0
	$T(^3B_{1u})$	3.1	3.1—5.6[c]
	$V(^1B_{1u})$	13.5	7.6[d]
Benzene	$^1A_{1g}$	0.0	0.0
	$^1B_{2u}$	5.9	4.9[e]
	$^1B_{1u}$	7.3	6.2[e]
	$^1E_{1u}$	9.8	7.0[e]
	$^3B_{2u}$	5.8	...
	$^3B_{1u}$	3.1	3.8[e]
	$^3E_{1u}$	4.4	...

[a] For notation, see references 3 and 4.
[b] Reference 3 and 4. Values given are for Slater $2p\pi$ AO's with effective charge 3.18. For benzene the values are those obtained with no consideration of configuration interaction beyond that dictated by the molecular symmetry. Values including more configuration interaction are somewhat different; see reference 4.
[c] The lowest triplet state of ethylene has not been unambiguously located, and its symmetry has not been definitely established. Several authors have assigned its location in the indicated range, and the symmetry $^3B_{1u}$ seems most reasonable.
[d] The strong ethylene absorption at 7.6 ev is undoubtedly due to a singlet excited state. The symmetry of this state is less sure.
[e] The locations and symmetries of the benzene excited states are still being debated. The absorption at 4.9 ev corresponds to a forbidden transition from the ground state and has most probably the symmetry $^1B_{2u}$. The triplet at 3.8 ev may be either a $^3B_{1u}$ or $^3B_{2u}$ state and is probably the lowest triplet state of the molecule. The excited state at 7.0 ev corresponds to an allowed transition; the one at 6.2 ev could be either allowed or symmetry forbidden.

molecule and the mutual shielding effects of the electrons on one another. That is to say, the semi-empirical method appears to be more correct than the purely theoretical method as a derangement of which it has been developed.

The methods employed in the present paper are to a certain extent arbitrary and tentative. The flexibility of the theory presents a welcome challenge, but it does mean that results obtained now may require revision later as the base of experience becomes more broad.

2. EXPERIMENT AND THEORY IN ETHYLENE AND BENZENE

The first question then is: To what extent do the results of the purely theoretical method (or alternatively the simplified method described in I which is numerically equivalent) agree with experiment? Unfortunately, even for the simple unsaturated molecules ethylene and benzene the experimental spectra are not completely understood, but enough is known to effect the desired comparison. Table I gives theoretical *versus* experimental electronic levels for these molecules.

There appear to be two major points of disagreement between theory and experiment. First, the quantitative agreement is rather poor, the theoretical energies of the lowest excited singlets being too high by several ev. Second, the splitting between corresponding singlets and triplets computed theoretically is much too large.

Before abandoning the purely theoretical method, one might try to extend it by including more configuration interaction or test it further by varying the effective charge parameter which enters the calculations. Both of these possibilities have been explored, however, and the modified results are not particularly encouraging.[5]

Thus, the purely theoretical LCAO-MO method is not entirely adequate for quantitative purposes, and a detailed and realistic re-examination of the basic quantities which enter the theory is in order. For this the theory outlined in I, being relatively simple, seems admirably suited.

3. BASIC QUANTITIES OF THE THEORY

As was pointed out in the last section of I, four basic types of quantities, W_p, β_{pq}, $(pp|qq)$, and $(q:pp)$, are sufficient to express the electronic energy of a molecule. Of these only the resonance integrals β_{pq} and the Coulomb repulsion integrals $(pp|qq)$ are required in the computation of the electronic excitation energies for ethylene and benzene.

One might try varying only β_{pq} empirically in order to fit the lowest excited singlet states of ethylene and benzene, the states $^1B_{1u}$ and $^1B_{2u}$, respectively, to the observed 7.6 and 4.9 ev. One then finds, setting nonneighbor β's equal to zero and calling $\beta=\beta_{12}$, $\beta=-1.5$ ev for ethylene and $\beta=-2.2$ ev for benzene.

Now the theoretical expression for β_{pq}, when p and q are alike, namely,[6]

$$\beta_{pq}=\sum_{l,\neq q}\left[S_{pq}(l:qq)+S_{pq}(ll:qq)-(l:pq)-(ll|pq)\right] +\sum_{r}\left[S_{pq}(r:qq)-(r:pq)\right], \quad (1)$$

implies that β_{pq} is zero for infinite separation of atoms p and q. This and other theoretical considerations, plus semi-empirical correlations of bond properties such as force constants and bond dissociation energies as functions of distance with resonance integrals as functions of distance,[7] all indicate strongly that the absolute value of β_{pq} should increase with decreasing distance. This behavior is clearly not followed by the above values of β for a carbon-carbon bond. Moreover, neither inclusion of nonneighbor resonance integrals nor inclusion of more configuration interaction[4] improves the situation. And a final, somewhat unsatisfactory, result of the adjustment of β in ethylene to give the correct singlet-singlet excitation energy is that the triplet $^3B_{1u}$ state becomes the theoretically predicted ground state!

One is thus led to re-examine the values, through the meanings, of the Coulomb repulsion integrals $(pp|qq)$.[8]

Consider two neutral infinitely separated carbon

[5] For the effect of configuration interaction in ethylene and benzene, see references 3 and 4, respectively. For the effect of variation of the effective charge in ethylene, see reference 3; in benzene, see H. Shull and F. Ellison. J. Chem. Phys. 19, 1215 (1951).

[6] For notation and definitions of the various terms, see reference 1. Equation 1 is obtained from the definition of β_{pq} as in footnote 11 of reference 1.

[7] See, for example, R. S. Mulliken, J. chim. phys. 46, 497, 695 (1949). The quantities called β in the present papers are called β^{core} by Mulliken.

[8] R. Pariser, J. Chem. Phys. 21, 568 (1953).

atoms in their sp^2 valence states. By the usual π-electron theory their combined energy would be given by $2W_p$, where W_p is the orbital energy or ionization potential of the $2p\pi$-electron. Now consider the ions C^+ and C^- which are formed by ionization of one of the π-electrons and placement of it in the $2p\pi$-orbital of the other atom. The energy of the ion pair is by the same theory $2W_p+(11|11)$, so that the difference of energy between the ion pair and the neutral pair is simply $(11|11)$. But experimentally this difference is the ionization potential I of a neutral carbon atom in its valence state minus the electron affinity A of such a neutral carbon atom. Thus, formally,

$$(11|11)=I-A. \qquad (2)$$

According to Mulliken,[9] $I=11.22$ ev and $A=0.69$ ev for carbon, so that Eq. (2) gives $(11|11)=10.53$ ev for carbon.

But theory, using Slater orbitals with $Z=3.18$ for carbon, gives $(11|11)=16.93$ ev! In view of Eq. (2), this imples either a high ionization potential of about 16 ev or a high negative electron affinity of about -6 ev, which values are inconsistent with the basic assumption that a carbon atom in a molecule behaves essentially as a free carbon atom in the appropriate valence state. The discrepancy is due, in the main, to the failure to consider in the derivation given above the change in σ-electron energy in passing from 2C to C^++C^-.

Further illustrations of the inadequacy of nonempirical values for the integral $(11|11)$ at large interatomic distances may be found in various relationships involving heteroatoms. Thus, one may compare the process

$$C(sp^3, V_4)+e\rightarrow C^-(sp^4, V_3),\ \Delta E_a$$

with the process

$$N(sp^4, V_3)+e\rightarrow N^-(sp^5, V_2),\ \Delta E_b.$$

According to the conventional theory,

$$\Delta E_a-\Delta E_b=W_C-W_N+(11|11)_C-(11|11)_N. \qquad (3)$$

Using Mulliken's valence state ionization potentials for W_C and W_N,[9] and theoretically computed values for $(11|11)_C$ and $(11|11)_N$ with $Z_N-Z_C=0.65$,[10] this energy difference is computed to be -0.05 ev. From valence state electron affinities the same difference may be computed to be $+1.67$ ev;[9] the nonempirical calculation predicts that it takes more energy to form N^- than C^-, whereas the reverse is unquestionably true.

If the usual interpretation of the π-electron approximation were taken literally, the self-penetration integral $(1:11)$ would be equal to the valence state electron affinity of the atom 1. For carbon, with $Z=3.25$, the computed value is 25.90 ev,[10] which is somewhat in excess of the carbon electron affinity of 0.69 ev.[9]

It would appear evident from these results that when theoretically computed values for Coulomb repulsion and Coulomb penetration integrals are used within the framework of the π-electron approximation, the results are neither realistic nor trustworthy. To retain the mathematical scheme of the π-electron approximation, one must alter the values of the integrals, especially $(11|11)$. The LCAO-MO method with all possible configuration interaction is equivalent to the valence-bond method including all ionic structures. Thus, an electronic wave function expressed in terms of LCAO-MO's can always be written out as a series of non-ionic and ionic resonance structures, and the appearance of the integral $(11|11)$ in the expression for the energy of some electronic state implies two electrons on the same atom and consequently some other atom devoid of its π-electron. In other words, an ion pair is formed, and to a first approximation the change in both π- and σ-electronic energy accompanying this change may be included in the integral $(11|11)$ by the use of Eq. (2) above.

These considerations provide justification for evaluation of one-center repulsion and penetration integrals from atomic ionization potentials and electron affinities. In the next section this evaluation is carried out for the integrals of this type required in the present calculations. There the corresponding two-center integrals are also evaluated by a method which is also partly semi-empirical. Justification for this is somewhat hard to make precise, but some lowering of $(pp|qq)$ and $(q:pp)$ values from those computed from Slater orbitals with $Z=3.18$ for carbon appears reasonable for reasons analogous to those given above for lowering of $(pp|pp)$ and $(p:pp)$ values and, at any rate, appears desirable from a semi-empirical point of view.

4. SEMI-EMPIRICAL EVALUATION OF THE BASIC QUANTITIES

The method now to be prescribed for evaluating the basic quantities represents an attempt to obtain a correct energy relationship between the ionic and non-ionic resonance structures of a π-bond by taking advantage of empirical ionization potentials and electron affinities of atoms.

A two-electron π-bond between atoms p and q may be described, in the usual approximation, as a superposition of four wave functions, the first two non-ionic, the second two ionic, namely,

$$\left.\begin{aligned}\Phi_a&=\frac{1}{\sqrt{2}}\begin{vmatrix}(\chi_p\alpha)^1(\chi_q\beta)^1\\(\chi_p\alpha)^2(\chi_q\beta)^2\end{vmatrix}\\ \Phi_b&=\frac{1}{\sqrt{2}}\begin{vmatrix}(\chi_p\beta)^1(\chi_q\alpha)^1\\(\chi_p\beta)^2(\chi_q\alpha)^2\end{vmatrix}\\ \Phi_c&=\frac{1}{\sqrt{2}}\begin{vmatrix}(\chi_p\alpha)^1(\chi_p\beta)^1\\(\chi_p\alpha)^2(\chi_p\beta)^2\end{vmatrix}\\ \Phi_d&=\frac{1}{\sqrt{2}}\begin{vmatrix}(\chi_q\alpha)^1(\chi_q\beta)^1\\(\chi_q\alpha)^2(\chi_q\beta)^2\end{vmatrix}\end{aligned}\right\}. \qquad (4)$$

[9] R. S. Mulliken, J. Chem. Phys. 2, 782 (1934).
[10] R. G. Parr and B. L. Crawford, Jr., J. Chem. Phys. 16, 1049 (1948).

TABLE II. Integrals over atomic orbitals (ev).

Integral[a]	R (in A)	Value[b]	Molecule[d]
$(11\|11)_{CC}$	0.00	10.53	all
$(11\|22)_{CC}$	1.35	7.38	ethylene
	1.39	7.30	Bz, Py, Pz, Pm
	1.46	7.16	cB, tB
	2.41	5.46	Bz, Py, Pz, Pm, T
	2.48	5.35	cB, tB
	2.78	4.90	Bz, Py, Pz, Pm
	2.97	4.65	cB
	3.72	3.75	tB
$(11\|11)_{NN}$	0.00	12.27	Py, Pz, Pm, T
$(11\|22)_{NN}$	1.36	8.00	none
	2.36	5.72	Pm, T
	2.75	5.03	Pz
$(11\|22)_{CN}$	1.36	7.68	Py, Pz, Pm, T
	2.38	5.60	Py, Pz, Pm
	2.76	4.97	Py, Pm, T
(N:CC)−(C:NN)	1.36	0.82[c]	Py, Pz, Pm, T
	2.37	0.14[c]	Py, Pz, Pm, T
	2.75	0.01[c]	Py, Pz, Pm, T

[a] Letters indicate the centers, C for carbon, N for nitrogen.
[b] See text for methods used for obtaining values, especially Sec. 4. $(11|11)_C = 11.22-0.69$, $(11|11)_N = 14.63-2.36$. For $r \gtrsim 2.8$A one uses Eq. (11), with $Z_C = 3.25$, $Z_N = 3.90$. For $r \lesssim 2.8$A, one obtains $(11|22)_{CC} = 0.2157r^2 - 2.625r + 10.53$, $(11|22)_{NN} = 0.3636r^2 - 3.634r + 12.27$, $(11|22)_{CN} = 0.2875r^2 - 3.123r + 11.40$. Also, from the average of Eqs. (14), $(N:CC)-(C:NN) = 0.2439r^2 - 1.585r + 2.525$.
[c] From Eq. (14). The values obtained by considering C^+-N^- are 0.818, 0.136, 0.015; by considering C^--N^+ are 0.824, 0.143, 0.008. The average is listed in the table and gives the formula in note *b*.
[d] The symbols refer to the molecule for which the integrals are employed in the present paper: cB = *cis*-butadiene, tB = *trans*-butadiene, Bz = benzene, Py = pyridine, Pz = pyrazine, Pm = pyrimidine, T = *s*-triazine.

The matrix elements for the determination of the energy then are, in the notation of I, since $\mathbf{H} = \mathbf{H}_{\text{core}}^{(1)} + \mathbf{H}_{\text{core}}^{(2)} + (e^2/r_{12})$,

$$\left.\begin{aligned} H_{aa} &= H_{bb} = \alpha_p + \alpha_q + (pp|qq) \\ H_{cc} &= 2\alpha_p + (pp|pp) \\ H_{dd} &= 2\alpha_q + (qq|qq) \end{aligned}\right\}. \tag{5}$$

Making use of Eq. (25) of I (that is, the conventional theory), one thus obtains

$$H_{cc} - H_{aa} = W_p - W_q + (p:qq) - (q:pp) + (pp|pp) - (pp|qq), \tag{6}$$

$$H_{dd} - H_{aa} = W_q - W_p + (q:pp) - (p:qq) + (qq|qq) - (pp|qq), \tag{7}$$

$$(1/2)(H_{cc} + H_{dd}) - H_{aa} = (1/2)[(pp|pp) + (qq|qq)] - (pp|qq). \tag{8}$$

For the case atoms p and q alike, these equations reduce to

$$H_{cc} - H_{aa} = (pp|pp) - (pp|qq) \quad [p \text{ and } q \text{ identical}]. \tag{9}$$

Equations (6) through (8) given energy differences between the hypothetical nonresonating structures described by Φ_a, Φ_b, Φ_c, Φ_d. Under the assumption of zero differential overlap, Eqs. (6) and (7) give the energy differences between the ionic forms $p^- - q^+$ and $p^+ - q^-$ and the purely covalent form $p = q$, respectively.

Equations (6) through (8) may serve as a basis for estimating Coulomb repulsion and penetration integrals as functions of the interatomic distance r, as follows. First, the atomic integrals $(pp|pp)$ are obtained from free atom valence state ionization potentials, $-W_p$, and electron affinities, A_p, through the relations

$$(pp|pp) = -W_p - A_p, \tag{10}$$

and are assumed constant. Secondly, the two-center electronic repulsion integrals $(pp|qq)$ are determined for $r \gtrsim 2.80$A from the uniformly charged sphere model formula.[11]

$$(pp|qq) = (7.1975/r)\{[1 + (1/2r)^2(R_p - R_q)^2]^{-\frac{1}{2}} + [1 + (1/2r)^2(R_p + R_q)^2]^{-\frac{1}{2}}\}\text{ev}, \tag{11}$$

in which

$$R_p = (4.597/Z_p) \times 10^{-8}\ \text{cm}, \tag{12}$$

where Z_p is Slater's effective nuclear charge; for $r \lesssim 2.80$A, the integrals $(pp|qq)$ are determined by extrapolations of Eq. (8) down to $r = 0$ by use of an equation of the form

$$ar + br^2 = (1/2)[(pp|pp) + (qq|qq)] - (pp|qq), \tag{13}$$

in which the constants a and b are obtained by fitting values calculated from Eq. (11) for $r = 2.80$A and $r = 3.70$A. Thirdly, the two-center penetration integrals $(p:qq)$ are assumed equal to zero for $r \gtrsim 2.80$A; for $r \lesssim 2.80$A, the differences $(q:pp) - (p:qq)$ are obtained by averaging extrapolations of Eqs. (6) and (7) down to $r = 0$ by use of equations of the form

$$\left.\begin{aligned} a'r + b'r^2 &= W_p - W_q + (p:qq) - (q:pp) + (pp|pp) - (pp|qq) \\ a''r + b''r^2 &= W_q - W_p + (q:pp) - (p:qq) + (qq|qq) - (pp|qq) \end{aligned}\right\}, \tag{14}$$

in which the constants a', a'', b', and b'' are again obtained by fitting values calculated for $r = 2.80$A and $r = 3.70$A. In many cases, only differences of penetration integrals are needed in calculations of spectroscopic intervals and intensities.

Table II gives values obtained in this way of integrals used in the calculations on hydrocarbons and heteromolecules to be described below. This method for obtaining the values is admittedly rough; a multitude of approximations is implied. Nevertheless, the theory gives the correct values to integrals of the type $(pp|pp)$ at $r = \infty$, and the behavior of the σ-electrons has been approximately taken into account without complicating the mathematics of the π-electron approximation. Furthermore, the values of the several quantities entering the formulas are now all consistent with the notion that the atoms in molecules behave like free atoms in their appropriate valence states.

As has already been indicated, the resonance integrals β will be evaluated empirically, from experimental results on molecules. With the other integrals adjusted semi-empirically, β turns out to have a dependence on

[11] R. G. Parr, J. Chem. Phys. 20, 1499 (1952).

distance of the sort required by the considerations of Sec. 3 above.

5. APPLICATION TO HYDROCARBONS

For the ground and excited states of ethylene and benzene the method of computation has already been outlined in I. Values for the MO repulsion integrals are obtained using Eqs. (33) and (35) of I and the AO repulsion integrals listed in Table II. Values of β are used which give the experimental value for the lowest singlet excited state in each case. The results thus obtained are summarized and compared with experiment in Tables III and IV. The agreement is good, especially with regard to the magnitude of the singlet-triplet splittings. And of the values of the resonance integrals,

$$\beta(\text{benzene}) = -2.39 \text{ ev},$$
$$\beta(\text{ethylene}) = -2.92 \text{ ev},$$

are satisfactory from the semi-empirical point of view.[12]

The treatment of butadiene differs from that of ethylene and benzene because the MO's in this case are not determined completely by symmetry. To avoid launching a complicated self-consistent field calculation, use will be made of the idea advanced in Sec. 3 of I, that any starting MO's will do, if configuration interaction is invoked. As starting MO's one may take, in order of increasing energy, the orthonormal (in zero differential overlap approximation) set

$$\left.\begin{aligned}\phi_1&=\tfrac{1}{2}(\chi_1+\chi_2+\chi_3+\chi_4)\\ \phi_2&=\tfrac{1}{2}(\chi_1+\chi_2-\chi_3-\chi_4)\\ \phi_3&=\tfrac{1}{2}(\chi_1-\chi_2-\chi_3+\chi_4)\\ \phi_4&=\tfrac{1}{2}(\chi_1-\chi_2+\chi_3-\chi_4)\end{aligned}\right\}, \tag{15}$$

where χ_p is a $2p\pi$ AO on carbon p, with carbons numbered consecutively along the (planar) chain. These orbitals are simple and convenient of manipulation; they have the requisite symmetries and are, in fact, fairly close to the best self-consistent field orbitals for the molecule.[13] Corrections to the energies of states described by various prescribed electron assignments of the MO's of Eq. (15) are obtainable through configuration interaction. Lower excited states will result from excitations of one electron from a lower to a higher MO; even when all the corresponding configurations are mixed the resultant corrections to the calculated energy spectrum are small.

The lowest configurational singlet state, of energy E_0 with wave function V_0, has two electrons in each of ϕ_1 and ϕ_2. A singlet excited state arises when an electron has been raised from ϕ_i to ϕ_j; let this be denoted by V_{ij}, with T_{ij} for the corresponding triplet. Computation of the energies then yields [Eq. (6) of I, but note that additional terms enter in cases such as V_{ij} in which the wave function is a combination of two or more determinants]

$$\left.\begin{aligned}E\begin{Bmatrix}V_{23}\\T_{23}\end{Bmatrix}-E_0&=I_3-I_2\pm K_{23}+K_{12}-K_{13}\\ E\begin{Bmatrix}V_{14}\\T_{14}\end{Bmatrix}-E_0&=I_4-I_1\pm K_{14}+K_{12}-K_{24}\\ E\begin{Bmatrix}V_{24}\\T_{24}\end{Bmatrix}-E_0&=I_4-I_2\pm K_{24}+K_{12}-K_{14}\\ E\begin{Bmatrix}V_{13}\\T_{13}\end{Bmatrix}-E_0&=I_3-I_1\pm K_{13}+K_{12}-K_{23}\end{aligned}\right\}, \tag{16}$$

where the upper and lower signs refer, respectively, to the singlet and triplet states indicated, the integrals

TABLE III. Electronic states of ethylene (ev).[a]

State	Calculated energy[b]	Observed energy
$N(^1A_{1g})$	0	0
$T(^3B_{1u})$	4.5	3.1—5.6
$V(^1B_{1u})$	7.6	7.6
$1(^1A_{1g})$	0.2	...[c]

[a] See explanatory notes to Table I.
[b] Calculated by the semi-empirical LCAO-MO theory of the present paper, using $\beta = -2.92$ ev and values of electronic repulsion integrals from Table II.
[c] "State 1" does not correspond to any actual molecular state.

TABLE IV. Electronic states of benzene (ev).[a]

State	Calculated energy[b]	Observed energy
$^1A_{1g}$	0	0
$^1B_{2u}$	4.9	4.9
$^1B_{1u}$	5.3	6.0
$^1E_{1u}$	7.0	7.0
$^3B_{2u}$	4.9	...
$^3B_{1u}$	4.0	3.8
$^3E_{1u}$	4.45	...

[a] See explanatory notes to Table I.
[b] Calculated by the semi-empirical LCAO-MO theory of the present paper, using $\beta = -2.39$ ev and values of electronic repulsion integrals from Table II.

[12] An interesting result of the use of the new semi-empirical values for Coulomb repulsion integrals is a marked reduction of the effects of configuration interaction. The lower value for integrals of the type $(pp|pp)$ decreases the energy of ionic forms and increases their contribution to the resonance hybrid. The MO method, without configuration interaction, postulates 50 percent ionic and 50 percent covalent character in the π-bond in ethylene. The wave functions for the ground state of ethylene, obtained with the inclusion of configuration interaction are

(a) $\Psi_N = 0.3185[\chi_1(1)\chi_1(2)+\chi_2(1)\chi_2(2)] + 0.6295[\chi_1(1)\chi_2(2)+\chi_2(1)\chi_1(2)]$,

corresponding to the use of integrals obtained by means of uniformly charged spheres (which are analogous to theoretical integrals), or

(b) $\Psi_N = 0.4300[\chi_1(1)\chi_1(2)+\chi_2(1)\chi_2(2)] + 0.5615[\chi_1(1)\chi_2(2)+\chi_2(1)\chi_1(2)]$,

corresponding to the use of the semi-empirical integrals of this paper. (a) Implies 21 percent ionic and 79 percent covalent character, whereas (b) gives 37 percent ionic and 63 percent covalent character. Thus the state expressed by (b) corresponds quite closely to the ground state configuration given by the MO method without configuration interaction.

[13] R. G. Parr and R. S. Mulliken, J. Chem. Phys. 18, 1338 (1950).

TABLE V. Butadiene matrix elements (ev).

Matrix element[a]	*trans*-butadiene	*cis*-butadiene
$E(V_{23})-E_0$	5.88	5.54
$E(V_{14})-E_0$	9.14	8.91
$E(V_{13})-E_0$	7.67	7.78
$E(V_{24})-E_0$	7.67	7.78
$E(T_{23})-E_0$	4.36	4.24
$E(T_{14})-E_0$	7.61	7.61
$E(T_{13})-E_0$	6.04	5.93
$E(T_{24})-E_0$	6.04	5.93
$(V_0 \mid V_{13})$	1.19	1.19
$(V_0 \mid V_{24})$	−1.19	−1.19
$(V_{13} \mid V_{24})$	−0.15	0.19
$(V_{23} \mid V_{14})$	−0.25	−0.37
$(T_{13} \mid T_{24})$	−1.78	−1.66
$(T_{23} \mid T_{14})$	−1.78	−1.66

[a] See text for definition of matrix elements.

are over the *molecular orbitals* of Eq. (15), and all integrals of the type J_{ij} cancel because of the simple form of these MO's.

The quantities appearing in Eqs. (16) may now be expressed in terms of integrals over *atomic orbitals*. The core energy terms, by Eqs. (17), (19), and (20) of I, are given by the formulas

$$\left.\begin{aligned} I_3-I_2&=-2\beta_{12}+\beta_{23}\\ I_4-I_1&=-2\beta_{12}-\beta_{23}\\ I_4-I_2=I_3-I_1&=-2\beta_{12}\end{aligned}\right\},\qquad(17)$$

provided nonneighbor resonance integrals are neglected. The electronic repulsion terms, by Eq. (30) of I, are given by the formulas

$$\left.\begin{aligned} K_{12}=K_{34}&=\tfrac{1}{8}[2(11|11)+2(11|22)\\ &\quad-(22|33)-2(11|33)-(11|44)]\\ K_{13}=K_{24}&=\tfrac{1}{8}[2(11|11)-2(11|22)\\ &\quad+(22|33)-2(11|33)+(11|44)]\\ K_{14}=K_{23}&=\tfrac{1}{8}[2(11|11)-2(11|22)\\ &\quad-(22|33)+2(11|33)-(11|44)]\end{aligned}\right\}.\qquad(18)$$

Here the integrals $(pp|qq)$ over AO's are the quantities listed in Table II.[14] The quantities β_{12} and β_{23} are merely the carbon-carbon resonance integral at distances 1.35A and 1.46A, respectively. The first of these may be taken as the already determined ethylene resonance integral

$$\beta_{12}=-2.92 \text{ ev}.$$

The second may be found by a suitable extrapolation based on the already determined ethylene ($r=1.35$A) and benzene ($r=1.39$A) resonance integrals. Thus the equation (r in A)

$$\beta(r)=-6442\exp(-5.6864r)\text{ ev},\qquad(19)$$

which fits the ethylene and benzene values, gives, for $r=1.46$A,

$$\beta_{23}=-1.68 \text{ ev}.$$

This value has been assumed for the present calculations.

To complete the calculation, one needs values for the appropriate interaction elements between the several configurations. The wave functions V_0, V_{24}, and V_{13}, all being of symmetry ${}^1A$, must be mixed, as must the functions V_{23} and V_{14} of symmetry ${}^1B$, the functions T_{23} and T_{14} of symmetry ${}^3B$, and the functions T_{13} and T_{24} of symmetry ${}^3A$. Letting

$$\int V_{ij}{}^*\mathbf{H}V_{kl}dv=(V_{ij}|V_{kl}),\qquad(20)$$

one finds the following expressions for the required matrix elements in terms of integrals over *molecular orbitals:*

$$\left.\begin{aligned} (V_0|V_{13})&=2^{\frac{1}{2}}[I_{13}+(11|13)\\ &\quad+2(22|13)-(12|23)]\\ (V_0|V_{24})&=2^{\frac{1}{2}}[I_{24}+(22|24)\\ &\quad+2(11|24)-(12|14)]\\ (V_{13}|V_{24})&=2(13|24)-(12|34),\\ (T_{13}|T_{24})&=-(12|34)\\ (V_{23}|V_{14})&=2(23|14)-(12|34),\\ (T_{23}|T_{14})&=-(12|34)\end{aligned}\right\}.\qquad(21)$$

The quantities appearing in these formulas may now be expressed in terms of integrals over *atomic orbitals*. The core energy terms, by Eqs. (17), (19), (20), and (25) of I, are given by the expressions

$$\left.\begin{aligned} I_{13}&=\tfrac{1}{2}[\alpha_1-\alpha_2-\beta_{23}]\approx\tfrac{1}{2}[(22|33)-(11|44)-\beta_{23}]\\ I_{24}&=\tfrac{1}{2}[\alpha_1-\alpha_2+\beta_{23}]\approx\tfrac{1}{2}[(22|33)-(11|44)+\beta_{23}]\end{aligned}\right\},\qquad(22)$$

where, in calculating $\alpha_1-\alpha_2$ by Eq. (25) of I, penetration integrals, since they are comparatively small and cancel each other to a large extent, have been neglected. Expansion of $(V_0|V_{13})$ and $(V_0|V_{24})$ in terms of β_{23} and AO repulsion integrals now results in complete

TABLE VI. Electronic states of butadiene (ev).

State		Calculated energy		Observed energy[a]
trans	*cis*	*trans*	*cis*	
${}^1A_g$	${}^1A_1$	0	0	0
${}^1B_u$	${}^1B_1$	6.21	5.91	6.0
${}^1A_g$	${}^1A_1$	7.87	8.29	7.2(?)
${}^1A_g$	${}^1A_1$	8.51	8.34	...
${}^1B_u$	${}^1B_1$	9.50	9.25	...
${}^3B_u$	${}^3B_1$	3.92	3.96	...
${}^3A_g$	${}^3A_1$	4.61	4.62	...
${}^3A_g$	${}^3A_1$	8.16	7.95	...
${}^3B_u$	${}^3B_1$	8.74	8.61	...

[a] The observed energies are probably for *trans*-butadiene, and are taken from R. S. Mulliken, Revs. Modern Phys. 14, 265 (1942), corrected for new values of fundamental constants.

[14] The geometries assumed for *cis*- and *trans*-butadiene are planar carbon skeletons, $C_1-C_2-C_3-C_4$, with $r_{12}=1.35$A, $r_{23}=1.46$A, and 1-2-3 and 2-3-4 angles=124°. See V. Schomaker and L. Pauling, J. Am. Chem. Soc. 61, 1769 (1939).

cancellation of the latter, giving

$$(V_0|V_{13}) = -(V_0|V_{24}) = -2^{-\frac{1}{2}}\beta_{23}. \tag{23}$$

There remain the electronic repulsion integrals in the last four of Eqs. (21); these are given by the formulas

$$\left.\begin{array}{l}(12|34)^{\mathrm{MO}} = K_{12}\\(13|24)^{\mathrm{MO}} = K_{13}\\(23|14)^{\mathrm{MO}} = K_{23}\end{array}\right\}, \tag{24}$$

where the superscripts have been added to indicate that MO's are involved in the various integrals.

Computation of the diagonal matrix elements of Eq. (16) and the off-diagonal matrix elements of Eq. (21), using the above formulas and the integral values given in Table II, yields the numerical results listed in Table V. Solutions of the secular equations for configuration interaction (of these there are one third-order and three second-order equations) then gives the final electronic states listed in Table VI. Agreement with the observed excitation energies, also given in the table, is good, although in this case the agreement, before configuration interaction is considered (Table V), is almost as good.

Any other unsaturated hydrocarbon containing no triple bonds could now be treated with the introduction of no further empirical data; the formulas for electronic repulsion integrals given in Table II and the formula for β, Eq. (19) being all that is required in the most general such case.

6. APPLICATION TO HETEROMOLECULES

As a test of the applicability of the theory to molecules containing other atoms than carbon in the conjugated system, the nitrogen-containing heterocyclic molecules, pyridine, pyrazine, pyrimidine, and *s*-triazine will now be treated. These molecules may be considered as derived from benzene by replacement of one or more CH groups by an N atom. Each N, like each CH, furnishes one π-electron to the conjugated system, so in the π-electron approximation each of these molecules presents a six-electron problem just as does benzene.

TABLE VII. Wave-function symmetries for benzene, pyridine, pyramidine, pyrazine, and *s*-triazine.[a]

Configuration	Combination[b]	Benzene	Pyridine	Pyrimidine	Pyrazine	*s*-Triazine
V_0		$^1A_{1g}$	$^1A_1$	$^1A_1$	$^1A_{1g}$	$^1A_1'$
V_{23}, V_{14}	−	$^1B_{2u}$	$^1B_1$	$^1B_1$	$^1B_{3u}$	$^1A_2'$
	+	$^1E_{1u}$	$^1B_1$	$^1B_1$	$^1B_{3u}$	$^1E'$
V_{13}, V_{24}	+	$^1B_{1u}$	$^1A_1$	$^1A_1$	$^1B_{2u}$	$^1A_1'$
	−	$^1E_{1u}$	$^1A_1$	$^1A_1$	$^1B_{2u}$	$^1E'$

[a] The table lists only singlet states. Symmetries of triplet wave functions are identical with symmetries of corresponding singlets.
[b] Combination + denotes a wave function of the type $\Psi = \sin\theta V_{ij} + \cos\theta V_{kl}$, − denotes one of the type $\Psi = \sin\theta V_{ij} - \cos\theta V_{kl}$, where $0 \leqslant \theta \leqslant \pi/2$.

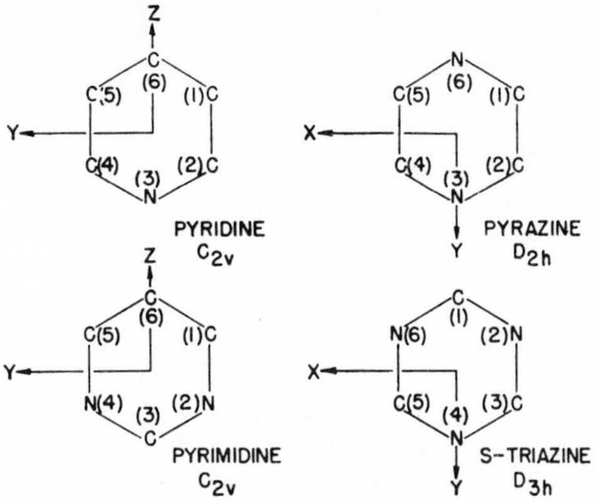

FIG. 1. Heterocyclic molecules.

The symmetries of these molecules (all planar) and the numbering employed for the atoms are shown in Fig. 1. For simplicity and the lack of more precise information, interatomic distances in all molecules will be taken as follows: nearest C−C distance, 1.39A (the benzene value); nearest C−N distance, 1.36A; nonneighbor C−C distances, 2.41 and 2.78A; nonneighbor C−N distances, 2.38 and 2.76A; nonneighbor N−N distances, 2.36 and 2.75A.[15]

The similarity of these molecules to benzene makes benzene MO's natural and convenient starting MO's. Real LCAO coefficients are preferable, so one takes the orthonormal (in zero differential overlap approximation) set, in order of increasing energy,

$$\left.\begin{array}{l}
\phi_0 = \dfrac{1}{6^{\frac{1}{2}}}(\chi_1+\chi_2+\chi_3+\chi_4+\chi_5+\chi_6)\\[2ex]
\phi_1 = \dfrac{1}{12^{\frac{1}{2}}}(\chi_1-\chi_2-2\chi_3-\chi_4+\chi_5+2\chi_6)\\[2ex]
\phi_2 = \dfrac{1}{4^{\frac{1}{2}}}(\chi_1+\chi_2-\chi_4-\chi_5)\\[2ex]
\phi_3 = \dfrac{1}{12^{\frac{1}{2}}}(\chi_1+\chi_2-2\chi_3+\chi_4+\chi_5-2\chi_6)\\[2ex]
\phi_4 = \dfrac{1}{4^{\frac{1}{2}}}(\chi_1-\chi_2+\chi_4-\chi_5)\\[2ex]
\phi_5 = \dfrac{1}{6^{\frac{1}{2}}}(\chi_1-\chi_2+\chi_3-\chi_4+\chi_5-\chi_6)
\end{array}\right\}, \tag{25}$$

where the numbering of the AO's follow the numbering of the atoms in Fig. 1.

[15] Nearest neighbor distances are average distances obtained by V. Schomaker and L. Pauling, reference 14. Nonneighbor distances are estimated as follows: for N−N: $\sqrt{3}(1.36)A$, and $(1.36+1.39)A$; for C−N: $\frac{1}{2}\sqrt{3}(1.36+1.39)A$, and $(\frac{1}{2}\times 1.36+\frac{3}{2}\times 1.39)A$.

TABLE VIII. Energy formulas for benzene and *s*-triazine.[a, b]

Benzene quantity	*s*-Triazine quantity	$-2\beta_{12}$	$\frac{1}{6}(11\|11)$	$\frac{1}{6}(22\|22)$	$\frac{1}{6}(11\|22)$	$\frac{1}{6}(11\|33)$	$\frac{1}{6}(22\|44)$	$\frac{1}{6}(11\|44)$
$E(^1B_{2u})-E_N$	$E(^1A_2')-E_N$	1	0	0	1	$-3/2$	$-3/2$	2
$E(^1B_{1u})-E_N$	$E(^1A_1')-E_N$	1	1	1	-5	7/2	7/2	-4
$E(^1E_{1u})-E_N$	$E(^1E_1')-E_N$	1	1/2	1/2	4	-2	-2	-1
$E(^3B_{2u})-E_N$	$E(^3A_2')-E_N$	1	0	0	1	$-3/2$	$-3/2$	2
$E(^3B_{1u})-E_N$	$E(^3A_1')-E_N$	1	-1	-1	3	$-1/2$	$-1/2$	0
$E(^3E_{1u})-E_N$	$E(^3E_1')-E_N$	1	$-1/2$	$-1/2$	2	-1	-1	1

[a] The numbers in a given row of the table give the coefficients of the indicated atomic orbital integrals in the formula for the energy quantity listed in the first column. E_N is the ground-state energy. See text for notation for other energy states and atomic orbital integrals; see Fig. 1 for the numbering of atoms. Note that, in deriving the table, nonneighbor resonance integrals have been neglected and the zero differential overlap approximation employed.
[b] For benzene, $(11|11)=(22|22)$, $(11|33)=(22|44)$.

In benzene, the lower excited states arise through the promotion of an electron from one of the ground-state filled MO's ϕ_1 or ϕ_2 (ϕ_0 is also filled) to one of the excited MO's ϕ_3 or ϕ_4. The core energies of the resultant eight states, four singlets and four triplets, are the same. Their total π-electron energies are, however, split by (a) electronic interaction and (b) configuration interaction among themselves. The situation in the present heterocyclic molecules may be regarded as essentially equivalent. The core energies of the eight excited states are no longer necessarily the same, but the splittings (a) and (b) are formally just as before.

The symmetry properties for the ground and the eight excited states for the several molecules are summarized in Table VII. These symmetries are such that the configurational interaction among the eight excited states (interaction with the ground state, which is possible in three cases, is neglected) reduces to interaction within four pairs: V_{23}, V_{14}; V_{13}, V_{24}; T_{23}, T_{14}; T_{13}, T_{24}. The interactions in the cases of benzene and *s*-triazine can be handled by group theory and the final wave functions written down; computation of the energies of the states by the methods already described is then straightforward. The final energy formulas in terms of integrals over atomic orbitals are given in Table VIII. For the other three molecules four quadratic secular equations must be solved numerically; formulas for the necessary matrix elements are given in Tables IX, X, and XI.

The intensities of transitions from ground to excited states may be calculated by the methods summarized by Mulliken and Rieke,[16] simplified by the neglect of differential overlap. For transitions between nondegenerate states described by wave functions Ψ_k and Ψ_l, the formula for the oscillator strength f is

$$f=1.085\times10^{11}\omega\sum_{i=x,y,z}Q_i^2, \tag{26}$$

where ω is the frequency of the transition in cm^{-1} and

$$Q_i=\int\Psi_k{}^*\bar{\imath}\Psi_l dv(i=x,\,y,\,z), \tag{27}$$

where $\bar{\imath}$ is the algebraic sum of the i's for the several electrons. Now, the wave function for the lowest excited singlet state of each of the molecules here being considered has the form

$$\Psi_l=(\sin\theta)V_{23}-(\cos\theta)V_{14},\quad 0\leqslant\theta\leqslant\pi/2. \tag{28}$$

Accordingly, for the transition from the ground state V_0, which has the configuration $\phi_0{}^2\phi_1{}^2\phi_2{}^2$, to the lowest

TABLE IX. Energy formulas for pyridine.[a]

Quantity[b,c]	(1/72)(11|11)	(1/72)(33|33)	(1/72)(11|22)	(1/72)(22|33)	(1/72)(11|55)	(1/72)(11|33)	(1/72)(11|44)	(1/72)(33|66)
$E(V_{14})-E_N-\Delta I_{1,4}$	18	-12	50	-20	-6	-36	46	-40
$E(V_{23})-E_N-\Delta I_{2,3}$	-6	12	2	28	-54	12	-50	56
$E(V_{13})-E_N-\Delta I_{1,3}$	10	8	-14	8	10	8	2	-32
$E(V_{24})-E_N-\Delta I_{2,4}$	18	0	-6	0	18	0	-30	0
$E(T_{14})-E_N-\Delta I_{1,4}$	6	-12	38	-20	6	-36	58	-40
$E(T_{23})-E_N-\Delta I_{2,3}$	-18	12	-10	28	-42	12	-38	56
$E(T_{13})-E_N-\Delta I_{1,3}$	-10	-8	6	24	-10	-8	6	0
$E(T_{24})-E_N-\Delta I_{2,4}$	-18	0	30	0	-18	0	6	0
$(V_{14}\|V_{23})$	6	0	18	0	-6	0	-18	0
$(V_{13}\|V_{24})$	6	0	-30	-24	42	24	-18	0
$(T_{14}\|T_{23})$, $(T_{13}\|T_{24})$	-6	0	6	0	6	0	-6	0

[a] See Table VIII, note a.
[b] Here $\Delta I_{1,4}\equiv I_4-I_3=\frac{1}{3}(\alpha_1+\alpha_2-\alpha_3-\alpha_6)-(4/3)\beta_{12}-\frac{2}{3}\beta_{23}$
$\Delta I_{2,3}\equiv I_3-I_2=-\frac{1}{3}(\alpha_1+\alpha_2-\alpha_3-\alpha_6)-(4/3)\beta_{12}-\frac{2}{3}\beta_{23}$
$\Delta I_{1,3}\equiv I_3-I_1=-\frac{2}{3}\beta_{12}-(4/3)\beta_{23}$
$\Delta I_{2,4}\equiv I_4-I_2=-2\beta_{12}$
$(\alpha_1+\alpha_2-\alpha_3-\alpha_6)=(W_1-W_3)-[(11|22)-(22|33)]-[(11/55)-(11|33)]-2[(11|44)-(33|66)]-[(3:22)-(2:33)]-[(3:11)-(1:33)]-[(6:33)-(3:66)]$.
[c] In computing the terms ΔI (note b), use has been made of approximations of the type: $(2:33)\approx(2:11)$.

[16] R. S. Mulliken and C. A. Rieke, Repts. Prog. Phys. **8**, 231 (1941).

TABLE X. Energy formulas for pyrazine.[a]

Quantity[b,c]	(1/36)(11|11)	(1/36)(33|33)	(1/36)(11|22)	(1/36)(22|33)	(1/36)(11|55)	(1/36)(11|33)	(1/36)(11|44)	(1/36)(33|66)
$E(V_{14})-E_N-\Delta I_{1,4}$	15	−12	35	−20	15	−36	23	−20
$E(V_{23})-E_N-\Delta I_{2,3}$	−9	12	−13	28	−33	12	−25	28
$E(V_{13})-E_N-\Delta I_{1,3}$	1	8	−11	8	1	8	1	−16
$E(V_{24})-E_N-\Delta I_{2,4}$	9	0	−3	0	9	0	−15	0
$E(T_{14})-E_N-\Delta I_{1,4}$	9	−12	29	−20	21	−36	29	−20
$E(T_{23})-E_N-\Delta I_{2,3}$	−15	12	−19	28	−27	12	−19	28
$E(T_{13})-E_N-\Delta I_{1,3}$	−1	−8	−9	24	−1	−8	3	0
$E(T_{24})-E_N-\Delta I_{2,4}$	−9	0	15	0	−9	0	3	0
$(V_{14}\|V_{23})$	3	0	9	0	−3	0	−9	0
$(V_{13}\|V_{24})$	3	0	−3	−24	9	24	−9	0
$(T_{14}\|T_3)$, $(T_{13}\|T_{24})$	−3	0	3	0	3	0	−3	0

[a] See Table VIII, note a.
[b] Here $\Delta I_{1,4}=\frac{2}{3}(\alpha_1-\alpha_3)-\frac{2}{3}\beta_{12}-(4/3)\beta_{23}$
$\Delta I_{2,3}=-\frac{2}{3}(\alpha_1-\alpha_3)-\frac{2}{3}\beta_{12}-(4/3)\beta_{23}$
$\Delta I_{1,3}=\frac{2}{3}\beta_{12}-(8/3)\beta_{23}$
$\Delta I_{2,4}=-2\beta_{12}$
$(\alpha_1-\alpha_3)=(W_1-W_3)-[(11|22)-(22|33)]-[(11|55)-(11|33)]-[(11|44)-(33|66)]-[(3:22)-(2:33)]-[(3:11)-(1:33)]-[(1:44)-(3:66)]$.
[c] In computing the terms ΔI (note b), use has been made of approximations of the type: $(2:33)\approx(2:11)$.

singlet excited state one has

$$Q_i=\sqrt{2}\left[\sin\theta\int\phi_3 i\phi_2 dv-\cos\theta\int\phi_4 i\phi_1 dv\right], \tag{29}$$

where i refers to, and the integrations are over the coordinates of, a single electron. But, assuming for all of the molecules the same distance between next nearest neighbors 2.4A, and invoking the assumption of zero differential overlap,[16]

$$\int\phi_3 i\phi_2 dv=\int\phi_4 i\phi_1 dv=0,$$

except

$$\int\phi_3 y\phi_2 dv=\int\phi_4 y\phi_1 dv=\frac{2.4}{2\sqrt{3}}A=0.693\times10^{-8}\text{ cm}$$

for pyridine and pyrimidine and

$$\int\phi_3 x\phi_2 dv=\int\phi_4 x\phi_1 dv=0.693\times10^{-8}\text{ cm} \tag{30}$$

for pyrazine.

Hence

$$Q_s=0, \tag{31}$$

except

$$Q_y^{\text{pryidine}}=Q_x^{\text{pyrazine}}=Q_y^{\text{pyrimidine}}=0.980\times10^{-8}[\sin\theta-\cos\theta]\text{ cm}.$$

These results upon insertion in Eq. (26) will give final expressions for the oscillator strengths.

Table XII presents the results of calculations on these molecules using the integral values of Table II, the formulas of Tables VIII–XI and this section, the $\beta_{CC}=-2.390$ ev value obtained in the previous section, and $\beta_{CN}=-2.576$ ev. The latter value has been chosen to give agreement with Halverson and Hirt's estimated value for the lowest singlet transition of the experimentally unknown *s*-triazine.[17] Given in the table are computed and experimental[17–19] values for the positions and oscillator strengths of the lowest-lying singlet and triplet states of these molecules. The agreement between calculated and observed values is very good and could be improved still further by adjustment of the β_{CN} value employed.

TABLE XI. Energy formulas for pyrimidine.[a]

Quantity[b,c]	(1/72)(11|11)	(1/72)(22|22)	(1/72)(11|66)	(1/72)(22|33)	(1/72)(11|33)	(1/72)(22|66)	(1/72)(22|44)	(1/72)(33|66)	(1/72)(11|44)
$E(V_{14})-E_N-\Delta I_{1,4}$	−9	15	−20	50	−21	−36	15	−40	46
$E(V_{23})-E_N-\Delta I_{2,3}$	15	−9	28	2	−21	12	−33	56	−50
$E(V_{13})-E_N-\Delta I_{1,3}$	17	1	8	−14	9	8	1	−32	2
$E(V_{24})-E_N-\Delta I_{2,4}$	9	9	0	−6	9	0	9	0	−30
$E(T_{14})-E_N-\Delta I_{1,4}$	−15	9	−20	38	−15	−36	21	−40	58
$E(T_{23})-E_N-\Delta I_{2,3}$	9	−15	28	−10	−15	12	−27	56	−38
$E(T_{13})-E_N-\Delta I_{1,3}$	−17	−1	24	6	−9	−8	−1	0	6
$E(T_{24})-E_N-\Delta I_{2,4}$	−9	−9	0	30	−9	0	−9	0	6
$(V_{14}\|V_{23})$	3	3	0	18	−3	0	−3	0	−18
$(V_{13}\|V_{24})$	3	3	−24	−30	33	24	9	0	−18
$(T_{14}\|T_{23})$, $(T_{13}\|T_{24})$	−3	−3	0	6	3	0	3	0	−6

[a] See Table VIII, note a.
[b] Here $\Delta I_{1,4}=\frac{1}{3}(\alpha_1+\alpha_2-\alpha_3-\alpha_6)-(4/3)\beta_{23}-\frac{2}{3}\beta_{16}$
$\Delta I_{2,3}=-\frac{1}{3}(\alpha_1+\alpha_2-\alpha_3-\alpha_6)-(4/3)\beta_{23}-\frac{2}{3}\beta_{16}$
$\Delta I_{1,3}=-\frac{2}{3}\beta_{23}-(4/3)\beta_{16}$
$\Delta I_{2,4}=-2\beta_{23}$
$(\alpha_3+\alpha_6-\alpha_1-\alpha_2)=(W_1-W_2)-[(11|66)-(11|22)]-[(22|66)-(22|44)]-2[(33|66)-(11|44)]-[(2:11)-(1:22)]-[(1:44)-(4:11)]-[(3:66)-(4:11)]$.
[c] In computing the terms ΔI (note b), use has been made of approximations of the type: $(1:22)\approx(1:66)$.

[17] F. Halverson and R. C. Hirt, J. Chem. Phys. **19**, 711 (1951).
[18] H. Shull, J. Chem. Phys. **17**, 295 (1949).
[19] Barany, Braude, and Pianka, J. Chem. Soc. **1949**, 1898.

TABLE XII. Lowest singlet and triplet excited electronic states of benzene, pyridine, pyrazine, pyrimidine, and *s*-triazine.

Molecule	State	Calculated energy (ev)	Observed energy (ev)	Calculated f	Observed f
pyrazine	$^1B_{3u}$	4.71	4.77[a]	0.121	0.130[d]
benzene	$^1B_{2u}$	4.90	4.90[a]	0	$\sim$0[a]
pyridine	$^1B_1$	4.90	4.95[a]	0.046	0.041[e]
pyrimidine	$^1B_1$	5.05	5.15[a]	0.038	...
s-triazine	$^1A_2'$	5.29	5.29[a]	0	($\sim$0)[a]
pyrazine	$^3B_{3u}$	3.85	3.35[b]	0	$\sim$0[b]
benzene	$^3B_{1u}$	4.01	3.65[c]	0	$\sim$0[c]
pyridine	$^3A_1$	4.08	...	0	...
pyrimidine	$^3A_1$	4.16	...	0	...
s-triazine	$^3A_1'$	4.26	...	0	...

[a] See reference 17, and references cited there. The various references differ as to the precise location of absorption maxima.
[b] Estimated, from a privately communicated pyrazine absorption spectrum by R. C. Hirt.
[c] Reference 18.
[d] f is estimated by assuming it proportional to the maximum extinction coefficient in hexane and determining the proportionality constant from pyridine data. $\epsilon_{max}=6350$ for pyrazine (reference 17), and $\epsilon_{max}=2000$ for pyridine (reference 19), both in hexane.
[e] H. P. Stephenson, presented at the Symposium on Molecular Structure and Spectroscopy, Ohio State University, June 9, 1952.

As indicated by the notes to Table XII, too much reliance should not be placed on the experimental values which are quoted for positions of absorption bands. There seems little doubt that the molecules absorb at increasing wavelengths in the order, *s*-triazine, pyrimidine, pyridine, benzene, and pyrazine, however. This is the order the theory predicts. The theory also indicates that the lowest triplets of these molecules should fall in the same order as the singlets; the observed triplets in benzene and pyrazine follow this rule. Calculated transition probabilities appear to be in excellent agreement with experimental values (here one should note that the calculation is absolute; no empirical correction factor has been employed). The theory thus fits thirteen experimental results or estimates with the use of only two empirical parameters (the CC and CN resonance integrals).

7. DISCUSSION

The flexibility of the theory that has been outlined and tested in these two papers is such that more experience must be acquired before a completely definitive recipe can be given for its application. In this very flexibility there appears to lie much power, however.

Among the fundamental questions that still should be asked, the following may be mentioned: How much configuration interaction should be included? Can resonance integrals be computed theoretically? Can nonneighbor resonance integrals be neglected? Can resonance integrals be carried from molecule to molecule? Can the theory be applied to molecules containing triple bonds? Can the theory be adapted to σ-bonds? Can a rationalization of the empirical $(pp|qq)$ and $(p:qq)$ *versus* distance curves be made in terms of Slater effective charges which vary with distance? Tentatively, the authors would answer: Some, but not very much, configuration interaction should be included. Resonance integrals can be estimated, sometimes computed, theoretically (a theoretical calculation of the resonance integrals for ethylene and benzene gives -2.80 and -2.48 ev, which compare favorably with the empirical values of -2.92 and -2.39 ev). Nonneighbor resonance integrals, even though perhaps in principle important, may usually be neglected, because what small effects they have can be taken into account elsewhere. Resonance integrals can be carried over from molecule to molecule as a first approximation, but small adjustments should be expected. Application of the theory to molecules containing triple bonds will be straightforward. Adaptation to σ-bonds is also feasible (calculations on the hydrogen molecule using the zero differential overlap approximation give quite startling results). And finally, rationalizations of the electronic repulsion integral and penetration integral curves are possible in terms of varying effective charges, but such rationalizations may be dangerous.

The authors are pleased to thank Professor R. S. Mulliken, Professor C. C. J. Roothaan, Dr. K. Rüdenberg, and Dr. F. G. Fumi for helpful discussions.

ELECTRON INTERACTION IN UNSATURATED HYDROCARBONS

By J. A. Pople
Dept. of Theoretical Chemistry, University of Cambridge

Received 24*th July*, 1953

An approximate form of the molecular orbital theory of unsaturated hydrocarbon molecules in their ground states is developed. The molecular orbital equations rigorously derived from the correct many-electron Hamiltonian are simplified by a series of systematic approximations and reduce to equations comparable with those used in the semi-empirical method based on an incompletely defined one-electron Hamiltonian. The two sets of equations differ, however, in that those of this paper include certain important terms representing electronic interaction. The theory is used to discuss the resonance energies, ionization potentials, charge densities, bond orders and bond lengths of some simple hydrocarbons. The electron interaction terms introduced in the theory are shown to play an important part in determining the ionization potentials. It is also shown that the uniform charge density theorem, proved by Coulson and Rushbrooke [1] for the simpler theory, holds also for the self-consistent orbitals derived by the method of this paper.

1. Introduction.—One of the methods most extensively used in the quantum-mechanical study of the mobile electrons of conjugated molecules is the semi-empirical molecular orbital theory developed by Hückel,[2] Lennard-Jones,[3] Coulson and Longuet-Higgins [4] and others. According to this well-known theory, the mobile electrons can be treated as occupying a set of delocalized molecular orbitals (not more than two electrons in each), these orbitals being eigenfunctions of a one-electron Hamiltonian representing the kinetic energy, the field of the nuclei and the smoothed-out distribution of the other electrons. The total energy of the mobile electrons is then obtained by adding together the energies of the individual electrons. By approximating the orbitals as linear combinations of atomic orbitals centred on the various atoms and estimating certain integrals empirically, the theory can be put in a simple form enabling it to be applied to a wide range of molecules.

Although it has the merit of great simplicity, the Hückel procedure has serious defects. These are connected with the difficulty of giving a precise definition of the one-electron Hamiltonian. Strictly the problem should be formulated in terms of the complete many-electron Hamiltonian in which the interelectronic repulsions are included explicitly. If the one-electron Hamiltonian is supposed to include a term allowing for the screening effect of other electrons, then interelectronic interactions will be counted twice in the total energy. These considerations have led some authors to develop more precise theories of mobile electrons based on the correct many electron Hamiltonian. Hall [5] has proposed an alternative interpretation of the empirical theory in which the parameters are closely related to the ionization potentials of an excited state in which all mobile electrons have the same spin. Most of the more refined theories, however, have been of a non-empirical nature, obtaining energy levels and other molecular properties by direct calculation from approximate analytical forms for the wave function. The molecular orbital calculations of Goeppert-Mayer and Sklar [6] on benzene and of Parr and Mulliken [7] on butadiene are based on a single configuration wave-function, that is, a single way of allocating electrons to orbitals. Other detailed calculations [8, 9] indicate, however, that different configurations cannot always be treated independently and that the interaction of configurations often leads to important changes in molecular properties, notably excitation levels. The significance of configuration interaction in conjugated molecules has been fully discussed by Coulson, Craig and Jacobs.[10]

The aim of this paper is to present a simplified molecular orbital theory of the ground states of hydrocarbons which is correctly based on the many-electron Hamiltonian but which is simple enough to be directly comparable with the Hückel procedure. The method is based on a single configuration wave function, the molecular orbitals being chosen as the best possible linear combinations of given atomic orbitals. The method starts from the self-consistent orbital equations given by Lennard-Jones,[11] Hall [12] and Roothaan.[13] These are simplified by systematic approximation of the integrals and reduce to expressions involving empirical parameters analogous to those of the Hückel theory, together with certain electron interaction terms given directly in terms of the geometrical dimensions of the molecule. The resulting wave functions can then be used in a discussion of resonance energies, ionization potentials and bond orders of some simple hydrocarbons.

The interaction of configurations can be included at a similar level of approximation.[14] This must eventually lead to an improved wave function, but in view of the difficulty of enumerating all configurations and the even greater difficulty of deciding which will interact most strongly, it is important to find out just how successful a single-determinant function can be. Only such a simple wave function will be considered in this paper.

2. THE DETERMINATION OF SELF-CONSISTENT MOLECULAR ORBITALS FOR CONJUGATED MOLECULES.—According to the molecular orbital theory, the wave function for the ground state of a molecule with $2N$ electrons is obtained by allocating one electron of each spin to each of a set of space orbitals $\psi_1 \ldots \psi_N$ and combining the products into a complete determinantal wave function

$$\Psi = \det\{\psi_1(1)\alpha(1) \ldots \psi_N(N)\alpha(N)\psi_1(N+1)\beta(N+1) \ldots \psi_N(2N)\beta(2N)\}. \quad (2.1)$$

Explicit equations for the functions ψ_i can be derived from the variational principle.[11]

If it is not practicable to use the best possible ψ_i, it is usual to use some approximate analytical forms containing adjustable parameters, these parameters being determined by the variational principle. The most convenient way of doing this is by writing the molecular orbitals as a linear combination of given atomic orbitals ϕ_μ centred on the various atoms of the molecule

$$\psi_i = \sum_\mu x_{i\mu}\phi_\mu. \quad (2.2)$$

Throughout this paper, Greek suffixes will be used for atomic orbitals and italics for molecular orbitals. The equations for the coefficients $x_{i\mu}$ are

$$\sum_\nu F_{\mu\nu}x_{i\nu} = E_i \sum_\nu S_{\mu\nu}x_{i\nu}, \quad (2.3)$$

where

$$F_{\mu\nu} = H_{\mu\nu} + \sum_{\lambda\sigma} P_{\lambda\sigma}\{(\mu\lambda \mid G \mid \nu\sigma) - \tfrac{1}{2}(\mu\lambda \mid G \mid \sigma\nu)\}, \quad (2.4)$$

$$H_{\mu\nu} = \int \bar{\phi}_\mu\{-\tfrac{1}{2}\nabla^2 - \sum_\alpha V_\alpha(\mathbf{r})\}\phi_\nu d\mathbf{r}, \quad (2.5)$$

$$(\mu\lambda \mid G \mid \nu\sigma) = \iint \bar{\phi}_\mu(1)\bar{\phi}_\lambda(2)(1/r_{12})\phi_\nu(1)\phi_\sigma(2)d\mathbf{r}_1 d\mathbf{r}_2, \quad (2.6)$$

$$S_{\mu\nu} = \int \bar{\phi}_\mu\phi_\nu d\mathbf{r}, \quad (2.7)$$

$$P_{\lambda\sigma} = 2\sum_i \bar{x}_{i\lambda}x_{i\sigma}. \quad (2.8)$$

In these expressions $V_\alpha(\mathbf{r})$ is the potential due to nucleus α, so that $H_{\mu\nu}$ is the matrix element of the one-electron Hamiltonian for motion in the field of the bare nuclei. The E_i in (2.3) are the N lowest roots of the secular equation

$$| F_{\mu\nu} - ES_{\mu\nu} | = 0, \tag{2.9}$$

and are the molecular orbital theory approximations to the ionization potentials.[15] Equations of this type for the coefficients $x_{i\mu}$ were given by Hall [12] and Roothaan.[13] It should be noted that they are not linear since $F_{\mu\nu}$ itself depends on $x_{i\mu}$. The expression for the total electronic energy using these orbitals can be written

$$\mathscr{E} = \tfrac{1}{2} \sum_{\mu\nu} P_{\mu\nu}(H_{\mu\nu} + F_{\mu\nu}). \tag{2.10}$$

This follows from the energy expression corresponding to the wave function (2.1) [16] if the molecular orbitals are written in the LCAO form (2.2). The total energy of the molecule is obtained by adding the nuclear repulsion terms to (2.10).

Strictly the above equations should be applied to all electrons in a molecule including inner shells. For conjugated molecules with a planar nuclear framework, however, it is possible to separate the orbitals into non-combining classes π and σ according as they have or have not a node in the nuclear plane. Since a complete treatment would be very difficult, it is usual to suppose that the effect of the σ-electrons on the π-structure can be represented by a rigid non-polarizable core whose potential can then be included in the $H_{\mu\nu}$ matrix elements. The only investigation of the effect of the details of π—σ interaction [17] indicates that this approximation is reasonable, at least for the ground state. If only one atomic orbital of π symmetry is used for each atom ($2p\pi$) then eqn. (2.3) lead to a set of self-consistent coefficients for the LCAO orbitals. The theory in this form has been applied to butadiene by Parr and Mulliken [7] and by Coulson and Jacobs.[9] As outlined in the introduction, we shall endeavour to simplify these equations by a series of approximations so that the method becomes comparable with the Hückel procedure but yet retains the important qualitative features of electron interaction. These approximations are as follows.

A. The σ-system is treated as a non-polarizable core and its effect included in the $H_{\mu\nu}$ terms as described above. This means that $V_\alpha(\mathbf{r})$ now represents the potential due to the nuclear charge and all the σ-electrons associated with atom α.

B. The overlap integral $S_{\mu\nu}$ will be neglected unless $\mu = \nu$, in which case it is unity. This approximation is not quantitatively accurate, but it simplifies the treatment considerably and is unlikely to alter the general features of the electronic distribution. The condition that the molecular orbitals ψ_i are normalized now becomes

$$\sum \bar{x}_{i\mu} x_{i\mu} = 1. \tag{2.11}$$

C. All two-electron integrals which depend on the overlapping of charge distributions of different orbitals are neglected. This means that $(\mu\lambda \,|\, G \,|\, \nu\sigma)$ is neglected unless $\mu = \nu$ and $\lambda = \sigma$. Approximations B and C are really consistent with one another for if the magnitude $S_{\mu\nu}$ of the charge distribution $\bar{\phi}_\mu \phi_\nu$ is neglected, its interaction with other distributions should also be left out of account. In fact, if approximation B were made without approximation C it would be equivalent to counting the interactions of more electrons than are actually present. With these simplifications the $F_{\mu\nu}$ can be written

$$F_{\mu\mu} = H_{\mu\mu} + \tfrac{1}{2} P_{\mu\mu}(\mu\mu \,|\, G \,|\, \mu\mu) + \sum_{\sigma(\neq\mu)} P_{\sigma\sigma}(\mu\sigma \,|\, G \,|\, \mu\sigma), \tag{2.12}$$

$$F_{\mu\nu} = H_{\mu\nu} - \tfrac{1}{2} P_{\mu\nu}(\mu\nu \,|\, G \,|\, \mu\nu), \qquad (\mu \neq \nu). \tag{2.13}$$

The $H_{\mu\mu}$ in (2.12) are the diagonal matrix elements of the core Hamiltonian for all atoms and will therefore include the interaction with distant cores. These distant interactions will not be small (in fact their sum diverges for a long polyene) but they will be largely cancelled by corresponding terms in the last part of (2.12). In order to replace $H_{\mu\mu}$ by something which may reasonably be taken as constant from molecule to molecule, it is convenient to rearrange (2.12). The matrix element $H_{\mu\mu}$ is

$$H_{\mu\mu} = (\mu \,|\, -\tfrac{1}{2}\nabla^2 - V_\mu \,|\, \mu) - \sum_{\alpha(\neq\mu)} (\mu \,|\, V_\alpha \,|\, \mu) = U_{\mu\mu} - \sum_{\alpha(\neq\mu)} (\mu \,|\, V_\alpha \,|\, \mu), \quad (2.14)$$

where $U_{\mu\mu}$ is now the diagonal matrix element of ϕ_μ with respect to the one-electron Hamiltonian containing the kinetic energy and the interaction with the core of atom μ. $U_{\mu\mu}$ may reasonably be taken as the same for all hydrocarbons.

D. To allow some of the cancelling mentioned above to be carried out explicitly we now replace all electron interaction integrals $(\mu\nu \,|\, G \,|\, \mu\nu)$ between electrons on different centres and also $(\mu \,|\, V_\alpha \,|\, \mu)$, $(\alpha \neq \mu)$, by the interaction energy of point charges at the nuclear centres.

$$(\mu\nu \,|\, G \,|\, \mu\nu) = R_{\mu\nu}^{-1}, \quad (2.15)$$

$$(\mu \,|\, V_\alpha \,|\, \mu) = - Z_\alpha R_{\mu\alpha}^{-1}, \quad (2.16)$$

where Z_α is the " effective charge " of the σ-core of atom α. For hydrocarbons $Z_\alpha = 1$ but in the extension of the theory to systems where one atom contributes two electrons to the π-system, it may take other values.

This set of approximations is similar to those suggested by Pariser and Parr.[14] These authors neglect all but the Coulomb-type two-electron integrals $(\mu\nu \,|\, G \,|\, \mu\nu)$ and approximate these by the interaction of suitably chosen uniformly charged spheres.

Using (2.15) and (2.16), eqn. (2.12) and (2.13) now reduce to

$$F_{\mu\mu} = U_{\mu\mu} + \tfrac{1}{2}P_{\mu\mu}(\mu\mu \,|\, G \,|\, \mu\mu) + \sum_{\sigma(\neq\mu)} (P_{\sigma\sigma} - Z_\sigma) R_{\mu\sigma}^{-1}, \quad (2.17)$$

$$F_{\mu\nu} = H_{\mu\nu} - \tfrac{1}{2}P_{\mu\nu}R_{\mu\nu}^{-1}, \qquad (\mu \neq \nu). \quad (2.18)$$

$(P_{\sigma\sigma} - Z_\sigma)$ may be described as the resultant electronic charge on atom σ. $H_{\mu\nu}$ $(\mu \neq \nu)$ is now a non-diagonal matrix element representing the fact that electrons can move in levels of lower energy by virtue of being in the field of two σ-cores simultaneously. This is the primary cause of chemical binding. If all the terms in (2.17) and (2.18) except $H_{\mu\mu}$ and $H_{\mu\nu}$ for nearest neighbours are omitted, the method reduces to the Hückel theory where the parameters are usually called α and β. In the present work we shall continue to treat $U_{\mu\mu}$ and $H_{\mu\nu}$ as empirical parameters, neglecting $H_{\mu\nu}$ for all but nearest neighbours, but shall also include the electron interaction terms in the forms given in (2.17) and (2.18).

To get an expression for the total π-electron energy, it is convenient to add to (2.10) an " effective nuclear interaction " term

$$\mathscr{E}' = \sum_{\mu<\nu} Z_\mu Z_\nu R_{\mu\nu}^{-1}. \quad (2.19)$$

This is really part of the energy of the σ-core itself, but it is convenient to include it as it leads to a simply additive expression. All expressions for resonance energies, ionization potentials and excitation energies, however, occur as the difference of two quantities both including $\mathscr{E}'$. The total π-electron energy is then given by

$$\begin{aligned}\mathscr{E}_\pi &= \mathscr{E}' + \tfrac{1}{2}\sum_{\mu\nu} P_{\mu\nu}(H_{\mu\nu} + F_{\mu\nu}) \\ &= \sum_{\mu} P_{\mu\mu}[U_{\mu\mu} + \tfrac{1}{4}P_{\mu\mu}(\mu\mu \,|\, G \,|\, \mu\mu)] + 2\sum_{\mu<\nu} P_{\mu\nu}H_{\mu\nu} \\ &\quad + \sum_{\mu<\nu} (P_{\mu\mu} - Z_\mu)(P_{\nu\nu} - Z_\nu)R_{\mu\nu}^{-1} - \tfrac{1}{2}\sum_{\mu<\nu} P_{\mu\nu}^2 R_{\mu\nu}^{-1}. \end{aligned} \quad (2.20)$$

3. RESONANCE ENERGIES AND IONIZATION POTENTIALS OF CONJUGATED HYDROCARBONS.—The expression (2.20) for the π-electron energy can be used for comparing the resonance or delocalization energies of simple conjugated hydrocarbons. In the simplest molecules (ethylene, benzene) the coefficients $x_{i\mu}$ are determined by symmetry and will be the same in this theory as in the Hückel method. For ethylene, which is treated as the standard double bond, there is only one occupied π-molecular orbital $(\phi_1 + \phi_2)/\sqrt{2}$ so that

$$P_{11} = P_{12} = P_{22} = Z_1 = Z_2 = 1. \tag{3.1}$$

The expression $\mathscr{E}_\pi$ then becomes

$$\mathscr{E}_\pi \text{ (ethylene)} = 2U_{11} + \tfrac{1}{2}(11 \mid G \mid 11) + 2H_{12} - \tfrac{1}{2}R_{12}^{-1}. \tag{3.2}$$

For benzene the orbitals are

$$\left.\begin{aligned} \psi_1 &= (\phi_1 + \phi_2 + \phi_3 + \phi_4 + \phi_5 + \phi_6)/\sqrt{6}, \\ \psi_2 &= (\phi_2 + \phi_3 - \phi_5 - \phi_6)/\sqrt{2}, \\ \psi_3 &= (\phi_1 + \tfrac{1}{2}\phi_2 - \tfrac{1}{2}\phi_3 - \phi_4 - \tfrac{1}{2}\phi_5 + \tfrac{1}{2}\phi_6)/\sqrt{3}, \end{aligned}\right\} \tag{3.3}$$

the atoms being numbered cyclically round the ring. It then follows that

$$P_{11} = 1; \quad P_{12} = \tfrac{2}{3}, \quad P_{13} = 0, \quad P_{14} = -\tfrac{1}{3}, \tag{3.4}$$

and $$\mathscr{E}_\pi \text{ (benzene)} = 6U_{11} + \tfrac{3}{2}(11 \mid G \mid 11) + 8H_{12} - \tfrac{4}{3}R_{12}^{-1} - \tfrac{1}{6}R_{14}^{-1}. \tag{3.5}$$

If it is now assumed that U_{11} may be taken as constant from molecule to molecule and if the bond lengths are assumed the same, the resonance energy of benzene is

$$\mathscr{E}_\pi \text{ (benzene)} - 3\mathscr{E}_\pi \text{ (ethylene)} = 2H_{12} + \tfrac{1}{6}R_{12}^{-1} - \tfrac{1}{6}R_{14}^{-1} = 2H_{12} + \tfrac{1}{12}R_{12}^{-1}. \tag{3.6}$$

The simpler theory gives $2H_{12}$ (usually written 2β). Eqn. (3.6) indicates that the positive electron interaction energy in the benzene molecule is greater than in one of its Kekulé structures where the electrons are paired in localized bonds.

Following Lennard-Jones [3] and others, the resonance energy (3.6) has to be compared with the difference between the energy of benzene and of one of its Kekulé structures with bond lengths equal to those in benzene (frequently called the vertical resonance energy). An experimental value for this can be obtained by adding the thermochemical resonance energy to an estimate of the energy required to distort a Kekulé structure with normal single and double bond lengths into the corresponding structure with equal bond lengths. The best available estimate obtained in this way is 78·4 kcal/mole.[18] * As R_{12} is 1·39 Å or 2·63 atomic units, $\frac{1}{12}R_{12}^{-1}$ is 19·8 kcal/mole, so the empirical value H_{12} is $-$ 49·1 kcal/mole.

If the symmetry of the molecule is insufficient to determine the coefficients $x_{i\mu}$, it is necessary either to solve the self-consistent equations (2.3), (2.17) and (2.18) exactly or to accept the orbitals calculated by the Hückel method as approximations and use these in the energy expression (2.20). In this section the latter course will be followed, but the solution of the self-consistent equations is further discussed in § 4.

The orbitals for butadiene are well known[9] and when used together with the assumption of equal bond lengths, the vertical resonance energy is found to be

$$\mathscr{E}_\pi \text{ (butadiene)} - 2\mathscr{E}_\pi \text{ (ethylene)} = 0{\cdot}4722H_{12} + 0{\cdot}1\,(R_{12}^{-1} - R_{14}^{-1}). \tag{3.7}$$

Again assuming $R_{12} = 1{\cdot}39$ Å as an average, the vertical resonance energy is calculated by this formula using the same value of H_{12} as for benzene, 11·3 kcal/mole for *cis*-butadiene and 8·4 kcal/mole for *trans*-butadiene. The experimental estimate for the vertical resonance energy of the equilibrium configuration

* Mulliken and Parr indicate that other small terms should be added to this estimate. But as the exact values are uncertain they are omitted here.

is 9·3 kcal/mole.[18] In view of the many approximations involved, it is unlikely that much significance can be attributed to the prediction that the *cis* isomer will be more stable. The physical reason behind this prediction is discussed in the final section. Parr and Mulliken,[7] making fewer approximations, obtain the opposite result. Other similar calculations of resonance energies could be carried out, but since these are already fairly well correlated by the simpler theory, it is unlikely that any significant results would emerge.

The molecular orbital theory expression for the ionization potential corresponding to the orbital i is

$$-I_i = \sum_{\mu\nu} \bar{x}_{i\mu} F_{\mu\nu} x_{i\nu}. \tag{3.8}$$

Given the coefficients $x_{i\mu}$, these can easily be calculated from eqn. (2.17) and (2.18). For ethylene,

$$\left.\begin{aligned} F_{11} = F_{22} &= U_{11} + \tfrac{1}{2}(11 \mid G \mid 11), \\ F_{12} &= H_{12} - \tfrac{1}{2}R_{12}^{-1}, \end{aligned}\right\} \tag{3.9}$$

so that the lowest ionization potential is given by

$$-I\,(\text{ethylene}) = U_{11} + \tfrac{1}{2}(11 \mid G \mid 11) + H_{12} - \tfrac{1}{2}R_{12}^{-1}. \tag{3.10}$$

For benzene the orbitals are given by (3.3) and

$$F_{11} = U_{11} + \tfrac{1}{2}(11 \mid G \mid 11),\; F_{12} = H_{12} - \tfrac{1}{3}R_{12}^{-1},\; F_{13} = 0,\; F_{14} = \tfrac{1}{6}R_{14}^{-1}, \tag{3.11}$$

so that

$$-I\,(\text{benzene}) = U_{11} + \tfrac{1}{2}(11 \mid G \mid 11) + H_{12} - \tfrac{1}{3}R_{12}^{-1} - \tfrac{1}{6}R_{14}^{-1}. \tag{3.12}$$

If the difference between bond lengths is neglected, comparison of (3·10) and (3·12) shows that the ionization potential of benzene should be smaller than that of ethylene by an amount $\tfrac{1}{6}(R_{12}^{-1} - R_{14}^{-1})$ or $\tfrac{1}{12}R_{12}^{-1}$. This is 0·86 eV to be compared with the experimental difference of 1·19 eV (table 1). The calculated difference, which does not appear at all in the Hückel theory, is independent of choice of the empirical parameters U_{11} and H_{12}.

Corresponding expressions for the ionization potentials of other conjugated hydrocarbons are fairly easily derived if it is assumed that the coefficients given by the Hückel theory are adequate. For even alternant hydrocarbons (that is hydrocarbons with an even number of carbon atoms which can be divided into two groups, no member of one group being directly bonded to another of the same group) it can be shown [1] that $P_{\mu\mu} = 1$ if the coefficients are calculated by the Hückel procedure. It follows that

$$F_{\mu\mu} = U_{11} + \tfrac{1}{2}(11 \mid G \mid 11). \tag{3.13}$$

Since $\sum_{\mu} \bar{x}_{i\mu} x_{i\mu} = 1$, this term is common to the calculated ionization potentials of all even alternant hydrocarbons and it is simplest to compare the differences between the ionization potentials of the conjugated molecules and that of ethylene. Some examples derived in this way are (assuming all carbon-carbon bonds to be of the same length R_{12} and using the geometry of the molecule to express $R_{\mu\nu}^{-1}$ in terms of R_{12}^{-1}):

$$\left.\begin{aligned} &\textit{cis}\text{-butadiene}, && I - I\,(\text{ethylene}) = 0{\cdot}3820\,H_{12} - 0{\cdot}0809\,R_{12}^{-1}, \\ &\textit{trans}\text{-butadiene}, && I - I\,(\text{ethylene}) = 0{\cdot}3820\,H_{12} - 0{\cdot}1006\,R_{12}^{-1}, \\ &\text{naphthalene}, && I - I\,(\text{ethylene}) = 0{\cdot}3820\,H_{12} - 0{\cdot}1474\,R_{12}^{-1}, \\ &\text{anthracene}, && I - I\,(\text{ethylene}) = 0{\cdot}5858\,H_{12} - 0{\cdot}1929\,R_{12}^{-1}, \\ &\text{hexatriene}, && I - I\,(\text{ethylene}) = 0{\cdot}5550\,H_{12} - 0{\cdot}1652\,R_{12}^{-1}. \end{aligned}\right\} \tag{3.14}$$

Taking $R_{12} = 2{\cdot}63$ a.u. and $H_{12} = -49{\cdot}1$ kcal/mole $= -2{\cdot}130$ eV as before, these formulae have been used to calculate the vertical ionization potentials of the molecules using the observed value for ethylene. The results are given in the second column of table 1. The first column contains the results of a similar calculation based on the simple theory without the electron interaction terms. Here the value of H_{12} has been taken as $-39{\cdot}2$ kcal/mole (the vertical resonance energy of benzene being $2H_{12}$ in the simple theory).

TABLE 1.—IONIZATION POTENTIALS OF CONJUGATED HYDROCARBONS (eV)

	calc. (without electron interaction)	calc. (with electron interaction)	obs.
ethylene	(10·62)	(10·62)	10·62 *a*
benzene	10·62	9·76	9·43 *a*
cis-butadiene	9·97	8·97	—
trans-butadiene	9·97	8·77	9·07 *b*
trans-hexatriene	9·68	7·73	8·23 *c*
naphthalene	9·97	8·28	8·30 *d*
anthracene	9·62	7·38	—

a Honig [19]; *b* Price and Walsh [20]; *c* Price and Walsh [21]; *d* Birge [22]. The values for butadiene and hexatriene are obtained spectroscopically and are not truly vertical. The corresponding vertical ionization potentials will be slightly larger.

The agreement between the calculated and experimental ionization potentials where the latter exist is encouraging. It is clear that the introduction of electron interaction terms leads to a marked improvement in the theory. In fact, the R_{12}^{-1} terms in (3.14) are the dominant parts and it is impossible to understand ionization potentials without them.

4. CHARGE DENSITIES AND BOND ORDERS IN THE SELF-CONSISTENT THEORY.— In the previous section we have used the molecular orbitals determined by the Hückel procedure rather than the truly self-consistent ones obtained from eqn. (2.3). As already noted, for certain highly symmetrical molecules, the two sets of coefficients will be the same but in general they will be different. In this section we shall investigate differences between the values of $P_{\mu\nu}$ calculated by the two methods. The quantity $P_{\mu\mu}$ represents the mobile electron charge density on atom μ. $P_{\mu\nu}$ for neighbouring atoms μ and ν is the molecular orbital theory bond order and has been widely used in discussions of bond lengths.[23]

The most convenient general way of solving the self-consistent equations is by a cyclic method. If the coefficients obtained by the Hückel procedure are used as a first approximation, they can be used to calculate $P_{\mu\nu}$ and $F_{\mu\nu}$ and then a further set of coefficients (the second approximation) can be obtained by direct solution of (2.3) as linear equations. The process can be repeated an indefinite number of times and should converge to the final self-consistent solution.

Coulson and Rushbrooke [1] proved that for alternant hydrocarbons $P_{\mu\mu} = 1$ for all μ if the coefficients obtained by the Hückel procedure are used. This important result, which indicates that electron charge is uniformly distributed over the atoms of an alternant hydrocarbon, still holds in the self-consistent theory based on eqn. (2.17) and (2.18). The proof of this is given in the appendix.

This result only follows from the approximations that have been made in the evaluation of the integrals. More accurate calculations on butadiene [9] indicate that without the approximations, charge migrations of the order of $0{\cdot}02\,\boldsymbol{e}$ may be predicted. The theorem proved in the appendix does indicate, however, that any charge migrations that do occur will arise because of finer details in the integrals and not from the general features of electron distribution as retained in the present treatment.

It is not possible to prove any general result for the bond orders $P_{\mu\nu}$ but some idea of the trend can be obtained from an examination of the non-diagonal elements

$$F_{\mu\nu} = H_{\mu\nu} - \tfrac{1}{2}P_{\mu\nu}R_{\mu\nu}^{-1}. \qquad (4.1)$$

The Hückel coefficients are obtained by assuming that all non-diagonal matrix elements between neighbours are the same. This leads to a non-uniform set of bond-orders $P_{\mu\nu}$, the larger values corresponding to those bonds with most double bond character. Since $H_{\mu\nu}$ is negative, it follows that in the first cycle of the self-consistent calculation $|F_{\mu\nu}|$ will be largest for the strongest bonds. This will tend to make these bonds even stronger in the second approximation. It is probable, therefore, that the self-consistent theory will tend to accentuate the amount of double bond fixation compared with the simple theory.

We shall illustrate the changes in bond orders by calculations on *trans*-butadiene and naphthalene. A self-consistent calculation has been carried out for *trans*-butadiene and leads to the following occupied molecular orbitals

$$\left.\begin{aligned}\phi_1 &= 0{\cdot}4246\,(\phi_1 + \phi_4) + 0{\cdot}5655\,(\phi_2 + \phi_3),\\ \phi_2 &= 0{\cdot}5655\,(\phi_1 - \phi_4) + 0{\cdot}4246\,(\phi_2 - \phi_3),\end{aligned}\right\} \quad (4.2)$$

The corresponding bond orders are $P_{12} = 0{\cdot}9604$ and $P_{23} = 0{\cdot}2790$, to be compared with values of 0·8944 and 0·4472 obtained from the simple theory. In this molecule the double bond character of the central bond is considerably diminished. The best experimental value for the length of this bond (1·46 Å) is, in fact, considerably greater than the value (1·43 Å) corresponding to a bond order of 0·4472.

For naphthalene

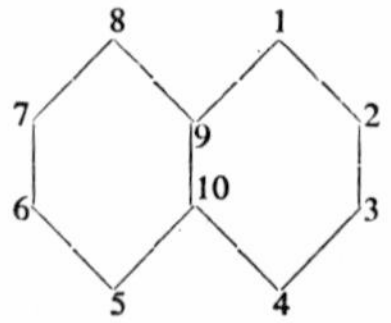

the self-consistent calculations lead to the bond orders ($P_{\mu\nu}$) given in table 2, where the values obtained by Coulson from the simple theory coefficients are also quoted.

TABLE 2.—BOND ORDERS FOR NAPHTHALENE

bond	1-2	9-10	2-3	1-9
bond order (Coulson)	1·725	1·518	1·603	1·554
bond order (self-consistent)	1·78	1·60	1·54	1·50

The naphthalene molecule is very suitable for a comparison with observed bond lengths for accurate experimental values are available.[24, 25] Previous methods for calculating the bond lengths in this molecule have been compared by Coulson, Daudel and Robertson.[26] The calculated values can be obtained from the bond orders using the Coulson [23] formula:

$$x = s - \frac{s - d}{1 + K(2 - p)/(p - 1)}, \quad (4.3)$$

where p is the bond order, s and d are the single and double bond lengths and K is a constant (0·765). The results using the Coulson and self-consistent bond orders are given in the first two rows of table 3.

TABLE 3.—BOND LENGTHS FOR NAPHTHALENE (Å)

bond	1-2	9-10	2-3	1-9
calc. (Coulson)	1·384	1·424	1·406	1·416
calc. (self-consistent theory)	1·376	1·408	1·420	1·428
calc. (self-consistent theory with adjusted mean)	1·366	1·398	1·410	1·418
obs.	1·365	1·393	1·404	1·424

The lengths calculated by the method of this paper are in rather better agreement with experiment than are Coulson's values. The correct order of lengths is now predicted and the central bond is no longer anomalous. The calculated values are all too large, but this may well be due to the inadequacy of the formula (4.3). If the calculated lengths are all reduced by 0·010 Å to give the correct mean, the values shown in the third row of table 3 are obtained. These are very well correlated with the experimental values.

5. THE CORRELATION OF ELECTRONS IN UNSATURATED HYDROCARBONS.—In order to appreciate the physical significance of the electron interaction terms appearing in the expressions for the resonance energies and ionization potentials, it is useful to examine some details of the electron distribution functions. These give the probabilities of relative distributions of electrons in multidimensional space and are obtained by suitable integration of the complete function $\bar{\Psi}\Psi$ The total electron-electron interaction energy can be calculated directly from the two-electron distribution function (in six-dimensional space). This function can be simplified in ways analogous to the approximations of § 2 and leads to some insight into the origin of the interelectronic terms.

Considering the π-electrons separately, let us write $P^{\alpha\alpha}(1, 2)\, dv_1 dv_2$ for the probability of there being two electrons of α spin simultaneously in volume elements dv_1 and dv_2 and define $P^{\alpha\beta}$ and $P^{\beta\beta}$ similarly. Then for the ground state in which there are N doubly occupied molecular orbitals $\psi_1 \ldots \psi_N$ it can be shown [11] that the single determinant wave function leads to expressions

$$P^{\alpha\alpha}(1, 2) = P^{\beta\beta}(1, 2) = \sum_{ij}^{N} \{[\psi_i(1)]^2 [\psi_j(2)]^2 - \psi_i(1)\psi_j(1)\psi_i(2)\psi_j(2)\}, \tag{5.1}$$

$$P^{\alpha\beta}(1, 2) = \sum_{ij}^{N} [\psi_i(1)]^2 [\psi_j(2)]^2. \tag{5.2}$$

If we now write these expressions in terms of atomic orbitals and omit all terms of the type $\phi_\mu(1)\phi_\nu(1)$, $(\mu \neq \nu)$, we obtain

$$P^{\alpha\alpha}(1, 2) = P^{\beta\beta}(1, 2) = \tfrac{1}{4} \sum_{\lambda\mu} [P_{\lambda\lambda}P_{\mu\mu} - P_{\mu\lambda}^2][\phi_\lambda(1)]^2 [\phi_\mu(2)]^2, \tag{5.3}$$

$$P^{\alpha\beta}(1, 2) = \tfrac{1}{4} \sum_{\lambda\mu} P_{\lambda\lambda}P_{\mu\mu}[\phi_\lambda(1)]^2 [\phi_\mu(2)]^2. \tag{5.4}$$

The omission of terms of the type $\phi_\mu\phi_\nu$ is strictly analogous to approximations B and C of the energy calculations.

The probability distributions (5.3) and (5.4) can now be interpreted with the assumption that different atomic orbitals do not significantly overlap. We shall say that electron 1 is at the atom λ if $\phi_\lambda(1) \neq 0$ and $\phi_\mu(1) = 0$ for all other μ. Once again this is an oversimplification of the real picture, but it does enable general features of the electron distribution to be examined. It is clear from (5.2) and (5.4) that $P^{\alpha\beta}$ is the product of a function of electron 1 with a function of electron 2 so that the two sets of electrons are uncorrelated with one another. Eqn. (5.3) enables us to find the probability of an α-electron being found on atom μ, given that there is one on atom λ. For alternant hydrocarbons for which $P_{\lambda\lambda} = P_{\mu\mu} = 1$, this is

$$\tfrac{1}{2}(1 - P_{\lambda\mu}^2), \tag{5.5}$$

whereas the corresponding probability of finding a β-electron is $\tfrac{1}{2}$.

The results are conveniently illustrated by simple diagrams of the type shown in fig. 1 for ethylene.

FIG. 1.—Correlation diagram for ethylene.

The figures above the line give the probability of there being another α-electron at the atom given that there is one at the position of the arrow. The figures below the line give the corresponding probabilities for a β-electron. The interaction between the α-electron and 0·5 β-electrons on the same atom gives rise to the term $\frac{1}{2}(11 \mid G \mid 11)$ in the energy expression (3.2) while its interaction with the σ-core of the other atom (screened by 0·5 β-electrons) gives $-\frac{1}{2}R_{12}^{-1}$.

Corresponding diagrams for benzene are given in fig. 2 (the β-probabilities being written inside the ring). The diagram for one of the Kekulé structures is shown in (*a*) (using three localized ethylene orbitals) and is to be compared with (*b*) derived from the molecular orbitals (3·3). Fig. 2(*b*) shows that if there is an α-electron at position 1, then according to the single-determinant wave function, there is a deficiency of α-electrons at the *ortho* and *para* positions. In the Kekulé structure, however, this same electron deficiency is concentrated at one of the *ortho* positions. The $\frac{1}{12}R_{12}^{-1}$ term in the expression for the resonance energy of benzene can be obtained by counting the interactions of α-electrons with all partially screened σ-cores in the two cases.

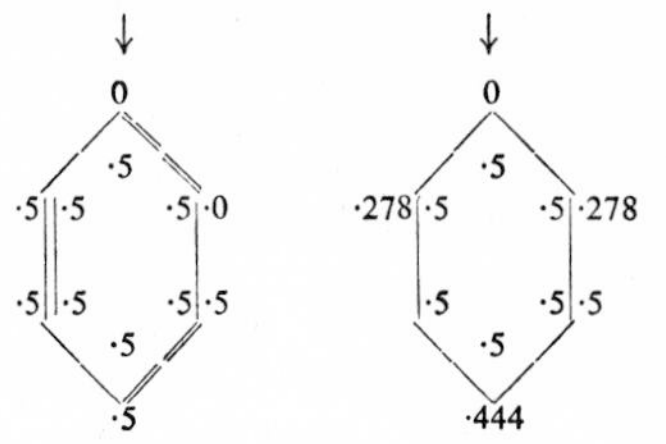

(*a*) (*b*)

FIG. 2.—Correlation diagrams for benzene.

As a third example we may consider butadiene. The correlation diagrams based on the orbitals obtained by the Hückel procedure are shown in fig. 3. It is seen that part of the stabilization energy arises from the interaction of an α-electron in position 1 with an incompletely screened σ-core at position 4. The theory of § 3 predicts this *cis* isomer to be more stable because the 1 and 4 positions are then closer. This extra stability, however, may be more than offset by other factors such as repulsion between the hydrogen atoms.

↓					↓		
0	0·1	0·5	0·4	0·1	0	0·4	0·5
0·5	0·5	0·5	0·5	0·5	0·5	0·5	0·5

FIG. 3.—Correlation diagrams for butadiene.

The author is indebted to Dr. G. G. Hall and Prof. C. A. Coulson for valuable discussion and criticism.

APPENDIX.—Here we shall prove the results $P_{\mu\mu} = 1$ for the cyclic process of solving the self-consistent equations for alternants described in § 4. The proof follows an inductive method. Let $x_{i\mu}^{(n)}$ be the *n*th approximation to the self-consistent coefficients $x_{i\mu}$ (obtained after $(n-1)$ cycles), $E_i^{(n)}$ being the corresponding energy. $x_{i\mu}^{(0)}$ are the coefficients obtained by the Hückel procedure (i.e. solving (2·3) with $S_{\mu\nu} = \delta_{\mu\nu}$, all $F_{\mu\mu}$ identical, $F_{\mu\nu} = \beta$ if μ and ν are bonded and zero otherwise). Define

$$P_{\mu\nu}^{(n)} = 2\sum_i \bar{x}_{i\mu}^{(n)} x_{i\nu}^{(n)}, \tag{6·1}$$

and let $F_{\mu\nu}^{(n)}$ be the corresponding matrix element calculated from (2·17) or (2·18). Divide the carbon centres into two classes ("starred" and "unstarred") so that each starred atom is bonded to only unstarred atoms and vice versa. We can then establish the following theorem which is a generalization of that proved by Coulson and Rushbrooke.[1]

Theorem.—If $H_{\mu\nu} = 0$ unless $\mu = \nu$ or μ and ν are neighbouring atoms, then for even alternant hydrocarbons it follows that $P_{\lambda\sigma}^{(n)} = \delta_{\lambda\sigma}$ for all *n* if λ and σ are both starred or both unstarred.

Proof.—Assume the result for $n-1$ as an inductive hypothesis. The coefficients $x_{i\mu}^{(n)}$ and the energy levels $E_i^{(n)}$ are then determined by the linear equations

$$[F_{\mu\mu}^{(n-1)} - E_i^{(n)}]x_{i\mu}^{(n)} + \sum_{\nu(\neq\mu)} F_{\mu\nu}^{(n-1)}x_{i\nu}^{(n)} = 0, \tag{6.2}$$

where, from the inductive hypothesis and eqn. (2.17) and (2.18)

$$F_{\mu\nu}^{(n-1)} = \{U_{11} + \tfrac{1}{2}(11 \mid G \mid 11)\}\delta_{\mu\nu}, \tag{6.3}$$

if μ and ν are both starred or both unstarred. It then follows from (6.2) that from the coefficients $x_{i\mu}^{(n)}$ of one orbital with energy $E_i^{(n)}$ the coefficients of another corresponding to an energy

$$2F_{\mu\mu}^{(n-1)} - E_i^{(n)}$$

can be obtained by changing the sign of the coefficients of the starred atomic orbitals. The molecular orbitals ψ_i can therefore be paired in this way, to each occupied orbital $\psi_1 \ldots \psi_N$ corresponding one of the unoccupied orbitals $\psi_{N+1}, \ldots \psi_{2N}$, $2N$ being the number of carbon centres. If i and j are orbitals corresponding in this way, it follows that, if μ and ν are both starred or both unstarred, then

$$\bar{x}_{i\mu}^{(n)}x_{i\nu}^{(n)} = \bar{x}_{j\mu}^{(n)}x_{j\nu}^{(n)} \tag{6.4}$$

Hence

$$\sum_{i=N}^{N} \bar{x}_{i\mu}^{(n)}x_{i\nu}^{(n)} = \sum_{i=N+1}^{2N} \bar{x}_{i\mu}^{(n)}x_{i\nu}^{(n)}. \tag{6.5}$$

But from the unitary property of the complex matrix $x_{i\mu}$

$$\sum_{i=1}^{2N} \bar{x}_{i\mu}^{(n)}x_{i\nu}^{(n)} = \delta_{\mu\nu}. \tag{6.6}$$

It follows immediately that $P_{\mu\nu}^{(n)} = \delta_{\mu\nu}$.

The proof for $n = 1$ follows identical lines, so the theorem is established. If convergence is assumed the same result must apply to the limiting self-consistent solution.

[1] Coulson and Rushbrooke, *Proc. Camb. Phil. Soc.*, 1940, **36**, 193.
[2] Hückel, *Z. Physik.*, 1931, **70**, 204, 279.
[3] Lennard-Jones, *Proc. Roy. Soc. A*, 1937, **158**, 280.
[4] Coulson and Longuet-Higgins, *Proc. Roy. Soc. A*, 1947, **191**, 39.
[5] Hall, *Proc. Roy. Soc. A*, 1952, **213**, 102, 113.
[6] Goeppert-Mayer and Sklar, *J. Chem. Physics*, 1938, **6**, 645.
[7] Parr and Mulliken, *J. Chem. Physics*, 1950, **18**, 1338.
[8] Parr, Craig and Ross, *J. Chem. Physics*, 1950, **18**, 1561.
[9] Coulson and Jacobs, *Proc. Roy. Soc. A*, 1951, **206**, 287.
[10] Coulson, Craig and Jacobs, *Proc. Roy. Soc. A*, 1951, **206**, 297.
[11] Lennard-Jones, *Proc. Roy. Soc. A*, 1949, **198**, 1, 14.
[12] Hall, *Proc. Roy. Soc. A*, 1951, **205**, 541.
[13] Roothaan, *Rev. Mod. Physics*, 1951, **23**, 61.
[14] Pariser and Parr, *J. Chem. Physics*, 1953, **21**, 466.
[15] Hall and Lennard-Jones, *Proc. Roy. Soc. A*, 1950, **202**, 155.
[16] Lennard-Jones and Pople, *Proc. Roy. Soc. A*, 1950, **202**, 166.
[17] Altmann, *Proc. Roy. Soc. A*, 1951, **210**, 327, 343.
[18] Mulliken and Parr, *J. Chem. Physics*, 1951, **19**, 1271.
[19] Hönig, *J. Chem. Physics*, 1948, **16**, 105.
[20] Price and Walsh, *Proc. Roy. Soc. A*, 1940, **174**, 220.
[21] Price and Walsh, *Proc. Roy. Soc. A*, 1946, **185**, 182.
[22] Birge, *Physic. Rev.*, 1937, **52**, 241.
[23] Coulson, *Proc. Roy. Soc. A*, 1939, **169**, 413.
[24] Abrahams, Robertson and White, *Acta Cryst.*, 1949, **2**, 233, 238.
[25] Ahmed and Cruickshank, *Acta Cryst.*, 1952, **5**, 852.
[26] Coulson, Daudel and Robertson, *Proc. Roy. Soc. A*, 1951, **207**, 306.
[27] Parr, *J. Chem. Physics*, 1952, **20**, 1499.

Reprinted from the *Transactions of the Faraday Society*,
No. 381, Vol. 50, Part 9, September, 1954

RESONANCE ENERGIES AND CHARGE DISTRIBUTIONS OF UNSATURATED HYDROCARBON RADICALS AND IONS

BY A. BRICKSTOCK AND J. A. POPLE
Dept. of Theoretical Chemistry, University of Cambridge

Received 10*th March*, 1954

A self-consistent molecular-orbital treatment, including electron interaction, is used to discuss resonance energies and charge distributions of certain conjugated hydrocarbon radicals and ions. The principal aim is to test the validity of conclusions reached on the basis of the simpler Hückel molecular-orbital theory, using an effective one-electron Hamiltonian. The following general conclusions are reached for alternant systems.

(i) The resonance energy of a conjugated ion (positive or negative) should be greater than that of the corresponding radical. (They are equal according to the Hückel theory.)

(ii) The distribution of charge in conjugated ions may differ considerably from that predicted by the Hückel theory, there being a tendency for electrons of cations to keep to the central parts of the system.

1. INTRODUCTION

In its most widely developed form, the molecular-orbital theory of conjugated hydrocarbons is based on the well-known Hückel method [1, 2] of obtaining the orbitals for the mobile electrons as approximate eigenfunctions of a one-electron Hamiltonian. One of the principal disadvantages of this technique is that it does not take adequate account of the electrostatic repulsion of the electrons. This can only be introduced satisfactorily if the theory is based on the complete many-electron Hamiltonian (which cannot be expressed as a sum of one-electron operators). A sounder starting-point is the general molecular-orbital theory developed by Lennard-Jones,[3] Hall [4] and Roothaan,[5] according to which the orbitals should be obtained as solutions or approximate solutions of a coupled set of self-consistent equations analogous to the Fock equations for atoms. The solution of these equations in their general form is laborious because of the difficult electron repulsion integrals. Recently, however, a series of approximations has been suggested [6, 7] which greatly simplify the treatment of electron interaction. One of the authors [7] has used these approximations to put the self-consistent equations into a form simple enough for the results to be compared directly with the Hückel method. The theory was applied to certain neutral alternant hydrocarbon molecules and it was found that although the electron interaction terms were by no means small, calculated resonance energies were only slightly altered. Further, the uniformity of charge distribution in conjugated hydrocarbons predicted by the Hückel theory [8] was shown to hold also for self-consistent orbitals at this level of approximation.

The aim of the present paper is to apply this self-consistent molecular-orbital method to odd alternant hydrocarbon radicals and ions. The Hückel method has been used for developing a theory of these systems [9] and leads to certain conclusions about resonance energies and charge distributions. It has been realized, however, that the procedure is less satisfactory for ions, for whereas the Hückel method for neutral alternant molecules starts by treating all carbon atoms as equally electron attractive and predicts uniformity of charge distribution, for ions it predicts a non-uniform charge distribution and so is not internally consistent. This is automatically put right in a self-consistent treatment.

2. THE DETERMINATION OF SELF-CONSISTENT ORBITALS

The self-consistent molecular orbital theory used is similar to that developed in the previous paper on neutral hydrocarbons,[7] so full details of its derivation will not be given. Certain minor changes in notation have been made. The principal extension needed is the determination of self-consistent orbitals for the mobile electrons of radicals.

For systems with an even number of mobile electrons in closed shell ground states, the molecular orbitals ψ_i are expressed as linear combinations of atomic orbitals ϕ_μ

$$\psi_i = \sum_\mu x_{i\mu}\phi_\mu , \tag{2.1}$$

the coefficients being solutions of the Roothaan equations

$$\sum_\nu F_{\mu\nu}x_{i\nu} = E_i x_{i\mu} . \tag{2.2}$$

The elements of the matrix $F_{\mu\nu}$ are given by

$$F_{\mu\mu} = U_{\mu\mu} + \tfrac{1}{2}P_{\mu\mu}\gamma_{\mu\mu} + \sum_{\sigma(\neq\mu)} (P_{\sigma\sigma} - 1)\gamma_{\mu\sigma} , \tag{2.3}$$

$$F_{\mu\nu} = \beta_{\mu\nu} - \tfrac{1}{2}P_{\mu\nu}\gamma_{\mu\nu}, \quad (\mu \neq \nu), \tag{2.4}$$

$$P_{\mu\nu} = 2\sum_i^{\text{occ}} x_{i\mu}x_{i\nu} . \tag{2.5}$$

The quantities E_i are the roots of the secular equation

$$| F_{\mu\nu} - E\delta_{\mu\nu} | = 0, \tag{2.6}$$

only the orbitals corresponding to the lower E_i being occupied (two electrons in each). Throughout Greek suffixes will be used for atomic orbitals and italics for molecular orbitals. The quantities $U_{\mu\mu}$ and $\beta_{\mu\nu}$ are closely analogous to the coulomb and resonance integrals of the simpler theory. $U_{\mu\mu}$ is the diagonal matrix element of ϕ_μ with respect to the one-electron Hamiltonian containing the kinetic energy and the effect of the core of atom μ. Strictly it should include the effect of " penetration " of neighbouring atoms, but for the purpose of this paper we shall only need to assume that $U_{\mu\mu}$ is equal to a constant U for each carbon atom. $\beta_{\mu\nu}$ (written $H_{\mu\nu}$ in the previous paper) is a corresponding non-diagonal matrix element taken to be zero for atoms μ and ν which are not directly bonded to each other and equal to β for each C—C bond. $\gamma_{\mu\nu}$ is the electrostatic coulomb interaction of an electron in ϕ_μ with one in ϕ_ν. In the previous paper,[7] $\gamma_{\mu\mu}$ (written $(\mu\mu \mid G \mid \mu\mu)$) was not specified and $\gamma_{\mu\nu}$ $(\mu \neq \nu)$ was taken to be the inverse distance between the nuclei $R_{\mu\nu}^{-1}$. This latter approximation is not an essential part of the theory and alternative numerical values are used in this paper. $P_{\mu\nu}$ is defined as a sum over occupied orbitals and, as in the Hückel theory, $P_{\mu\mu}$ is taken as the definition of π-electron density on atom μ and $P_{\mu\nu}$ for bonded atoms as the definition of bond order.

The same set of approximations leads to the following expression for the total energy associated with the π-electrons

$$\mathscr{E}_\pi = \sum_\mu P_{\mu\mu}(U_{\mu\mu} + \tfrac{1}{4}P_{\mu\mu}\gamma_{\mu\mu}) + 2\sum_{\mu<\nu} P_{\mu\nu}\beta_{\mu\nu} + \sum_{\mu<\nu} \{(P_{\mu\mu} - 1)(P_{\nu\nu} - 1) - \tfrac{1}{2}P_{\mu\nu}^2\}\gamma_{\mu\nu}. \tag{2.7}$$

All these equations reduce to those of the Hückel theory if all $\gamma_{\mu\nu}$ are neglected for then $F_{\mu\mu} = U_{\mu\mu}$ and $F_{\mu\nu} = \beta_{\mu\nu}$. In fact, the $\gamma_{\mu\nu}$ are by no means small and their introduction, particularly in the energy expression (2.7), may modify results considerably.

In order to obtain corresponding formulae for radicals with an odd number of mobile electrons, it is necessary to use the generalization of Roothaan's procedure suggested by Pople and Nesbet.[10] According to this, electrons of α- and β-spin are supposed to occupy two entirely distinct sets of molecular orbitals ψ_i^α and ψ_i^β. There will be two corresponding sets of coefficients $x_{i\mu}^\alpha$ and $x_{i\mu}^\beta$, satisfying equations analogous to those of Roothaan.[5] These two sets of equations can be simplified by the same approximations and become

$$\sum F_{\mu\nu}^\alpha x_{i\nu}^\alpha = E_i^\alpha x_{i\mu}^\alpha; \quad \sum_\nu F_{\mu\nu}^\beta x_{i\nu}^\beta = E_i^\beta x_{i\mu}^\beta, \tag{2.8}$$

where

$$F_{\mu\mu}^\alpha = U_{\mu\mu} + P_{\mu\mu}^\beta \gamma_{\mu\mu} + \sum_{\sigma(\neq\mu)} (P_{\sigma\sigma} - 1)\gamma_{\mu\sigma}, \tag{2.9}$$

$$F_{\mu\mu}^\beta = U_{\mu\mu} + P_{\mu\mu}^\alpha \gamma_{\mu\mu} + \sum_{\sigma(\neq\mu)} (P_{\sigma\sigma} - 1)\gamma_{\mu\sigma}, \tag{2.10}$$

$$F_{\mu\nu}^\alpha = \beta_{\mu\nu} - P_{\mu\nu}^\alpha \gamma_{\mu\nu}, \quad (\mu \neq \nu), \tag{2.11}$$

$$F_{\mu\nu}^\beta = \beta_{\mu\nu} - P_{\mu\nu}^\beta \gamma_{\mu\nu}, \quad (\mu \neq \nu), \tag{2.12}$$

$$P_{\mu\nu}^\alpha = \sum_i^{\text{occ}}{}^\alpha x_{i\mu}^\alpha x_{i\nu}^\alpha, \quad P_{\mu\nu}^\beta = \sum_i^{\text{occ}}{}^\beta x_{i\mu}^\beta x_{i\nu}^\beta, \tag{2.13}$$

$$P_{\mu\nu} = P_{\mu\nu}^\alpha + P_{\mu\nu}^\beta, \tag{2.14}$$

$\sum^{\text{occ}\,\alpha}$ and $\sum^{\text{occ}\,\beta}$ being sums over molecular orbitals occupied by α- and β-electrons respectively. If the number of α-electrons is equal to the number of β-electrons, the two sets of equations become equivalent and reduce to (2.2)-(2.5). For radicals with an odd number of electrons this cannot be so and the two sets of equations have to be solved independently. The corresponding total energy expression is

$$\mathscr{E}_\pi = \sum_\mu (P_{\mu\mu}U_{\mu\mu} + P_{\mu\mu}^\alpha P_{\mu\mu}^\beta \gamma_{\mu\mu}) + 2\sum_{\mu<\nu} P_{\mu\nu}\beta_{\mu\nu}$$
$$+ \sum_{\mu<\nu} \{(P_{\mu\mu} - 1)(P_{\nu\nu} - 1) - [(P_{\mu\nu}^\alpha)^2 + (P_{\mu\nu}^\beta)^2]\}\gamma_{\mu\nu}. \tag{2.15}$$

Again if the $\gamma_{\mu\nu}$ are neglected, these equations become equivalent to those of the Hückel theory, the two sets having the same solutions so that we may speak of certain orbitals being doubly occupied and others only singly occupied.

In this paper we shall be primarily concerned with the properties of a limited class of alternant hydrocarbon systems. Alternant systems are those without any odd-numbered rings, so that the carbon atoms can be divided into two classes, each member of one class being directly bonded only to members of the other. We shall only deal with radicals and singly-charged ions with an odd number of carbon atoms (odd alternants). For such ions, it is possible to establish simple relations between the $P_{\mu\nu}$ for corresponding carbanions ($P_{\mu\nu}^-$) and carbonium ions ($P_{\mu\nu}^+$). These follow from the self-consistent equations (2.2) and are

$$P_{\mu\mu}^+ + P_{\mu\mu} = 2, \tag{2.16}$$

$$P_{\mu\nu}^+ = -P_{\mu\nu} \ (\mu \neq \nu \text{ but in the same class}), \tag{2.17}$$

$$P_{\mu\nu}^+ = P_{\mu\nu}, \ (\mu, \nu \text{ in different classes}). \tag{2.18}$$

Details of the proof are given in the appendix. (2.16) shows that the distribution of resultant positive charge in a carbonium ion is the same as the distribution of negative charge in the corresponding carbanion. (2.18) shows that the bond orders are equal. For odd alternant radicals, similar relations connect $P^{\alpha}_{\mu\nu}$ and $P^{\beta}_{\mu\nu}$:

$$P_{\mu\mu} = P^{\alpha}_{\mu\mu} + P^{\beta}_{\mu\mu} = 1, \tag{2.19}$$

$$P^{\alpha}_{\mu\nu} = - P^{\beta}_{\mu\nu}, \quad (\mu \neq \nu \text{ but in same class}), \tag{2.20}$$

$$P^{\alpha}_{\mu\nu} = P^{\beta}_{\mu\nu}, \quad (\mu, \nu \text{ in different classes}). \tag{2.21}$$

These are also proved in the appendix. (2.19) shows that the uniformity of charge density proved for even alternant molecules in ref. (7) applies also to odd radicals.

3. RESONANCE ENERGIES

The resonance energy of any molecule, radical, or ion may be defined as the negative of the difference between the total π-electron energy of the actual system and the corresponding energy of the hypothetical system of bonds, charges and free electrons as represented by one of its classical structures. To make the concept more precise, the systems considered will be supposed to have C—C bond lengths all equal to some standard (the bond length of benzene) and all bond angles equal to 120°. The energy of such a molecule will be compared with that of single and double bonds *with the same standard bond length.* The resonance energy defined in this way may be described as the vertical resonance energy of the configuration with standard bond lengths and angles.

Consider first a conjugated hydrocarbon molecule with $2N$ carbon atoms and $2N$ mobile electrons. $\mathscr{E}_\pi$ for one of the classical structures is $N\mathscr{E}_\pi$ (ethylene) where

$$\mathscr{E}_\pi\,(\text{ethylene}) = 2U + \tfrac{1}{2}\gamma_{11} + 2\beta - \tfrac{1}{2}\gamma_{12}, \tag{3.1}$$

so that

$$- \mathscr{E}_R\,(\text{molecule}) = 2\Big[\sum_{\mu<\nu}^{*} P_{\mu\nu} - N\Big]\beta + \Big[\tfrac{1}{4}\sum_{\mu} P^2_{\mu\mu} - \tfrac{1}{2}N\Big]\gamma_{11} + \sum_{\mu<\nu} [(P_{\mu\mu} - 1)(P_{\nu\nu} - 1) - \tfrac{1}{2}P^2_{\mu\nu}]\gamma_{\mu\nu} + \tfrac{1}{2}N\gamma_{12}, \tag{3.2}$$

$\sum^{*}$ being written for summation over nearest neighbour pairs only. For alternant molecules it can be proved [7] that $P_{\mu\mu} = 1$. Also

$$\sum_{\nu} P^2_{\mu\nu} = 4\sum_{i}^{\text{occ}}\sum_{j}^{\text{occ}} x_{i\mu}x_{j\mu}\sum_{\nu} x_{i\nu}x_{j\nu} = 4\sum_{i}^{\text{occ}}\sum^{\text{occ}} x_{i\mu}x_{j\mu}\delta_{ij} = 2P_{\mu\mu}, \tag{3.3}$$

so that (3.2) can be written

$$- \mathscr{E}_R\,(\text{alternant molecule}) = 2\Big[\sum_{\mu<\nu}^{*} P_{\mu\nu} - N\Big]\beta + \tfrac{1}{2}\sum_{\mu<\nu} P^2_{\mu\nu}(\gamma_{12} - \gamma_{\mu\nu}). \tag{3.4}$$

The two terms in (3.4) are easily interpreted physically. The first is the usual type of term arising in the theory without explicit electron interaction because the electrons are able to take greater advantage of the σ-core field in the actual molecule than in one of the classical structures. The other term, which is necessarily positive (reducing stability) indicates that more pairs of electrons are found on neighbouring atoms in the actual state. But this is not a large term (*a*) because there are no contributions from nearest neighbours and (*b*) because $P_{\mu\nu}$ falls off rapidly with increasing separation of ϕ_μ and ϕ_ν. Eqn. (3.4) is therefore a justification of the elementary Hückel molecular-orbital method of estimating resonance energies of hydrocarbon molecules.

Now consider the application to odd alternant radicals and ions. The resonance energy of a radical with $2N + 1$ electrons and $2N + 1$ conjugating atoms is obtained by subtracting (2·15) from $U + N\mathscr{E}_\pi$ (ethylene). For the positive and negative ions obtained by removing or adding an electron, (2.16)-(2.18) apply and it is not difficult to show from (2.7) that

$$\mathscr{E}_\pi\,(\text{carbanion}) - \mathscr{E}_\pi\,(\text{carbonium ion}) = 2U + \gamma_{11}. \tag{3.5}$$

This is also the difference between the energies of single classical structures, so the theory predicts that the resonance energies will be equal. Only carbonium ions will be considered in the rest of this section, it being understood that the same results apply to the corresponding carbanions.

For complete resonance energy calculations based on these formulae, solutions of the self-consistent equations (2.2) or (2.8) are needed. As this involves rather heavy computation for larger systems we shall be content in this section to use $P_{\mu\nu}$ corresponding to Hückel orbitals as approximations to the self-consistent $P_{\mu\nu}$. This will at least give some idea of the relative magnitude of the various contributions to the resonance energy. When charge distributions are discussed, however, it is necessary to know how solutions of the self-consistent equations differ from the Hückel coefficients. This will be discussed in the next section.

The form of the Hückel orbitals (unlike self-consistent orbitals) depends on the arrangement of carbon atoms only and not on the number of electrons occupying them. They are therefore the same for corresponding radicals and ions. Also, for odd alternants, one orbital (unoccupied in the cation, singly occupied in the radical and doubly occupied in the anion) is restricted to one class of atoms. This is generally known as the non-bonding orbital * and its coefficients will be denoted by $x_{0\mu}$. (We shall not consider odd alternants possessing more than one non-bonding orbital.) The atoms belonging to the class from which the non-bonding orbital is formed will be referred to as starred, the rest being unstarred. The coefficients are then easily determined from the condition [9] that $\sum_{\mu}^{\ddagger} x_{0\mu}$ is zero, where the sum $\sum^{\ddagger}$ is over all starred atoms directly bonded to any given unstarred atom. It is shown in the appendix that, for ions

$$P_{\mu\mu}^{\pm} = 1 \mp x_{0\mu}^2, \tag{3.6}$$

$$P_{\mu\nu}^{\pm} = \mp x_{0\mu}x_{0\nu}, \quad (\mu \neq \nu, \text{ both starred or both unstarred}). \tag{3.7}$$

For radicals we shall suppose that there are $N+1$ electrons of α-spin and N of β-spin. Then (see appendix),

$$P_{\mu\mu}^{\alpha} = \tfrac{1}{2}(1 + x_{0\mu}^2), \quad P_{\mu\mu}^{\beta} = \tfrac{1}{2}(1 - x_{0\mu}^2), \tag{3.8}$$

$$P_{\mu\nu}^{\alpha} = \tfrac{1}{2}x_{0\mu}x_{0\nu}, \qquad P_{\mu\nu}^{\beta} = -\tfrac{1}{2}x_{0\mu}x_{0\nu} \; (\mu \neq \nu, \text{ both starred or both unstarred}). \tag{3.9}$$

These results can be used to derive simple expressions for the resonance energies of carbonium ions and radicals. The resonance energy of a carbonium ion with $2N$ mobile electrons and $2N+1$ carbon centres is the same as the expression (3.2) for a neutral molecule. Eqn. (3.3) applies generally, so that if μ is unstarred

$$\sum_{\nu}^{\text{st}} P_{\mu\nu}^2 = 1, \quad \sum_{\mu}^{\text{unst}} \sum_{\nu}^{\text{st}} P_{\mu\nu}^2 = N, \tag{3.10}$$

where $\sum^{\text{st}}$ and $\sum^{\text{unst}}$ indicate summation over starred and unstarred atoms respectively. The resonance energy expression (3.2) can therefore be written

$$-\mathscr{E}_R\,(\text{carbonium ion}) = 2\Big[\sum_{\mu<\nu}^{*} P_{\mu\nu} - N\Big]\beta + \tfrac{1}{4}\sum_{\mu} P_{\mu\mu}(P_{\mu\mu} - 1)\gamma_{11}$$
$$+ \sum_{\mu<\nu}^{\text{st}} [(P_{\mu\mu} - 1)(P_{\nu\nu} - 1) - \tfrac{1}{2}P_{\mu\nu}^2]\gamma_{\mu\nu} + \tfrac{1}{2}\sum_{\mu}^{\text{unst}}\sum_{\nu}^{\text{st}} P_{\mu\nu}^2(\gamma_{12} - \gamma_{\mu\nu}). \tag{3.11}$$

* It should be noted that non-bonding orbitals only exist in the Hückel approximation. The self-consistent equations do not necessarily have such a solution.

Using (3.6) and (3.7) this can be transformed to

$$-\mathscr{E}_R\text{ (carbonium ion)} = 2\Big[\sum_{\mu<\nu}^{*} P_{\mu\nu} - N\Big]\beta - \tfrac{1}{2}\sum_{\mu<\nu}^{\text{st}} x_{0\mu}^2 x_{0\nu}^2(\gamma_{11} - \gamma_{\mu\nu})$$

$$+ \tfrac{1}{2}\sum_{\mu}^{\text{unst}}\sum_{\nu}^{\text{st}} P_{\mu\nu}^2(\gamma_{12} - \gamma_{\mu\nu}). \quad (3.12)$$

By similar steps, the following expression for the resonance energy of a radical is obtained from (2·15),

$$-\mathscr{E}_R\text{ (radical)} = 2\Big[\sum_{\mu<\nu}^{*} P_{\mu\nu} - N\Big]\beta + \tfrac{1}{2}\sum_{\mu<\nu}^{\text{st}} x_{0\mu}^2 x_{0\nu}^2(\gamma_{11} - \gamma_{\mu\nu})$$

$$+ \tfrac{1}{2}\sum_{\mu}^{\text{unst}}\sum_{\nu}^{\text{st}} P_{\mu\nu}^2(\gamma_{12} - \gamma_{\mu\nu}). \quad (3.13)$$

Since we are using Hückel orbitals, $P_{\mu\nu}$ (μ, ν in different classes) is the same for the carbonium ion and the radical so that

$$\mathscr{E}_R\text{ (carbonium ion)} - \mathscr{E}_R\text{ (radical)} = \sum_{\mu<\nu}^{\text{st}} x_{0\mu}^2 x_{0\nu}^2(\gamma_{11} - \gamma_{\mu\nu}). \quad (3.14)$$

Since $\gamma_{11} > \gamma_{\mu\nu}$, this is positive, so that the theory predicts the resonance energy of the carbonium ion to be greater than that of the radical. The simple Hückel theory, however, neglecting electron interaction throughout, gives the same value for both.*

The first and third terms in (3.12) have the same physical interpretation as they had for neutral molecules. The second term is additional and represents the stabilization due to there being less probability of two electrons being on the same atom in the conjugated state than there is in one of the classical structures. For the radical (eqn. (3.13)) there is an increase in the corresponding probability. Numerical values of the three parts of (3.12) and (3.13) for some odd alternant systems are given in table 1.

The resonance energies of these radicals and ions can only be estimated from experimental data by indirect means. Some values obtained from dissociation energies and appearance potentials are quoted in table 2.

The theoretical estimates obtained by the method of this paper are in rough agreement with the available experimental data. It should be remembered, however, that the theoretical results are for vertical resonance energies. Strictly a correction should be applied for the " compression energies " to distort both the actual molecule and one of the classical structures to artificial systems with a standard bond length. This would reduce the theoretical estimates somewhat. On the other hand, the use of truly self-consistent orbitals, rather than Hückel orbitals, would lead to larger resonance energies. For the allyl radical, whose self-consistent orbitals are easily determined from eqn. (2.8), this increases the theoretical resonance energy from 31·0 to 34·8 kcal/mole.

Perhaps the most significant result emerging from table 2 is the confirmation it provides of the theoretical prediction that the resonance energy of a carbonium ion is larger than that of the corresponding radical. Although the experimental estimates are only rough, the expression (3.13) for the difference seems to be quantitatively satisfactory.

* Franklin and Lumpkin [11] have suggested that carbonium ions, unlike radicals, have no resonance energy. Eqn. (3·14) shows that this directly contradicts molecular-orbital theory.

TABLE 1.—CONTRIBUTIONS TO THE VERTICAL RESONANCE ENERGY OF SOME CARBONIUM IONS AND HYDROCARBON RADICALS * (kcal/mole)

system	$2\left[\sum^{*}_{\mu<\nu} P_{\mu\nu} - N\right]\beta$	$\frac{1}{2}\sum_{\mu<\nu} x_{0\mu}^2 x_{0\nu}^2(\gamma_{11}-\gamma_{\mu\nu})$	$\frac{1}{2}\sum^{st}_{\mu}\sum^{unst}_{\nu} P^2_{\mu\nu}(\gamma_{12}-\gamma_{\mu\nu})$	$\mathscr{E}_R$ (cation)	$\mathscr{E}_R$ (radical)
allyl	− 45·6	14·6	—	60·2	31·0
trans-pentadienyl	− 80·7	22·6	3·5	99·8	54·6
benzyl	−149·9	19·8	7·2	162·5	122·9
diphenylmethyl	−292·0	27·1	16·2	302·9	248·7
triphenylmethyl†	−429·7	30·9	28·5	432·1	370·3
1-phenylallyl	−186·5	24·4	11·0	199·9	151·1
2 phenylallyl	−175·7	14·6	13·3	177·0	147·8

* In all numerical calculations a standard bond length is assumed (1·39 Å) and all bond angles are taken to be 120°. Values for the integrals are taken from the work of Pariser and Parr.[6] Thus $\beta = 55{\cdot}1$, $\gamma_{11} = 242{\cdot}7$, $\gamma_{12} = 168{\cdot}3$, $\gamma_{13} = 125{\cdot}9$, $\gamma_{14}(cis) = 113{\cdot}0$ kcal/mole. For larger internuclear separations $R_{\mu\nu}$, the point charge model of ref. (7) is used. These values, which are discussed in detail by Pariser and Parr, fit the benzene spectrum well. The corresponding value for the vertical resonance energy of benzene is $-2\beta - \frac{1}{6}(\gamma_{12} - \gamma_{14}) = 101{\cdot}0$ kcal/mole. This is rather higher than the value put forward by Mulliken and Parr [12] (78·5 kcal/mole), but is not far from the estimate of Glockler [13] (111 kcal/mole).

† The triphenylmethyl radical is treated as if it were planar. There is evidence that this is not so, presumably for steric reasons. The resonance energy of a non-planar configuration will be slightly lower.

TABLE 2.—THEORETICAL AND EXPERIMENTAL ESTIMATES OF SOME RESONANCE ENERGIES (kcal/mole)

energy	theor. estimate	expt. estimate	source *
$\mathscr{E}_R$ (allyl)	31·0	19·0	$D(CH_2:CH.CH_2-Br) - D(CH_3-Br)$
		24·0	$\frac{1}{2}[D(CH_2:CH.CH_2-CH_2.CH:CH_2) - D(CH_3-CH_3)]$
		24·0	$D(CH_2:CH.CH_2-Cl) - D(CH_3-Cl)$
$\mathscr{E}_R$ (allyl⁺)	60·2	58·0	appearance potential of allyl⁺ from allyl chloride [11]
$\mathscr{E}_R$ (benzyl) − $\mathscr{E}_R$(benzene)	21·9	23·5	$D(PhCH_2-H) - D(CH_3-H)$
		17·0	$D(PhCH_2-Br) - D(CH_3-Br)$
		19·5	$\frac{1}{2}[D(PhCH_2-CH_2Ph) - D(CH_3-CH_3)]$
$\mathscr{E}_R$ (benzyl⁺) − $\mathscr{E}_R$ (benzene)	61·5	50·0	appearance potential of benzyl⁺ from benzyl chloride [11]
$\mathscr{E}_R$ (triphenylmethyl) − 3$\mathscr{E}_R$ (benzene)	67·3	26·0	$D(Ph_3C-H) - D(CH_3-H)$
		37·5	$\frac{1}{2}[D(Ph_3C-CPh_3) - D(CH_3-CH_3)]$

* All dissociation energies are taken from the review of Szwarc.[14] Resonance energies of carbonium ions are estimated from appearance potentials $A(R^+)$ by assuming that this potential corresponds to the energy required for the process $RX \rightarrow R^+ + X^\cdot + e$. Then, following the method outlined by Halpern,[15] we have

$$\mathscr{E}_R(R^+) - \mathscr{E}_R(RX) = A(MeX \rightarrow Me^+ + X^\cdot + e) - A(RX \rightarrow R^+ + X^\cdot + e)$$

$$= I(Me^\cdot) + D(Me - X) - A(RX \rightarrow R^+ + X^\cdot + e),$$

where $I(Me^\cdot)$ is the ionization potential of the methyl radical (10·1 eV).[16] The estimates of $\mathscr{E}_R$ (allyl⁺) and $\mathscr{E}_R$ (benzyl⁺), are obtained by neglecting any resonance due to the —CH_2Cl group in the undissociated compound.

4. CHARGE DISTRIBUTION IN CARBONIUM IONS

It has already been shown in § 2 that this theory predicts equal and opposite charge distributions for corresponding carbonium ions and carbanions. In this section, therefore, we need only consider positive ions in detail, it being understood that corresponding conclusions apply to negative ions.

If the molecular orbitals are obtained by the Hückel procedure, the mobile electron charge densities on the carbon atoms of a singly charged carbonium ion are given by (3.6). That is, the resultant charge is restricted to starred atoms and its magnitude at any atom is equal to the square of the corresponding coefficient of the non-bonding orbital. A similar result is obtained from the resonance picture. The benzyl cation, for example, is supposed to resonate between structures such as

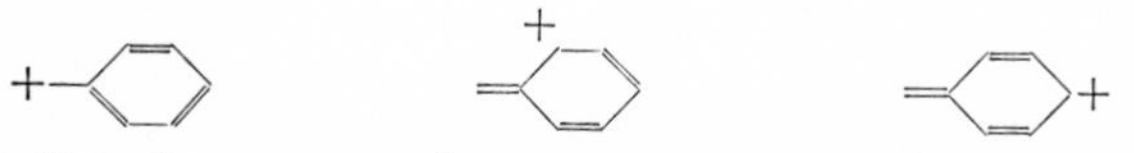

so that the positive charge may only appear on the CH_2 group or on the *ortho* or *para* positions. The mathematical equivalence of these two procedures has recently been demonstrated by Dewar and Longuet-Higgins.[17]

The equations for self-consistent orbitals given earlier in this paper can be used to investigate the validity of these conclusions. To do this we need to know how the $P_{\mu\mu}$ obtained from eqn. (2.2) differ from those obtained by the Hückel theory. This can be done by solving the self-consistent equations exactly, but a rather simpler procedure that will give the general information required is to treat the introduction of explicit electron interaction terms as a perturbation on the Hückel equations, only first-order changes being evaluated. As the perturbations are not small, the results obtained in this way will not be accurate, but they should be sufficient to indicate the direction and order of magnitude of any changes that occur.

If the $\gamma_{\mu\nu}$ are omitted, the matrix elements (2.3) and (2.4) become

$$F^{(0)}_{\mu\mu} = U_{\mu\mu}\,, \tag{4.1}$$

$$F^{(0)}_{\mu\nu} = \beta_{\mu\nu}\,, \quad (\mu \neq \nu), \tag{4.2}$$

and the corresponding charge densities $P^{(0)}_{\mu\mu}$ and bond orders $P^{(0)}_{\mu\nu}$ are the Hückel values. We shall use a bracketted zero superscript for quantities associated with the Hückel orbitals (the zeroth approximation to the solution of the self-consistent equations). If the $\gamma_{\mu\nu}$ are now introduced, the first-order changes in the matrix elements are

$$F^{(1)}_{\mu\mu} = \tfrac{1}{2}P^{(0)}_{\mu\mu}\gamma_{\mu\mu} + \sum_{\sigma(\neq\mu)} (P^{(0)}_{\sigma\sigma} - 1)\gamma_{\mu\sigma}, \tag{4.3}$$

$$F^{(1)}_{\mu\nu} = -\tfrac{1}{2}P^{(0)}_{\mu\nu}\gamma_{\mu\nu}\,, \quad (\mu \neq \nu). \tag{4.4}$$

The corresponding changes in the charge densities $P^{(1)}_{\lambda\lambda}$ can be obtained from the theory of perturbations to the Hückel equations developed by Coulson and Longuet-Higgins.[18] Thus

$$P^{(1)}_{\lambda\lambda} = \sum_{\mu} \pi^{(0)}_{\lambda,\,\mu} F^{(1)}_{\mu\mu} + \sum_{\mu<\nu} \pi^{(0)}_{\lambda,\,\mu\nu} F^{(1)}_{\mu\nu}, \tag{4.5}$$

where $\pi^{(0)}_{\lambda,\,\mu}$ and $\pi^{(0)}_{\lambda,\,\mu\nu}$ are certain polarizability coefficients for which Coulson and Longuet-Higgins give explicit formulae. $P^{(0)}_{\lambda\lambda} + P^{(1)}_{\lambda\lambda}$ is then the improved estimate of the charge density on atom λ.

This procedure has been carried out for several carbonium ions using the same integrals as in table 1. The results are given in fig. 1. For $(\text{allyl})^+$ the exact solutions of eqn. (2.2) are easily obtained, so both sets of values are given for comparison.

These figures show several interesting features. Some of the $P_{\mu\mu}$ are greater than unity, indicating that an atom in a positive ion may bear a resultant negative charge. This appears surprising at first, but further consideration shows that the repulsion between electrons in the same atomic orbital may not be the dominating factor. In (allyl)$^+$, for example, numbering the atoms 1, 2 and 3, we find for the first-order changes in diagonal matrix elements (from (4.3))

$$F_{11}^{(1)} = F_{33}^{(1)} = \tfrac{1}{4}\gamma_{11} - \tfrac{1}{2}\gamma_{13} = -\,0{\cdot}10\ \text{eV}, \quad F_{22}^{(1)} = \tfrac{1}{2}\gamma_{11} - \gamma_{12} = -\,2{\cdot}03\ \text{eV}. \tag{4.6}$$

This means that for the central atom the proximity of two neighbours bearing a considerable resultant charge more than offsets the interaction of electrons in the same orbital and so its charge density is increased in the next approximation.

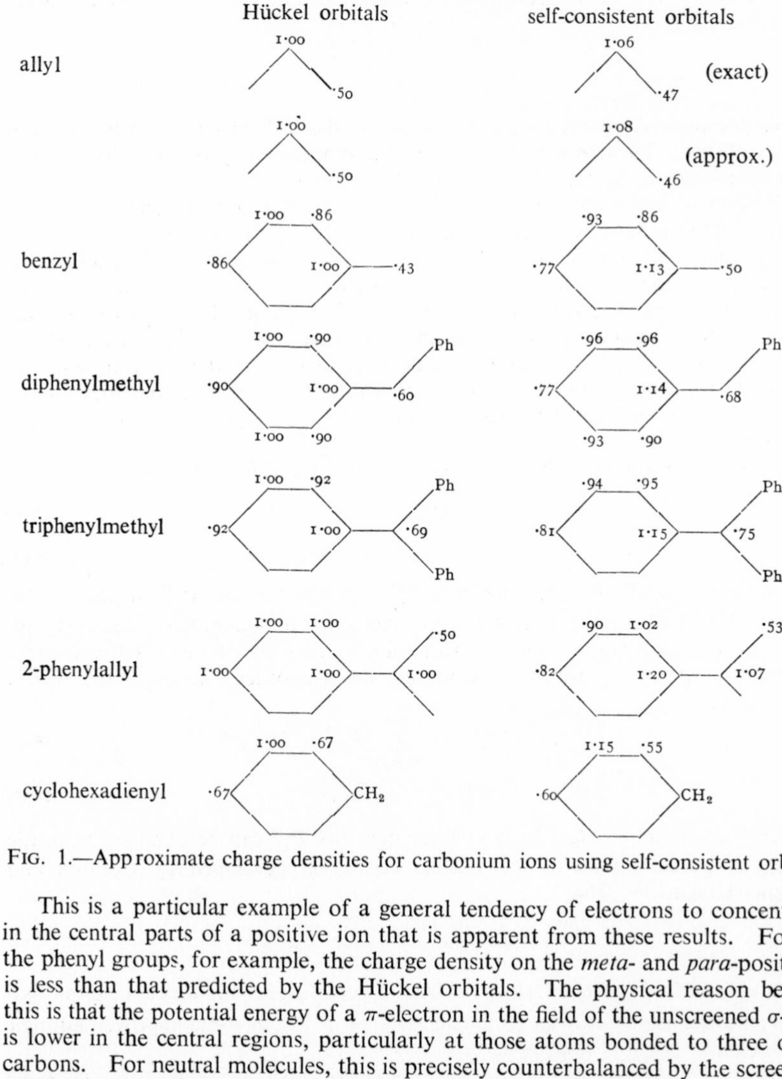

FIG. 1.—Approximate charge densities for carbonium ions using self-consistent orbitals

This is a particular example of a general tendency of electrons to concentrate in the central parts of a positive ion that is apparent from these results. For all the phenyl groups, for example, the charge density on the *meta*- and *para*-positions is less than that predicted by the Hückel orbitals. The physical reason behind this is that the potential energy of a π-electron in the field of the unscreened σ-core is lower in the central regions, particularly at those atoms bonded to three other carbons. For neutral molecules, this is precisely counterbalanced by the screening effect of other π-electrons and uniform charge density is obtained. For carbonium ions, however, the screening is incomplete and there remains a tendency for electrons to keep away from the perimeter.

The results for the cyclohexadienyl ion (neglecting any hyperconjugative effect of the CH_2 group) are of particular interest as this system is closely analogous to the transition state for the electrophilic substitution of benzene. Wheland [19] suggested that the effect of the approaching reagent was to localize two of the π-electrons on the carbon atom attacked, leaving the other four in a pentadienyl-like system. According to the Hückel theory, the positive charge is then distributed equally over the positions *ortho* and *para* to the position under attack. The presence of electron-donating substituents at these positions, therefore, lowers the energy of the transition state and increases the reaction rate. This explanation of *ortho-para* direction is reinforced by the self-consistent calculations which suggest that the non-uniformity of charge distribution in the transition state is more marked than has hitherto been supposed.

APPENDIX

Here we shall obtain certain general properties of self-consistent orbitals for odd alternant systems. The proofs depend on the concept of "pairing of orbitals". Two orbitals ψ_i and ψ_j are said to be paired if the corresponding coefficients satisfy $x_{i\mu} = \pm x_{j\mu}$ according as μ is starred or unstarred.

Consider first the Hückel orbitals for an odd alternant with $2N + 1$ carbon centres. It is well known [8, 9] that these orbitals must be paired or be of the non-bonding type (i.e. restricted to one of the two classes of atoms). We shall only consider systems with one non-bonding orbital ψ_0 confined to starred atoms. The remaining orbitals may be numbered so that $\psi_i (i > 0)$ is occupied and is paired with ψ_{-i} (unoccupied). ψ_0 is unoccupied, singly and doubly occupied in the cation, radical and anion respectively. Now since $x_{i\mu}$ are obtained as eigenvectors of a unitary matrix, we must have

$$\sum_i^{\text{all}} \bar{x}_{i\mu} x_{i\nu} = \delta_{\mu\nu}, \tag{5.1}$$

$\delta_{\mu\nu}$ being unity if $\mu = \nu$ and zero otherwise. This may be written

$$\sum_{i>0} \bar{x}_{i\mu} x_{i\nu} + \sum_{i<0} \bar{x}_{i\mu} x_{i\nu} = \delta_{\mu\nu} - \bar{x}_{0\mu} x_{0\nu}. \tag{5.2}$$

If μ and ν belong to the same class, the two terms on the left-hand side are equal and (3.6)-(3.9) follow immediately from the definitions of $P_{\mu\nu}$.

We now come to the proofs of the results for self-consistent orbitals quoted at the end of § 2. Consider first eqn. (2.2) for the positive and negative singly-charged ions of an odd alternant system. These may be written in the form

$$\sum_\nu \mathscr{F}_{\mu\nu} x_{i\nu} = \eta_i x_{i\mu}, \tag{5.3}$$

where

$$\mathscr{F}_{\mu\nu} = F_{\mu\nu} - (U + \tfrac{1}{2}\gamma_{11})\delta_{\mu\nu},$$
$$\eta_i = E_i - (U + \tfrac{1}{2}\gamma_{11}). \tag{5.4}$$

They can be solved by a cyclic procedure. The Hückel orbitals can be used to obtain approximate $\mathscr{F}_{\mu\nu}$ and (5.3) can then be solved as linear equations giving a better approximation to $x_{i\mu}$. The process can then be repeated until self-consistency is obtained.

Now we have shown above that eqn. (2.16)-(2.17) hold for Hückel orbitals. From the form of $F_{\mu\nu}$, these imply

$$\mathscr{F}^+_{\mu\nu} = -\mathscr{F}^-_{\mu\nu}, \ (\mu, \nu \text{ in same class}),$$
$$\mathscr{F}^+_{\mu\nu} = \mathscr{F}^-_{\mu\nu}, \ (\mu, \nu \text{ in different classes}). \tag{5.5}$$

From these we can deduce that, in the next approximation, the occupied and unoccupied orbitals of the positive ion are paired with the unoccupied and occupied orbitals of the negative ion respectively. For (5.3) can be written

$$-\sum_\nu^{\text{st}} \mathscr{F}^-_{\mu\nu} x^+_{i\nu} + \sum_\nu^{\text{unst}} \mathscr{F}^-_{\mu\nu} x^+_{i\nu} = \eta^+_i x^+_{i\mu}, \tag{5.6}$$

from which it follows that $\pm x^{+}_{i\mu}$ are the coefficients of an orbital with energy $-\eta^{+}_{i}$ in the negative ion.

As a consequence of this pairing, we have (using (5.1))

$$P^{+}_{\mu\nu} = 2\sum_{i}^{\text{occ}} \overline{x^{+}_{i\mu}x^{+}_{i\nu}} = 2\sum_{i}^{\text{unocc}} \overline{x^{-}_{i\mu}x^{-}_{i\nu}} = 2\delta_{\mu\nu} - P^{-}_{\mu\nu}, \quad (\mu, \nu \text{ in same class}),$$

$$P^{+}_{\mu\nu} = 2\sum_{i}^{\text{occ}} \overline{x^{+}_{i\mu}x^{+}_{i\nu}} = -2\sum_{i}^{\text{unocc}} \overline{x^{-}_{i\mu}x^{-}_{i\nu}} = P^{-}_{\mu\nu}, \quad (\mu, \nu \text{ in different classes}), \qquad (5.7)$$

so that (2.16)-(2.18) hold also for the orbitals obtained after one cycle. A corresponding proof applies to every cycle, so the results apply to the final self-consistent solution (assuming convergence).

The proof of (2.19)-(2.21) for radicals follows very similar lines. If Hückel orbitals are used, then

$$\mathscr{F}^{\alpha}_{\mu\nu} = -\mathscr{F}^{\beta}_{\mu\nu}, \quad (\mu, \nu \text{ in same class}),$$

$$\mathscr{F}^{\alpha}_{\mu\nu} = \mathscr{F}^{\beta}_{\mu\nu}, \quad (\mu, \nu \text{ in different classes}).$$

By similar arguments it follows that the occupied α-orbitals are paired with the unoccupied β-orbitals and that (2.19)-(2.21) hold after each cycle of the calculation.

1 Hückel, *Z. Physik*, 1931, **70**, 204, 279.
2 Coulson, *Valence* (Oxford, 1952).
3 Lennard-Jones, *Proc. Roy. Soc. A*, 1949, **198**, 1, 14.
4 Hall, *Proc. Roy. Soc. A*, 1951, **205**, 541.
5 Roothaan, *Rev. Mod. Physics*, 1951, **23**, 61.
6 Pariser and Parr, *J. Chem. Physics*, 1953, **21**, 466, 767.
7 Pople, *Trans. Faraday Soc.*, 1953, **49**, 1375.
8 Coulson and Rushbrooke, *Proc. Camb. Phil. Soc.*, 1940, **36**, 193.
9 Longuet-Higgins, *J. Chem. Physics*, 1950, **18**, 265.
10 Pople and Nesbet, *J. Chem. Physics* (to be published).
11 Franklin and Lumpkin, *J. Chem. Physics*, 1951, **19**, 1073.
12 Mulliken and Parr, *J. Chem. Physics*, 1941, **19**, 1271.
13 Glockler, *J. Chem. Physics*, 1953, **21**, 1249.
14 Szwarc, *Chem. Rev.*, 1950, **47**, 75.
15 Halpern, *J. Chem. Physics*, 1952, **20**, 744.
16 Stevenson and Hipple, *Physic. Rev.*, 1943, **63**, 621.
17 Dewar and Longuet-Higgins, *Proc. Roy. Soc. A*, 1952, **214**, 482.
18 Coulson and Longuet-Higgins, *Proc. Roy. Soc. A*, 1947, **191**, 39.
19 Wheland, *J. Amer. Chem. Soc.*, 1942, **64**, 900.

IONIZATION POTENTIALS AND ELECTRON AFFINITIES OF CONJUGATED HYDROCARBON MOLECULES AND RADICALS

By N. S. Hush and J. A. Pople

Dept. of Physical and Inorganic Chemistry, University of Bristol
Dept. of Theoretical Chemistry, University of Cambridge

Received 23*rd July*, 1954; *in final form*, 22*nd November*, 1954

The self-consistent molecular orbital theory with systematic approximation for electron interaction integrals is applied to the calculation of the ionization potential I and the electron affinity A of alternant conjugated hydrocarbon molecules and radicals. The theory predicts the simple result

$$I + A = \text{const.}$$

for all such molecules and radicals. Calculations have been made for a series of molecules and radicals using semi-empirical values of electron interaction integrals proposed by Pariser and Parr. The agreement with experimental data is satisfactory In particular, it is shown that certain features of the experimental results cannot be understood unless electron interaction is taken into account explicitly.

1. Introduction

The simplest molecular orbital theories of the mobile electrons of conjugated hydrocarbons (the free electron model and the Hückel l.c.a.o. theory), which neglect the specific effects of electron interaction, have not been able to give a satisfactory account of observed ionization potentials I and electron affinities A. For molecules with closed shell ground states, the difference between I and A is predicted to be too small if the parameters used are those required to give reasonable resonance energies or spectroscopic levels. For many free radicals, the simpler theories imply that $I = A$, in gross disagreement with experimental data.

The basic reason for these poor results is the failure of the simpler theories to make the energy of an electron in any one orbital dependent on whether the others are occupied or not. Such effects arise from the electrostatic interaction of electrons. Recent developments [1, 2, 3] have enabled the principal effects of electron interaction to be examined approximately within the framework of a relatively simple theory. The present paper is concerned with the application of these new methods to a study of ionization potentials and electron affinities.

2. Even alternant hydrocarbon molecules

Following previous molecular orbital theories of conjugated hydrocarbons. we suppose that the mobile or π-electrons can be allocated to a set of delocalized molecular orbitals ψ_i, these being linear combinations of atomic orbitals (l.c.a.o.),

$$\psi_i = \sum_{\mu} x_{i\mu}\phi_{\mu}. \tag{2.1}$$

Throughout, Greek suffixes will be used for atomic orbitals and italics for molecular orbitals. We shall neglect the overlap integral between different atomic orbitals, so that normalization of the molecular orbitals implies

$$\sum_{\mu} \bar{x}_{i\mu}x_{i\mu}' = 1. \tag{2.2}$$

Suppose we are dealing with a conjugated hydrocarbon with $2N$ mobile electrons occupying N molecular orbitals. If the field of the σ-electrons is treated as an effective fixed potential, the coefficients $x_{i\mu}$ should be determined from the Roothaan self-consistent equations [4]

$$\sum_{\nu} F_{\mu\nu}x_{i\nu} = E_i x_{i\mu}, \tag{2.3}$$

where $F_{\mu\nu}$ are matrix elements of the Hartree-Fock Hamiltonian. The eigenvalues E_i are roots of the secular equation

$$| F_{\mu\nu} - E\delta_{\mu\nu} | = 0. \tag{2.4}$$

Eqn. (2.1)-(2.3) define $2N$ molecular orbitals, of which only N (corresponding to lower E_i) are occupied in the ground state. We shall number the molecular orbitals in order of increasing E_i.

If we assume that the other molecular orbitals are unaltered when an electron is removed from a molecular orbital ψ_i, Roothaan [4] has shown that $-E_i$ is equal to the corresponding ionization potential. Thus the first ionization potential I is given by

$$-I = E_N = \sum_{\mu\nu} \bar{x}_{N\mu}F_{\mu\nu}x_{N\nu}. \tag{2.5}$$

In a similar way, if we assume that other orbitals are unaltered when an electron is added to one of the higher orbitals ψ_k, it can be shown that $-E_k$ is equal to the corresponding electron affinity. Thus the first electron affinity A is given by

$$-A = E_{N+1} = \sum_{\mu\nu} \bar{x}_{N+1,\mu}F_{\mu\nu}x_{N+1,\nu}. \tag{2.6}$$

This result is derived by a method completely analogous to that used by Roothaan for ionization potentials, so details need not be given.

Using certain approximations for the integrals, Pople [3] has shown that the matrix elements $F_{\mu\nu}$ can be written

$$F_{\mu\mu} = U_{\mu\mu} + \tfrac{1}{2}P_{\mu\mu}\gamma_{\mu\mu} + \sum_{\sigma(\neq\mu)} (P_{\sigma\sigma} - 1)\gamma_{\mu\sigma}, \tag{2.7}$$

$$F_{\mu\nu} = \beta_{\mu\nu} - \tfrac{1}{2}P_{\mu\nu}\gamma_{\mu\nu}, \qquad (\mu \neq \nu), \tag{2.8}$$

$$P_{\mu\nu} = 2\sum_{i=1}^{N} x_{i\mu}x_{i\nu}. \tag{2.9}$$

Here $U_{\mu\mu}$ and $\beta_{\mu\nu}$ are matrix elements involving the core Hamiltonian, which may reasonably be taken to have equal values for all carbon atoms and carbon-carbon bonds respectively. $\beta_{\mu\nu}$ is supposed to be zero for non-neighbour μ and ν. $\gamma_{\mu\nu}$ are two-electron integrals of the type

$$\gamma_{\mu\nu} = \iint \bar{\phi}_\mu(1)\, \bar{\phi}_\nu(2)(1/r_{12})\phi_\mu(1)\phi_\nu(2)dv_1dv_2. \tag{2.10}$$

For alternant hydrocarbons, whose carbon atoms can be divided into two groups, no member of one group being directly bonded to another of the same group, certain general conclusions can be drawn from this approximate version of the self-consistent theory.[3] These are

(i) $P_{\mu\mu} = 1$ for all μ. It follows that

$$F_{\mu\mu} = U_{\mu\mu} + \tfrac{1}{2}\gamma_{\mu\mu} = \text{constant}. \tag{2.11}$$

(ii) The orbitals are paired, so that the coefficients $x_{N+1,\mu}$ are related to $x_{N\mu}$ by

$$x_{N+1,\mu} = \pm x_{N\mu}, \tag{2.12}$$

the positive sign being taken for one group and the negative for the other.

(iii) $P_{\mu\nu}$ and hence $F_{\mu\nu}$ are zero if μ and ν are different atoms of the same group.

Using these three properties, we find from (2.5) and (2.6) that the ionization potential and electron affinity of the hydrocarbon are given by

$$-I = U + \tfrac{1}{2}\gamma_{11} - Q, \qquad (2.13)$$
$$-A = U + \tfrac{1}{2}\gamma_{11} + Q,$$

where

$$Q = -2\sum_{\mu<\nu} x_{N\mu}F_{\mu\nu}x_{N\nu}. \qquad (2.14)$$

Eqn. (2.13) immediately leads to the interesting prediction that the sum of the ionization potential and the electron affinity should be a constant independent of the hydrocarbon.

Given numerical values for the various parameters, these equations enable theoretical estimates of I and A to be calculated. In practice the self-consistent equations are rather tedious to solve completely so in the calculations given later in the paper the coefficients $x_{i\mu}$ obtained by the Hückel method are used as approximations.

Before proceeding to the prediction of ionization potentials and electron affinities of particular hydrocarbons, we shall derive expressions for alternant free radicals (with an odd number of carbon centres) corresponding to (2.13).

3. Odd alternant hydrocarbon radicals

For odd alternant radicals with $2N - 1$ centres, the carbon atoms can be divided into two groups as before, one group containing more than the other. We shall only consider radicals in which there are N of one class (starred) and $N - 1$ of the other (unstarred). We shall use the simple Hückel values for the l.c.a.o. coefficients $x_{i\mu}$. Longuet-Higgins has shown [5] that the coefficients $x_{N\mu}$ of the singly occupied orbital ψ_N are zero on all unstarred atoms. ψ_N is often referred to as the non-bonding orbital.

We wish to consider energy changes when an electron is removed or added to the non-bonding orbital. This is a slightly different theoretical problem from that considered in the last section where we were dealing with adding or removing an electron from a closed-shell ground state. However, we may note that the ionization potential of the radical is equal to the electron affinity of the positive ion and is therefore

$$-I = \sum_{\mu\nu} x_{N\mu}F^{+}_{\mu\nu}x_{N\nu}, \qquad (3.1)$$

$F^{+}_{\mu\nu}$ being the matrix for the ion (which is in a closed-shell ground state). Similarly, the electron affinity of the radical is equal to the ionization potential of the anion, so that

$$-A = \sum_{\mu\nu} x_{N\mu}F_{\mu\nu}x_{N\nu}. \qquad (3.2)$$

Since the non-bonding orbital ψ_N is restricted to starred atoms, we only need $F_{\mu\nu}$ for μ, ν both starred. The corresponding values of $P_{\mu\nu}$ are [5, 6]

POSITIVE IONS	NEGATIVE IONS	
$P^{+}_{\mu\mu} = 1 - x^2_{N\mu}$	$P^{-}_{\mu\mu} = 1 + x^2_{N}$	
$P^{+}_{\mu\nu} = -x_{N\mu}x_{N\nu}$	$P^{-}_{\mu\nu} = x_{N\mu}x_{N\nu}$	(3.3)
	($\mu \neq \nu$, both starred).	

Eqn. (2.7) and (2.8) apply, so that we find

$$-I = U + \tfrac{1}{2}\gamma_{11} - Q', \qquad (3.4)$$
$$-A = U + \tfrac{1}{2}\gamma_{11} + Q',$$

where

$$Q' = \tfrac{1}{2}\sum_{\mu\nu} x^2_{N\mu}x^2_{N\nu}\gamma'_{\mu\nu}. \qquad (3.5)$$

Physically, $2Q'$ corresponds to the electronic repulsion energy between two electrons in the non-bonding orbital.

Two interesting results follow from (3.4) and (3.5). In the first place we have a formula which predicts that the ionization potential of an odd alternant radical will be lower if the non-bonding orbital is more spread out. The simple Hückel theory based on a one-electron Hamiltonian, however, predicts that they are all the same. Secondly, the rule

$$I + A = \text{constant} \tag{3.6}$$

should apply equally to radicals, the constant being the same as for even alternant molecules.

4. Empirical values of integrals

The basic parameters occurring in the theory outlined above are the core integrals U and β and the coulomb electron repulsion integrals $\gamma_{\mu\nu}$. In ref. (3) the latter were approximated (in atomic units) by the inverse distance between corresponding nuclei $R_{\mu\nu}$ if $\mu \neq \nu$, the integral γ_{11} (written $(11 \mid G \mid 11)$) being left unspecified. γ_{11} can be evaluated using an analytical form for the atomic orbital (such as the Slater exponential) but Pariser [7] has suggested that it is more appropriate to choose it empirically as the difference between the ionization potential and electron affinity of the valence state of neutral carbon. Such a choice gives the correct energy for the process $C^+ + C^- \rightarrow 2C$ and makes some allowance for the polarization effects in the σ-core. This empirical γ_{11} is particularly appropriate for a theory of ionization potentials and electron affinities of molecules for such a theory is likely to be more successful if it is based on parameters which give a correct description of the corresponding atomic quantities, rather than on *a priori* estimates.

γ_{11} determined from atomic data is considerably less than the theoretical value, so Pariser and Parr [1] also use reduced values for other $\gamma_{\mu\nu}$. In this paper we shall assume that all bond-lengths are equal to that of benzene (1·39 Å) and all bond angles 120°. $\gamma_{\mu\nu}$ is then needed for various multiples of this distance. We shall use the Pariser-Parr [2] values $\gamma_{\mu\nu} = 10{\cdot}53$, 7·30, 5·46 and 4·90 eV for internuclear distances 0, 1, $\sqrt{3}$ and 2 times the benzene distance. For larger separations the point-charge approximation of reference 3 will be used. The value of β will be taken as $-$ 2·39 eV (following Pariser and Parr). This set of parameters was found to give a satisfactory picture of the electronic transitions in benzene. They also fit data on vertical resonance energies quite well.

The remaining parameter U is common to all ionization potentials and electron affinities, differences among a series of compounds being independent of it. We shall therefore leave this as a further empirical parameter to be discussed in direct relation to the data.

5. Comparison of theory with experimental data

The quantities Q and Q' of eqn. (2.13) and (3.4) have been evaluated for a series of molecules and radicals, using the parameters given in the previous section. It is found that the best overall fit of the experimental data is obtained if U is taken to be about $-$ 9·50 eV. Ionization potentials and electron affinities based on this value are given in tables 1 and 2.

Experimental values are also listed where they are known. Of these, the ionization potentials are the more reliable. Nearly all the values listed are vertical ionization potentials derived from electron-impact data, the probable error being usually in the range 0·03-0·1 eV. The electron affinities for both molecules and radicals (particularly the latter) are more approximate. Relative values of A have been estimated from measurements of the kinetics of electron transfer to the hydrocarbon at a mercury electrode, and the absolute values quoted are all standardized on Swift's value of $A = 2{\cdot}1$ eV for the triphenylmethyl radical (table 2, notes (*c*) and (*d*)).

The calculated ionization potentials of both molecules and radicals in general correspond quite closely to the experimental values. Such an agreement would not have been obtained if electron interaction terms had been omitted. This is strikingly illustrated by the results for radicals; the simple Hückel theory predicts that I for all radicals is the energy required to remove an electron from a non-bonding molecular orbital and will therefore be constant, which is experimentally far from being true. Variations of electron affinity in molecules are also fairly

TABLE 1.—CALCULATED AND EXPERIMENTAL DATA FOR SOME HYDROCARBON MOLECULES

	I, eV		A, eV	
	calc.	obs.	calc.	obs.
benzene	9·87	9·43[a]	— 1·40	— 0·54*
ethylene	10·28†	10·62[a]	— 1·81	—
trans-butadiene	8·81	9·07[b]	— 0·34	—
styrene	8·76	8·86[c]	— 0·29	—
diphenyl	8·84	8·30[d]	— 0·37	+ 0·41[f]
naphthalene	8·61	8·30[e]	— 0·14	+ 0·65[f]
phenanthrene	8·53	—	— 0·06	+ 0·69[f]
anthracene	7·83	—	+ 0·64	+ 1·19[f]
graphite sheet	4·23	4·39[g]	+ 4·23	4·39[g]

* extrapolated. † A different value of β should really be used for the shorter C—C bond in ethylene.

a Honig, *J. Chem. Physics*, 1948, **16**, 105.
b Price and Walsh, *Proc. Roy. Soc. A*, 1940, **174**, 220.
c Morrison, *J. Chem. Physics*, 1952, **20**, 1021.
d Syrkin and Diatkina, *The Structure of Molecules* (Butterworth, 1950), p. 265.
e Birge, *Physic. Rev.*, 1937, **52**, 241.
f Blackedge and Hush, in course of publication.
g photoelectric work function of graphite quoted by Mulliken, *Physic. Rev.*, 1948. **74**, 736.

TABLE 2.—CALCULATED AND EXPERIMENTAL DATA FOR HYDROCARBON RADICALS

	I, eV		A, eV	
	calc.	obs.	calc.	obs.
methyl	9·50	9·95[a]	— 1·03	1·1[c]
allyl	8·23	8·16[a]	+ 0·24	2·1[c]
benzyl	7·78	7·73[a]	+ 0·69	1·8[c]
α-naphthylmethyl	7·35	—	+ 1·12	1·6[c]
diphenylmethyl	7·26	—	+ 1·21	—
triphenylmethyl	6·82	6·5[b]	+ 1·65	2·1[d]

[a] Lossing, Ingold and Henderson, *J. Chem. Physics*, 1954, **22**, 621.
[b] approximate value derived from standard potential of ϕ_3Me^+/ϕ_3Me couple reported by Conant and Chow, *J. Amer. Chem. Soc.*, 1933, **55**, 3752; the solvation energy of ϕ_3Me^+ has been estimated by the method of Evans, *Trans. Faraday Soc.*, 1946, **42**, 719.
[c] Hush and Oldham, in course of publication; cf. Pritchard, *Chem. Rev.*, 1953, **52**, 529.
[d] Swift, *J. Amer. Chem. Soc.*, 1938, **60**, 1403.

well fitted by the calculations, and the predicted constancy of $I + A$ (eqn. (3.6)) is approximately borne out. Absolute theoretical values of A for molecules are lower by $\sim 0{\cdot}7$ eV than the listed experimental quantities; this is possibly connected with the fact that the calculated electron affinity of triphenylmethyl is also rather less (0·45 eV) than the experimental value which has been used to calibrate the series. For radicals, the relative electron affinities of the larger species are fairly well correlated, but the data for smaller radicals (methyl, allyl, benzyl) are not well fitted. For methyl, this is partly due to a choice of U which under-estimates I for methyl by 0·45 eV; the cause of the remaining discrepancies is not clear. However, as the experimental electron affinities for radicals are still somewhat tentative, it seems best to postpone any further discussion of the significance of these differences. With these reservations, the correspondence between theory and experiment is most encouraging, and this is particularly so in view of the fact that we have used Hückel orbitals, which are only a first approximation to the properly self-consistent wave-funcions.

The value of the parameter U which has been assumed in these calculations is the mean of the values which fit the experimental ionization potentials of methyl radical and benzene, i.e. $-9{\cdot}95$ and $-9{\cdot}06$ eV respectively. Although we have assumed U to be constant and independent of the environment of the carbon atom, it is evident that some variation is to be expected when directly-bonded hydrogen atoms are substituted by carbon atoms. Further refinements of the theory must take this into account. Apart from the extreme cases cited, however, it seems probable that the error introduced into the calculation of ionization potential by the assumption of constant U will be at least partially cancelled by variations in electron interaction integrals $\gamma_{\mu\nu}$, particularly γ_{11}, the values of which have correspondingly been assumed to be independent of the nature of σ-bonded atoms. In terms of Slater atomic functions, an increase in $-U$ corresponds to an increased effective nuclear charge, and hence also to an increase in γ_{11}, so that the sum $U + \frac{1}{2}\gamma_{11}$ should be less sensitive to the bonding environment of the atom than either of the individual terms.[8]

We are indebted to Mr. F. Sumner, Manchester University, for making available some electronic digital computer calculations of Hückel orbital coefficients.

1 Pariser and Parr, *J. Chem. Physics*, 1953, **21**, 466.
2 Pariser and Parr, *J. Chem. Physics*, 1953, **21**, 767.
3 Pople, *Trans. Faraday Soc.*, 1953, **49**, 1375.
4 Roothaan, *Rev. Mod. Physics*, 1951, **23**, 61.
5 Longuet-Higgins, *J. Chem. Physics*, 1950, **18**, 265.
6 Brickstock and Pople, *Trans. Faraday Soc.*, 1954, **50**, 901.
7 Pariser, *J. Chem. Physics*, 1953, **21**, 568.
8 Blackledge and Hush, *J. Chem. Physics*, in press.

[Reprinted from the Bulletin of the Chemical Society of Japan, Vol. 28, No. 4 (1955)]

A Semi-empirical Approach to the SCF Molecular Orbitals

By Hideo KON

(Received January 27, 1955)

Introduction

The semi-empirical ASMO method recently proposed by Pariser and Parr[1] presents a way to calculate the transition energies and oscillator strengths of a variety of π-electron systems without much labour, in such a quantitative conformity with experiments as is rarely found in this kind of calculation. One of the essential points of their method is to alter the values of Coulomb repulsion integrals over atomic orbitals by introducing semi-empirical elements on a similar ground as in the method of "atoms in molecules" of Moffit[2]. The reasonable nature of such revision of integral values is illustrated by

1) R. Pariser and R.G. Parr, *J. Chem. Phys.*, 21, 466, 767 (1953).

2) W. Moffit, *Proc. Roy. Soc.*, A210, 245 (1951).

the improvements in the results of their calculations. Nothing is known, however, of the improvements in the form of MO's which might be brought about by introducing the revised integrals, and one has to be content with the naive Hückel method or to resort to the elaborate, laborious, self-consistent field method of Roothaan[3].

In this preparatory note, a trial is given to incorporate the Pariser and Parr's semi-empirical method into the iterative procedure of Roothaan in order to reflect their reasonable revision of the integral values on the form of molecular orbitals. In the course of this calculation, the author found that Pople's treatment of unsaturated hydrocarbon[4] was based on a similar idea, but there, the Coulomb repulsion integrals were approximated by the Coulomb energy between two point charges instead of the charged sphere model of Pariser and Parr, and the details were somewhat different from the present treatment.

Modification of Roothaan's SCF Equation

A molecular orbital (ϕ_i) of a π-electron system is expressed as a linear combination of atomic orbitals (χ_p),

$$\phi_i=\sum_p c_{ip}\chi_p.$$

The coefficients c_{ip} are determined by a homogeneous set of equations derived by Roothaan.

$$\sum_q c_{ip}(L_{pq}-S_{pq}\varepsilon_i=0,$$

$$L_{pq}=G_{pq}+I_{pq},$$

$$G_{pq}=\sum_i^{occ}[2J_{i,pq}-K_{i,pq}],$$

$$I_{pq}=\int\chi_p(\nu)H_{core}\chi_q(\nu)d\tau_\nu$$
$$=\int\chi_p(\nu)[T(\nu)+\sum_r U_r(\nu)]\chi_q(\nu)d\tau_\nu\,.$$

$U_r(\nu)$ is the potential on the electron ν due to the atom r stripped of its π-electron. $J_{i,pq}$ and $K_{i,pq}$ are defined as follows:

$$J_{i,pq}=\int\int\phi^*_i(\mu)\phi_i(\mu)[e^2/r_{\mu\nu}]\,\chi^*_p(\nu)\chi_q(\nu)d\tau_\nu\,d\tau_\mu,$$
$$K_{i,pq}=\int\int\phi_i^*(\mu)\phi_i(\nu)[e^2/r_{\mu\nu}]\,\chi^*_q(\mu)\chi_q(\nu)d\tau_\mu d\tau_\nu\,.$$

The simplifying assumptions of Pariser and Parr such as; 1) zero differential overlap, $\chi_p\chi_q=0$, 2) neglect of non-neighbour core integral I_{pq}, are taken into account here, so that $J_{i,pq}$ and $K_{i,pq}$ are rewritten in terms only of atomic Coulomb repulsion integrals as follows,

$$J_{i,pq}=0,\ p\neq q,$$
$$J_{i,pp}=\sum_q c^2_{iq}\int\chi^*_q(\mu)\chi_q(\mu)[e^2/r_{\mu\nu}]\chi^*_p(\nu)\chi_p(\nu)d\tau_\mu d\tau_\nu=\sum_q c^2_{iq}(qq|pp)$$
$$=c^2_{ip}\,(pp|pp)+\sum_{q\neq p}c^2_{iq}(qq|pp),$$

$$K_{i,pq}=c_{ip}c_{iq}\,(pp|qq).$$

Similarly, the core integrals reduce to two integrals:

$$I_{pq}=\alpha_p,\quad p=q,$$
$$=\beta_{pq},\quad p\neq q,\ \text{atom } p \text{ being linked directly to atom } q,$$
$$=0,\quad \text{otherwise}.$$

Thus the expression for the quantity L_{pq} is replaced by

$$L_{pp}=\alpha_p+\sum_i 2c^2_{ip}(pp|pp)+\sum_i\sum_{q\neq p}2c^2_{iq}(pp|qq)-\sum_i c^2_{ip}\,(pp|pp)$$

$$=\alpha_p+\frac{1}{2}Q_p(pp|pp)+\sum_{q\neq p}Q_q(qq|pp),$$

$$L_{pq}=\beta_{pq}-\sum_i c_{ip}c_{iq}(pp|qq)$$

$$=\beta_{pq}-\frac{1}{2}P_{pq}(pp|qq),\quad p\neq q.$$

Here Q_p is the π-electron density on p-atom and P_{pq} reduces to the mobile bond order, if atoms p and q are the neighbouring atoms, but if not, it has not any definite physical meaning. In addition to these simplifications, the following assumptions are made in this paper in dealing with the core integrals α_p and β_{pq}.

1) The Coulomb integral α_p can be approximated as the valence state ionization potential (W_{2p}) of a $2p$ electron on a free atom, less the sum only of the Coulomb repulsion integrals $(pp|qq)$, summation being carried out over all the other atoms q involved in the π-electron system. This neglect of Coulomb penetration integrals is found to reduce the labour without having a significant influence on the good numerical performance of Pariser and Parr's original work. 2) The resonance integral β_{pq} which as in ref. 1, is one of the empirical parameters and is carried from molecule to molecule, is assumed, apart from Pariser and Parr, to be proportional to the inverse sixth-power of the bond distance r_{pq} and the proportionality constants are so chosen as to reproduce the observed first transition energy of a particular molecule as closely as possible. As the reference molecule, ethylene, formaldehyde and pyrazine

3) C.C.J. Roothaan, *Rev. Mod. Phys.*, 23, 69 (1951); R. G. Parr and R.S. Mulliken, *J. Chem. Phys.*, 18, 1338 (1950).

4) J.A. Pople, *Trans. Farad. Soc.*, 49, 1375 (1953).

are chosen for the bond C=C, C=O and C=N, respectively. In ref. 1, it is postulated that β_{pq} can be expressed as, $\beta_{pq}=a\exp(-br_{pq})$. Two experimental data being needed to fix the parameters a and b, it is not easy to extend it to other cases than C=C bonds. Whether or not the inverse sixth-power equation is appropriate will be tested by applying it to a variety of compounds and by comparing the results with observations. Taking these assumptions into account, the matrix element L_{pp} can be written down as,

$$L_{pp}=W_{2p}+\frac{1}{2}Q_p(pp|pp)+\sum_{q\neq p}(Q_q-1)(qq|pp).$$

If we put, $Q_p=Q_q=1$, then L_{pp} becomes a constant. As L_{pp} in the present treatment plays an analogous role to the Coulomb integral in the simple molecular orbital method, the constant L_{pp} will bring about a uniform distribution of π-electrons as in the alternant hydrocarbons treated by the simple molecular orbital method. For non-alternant hydrocarbons and hetero-molecules, Q_p, $Q_q\neq1$ and L_{pp} depends in a complicated manner on the geometrical configuration of the molecule, that is L_{pp} is a function not only of the charge density of p-atom and q-atoms. In Wheland and Mann's iterative method, the Coulomb integral on an atom p is dependent only on Q_p[5]. The above mentioned functional relation, however, is a more satisfactory one and is in harmony with the Coulson and Longuet-Higgins' theory[6], where the charge density on an atom and the Coulomb integral of other atoms are connected to each other by their mutual polarizability (π_{pq}).

Roothaan's iterative procedure to find the self-consistent set of c_{ip}'s is then followed, making at each step a guess at a better set of c_{ip} values to attain a rapid convergence. The symmetry coordinates are fully made use of in order to reduce the order of secular equations. Of the molecules calculated in this paper, ethylene and benzene have geometrical symmetry sufficient for finding the self-consistent set of c_{ip}'s only through the symmetry requirements, and so the iteration is unnecessary.

Numerical Values of the Basic Quantities

Following Pariser and Parr, the Coulomb repulsion integrals $(pp|qq)$ are computed by making use of their uniformly charged sphere model for bond distances longer than 2.80 Å and proper quadratic extrapolation formulae are used for bonds shorter than 2.80 Å. The resonance integral β_{pq} is computed as mentioned above from the formula, $\beta_{pq}=k/r^6_{pq}$, k being the proportionality constant, to which numerical values −17.464, −13.983 and −8.8086 are assigned for C=C, C=N and C=O bond, respectively. In Fig. 1 are shown the geometricals and designations for the calculated eight molecules. Except for s-triazine, geometricals are all based on the experimental data.

5) G.W. Wheland and D.E. Mann, *J. Chem. Phys.*, **17**, 264 (1949).

6) C. A. Coulson and H. C. Longuet-Higgins, *Proc. Roy. Soc.*, **A191**, 39; **A192**, 16 (1947).

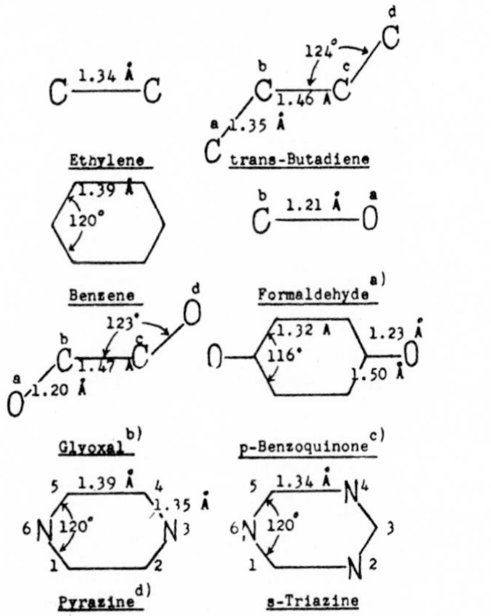

Fig. 1. Geometricals and designations of the calculated molecules.

a) D. P. Stevenson, J. E. LuValle and V. Schomaker, *J. Am. Chem. Soc.*, **61**, 2508 (1939).

b) J. E. LuValle and V. Schomaker, ibid., **61**, 3520 (1939).

c) S.M. Swingle, ibid., **76**, 1409 (1954).

d) V. Schomaker and L. Pauling, ibid., **61**, 1769 (1939).

Results of Calculation

After the iterative processes have come to convergence, the electronic transition energies are calculated by use of the following formula, no configuration interaction being allowed for, except in the symmetry degenerate cases of benzene and s-triazine.

$$\left.\begin{matrix}E_{Vij}\\E_{Tij}\end{matrix}\right\}-E_N=(\epsilon_j-\epsilon_i)-(J_{ij}-K_{ij})\pm K_{ij}.$$

Here, E_N, E_V and E_T designate the energy of the ground, excited singlet and excited triplet configuration, respectively, electronic excitation being from orbital i to j. J and K are the Coulomb repulsion and exchange repulsion integrals in terms of molecular orbitals.

$$J_{ij}=\iint\phi^*_i(\mu)\phi_i(\mu)[e^2/r]\phi^*_j(\nu)\phi_j(\nu)d\tau_\mu d\tau_\nu\ ,$$
$$K_{ij}=\iint\phi^*_i(\mu)\phi^*_j(\mu)[e^2/r]\phi_i(\nu)\phi_j(\nu)d\tau_\mu d\tau_\nu\ .$$

The calculated results are compared in Tables I-III with the observed values and with those by Pariser and Parr.

TABLE I

CALCULATED TRANSITION ENERGIES VS. EXPERIMENTAL VALUES OF HYDROCARBONS

Molecule	State	Calculated energy above the ground state (ev): This paper	Pariser-Parr	Obs.*) (ev)
Ethylene	$^1B_{1u}$	(7.60)	(7.60)	7.60
	$^3B_{1u}$	4.47	4.5	3.1—5.6
trans-	^1B_u	6.19	6.21	6.0
Butadiene	^1A_g	7.72	7.87	7.2(?)
	^3B_u	4.10	3.92	—
	^3A_g	6.17	4.61	—
Benzene	$^1B_{2u}$	4.96	4.9	4.9
	$^1B_{1u}$	5.37	5.3	6.0
	$^1E_{1u}$	7.01	7.0	7.0
	$^3B_{1u}$	3.62	4.0	3.8
	$^3E_{1u}$	4.52	4.45	—
	$^3B_{2u}$	4.96	4.9	—

*) See ref. 1 and those cited there.

It can be seen there that, in spite of the neglect of the Coulomb penetration integrals, the calculated values agree well with those observed, almost to the same extent as do the Pariser and Parr's values. It must, also, be noted that these agreements are obtained without taking account of the configuration interactions, except in benzene and triazine. This may be accepted as a good reason for neglecting the Coulomb penetration integrals and for the availability of the simple inverse sixth-power formula to compute β_{pq}, at least in hydrocarbons.

TABLE II

CALCULATED TRANSITION ENERGIES VS. EXPERIMENTAL VALUES FOR PYRAZINE AND S-TRIAZINE

Molecule	State	Calculated energy above the ground state (ev): This paper	Pariser-Parr	Obs. (ev)
Pyrazine	$^1B_{3u}$	4.74	4.71	4.77
	$^3B_{3u}$	3.03	3.85	3.35
s-Triazine	$^1A'_2$, $^3A'_2$	5.43	5.29	5.62*)
	$^1A'_1$	6.17	—	—
	$^1E'_1$	7.41	—	—
	$^3A'_1$	4.97	4.26	—

* R.C. Hirt, F. Halverson and R.G. Schmitt, *J. Chem. Phys.*, 22, 1148 (1954).

The calculation of *s*-triazine is based on the assumed bond length shown in Fig. 1, because it was non-existent. A slightly shorter C=N bond distance (1.34 Å) than in pyrazine is presumed for *s*-triazine, taking into account that the C=N bond in cyanuric triazide is shorter than 1.35 Å. As shown in Table II, the calculated result for N→V transition in *s*-triazine is improved, compared with Pariser-Parr's value. Recently it is reported that the existence of this molecule was shown by Grundmann and Kreutzberger. The experimental data of ultraviolet and infrared absorption spectra are published, and the detailed x-ray analysis is reported in progress, by which the present calculation might be revised so as to allow for the experimentally determined bond lengths.

TABLE III

CALCULATED TRANSITION ENERGIES VS. EXPERIMENTAL VALUES FOR OXYGEN CONTAINING MOLECULES

Molecule	State	Calculated energy above the ground state (ev)	Obs. (ev)
Form-aldehyde*)	$^1A_1$	7.80	7.96
	$^3A_1$	4.49	—
Glyoxal	^1B_u	7.47	7.51**)
	^3B_u	5.09	—
p-Benzo-quinone	$^1B_{2u}$	6.08	5.21***)
	$^3B_{2u}$	4.37	—

* Slight differences in calculated results between the present and the previous communication (This Bulletin, 27, 565 (1954).) are due to the different bond lengths adopted.

** Estimated value; see the previous communication (This Bulletin, loc. cit.)

*** G. Scheibe et al., *Ber.*, 59, 2617 (1926).

A comment on the calculated results of *p*-benzoquinone will be given in Sec. V.

The self-consistent molecular orbitals finally obtained are tabulated in Tables IV-V. Unfortunately, none of the molecules treated in this paper has definite dipole moment and there seems to be no means of crucial test for the quality of the molecular orbitals obtained. A few points are still to be noted. 1) The bond lengths r_{ab} and r_{bc} of *trans*-butadiene calculated from the theoretical bond orders through the bond order-bond length relation of Coulson are 1.35 Å and 1.49 Å, while the assumed values are 1.35 Å and 1.46 Å, respectively, a situation satisfactorily self-consistent. For other molecules containing hetero-atoms, the existence of excess charge prevents one from setting up a simple relation between bond orders and bond lengths. However, the bond length r_{12} of pyrazine, where the net positive charge on carbon atoms is comparatively small, the computed and assumed (experimental) bond lengths are in complete agreement, 1.39 Å.

2) The π-electron density on nitrogen atoms of pyrazine is computed by the simple molecular orbital method using the set of correction parameter for nitrogen atom which was found by Lowdin[7] to result in satisfactory agreements between the computed and observed values of dipole moment in diazines. It is 1.155 in units of electronic charge, while the present method gives only a little higher value, 1. 238.

These together with the fact that the present method applied to fulvene[8], yields the value of dipole moment in satisfactory agreement with the estimated value, might be helpful for judging the quality of the molecular orbitals obtained here.

TABLE IV

SELF-CONSISTENT MOLECULAR ORBITALS*)

Molecule	ε (ev)	Molecular Orbital	
trans-Butadiene	− 2. 480	$\phi_1=0.4397\ (\chi_a+\chi_d)+0.5538\ (\chi_b+\chi_c)$	$q_a=1$
	− 0. 296	$\phi_2=0.5538\ (\chi_a-\chi_d)+0.4397\ (\chi_b-\chi_c)$	$q_b=1$
	10. 826	$\phi_3=0.5538\ (\chi_a+\chi_d)-0.4397\ (\chi_b+\chi_c)$	$p_{ab}=0.974$
	13. 010	$\phi_4=0.4397\ (\chi_a-\chi_d)-0.5538\ (\chi_b-\chi_c)$	$p_{bc}=0.227$
Formaldehyde	− 3. 701	$\phi_1=0.5472\ \chi_a+0.8370\ \chi_b$	$q_a=1.401$
	10. 916	$\phi_2=0.8370\ \chi_a-0.5472\ \chi_b,\ q_b=0.599$	$p_{ab}=0.916$
Glyoxal	− 5. 140	$\phi_1=0.5541\ (\chi_a+\chi_d)+0.4393\ (\chi_b+\chi_c)$	$q_a=1.384$
	− 3. 853	$\phi_2=0.6205\ (\chi_a-\chi_d)+0.3390\ (\chi_b-\chi_c)$	$q_b=0.616$
	9. 202	$\phi_3=0.4393\ (\chi_a+\chi_d)-0.5541\ (\chi_b+\chi_c)$	$p_{ab}=0.908$
	11. 847	$\phi_4=0.3390\ (\chi_a-\chi_d)-0.6205\ (\chi_b-\chi_c)$	$p_{bc}=0.156$

*) q: π-electron density in units of e; p: mobile bond order

TABLE V

SELF-CONSISTENT MOLECULAR ORBITALS

Molecule	ε (ev)	Molecular Orbital	
Pyrazine	− 4. 507	$\phi_1=0.3646\ (\chi_1+\chi_2+\chi_4+\chi_5)+0.4838\ (\chi_3+\chi_6)$	$q_1=0.881$
	− 2. 107	$\phi_2=0.2397\ (\chi_1-\chi_2-\chi_4+\chi_5)-0.6205\ (\chi_3-\chi_6)$	$q_3=1.238$
	− 0. 316	$\phi_3=0.5000\ (\chi_1+\chi_2-\chi_4-\chi_5)$	$p_{12}=0.651$
	9. 572	$\phi_4=0.3421\ (\chi_1+\chi_2+\chi_4+\chi_5)-0.5157\ (\chi_3+\chi_6)$	$p_{23}=0.650$
	11. 013	$\phi_5=0.5000\ (\chi_1-\chi_2+\chi_4-\chi_5)$	
	13. 506	$\phi_6=0.4388\ (\chi_1-\chi_2-\chi_4+\chi_5)+0.3390\ (\chi_3-\chi_6)$	
s-Triazine	− 4. 965	$\phi_1=0.3569\ (\chi_1+\ \chi_3+\chi_5)+0.4538\ (\chi_2+\chi_4+\ \chi_1)$	$q_1=0.620$
	− 1. 940	$\phi_2=0.2138\ (\chi_1-2\chi_3+\chi_5)-0.3478\ (\chi_2+\chi_4-2\chi_6)$	$q_2=1.380$
	− 1. 940	$\phi_3=0.3703\ (\chi_1-\chi_5)\quad +0.6024\ (\chi_2-\chi_4)$	$p_{12}=0.621$
	10. 402	$\phi_4=0.6024\ (\chi_1-\chi_5)\quad -0.3703\ (\chi_2-\chi_4)$	
	10. 402	$\phi_5=0.3478\ (\chi_1-2\chi_3+\chi_5)+0.2138\ (\chi_2+\chi_4-2\chi_6)$	
	13. 448	$\phi_6=0.4538\ (\chi_1+\ \chi_3+\chi_5)-0.3569\ (\chi_2+\chi_4+\ \chi_6)$	

Criticism of the Assumption-1

Now it seems necessary to make a remark on the validity of assumption-1, made in sec. II. According to the approximation of zero-differential overlap adopted throughout the present calculation, the Coulomb integral (α_p) of an electron in the potential field due to the atomic cores in a molecule is expressed in terms of the Coulomb repulsion integrals as well as of the Coulomb penetration integrals as follows:

$$\alpha_p=W_{2p}-\sum_q[(pp\,|\,qq)+(q:\,pp)],$$

Of the integrals in this equation, the Coulomb penetration integrals $(q:\,pp)$ can not be computed easily, in cases where the atoms p and q are of different species. As, in addition, the order of magnitude of $(q:\,pp)$ is supposed to be relatively small, they are left out, as a first approximation, in the calculations in the preceding sections. In order to see how much the results would be affected by this simplification, *trans*-butadiene is treated by use of the Coulomb integrals computed without leaving out the Coulomb penetration integrals. Instead of computing $(q:\,pp)$ exactly, corrections are made for L's by subtracting 1.0 and 1.5 ev, respectively, from the L_{pp}(atom p being a methylene carbon)

7) P.O. Lowdin, *J. Chem. Phys.*, **19**, 1323 (1951).

8) H. Kon, to be published soon.

9) R.G. Parr and B.L. Crawford, Jr., *J. Chem. Phys.*, **16**, 1049 (1948).

and L_{qq} (atom q being a methine carbon). This manner of correction comes from the following consideration: The values of Coulomb penetration integrals $(p:qq)$, where atom p and q are both carbon, can be obtained through the formula derived by Parr and Crawford[9] using the Slater type atomic orbitals. They are 0.91 and 0.58 ev for the interatomic distances 1.35 Å and 1.46 Å, respectively. The methylene carbon atoms in butadiene have one formal double bond (1.35 Å), while the methine carbons have one formal single (1.46 Å) and double bond. Assuming the contributions from the other atoms than those linked together directly to be small, the corrections to be made for L's of a methylene and methine carbon atoms are 0.91 and 1.49 ev, respectively, which are rounded to 1.0 and 1.50 ev as given above. This correction, though it is only approximate because of ignoring the effect of the hydrogen atom and the non-neighbouring carbon atoms, would be sufficient for the qualitative purpose.

TABLE VI

COMPARISON OF CALCULATED RESULTS WITH AND WITHOUT CORRECTION

	Correction	
	with	without
Orbital energy (ev)	− 2.730	− 2.480
	− 0.434	− 0.296
	10.689	10.826
	12.777	13.010
Excit. energy (ev)		
^1B_u	6.20	6.19
^3B_u	4.10	4.10
Coeff. of AO		
c_{1a}	0.4258	0.4397
c_{2a}	0.5645	0.5538
π-elec. density		
q_a	0.953	1.000
q_b	1.046	1.000
Bond order		
p_{ab}	0.972	0.974
p_{bc}	0.228	0.227

The calculated results of transition energy, coefficients of AO, π-electron densities and mobile bond orders, with and without correction are compared in Table VI. As can be seen there, the overall alteration brought about by introducing the correction is a minor one. And though the orbital energies are changed a little after correction, the transition energies are almost unchanged. The same holds for the relation between the AO coefficients and the bond orders derived from the former.

Conspicuous among the results may be the fact that the uniformity of π-electron distribution in butadiene (or, the hydrocarbons in general), which is assured in the Hückel method is broken down by the correction. At any rate the results in Table VI, together with the good agreements between the calculated and the observed transition energies show that one can safely dispense with Coulomb penetration integrals at least in computing the transition energies of hydrocarbons (and those hetero-molecules where the perturbation due to the hetero-atoms are not so serious), and that the wave functions so obtained would be fairly good approximations to the best possible ones.

The numerical agreement between the computed and experimental transition energy of p-benzoquinone is shown to be inferior to other cases. (Table III) The situation may probably be improved by making such a correction as mentioned above, especially for the tertiary carbon atoms (p) where, owing to the adjacent electronegative oxygen atoms, the amount to be subtracted from L_{pp} is considered too great to be ignored. It can also be understood from the similar point of view that the π-electron densities on nitrogen atoms listed in Table V appear a little higher than desirable.

The author expresses his deep thanks to Professor H. Tominaga for his interest and encouragement throughout the course of this work.

Department of Chemistry, Faculty of Science, Tôhoku University, Sendai

Reprinted from THE JOURNAL OF CHEMICAL PHYSICS, Vol. 22, No. 2, 320–333, February, 1954
Printed in U. S. A.

The Electronic Spectra of Cata-Condensed Hydrocarbons

WILLIAM MOFFITT
Department of Chemistry, Harvard University, Cambridge, Massachusetts
(Received August 20, 1953)

It is shown how the main features of the spectra of cata-condensed hydrocarbons may be explained on the basis of a very simple model. This, so-called perimeter model was used, in its free-electron variant, by Platt in order to classify the spectra. In this note, a more quantitative version is formulated which enables calculations to be made; it may be considered as an approximation either to an antisymmetrized molecular orbital treatment or to the method of atoms in molecules.

INTRODUCTION

THE electronic spectra of benzene, of its homologs, the polyacenes, and their isomers have been the subject of considerable experimental study. And this study has been rewarded by the appearance of remarkable similarities and regularities in the properties of the concomitant band systems. It is the purpose of this note to show how the more striking of these generic relationships may be understood.

The so-called cata-condensed hydrocarbons generally exhibit three main band systems in the near ultraviolet or visible region of the spectrum. The prototypes of all these systems are to be found in benzene, which absorbs strongly near 1750A, exhibits absorption of moderate intensity around 2000A, and shows a weak band system in the 2500A region. Clar demonstrated that band systems of a similar type also occur for the higher homologs of benzene.[1] He classified these as β, p, and α systems, respectively. This note will be concerned with the following aspects of the spectra:

I. The regular appearance of the three systems enumerated by Clar throughout the range from benzene to its very complex homologs containing fused rings.

II. The regular intensity relationships which they exhibit; very intense β bands, moderately intense p bands, and very weak α bands.

III. The relative insensitivity of the location of the α and β bands to isomerism, but the characteristic movement of the p bands, e.g., on going from anthracene to phenanthrene.

IV. The particular intensification of the α bands under inductive substitution, such as occurs on going from naphthalene to quinoline.

V. The relation between the spectra of naphthalene and azulene, in which analogous band systems may also be identified.

VI. The characteristic shifts exhibited by the α bands of azulene, to the red or to the violet, depending on the nature and position of different substituents in the aromatic system. Most of these topics have already been discussed by various authors, particularly during the last decade, and some reference to their work will be made later. The empirical characterization of these effects is particularly due to Clar,[1] and more recently to Jones[2] and to Klevens and Platt.[3] But no unified theoretical treatment has been put forward, for reasons which are not difficult to understand.

The potentialities of a given theory may be tested with reference to the account it gives of the benzene spectrum, and it is already here that calculations founder. The most appealing theory, on grounds of conceptual simplicity and predictive immediacy, namely the molecular orbital method, has been applied to benzene in stages of increasing sophistication. The first of these, which is based on purely qualitative considerations of simple orbital configurations, is undoubtedly the most successful. It correctly predicts the number and most probably also the symmetries of the low-lying singlet levels. However, the various attempts to locate these quantitatively, which mark succeeding stages, have met with indifferent results. The only formalism capable of ready generalization to more complicated systems without enormous increase in labor—the semi-empirical LCAO theory[4]—is incapable of distinguishing between the energies of the first three excited-singlet states (transitions to which account for the α, p, and β band systems). It is only by trying to assess the complicated electron repulsion terms that these states may be separated. And it appears that present computational techniques do not have sufficient accuracy to merit the attempt for all but the simplest systems. Moreover, the intricate methodology associated with such calculations would seem to mask rather than to reveal the generalizations that appear to underlie the spectra.

Platt has proposed a peculiarly simple approach to the classification of the spectra of these cata-condensed hydrocarbons.[5] It is based on what may be called the "perimeter" model of these systems, which is a simplification of the molecular orbital method. Essentially, he relates the electronic states of a given hydrocarbon to those of the corresponding cyclic polyene (e.g., of naphthalene to cyclodecapentaene). The first excited states of such cyclic polyenes, of general formula

[1] E. Clar, *Aromatische Kohlenwasserstoffe* (Julius Springer, Berlin), first edition 1941, second edition 1952.

[2] R. N. Jones, Chem. Rev. **32**, 1 (1943); **41**, 353 (1947).

[3] H. B. Klevens and J. R. Platt, J. Chem. Phys. **17**, 470 (1949).

[4] J. E. Lennard-Jones and C. A. Coulson, Trans. Faraday Soc. **35**, 811 (1939).

[5] J. R. Platt, J. Chem. Phys. **17**, 484 (1949).

TABLE I. The character table for the point group. $\mathbf{D}_{(4\nu+2)h}=\mathbf{C}_{(4\nu+2)v}\times\mathbf{C}_s$.

$\mathbf{C}_{(4\nu+2)v}$	I	$2C_{4\nu+2}$	$2C_{4\nu+2}^2$	$\cdots$	$C_{4\nu+2}^{2\nu+1}=C_2$	$(2\nu+1)\sigma_v$	$(2\nu+1)\sigma_d$	
A_1	1	1	1	$\cdots$	1	1	1	T_z
A_2	1	1	1	$\cdots$	1	-1	-1	
B_1	1	-1	1	$\cdots$	-1	1	-1	
B_2	1	-1	1	$\cdots$	-1	-1	1	
E_1	2	$2Rl(\omega)$	$2Rl(\omega^2)$	$\cdots$	-2	0	0	T_x, T_y
$\vdots$	$\vdots$	$\vdots$	$\vdots$		$\vdots$	$\vdots$	$\vdots$	
E_ν	2	$2Rl(\omega^\nu)$	$2Rl(\omega^{2\nu})$	$\cdots$	$(-1)^\nu 2$	0	0	
$E_{\nu+1}$	2	$2Rl(\omega^{\nu+1})$	$2Rl(\omega^{2\nu+2})$	$\cdots$	$(-1)^{\nu+1}2$	0	0	
$\vdots$	$\vdots$	$\vdots$	$\vdots$		$\vdots$	$\vdots$	$\vdots$	
$E_{2\nu}$	2	$2Rl(\omega^{2\nu})$	$2Rl(\omega^{4\nu})$	$\cdots$	2	0	0	

I = identity operator; $C_{4\nu+2}$ = rotation by $2\pi/(4\nu+2)$ about the z axis; σ_v = reflection in a vertical plane of symmetry containing carbon atoms; σ_d = reflection in a vertical plane of symmetry bisecting carbon-carbon bonds. $\omega=\exp\{2\pi i/(4\nu+2)\}$.

$\mathbf{C}_s$ has only two elements, I and the reflection σ_h in the horizontal (xy-) plane of symmetry. Representations of the full group are therefore characterized first with respect to its $\mathbf{C}_{(4\nu+2)v}$ subgroup and then with respect to the inversion $i=C_2\cdot\sigma_h$ in the center of symmetry.

$C_{4\nu+2}H_{4\nu+2}$ ($\nu=1, 2, \cdots$), have certain symmetry properties which are preserved throughout the series of homologs. And these characteristics are empirically parallelled by the permanence of certain band types in the cata-condensed molecules, of general formula $C_{4\nu+2}H_{2\nu+4}$. This leads to an exceedingly fruitful classification of the spectra. There is, however, a variety of questions which Platt's treatment throws into relief—particularly those related to features II–VI above.

In the present note, a preliminary solution to these questions is outlined. To this end, simple LCAO theory will be used in conjunction with perturbation theory. Adopting the perimeter model, a description of the (hypothetical, planar) cyclic polyenes is first put forward and some plausible assumptions are made regarding their spectra—essentially an extrapolation from diatomic molecules and benzene to cyclic homologs of the latter. These are then regarded as unperturbed states, from which the cata-condensed systems are formed by perturbation. In this way, there is a direct correspondence between the two types of molecule and the essential properties of the perimeter model may be handled simply and semiquantitatively.

There is one important respect in which the treatment will differ from that of conventional LCAO theory. It is in the recognition that configurational interaction may be of two types. This classification is only rigid for the cyclic polyenes, but it is also important in other cases. The first type is due to the degeneracy of a particular configuration and may be considered as a first-order effect. The second is of little account in the cyclic polyenes, involving the "high-frequency" terms of second-order perturbation theory.[6] When the high symmetry of the cyclic polyenes is broken down, the distinction between these different types is obscured. By adopting the perimeter model, however, it remains a fairly real distinction and it is possible to refer the first-order assessment of configurational interaction in the cata-condensed molecules to that in the cyclic polyenes.

[6] W. Moffitt and J. Scanlan, Proc. Roy. Soc. (London) (to be published).

1. THE CYCLIC POLYENES

(a) Molecular Orbitals and Electronic Configurations

Consider a cyclic polyene of general formula $C_{4\nu+2}H_{4\nu+2}$ in which the carbon atoms are regularly spaced on the circumference of a circle. For convenience, let the $(4\nu+2)$-fold axis of symmetry be called the z axis. As origin of coordinates take the center of the circle and number the carbon atoms serially from 0 to $(4\nu+1)$ on going around the ring. The x axis is taken as passing through the carbon atom labeled 0, and therefore also through atom $(2\nu+1)$; the y axis then bisects the bonds linking atoms ν, $(3\nu+1)$ with atoms $(\nu+1)$, $(3\nu+2)$, respectively. Except in the simplest case of benzene ($\nu=1$), these cyclic polyenes are hypothetical, planar molecules defined for convenience in handling only the unsaturation electrons; the associated σ-bond strain energies and so forth are of no concern.

Owing to the high symmetry of the cyclic polyenes, the appropriate molecular orbitals ψ_ξ may be prescribed as linear combinations of $2p\pi$ atomic orbitals ϕ_m straight away,

$$\psi_\xi=\sigma_\xi \sum_{m=0}^{4\gamma+1} \omega^{m\xi}\phi_m, \quad (\xi=0, \pm 1, \cdots, \pm 2\nu, 2\nu+1), \quad (1.1)$$

where

$$\omega=e^{i\theta}=\exp\{2\pi i/(4\nu+2)\},$$

and σ_ξ is a normalizing factor which we shall take to be real and positive. It is easily verified that $\psi_{-\xi}=\psi_\xi^*$. By considering their transformation properties (see the following), we may set these orbitals in correspondence with Platt's free-electron orbitals: ψ_ξ is then the LCAO equivalent of his orbital of angular momentum $\xi h/2\pi$ about the z axis. The one-electron energy ϵ_ξ associated

TABLE II. The transformation properties of the molecular orbitals.

	ψ_ν	$\psi_{-\nu}$	$\psi_{\nu+1}$	$\psi_{-\nu-1}$
$C_{4\nu+2}$	$\omega^\nu\psi_\nu$	$\omega^{-\nu}\psi_{-\nu}$	$\omega^{\nu+1}\psi_{\nu+1}$	$\omega^{-\nu-1}\psi_{-\nu-1}$
σ_v	$\psi_{-\nu}$	ψ_ν	$\psi_{-\nu-1}$	$\psi_{\nu+1}$
σ_d	$(-1)^\nu\psi_{-\nu}$	$(-1)^\nu\psi_\nu$	$(-1)^{\nu+1}\psi_{-\nu-1}$	$(-1)^{\nu+1}\psi_{\nu+1}$
σ_h	$-\psi_\nu$	$-\psi_{-\nu}$	$-\psi_{\nu+1}$	$-\psi_{-\nu-1}$

with ψ_ξ will be a monotonically increasing function of $|\xi|$, with the identity $\epsilon_{-\xi}=\epsilon_\xi$. Thus all orbitals apart from the most stable (ψ_0) and the most highly excited ($\psi_{2\nu+1}$) are doubly-degenerate. (The precise definition of the Hartree-Fock energy parameter ϵ_ξ will, of course, be a function not only of ν and ξ, but also of the particular molecular state with which it is associated; it is not, however, necessary to pursue this subject here.)

The molecular orbitals ψ_ξ span an irreducible representation of the molecule's spatial symmetry group, namely, $\mathbf{D}_{(4\nu+2)h}=\mathbf{C}_{(4\nu+2)v}\times\mathbf{C}_s$, whose characters are assembled in Table I. $\mathbf{C}_{(4\nu+2)v}$ is a group of order $(8\nu+4)$ whose elements fall into $(2\nu+4)$ classes, so that it has four one-dimensional and 2ν two-dimensional irreducible representations. $\mathbf{C}_s$ consists of only two elements, the identity I and the reflection σ_h in the horizontal plane of symmetry. The full group therefore has twice as many representations as $\mathbf{C}_{(4\nu+2)v}$, which are described by symbols characteristic of representations of this invariant subgroup, together with subscripts g or u according as these are even or odd with respect to the inversion $i=C_2\cdot\sigma_h$. In Table II, it is shown how the ψ_ξ transform; the particular reflections σ_v, σ_d which are chosen here and in Table III refer to the zx and yz planes, respectively. It should be noticed that, as is customary for benzene, the σ_v planes contain carbon atoms, whereas the σ_d planes bisect bonds. By inspection, it is clear that the molecular orbitals may be labeled according to their symmetry properties as follows:

$$\psi_0=a_{1u}=a_1,\quad \psi_{2\nu+1}=b_{1g}=b_1,$$
$$\psi_{\pm|\xi|}=e_{|\xi|s}{}^{\pm}=e_{|\xi|}{}^{\pm},\quad (|\xi|=1,2,\cdots,2\nu),\tag{1.2}$$

where $s=g$ when $|\xi|$ is odd and $s=u$ when $|\xi|$ is even. The last form of writing is that which we shall use in the sequel; it will always be used in conjunction with (1.1) rather than with Table II, so that this analytical form for the molecular orbitals is preserved even when the molecule is distorted in such a way that the symmetry is partially or completely lost.

Molecular states are now built up in the usual way by constructing orbital configurations, or making electron assignments. The ground configuration will be

$$\mathfrak{N}:\ (a_1)^2(e_1)^4\cdots(e_\nu)^4,$$

and the first-excited configuration is

$$\mathfrak{A}:\ (a_1)^2(e_1)^4\cdots(e_\nu)^3(e_{\nu+1}).$$

In prescribing these configurations, we do not at first distinguish, for example, $e_\nu{}^+$ from its complex conjugate $e_\nu{}^-$. This is of no consequence to the specification of $\mathfrak{N}$, for which there is only one permissible electron assignment, corresponding to the antisymmetric function

$$\Theta_N=\{(4\nu+2)!\}^{-\frac{1}{2}}\det\{a_1(1)\alpha(1),\ a_1(2)\beta(2),\ \cdots,\ e_\nu{}^-(4\nu+2)\beta(4\nu+2)\}$$
$$=|a_1\bar{a}_1e_1{}^+\bar{e}_1{}^+\cdots e_\nu{}^+\bar{e}_\nu{}^+e_\nu{}^-\bar{e}_\nu{}^-|,\quad\text{say.}\tag{1.3}$$

On the other hand, there are several linearly independent functions of this type which may be constructured from configuration $\mathfrak{A}$, which is therefore said to be degenerate; all are associated with the same zeroth-order energy. Confining our attention to the singlets, although the subsequent development is in no way restricted to these, we may specify only four independent functions:

$$\Theta_1=1/\sqrt{2}\{|\cdots e_\nu{}^+\bar{e}_\nu{}^+e_\nu{}^-\bar{e}_{\nu+1}{}^-|+|\cdots e_\nu{}^+\bar{e}_\nu{}^+e_{\nu+1}{}^-\bar{e}_\nu{}^-|\},$$
$$\Theta_2=1/\sqrt{2}\{|\cdots e_\nu{}^-\bar{e}_\nu{}^-e_\nu{}^+\bar{e}_{\nu+1}{}^+|+|\cdots e_\nu{}^-\bar{e}_\nu{}^-e_{\nu+1}{}^+\bar{e}_\nu{}^+|\},$$
$$\Theta_3=1/\sqrt{2}\{|\cdots e_\nu{}^+\bar{e}_\nu{}^+e_\nu{}^-\bar{e}_{\nu+1}{}^+|+|\cdots e_\nu{}^+\bar{e}_\nu{}^+e_{\nu+1}{}^+\bar{e}_\nu{}^-|\},\tag{1.4}$$
$$\Theta_4=1/\sqrt{2}\{|\cdots e_\nu{}^-\bar{e}_\nu{}^-e_\nu{}^+\bar{e}_{\nu+1}{}^-|+|\cdots e_\nu{}^-\bar{e}_\nu{}^-e_{\nu+1}{}^-\bar{e}_\nu{}^+|\}.$$

Their transformation properties are gathered together in Table III, as are those of the linear combinations

$$\Theta_X=1/\sqrt{2}(\Theta_1+\Theta_2),\quad \Theta_Y=1/i\sqrt{2}(\Theta_1-\Theta_2),$$
$$\Theta_U=1/\sqrt{2}(\Theta_3+\Theta_4),\quad \Theta_V=1/i\sqrt{2}(\Theta_3-\Theta_4).\tag{1.5}$$

It will be noticed that whereas Θ_1, Θ_2 (or Θ_X, Θ_Y) together span the irreducible representation ${}^1E_{1u}$ of the molecular symmetry group, Θ_3 and Θ_4 span a reducible representation. The linear combinations Θ_U, Θ_V are appropriate in this case and are of species ${}^1B_{1u}$, ${}^1B_{2u}$, respectively. Since $\Theta_2=\Theta_1{}^*$, $\Theta_4=\Theta_3{}^*$, it will be noticed

TABLE III. The transformation properties of the configurational functions.

	Θ_1	Θ_2	Θ_3	Θ_4	Θ_X	Θ_Y	Θ_U	Θ_V
$C_{4\nu+2}$	$\omega^{-1}\Theta_1$	$\omega\Theta_2$	$-\Theta_3$	$-\Theta_4$	$Rl(\omega)\Theta_X+Im(\omega)\Theta_Y$	$Rl(\omega)\Theta_Y-Im(\omega)\Theta_X$	$-\Theta_U$	$-\Theta_V$
σ_v	Θ_2	Θ_1	Θ_4	Θ_3	Θ_X	$-\Theta_Y$	Θ_U	$-\Theta_V$
σ_d	$-\Theta_2$	$-\Theta_1$	$-\Theta_4$	$-\Theta_3$	$-\Theta_X$	Θ_Y	$-\Theta_U$	Θ_V
σ_h	Θ_1	Θ_2	Θ_3	Θ_4	Θ_X	Θ_Y	Θ_U	Θ_V

that all the functions Θ_S, (S=X, Y, U, V) are real. Moreover, Θ_X, Θ_Y transform like translations along $0x$, $0y$, respectively; this is useful to remember when the symmetry is partially destroyed, since a suitable numbering of the carbon atoms will ensure that Θ_X, Θ_Y, as also Θ_U, Θ_V, conform to primitive symmetry species of the lower group.

Thus in every case (i.e., for all $\nu \geq 1$), the first excited configuration gives rise to three singlet functions, ${}^1B_{1u}$, ${}^1B_{2u}$ and doubly-degenerate ${}^1E_{1u}$, which Platt calls ${}^1L_a$, ${}^1L_b$, and ${}^1B$, respectively (see Table IV). That these states differ in energy may be attributed to "intra-configurational" interaction or, as we shall prefer to call it, first-order *CI*. Now states of the same symmetry are obtained from more highly excited configurations as well: there is, formally at least, another type of interaction which is "inter-configurational" in origin; this we call second-order *CI*. For the purposes of this note, we shall neglect second-order *CI* altogether, justifying this by a reference to recent work on simple hydrocarbons.[6,7]

In what follows we shall reserve the symbols Θ_S, (S=X, Y, U, V) for the singlet functions (1.5). When second-order *CI* is ignored, these represent the associated singlet states arising from $\mathfrak{A}$, and in this specific sense, we may call them $\Omega_S{}^0$, ($S=X, Y, U, V$). The distinction, though real, is not important for the cyclic polyenes themselves, but is introduced for the purposes of later perturbation theory, when the Θ_S are used as the basis of representation for perturbed states Ω_S of the cyclic polyenes.

The pictorial representation and qualitative description of transitions between the states of $\mathfrak{N}$ and $\mathfrak{A}$ have been discussed by Platt in some detail. Having formalized his perimeter model in LCAO terms, we shall not trouble to repeat such descriptions here. It may be noticed, however, that Θ_U has 2ν nodal planes (σ_d) normal to the polyene ring which bisect carbon-carbon bonds, whereas Θ_V has 2ν nodal planes (σ_v) which pass through carbon atoms.

(b) Orbital Energies

We shall now give an outline of the simplest LCAO calculations which can be made.[4] For this purpose, we neglect overlap and interactions between all but nearest neighbors. Energies are then expressed in terms of the usual Coulomb integral α and the resonance integral β.

Firstly, the orbital energy of an electron in ψ_ξ is easily seen to be

$$\epsilon_\xi=\alpha+2\beta\cos(\xi\theta),\quad \theta=\pi/(2\nu+1). \tag{1.6}$$

The energy of the unsaturation electrons in their ground state $\mathfrak{N}$ is therefore

$$2\{\epsilon_0+\sum_{\xi=1}^{\nu}(\epsilon_\xi+\epsilon_{-\xi})\}=(4\nu+2)\alpha+4\beta\operatorname{cosec}(\theta/2), \tag{1.7}$$

[7] W. Moffitt and J. Scanlan, Proc. Roy. Soc. (London) **A218**, 464 (1953); W. Moffitt, Proc. Roy. Soc. (London) **A218**, 486 (1953).

TABLE IV. Different nomenclatures for states of cyclic polyenes and polyacenes.

This paper	Platt (reference 5)	Group theory
X, Y	${}^1B$	${}^1E_{1u}$
U	${}^1L_a$	${}^1B_{1u}$
V	${}^1L_b$	${}^1B_{2u}$

(a) Cyclic polyenes.

This paper	Platt (reference 5)	Group theory (reference 11)	Upper state of Clar's (reference 1)
Y	${}^1B_b$	${}^1B_{1u}$	β bands
U	${}^1L_a$	${}^1B_{2u}$	p bands
V	${}^1L_b$	${}^1B_{1u}$	α bands

(b) Polyacenes.

which corresponds to a resonance energy of

$$2|\beta|\{2\operatorname{cosec}(\theta/2)-(2\nu+1)\} \tag{1.8}$$

and a mobile bond order of

$$(2\nu+1)^{-1}\operatorname{cosec}(\theta/2). \tag{1.9}$$

As the number of carbon atoms, and thus ν, increases, so the mobile bond order approaches the value $(2/\pi)$.

Secondly, we may give an estimate for the lowest excitation energy, which corresponds to the process $(e_\nu)^{-1}(e_{\nu+1})$. This is then simply

$$\epsilon_{\nu+1}-\epsilon_\nu=4|\beta|\sin(\theta/2), \tag{1.10}$$

which vanishes as ν increases indefinitely. Now, this prediction gives, at best, only some mean excitation energy of the totality of states (${}^{1,3}B_{1u}$, ${}^{1,3}B_{2u}$, ${}^{1,3}E_{1u}$) arising from $\mathfrak{A}$, with respect to the ground state. The method is insufficiently sensitive to separate these states energetically.

The methods of antisymmetrized molecular orbitals and of atoms in molecules are sufficiently discerning in this respect, but not sufficiently accurate for us to apply them with any confidence.[6] For this reason, we make the assumption that (1.10) may be used to compute the mean excitation energies of the higher cyclic polyenes, taking for β that value which is appropriate for benzene. In order to locate the particular states of $\mathfrak{A}$ relative to this mean, we shall also adopt an extrapolation method from benzene, which will now be described.

(c) Excitation Energies

As Göppert-Mayer and Sklar first pointed out, the molecular orbital theory correctly predicts the number of low-lying singlet states of benzene as three.[8] The first, very weak absorption system, with an excitation energy of ~4.9 ev, they identified as the ${}^1A_{1g}\rightarrow{}^1B_{2u}$ transition (Clar's α bands), which is electronically forbidden. The second, stronger system around 6.2 ev they attributed to the forbidden process ${}^1A_{1g}\rightarrow{}^1B_{1u}$ (p bands), whereas the intense 7.0 ev absorption is clearly due to

[8] M. Göppert-Mayer and A. L. Sklar, J. Chem. Phys. **6**, 645 (1938).

the allowed transition ${}^1A_{1g} \rightarrow {}^1E_{1u}$ (β bands). We shall accept their assignments in this note, as did Platt.

Now it is easily shown that as ν increases, so the separation of the different electronic states arising from configuration $\mathfrak{A}$ decreases, vanishing asymptotically. Since in the higher cyclic polyenes ($\nu > 1$), the transformation properties of the associated eigenfunctions remain identical, we may expect the relative separations of these states to be roughly proportional: $({}^1E_{1u} - {}^1B_{1u})/({}^1B_{1u} - {}^1B_{2u})$ for benzene will be the same as $({}^1E_{1u} - {}^1B_{1u})/({}^1B_{1u} - {}^1B_{2u})$ for cyclodecapentaene, and so on. And we shall further suppose that this similarity extends to the separation of these states from the corresponding ground states. On the basis of these qualitative arguments, we may now make (admittedly rather approximate) estimates of the relevant excitation energies in the higher cyclic polyenes:

Using (1.10) to furnish the mean excitation energies and exploiting our proportionality assumptions it is easily seen that the excitation energy of a particular state $\Xi (= {}^1E_{1u}, {}^1B_{1u}, {}^1B_{2u})$ is given by

$$4|\beta(\Xi)|\sin(\theta/2), \tag{1.11}$$

where $\beta(\Xi)$ is chosen separately for each symmetry species from the known benzene spectrum. For example, since $\nu = 1$ and therefore $\theta = \pi/3$ for benzene, $|\beta({}^1B_{1u})| = \frac{1}{4}(6.2)\operatorname{cosec}(\pi/6) = 3.1$ ev; and, accordingly, the ${}^1B_{1u} - {}^1A_{1g}$ interval for cyclodecapentaene is predicted to be of the order $4(3.1)\sin(\pi/10)$ ev.

There seems to be little doubt that these very approximate calculations are qualitatively correct. And, in the absence of a more reliable method, it seems rather pointless to use more elaborate techniques to attain results which are bound to be qualitatively similar and no more accurate. Essentially, we use the simplest LCAO theory as a means of extrapolating the spectra of the higher cyclic polyenes from the known benzene spectrum.

(d) Perturbation Theory

We have now constructed a semi-empirical description of our cyclic polyenes (the "perimeters") in both their ground and lower excited states. Their spectroscopic properties can be assessed roughly by means of (1.11) and their approximate eigenfunctions are given by (1.3) and (1.5). In these paragraphs, we shall outline the way in which the lower states of the cyclic polyenes are modified by perturbations of a particular type.

Of these perturbations, we shall require: (i) that they are small with respect to the separation of different electronic configurations giving rise to states of the same symmetry, if comparable to the separation of different electronic levels within the same configuration; (ii) that they may be expressed as the sum of one-electron Hermitian operators

$$\mathcal{P} = \sum_{i=1}^{4\nu+2} \mathfrak{p}_i.$$

With respect to the molecular orbitals ψ_ξ as basis, a typical perturbation $\mathcal{P}$ is represented by a matrix $[P_{\xi\eta}]$, where

$$P_{\xi\eta} = \int \psi_\xi^* \mathfrak{p} \psi_\eta dv = P_{\eta\xi}^*$$
$$= \sigma_\xi \sigma_\eta \{ \sum_m \omega^{(\eta-\xi)m} A_m + \sum_m \sum_{n>m} (\omega^{n\eta - m\xi} + \omega^{m\eta - n\xi}) B_{mn} \} \tag{1.12}$$

and

$$A_m = \int \phi_m^* \mathfrak{p} \phi_m dv, \quad B_{mn} = \int \phi_m^* \mathfrak{p} \phi_n dv \tag{1.13}$$

are the elements of the matrix representing the separate one-electron operators in a basis of AO functions. However, it is not in the molecular orbitals, but rather in the molecular states themselves that we shall be interested. In particular, referred to the four singlet functions Θ_S, which we regard as the approximate unperturbed eigenfunctions of the states arising from $\mathfrak{A}$, the perturbation operator is represented by the matrix

$$\begin{array}{ccccc} \mathrm{X} & \kappa & 0 & Rl(\lambda) & Im(\mu) \\ \mathrm{Y} & 0 & \kappa & -Im(\lambda) & Rl(\mu) \\ \mathrm{U} & Rl(\lambda) & -Im(\lambda) & \kappa & 0 \\ \mathrm{V} & Im(\mu) & Rl(\mu) & 0 & \kappa \end{array}, \tag{1.14}$$

where κ is a constant, and

$$\lambda = P_{-\nu-1,\nu+1} - P_{\nu,-\nu},$$
$$\mu = P_{-\nu-1,\nu+1} + P_{\nu,-\nu}. \tag{1.15}$$

Here the element of the Sth row and Tth column gives the value of the integral

$$P_{\mathrm{ST}} = \int \Theta_{\mathrm{S}}^* \mathcal{P} \Theta_{\mathrm{T}} dV. \tag{1.16}$$

The common diagonal term, namely κ, is related to the diagonal element corresponding to the ground state by the formula

$$\int \Theta_{\mathrm{N}}^* \mathcal{P} \Theta_{\mathrm{N}} dV = \kappa + P_{\nu,\nu} - P_{\nu+1,\nu+1} = \chi, \text{ say.} \tag{1.17}$$

Since it is supposed at the outset that the perturbation is small with respect to the energetic intervals separating Θ_{N} from the Θ_{S}, the matrix elements of $\mathcal{P}$ connecting Θ_{N} with the Θ_{S} are of no interest.

Now, apart from the obvious appearance of zeros in (1.14), this matrix has certain other most illuminating properties. Suppose we neglect overlap, when $\sigma_\xi = (4\nu+2)^{-\frac{1}{2}}$ for all ξ. It is then easily shown that

$$\lambda = (2\nu+1)^{-1} \sum_m \sum_{n>m}{}^{\S}\, 2\omega^{(\nu+1)(m+n)} B_{mn},$$

$$\mu = (2\nu+1)^{-1} \{ \sum_m \omega^{2(\nu+1)m} A_m + 2 \sum_m \sum_{n>m}{}^{\dagger}\, \omega^{(\nu+1)(m+n)} B_{mn} \}, \tag{1.18}$$

where the first double summation (§) is taken over only those pairs of atoms for which $(m+n)$ is odd, and the second (†) is taken over only those pairs for which $(m+n)$ is even. Moreover, Θ_U is connected with the degenerate Θ_X, Θ_Y pair only through λ, and Θ_V is connected with Θ_X, Θ_Y only through μ, the matrix elements between Θ_U and Θ_V vanishing. This means that the $^1B_{1u}$ and $^1B_{2u}$ states will in general behave differently, and characteristically so, under the influence of a particular perturbation $\mathcal{P}$.

For example, suppose $\mathcal{P}$ to be such that $A_m=0$ for all m and $B_{mn}=0$ whenever $(m+n)$ is even. Then $\mu=0$, and that part of the energy matrix referring to configuration $\mathcal{A}$ has the form

$$\begin{array}{cccc} W_X+\kappa & 0 & Rl(\lambda) & 0 \\ 0 & W_Y+\kappa & -Im(\lambda) & 0 \\ Rl(\lambda) & -Im(\lambda) & W_U+\kappa & 0 \\ 0 & 0 & 0 & W_V+\kappa \end{array}, \quad (1.19)$$

$W_X=W_Y$ being the energy of the cyclic polyene in its unperturbed $^1E_{1u}$ state and W_U, W_V being the energies of its unperturbed $^1B_{1u}$, $^1B_{2u}$ states, respectively. The eigenfunctions of the perturbed states then have the form

$$\begin{aligned} \Omega_V&=\Theta_V, \quad \Omega_Y=\cos\tau\Theta_Y-\sin\tau\Theta_X, \\ \Omega_X&=\cos\rho\{\cos\tau\Theta_X+\sin\tau\Theta_Y\}-\sin\rho\Theta_U, \quad (1.20) \\ \Omega_U&=\cos\rho\Theta_U+\sin\rho\{\cos\tau\Theta_X+\sin\tau\Theta_Y\}, \end{aligned}$$

where the parameters τ, ρ are easily determined when the latent roots of (1.19) are obtained. Under such a perturbation we see that apart from the common additive term κ, the state V and one of the components Y of the degenerate Θ_X, Θ_Y pair are left unchanged, whereas the Θ_U state and the remaining component of this pair interact, to form states X and U. Such a perturbation is illustrated graphically in Fig. 1(a).

Similarly, if $\mathcal{P}$ is such that $B_{mn}=0$ whenever $(m+n)$ is odd, it is seen that one component X of the Θ_X, Θ_Y pair, and U remain pure, whereas its remaining component mixes with Θ_V to form states Y and V. This type of interaction is illustrated in Fig. 1(b).

For convenience, we shall refer to these two different types of perturbation as "odd" and "even," respectively. The selectivity which they show is very important for the ensuing discussion.

2. BENZENE PERTURBATIONS

(a) "Even" Perturbations

As a first example of the perturbation technique outlined in the last section, we shall consider the effect of inductive substituents on the intensity of the forbidden electronic transitions in benzene. The appropriate perturbation operator in LCAO theory may be defined with respect to its representatives referred to a basis of atomic orbitals. If atoms $r, s, \cdots, t$ have a common inductive substituent, then the relations

$$B_{mn}=0, \quad A_m=A(\delta_{mr}+\delta_{ms}+\cdots+\delta_{mt}) \quad (2.1)$$

define the perturbation. The constant A is the difference between the substituted and unsubstituted Coulomb integral α associated with a particular carbon atom. Clearly this substitution is "even" in the sense of Fig. 1. It follows immediately that only the $^1B_{2u}$ state is affected by the perturbation—at least to a first approximation. This means that the $^1A_{1g}\rightarrow{}^1B_{2u}$ band system should be more strongly affected by purely inductive substituents than the $^1A_{1g}\rightarrow{}^1B_{1u}$ system, other things being equal.

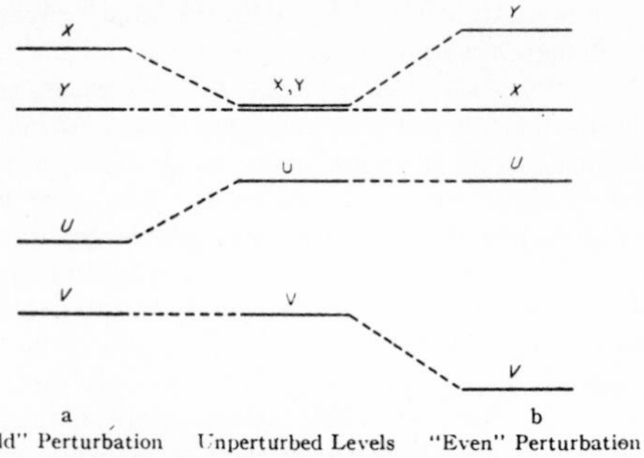

FIG. 1. The behavior of the lower-excited singlet states of the cyclic polyenes under perturbations. (Shifts K common to all levels have not been indicated.)

Putting these arguments on a more quantitative basis, we may suppose $|\mu|\ll(W_X-W_V)$ and therefore write

$$\Omega_V=\Theta_V+R(\cos\tau\Theta_Y+\sin\tau\Theta_X), \quad (2.2)$$

where

$$R=-|\mu|/(W_X-W_V), \quad \tau=\arg\mu, \quad (2.3)$$

for the perturbed $^1B_{2u}$ state. Since Ω_V now contains a small contribution from the $^1E_{1u}$ state, to which transitions from the ground state are allowed, we see that the intensity of the $^1A_{1g}\rightarrow{}^1B_{2u}$ absorption should be enhanced. For different types of inductive substitution, this enhancement will be roughly proportional to $|R|^2$ and therefore to $|\mu|^2$.

In Table V we give values of $|3\mu/A|^2$ for mono-, di-, and tri-substitution by a common substituent type (constant value of A). These rules agree perfectly with those derived on different grounds by Sklar[9] and by

TABLE V. The effect of substitution on the intensities of the α bands in the benzene spectrum.

Type of di-substitution	Enhancement factor	Type of tri-substitution	Enhancement factor[a]
ortho-	1	1, 2, 3	0
meta-	1	1, 2, 4	3
para-	4	1, 3, 5	0

[a] The enhancement factor is taken relative to the effect $|3\mu/A|^2$ of mono-substitution.

[9] A. L. Sklar, J. Chem. Phys. 10, 135 (1942).

Förster[10] and, as these authors showed, are in excellent accord with the known spectra of substituted benzenes. By our method of derivation, however, it becomes clear why the 2600A band system in benzene is more sensitive to inductive substitution than the 2000A system, despite the fact that the upper state of the latter transition is nearer to the state from which the intensity is borrowed. This result may be considered as confirming, if somewhat indirectly, the assignment of the longest wave length absorption to the ${}^1A_{1g}\rightarrow{}^1B_{2u}$ transition.

(b) "Odd" Perturbations

As an example of an "odd" perturbation in benzene, let us take the case where $A_m=0$ for all m, and B_{mn} also vanishes unless m and n are neighbors ($m+n$ odd). Under these conditions, it is seen from (1.18) that μ vanishes identically and of the lower states ${}^1B_{1u}$, ${}^1B_{2u}$ only the former interacts with the degenerate ${}^1E_{1u}$ state. Now this is exactly the type of perturbation associated with a distortion of the benzene ring in LCAO terms. The nonvanishing B_{mn} correspond to the changes in the values of the resonance integrals β_{mn} associated with the distortion. Clearly it is just such an operator which must be used to describe vibrational perturbations of the benzene system. Rather naively, we may say that vibrations will allow the ${}^1E_{1u}$ state to contribute only to the ${}^1B_{1u}$ state and not to the ${}^1B_{2u}$ state. That is, the borrowed intensity which permits the observation of the forbidden ${}^1A_{1g}\rightarrow{}^1B_{1u}$, ${}^1B_{2u}$ transitions should be greater for the former, 2000A system than for the latter, longer wavelength system, other things being equal.

Now, it has been verified that both ${}^1B_u$ states may formally interact with the ${}^1E_{1u}$ state on symmetry grounds, suitable vibrational species being present for both. On the other hand, the closer proximity of the ${}^1B_{1u}$ to the ${}^1E_{1u}$ state, should lead to a greater intensity for the ${}^1A_{1g}\rightarrow{}^1B_{1u}$ transition than for the ${}^1A_{1g}\rightarrow{}^1B_{2u}$ system by the factor $\{(W_X-W_V)/(W_X-W_U)\}^2\approx 6$. That the ${}^1A_{1g}\rightarrow{}^1B_{1u}$ system is in fact between six and eight times as strong again in absorption than this proximity reasoning would suggest, or rather that the ${}^1A_{1g}\rightarrow{}^1B_{2u}$ system is between six and eight times as weak, we may tentatively attribute to the insensitivity of the ${}^1B_{2u}$ state to "odd" perturbations. More thoroughgoing calculations are in progress to amplify this reasoning.

3. THE POLYACENES

(a) Excitation Energies

We now apply the perimeter model to the polyacenes. To this end, we take a typical cyclic polyene $C_{4\nu+2}H_{4\nu+2}$ and perturb it in such a way that its unsaturation electrons simulate those of the corresponding polyacene $C_{4\nu+2}H_{2\nu+4}$. For example, by introducing a perturbation whose nonvanishing elements in a representation referred to the AO's are $B_{05}=B_{50}=B$, say, we form a "bond" between atoms 0 and 5 of cyclodecapentaene, which then becomes, to all intents and purposes, naphthalene. Similarly, we form π-electron systems analogous to anthracene, naphthacene, and pentacene by introducing suitable cross-linking perturbations to the cyclic polyenes with the same number of carbon atoms. At the same time we complete the distortion of our cyclic polyenes in such a way that its unsaturation electrons become isosteric with the corresponding polyacene; this is of no importance for the prediction of excitation energies, since we employ an approximation which neglects interactions between non-nearest neighbors, but is vital when we come to compute oscillator strengths.

For convenience, we number the carbon atoms in such a way that the x axis, which contains atoms 0 and $(2\nu+1)$, is the transverse (shorter) axis of twofold symmetry. The origin then lies at the center of symmetry of the polyacene, and the y axis is the molecule's longitudinal axis. The polyacene-forming perturbations are symmetrical (under their action, only states of the same symmetry interact) and the unperturbed functions Θ_X, Θ_U transform like translations along $0x$, and Θ_Y, Θ_V like translations along $0y$. In the notation appropriate to the point group $\mathbf{D}_{2h}$, Θ_X, Θ_U are of species ${}^1B_{2u}$, whereas Θ_Y, Θ_V are of species ${}^1B_{1u}$.[11] On grounds of symmetry alone, all four unperturbed states are now accessible by dipole transitions from the ground state, owing to the distortion of the π-electron system.

Before proceeding with the calculations, our attitude to these might be clarified. In the first place, we assume that the perturbations may be handled in terms of the simplest LCAO theory. This is certainly only true as a first approximation, but it is not intended to aspire to greater quantitative accuracy. It is rather in the qualitative behavior of the resultant states that we shall be interested, and in the more important sources of this behavior. Secondly, we shall suppose that the relevant perturbations may be handled in the manner of Sec. 1(d): that only states arising from the same configuration of the cyclic polyene will interact under their influence. This will not be a good approximation for the more highly excited states, but should be adequate, within our prescribed limits of accuracy, for the lower states.

In order to illustrate the nature of the perturbations, we shall first compute the diagonal terms of the perturbed energy matrix. For the states arising from $\mathcal{A}$, these are simply the $(W_S+\kappa)$ and for the ground state $(W_N+\chi)$. We shall plot our results with respect to $(W_N+\chi)$ as the origin of energy units, so that they are

[10] T. Förster, Z. Naturforsch. **2A**, 149 (1947).

[11] C. A. Coulson, Proc. Phys. Soc. (London) **60**, 257 (1948). We use the same group notation for the transverse and longitudinal polarizations as Coulson, although we have had to use a different choice of x, y, and z axes; this is due to the fact that the principal axis of symmetry for the cyclic polyenes is, by convention, the z axis.

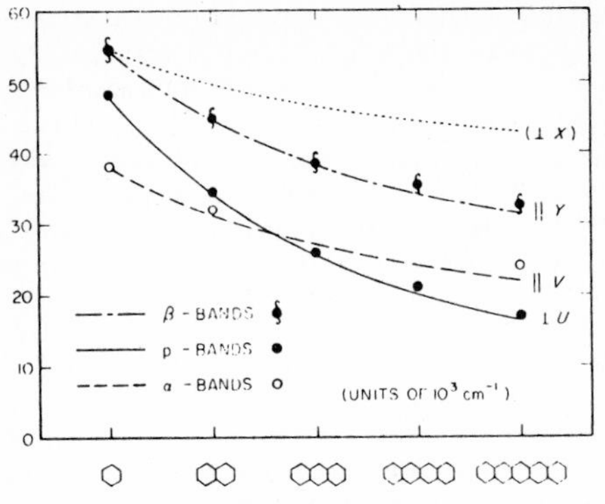

FIG. 2. A preliminary stage in the calculation of the excitation energies of the polyacenes.

expressed as "excitation" energies in Fig. 2. For a particular state, Θ_U say, we use (1.11), (1.12), and (1.17), setting the perturbation parameter $B=\beta(^1B_{1u})$, the resonance integral used in (1.11) for this particular symmetry species. And similarly for Θ_X, Θ_Y, and Θ_V. The behavior of these curves, as functions of ν, is determined very largely by the form of the excitation energies of the cyclic polyenes; they do not, however, fall off as rapidly with increasing ν as do the latter. The degeneracy of the Θ_X, Θ_Y pair has not yet been lifted.

The second, and final stage of the calculations is concerned with the scrambling of the unperturbed states arising from configuration $\mathfrak{A}$ under the influence of the perturbations. By symmetry, Θ_X may interact with Θ_U, and so may Θ_Y with Θ_V. However, it is easily seen that the sum of the indices of the atoms linked by the newly-formed bonds is always odd. The perturbation is therefore also "odd" and the possibility of mixing Θ_Y with Θ_V is never realized: the perturbed states are represented by the unperturbed functions

$$\Omega_V=\Theta_V, \quad \Omega_Y=\Theta_Y. \tag{3.1}$$

These correspond to the upper states of Clar's α and β bands, respectively (see the following). However, under an "odd" perturbation of this type, Θ_U and Θ_X interact to form the perturbed states

$$\begin{aligned}\Omega_X&=\cos\rho\Theta_X-\sin\rho\Theta_U,\\ \Omega_U&=\cos\rho\Theta_U+\sin\rho\Theta_X,\end{aligned} \tag{3.2}$$

where

$$\rho=\tfrac{1}{2}\tan^{-1}\{2\lambda/(W_U-W_X)\}. \tag{3.3}$$

As a result, the curves representing Θ_X and Θ_U in Fig. 2 repel each other and the complete excitation diagram follows Fig. 3. The rapid movement downwards of the p bands is ascribed to the resulting stabilization of its upper state, namely Ω_U.

It is easily seen that λ of (1.18) is real in all these cases, and a multiple of the perturbation parameter B. More specifically, it is found that

$$\lambda=2B(-1)^{\nu+1}(\nu-1)/(2\nu+1). \tag{3.4}$$

For the excitation energies shown in Fig. 2, we set B equal to the "resonance integrals" β, appropriately chosen for the different states using the observed benzene levels, and therefore consistently with the extrapolations from benzene we had used to determine the spectra of the cyclic polyenes. The off-diagonal parameter B cannot be chosen in this way, except in so far as it must obviously be of the same order of magnitude as the three $\beta(\Xi)$'s. We choose it semiempirically as $\sim$2.5 ev. It should be remembered that we are not aiming at quantitative results, and fortunately the accuracy we do obtain owes little to the particular values assigned to the perturbation parameters, always provided that these are in the neighborhood of 3 ev.

In addition to the predicted curves of Fig. 3, we show the observed spectroscopic intervals as points. We have only included data for the three lowest states Y, U, and V (or ^1B_b, ^1L_a and ^1L_b in Platt's notation), since the X state probably begins to interact with states from higher configurations on the one hand, and because the empirical identification of the higher states is neither complete, nor does it appear so reliable. The quantitative agreement is remarkably good but probably fortuitous in part. It is "stable" with respect to the parameters B and derives almost entirely from the qualitative properties of the "perimeters," the cyclic polyenes. The lowest states of the polyacenes may be described as arising from states of the corresponding cyclic polyenes under the appropriate cross-linking perturbations. Of these states, only Θ_X and Θ_U may interact with the result that the simple behavior in Fig. 2 is modified only by the more rapid descent of the curve representing state U, as in Fig. 3.

(b) Isomerism

In order to confirm and to extend our description of the lower excited states of the polyacenes, we may apply

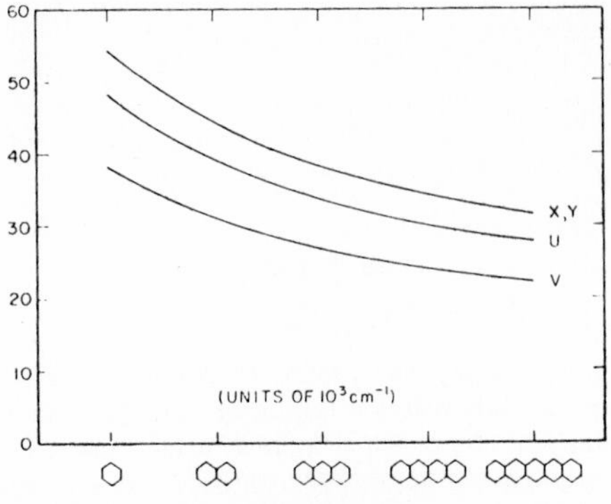

FIG. 3. The predicted and observed excitation energies in the polyacene spectra.

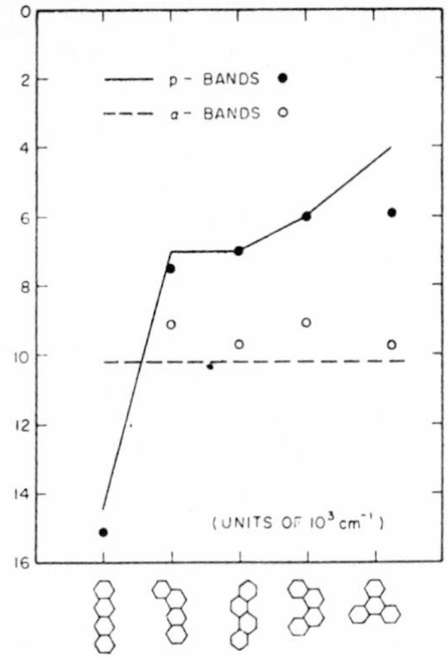

FIG. 4. The movement of the $\alpha+$ and $p+$ bands of napthacene and its isomers, relative to their $\beta+$ bands.

the same considerations to their isomers. Two distinct cases arise. If we suppose the new cata-condensed systems to be built up from fused benzene rings, e.g., phenanthrene, then the cross-linking perturbations remain "odd." However, if the isomeric molecules contain odd-membered rings, e.g., azulene, we shall discover a different type of behavior. In these paragraphs, we shall confine our attention to the cases where the ring systems all contain six carbon atoms; the case of azulene will be taken up again in the next section.

The positions at which cross linking is effected to produce cata-condensed systems from cyclic polyenes are important not only in deciding whether the appropriate perturbations are "even," "odd" or have some more complicated form, but also in determining their more quantitative aspects. Thus, for any "odd" perturbations, the behavior symbolized in (1.20) is obeyed. But the extent to which the Θ_U state is stabilized by interaction with the Θ_X, Θ_Y pair is determined by the magnitude of the parameter λ of (1.18). It is in this way that phenanthrene differs from isomeric anthracene.

Let us number our cyclic polyene ($\nu=3$) in such a way that its atoms 3 and 4 occupy the meso-positions of phenanthrene, and atoms 0 and 7 the meso-positions of anthracene. Then it is easily seen that $\lambda=(4B/7)\times\cos(4\pi/7)$ in the former case, whereas $\lambda=(4B/7)$ in the latter, $(\kappa-\chi)$ being the same in both. (The magnitude of the perturbation is determined by $|\lambda|$, which is independent of the origin of indexing, of course, but by adopting this specific form, we ensure that Θ_X, Θ_Y transform independently and that only Θ_X can then interact with Θ_U.) Accordingly it is clear from (1.19) that Θ_U and Θ_X do not interact nearly as strongly in phenanthrene as they do in anthracene. As a consequence, we should expect that of the three lower excited states of these two molecules, Y and V have the same excitation energies in both whereas the excitation energy of the state U is 4.0 ev in phenanthrene and only 3.2 ev in anthracene. This is in excellent agreement with the comparison of their spectra made by Klevens and Platt,[3] who call the relevant transition $^1A\rightarrow{}^1L_a$.

Similar comparisons may be made for the cata-condensed systems with four or five nuclei. Since $(\kappa-\chi)$ is the same for nearly all the isomers, and does not vary significantly for the few exceptions, we should expect, to a first approximation, that the location of the V and Y states of (1.20) is the same in all isomeric spectra. These states are not mixed by the "odd" cross-linked perturbations. They are called ^1L_b and ^1B_b respectively by Klevens and Platt, and the data assembled by these authors confirm our conclusion. On the other hand, the behavior of the U state depends on λ and this quantity is the only one which distinguishes different isomers in our work. Accordingly we show the predicted movement of this band, and of the V band (which should remain inactive) relative to the Y band in Figs. 4 and 5. It will be seen that the characterization of the isomers is very satisfactory, especially when the relative crudity of our method is taken into account. The specificity of Clar's p bands (our $N\rightarrow U$) to isomerization and the concomitant insensitivity of his α and β bands ($N\rightarrow V$, Y respectively) is easily understood.

(c) Intensities

So far, we have been able to see how the α, p, and β bands persist in the spectra of the cata-condensed hydrocarbons. We have shown how their locations may be explained and, in particular, we have followed the characteristic movement of the p bands. Before going

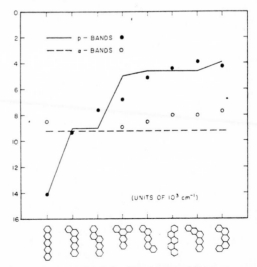

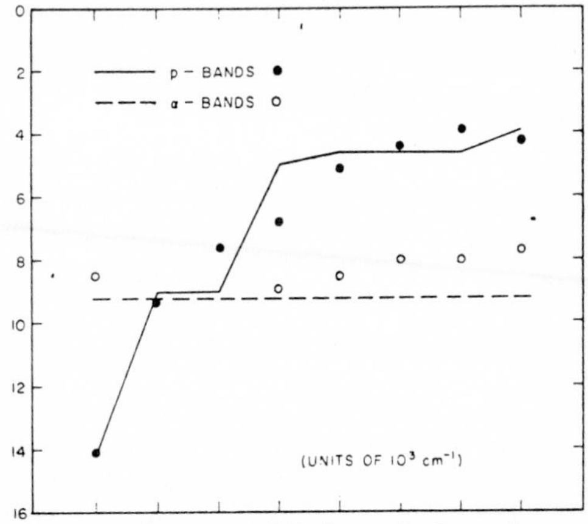

FIG. 5. The movement of the $\alpha+$ and $p+$ bands of pentacene and its isomers, relative to their $\beta+$ bands.

on to discuss azulene (features V and VI of the introduction), we must attend to the intensity relationships (II) and the effects of substitution (IV). For benzene, these have already been considered in Sec. 2.

Let us first assess the intensities of transitions from the ground state Θ_N to the unperturbed states Θ_S of some cyclic polyene, which has been distorted so as to have the same shape as a particular cata-condensed hydrocarbon. (For the undistorted rings, of course, transitions $N\rightarrow X$, Y are electronically allowed, whereas $N\rightarrow U$, V are electronically forbidden; vibrational perturbations enable the latter to "borrow" intensity from the former, but the $N\rightarrow U$ transition is more susceptible to this than the $N\rightarrow V$ transition.) As a first step in this calculation, we follow Mulliken[12] and evaluate the effective dipole vectors

$$\mathbf{Q}_{\mathrm{NS}}{}^0=\int \Theta_{\mathrm{N}}{}^*(\sum_i \mathbf{r}_i)\Theta_{\mathrm{S}}dV, \quad (\mathrm{S=X,Y,U,V}), \tag{3.5}$$

where $\mathbf{r}_i$ is the position vector of the ith unsaturation electron, referred to the centroid of charge as origin. If the molecular orbitals are considered to remain orthogonal, despite the distortion, it is easily seen that

$$\mathbf{Q}_{\mathrm{NX}}{}^0=2Rl\mathbf{q}_{-\nu,-\nu-1},\quad \mathbf{Q}_{\mathrm{NY}}{}^0=2Im\mathbf{q}_{-\nu,-\nu-1},$$
$$\mathbf{Q}_{\mathrm{NU}}{}^0=2Rl\mathbf{q}_{-\nu,\nu+1},\quad \mathbf{Q}_{\mathrm{NV}}{}^0=2Im\mathbf{q}_{-\nu,\nu+1}, \tag{3.6}$$

where

$$\mathbf{q}_{\xi\eta}=\int \psi_\xi{}^*\mathbf{r}\psi_\eta dv. \tag{3.7}$$

So that, neglecting overlap between all but adjacent carbon atoms,

$$\mathbf{Q}_{\mathrm{NX}}{}^0=2\sigma_\nu\sigma_{\nu+1}\sum_m \cos\{m\pi/(2\nu+1)\}\mathbf{a}_m,$$

$$\mathbf{Q}_{\mathrm{NY}}{}^0=2\sigma_\nu\sigma_{\nu+1}\sum_m \sin\{-m\pi/(2\nu+1)\}\mathbf{a}_m,$$

$$\mathbf{Q}_{\mathrm{NU}}{}^0=2\sigma_\nu\sigma_{\nu+1}\sum_m \cos(m\pi)\mathbf{a}_m, \tag{3.8}$$

$$\mathbf{Q}_{\mathrm{NV}}{}^0=4\sigma_\nu\sigma_{\nu+1}\sum_m\sum_{n>m} \sin\{(m+n)\pi/2\}\times\cos\{(m-n)\pi/(4\nu+2)\}\mathbf{b}_{mn},$$

where

$$\mathbf{a}_m=\int \phi_m{}^*\mathbf{r}\phi_m dv=\mathbf{r}_m,$$
$$\mathbf{b}_{mn}=\int \phi_m{}^*\mathbf{r}\phi_n dv=\tfrac{1}{2}(\mathbf{r}_m+\mathbf{r}_n)S_{mn}, \tag{3.9}$$

$\mathbf{r}_m$, $\mathbf{r}_n$ being the position vectors of the m, nth carbon atoms and S_{mn} being the overlap integral between ϕ_m and ϕ_n. We have used the fact that, under the distortion, the cyclic polyene assumes the geometry of some cata-condensed hydrocarbon containing only even-membered rings, so that all adjacent carbon atoms differ in their indices by an odd number. It will be noticed, immediately, that contributions to the effective dipole vectors $\mathbf{Q}^0$ arise only from atoms for "transitions" N→X, Y, U, whereas $\mathbf{Q}_{\mathrm{NV}}{}^0$ consists of contributions from bonds only, and therefore contains the overlap integral as a factor.

[12] R. S. Mulliken, J. Chem. Phys. 7, 14 (1939).

Even though these formulas are only approximate—we have assumed the MO's to remain orthogonal under the distortion—it is very instructive to evaluate the $\mathbf{Q}^0$'s. For this purpose, we choose the polyacenes themselves, which serve to illustrate the essential factors determining intensities. Similar results are easily obtained for their isomers, whose condensation is not linear. For simplicity, we suppose the molecules to consist of fused regular hexagons with sides of length $R=1.4$A. Using the approximation $\sigma_\nu\approx(4\nu+2)^{-\frac{1}{2}}\approx\sigma_{\nu+1}$, it is found that

$$\mathbf{Q}_{\mathrm{NX}}{}^0=R\mathbf{i}\{3/(4\nu+2)\}\operatorname{cosec}(\theta/2),$$
$$\mathbf{Q}_{\mathrm{NY}}{}^0=-R\mathbf{j}\{\sqrt{3}/(4\nu+2)\}\operatorname{cosec}(\theta/2)\cot(\theta/2),$$
$$\mathbf{Q}_{\mathrm{NU}}{}^0=R\mathbf{i}(-1)^{\nu+1}\{(\nu-1)/(2\nu+1)\}, \tag{3.10}$$
$$\mathbf{Q}_{\mathrm{NV}}{}^0=SR\mathbf{j}(-1)^\nu\{\sqrt{3}/(4\nu+2)\}\operatorname{cosec}\theta\{\operatorname{cosec}(\theta/2)-2\nu\sin(3\theta/2)\},\quad (\theta=\pi/(2\nu+1))$$

where $\mathbf{i}$, $\mathbf{j}$ are unit vectors along $0x$, $0y$ respectively and we have put $S_{mn}=S$ whenever m, n are adjacent. Certain results are apparent at once.

For example, $|Q_{\mathrm{NX}}{}^0|$ never becomes large; its magnitude for benzene is R and for a very long polyacene, it approaches $(3/\pi)R$ monotonically. $|Q_{\mathrm{NY}}{}^0|$, on the other hand, increases almost linearly on increasing the number of fused rings. $|Q_{\mathrm{NU}}{}^0|$ is again bounded, and never exceeds $\frac{1}{2}R$. $|Q_{\mathrm{NV}}{}^0|$ vanishes identically for distorted cyclodecapentaene, which is the perimeter of naphthalene, and remains small even as far as pentacene; it contains the overlap integral. For benzene itself, of course, we have $|Q_{\mathrm{NX}}{}^0|=|Q_{\mathrm{NY}}{}^0|=R$ and $|Q_{\mathrm{NU}}{}^0|=|Q_{\mathrm{NV}}{}^0|=0$.

We are now in a position to make estimates of the intensities of the various bands which arise in the spectra of the polyacenes. These are best compared on the basis of their oscillator strengths f, which are proportional to the excitation energy of the upper state and to the square of the effective dipole lengths associated with the transitions.[12] When Ω_N is the ground-state function, and Ω_S the eigenfunction of the upper state, the effective dipole length is defined as

$$\mathbf{Q}_{NS}=\int \Omega_N{}^*(\sum_i \mathbf{r}_i)\Omega_S dV. \tag{3.11}$$

Thus $|Q_{NS}|^2$ is the main criterion for the purely electronic contribution to the intensity of the $N\rightarrow S$ bands. We shall discuss the three different band systems in turn.

The very intense bands which Clar calls β bands are those due to the transitions $N\rightarrow Y$ in our notation

(Platt's $^1A \rightarrow {}^1B_b$). They are longitudinally polarized. Now, in our approximation, we have, according to (3.1), $\Omega_N = \Theta_N$, $\Omega_Y = \Theta_Y$, so that the effective dipole lengths are given by the $\mathbf{Q}_{NY}^0$ of Eq. (3.10). Thus we should expect the intensities of these transitions to increase as we go to the higher polyacenes. They correspond to the allowed transition ($^1A_{1g} \rightarrow {}^1E_{1u}$) in benzene, and therefore absorb very strongly.

The very weak α bands, which are obscured by the stronger p bands in anthracene and naphthacene, correspond to our transition $N \rightarrow V$. Just as for the β bands, we may use Eq. (3.10) to calculate the effective dipole lengths, since $\Omega_V = \Theta_V$ in our approximation. Now the $N \rightarrow V$ transitions are formally allowed electronically, since they too are polarized longitudinally. However, we have seen that $|Q_{NV}^0|$ vanishes identically for naphthalene and is still very small for pentacene. The absorptions associated with these transitions are therefore exceedingly weak. It is, moreover, easily shown, by arguments analogous to those used for benzene, that the upper states of these bands are insensitive to vibrational ("odd") perturbations. So that, although they are often not far from more intense systems, they do not "borrow" intensity at all effectively. (The f value for benzene is only 0.002.)

Lastly, we consider the p bands, whose moderate to strong intensity is attributed to the transition $N \rightarrow U$. The situation is slightly more complicated, since the U state is represented as the linear combination

$$\Omega_U = \cos\rho\Theta_U + \sin\rho\Theta_X. \quad (3.12)$$

Accordingly, the effective dipole length is given by

$$\mathbf{Q}_{NU} = \cos\rho\mathbf{Q}_{NU}^0 + \sin\rho\mathbf{Q}_{NX}^0. \quad (3.13)$$

Now, we have seen that $|Q_{NU}^0|$ is small for small ν and approaches $\frac{1}{2}R$ for very long polyacenes; $|Q_{NX}^0|$ is always very close to R. Thus $|Q_{NU}|$ begins by being rather small and never exceeds $1/\sqrt{2}[\frac{1}{2}+(3/\pi)]R$. The intensity of these bands is markedly affected by the vibrational couplings ("odd" perturbations), which we have considered qualitatively for benzene. As we shall see more specifically below, this accounts for the moderate intensity of the p bands quite nicely.

TABLE VI. The calculated and observed oscillator strengths of band systems in the polyacene spectra.

Method	Transition	Benzene	Naphthalene	Anthracene	Naphthacene	Pentacene
calc. I	$N \rightarrow V$	0	0	0.0016	0.008	0.019
calc. II	(α bands)	0	0	0.0005	0.002	0.006
obs.		0.002	0.002	?	?	~0.006
calc. I	$N \rightarrow U$	0	0.38	0.37	0.32	0.29
calc. II	(p bands)	0	0.11	0.11	0.10	0.09
obs.		0.10	0.18?	0.10	0.08	0.08
calc. I	$N \rightarrow Y$	1.2	2.8	4.8	7.2	9.9
calc. II	(β bands)	(0.35)	0.85	1.45	2.16	2.97
obs.		0.35	1.70	2.28	1.85	2.2

The important contributions of vibrational coupling to the observed oscillator strengths, particularly for the α and p bands are discussed in the text.

To illustrate the more quantitative aspects of these arguments, we shall estimate the oscillator strengths f of the three band systems using the formula[12]

$$f_{N\rightarrow S} = 1.085 \times 10^{11} \times |Q_{NS}|^2 \times E_{NS}, \quad (S = V, U, Y), \quad (3.14)$$

where $\mathbf{Q}_{NS}$ is expressed in cm and E_{NS}, the excitation energy of the relevant upper state, is expressed in cm^{-1}. Then, using (1.19), (3.10), and (3.13) in conjunction with (3.14), we prepare Table VI. In the first row, we use (3.14) directly. But, as Mulliken has shown, calculations of oscillator strengths by means of this equation always lead to results whose values are too high. Accordingly he used correction factors in the range from 0.4 to 0.25. To obtain a better comparison with the experimental results, we therefore multiply all oscillator strengths in the first row by 0.3, thereby "normalizing" with respect to benzene, whose oscillator strength then comes out correctly. (Only $N \rightarrow Y$ is shown for benzene, since we do not include $N \rightarrow X$ for the polyacenes.) These modified values are given in the second row. The third row lists the observed values, which are taken from Klevens and Platt's compilation.

The agreement is strikingly good. For example, the calculated range of intensities falls sharply into the three observed domains. Those band systems of exceedingly low oscillator strengths ($N \rightarrow V$) cannot be compared at all closely with the empirical values, since the predicted intensities for the electronic processes are lower than those due to the vibrational coupling ($\Delta f \sim 0.002$). The bands of moderate intensity ($N \rightarrow U$) are more strongly affected by vibrational perturbations ($\Delta f \sim 0.1$) but presumably also have electronic contributions to their intensity. Our estimates of the latter show these to be of the right order of magnitude. Finally, the strong $N \rightarrow Y$ bands are predicted to be in just the right intensity range. A more detailed comparison of the numerical results does not seem very profitable. In the first place, our theoretical method was not aimed at great accuracy, and in the second, the oscillator strengths in the shorter wavelength region are not easy to measure exactly. The uniform increase of f with ν predicted for the β bands may well occur, but its observation may be obscured by possible interference from neighboring, more highly excited levels; the experimental behavior of ϵ_{max} certainly confirms the regular intensification which we have calculated.

As a last feature of the intensities of these three band systems, we may consider the effect of inductive substituents. The most striking change that is observed on going from a cata-condensed hydrocarbon to its aza-derivative, by the replacement of $-CH=$ by $-N=$, is the sharp intensification of the α bands.[13] And similar changes occur on replacing hydrogen atoms by more or

[13] Badger, Pearce, and Pettit, J. Chem. Soc. **1951**, 3199.

less electronegative groups. Now the upper state of these bands is our V state which is sensitive only to the "even" perturbations analyzed in Sec. 1(d). As an example of these, variations (A_m) of the Coulomb integrals at particular atomic centers constitute an "even" perturbation. And such inductive changes at a carbon atom are of just this type. Accordingly, the effect of these perturbations is to mix the unperturbed V states, to which transitions from the ground state are virtually "forbidden," with contributions from X and Y, to which transitions are strongly allowed. The observed intensification of the ensuing bands is easily explained on this basis.

4. AZULENE

(a) Excitation Energies

In the preceding section, we have dealt with the "formation" of cata-condensed hydrocarbons containing fused benzene rings, from their perimeters. It was always found that the cross-linking perturbations were "odd." However, stable aromatic systems may also be formed in which the fused rings contain odd numbers of carbon atoms. The most simple of these is azulene which, like naphthalene, we relate to cyclodecapentaene. In this case, the relevant perturbation, when referred to an AO representation, has only two nonvanishing elements, namely, $B_{28}=B_{82}=B$, say. This will link together atoms 2 and 8, so that the new aromatic system contains fused five- and seven-membered rings. Since the sum of the atomic indices is now even, we are dealing with an "even" perturbation.

The atoms have been labeled in such a way that 0 and 5 lie on the twofold (x) axis of symmetry, with the former belonging to the five-membered ring. It is then easily verified that Θ_Y, Θ_V transform like translations along the shorter, transverse (y) axis of the molecule, whereas Θ_X, Θ_U are longitudinally polarized. Once again, it is formally possible for Θ_X and Θ_U to interact under the perturbation, and similarly for Θ_Y and Θ_V. In contrast to the behavior found for naphthalene, however, it is Θ_Y and Θ_V which interact under the "even" perturbation, whereas the possibility of mixing Θ_X with Θ_U is not realized.

A comparison of the predicted properties of naphthalene and azulene is made in Fig. 6. At the sides of this figure, we show the location of the diagonal terms of the energy matrix (1.14), referred to their respective ground states, for both cases. It will be noticed that $(\kappa-\chi)$ is greater for naphthalene than for azulene. In the middle, the results of the full perturbation calculations are illustrated. For azulene, we see that the interaction of Θ_Y and Θ_V accounts for the low level of the V state, whereas the remaining states are unaffected. For naphthalene, on the other hand, it is the location of the U state which is affected by the appropriate cross-linking perturbation. We also indicate the observed energies of the three lowest-excited singlet states by

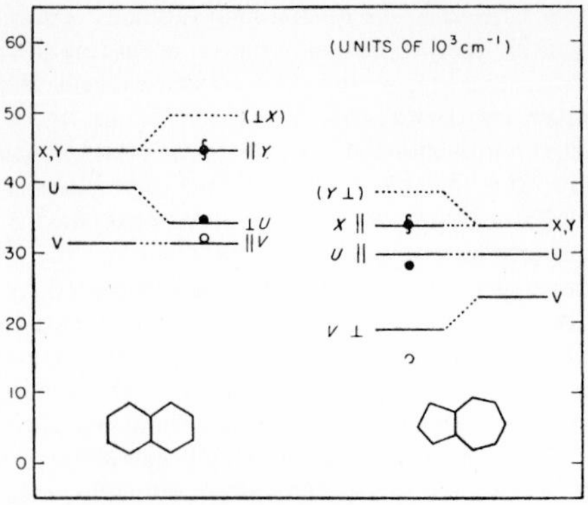

FIG. 6. A comparison of the spectra of azulene and naphthalene.

circles on this diagram.[14] It will be seen that the qualitative behavior we predict is perfectly correct. The quantitative results are also quite good. Least accurate is the location of the lowest state in azulene. Considering the relative crudity of our method, it does not seem profitable at present to speculate on the reason for the greater disparity in this particular case.

(b) Intensities

In the case of the polyacenes, it was possible to confirm the assignment of the observed band systems, to the theoretically located transitions, on grounds other than those of excitation energies alone. Similar considerations must now be applied to the azulene levels. As before, we shall use the intensity of the bands for this purpose. (For the polyacenes, it was also possible to use isomerism and sensitivity to inductive substitution; the application of an additional criterion will also be discussed for azulene below.)

Calculations of the oscillator strengths associated with the three azulene transitions $N \rightarrow V$, U, X may be made in the same manner that similar computations were undertaken in Sec. 3(c) for the polyacenes. We assume that the geometry of the molecule is not far from that of a system which fuses a regular pentagon together with a regular heptagon of side $R=1.4$A. The calculations are then straightforward and it is unnecessary to comment further on them, except to state that the same correction factor of 0.3 is applied to these cases, as was applied to benzene and the polyacenes.

For the lowest $N \rightarrow V$ transition, the electronic contribution to the intensity is almost entirely due to the admixture of Θ_Y contained in Ω_V. This is predicted to lead to an oscillator strength which is rather less than 0.02. Skeletal vibrations will not affect the intensity of these bands very much, since variations in the lengths of the ten perimetric bonds constitute "odd" perturbations, to which the upper and lower states are relatively insensitive. This is in good agreement with the oscillator

[14] Mann, Platt, and Klevens, J. Chem. Phys. 17, 481 (1949).

strength determined empirically by Mann, Platt, and Klevens ($f\approx 0.01$), who call this transition $^1A\rightarrow{}^1L_b$. It corresponds to a transversely polarized absorption.

The second band system, $N\rightarrow U$, has a very small electronic contribution to the oscillator strength, namely, 0.01. On the other hand, the upper state associated with this system is strongly affected by the "odd" perturbations which describe the more important effects of nuclear vibrations. By analogy with benzene, we should expect this coupling to enhance electronically negligible intensities by an amount $\Delta f\approx 0.1$. That the observed oscillator strength is in the neighborhood of 0.08, is in excellent agreement with these expectations. The $N\rightarrow U$ system is longitudinally polarized.

Lastly, we consider the longitudinally polarized $N\rightarrow X$ bands. Here the transition is very strongly allowed, electronically, and we compute an oscillator strength $f\approx 0.6$. This also agrees quite nicely with the empirical value of $f\approx 1.1$. (Mann, Platt, and Klevens call this transition $^1A\rightarrow{}^1B_b$. It would seem, however, that the upper state of this system could profitably be renamed ^1B_a. For both ^1L_a and ^1B_a would then be polarized along the same twofold axis of symmetry, and the subscripts a and b for Platt's ^1B states would have an enhanced significance. It would also appear to be more consistent with his usage for the polyacenes, where ^1L_b and ^1B_b have the same axis of polarization.)

It will be noticed in these cases, as for the polyacenes, that the intensity criterion is particularly good since the observed, as well as the calculated oscillator strengths differ sharply for the three lowest band systems. But it is most important in this connection to assess, however approximately, the vibrational contributions to those band systems whose purely electronic dipole lengths are small. In this note, we have used the criterion $\Delta f\approx 0.1$ for those transitions whose upper states are vulnerable to "odd" perturbations, whereas $\Delta f\approx 0.002$ for the remainder—using the known benzene spectrum as the basis for these estimates. A more fundamental treatment of this topic is being carried out and will be published at a later date.

(c) The Effect of Inductive Substituents

One of the most striking features of the azulene spectrum is the sensitivity exhibited by the lowest $N\rightarrow V$ band system. On effecting substitutions for hydrogen atoms by more or less electronegative groups at different positions in either or both of the fused rings, characteristic and quite appreciable shifts to greater or to lower wavelengths are observed. But concomitant shifts in the other two band systems are much smaller and of the usual bathochromic type. Coulson and others have discussed this phenomenon but, as he remarked,[15] it has remained a mystery why the $N\rightarrow V$ system should be unique in this respect. The present approach offers a very natural explanation of these effects.

[15] C. A. Coulson, Proc. Phys. Soc. (London) **A65**, 933 (1952).

Consider first the cyclic polyenes of $(4\nu+2)$ carbon atoms. It is easily verified that the description of these molecules given in Sec. 1 assigns the electronic charges uniformly among the equivalent carbon atoms in all their states $\Omega_T{}^0$, $(T=N, X, Y, U, V)$. Under an "odd" perturbation, these charge distributions remain unaltered. However, under an "even" perturbation, the situation is different. The separate, unperturbed functions Θ_T, $(T=N, X, Y, U, V)$ describe states of the molecules in which no atom has a net charge. And therefore the N, U, and X states are unaffected by the perturbation in this respect. But the linear combination of Θ_V and, in our case, Θ_Y—which is needed to describe the perturbed V state (of azulene, say)—is such that the charge distribution is no longer uniform: fractional positive and negative charges appear on the various carbon atoms in this particular state, and in this state only.

More specifically, we may write for the eigenfunction of the V state in azulene

$$\Omega_V=\cos\rho\Theta_V+\sin\rho\Theta_Y,$$

where the parameter ρ is determined by the usual methods of Sec. 1; it turns out to be in the neighborhood of $27\frac{1}{2}°$. Then, although the separate distributions Θ_V, Θ_Y are uniform, it is readily shown that their interference induces a net charge of

$$-(1/5)\sin 2\rho\cos(6m\pi/5)$$

at the carbon atom which we have labeled m. It may be noticed that the ratios of these charge increments are independent of the specific value calculated for ρ. Up to the present, we have found it convenient analytically to index carbons serially on going around the ring of the parent cyclic polyene. Since this is at variance with chemical nomenclature, we shall adopt the latter from now on and abandon our original designation. The net charges are therefore given numerically, together with the conventional labelling, in Fig. 7.

That such charge separation should occur for the V state of azulene, which arises from an "even" perturbation of cyclodecapentaene, is not in any way surprising. It will be recalled that electrostatic perturbations of benzene induced a mixing of its $^1B_{2u}(V)$ and $^1E_{1u}(X, Y)$ states in Sec. 2(a). The cyclic polyene in this case ($\nu=1$) rearranged its electronic densities in such a way as best to accommodate itself to the different conditions defined by its substituents; some charge separation

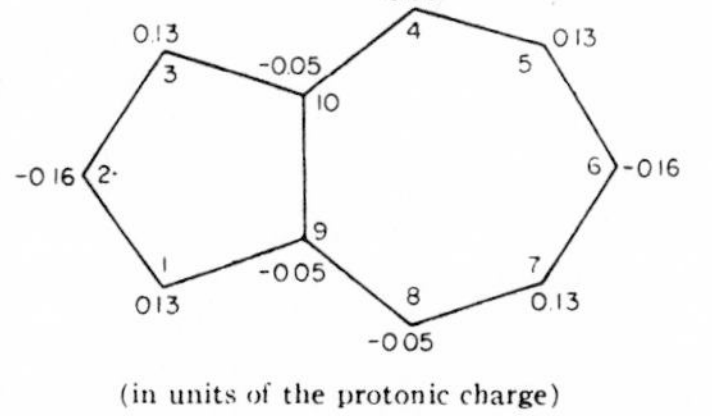

FIG. 7. The charge distribution in the first excited state of azulene.

occurred. This effect was also due to an "even" perturbation.

The changes to be observed in the azulene spectrum on replacing hydrogen atoms by electron donors or acceptors may now be worked out quite simply—to a first approximation, at least. The charge distribution being uniform in states N, U, and X, we should anticipate only second-order shifts in the band systems $N \rightarrow U$ and $N \rightarrow X$. However, an inspection of Fig. 7 shows that if electron donors (e.g., methyl groups) replace hydrogen atoms at positions 1, 3, 5, and 7, the V state is stabilized and we should expect corresponding first-order shifts in the $N \rightarrow V$ bands to longer wavelengths (bathochromically). Conversely, similar substitutions at positions 2, 4, 6, and 8 should lead to hypsochromic shifts. Moreover, within the limits of accuracy set by our first-order treatment, the effect of successive replacements should be additive. Substitution by electron acceptors (more electronegative atoms or groups, like $-COOH$), on the other hand, should follow exactly the opposite laws: at positions 1, 3, 5, and 7 hypsochromic shifts are expected, whereas at 2, 4, 6, and 8 the $N \rightarrow V$ bands should be moved to longer wavelengths.

These qualitative rules reproduce precisely the empirical behavior of the $N \rightarrow V$ band system.[16] Moreover, the shifts observed are much larger than those obtained for the $N \rightarrow U$, X systems, which is again what we should have expected. Using the magnitudes of the charge increments of Fig. 7 as a quantitative guide, it appears that the numerical value of the methyl shifts at positions 1 and 4 is rather larger than would have been anticipated. No importance is attached to this, however, since neither the second-order effects of the substitutions nor their hyperconjugative propensities—which are probably also subsidiary factors—have been considered. We should be content that a treatment as simple as that described is qualitatively so successful. It lends powerful support to the identification of the band systems.

[16] P. A. Plattner, Helv. Chim. Acta **24**, 283 (1941); **34**, 971 (1951); P. A. Plattner and E. Heilbronner, Helv. Chim. Acta **31**, 804 (1948).

DISCUSSION

It has been shown how the perimeter model accounts for the more prominent features of the electronic spectra of cata-condensed hydrocarbons. These include the location of the three lowest band systems, their intensities and particularly the way in which these are affected by vibrational coupling and substitution, the effects of isomerism and the characteristic shifts accompanying substitution in azulene. Starting with the supposedly known benzene spectrum, the properties of the cyclic polyenes were estimated. These hypothetical molecules were then subjected to perturbations under which their unsaturation electrons simulated the behavior of the cata-condensed systems of interest. The most interesting properties which emerged were due to the very specific, almost geometrical nature of these perturbations.

The method which was used has several advantages. More particularly, it is sufficiently simple for its general results to become apparent almost immediately on qualitative grounds. The calculations never require the solution of difficult secular equations, but may be carried out directly using trigonometric tables. Another of its more important aspects concerns the sense in which perturbation theory is employed: the zeroth-order levels in the treatment refer to states, and not to orbitals. It is in this way that many of the complications (particularly those connected with configurational interaction) of previous theoretical work are avoided. There are many points of interest which arise relating the perimeter theory to the conventional methods of approach. In view of the very limited ability of the latter to rationalize the spectral features, it would be desirable in many ways to pursue this topic here. It seems, however, that this could more profitably be discussed in a later and quite separate communication.

The work reported in this note was largely stimulated by the publications of Clar, Jones, and particularly of Platt, references to which have been made above.

REPRINTED FROM THE
PROCEEDINGS OF THE PHYSICAL SOCIETY, A, VOL. LXVIII, p. 81, 1955

The Electronic Spectra of Aromatic Molecules

II : A Theoretical Treatment of Excited States of Alternant Hydrocarbon Molecules based on Self-Consistent Molecular Orbitals

BY J. A. POPLE
Department of Theoretical Chemistry, University of Cambridge

MS. received 13*th August* 1954

Abstract. The theoretical treatment of the electronic spectrum of benzenoid hydrocarbons recently given by Dewar and Longuet-Higgins (Part I) is generalized so that full account is taken of electron interaction. The method is based on the use of a self-consistent molecular orbital function for the ground state and corresponding functions for excited states. It is found that all the general features of the method of Part I carry over, although certain accidental degeneracies are removed. Approximate numerical calculations based on the new method give support to the assignments made by Dewar and Longuet-Higgins.

§ 1. INTRODUCTION

In a previous paper, Dewar and Longuet-Higgins (1954) have given a theoretical interpretation of the singlet electronic spectra associated with the mobile electrons of benzenoid hydrocarbons. Their procedure, in outline, is as follows:

(1) A set of orbital energies is obtained from the Hückel LCAO molecular orbital theory (based on an effective one-electron Hamiltonian and neglecting overlap). If the mobile electrons were really independent and non-interacting, the excitation levels would be the differences between these energies.

(2) It is well known that the Hückel theory by itself leads to an oversimplified picture of the spectra. The mutual repulsion of the electrons leads to interaction between the various excited configurations and modifies the energy levels. To allow for this in a simple way, interaction is permitted between configurations which the Hückel theory predicts to be degenerate. Such levels are then split by amounts which are related to the matrix elements of the complete many-electron Hamiltonian between the corresponding antisymmetrized configurational wave functions. By applying this method to the lowest levels, Dewar and Longuet-Higgins are able to interpret the general features of the p, α, β and β' bands classified by Clar.

Although this is undoubtedly an improvement over the Hückel theory by itself, the use of the incompletely defined one-electron Hamiltonian in step (1) is still rather unsatisfactory. It would be better if the *whole* treatment could be based on the many-electron Hamiltonian with electron interaction. That some such further development is needed is suggested by the fact that the Dewar–Longuet-Higgins method still oversimplifies the spectra in some respects. For example, it predicts that the B_{1u} and B_{2u} levels of benzene should be degenerate, whereas in fact they are distinct. A second reason for improving the theory is that a treatment including electron interaction at all stages should show the relation between singlet and triplet levels.

Recently the work of Pariser and Parr (1953) on the spectra of ethylene and benzene has suggested that useful conclusions about the effect of electron interaction can be drawn without detailed calculation of complicated integrals characteristic of earlier work. Using a similar series of approximations, the present author (Pople 1953) has discussed the determination of self-consistent orbitals for the ground states of alternant hydrocarbons and has shown how many of the features of the Hückel theory (uniform charge-density, pairing of orbitals, etc.) hold also when electron interaction is taken into account explicitly. The present paper introduces a generalization of the work of Dewar and Longuet-Higgins which is based on the self-consistent molecular orbital function and which allows for electron interaction at all stages. The principal features of their work carry over almost without change to this more rigorous method, although certain accidental degeneracies are removed. It is possible to get explicit expressions for the lowest energy levels in terms of the self-consistent orbital coefficients, so that the integrals of Pariser and Parr can be used to make a more quantitative test of the assignments.

§ 2. Excited States of Alternant Hydrocarbons

The wave function χ_0 for the π-electrons in the ground state of an alternant hydrocarbon will be taken as a Slater determinant built up from orthogonal molecular orbitals $\psi_1, \ldots . \psi_m$ which are themselves linear combinations of carbon 2pπ atomic orbitals $\phi_1 \ldots . \phi_{2m}$

$$\psi_i = \sum_\mu c_{i\mu}\phi_\mu. \qquad \ldots\ldots(2.1)$$

In the self-consistent treatment, the coefficients $c_{i\mu}$ are chosen to minimize the electronic energy

$$\mathscr{E} = \int \ldots . \int \bar{\chi}_0 \mathscr{H} \chi_0 d\tau \qquad \ldots\ldots(2.2)$$

where $\mathscr{H}$ is the complete electronic Hamiltonian

$$\mathscr{H} = \sum_i H_i^{\text{core}} + \sum_{i<j}^{2m} (1/r_{ij}). \qquad \ldots\ldots(2.3)$$

H^{core} represents the kinetic energy and the potential energy of the σ-core.

A general set of equations for $c_{i\mu}$ has been given by Roothaan (1951). Making certain simplifying approximations about the integrals that arise (Pople 1953), these can be reduced to the eigenvalue equations

$$\sum_\nu F_{\mu\nu} c_{i\nu} = E_i c_{i\mu}. \qquad \ldots\ldots(2.4)$$

where

$$F_{\mu\mu} = U_{\mu\mu} + \tfrac{1}{2} p_{\mu\mu}\gamma_{\mu\mu} + \sum_{\sigma(\neq\mu)} (p_{\sigma\sigma} - 1)\gamma_{\mu\sigma} \qquad \ldots\ldots(2.5)$$

$$F_{\mu\nu} = H_{\mu\nu} - \tfrac{1}{2} p_{\mu\nu}\gamma_{\mu\nu} \qquad \ldots\ldots(2.6)$$

$$P_{\mu\nu} = 2\sum_{i=1}^{m} \bar{c}_{i\mu} c_{i\nu}. \qquad \ldots\ldots(2.7)$$

In these expressions $\gamma_{\mu\nu}$ has been written for the coulomb electrostatic repulsion integral

$$\gamma_{\mu\nu} = \iint \phi_\mu{}^2(1)(1/r_{12})\phi_\nu{}^2(2)\, dv_1\, dv_2. \qquad \ldots\ldots(2.8)$$

$U_{\mu\mu}$ is a core matrix element which may reasonably be taken as the same for all carbon centres and $H_{\mu\nu}$ is the off-diagonal matrix element of the core Hamiltonian

$$H_{\mu\nu} = \int \phi_\mu(1) H_1^{\text{core}} \phi_\nu(1)\, dv_1. \qquad \ldots\ldots(2.9).$$

This is taken to be equal to a constant β for all pairs of neighbours and zero otherwise. E_i are the eigenvalues of the matrix $F_{\mu\nu}$.

Since there are $2m$ atomic orbitals, equations (2.2) determine $2m$ molecular orbitals. Of these only m corresponding to the lower E_i are occupied in the ground state. The other unoccupied orbitals will be used in formulating wave functions for excited states.

From the form of the self-consistent equations (2.4) certain general results can be derived which are applicable to all alternant hydrocarbons (Pople 1953). In particular,

(i) $p_{\mu\mu} = 1$ for all μ.

(ii) The eigenvalues E_i are symmetrically arranged about the value $U + \frac{1}{2}\gamma_{11}$. That is, if $U + \frac{1}{2}\gamma_{11} - \epsilon$ is an eigenvalue, so is $U + \frac{1}{2}\gamma_{11} + \epsilon$.

(iii) The coefficients of the orbitals are paired. This means that, if the atoms are divided into starred and unstarred sets in the usual way, then the pair of molecular orbitals with energies $U + \frac{1}{2}\gamma_{11} \pm \epsilon$ can be written

$$\left.\begin{aligned} \psi_i &= \sum_\mu{}^* c_{i\mu}\phi_\mu + \sum_\mu{}^0 c_{i\mu}\phi_\mu \\ \psi_{2m+1-i} &= \sum_\mu{}^* c_{i\mu}\phi_\mu - \sum_\mu{}^0 c_{i\mu}\phi_\mu \end{aligned}\right\} \qquad \ldots\ldots(2.10)$$

where the molecular orbitals are numbered 1, 2.... $2m$ with increasing eigenvalues E_i; Σ^* and Σ^0 are written for sums over starred and unstarred atoms respectively.

Once the self-consistent problem for the ground state has been solved, the unoccupied molecular orbitals $\psi_{m+1} \ldots \psi_{2m}$ can be used to construct configurational wave functions for excited states. We shall write ${}^1\chi_{i\to k}$ for the singlet configurational wave function in which one electron is excited from an occupied orbital ψ_i to an unoccupied one ψ_k. ${}^1\chi_{i\to k}$ will be a sum of two Slater determinants (Roothaan 1951). The corresponding triplet wave function will be written ${}^3\chi_{i\to k}$. (There are in fact three triplet functions with three different spin component eigenvalues. It is immaterial which component is selected as long as the same one is used for all configurations.) Other functions for two-electron excitations could be developed, but for a discussion of the lower absorption levels they will not be taken into account.

The matrix elements of the total Hamiltonian $\mathscr{H}$ between the $\chi_{i\to k}$ and χ_0 can be reduced to integrals over one or two electrons utilizing the orthogonality property of molecular orbitals. The results are (see Appendix)

$$({}^1\chi_{i\to k}|\mathscr{H}|{}^1\chi_{i\to k}) - (\chi_0|\mathscr{H}|\chi_0) = E_k - E_i - (ik|G|ik) + 2(ik|G|ki) \qquad \ldots\ldots(2.11)$$

$$({}^3\chi_{i\to k}|\mathscr{H}|{}^3\chi_{i\to k}) - (\chi_0|\mathscr{H}|\chi_0) = E_k - E_i - (ik|G|ik) \qquad \ldots\ldots(2.12)$$

$$({}^1\chi_{i\to k}|\mathscr{H}|\chi_0) = 0 \qquad \ldots\ldots(2.13)$$

$$({}^1\chi_{i\to k}|\mathscr{H}|{}^1\chi_{j\to l}) = 2(jk|G|li) - (jk|G|il) \text{ (unless } i=j \text{ and } k=l) \qquad \ldots\ldots(2.14)$$

$$({}^3\chi_{i\to k}|\mathscr{H}|{}^3\chi_{j\to l}) = -(jk|G|il) \text{ (unless } i=j \text{ and } k=l) \qquad \ldots\ldots(2.15)$$

the two-electron matrix elements being defined by

$$(pq|G|rs)=\int\int\bar{\psi}_p(1)\bar{\psi}_q(2)(1/r_{12})\psi_r(1)\psi_s(2)\,dv_1\,dv_2. \quad ......(2.16)$$

All matrix elements between singlet and triplet functions are zero by integration over spin.

Equations (2.11) and (2.12) show that $({}^1\chi_{i\to k}|\mathscr{H}|{}^1\chi_{i\to k})-(\chi_0|\mathscr{H}|\chi_0)$ and $({}^3\chi_{i\to k}|\mathscr{H}|{}^3\chi_{i\to k})-(\chi_0|\mathscr{H}|\chi_0)$, which may be described as configurational excitation energies, are not equal to the difference between the two eigenvalues if electron interaction is included. In fact E_k-E_i is generally larger.

In spite of this, it is still possible to generalize the method of Dewar and Longuet-Higgins, using the pairing properties described above. As explained in the introduction, their procedure is to include interaction only between configurations which are degenerate according to the one-electron Hamiltonian theory. The obvious generalization of this is to include interaction between configurations whose excitation energies are equal according to (2.11) and (2.12).

The most important degeneracy predicted by the Hückel theory for the general alternant hydrocarbon is that between the configurational excitations $m-1\to m+1$ and $m\to m+2$. An interaction element of the type (2.14) splits the singlets into two levels which Dewar and Longuet-Higgins identify with Clar's α and β bands. We shall now show that the same degeneracy occurs for both singlets and triplets in the self-consistent theory, that is

$$({}^1\chi_{m-1\to m+1}|\mathscr{H}|{}^1\chi_{m-1\to m+1})=({}^1\chi_{m\to m+2}|\mathscr{H}|{}^1\chi_{m\to m+2}) \quad ......(2.17)$$

$$({}^3\chi_{m-1\to m+1}|\mathscr{H}|{}^3\chi_{m-1\to m+1})=({}^3\chi_{m\to m+2}|\mathscr{H}|{}^3\chi_{m\to m+2}). \quad ......(2.18)$$

$E_{m+1}-E_{m-1}$ is clearly equal to $E_{m+2}-E_m$ on account of the pairing property noted above, so it only remains to demonstrate equality of the two-electron integrals. This is easily done by expanding the molecular orbitals in terms of atomic orbitals and neglecting all integrals except those of the Coulomb type (2.8). If, following Dewar and Longuet-Higgins, we write the highest occupied and lowest unoccupied orbitals in the form

$$\left.\begin{aligned}\psi_{m-1}&=\textstyle\sum^* b_\mu\phi_\mu+\sum^0 b_\mu\phi_\mu\\ \psi_m&=\textstyle\sum^* a_\mu\phi_\mu+\sum^0 a_\mu\phi_\mu\\ \psi_{m+1}&=\textstyle\sum^* a_\mu\phi_\mu-\sum^0 a_\mu\phi_\mu\\ \psi_{m+2}&=\textstyle\sum^* b_\mu\phi_\mu-\sum^0 b_\mu\phi_\mu\end{aligned}\right\} \quad ......(2.19)$$

then

$$(m-1,m+1|G|m-1,m+1)=(m,m+2|G|m,m+2)=\sum_{\mu\nu}a_\mu^2b_\nu^2\gamma_{\mu\nu} \quad .....(2.20)$$

$$(m-1,m+1|G|m+1,m-1)=(m,m+2|G|m+2,m)=\Big[\sum_\mu{}^*\sum_\nu{}^*+\sum_\mu{}^0\sum_\nu{}^0-2\sum_\mu{}^*\sum_\nu{}^0\Big]a_\mu b_\mu a_\nu b_\nu\gamma_{\mu\nu}. \quad .....(2.21)$$

For the interaction elements

$$({}^1\chi_{m-1\to m+1}|\mathscr{H}|{}^1\chi_{m\to m+2})=\Big[\sum_\mu{}^*\sum_\nu{}^*+\sum_\mu{}^0\sum_\nu{}^0-6\sum_\mu{}^*\sum_\nu{}^0\Big]a_\mu b_\mu a_\nu b_\nu\gamma_{\mu\nu} \quad ......(2.22)$$

$$({}^3\chi_{m-1\to m+1}|\mathscr{H}|{}^3\chi_{m\to m+2})=-\Big[\sum_\mu{}^*\sum_\nu{}^*+\sum_\mu{}^0\sum_\nu{}^0+2\sum_\mu{}^*\sum_\nu{}^0\Big]a_\mu b_\mu a_\nu b_\nu\gamma_{\mu\nu}. \quad ....(2.23)$$

Equation (2.22) has already been given by Dewar and Longuet-Higgins. Other integrals are easily evaluated by the same method.

In the absence of further degeneracy, Dewar and Longuet-Higgins assign wave-functions to the excited states as follows

$$\mathrm{p}:\ {}^1\chi_{m\to m+1} \qquad \alpha:\ ({}^1\chi_{m-1\to m+2}-{}^1\chi_{m\to m+2})/\sqrt{2}$$

$$\beta':\ {}^1\chi_{m-1\to m+2} \qquad \beta:\ ({}^1\chi_{m-1\to m+1}+{}^1\chi_{m\to m+2})/\sqrt{2}. \qquad \ldots\ldots(2.24)$$

By analogy, we may classify a corresponding set of triplet states.

$${}^3\mathrm{p}:\ {}^3\chi_{m\to m+1} \qquad {}^3\alpha:\ ({}^3\chi_{m-1\to m+1}-{}^3\chi_{m\to m+2})/\sqrt{2}$$

$${}^3\beta':\ {}^3\chi_{m-1\to m+2} \qquad {}^3\beta:\ ({}^3\chi_{m-1\to m+1}+{}^3\chi_{m\to m+2})/\sqrt{2}. \qquad \ldots\ldots(2.25)$$

The excitation energies can be found from the matrix elements. For the singlet bands they are

$$\mathscr{E}(\mathrm{p})-\mathscr{E}_0=E_{m+1}-E_m+\Big[\sum_\mu{}^*\sum_\nu{}^*+\sum_\mu{}^0\sum_\nu{}^0-6\sum_\mu{}^*\sum_\nu{}^0\Big]a_\mu{}^2a_\nu{}^2\gamma_{\mu\nu} \qquad \ldots\ldots(2.26)$$

$$\mathscr{E}(\alpha)-\mathscr{E}_0=E_{m+1}-E_{m-1}-\sum_{\mu\nu}a_\mu{}^2b_\nu{}^2\gamma_{\mu\nu}+\Big[\sum_\mu{}^*\sum_\nu{}^*+\sum_\mu{}^0\sum_\nu{}^0+2\sum_\mu{}^*\sum_\nu{}^0\Big]a_\mu b_\mu a_\nu b_\nu\gamma_{\mu\nu} \qquad \ldots\ldots(2.27)$$

$$\mathscr{E}(\beta)-\mathscr{E}_0=E_{m+1}-E_{m-1}-\sum_{\mu\nu}a_\mu{}^2b_\nu{}^2\gamma_{\mu\nu}+\Big[3\sum_\mu{}^*\sum_\nu{}^*+3\sum_\mu{}^0\sum_\nu{}^0-10\sum_\mu{}^*\sum_\nu{}^0\Big]a_\mu b_\mu a_\nu b_\nu\gamma_{\mu\nu} \qquad \ldots\ldots(2.28)$$

$$\mathscr{E}(\beta')-\mathscr{E}_0=E_{m+2}-E_{m-1}+\Big[\sum_\mu{}^*\sum_\nu{}^*+\sum_\mu{}^0\sum_\nu{}^0-6\sum_\mu{}^*\sum_\nu{}^0\Big]b_\mu{}^2b_\nu{}^2\gamma_{\mu\nu} \qquad \ldots\ldots(2.29)$$

and for the triplets

$$\mathscr{E}({}^3\mathrm{p})-\mathscr{E}_0=E_{m+1}-E_m-\sum_{\mu\nu}a_\mu{}^2a_\nu{}^2\gamma_{\mu\nu} \qquad \ldots\ldots(2.30)$$

$$\mathscr{E}({}^3\alpha)-\mathscr{E}_0=E_{m+1}-E_{m-1}-\sum_{\mu\nu}a_\mu{}^2b_\nu{}^2\gamma_{\mu\nu}+\Big[\sum_\mu{}^*\sum_\nu{}^*+\sum_\mu{}^0\sum_\nu{}^0+2\sum_\mu{}^*\sum_\nu{}^0\Big]a_\mu b_\mu a_\nu b_\nu\gamma_{\mu\nu} \qquad \ldots\ldots(2.31)$$

$$\mathscr{E}({}^3\beta)-\mathscr{E}_0=E_{m+1}-E_{m-1}-\sum_{\mu\nu}a_\mu{}^2b_\nu{}^2\gamma_{\mu\nu}-\Big[\sum_\mu{}^*\sum_\nu{}^*+\sum_\mu{}^0\sum_\nu{}^0+2\sum_\mu{}^*\sum_\nu\Big]{}^0a_\mu b_\mu a_\nu b_\nu\gamma_{\mu\nu} \qquad \ldots\ldots(2.32)$$

$$\mathscr{E}({}^3\beta')-\mathscr{E}_0=E_{m+2}-E_{m-1}-\sum_{\mu\nu}b_\mu{}^2b_\nu{}^2\gamma_{\mu\nu}. \qquad \ldots\ldots(2.33)$$

Even without detailed calculations, certain general features of the spectra can be deduced from these formulae. Dewar and Longuet-Higgins have indicated that the interaction element (2.22) leading to the separation of the α and β levels will be positive so that $\mathscr{E}(\beta)>\mathscr{E}(\alpha)$. They also showed that the transition moment between the ground state and the α-state is theoretically zero. This depends only on the pairing of orbitals and is still valid in the present theory. In a similar way we now predict the existence of a pair of associated triplet states ${}^3\alpha$ and ${}^3\beta$. The matrix element (2.23) is negative, so that $\mathscr{E}({}^3\alpha)>\mathscr{E}({}^3\beta)$. One interesting point is that the theory leads to degeneracy between the α and ${}^3\alpha$ states. This, no doubt, is partly a fortuitous result of the approximations made and would not hold accurately in a more refined calculation. There are not yet sufficient experimental data to test predictions about triplet states other than the lowest. The general effect of configuration interaction on the singlet and triplet levels is illustrated diagrammatically in the figure.

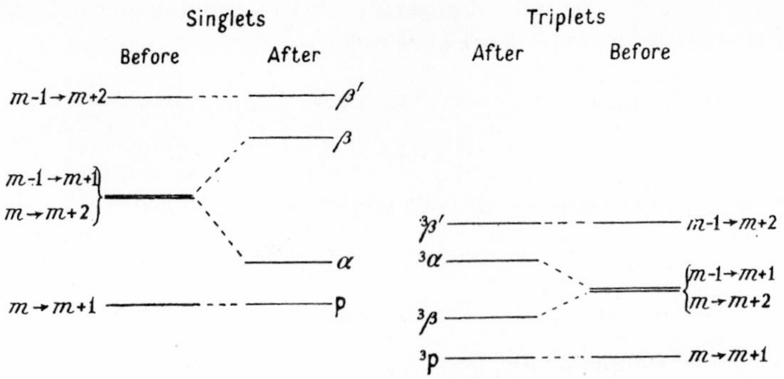

Effect of configuration interaction between degenerate configurational excitations

§ 3. Application to Particular Hydrocarbons

When applied to benzene, the present treatment is equivalent to that of Pariser and Parr (1953). The molecular orbitals $\psi_{m-1} \ldots \psi_{m+2}$ are determined by symmetry and, in their real form, are

$$\left.\begin{aligned} \psi_2 &= \tfrac{1}{2}(\phi_2+\phi_3-\phi_5-\phi_6) \\ \psi_3 &= \tfrac{1}{\sqrt{3}}(\phi_1+\tfrac{1}{2}\phi_2-\tfrac{1}{2}\phi_3-\phi_4-\tfrac{1}{2}\phi_5+\tfrac{1}{2}\phi_6) \\ \psi_4 &= \tfrac{1}{\sqrt{3}}(\phi_1-\tfrac{1}{2}\phi_2-\tfrac{1}{2}\phi_3+\phi_4-\tfrac{1}{2}\phi_5-\tfrac{1}{2}\phi_6) \\ \psi_5 &= \tfrac{1}{2}(-\phi_2+\phi_3-\phi_5+\phi_6) \end{aligned}\right\} \quad \ldots\ldots(3.1)$$

Since ψ_2, ψ_3 and ψ_4, ψ_5 are degenerate pairs of orbitals, there will be degeneracy between the configurational excitations $3\to4$ and $2\to5$ as well as that between $3\to5$ and $2\to4$. But since the configurational excitation energies are no longer differences between one-electron energies, all four need not be degenerate. In fact they are not. The method of the previous section gives

$$({}^1\chi_{3\to4}|\mathscr{H}|{}^1\chi_{3\to4})-(\chi_0|\mathscr{H}|\chi_0) = -2\beta+\tfrac{1}{4}\gamma_{11}-\tfrac{1}{12}\gamma_{12}+\tfrac{1}{4}\gamma_{13}-\tfrac{5}{12}\gamma_{14} \quad \ldots\ldots(3.2)$$

$$({}^1\chi_{2\to4}|\mathscr{H}|{}^1\chi_{2\to4})-(\chi_0|\mathscr{H}|\chi_0) = -2\beta+\tfrac{1}{12}\gamma_{11}+\tfrac{5}{12}\gamma_{12}-\tfrac{7}{12}\gamma_{13}+\tfrac{1}{12}\gamma_{14}. \quad \ldots\ldots(3.3)$$

For this molecule, additional configuration interaction must be taken into account between $\chi_{3\to4}$ and $\chi_{2\to5}$.

The appropriate values for the β and γ integrals have been thoroughly discussed by Pariser and Parr (1953) (they use the symbol $(\mu\mu|\nu\nu)$ for $\gamma_{\mu\nu}$). On a partly empirical basis they select $\beta=-2{\cdot}39$ ev, $\gamma_{11}=10{\cdot}53$ev, $\gamma_{12}=7{\cdot}30$ev, $\gamma_{13}=5{\cdot}46$ev and $\gamma_{14}=4{\cdot}90$ev. Using these values and including configuration interaction, they calculate the energy levels of excited states as shown in table 1. It is clear that the difference between (3.2) and (3.3) removes the degeneracy between the ${}^1\beta_{1u}$ and ${}^1\beta_{2u}$ levels predicted by the method of Dewar and Longuet-Higgins.

The numerical parameters quoted above can be used to apply the method of this paper to other less symmetrical hydrocarbons. Since the application to benzene is comparatively successful, this should provide a quantitative test of the general assignments made by Dewar and Longuet-Higgins. It should also lead to energy-level predictions for as yet unobserved triplets.

Detailed calculations have been carried out for napthalene and anthracene. It has been assumed that all bond lengths can be taken as equal to that in benzene, each ring forming a perfect hexagon. The inverse distance approximation (Pople 1953) has been used for $\gamma_{\mu\nu}$ for atoms further apart than the opposite pair in benzene. The self-consistent equations (2.4) were solved by a cyclic process and the coefficients then used in the energy level expressions (2.26)–(2.33). The results are given in tables 2 and 3.

Table 1. Spectrum of Benzene

Band	Wave function	Symmetry	Frequency (cm^{-1}) calc	Frequency (cm^{-1}) expt
α	$\chi_{2\to4}-\chi_{3\to5}$	$^1B_{2u}$	39500	38000 (*a*)
p	$\chi_{3\to4}+\chi_{2\to5}$	$^1B_{1u}$	43000	48000 (*a*)
β, β'	$\left\{\begin{matrix}\chi_{2\to4}+\chi_{3\to5}\\ \chi_{3\to4}-\chi_{2\to5}\end{matrix}\right\}$	$^1E_{1u}$	56500	54500 (*a*)
^{3}p	$^3\chi_{3\to4}+{}^3\chi_{2\to5}$	$^3B_{1u}$	32000	29500 (*b*)
$^3\beta, {}^3\beta'$	$\left\{\begin{matrix}^3\chi_{2\to4}+{}^3\chi_{3\to5}\\ ^3\chi_{3\to4}-{}^3\chi_{2\to5}\end{matrix}\right\}$	$^3E_{1u}$	36000	—
$^3\alpha$	$^3\chi_{2\to4}-{}^3\chi_{3\to5}$	$^3B_{2u}$	39500	—

(*a*) Klevens and Platt (1949). (*b*) McClure (1949).

Table 2. Spectrum of Naphthalene

Band	Wave function	Symmetry	Frequency (cm^{-1}) calc	Frequency (cm^{-1}) expt
α	$\chi_{4\to6}-\chi_{5\to7}$	$^1B_{1u}$	35500	32000 (*a*)
p	$\chi_{5\to6}$	$^1B_{2u}$	37500	34500 (*a*)
β	$\chi_{4\to6}+\chi_{5\to7}$	$^1B_{1u}$	49500	45500 (*a*)
β'	$\chi_{4\to7}$	$^1B_{2u}$	50000	60000 (*a*)
^{3}p	$^3\chi_{5\to6}$	$^3B_{2u}$	25000	21300 (*b*)
$^3\beta$	$^3\chi_{4\to6}+{}^3\chi_{5\to7}$	$^3B_{1u}$	33000	—
$^3\alpha$	$^3\chi_{4\to6}-{}^3\chi_{5\to7}$	$^3B_{1u}$	35500	—
$^3\beta'$	$^3\chi_{4\to7}$	$^3B_{2u}$	39000	—

(*a*) Klevens and Platt (1949). (*b*) McClure (1949).

Table 3. Spectrum of Anthracene

Band	Wave function	Symmetry	Frequency (cm^{-1}) calc	Frequency (cm^{-1}) expt
p	$\chi_{7\to8}$	$^1B_{2u}$	30000	26500 (*a*)
α	$\chi_{6\to8}-\chi_{7\to9}$	$^1B_{1u}$	33500	[28000]
β	$\chi_{6\to8}+\chi_{7\to9}$	$^1B_{1u}$	45500	39000 (*a*)
β'	$\chi_{6\to9}$	$^1B_{2u}$	52000	45500 (*a*)
^{3}p	$^3\chi_{7\to8}$	$^3B_{2u}$	18000	14700 (*b*)
$^3\beta$	$^3\chi_{6\to8}+{}^3\chi_{7\to9}$	$^3B_{1u}$	32000	—
$^3\alpha$	$^3\chi_{6\to8}-{}^3\chi_{7\to9}$	$^3B_{1u}$	33500	—
$^3\beta'$	$^3\chi_{6\to9}$	$^3B_{2u}$	43500	—

(*a*) Klevens and Platt (1949). (*b*) Lewis and Kasha (1944).

There is satisfactory general agreement between the calculated and observed frequencies listed in these tables. The calculated values are mostly too high, but the relative arrangement tallies very well with the experimental assignments.

It is probable that further configuration interaction with other singly excited configurations would improve the detailed agreement, but these calculations do show that the general features of the low-frequency electronic spectra can be understood in terms of the simple relations derived in this paper.†

The assignment in anthracene differs slightly from that of Dewar and Longuet-Higgins and deserves comment. They note that according to the Hückel theory the transitions $6\to 9$ and $5\to 10$ are degenerate, so they assign wave functions $\chi_{6\to 9}+\chi_{5\to 10}$ and $\chi_{6\to 9}-\chi_{5\to 10}$ to two bands at 45 500 cm^{-1} and 53 500 cm^{-1}. This accidental degeneracy disappears when electron interaction is included, however, the energy of $\chi_{6\to 9}$ being lower. As a result, the β' state is assigned a wave function $\chi_{6\to 9}$. In a complete calculation there will probably be partial mixing between these two.

ACKNOWLEDGMENT

The author is indebted to Professor H. C. Longuet-Higgins for some valuable discussions on this topic.

APPENDIX

Reduction of Matrix Elements for Self-Consistent Determinantal Functions

Equations (2.11) and (2.12) for the diagonal matrix elements of the many-electron Hamiltonian between determinantal functions are well known (Roothaan 1951). The off-diagonal elements (2.13)–(2.15) are also of considerable interest, so a brief outline of their derivation is given here.

The molecular orbital wave function for the ground state χ_0 can be written as an antisymmetrized product

$$\chi_0=[(2m)!]^{-1/2}\sum_P(-1)^P P\{(\psi_1\alpha)(\psi_1\beta)(\psi_2\alpha)\ldots(\psi_m\beta)\}. \qquad \ldots\ldots(\mathrm{A1})$$

Here $\Sigma_P(-1)^P P$ is the usual antisymmetrizing summation over all permutations of the electrons. The corresponding expressions for $^1\chi_{i\to k}$ and one component of $^3\chi_{i\to k}$ are

$$\chi_{i\to k}=[2(2_m)!]^{-1/2}\sum_P(-1)^P P\{(\psi_1\alpha)\ldots(\psi_{i-1}\beta)(\psi_i\alpha)(\psi_k\beta)\ldots(\psi_m\beta)$$
$$\pm(\psi_1\alpha)\ldots(\psi_{i-1}\beta)(\psi_k\alpha)(\psi_i\beta)\ldots(\psi_m\beta)\} \qquad \ldots\ldots(\mathrm{A2})$$

the positive and negative signs being taken for singlet and triplet respectively.

The reduction of the many-electrons integrals between the determinantal functions can be performed by the usual method (Condon and Shortley 1935).

† Dr. R. G. Parr informs the author that Dr. Pariser has recently completed a more extensive treatment of the polyacene spectra using an electronic calculating machine and does, in fact, get better results.

This leads to

$$\left.\begin{aligned}
&({}^1\chi_{i\to k}|\mathscr{H}|\chi_0)=\sqrt{2}F_{ki}\\
&\left.\begin{aligned}({}^1\chi_{i\to k}|\mathscr{H}|{}^1\chi_{i\to l})&=F_{kl}+2(ik|li)-|G(ik|G|il)\\ ({}^3\chi_{i\to k}|\mathscr{H}|{}^3\chi_{i\to l})&=F_{kl}-(ik|G|il)\end{aligned}\right\}(k\neq l)\\
&\left.\begin{aligned}({}^1\chi_{i\to k}|\mathscr{H}|{}^1\chi_{j\to k})&=-F_{ji}+2(kj|G|ik)-(kj|G|ki)\\ ({}^3\chi_{i\to k}|\mathscr{H}|{}^3\chi_{j\to k})&=-F_{ji}-(kj|G|ki)\end{aligned}\right\}(i\neq j)\\
&\left.\begin{aligned}({}^1\chi_{i\to k}|\mathscr{H}|{}^1\chi_{j\to l})&=2(jk|G|li)-(jk|G|il)\\ ({}^3\chi_{i\to k}|\mathscr{H}|{}^3\chi_{j\to l})&=-(jk|G|il)\end{aligned}\right\}(i\neq k,\,k\neq l)
\end{aligned}\right\}\quad\ldots\ldots(A3)$$

where

$$F_{ki}=(H^{\text{core}})_{ki}+\sum_{j=i}^{m}\{2(jk|G|ji)-(jk|G|ij)\}.\qquad\ldots\ldots(A4)$$

But if we are using self-consistent orbitals, the matrix F_{ki} is diagonal. Nesbet (1955) has emphasised the importance of this property in the reduction of similar matrix elements. Equations (A3) can then be written in the compact form (2.13)–(2.15).

References

Condon, E. U., and Shortley, G. H., 1935, *The Theory of Atomic Spectra* (Cambridge: University Press).

Dewar, M. J. S., and Longuet-Higgins, H. C., 1954, *Proc. Phys. Soc.* A, **67**, 795.

Klevens, H. B., and Platt, J. R., 1949, *J. Chem. Phys.*, **17**, 470.

Lewis, G. N., and Kasha, M., 1944, *J. Amer. Chem. Soc.*, **66**, 2100.

McClure, D. S., 1949, *J. Chem. Phys.*, **17**, 905.

Nesbet, R. K., 1955, *Proc. Roy. Soc.*, in preparation.

Pariser, R., and Parr, R. G., 1953, *J. Chem. Phys.*, **21**, 767.

Pople, J. A., 1953, *Trans. Faraday Soc.*, **49**, 1375.

Roothaan, C. C. J., 1951, *Rev. Mod. Phys.*, **23**, 61.

REPRINTED FROM THE
PROCEEDINGS OF THE PHYSICAL SOCIETY, A, VOL. LXVIII, p. 591, 1955

The Electronic Spectra of Aromatic Molecules
IV : Excited States of Odd Alternant Hydrocarbon Radicals and Ions

BY H. C. LONGUET-HIGGINS AND J. A. POPLE
University Chemical Laboratory, Cambridge

MS. received 9th December 1954

Abstract. The lower excited electronic states of some unsaturated hydrocarbon radicals and ions are discussed in terms of molecular orbital theory, taking account of electron interaction. The following results emerge:

(i) In the absorption spectrum of an alternant radical there should appear two long wavelength bands. These arise jointly from excitations of electrons into and out of the singly occupied orbital. The lower frequency band should be weak, and the higher frequency band relatively strong. The existence of a low-lying quartet level is also predicted.

(ii) The absorption spectra of the corresponding anion and cation should be closely related, the lowest two excited states being for both types of ion a triplet and a singlet.

(iii) The singlet–triplet separation in the ions should be roughly equal to the separation of the two low-lying doublets of the radical.

These generalizations are supported by the experimental data for certain triaryl-methyl systems.

§ 1. INTRODUCTION

ODD alternant hydrocarbons are conjugated systems with an odd number of carbon atoms connected together in such a way that they can be divided into two classes, each member of one being bonded only to members of the other. According to the number of electrons present, they may be charged ions or free radicals. They form an important class of compounds whose spectra should be understandable in terms of molecular orbital theory.

The simplest molecular orbital theory of conjugated hydrocarbons is that due to Hückel (1931) according to which the orbitals are supposed to be approximate eigenfunctions of an effective one-electron Hamiltonian. The Hückel theory has been applied to odd alternants by Longuet-Higgins (1950) who showed that there are certain non-bonding orbitals restricted to one of the two classes of carbon atoms. We shall only consider systems of $2m-1$ centres with one non-bonding orbital restricted to starred atoms. This orbital will be empty in the cation, singly occupied in the radical and doubly occupied in the anion. The eigenvalues of the remaining orbitals are symmetrically placed in pairs above and below the energy of the non-bonding orbital.

If the excitation energies are taken to be the difference of Hückel orbital eigenvalues, then the lowest excited configurations of the cation, radical and anion will all be equally raised above their ground states (figure 1). These configurations will lead to a singlet and a triplet level for each of the two ions and two doublets for the radical. In addition, the radical will have an excited quartet state and two further doublets due to the configuration in which an electron is moved from the lowest to the highest of the three orbitals. However, these predictions of the Hückel theory are over-simplified because of the neglect of electron interaction. A similar situation arises in the corresponding theory of even alternants. In part I of this series, Dewar and Longuet-Higgins (1954) suggested an interpretation of the long-wave spectra of alternant hydrocarbons in which they allowed for the particular effect of electron interaction in splitting levels which were degenerate according to the Hückel theory. When applied to odd alternant radicals, they showed that this led to a splitting of the two lower doublet levels. In part II (Pople 1955), it was shown how the conclusions of Dewar and

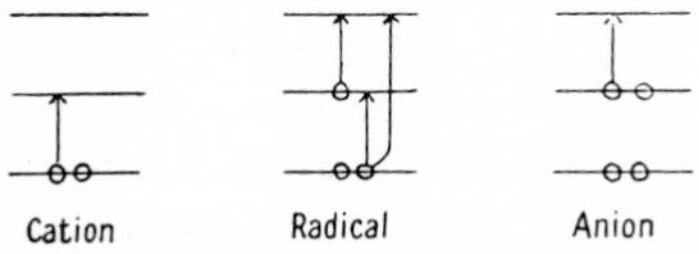

Figure 1. Configurational excitations in odd alternant hydrocarbons.

Longuet-Higgins on even alternants could be justified in terms of a more rigorous theory, based on self-consistent orbitals, in which electron interaction was taken into account at all stages. The first aim of the present paper is to develop a similar background for the application to odd radicals. This is followed by a treatment of the excited states of corresponding singly charged ions, also based on the use of self-consistent orbitals. It is important that electron interaction should be adequately allowed for in a discussion of the structure of ions, for one of the principal weaknesses of the Hückel theory is its assumption that the energy of an electron in one orbital is independent of whether the others are occupied or not. In the final section, the general relation between the spectra of corresponding radicals and ions is reconsidered.

§ 2. Self-Consistent Orbital Functions for Alternant Radicals

The determination of LCAO self-consistent orbitals for radicals has been discussed generally by Pople and Nesbet (1954), who derived equations for the coefficients, and these equations were applied to odd alternant hydrocarbons by Brickstock and Pople (1954).

Pople and Nesbet suggested that the ground state of a radical containing $2m-1$ mobile electrons should be described by a wave function of the form

$$\chi_0 = |\psi_1^{\alpha} \ldots \psi_m^{\alpha} \bar{\psi}_1^{\beta} \ldots \bar{\psi}_{m-1}^{\beta}| \qquad \ldots\ldots(2.1)$$

in which m electrons are assigned to space orbitals $\psi_1^{\alpha} \ldots \psi_m^{\alpha}$, with spin $\frac{1}{2}$, and the other $m-1$ electrons are assigned to orbitals $\psi_1^{\beta} \ldots \psi_{m-1}^{\beta}$, with spin $-\frac{1}{2}$. They removed the restriction that the spatial orbitals ψ_i^{α} and ψ_i^{β} be identical, so that one could no longer speak of doubly occupied molecular orbitals.

This description is convenient for a discussion of the unexcited radical, but is not altogether suitable for discussing electronic excitations, for the following reason. It is known that any eigenstate of a many-electron system must be not only an eigenfunction of the Hamiltonian $\mathscr{H}$ (assumed spin-free) but also of the spin component $\mathbf{S}_z$ and the total spin operator $\mathbf{S}^2$. The eigenvalue of $\mathbf{S}^2$, namely $S(S+1)\hbar^2$, determines the multiplicity $2S+1$ of the eigenstate; and the classification of electronic states according to their multiplicity is of fundamental importance in spectroscopy, since transitions are forbidden between states of different multiplicity. Now the function of Pople and Nesbet (1954), though an eigenfunction of $\mathbf{S}_z$ with eigenvalue $\frac{1}{2}\hbar$, is not an eigenfunction of $\mathbf{S}^2$, whereas the simpler function

$$^2\chi_0 = |\psi_1 \bar{\psi}_1 \ldots \psi_{m-1} \bar{\psi}_{m-1} \psi_m| \qquad \ldots\ldots(2.2)$$

in which the space parts of ψ_i and $\bar{\psi}_i$ are identical, may be shown to be an eigenfunction of $\mathbf{S}^2$ with eigenvalue $\frac{1}{2}(\frac{1}{2}+1)\hbar^2$, and is therefore one component ($S_z=\frac{1}{2}\hbar$) of a doublet. In this respect, therefore, the latter function is to be preferred to the former as a description of the ground state, which is normally a doublet.

One must now enquire how the orbitals $\psi_1 \ldots \psi_m$ are to be determined. The best orbitals are those which minimize the energy of the ground state $^2\chi_0$, subject to the orbitals themselves being orthonormal—a condition which involves no loss of generality. Assume for the moment that $\psi_1 \ldots \psi_m$ have been found, and that $\psi_k(k=m+1, m+2 \ldots)$ is some set of other functions which together with $\psi_1 \ldots \psi_m$ constitute a complete orthonormal set. Then any infinitesimal variation in the orbitals $\psi_1 \ldots \psi_m$, subject to the condition of orthonormality, has the effect of adding to $^2\chi_0$ small amounts of singly excited configurations, as follows:

$$\begin{aligned} {}^2\chi_0 \to & |\psi_1\bar{\psi}_1 \ldots \psi_i\bar{\psi}_i \ldots \psi_{m-1}\bar{\psi}_{m-1}\psi_m| \\ & + \sum_{i=1}^{m-1} \lambda_{im} |\psi_1\bar{\psi}_1 \ldots \psi_i\bar{\psi}_m \ldots \psi_{m-1}\bar{\psi}_{m-1}\psi_m| \\ & + \sum_{k=m+1}^{\infty} \lambda_{mk} |\psi_1\bar{\psi}_1 \ldots \psi_i\bar{\psi}_i \ldots \psi_{m-1}\bar{\psi}_{m-1}\psi_k| \\ & + \sum_{i=1}^{m-1} \sum_{k=m+1}^{\infty} \lambda_{ik} \{ |\psi_1\bar{\psi}_1 \ldots \psi_i\bar{\psi}_k \ldots \psi_{m-1}\bar{\psi}_{m-1}\psi_m| \\ & + |\psi_1\bar{\psi}_1 \ldots \psi_k\bar{\psi}_i \ldots \psi_{m-1}\bar{\psi}_{m-1}\psi_m| \}. \end{aligned} \qquad \ldots\ldots(2.3)$$

The associated change in energy is given by the expression

$$\begin{aligned} & \sum_{i=1}^{m-1} \lambda_{im} \langle {}^2\chi_0 | \mathscr{H} | \psi_i^{-1}\psi_m \rangle + \sum_{k=m+1}^{\infty} \lambda_{mk} \langle {}^2\chi_0 | \mathscr{H} | \psi_m^{-1}\psi_k \rangle \\ & + \sum_{i=1}^{m-1} \sum_{k=m+1}^{\infty} \lambda_{ik} \langle {}^2\chi_0 | \mathscr{H} | \psi_i^{-1}\psi_k \rangle, \end{aligned} \qquad \ldots\ldots(2.4)$$

where $\langle {}^2\chi_0 | \mathscr{H} | \psi_i^{-1}\psi_m \rangle$ represents the matrix element of the Hamiltonian $\mathscr{H}$ between $^2\chi_0$ and the wave function multiplying λ_{im} in (2.3), the other terms in (2.4) being similarly defined.

In passing we may note that the wave functions represented by $\psi_i^{-1}\psi_m$, $\psi_m^{-1}\psi_k$ and $\psi_i^{-1}\psi_k$ are eigenfunctions not only of $\mathbf{S}_z$ but of $\mathbf{S}^2$ also, with eigenvalue $\frac{1}{2}(\frac{1}{2}+1)\hbar^2$. They are therefore doublets, like $^2\chi_0$. For the energy of $^2\chi_0$ to be stationary, then, the matrix elements in (2.4) must all vanish, and this implies that the ground state $^2\chi_0$ cannot interact with any of the singly excited configurations appearing in (2.3).

We now express the Hamiltonian $\mathscr{H}$ in the form $H+G$, where H is a sum of one-electron operators (the 'core field' Hamiltonian) and G includes all the two-electron repulsion terms. This leads to the equations

$$\left.\begin{aligned} 0 = \langle {}^2\chi_0 | \mathscr{H} | \psi_i^{-1}\psi_m \rangle &= H_{im} + \sum_{j=1}^{m-1} \{2(ji|G|jm) - (ji|G|mj)\} \\ &\quad + (mi|G|mm) \\ & (i=1, 2, \ldots, m-1) \\ 0 = \langle {}^2\chi_0 | \mathscr{H} | \psi_m^{-1}\psi_k \rangle &= H_{mk} + \sum_{j=1}^{m-1} \{2(jm|G|jk) - (jm|G|kj)\} \\ & (k=m+1, m+2, \ldots) \\ 0 = \langle {}^2\chi_0 | \mathscr{H} | \psi_i^{-1}\psi_k \rangle &= H_{ik} + \sum_{j=1}^{m-1} \{2(ji|G|jk) - (ji|G|kj)\} \\ &\quad + \tfrac{1}{2}\{2(mi|G|mk) - (mi|G|km)\} \\ & (i=1, 2, \ldots, m-1; k=m+1, m+2, \ldots). \end{aligned}\right\} \qquad \ldots(2.5)$$

In these equations H_{pq} represents the matrix element of the one-electron core Hamiltonian between ψ_p and ψ_q, and $(pq\,|\,G\,|\,rs)$ denotes the two-electron integral

$$\iint \psi_p^*(1)\psi_q^*(2)\,\frac{e^2}{r_{12}}\,\psi_r(1)\psi_s(2)d\tau_1 d\tau_2.$$

Proceeding by analogy with the closed-shell case we now introduce a one-electron operator F defined by the equation

$$\int \psi_p F\psi_q = F_{pq} = H_{pq} + \sum_{j=1}^{m-1}\{2(jp\,|\,G\,|\,jq) - (jp\,|\,G\,|\,qj)\}$$
$$+\tfrac{1}{2}\{2(mp\,|\,G\,|\,mq) - (mp\,|\,G\,|\,qm)\}.$$

This makes it possible to rewrite equations (2.5) in the more compact form:

$$F_{im} + \tfrac{1}{2}(mi\,|\,G\,|\,mm) = 0$$
$$F_{mk} - \tfrac{1}{2}(mm\,|\,G\,|\,mk) = 0$$
$$F_{ik} = 0$$

where $\quad i = 1, 2, \ldots, m-1;\, k = m+1, m+2, \ldots \qquad \ldots\ldots(2.7)$

These equations are not quite so simple as the corresponding equations for a closed shell; but if the terms $(mi\,|\,G\,|\,mm)$ and $(mm\,|\,G\,|\,mk)$ are small, as they will appear to be, the molecular orbitals may be taken to satisfy the simpler equations

$$F_{pq} = 0. \qquad \ldots\ldots(2.8)$$

Now F, being a linear Hermitian operator, generates a complete set of orthonormal eigenfunctions with real eigenvalues. Furthermore, the matrix element of F between any two of these eigenfunctions is necessarily zero. It follows then that the molecular orbitals we require are just eigenfunctions of the operator F, satisfying the eigenvalue equation

$$F\psi_i = E_i\psi_i. \qquad \ldots\ldots(2.9)$$

The eigenvalues E_1 to E_{m-1} are then the 'energies' of the doubly occupied orbitals and E_m the energy of the singly occupied orbital. E_{m+1}, E_{m+2}, and so on, are the energies of the orbitals which are unoccupied in the ground state. It is not possible to identify the energies $E_1 \ldots E_m$ with the various ionization potentials, as in the closed shell case, but E_m can be identified with the mean of the ionization potential and electron affinity of the radical.

These orbitals can now be used to construct wave functions for excited states. The configurations most likely to contribute to the lowest excited states are those in which an electron is raised (i) from ψ_{m-1} to ψ_m, (ii) from ψ_m to ψ_{m+1} and (iii) from ψ_{m-1} to ψ_{m+1}. The first of these gives rise to a doublet configuration whose wave function is

$$^2\chi_1 = |\psi_1\bar{\psi}_1 \ldots \psi_{m-1}\bar{\psi}_m\psi_m|. \qquad \ldots\ldots(2.10)$$

The second also gives rise to a doublet configuration, namely

$$^2\chi_2 = |\psi_1\bar{\psi}_1 \ldots \psi_{m-1}\bar{\psi}_{m-1}\psi_{m+1}|. \qquad \ldots\ldots(2.11)$$

The third, however, gives rise to two doublets and a quartet. The doublet configurations may be taken in the forms

$$^2\chi_3 = \sqrt{\tfrac{1}{2}}\,|\psi_1\bar{\psi}_1 \ldots \psi_{m-1}\bar{\psi}_{m+1}\psi_m| + \sqrt{\tfrac{1}{2}}\,|\psi_1\bar{\psi}_1 \ldots \psi_{m+1}\bar{\psi}_{m-1}\psi_m|, \qquad \ldots\ldots(2.12)$$

$$^2\chi_3' = \sqrt{\tfrac{2}{3}}\,|\psi_1\bar{\psi}_1 \ldots \psi_{m-1}\psi_{m+1}\bar{\psi}_m| - \sqrt{\tfrac{1}{6}}\,|\psi_1\bar{\psi}_1 \ldots \psi_{m-1}\bar{\psi}_{m+1}\psi_m|$$
$$- \sqrt{\tfrac{1}{6}}\,|\psi_1\bar{\psi}_1 \ldots \bar{\psi}_{m-1}\psi_{m+1}\psi_m|, \qquad \ldots\ldots(2.13)$$

while the quartet configuration is

$$^4\chi_3 = \sqrt{\tfrac{1}{3}}\,|\psi_1\bar{\psi}_1\ldots\psi_{m-1}\psi_{m+1}\bar{\psi}_m| + \sqrt{\tfrac{1}{3}}\,|\psi_1\bar{\psi}_1\ldots\psi_{m-1}\bar{\psi}_{m+1}\psi_m| + \sqrt{\tfrac{1}{3}}\,|\psi_1\bar{\psi}_1\ldots\bar{\psi}_{m-1}\psi_{m+1}\psi_m|. \qquad \ldots\ldots(2.14)$$

It has already been established that $^2\chi_1$, $^2\chi_2$ and $^2\chi_3$ do not interact with $^2\chi_0$; and $^4\chi_3$ cannot do so either, as configurations of different multiplicity do not interact. $^2\chi_3'$, on the other hand, does interact with the ground state. However, it may be verified without difficulty that the transition moment between $^2\chi_0$ and $^2\chi_3'$ is zero, so that optical transitions between these two configurations are strictly forbidden. $^2\chi_3'$ is therefore analogous to a doubly excited configuration of a closed shell system, and we shall not consider it further.

The excitation energies of the configurations $^2\chi_1$, $^2\chi_2$, $^2\chi_3$ and $^4\chi_3$ may be evaluated in a straightforward manner, using the relationship

$$E_i = F_{ii} = H_{ii} + \sum_{j=1}^{m-1}\{2(ji|G|ji) - (ji|G|ij)\} + \tfrac{1}{2}\{2(mi|G|mi) - (mi|G|im)\}. \qquad \ldots\ldots(2.15)$$

The results are:

Configuration	Excitation energy
$^2\chi_1$	$E_m - E_{m-1} - (m-1, m\,|G|\,m-1, m) + \tfrac{1}{2}(m-1, m\,|G|\,m, m-1) + \tfrac{1}{2}(mm\,|G|\,mm)$
$^2\chi_2$	$E_{m+1} - E_m - (m, m+1\,|G|\,m, m+1) + \tfrac{1}{2}(m, m+1\,|G|\,m+1, m) + \tfrac{1}{2}(mm\,|G|\,mm)$
$^2\chi_3$	$E_{m+1} - E_{m-1} - (m-1, m+1\,|G|\,m-1, m+1) + 2(m-1, m+1\,|G|\,m+1, m-1)$
$^4\chi_3$	$E_{m+1} - E_{m-1} - (m-1, m+1\,|G|\,m-1, m+1) - \tfrac{1}{2}(m+1, m\,|G|\,m, m+1) - \tfrac{1}{2}(m-1, m\,|G|\,m, m-1)$.

(2.16)

In dealing with a conjugated radical such as benzyl it is most convenient to express these results in LCAO form. We set

$$\psi_i = \sum_\nu c_{i\nu}\phi_\nu \qquad \ldots\ldots(2.17)$$

where ϕ_ν are the various atomic orbitals of the conjugated system. Equation (2.9) then becomes

$$\sum_\nu c_{i\nu}F\phi_\nu = E_i \sum_\nu c_{i\nu}\phi_\nu. \qquad \ldots\ldots(2.18)$$

Multiplying both sides by ϕ_μ^*, integrating, and setting $\int\phi_\mu^*\phi_\nu d\tau = \delta_{\mu\nu}$, we obtain the secular equations

$$\sum_\nu F_{\mu\nu}c_{i\nu} = E_i c_{i\mu} \qquad \ldots\ldots(2.19)$$

where $F_{\mu\nu}$ is the matrix element of F between ϕ_μ and ϕ_ν. With the simplifying assumptions of Brickstock and Pople (1954), these elements take the form

$$\left.\begin{aligned} F_{\mu\mu} &= U_{\mu\mu} + \tfrac{1}{2}p_{\mu\mu}\gamma_{\mu\mu} + \sum_\sigma^{\neq\mu}(p_{\sigma\sigma}-1)\gamma_{\mu\sigma} \\ F_{\mu\nu} &= H_{\mu\nu} - \tfrac{1}{2}p_{\mu\nu}\gamma_{\mu\nu} \\ \text{where}\quad p_{\mu\nu} &= \sum_{i=1}^{m-1} 2c_{i\mu}c_{i\nu} + c_{m\mu}c_{m\nu} \end{aligned}\right\} \qquad \ldots\ldots(2.20)$$

and $\gamma_{\mu\mu}$, $U_{\mu\mu}$ and $H_{\mu\nu}$ are coulomb repulsion integrals and core integrals as in part II. Let us now apply these equations to an alternant hydrocarbon radical, containing $2m-1$ conjugated atoms of which m are 'starred' and $m-1$ 'unstarred', each starred atom being linked only to unstarred atoms and vice versa.

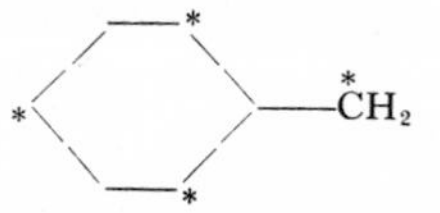

Let us assume that at some stage in the iterative calculation of the $c_{i\nu}$ (*a*) the diagonal elements $F_{\mu\mu}$ are all equal and (*b*) the off-diagonal elements $F_{\mu\nu}$ vanish if μ, ν are both starred or both unstarred. Then if equations (2.9) are solved to obtain the $p_{\mu\nu}$ it will be found that (α) the $p_{\mu\mu}$ are all unity and (β) the $p_{\mu\nu}$ vanish if μ, ν are both starred or both unstarred. This means that in the next iteration we must take

(*a*) $F_{\mu\mu} = U_{\mu\mu} + \frac{1}{2}\gamma_{\mu\mu}$,

(*b*) $F_{\mu\nu} = H_{\mu\nu} = 0$ if μ, ν are both starred or both unstarred,

(*c*) $F_{\mu\nu} = H_{\mu\nu} - \frac{1}{2}p_{\mu\nu}\gamma_{\mu\nu}$ if one of μ, ν is starred and the other unstarred (2.21).

Therefore if at one stage in the iterative calculation conditions (*a*) and (*b*) are satisfied, they will be satisfied at the next stage too; so we conclude that they will be satisfied by the elements $F_{\mu\nu}$ of the self-consistent Hamiltonian itself.

In consequence, the familiar pairing properties of the Hückel orbitals in a radical are exhibited by the self-consistent orbitals also. These properties are:

(i) If $\psi_i (i = 1, \ldots, m-1)$ is a doubly occupied orbital, then there is a 'conjugate' unoccupied orbital ψ_{2m-i} such that

$$\left.\begin{aligned} c_{2m-i,\mu} &= c_{i\mu} \quad &(\mu \text{ starred})\\ c_{2m-i,\mu} &= -c_{i\mu} \quad &(\mu \text{ unstarred}).\end{aligned}\right\} \qquad \ldots\ldots(2.22)$$

(ii) The energy parameters of a pair of conjugate orbitals are related by the equation

$$E_i + E_{2m-i} = 2U_{\mu\mu} + \gamma_{\mu\mu}. \qquad \ldots\ldots(2.23)$$

(iii) The singly occupied orbital ψ_m has the form

$$\psi_m = \sum{}^{*} c_{m\mu}\phi_\mu \qquad \ldots\ldots(2.24)$$

where the summation is confined to starred atoms only, and is non-bonding in the sense that

$$E_m = U_{\mu\mu} + \tfrac{1}{2}\gamma_{\mu\mu}. \qquad \ldots\ldots(2.25)$$

In view of these pairing properties the molecular orbitals ψ_{m+1}, ψ_m can be written

$$\left.\begin{aligned} \psi_{m-1} &= \sum{}^{*} b_\mu\phi_\mu + \sum{}^{0} b_\mu\phi_\mu\\ \psi_m &= \sum{}^{*} a_\mu\phi_\mu\\ \psi_{m+1} &= \sum{}^{*} b_\mu\phi_\mu - \sum{}^{0} b_\mu\phi_\mu,\end{aligned}\right\} \qquad \ldots\ldots(2.26)$$

where Σ^*, Σ^0 are sums over starred and unstarred atoms respectively. Their orbital energies satisfy the equality:

$$E_{m+1} - E_m = E_m - E_{m-1} = \Delta E, \text{ say.} \qquad \ldots\ldots(2.27)$$

Using (2.26) and (2.27), and the approximations introduced in II, we may express the excitation energies in (2.16) in terms of ΔE and the repulsion integrals $\gamma_{\mu\nu}$. It turns out that the excitation energies of ${}^2\chi_1$ and ${}^2\chi_2$ are identical, as predicted by the Hückel theory and illustrated schematically in figure 1. This means that there will be first-order configuration interaction between ${}^2\chi_1$ and ${}^2\chi_2$, the magnitude of the splitting (see I) being determined by the integral

$$\begin{aligned}\langle {}^2\chi_1 | \mathscr{H} | {}^2\chi_2 \rangle &= -(m+1, m-1 | G | m, m) \\ &= -\sum_{\mu\nu} a_\mu b_\mu a_\nu b_\nu \gamma_{\mu\nu}. \qquad \ldots\ldots(2.28)\end{aligned}$$

When this configurational interaction is taken into account, the excited states and their excitation energies become:

State	Excitation energy
$\surd\frac{1}{2}({}^2\chi_1 + {}^2\chi_2)$	$\Delta E - \sum_{\mu\nu} a_\mu^2 b_\nu^2 \gamma_{\mu\nu} + \frac{1}{2}\sum_{\mu\nu} a_\mu^2 a_\nu^2 \gamma_{\mu\nu} - \frac{1}{2}\sum_{\mu\nu} a_\mu b_\mu a_\nu b_\nu \gamma_{\mu\nu}$
$\surd\frac{1}{2}({}^2\chi_1 - {}^2\chi_2)$	$\Delta E - \sum_{\mu\nu} a_\mu^2 b_\nu^2 \gamma_{\mu\nu} + \frac{3}{2}\sum_{\mu\nu} a_\mu b_\mu a_\nu b_\nu \gamma_{\mu\nu} + \frac{1}{2}\sum_{\mu\nu} a_\mu^2 a_\nu^2 \gamma_{\mu\nu}$
${}^2\chi_3$	$2\Delta E - \sum_{\mu\nu} b_\mu^2 b_\nu^2 \gamma_{\mu\nu} + 2(\sum_\mu^* - \sum_\mu^0)(\sum_\nu^* - \sum_\nu^0) b_\mu^2 b_\nu^2 \gamma_{\mu\nu}$
${}^4\chi_3$	$2\Delta E - \sum_{\mu\nu} b_\mu^2 b_\nu^2 \gamma_{\mu\nu} - \sum_{\mu\nu} a_\mu b_\mu a_\nu b_\nu \gamma_{\mu\nu}.$

Dewar and Longuet-Higgins showed in I that the lowest of these states, namely $\surd\frac{1}{2}({}^2\chi_1 + {}^2\chi_2)$, should give only a weak band in the spectrum, but that the transition ${}^2\chi_0 \to \surd\frac{1}{2}({}^2\chi_1 - {}^2\chi_2)$ should give rise to a relatively intense band. This result still holds with self-consistent orbitals, since the pairing properties of the Hückel orbitals are preserved. The interpretation of alternant radical spectra suggested by Dewar and Longuet-Higgins is therefore confirmed by the self-consistent orbital theory.

Before discussing the alternant ions we should recall that the passage from equations (2.7) to (2.8) depends on the integrals $(im | G | mm)$ and $(mm | G | mk)$ being negligible. It is difficult to assess the accuracy of this assumption in general, but in the particular case of allyl the integrals $(12 | G | 22)$ and $(22 | G | 23)$ vanish by symmetry. Though this will not happen in general, we doubt whether the errors so introduced will be large, and feel that the assumption is justified in large measure by the great simplification which it makes possible.

§ 3. Self-Consistent Orbital Functions for Odd Alternant Ions

Singly charged odd alternant ions generally have closed shell ground states. The theory of excited states based on self-consistent orbitals is therefore similar to the treatment of even alternants given in II. In this section we shall show how certain pairing properties can be used to predict similarities between corresponding positive and negative ions.

The solution of the self-consistent equations has been discussed by Brickstock and Pople (1954). The LCAO coefficients for positive and negative ions must satisfy

$$\left.\begin{aligned}\sum_\nu F_{\mu\nu}^+ c_{i\nu}^+ &= E_i^+ c_{i\mu}^+ \\ \sum_\nu F_{\mu\nu}^- c_{i\nu}^- &= E_i^- c_{i\mu}^-\end{aligned}\right\} \qquad \ldots\ldots(3.1)$$

where F_μ^+, F_μ^- are defined as in (2.20) except that

$$\left.\begin{aligned} p_{\mu\nu}^+ &= 2\sum_{i=1}^{m-1} c_{i\mu}^+ c_{i\nu}^+ \\ p_{\mu\nu}^- &= 2\sum_{i=1}^{m} c_{i\mu}^- c_{i\nu}^- . \end{aligned}\right\} \quad \ldots\ldots (3.2)$$

With the same set of approximations, the following pairing properties can be deduced:

(i) $$p_{\mu\mu}^+ + p_{\mu\mu}^- = 2 \quad \ldots\ldots (3.3)$$

(ii) $$E_i^+ + E_{2m-i}^- = 2U_{\mu\mu} + \gamma_{\mu\mu} \quad \ldots\ldots (3.4)$$

(iii) $$\left.\begin{aligned} c_{i\mu}^+ &= c_{2m-i,\mu}^- \quad (\mu \text{ starred}) \\ c_{i\mu}^+ &= -c_{2m-i,\mu}^- \quad (\mu \text{ unstarred}). \end{aligned}\right\} \quad \ldots\ldots (3.5)$$

The simplest configurational excitations are $\psi_{m-1}^+ \rightarrow \psi_m^+$ for the cation and $\psi_m^- \rightarrow \psi_{m+1}^-$ for the anion. The corresponding determinantal wave functions for the ground states will be denoted by χ_0^+, χ_0^- and for the excited states by ${}^1\chi_1^+$, ${}^3\chi_1^+$ and ${}^1\chi_1^-$, ${}^3\chi_1^-$. By the pairing property (3.5) the orbitals involved can be written

$$\left.\begin{aligned} \psi_{m-1}^+ &= \sum_\mu{}^* b_\mu^+ \phi_\mu + \sum_\mu{}^0 b_\mu^+ \phi_\mu \\ \psi_m^+ &= \sum_\mu{}^* a_\mu^+ \phi_\mu + \sum_\mu{}^0 a_\mu^+ \phi_\mu \\ \psi_m^- &= \sum_\mu{}^* a_\mu^+ \phi_\mu - \sum_\mu{}^0 a_\mu^+ \phi_\mu \\ \psi_{m+1}^- &= \sum_\mu{}^* b_\mu^+ \phi_\mu - \sum_\mu{}^0 b_\mu^+ \phi_\mu . \end{aligned}\right\} \quad \ldots\ldots (3.6)$$

The excitation energies of these states can be evaluated by standard methods and are:

States	Excitation energies
${}^1\chi_1^+$, ${}^1\chi_1^-$	$E_m^+ - E_{m-1}^+ - \sum_{\mu\nu} a_\mu^{+2} b_\nu^{+2} \gamma_{\mu\nu} + 2\sum_{\mu\nu} a_\mu^+ b_\mu^+ a_\nu^+ b_\nu^+ \gamma_{\mu\nu}$
${}^3\chi_1^+$, ${}^3\chi_1^-$	$E_m^+ - E_{m-1}^+ - \sum_{\mu\nu} a_\mu^{+2} b_\nu^{+2} \gamma_{\mu\nu}$

The theory in this form therefore predicts that the energy levels of the lowest singlet and triplet states should be the same for corresponding positive and negative ions. In the next section we shall attempt to compare these with the excitation energies for the radicals derived previously.

§ 4. Comparison between Corresponding Radicals and Ions

It is not possible to make a direct comparison between radicals and ions on the basis of the formulae of the previous sections as the self-consistent coefficients are not simply related. We may get some idea of the relationship, however, by using the radical orbitals (2.26) as approximations in all cases. It then follows, if μ and ν are both starred or both unstarred, that

$$\left.\begin{aligned} p_{\mu\mu}^\pm &= 1 \mp a_\mu^2 \\ p_{\mu\nu}^\pm &= \mp a_\mu a_\nu . \end{aligned}\right\} \quad \ldots\ldots (4.1)$$

Further, if μ and ν belong to different classes, $p_{\mu\nu}$ is the same for the radical and both ions.

Although the orbitals are now taken to be identical, the eigenvalues E_i^+, E_i and E_i^- will not coincide. They are easily evaluated as diagonal elements of the corresponding operators, however, and it is found that

$$E_{m+1}-E_m=E_m-E_{m-1}=-2\sum_{\mu}{}^{*}\sum_{\nu}{}^{0} b_\mu b_\nu(H_{\mu\nu}-\tfrac{1}{2}p_{\mu\nu}\gamma_{\mu\nu}) \qquad \ldots\ldots(4.2)$$

$$E_{m+1}^- - E_m^- = E_m^+ - E_{m-1}^+ = -2\sum_{\mu}{}^{*}\sum_{\nu}{}^{0} b_\mu b_\nu(H_{\mu\nu}-\tfrac{1}{2}p_{\mu\nu}\gamma_{\mu\nu})$$

$$+\sum_{\mu\nu} a_\mu^2 b_\nu^2\gamma_{\mu\nu}-\tfrac{1}{2}\sum_{\mu\nu} a_\mu^2 a_\nu^2\gamma_{\mu\nu}-\tfrac{1}{2}\sum_{\mu\nu} a_\mu b_\mu a_\nu b_\nu\gamma_{\mu\nu}. \qquad \ldots\ldots(4.3)$$

Using these results the excitation energies of radicals and ions, (2.29) and (3.7) respectively, can be directly compared. The following general features of the results are of interest.

(i) The separation of the two doublet levels $\sqrt{\tfrac{1}{2}}({}^2\chi_1 \pm {}^2\chi_2)$ is equal to the singlet–triplet splitting of the ionic states ${}^1\chi_1^{\pm}$ and ${}^3\chi_1^{\pm}$.

(ii) The excitation energies of these two excited doublet levels are greater than those of the corresponding ionic singlet–triplet pair by an amount

$$\sum_{\mu\nu} a_\mu^2(a_\nu^2-b_\nu^2)\gamma_{\mu\nu}.$$

This is the difference between the averaged coulomb interaction between two electrons in ψ_m and that between one in ψ_m and one in ψ_{m-1}. It is not possible to prove that this is strictly positive, but it seems likely that it will usually be so.

(iii) The lowest quartet level of the radical will be considerably lower than would be expected on the basis of the Hückel theory, which would predict the excitation energy to be twice that of the doublets. Using the notation $\mathscr{E}(\chi)$ for the excitation energy of state χ, we have

$$\mathscr{E}({}^4\chi)-2\mathscr{E}(\sqrt{\tfrac{1}{2}}({}^2\chi_1+{}^2\chi_2))=-\sum_{\mu\nu}(a_\mu^2-b_\mu^2)(a_\nu^2-b_\nu^2)\gamma_{\mu\nu} \qquad \ldots\ldots(4.4)$$

which should be negative. This means that the excitation energy of the quartet is less than twice that of the *lower* doublet. But it is not possible to say whether it will be above or below the doublet $\sqrt{\tfrac{1}{2}}({}^2\chi_1-{}^2\chi_2)$ without detailed calculations.

(iv) The doublet ${}^2\chi_3$ will lie above the quartet ${}^4\chi$ and will probably be the highest of the excited states considered.

These conclusions are illustrated schematically in the energy level diagram of figure 2.

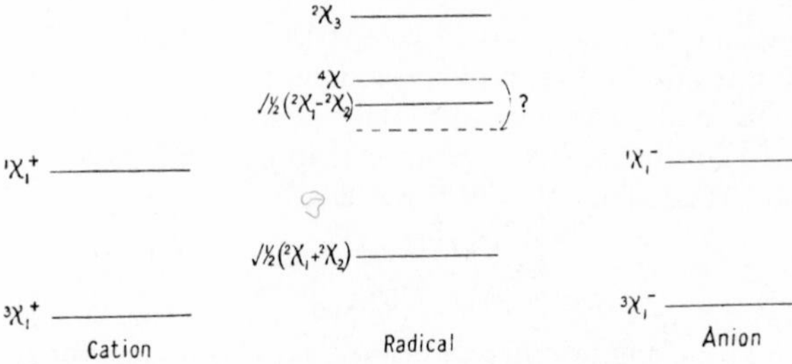

Figure 2. General arrangement of predicted energy levels.

The quantitative application of the theory can be illustrated by calculations on allyl and benzyl, two simple odd alternants (table 1). These are based on the formulae (4.4) using the same integrals β and $\gamma_{\mu\nu}$ as in part II.

Table 1. Calculated Excitation Energies of Odd Alternants (ev)

	Ion		Radical			
State	${}^3\chi_1{}^+$	${}^1\chi_1{}^+$	$\sqrt{\tfrac{1}{2}}({}^2\chi_1+{}^2\chi_2)$ (weak)	$\sqrt{\tfrac{1}{2}}({}^2\chi_1-{}^2\chi_2)$ (strong)	${}^2\chi_3$	${}^4\chi$
Allyl	2·39	4·94	2·74	5·29	7·74	4·51
Benzyl	1·96	2·68	3·46	4·18	6·23	3·97

The calculations of the allyl radical may be compared with those of Moffitt (1953). The results are similar, although Moffitt predicts the quartet level to be above both doublets $\sqrt{\tfrac{1}{2}}({}^2\chi_1 \pm {}^2\chi_2)$.

Experimental data on the spectra of odd alternants is rather limited, but what there is fits in with the qualitative description. Recently, Chu and Weissman (1954) have observed the spectra of some triaryl-methyl radicals and their cations. They found that each free radical shows a weak absorption in the visible region and a much stronger one in the near ultra-violet. The corresponding cations have a region of intense absorption at an intermediate wavelength. The approximate energy levels (peak absorption) are given in table 2.

Table 2. Energy Levels in Triaryl-Methyl Radicals and Cations (cm^{-1})

Substance	Radical		Cation
	Weak	Strong	Strong
Triphenyl-methyl	19,000	29,000	23,500
Diphenyl-p-xenylmethyl	17,500	26,000	19,500
Phenyl-di-p-xenylmethyl	16,000	24,500	18,500
Tri-p-xenylmethyl	15,000	24,000	18,000

Although these systems are probably not planar, the theory of this paper ought to give a qualitative explanation of these results. It is suggested, therefore, that the two principal bands of the radicals arise from the doublet states with wave functions $\sqrt{\tfrac{1}{2}}({}^2\chi_1 \pm {}^2\chi_2)$, while the excited state of the cation is ${}^1\chi_1{}^+$. For triphenyl-methyl and tri-p-xenylmethyl, Chu and Weissmann assign the weak radical band to a symmetry-forbidden transition. But if the present interpretation is correct, it will be of the same symmetry as the strong ultra-violet band.

References

Brickstock, A., and Pople, J. A., 1954, *Trans. Faraday Soc.*, **50,** 901.
Chu, T. L., and Weissman, S. I., 1954, *J. Chem. Phys.*, **22,** 21.
Dewar, M. J. S., and Longuet-Higgins, H. C., 1954, *Proc. Phys. Soc.* A, **67,** 795. (Part I of present paper.)
Hückel, W., 1931, *Z. Phys.*, **70,** 204, 279.
Longuet-Higgins, H. C., 1950, *J. Chem. Phys.*, **18,** 265.
Moffitt, W., 1953, *Proc. Roy. Soc.* A, **218,** 486.
Pople, J. A., 1955, *Proc. Phys. Soc.* A, **68,** 81. (Part II of present paper.)
Pople, J. A., and Nesbet, R. K., 1954, *J. Chem. Phys.*, **22,** 571.

Reprinted from THE JOURNAL OF CHEMICAL PHYSICS, Vol. 24, No. 2, 250–268, February, 1956
Printed in U. S. A.

Theory of the Electronic Spectra and Structure of the Polyacenes and of Alternant Hydrocarbons*

RUDOLPH PARISER
Jackson Laboratory, E. I. du Pont de Nemours and Company, Wilmington, Delaware
(Received February 28, 1955)

A previously given theory of the electronic spectra and structure of complex unsaturated molecules is further elucidated by listing specific formulas for the charge density, bond order, transition moment, and configuration interaction matrix elements.

The theory is then applied to give a number of simple rules for alternant hydrocarbons. These refer to the energies of the singly excited states and the effects of configuration interaction, the degeneracy between certain singlet and triplet states, the prohibition of certain electronic transitions which would be allowed from a group theoretical point of view, and the charge density distribution of the ground and singly excited states. A mechanism is proposed to explain some of the anomalously rapid singlet-triplet radiationless transitions which are observed in connection with studies of the lower triplet states of complex molecules.

Quantitative application of the theory is made to the spectra of the polyacenes, benzene through pentacene, and to the bond orders of naphthalene and anthracene, employing a high-speed digital computer. The calculated results are compared with experiment. Some previous assignments of electronic bands are confirmed, and some new assignments are suggested. The location of a number of excited states which have not, as yet, been observed is predicted.

I. INTRODUCTION

RECENTLY a semiempirical theoretical method has been proposed which is designed for the correlation and prediction of the lower electronic absorption bands and other properties of unsaturated molecules.[1] To test and apply this method further, consideration is given here to more complex molecules.

Sections II and III summarize the theoretical approach. In Sec. IV certain general relationships are derived which are applicable to all even alternant hydrocarbons where treated subject to the assumptions of the present theory. These relationships are not only helpful in carrying out precise calculations but could also be useful in qualitative and semiquantitative interpretations of the electronic spectra and structure of molecules. The second part of the paper, including Secs. V–XI, deals with various applications of the theory. A detailed calculation of the spectra of the polyacenes is carried out, and the results are compared with experiment (Secs. V–IX). In Sec. X application is made to phosphorescence phenomena, while Sec. XI deals with some aspects of the electronic structure of the ground state of naphthalene and anthracene.

II. OUTLINE OF THEORETICAL METHOD

The theoretical method is based on the framework of the method of antisymmetrized products, in LCAO approximation, including configuration interaction, with only the π electrons considered explicitly.[2] Two features are chiefly responsible for setting the present method apart from the more rigorous purely theoretical approaches. These are

(a) the formal consistent neglect of differential overlap between atomic orbitals[3,1] and
(b) the adjustment of some theoretical quantities by empirical or semiempirical procedures.[4,1]

The neglect of overlap is responsible for making it practicable to treat quantitatively molecules as large as pentacene. Of the many types of interelectronic repulsion integrals, only Coulomb integrals need to be considered, thus tremendously simplifying the computation. However, it has been demonstrated that this simplification sacrifices essentially no accuracy in π electron calculations of spectra.[1] The duplication of the results of the rigorous π electron approximation is, however, not a primary objective of the present approach, since these results are normally in rather poor agreement with experiment. It is evident that empirical elements will have to be introduced into any reasonably simple theory if quantitatively significant results are to be obtained.

The *ortho*-normal molecular orbitals (MO), ϕ_i, are given by

$$\phi_i=\sum_p C_{pi}\chi_p, \tag{1}$$

where χ_p is the pth $2p\pi$ atomic orbital (AO). A particular spin-orbital configuration is obtained by assigning electrons to the MO's, ϕ_i, multiplied by the spin function α or β. The many-electron configurational wave function is represented by an antisymmetrized product, or Slater determinant. To a first approximation each LCAO MO has associated with it a certain orbital

* Presented in part at the Symposium on Molecular Structure and Spectroscopy, Ohio State University, June, 1954.

[1] R. Pariser and R. G. Parr, J. Chem. Phys. 21, 466 (1953); *ibid* 21, 767 (1953). F. G. Fumi and R. G. Parr, J. Chem. Phys. 21, 1864 (1953). R. G. Parr and R. Pariser, J. Chem. Phys. 23, 711 (1955).

[2] M. Goeppert-Mayer and A. L. Sklar, J. Chem. Phys. 6, 645 (1938). D. P. Craig, Proc. Roy. Soc. (London) A200, 474 (1950). R. S. Mulliken, J. chim. phys. 46, 497 (1944). Parr, Craig, and Ross, J. Chem. Phys. 18, 1561 (1950).

[3] R. G. Parr, J. Chem. Phys. 21, 1499 (1952).

[4] R. Pariser, J. Chem. Phys. 21, 568 (1953). See also W. Moffitt, Proc. Roy. Soc. (London) A210, 224 (1951).

energy. This energy is defined so that the energy of a configuration is approximated by the sum of the energies of the occupied MO's.[5] Thus, in most cases, for molecules with an even number of π electrons, the lowest energy configuration will have its N π electrons assigned to the $N/2$ lowest energy MO's. The wave function for this configuration, V_0, is given by

$$V_0=(N!)^{-\frac{1}{2}}\begin{vmatrix} (\phi_1\alpha)^1(\phi_1\beta)^1 & \cdots & (\phi_{N/2}\alpha)^1(\phi_{N/2}\beta)^1 \\ (\phi_1\alpha)^2(\phi_1\beta)^2 & \cdots & (\phi_{N/2}\alpha)^2(\phi_{N/2}\beta)^2 \\ \cdot\quad\cdot & & \cdot\quad\cdot \\ \cdot\quad\cdot & & \cdot\quad\cdot \\ \cdot\quad\cdot & & \cdot\quad\cdot \\ \cdot\quad\cdot & & (\phi_{N/2}\alpha)^N(\phi_{N/2}\beta)^N \end{vmatrix} \tag{2}$$

$$\equiv(1\bar{1};\,2\bar{2}\cdots\tfrac{1}{2}N\tfrac{1}{2}\bar{N}).$$

When an electron is excited from some orbital ϕ_i, filled in V_0, to a higher unfilled orbital, $\phi_{k'}$, the resulting *singly excited* configuration, which may either be a singlet or triplet, is represented by the determinantal wave function

$$\begin{matrix} V_{ik'} \\ T_{ik'} \end{matrix}=2^{-\frac{1}{2}}(1\bar{1}\cdots i\bar{k'}\cdots\tfrac{1}{2}N\tfrac{1}{2}\bar{N})\mp2^{-\frac{1}{2}}(1\bar{1}\cdots\bar{i}k'\cdots\tfrac{1}{2}N\tfrac{1}{2}\bar{N}), \tag{3}$$

where the upper and lower sign is associated with the singlet, V, and triplet, T, configuration, respectively. In the present treatment a given electronic state function, Ψ_a, is approximated by a linear combination of singly excited configuration functions. For the singlets, for example,

$$\Psi_a=A_{1a}V_1+A_{2a}V_2+\cdots, \tag{4}$$

where the generalized subscripts 1, 2, $\cdots$ stand for subscripts such as 0, ik', $\cdots$ of Eqs. (2) and (3). This leads to the familiar equations:

$$|H_{mn}-\delta_{mn}E|=0, \tag{5}$$

and

$$\sum_m A_m(H_{mn}-\delta_{mn}E)=0. \tag{6}$$

The matrix elements H_{mn} for the singlets, for example, are defined by

$$H_{mn}=\int V_m{}^*\mathbf{H}V_n dv\equiv\{V_m|V_n\}, \tag{7}$$

with $\mathbf{H}$ of the form,

$$\mathbf{H}=\mathbf{H}_{\text{core}}+\tfrac{1}{2}\sum_{pq}\frac{e^2}{r_{pq}},\quad p\neq q. \tag{8}$$

The matrix elements H_{mn} upon substitution by means of Eqs. (2), (3), and (8) into Eq. (7) fall into six distinct types. These are expressed in terms of Coulomb and core integrals over MO's below[6]:

$$\begin{matrix}\{V_{ik'}|V_{ik'}\} \\ \{T_{ik'}|T_{ik'}\}\end{matrix}-\{V_0|V_0\}\equiv\begin{matrix}E(V_{ik'}) \\ E(T_{ik'})\end{matrix}-E(V_0)$$
$$=I_{k'k'}-I_{ii}+[ii|k'k']\pm[ik'|ik']-[ii|ii]-\sum_{f\neq i}2[ff|ii]-2[ff|k'k']-[fi|fi]+[fk'|fk'], \tag{9}$$

$$\{V_0|V_{ik'}\}=2^{\frac{1}{2}}(I_{ik'}+[ii|ik']+\sum_{f\neq i}2[ff|ik']-[fi|fk']),$$
$$\{V_0|T_{ik'}\}=0, \tag{10}$$

$$\{V_{ik'}|V_{jk'}\}=-I_{ij}+2[ik'|jk']-[ij|ii]-[ij/k'k']-[ij|ii]-\sum_{f\neq i,j}2[ff|ij]-[fi|fj],$$

$$\{T_{ik'}|T_{jk'}\}=\{V_{ik'}|V_{jk'}\}-2[ik'|jk'], \tag{11}$$

$$\begin{matrix}\{V_{ik'}|V_{il'}\} \\ \{T_{ik'}|T_{il'}\}\end{matrix}=I_{k'l'}\pm[ik'|il']+[ii|k'l']+\sum_{f\neq k'l'}2[ff|k'l']-[fk'|fl'], \tag{12}$$

$$\{V_{ik'}|V_{jl'}\}=2[ik'|jl']-[ij|k'l'],$$
$$\{T_{ik'}|T_{jl'}\}=-[ij|k'l']. \tag{13}$$

All sums over the index f are over the occupied MO's in V_0; also, in Eqs. (9) to (13)$\cdots i$, j refer to filled MO's in the ground configuration, V_0, whereas k', $l'\cdots$ designate unfilled MO's. By definition,

$$[ij|kl]=\int\phi_i{}^*(1)\phi_k{}^*(2)\frac{e^2}{r_{12}}\phi_j(1)\phi_l(2)dv, \tag{14}$$

$$I_{ij}=\int\phi_i{}^*(1)\mathbf{H}_{\text{core}}\phi_j(1)dv, \tag{15}$$

where here i, j, k, l may refer to any orbital. These integrals over MO's are here best expanded into integrals over AO's for numerical evaluation.

The transition moment between the states Ψ_a and Ψ_b is defined by

$$\mathbf{M}_{ab}=\int\Psi_a{}^*\mathbf{M}\Psi_b dv, \tag{16}$$

where

$$\mathbf{M}=\sum_t e_t\mathbf{r}_t. \tag{17}$$

e_t and $\mathbf{r}_t$ are the charge and the position vector of the tth charged particle, respectively. For the case where only π electrons are being considered explicitly, one can

[5] R. S. Mulliken, J. chim. phys. **46**, 497, 695 (1949).

[6] See, for example, E. U. Condon and G. H. Shortley, *The Theory of Atomic Spectra* (Cambridge University Press, Cambridge, London, 1951), p. 169–174.

separate **M**,

$$\mathbf{M}=e\sum_u \mathbf{r}_u+\sum_s e_s\mathbf{r}_s, \tag{18}$$

the summation u being over all π electrons and s over the core nuclei. Expansion of Eq. (16) in terms of cartesian coordinates for the x component, as an example, gives

$$M_{ab}^x=e\int\Psi_a^*\sum_u x_u\Psi_b dv+\int\Psi_a^*\sum_s e_s x_s\Psi_b dv. \tag{19}$$

Since the state functions Ψ_a are linear combinations of configuration wave functions, substitution of Eq. (4) into Eq. (19) will express $\mathbf{M}_{ab}$ in terms of a sum of transition moment integrals taken between configurations. These, in turn, are expanded in terms of integrals over MO's. For the x component

$$\int V_0^*\sum_t e_t x_t V_0 dv=2e\sum_f m_{ff}^x+\sum_s e_s x_s,$$

$$\int V_{ik'}^*\sum_t e_t x_t V_{ik'}dv=2e\sum_{f\neq i} m_{ff}^x$$

$$+m_{ii}^x+m_{k'k'}^x+\sum_s e_s x_s, \tag{20}$$

$$\int V_0^*\sum_t e_t x_t V_{ik'}dv=2^{\frac{1}{2}}em_{ik'}^x,$$

$$\int V_{ik'}^*\sum_t e_t x_t V_{jk'}dv=-em_{ij}^x,$$

$$\int V_{ik'}^*\sum_t e_t x_t V_{il'}dv=em_{k'l'}^x,$$

$$\int V_{ik'}^*\sum_t e_t x_t V_{jl'}dv=0,$$

where

$$m_{ij}^x\equiv\int\phi_i^*(1)x(1)\phi_j(1)dv, \tag{21}$$

and all sums over the index f are for filled MO's in V_0.

All transition moments between singlet and triplet configurations vanish, since the spin functions α and β are orthogonal. Moments between the triplets are given by Eqs. (20) upon replacing V by T.

By the methods described by Mulliken and Rieke,[7] the oscillator strength, f, is:

$$f=1.085\times10^{11}\omega_{ab}\sum_{i=x,y,z}(M_{ab}^i)^2, \tag{22}$$

where ω_{ab} is the frequency of the transition in cm^{-1}

Charge distributions may be obtained in a manner analogous to that for the transition moments. Specifically, the integrated π-electron density distribution for the state Ψ_a is

$$\int\Psi_a^*\sum_u e_u\Psi_a dv. \tag{23}$$

Expansion of Eq. (23) into integrals over MO's gives the result of Eq. (20) with x_u replaced by e_u, $x_s=0$, and m replaced by d, d_{ij} being defined as

$$d_{ij}\equiv\int\phi_i^*(1)e\phi_j(1)dv. \tag{24}$$

The last integral is zero for $i\neq j$ when integrated over all space. However, for certain applications it will be necessary to consider limited regions.

The expansion of the integrals involving MO's in Eqs. (14), (15), (21), and (24) into integrals over AO's is carried out in the following section.

III. FORMULATION THROUGH AO INTEGRALS

It is convenient to formulate the expansion of the various integrals over MO's into integrals over AO's in terms of a matrix notation. This is a useful notation in proving the general relationships for alternant hydrocarbons (Sec. IV) and for designing an automatic computational procedure (Sec. VI).

Adopting a notation similar to Dirac's,[8] let $[\mathbf{ij}|$ or $|\mathbf{ij}]$ represent row and column vectors, respectively, which have the components $[C_{1i}^*C_{1j};\ C_{2i}^*C_{2j};\ \cdots C_{Ni}^*C_{Nj}|$ and $|C_{1i}C_{1j}^*;\ C_{2i}C_{2j}^*;\ \cdots C_{Ni}C_{Nj}^*]$. Similarly, let the vectors $[\mathbf{i}|$ or $|\mathbf{i}]$ be defined by the components $[C_{1i}^*;\ C_{2i}^*;\ \cdots C_{Ni}^*|$ and $|C_{1i};\ C_{2i};\ \cdots C_{Ni}]$. Then let the symmetric matrix $\mathbf{H}^c$ collect the elements,

$$H_{pq}^{\text{core}}=\int\chi_p^*(1)\mathbf{H}_{\text{core}}(1)\chi_q(1)dv, \tag{25}$$

where, alternatively,

$$H_{pp}^{\text{core}}\equiv\alpha_p,\quad H_{pq}^{\text{core}}\equiv\beta_{pq},\quad p\neq q. \tag{26}$$

Then

$$I_{ij}=[\mathbf{i}^*|\mathbf{H}^c|\mathbf{j}]. \tag{27}$$

Here α_p and β_{pq} may be estimated in terms of Coulomb and penetration integrals[2] or by other means. A formula for α_p, based on neglect of penetration integrals (or an equal contribution to each atom), is[1]

$$\alpha_p=W_p-\sum_{p\neq q}(pp|qq)=-\sum_p(pp|qq)-A_p, \tag{28}$$

where W_p and A_p are the valence state ionization potential and electron affinity of the pth AO, respectively.

Now if one collects the Coulomb integrals over AO's

[7] R. S. Mulliken and C. A. Rieke, Repts. Progr. Phys. 8, 231 (1941).

[8] P. A. M. Dirac, *The Principles of Quantum Mechanics* (Clarendon Press, Oxford, 1947); p. 14–22.

into a symmetric matrix $\mathbf{\Gamma}$ with elements

$$\gamma_{pq} \equiv (pp|qq) \equiv \int \chi_p^*(1)\chi_q^*(2)\frac{e^2}{r_{12}}\chi_p(1)\chi_q(2)dv, \quad (29)$$

one obtains (subject to zero differential overlap between AO's),

$$[ij|kl] = [\mathbf{ij}^*|\mathbf{\Gamma}|\mathbf{kl}^*]. \quad (30)$$

Application of Eqs. (27) and (30) to Eqs. (9)–(13) gives them in terms of integrals over AO's. These, in turn, may be calculated from the AO's or estimated semiempirically.

Let the matrix $\mathbf{X}$ be composed of elements

$$x_{pq} = \int \chi_p^*(1)x(1)\chi_q(1)dv. \quad (31)$$

Then it follows that

$$m_{ij} = [\mathbf{i}^*|\mathbf{X}|\mathbf{j}]. \quad (32)$$

Subject to the neglect of overlap, $\mathbf{X}$ is diagonal; and, further, the diagonal elements x_{ss} are taken as equal to x_s, the position coordinate of the nucleus of the sth AO.[7] Thus through Eq. (32) the transition moments and oscillator strengths may be calculated.

Finally, let the symmetric matrix $\mathbf{Q}$ be composed of the elements

$$Q_{pq} = \int \chi_p^*(1)e\chi_q(1)dv. \quad (33)$$

Although $Q_{pp}=e$, and $Q_{pq}=0$ (subject to the neglect of differential overlap), it is convenient to leave Eq. (33) in its present form. d_{ij} may now be expanded as

$$d_{ij} = [\mathbf{i}|\mathbf{Q}|\mathbf{j}]. \quad (34)$$

The charge distribution, in the light of the present discussion, for a state characterized by Ψ_a can finally be expressed as

$$\int \Psi_a^*\sum e_u\Psi_a dv = b_{11}Q_{11} + 2b_{12}Q_{12} + \cdots b_{22}Q_{22} + \cdots, \quad (35)$$

where, by definition, $b_{pp} \equiv$ "charge density" on atom p, and $b_{pq} \equiv$ "bond order" between atoms p and q. b_{pp} and b_{pq} are given by Coulson and Longuet-Higgins'[9] definition for charge density and bond order for the case where Ψ_a is expressed by a single configurational wave function.

To summarize, if the matrix $\mathbf{C}$ collects the MO coefficients C_{pi} (or, alternatively, let $\mathbf{C}$ collect the vectors $\mathbf{i}$]), then a knowledge of $\mathbf{C}$, the Coulomb integral matrix $\mathbf{\Gamma}$, the core matrix $\mathbf{H}^c$, and the matrices $\mathbf{X}$, $\mathbf{Y}$, $\mathbf{Z}$ enables one to compute the transition energies, transition moments, and charge distributions.

[9] C. A. Coulson and H. C. Longuett-Higgins, Proc. Roy. Soc. (London) **A191**, 39 (1947).

IV. ALTERNANT HYDROCARBONS[10]

In the course of the polyacene calculations, it became evident that certain generalizations are applicable to the energies, transition moments, and charge distributions of even alternant hydrocarbons. In the proof of these general rules, the following theoretical approximations are applied:

(a) Differential overlap is neglected.

(b) Configuration interaction is limited to the ground state and singly excited configurations.

(c) The core is treated in a simplified manner. Specifically, only nearest neighbor resonance interaction β is considered. Further, in the computation of the core integral α, penetration integrals are either neglected or else taken to give a constant contribution to each C atom, and the valence state ionization potentials $-W$ are set equal for all C atoms. [See Eq. (28)]. Removal of these assumptions, however, should not affect the results a great deal, and the rules would still be approximately valid.

These rules can only be derived from a set of MO's which are alternant, [i.e., satisfy Eq. (37)]. Such MO's are the usual result for alternant hydrocarbons as they are derived through the conventional semiempirical LCAO MO theory. But as has been shown by Pople,[11] alternant MO's will also be the result of Roothaan's[12] more elaborate self-consistent field LCAO MO method; however, one must make use of the simplifying assumptions (a), (b), and (c) above, just as is done here.

In an even alternant hydrocarbon it is possible to divide the atoms into two classes, a "starred" and "unstarred" class, the number of "starred" and "unstarred" atoms being equal.[13] The characteristic secular equation, which determines the MO's, must be such that only interaction elements between "starred" and "unstarred" atoms be nonzero and that all the diagonal elements be equal. Then, according to Coulson and Rushbrooke, a number of useful relationships prevail.[11]

Let the MO's, which are normally filled in the lowest energy configuration, be designated by $i, j, k, l \cdots$, and those which are not filled, by $i', j', k', l' \cdots$. Further, let the atoms be numbered 1, 2, 3, 4, $\cdots$, and let all of the "starred" atoms be designated by odd numbers, and the "unstarred" atoms by even numbers. Then, the characteristic values k of the equations which determine the MO's will be spaced symmetrically.

[10] Since the completion of this work it has come to the author's attention that a number of other workers have been investigating generalizations for hydrocarbons, at least similar to the ones reported here. Some of this work is now published. A theoretical approach quite similar to the present one has been used by J. A. Pople, Proc. Phys. Soc. (London) **A68**, 81 (1955). See also the work by W. Moffitt, J. Chem. Phys. **22**, 1820 (1954) and by M. J. S. Dewar and H. C. Longuett-Higgins, Proc. Phys. Soc. (London) **A67**, 795 (1954), which reaches some of the same conclusions as here.

[11] J. A. Pople, Trans. Faraday Soc. **44**, 1375 (1953).

[12] C. C. J. Roothaan, Revs. Modern Phys. **23**, 69 (1951).

[13] C. A. Coulson and G. S. Rushbrooke, Proc. Cambridge Phil. Soc. **36**, 193 (1940).

That is,

$$k_i = -k_{i'}. \tag{36}$$

And

$$C_{p^*i} = C_{p^*i'} \quad \text{for } p \text{ odd, i.e., "starred,"} \tag{37}$$
$$C_{pi} = -C_{pi'} \quad \text{for } p \text{ even, i.e., "unstarred."}$$

The choice of sign in the first equation of (37) is quite arbitrary. In order that there be no confusion with respect to sign, it is important that the MO's, ϕ_i, conform with Eq. (37). Or more simply, choose some coefficient, say C_{1i}, and let it be positive in all MO's; this may always be achieved by multiplication of the ϕ_i's by ± 1. Also

$$2\sum_f C_{pf}^2 = 1, \quad p \text{ may be "starred" or not} \tag{38}$$

(sum over unprimed MO's), that is, the "charge density" is 1. And

$$2\sum_f C_{p^*f}C_{q^*f} = 0, \quad 2\sum_f C_{pf}C_{qf} = 0 \tag{39}$$

(sum over unprimed MO's), that is, the "bond order" between "starred" atoms or between "unstarred" atoms vanishes. Equations (36)–(39) summarize Coulson and Rushbrooke's results which are most useful for the present purpose.

It is evident that the various configurations fall into three types. Namely, one has the lowest energy configuration with MO's $i, j, k, l\cdots$ each occupied by two electrons, configurations arising by exciting an electron from i to i', j to j', etc., and finally configurations in which an electron is excited from i to j', j to i', etc. In the last type, configurations will always occur in degenerate pairs; that is, $k_{i'} - k_j = k_{j'} - k_i$, by Eq. (36).

One is now in a position to summarize the rules for even alternant hydrocarbons:

1. A. The energy of the configuration obtained by exciting an electron from the MO i to the MO j' is equal to that obtained by excitation from j to i', *even with the inclusion of electronic interaction*, that is, by application of Eq. (9). Or

$$E(V_{ij'}) = E(V_{ji'}), \quad E(T_{ij'}) = E(T_{ji'}). \tag{40}$$

B. The configurations $V_{ij'}$ and $V_{ji'}$, or $T_{ij'}$ and $T_{ji'}$ are degenerate. And the linear combinations

$${}^1\Omega_{ij}^{\pm} = 2^{-\frac{1}{2}}[V_{ij'} \pm V_{ji'}], \quad {}^3\Omega_{ij}^{\pm} = 2^{-\frac{1}{2}}[T_{ij'} \pm T_{ji'}], \tag{41}$$

enable one to factor each configurational secular determinant, singlet and triplet, into two determinants, where Ω^+, or *plus* states, do not interact with Ω^-, or *minus* states.[14]

In this connection the lowest energy configuration, V_0, behaves like a *minus* state, since it interacts only with ${}^1\Omega^-$. The excited configurations of the type $V_{ii'}$, however, behave like *plus* states, interacting only with Ω^+ states. Or

$$\{V_{ij'}|V_{kl'}\} = \{V_{ji'}|V_{lk'}\},$$
$$\{T_{ij'}|T_{kl'}\} = \{T_{ji'}|T_{lk'}\},$$
$$\{V_0|V_{ij'}\} = -\{V_0|V_{ji'}\}, \quad \{V_0|V_{ii'}\} = 0, \tag{42}$$
$$\{V_{ii'}|V_{kl'}\} = \{V_{ii'}|V_{lk'}\},$$
$$\{T_{ii'}|T_{kl'}\} = \{T_{ii'}|T_{lk'}\}.$$

2. The configurational energies and interaction elements of the secular determinant constructed from ${}^1\Omega^-$ functions are identical with those for ${}^3\Omega^-$. In other words, the energies of singlet and triplet *minus* states will be the same before as well as after configuration interaction of singly excited states. Or

$$\{{}^1\Omega_{ij}^-|{}^1\Omega_{kl}^-\} = \{{}^3\Omega_{ij}^-|{}^3\Omega_{kl}^-\}, \tag{43}$$

and also

$$E({}^1\Omega_{ij}^-) = E({}^3\Omega_{ij}^-) \geq E({}^3\Omega_{ij}^+),$$
$$E({}^1\Omega_{ij}^+) \geq E({}^3\Omega_{ij}^+). \tag{44}$$

3. The dipole transition moment between any two Ω^+ states or between any two Ω^- states is zero. That is, only transitions between *plus* and *minus* states are allowed.

4. The charge density of the ground state and all the singly excited states is 1 at each carbon atom, unaffected by mixing among the ground configuration and the singly excited configurations. The bond orders, however, will usually be affected by configuration interaction.

Conclusions similar to the ones expressed by rules 1 through 4 have been derived by Pople in a recent publication.[10] He starts from essentially the same basic assumptions and considers SCF MO's with interaction among degenerate configurations.

To prove rules 1 and 2, use the following relations, which are readily derived by using the equations of Sec. III and Eqs. (36)–(39):

$$[\mathbf{ij}'| = [\mathbf{i}'\mathbf{j}|, \quad [\mathbf{ii}| = [\mathbf{i}'\mathbf{i}'|, \quad [\mathbf{ij}| = [\mathbf{i}'\mathbf{j}'|, \tag{45}$$

$$2\sum_f [ii|ff] = [ii|1], \quad 2\sum_f [ij|ff] \quad [ij|1], \tag{46}$$

$$\sum_f [fi|fi] + [fi'|fi'] = (11|11), \quad \sum_f [fi|fj'] + [fi'|fj] = 0, \tag{47}$$

$$\sum_f [fi|fj] + [fi'|fj'] = 0, \quad \sum_f [fi|fi'] = 0, \tag{48}$$

$$I_{ii} = -[ii|1] + K_i\beta - A, \quad I_{i'i'} = -[ii|1] - K_i\beta - A, \tag{49}$$

$$I_{ij} = -[ij|1] + K_{ij}\beta, \quad I_{i'j'} = -[ij|1] - K_{ij}\beta, \tag{50}$$

$$I_{ij'} = -[ij'|1] + K_{ij'}\beta, \quad I_{i'j} = -[ij'|1] - K_{ij'}\beta. \tag{51}$$

In Eqs. (45)–(51) all sums are over unprimed MO's, $[\mathbf{ij}|\cdots$ are vectors as defined in Sec. III, $(11|11)$ is the atomic one-center carbon Coulomb integral, and $A = -W - (11|11)$,[1,4] where $-W$ is the valence state $2p\pi$ ionization potential. Further, if one considers the matrix $\mathbf{H}^c$ as the sum of two matrices, the diagonal matrix $\boldsymbol{\alpha}$ and the matrix $\boldsymbol{\beta}$ which is zero along the diagonal,

$$\mathbf{H}^c = \boldsymbol{\alpha} + \boldsymbol{\beta}, \tag{52}$$

where the matrix elements α_p and β_{pq} are defined by Eq. (26); also $\beta_{pq} = \beta$ for nearest neighbors. Then by definition

$$[\mathbf{i}|\boldsymbol{\beta}|\mathbf{i}] = K_i\beta, \quad [\mathbf{i}|\boldsymbol{\beta}|\mathbf{j}] = K_{ij}\beta \tag{53}$$

[14] The *plus* and *minus* states here should not be confused with a similar notation used in diatomic molecular spectra.

Here one notes that if $|\mathbf{i}]$ and $|\mathbf{j}]$ are eigenvectors of $\boldsymbol{\beta}$, $K_i=k_i$, $K_j=k_j$, and $K_{ij}=0$.

Rules 1 and 2 may now be readily derived by applying the Eqs. (45)–(51) to Eqs. (9)–(13). To consider two specific examples, suppose one wishes to prove rule 1. A., or that $E(V_{ij'})=E(V_{ji'})$:

Rewriting Eq. (9) so as to change the summation over the index f to include all unprimed MO's, one has

$$\begin{aligned} E(V_{ij'})-E(V_0)=&I_{j'j'}-I_{ii}-[ii|j'j']+2[ij'|ij'] \\ &+\sum_f 2[ff|j'j']-2[ff|ii]-[fj'|fj']+[fi|fi], \\ E(V_{ji'})-E(V_0)=&I_{i'i'}-I_{jj}-[jj|i'i']+2[ji'|ji'] \\ &+\sum_f 2[ff|i'i']-2[ff|jj]-[fi'|fi']+[fj|fj]. \end{aligned} \tag{54}$$

Now make use of Eqs. (36), (45), (46), and (49); Eqs. (54) are immediately simplified to

$$\begin{aligned} E(V_{ij'})-E(V_0)=&-(K_j+K_i)\beta-[ii|jj]+2[ij'|ij'] \\ &+\sum_f [fi|fi]-[fj'|fj'], \\ E(V_{ji'})-E(V_0)=&-(K_j+K_i)\beta-[ii|jj]+2[ij'|ij'] \\ &+\sum_f [fj|fj]-[fi'|fi']. \end{aligned} \tag{55}$$

This result is a simpler formulation of Eq. (9), applicable to even alternant hydrocarbons. Subtracting the last two relationships from one another and making use of Eq. (47), one finds that $E(V_{ij'})-E(V_{ji'})=0$.

As a further example consider the derivation of Eqs. (44). Starting with the Eqs. (41), one can write for the corresponding energies by the use of Eqs. (9), (13), and rule 1. A.:

$$\begin{aligned} E(^1\Omega_{ij}^+)&=E(V_{ij'})+2[ij'|ji']-[ij|j'i'], \\ E(^1\Omega_{ij}^-)&=E(V_{ij'})-2[ij'|ji']+[ij|j'i'], \\ E(^3\Omega_{ij}^+)&=E(V_{ij'})-2[ij'|ij']-[ij|j'i'], \\ E(^3\Omega_{ij}^-)&=E(V_{ij'})-2[ij'|ij']+[ij|j'i']. \end{aligned} \tag{56}$$

Now through application of Eqs. (45), it is evident that $E(^1\Omega_{ij}^-)=E(^3\Omega_{ij}^-)$. To show the inequalities in Eq. (44), one has to make use of Roothaan's theorem[12] that two center Coulomb exchange integrals, namely, $[ij'|ij']$ and $[ij|ij]$, in this case, are always positive.

To verify rule 3, use the auxiliary equations

$$2\sum_f m_{ff}{}^x=\sum_s x_s,\quad m_{ii}{}^x=m_{i'i'}{}^x,\quad m_{ij'}{}^x=m_{i'j}{}^x, \tag{57}$$

with analogous relationships for the y and z coordinates. These equations are readily derived from Eqs. (32), (37), and (38). Now consider the two generalized states:

$$\begin{aligned} {}^1\Psi_a^-&=A_0V_0+A_{ik}{}^1\Omega_{ik}^-+A_{jk}{}^1\Omega_{jk}^-+A_{il}{}^1\Omega_{il}^-+\cdots, \\ {}^1\Psi_b^-&=B_0V_0+B_{ik}{}^1\Omega_{ik}^-+B_{jk}{}^1\Omega_{jk}^-+B_{il}{}^1\Omega_{il}^-+\cdots. \end{aligned} \tag{58}$$

With the x component as an example, substitution of ${}^1\Psi_a^-$ and ${}^1\Psi_b^-$ into Eq. (19) gives transition moments among ${}^1\Omega^-$ functions of five distinct types. These, in turn, are easily expanded, and by Eq. (20) one obtains

$$\int V_0{}^*\sum_t e_tx_tV_0dv=2e\sum_f m_{ff}+\sum_s e_sx_s=0, \tag{59}$$

$$\int {}^1\Omega_{ik}{}^{-,*}\sum_t e_tx_t{}^1\Omega_{ik}^-dv=2e\sum_f m_{ff}+\sum_s e_sx_s=0, \tag{60}$$

$$\int V_0{}^*\sum_t e_tx_t{}^1\Omega_{ik}^-dv=em_{ik'}-em_{ki'}=0, \tag{61}$$

$$\int {}^1\Omega_{ik}{}^{-,*}\sum_t e_tx_t{}^1\Omega_{jk}^-dv=em_{i'j'}-em_{ij}=0, \tag{62}$$

$$\int {}^1\Omega_{jk}{}^{-,*}\sum_t e_tx_t{}^1\Omega_{il}^-dv=0. \tag{63}$$

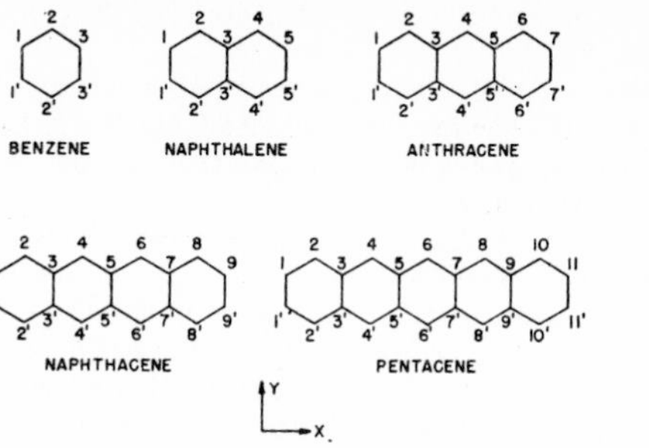

FIG. 1. Carbon skeleton of polyacenes.

Equations (59) and (60) equal zero by (57) and by the obvious relation for hydrocarbons, where each carbon atom contributes only one π electron, namely, $\sum_s e_sx_s=-e\sum_s x_s$. Equations (61) and (62) equal zero through (57). The proof that the transition moment vanishes among ${}^3\Omega^-$ functions, among ${}^1\Omega^+$ functions, and among ${}^3\Omega^+$ functions is the same as has just been shown for ${}^1\Omega^-$ functions. Only transition moments between *plus* and *minus* states of the same multiplicity do not necessarily vanish.

Finally, one wishes to show the validity of rule 4 for the charge density as defined in Secs. II and III. Since one is dealing only with the charge density and not the bond order, it is best to replace the matrix $\mathbf{Q}_D$ with elements Q_{11}, Q_{22}, $Q_{33}\cdots$. Now, defining d^D as

$$d_{ij}{}^D=[\mathbf{i}^*|\mathbf{Q}_D|\mathbf{j}], \tag{64}$$

one finds the following auxiliary relations to be true for even alternant hydrocarbons:

$$2\sum_f d_{ff}{}^D=\sum_s Q_{ss},\quad d_{i'i'}{}^D=d_{ii}{}^D,\quad d_{i'j}{}^D=d_{ij'}{}^D \tag{65}$$

where f is summed over filled MO's in V_0 and s over the AO's.

Considering, for example, the charge density of the state ${}^1\Psi_a^-$ [Eq. (58)] and substituting ${}^1\Psi_a^-$ into Eq. (23), one obtains a sum of integrals quite analogous to Eqs. (59)–(63), but with $\sum_t e_tx_t$ replaced by $\sum_u e_u$. Expansion of these integrals in terms of the d^D's is again quite analogous to the expansion of Eqs. (59)–(63), but with d^D replacing m and $\sum_s e_sx_s=0$. Application of Eq. (65) now proves the integrals corresponding to Eqs. (61)–(62) equal to zero, just as before; but the integrals corresponding to Eqs. (59) and (60) now equal $2\sum_f d_{ff}{}^D$. Thus one has

$$\int {}^1\Psi_A{}^{-,*}\sum_u e_u{}^1\Psi_A^-dv=2\sum_f d_{ff}{}^D[A_0{}^2+A_{ik}{}^2+\cdots]+\cdots, \tag{66}$$

But since the coefficients A are normalized,

$$\int {}^1\Psi_a{}^{-,*}\sum_u e_u{}^1\Psi_a^-dv=Q_{11}+Q_{22}+Q_{33}+\cdots 2b_{12}Q_{12}+\cdots, \tag{67}$$

or according to the discussion at the end of Sec. III, $b_{11}=b_{22}=b_{33}=\cdots 1$, showing that the charge density at each carbon atom is 1. An analogous proof applies to *plus* states and triplet states.

V. THE POLYACENES: PRELIMINARY CONSIDERATIONS

The carbon skeleton structure of the polyacenes is shown in Fig. 1. They are taken as planar, made up of regular hexagons, with all carbon-carbon distances equal to 1.390 A. Naphthalene, anthracene, naphthacene, and pentacene belong to the point group D_{2h}, and the ground and singly excited electronic states have the symmetry A_{1g}, B_{1g}, B_{2u}, and B_{3u} (with the axes chosen as in Fig. 1). The corresponding states in benzene, which belongs to D_{6h}, are A_{1g}, E_{2g}, B_{1u}, B_{2u}, and, E_{2u}.[15]

As preliminary information, for each of the polyacene molecules, one requires a set of LCAO MO's, Coulomb integrals, and core integrals, that is, the matrices $\mathbf{C}$, $\mathbf{\Gamma}$, $\mathbf{H}^c$ (or, $\boldsymbol{\alpha}$ and $\boldsymbol{\beta}$).

The molecular orbitals of the conventional semi-empirical LCAO MO theory were chosen for this calculation. However, in the case of naphthalene, a computation using perimeter MO's[16] was carried out as well. Coulson has solved the semiempirical secular equation for the polyacenes analytically for the eigenvalues.[17] His results can be extended to give the MO's.[18] Since the numbering of MO's and AO's follows a different method in this section from that in Sec. IV, it is best to rewrite Eq. (1) as:

$$\phi_\lambda=\sum_\mu C_{\mu\lambda}\chi_\mu. \tag{68}$$

Here the index μ numbers the AO's according to Coulson, as in Fig. 1. The MO's can now be divided into two sets: those made up of symmetry orbitals, σ, of the type:

$$\sigma_\mu{}^+=\chi_\mu+\chi_{\mu'},\quad \sigma_\mu{}^-=\chi_\mu-\chi_{\mu'}. \tag{69}$$

Then

$$\phi_\lambda{}^\pm=\sum_{\mu=1}^{2n+1} C_{\mu\lambda}{}^\pm\sigma_\mu{}^\pm, \tag{70}$$

where

$$C_{\mu\lambda}{}^\pm=\left[\frac{(k_\lambda\mp1)}{(2k_\lambda\mp1)(n+1)}\right]^{\frac{1}{2}}\sin\frac{\mu\lambda\pi}{2(n+1)} \times\left[\cos^2\frac{\mu\pi}{2}+\left(\frac{k_\lambda}{k_\lambda\mp1}\right)^{\frac{1}{2}}\sin^2\frac{\mu\pi}{2}\right], \tag{71}$$

for k_λ as given by Eq. (73), and $\lambda=1, 2\cdots 2n+1$, $\lambda\neq n+1$, where n equals the number of rings in the polyacene under consideration. Further,

$$C_{\mu,\,n+1}{}^\pm=\left[\frac{1}{2(n+1)}\right]^{\frac{1}{2}}\sin\frac{\mu\pi}{2} \tag{72}$$

for the case $\lambda=n+1$, and k_{n+1} as in Eq. (74). The expressions for k_λ are:

$$k_\lambda=\pm\tfrac{1}{2}+\tfrac{1}{2}\cos\frac{\lambda\pi}{2(n+1)}\left[16+\sec^2\frac{\lambda\pi}{2(n+1)}\right]^{\frac{1}{2}}, \tag{73}$$

$$k_{n+1}=\pm1. \tag{74}$$

In Eqs. (70)–(74) the upper sign always refers to the ϕ^+ MO's and the lower sign to the ϕ^- MO's. The positive square root is always taken. The symmetry classes to which the MO's belong may be ascertained to be as follows:

For ϕ^+: If λ is odd, MO belongs to b_{1u}. if λ is even, MO belongs to b_{2g},

For ϕ^-: if λ is odd, MO belongs to b_{3g}. if λ is even, MO belongs to a_{1u}.

One might expect that the configuration of lowest energy would have the $2n+1$ MO's which are characterized by positive k_λ values, filled with the $4n+2\pi$ electrons. As it turns out, with electronic interaction included this is still the lowest energy configuration for the polyacenes.

With the exception of the one-center and nearest neighbor two-center integrals, all Coulomb integrals were calculated from Slater carbon $2p_z$ AO's, with $Z=3.18$.[19] Table I summarizes these results. It is useful to note that at interatomic distances $r\geq2.780$ A, these integrals are simply obtained exact to at least three decimal places from the largest three terms of the theoretical expression:

$$(pp|qq)=\frac{\zeta}{\rho_{pq}}-\frac{3\zeta}{\rho_{pq}{}^3}+\frac{81\zeta}{4\rho_{pq}{}^5}, \tag{75}$$

where $\zeta=Ze^2/2a_0$, $\rho=Zr_{pq}/2a_0$, and r_{pq} is the distance between AO's χ_p and χ_q.

The one-center and nearest neighbor Coulomb integrals were obtained semiempirically from the benzene spectrum; this is discussed in detail in Sec. VII.

One now considers the core integrals α_p and β_{pq}. One might expect that the value of core resonance integral, β_{pq}, drops off rather rapidly with interatomic distance and also that non-nearest neighbor resonance interaction would cancel out to a great extent. With this in mind and for the sake of simplicity, it has been assumed here that $\beta_{pq}=0$, when k and j do not refer to nearest neighbor AO's. For neighboring AO's, β_{pq} has been taken as the constant $\beta=-2.371$ ev. This value, as was the case for the two Coulomb integrals discussed above, was obtained semiempirically from the benzene spectrum; it is the third and last parameter obtained in this manner.

The α_p's were computed by Eq. (28). Justification for the neglect of penetration integrals may be found in the smallness of their values, combined with the approximation that they contribute equally to each α_p. They would, therefore, largely cancel out in the computation of transition energies. Similarly, $-W_p$ (valence state ionization potential) and A_p (valence state electron affinity) were taken as the same for each carbon atom, causing them to cancel as well.

VI. COMPUTATIONAL PROCEDURES

The numerical calculation of configurational expectation energies and of interaction elements between configurations and the subsequent solution for the eigenvalues and eigenvectors are

[15] For group theoretical notation and character tables, see Eyring, Walter, and Kimball, *Quantum Chemistry* (John Wiley and Sons, Inc., New York, 1944), p. 376.
[16] J. R. Platt, J. Chem. Phys. **17**, 484 (1949).
[17] C. A. Coulson, Proc. Phys. Soc. (London) **A60**, 257 (1948).
[18] R. McWeeny, Proc. Phys. Soc. (London) **A65**, 839 (1952).
[19] For the theoretical formulas see, for example, C. C. J. Roothaan, J. Chem. Phys. **19**, 1445 (1951).

usually quite time consuming when done by hand. To facilitate the calculation, a high-speed digital computer, I.B.M.'s EDPM, type 701, was programmed to perform two generalized computational procedures.

The first of these programs is designed to compute the matrix elements for configuration interaction. This program does not take advantage of the simplifications for alternant hydrocarbons (Sec. IV), nor does it require that only nearest neighbor β_{pq}'s be considered or that any of these be the same. In other words, one requires the matrices $\mathbf{C}, \mathbf{\Gamma}$, and $\mathbf{H}^c$ with no special restriction on the values of the elements. No additional programming is necessary in going from one molecule to another.

The matrices $\mathbf{C}, \mathbf{\Gamma}$, and $\mathbf{H}^c$ and a table of symbolically expressed configuration interaction elements (Eqs. (9)–(13) are stored as input in the high speed electrostatic memory of the 701. Under command of the program, the computer proceeds to analyze each configuration interaction element as to type of expansion into integrals over MO's, evaluates and sums the necessary integrals, and prints out the desired result. Each matrix multiplication (see Sec. III) is checked by repeating it in reverse order; various other checking procedures are built into the program. Computations are carried out with fixed decimal point and with ten-digit precision.

As an example, the total time required for a 7th order matrix (such as for all singly excited naphthalene $^1A_{1g}$ configurations) is 2.5 minutes, or an average of about 5 seconds per matrix element. The average time per element increases about proportionally to the cube of the number of AO's. The largest MO which can be handled entirely within the high speed memory of the machine, that is, without resort to the slower magnetic tape and drum memories, is one containing 40 AO's.

The second program is designed to find the eigenvalues and eigenvectors [Eqs. (5)–(6)] or more generally, the characteristic roots and vectors of any real symmetric matrix.[20] The mathematical procedure was originally motivated by Jacobi.[21] It is an iterative procedure converging upon all of the eigenvectors and eigenvalues simultaneously. Essentially, a sequence of orthogonal transformations, or rotations in coordinate planes, is executed until the original matrix has been diagonalized. A 33rd order matrix may be handled by operating entirely within the electrostatic memory. About 15 minutes computing time is required to diagonalize this size matrix. The time increases about with the cube of the order. When the eigenvectors are known, transition moments and bond orders are easily calculated without the aid of an automatic computing program.

VII. BENZENE

Before one proceeds with the polyacenes, it is helpful to examine theoretically, but not without the aid of some experimental results, the assignments for the lower excited states of benzene.

One knows experimentally that the lowest benzene triplet is at 3.59 ev.[22] Also, the lowest three singlet bands fall at about 4.71 ev, 5.96 ev, and 6.76 ev; the first of these is very weak, the next is medium weak, and the last is very strong.[23] As a basis for the subsequent discussion, one now makes a number of theoretical assumptions with regard to AO integrals. With the atoms numbered as in Fig. 1, one would expect that $(11|11) > (11|22) > (11|33) > (11|3'3')$. The value for $(11|11)$ should be about 11.54–. 46 = 11.08 ev.[24,4] $(11|33)$ and $(11|3'3')$ should be reasonably close to the values computed by Slater AO's with $Z = 3.18$, i.e., 5.682 ev and 4.978 ev, respectively. And $(11|22)$ might be expected to fall between 9.065 ev, the Slater AO value, and 5.682 ev. A theoretically estimated value for β is -2.477 ev.[25] With this experimental and theoretical information at hand, one now asks whether a satisfactory assignment may be found for the lower states of benzene.

TABLE I.[a] Coulomb integrals.

p, q	r_{pq}	$(pp\|qq)$
1, 1	0 A	10.959 ev
1, 2	1.390	6.895
1, 3	2.407	5.682
1, 3′	2.780	4.978
1, 4	3.678	3.824
1, 4′	4.170	3.390
1, 5	4.812	2.949
1, 5′	5.012	2.836
2, 6′	5.560	2.563
1, 6	6.059	2.355
1, 6′	6.370	2.242
1, 7	7.223	1.981
1, 7′	7.355	1.946
2, 8′	7.739	1.850
1, 8	8.455	1.695
1, 8′	8.680	1.652
1, 9	9.630	1.490
1, 9′	9.730	1.475
2, 10′	10.023	1.432
1, 10	10.856	1.323
1, 10′	11.033	1.302
1, 11	12.038	1.193
1, 11′	12.118	1.186

[a] Atoms are numbered as in Fig. 1.

Consider first the problem of interaction among singly excited configurations in benzene. Each of the lower singly excited states is required by symmetry to be expressed by a sum of four Slater determinants instead of the usual two. Therefore, in a sense, configuration interaction among the singly excited states is being considered. In fact, this includes interaction among all singly excited configurations in benzene except for one: the B_{1u} configuration arising from the excitation of an electron from the lowest filled to the highest unfilled MO. The interaction with this high energy state is for the most part neglected in the subsequent discussion.

According to the present theoretical method, it is relatively easy to derive the following expressions for the energy of the six lowest states with respect to the

[20] The author is indebted to Mr. J. Sheldon and Mr. D. Ladd, both formerly of the I.B.M. Corp., for analyzing and coding most of this program. He is also grateful to them for their helpful cooperation throughout all of the computational work.

[21] See, for example, A. S. Householder, *Principles of Numerical Analysis* (McGraw-Hill Book Company, Inc., New York, 1953), p. 160–162, and references p. 184.

[22] G. N. Lewis and M. Kasha, J. Am. Chem. Soc. **66**, 2100 (1944); **67**, 994 (1945); H. Shull, J. Chem. Phys. **17**, 295 (1949); D. S. McClure, J. Chem. Phys. **17**, 905 (1949).

[23] H. B. Klevens and J. R. Platt, J. Chem. Phys. **17**, 470 (1949).

[24] H. D. Pritchard, Chem. Revs. **52**, 529 (1955).

[25] β was calculated by Eq. (1) of the second paper of reference 1 and the integral table of Parr, Craig, and Ross.[2]

TABLE II. Assignment of benzene electronic states.

Assignment: State	I	II	III
$^1B_{2u}$	4.71 ev	4.71 ev	5.96 ev
$^1B_{1u}$	5.96	6.76	4.71
$^1E_{1u}$	6.76	5.96	6.76
$^3B_{1u}$	3.59	3.59	3.59

ground state[26]:

$$E(^1B_{2u}) = -2\beta + \tfrac{1}{6}[(11|22) - 3(11|33) + 2(11|3'3)],$$

$$E(^1B_{1u}) = -2\beta + \tfrac{1}{6}[2(11|11) - 5(11|22) + 7(11|33) - 4(11|3'3')],$$

$$E(^1E_{1u}) = -2\beta + \tfrac{1}{6}[(11|11) + 4(11|22) - 4(11|33) - (11|3'3')], \quad (76)$$

$$E(^3B_{2u}) = -2\beta + \tfrac{1}{6}[(11|22) - 3(11|33) + 2(11|3'3')],$$

$$E(^3B_{1u}) = -2\beta + \tfrac{1}{6}[-2(11|11) + 3(11|22) - (11|33)],$$

$$E(^3E_{1u}) = -2\beta + \tfrac{1}{6}[-(11|11) + 2(11|22) - 2(11|33) + (11|3'3')].$$

It is evident that

$$E(^3E_{1u}) = \tfrac{1}{2}[E(^3B_{2u}) + E(^3B_{1u})], \quad E(^3B_{2u}) = E(^1B_{2u}). \quad (77)$$

Hence $^3E_{1u}$ cannot be the lowest theoretical triplet. Further, experimentally the lowest triplet is considerably below any singlet, and only $^3B_{1u}$ can satisfy this condition. This comes about when $(11|11) - (11|22) > (11|33) - (11|3'3')$, a reasonable condition.

About the singlets, by Eqs. (76),

$$E(^1E_{1u}) - E(^1B_{2u}) = \tfrac{1}{6}[(11|11) + 3(11|22) - (11|33) - 3(11|44)], \quad (78)$$

and since $(11|11) > (11|22) > (11|33) > (11|3'3')$,

$$E(^1E_{1u}) > E(^1B_{2u}). \quad (79)$$

This confirms the observation that $^1E_{1u}$ is not the lowest singlet but that the band at 4.71 ev corresponds to a forbidden transition, to either $^1B_{1u}$ or $^1B_{2u}$. The only remaining possibilities for assignment in benzene are given in Table II.

By application of Eq. (76), the several Coulomb integrals and β are readily expressed in terms of the state energies. Then assuming the theoretical value

TABLE III. Empirical and theoretical benzene integrals.

Assignment: Integrals	I	II	III	Theoret. approx
$-\beta$	2.371 ev	2.471 ev	2.527 ev	2.477
(11|11)	11.383	10.183	9.508	11.08
(11|22)	7.213	6.013	4.400	<9.065
(11|33)	5.788	5.788	2.976	5.682
(11|3'3')	4.978	4.978	4.978	4.978

[26] See Table VIII of the second paper of reference 1.

TABLE IV. Calculated energies and intensities for benzene excited states.

State[a]	Energy[b] (ev)	f[c]	State[a]	Energy[b] (ev)	f[c]
$^1A_{1g}^-$	0.000	Ref.	$^3B_{1u}^+$	3.590	Ref.
$^1B_{2u}^-$	4.710	0	$^3E_{1u}^+$	4.149	0
$^1B_{1u}^+$	5.960	0	$^3B_{2u}^-$	4.710	0
$^1E_{1u}^+$	6.548	2.215	$^3E_{2g}^+$	5.961	0
$^1E_{2g}^+$	8.201	0	$^3E_{2g}^-$	8.359	0.807
$^1E_{2g}^-$	8.359	0	$^3B_{1u}^+$	10.170	0
$^1B_{1u}^+$	11.355	0			

[a] The ± superscripts have been added to the usual symmetry notation for easy correlation with polyacene states; see discussion in Sec. IV.
[b] The energies as listed are obtained without configurational interaction among the two singly excited B_{1u} states. With interaction included, the $^1B_{1u}$ energies are unchanged (the interaction is very weak), but the $^3B_{1u}$ energies are replaced by 3.179 ev and 10.581 ev.
[c] f's for the singlets are for transitions from $^1A_{1g}^-$, and for the triplets, f's are for transition from the lower $^3B_{1u}^+$ state.

4.978 ev for $(11|3'3')$, one obtains the results of Table III. Assignment III obviously does not give reasonable values for the integrals. Assignment II can be eliminated on experimental grounds, since the strong 6.76 ev band should correspond to the allowed transition to $^1E_{1u}$. Thus only Assignment I appears satisfactory in terms of both theory and experiment.

The three empirically determined integrals used in the polyacene computation, namely, the values for

TABLE V[a,b] Calculated energies and intensities for naphthalene excited states.

State	Energy (ev)	f	State	Energy (ev)	f
$^1A_{1g}^-$	0.000	Ref.	$^3A_{1g}^-$		
	5.729	0		5.715	0.084
	7.359	0		7.351	0.360
	10.741	0		10.738	
$^1A_{1g}^+$	7.095	0	$^3A_{1g}^+$	4.435	0
	7.422	0		6.020	0
	10.213	0		9.490	0
$^1B_{1g}^-$	5.985	0	$^3B_{1g}^-$	5.985	0.451
	8.222	0		8.222	0.001
	12.524	0		12.524	
$^1B_{1g}^+$	5.507	0	$^3B_{1g}^+$	3.424	0
	7.559	0		5.526	0
	11.063	0		10.602	0
$^1B_{2u}^-$	9.206	0	$^3B_{2u}^-$	9.206	0
$^1B_{2u}^+$	4.493	0.256	$^3B_{2u}^+$	2.180	Ref.
	6.309	0.699		4.220	0
	8.182	0.851		6.705	0
	8.778			7.248	0
	10.864			10.243	0
	13.390			13.058	0
$^1B_{3u}^-$	4.018	0	$^3B_{3u}^-$	4.018	0
	8.010	0		8.010	0
	9.103	0		9.103	0
$^1B_{3u}^+$	5.939	2.115	$^3B_{3u}^+$	3.639	0
	7.959	0.043		6.331	0
	9.627			9.710	0

[a] The notation with respect to + and − is discussed in Sec. IV.
[b] For transitions from $^1A_{1g}$ to $^1B_{2u}$ the electric vector is polarized along the short molecular axis, while for transitions to $^1B_{3u}$ it is polarized along the long axis. With $^3B_{2u}$ as reference state, transitions to $^3A_{1g}$ are polarized along the short axis, while those to $^3B_{1g}$ are polarized along the long axis.

TABLE VI.[a] Calculated energies and intensities for anthracene excited states.

State	Energy (ev)	f	State	Energy (ev)	f
$^1A_{1g}^-$	0.000	Ref.	$^3A_{1g}^-$		
	5.000	0		4.977	0.166
	6.815	0		6.799	0.433
	7.752	0		7.798	0.000
	9.173	0		9.091	
	10.616	0		10.640	
$^1A_{1g}^+$	6.742	0	$^3A_{1g}^+$	3.981	0
	7.026	0		5.914	0
	7.683	0		6.195	0
	9.506	0		9.419	0
	10.550	0		10.231	0
$^1B_{1g}^-$	4.944	0	$^3B_{1g}^-$	4.944	0.540
	8.683	0		8.683	
	8.872	0		8.872	
$^1B_{1g}^+$	4.608	0	$^3B_{1g}^+$	2.844	0
	7.187	0		5.515	0
	7.393	0		6.558	0
$^1B_{2u}^-$	5.692	0	$^3B_{2u}^-$	5.692	0
$^1B_{2u}^+$	3.648	0.386	$^3B_{2u}^+$	1.660	Ref.
	5.251	0.091		3.555	0
	6.586	0.644		5.230	0
	7.846			7.232	0
$^1B_{3u}^-$	3.715	0	$^3B_{3u}^-$	3.715	0
	6.239	0		6.239	0
	7.732	0		7.732	0
	8.887	0		8.887	0
$^1B_{3u}^+$	5.499	3.229	$^3B_{3u}^+$	3.503	0
	7.221	0.091		4.911	0
	7.760			7.474	0
	9.108			9.085	0

[a] See notes to Table V.

TABLE VII. Calculated energies and intensities for naphthacene excited states.

State	Energy (ev)	f	State	Energy (ev)	f
$^1A_{1g}^-$	0.000	Ref.	$^3A_{1g}^-$		
	4.513	0		4.498	0.130
	6.308	0		6.279	0.243
	6.568	0		6.561	0.136
	8.287	0		8.285	
	9.089	0		9.089	
	9.849	0		9.850	
$^1A_{1g}^+$	6.332	0	$^3A_{1g}^+$	3.753	0
	6.675	0		5.130	0
	7.229	0		5.865	0
	8.361	0		7.993	0
	9.325	0		9.282	0
	9.795	0		9.538	
$^1B_{1g}^-$	4.260	0	$^3B_{1g}^-$	4.260	1.304
	5.562	0		5.562	0.299
	8.117	0		8.117	
	8.787	0		8.787	
$^1B_{1g}^+$	3.900	0	$^3B_{1g}^+$	1.866	0
	5.097	0		4.105	0
	7.019	0		5.506	0
	7.519	0		6.908	0
$^1B_{2u}^-$	5.142	0	$^3B_{2u}^-$	5.142	0
	8.326	0		8.326	0
$^1B_{2u}^+$	3.109	0.442	$^3B_{2u}^+$	1.103	Ref.
	4.686	0.159		3.192	0
	6.541	0.000		5.651	0
	6.942	1.203		6.023	0
	7.815			7.466	0
$^1B_{3u}^-$	3.565	0	$^3B_{3u}^-$	3.565	0
	5.783	0		5.783	0
	7.386	0		7.386	0
	8.447	0		8.447	0
$^1B_{3u}^+$	5.087	3.780	$^3B_{3u}^+$	3.450	0
	7.190	0.086		4.645	0
	7.566			7.278	0
	8.568			8.526	

[a] See notes to Table V.

$(11|11)$, $(11|22)$, and β are not those of Table III. Rather, the experimental energies of only three benzene states, $^1B_{1u}$, $^1B_{2u}$, and $^3B_{1u}$ by assignment I of Table II, were taken as known; theoretical values were used for $(11|33)$ and $(11|3'3')$. The result for $(11|11)$ and $(11|22)$ is listed in Table I, while $\beta=-2.371$ ev.

The results for benzene are summarized in Table IV. The assignments are the same for the lower states as proposed by Goeppert-Mayer and Sklar,[2] and by Roothaan and Parr.[27]

VIII. CALCULATED SPECTRA OF THE POLYACENES

The calculated results for the polyacenes are summarized in Tables IV–VIII. Here all the energies which are a result of configuration interaction among the chosen singly excited states are given. The calculated oscillator strengths uncorrected by any empirical factor are also given for the lower excited states.

In Figs. 2 and 3 the interrelations between the lower excited states are shown. It is clear that the results for the lowest $^1B_{2u}$ and $^3B_{2u}$, and the two lower $^1B_{3u}$ states bear out the relationships pointed out by Klevens and Platt.[23] It is encouraging that the energies and intensities for the $^1B_{2u}$ and the two lower $^1B_{3u}$ states are essentially the same as those recently obtained by Moffitt[28] and that the lowest triplets are in good agreement with those calculated by Hall.[29] Both of these authors have used different theoretical methods from the one employed here. The results are also in reasonable correspondence with Pople's calculation.[10]

In the Appendix a more complete presentation of the results for naphthalene is given. Namely, the MO's, the configuration interaction secular equations for all of the singly excited states, and the solution of these secular equations to give the final energies and wavefunctions are tabulated.[30] A comparison can be made

[27] C. C. J. Roothaan and R. G. Parr, J. Chem. Phys. 17, 1001 (1949).

[28] W. Moffitt, J. Chem. Phys. 22, 320 (1954).

[29] G. G. Hall, Proc. Roy. Soc. (London) A213, 113 (1952).

[30] Similar information for the other polyacenes is available.

Table VIII.[a] Calculated energies and intensities for pentacene excited states.

State	Energy (ev)	f	State	Energy (ev)	f
$^1A_{1g}^-$	0.000	Ref.	$^3A_{1g}^-$		
	4.238	0		4.229	0.140
	6.168	0		6.151	0.092
	6.275	0		6.254	0.226
	7.655	0		7.648	0.001
	8.840	0		8.840	
	9.411	0		9.411	
$^1A_{1g}^+$	6.062	0	$^3A_{1g}^+$	3.699	0
	6.518	0		4.944	0
	7.324	0		5.760	0
	7.849	0		7.631	0
	8.879	0		8.746	0
	9.423	0		9.321	0
$^1B_{1g}^-$	3.687	0	$^3B_{1g}^-$	3.687	1.582
	5.228	0		5.228	0.028
	7.040	0		7.040	0.014
	7.997	0		7.997	
	8.880	0		8.880	
	9.686	0		9.686	
$^1B_{1g}^+$	3.429	0	$^3B_{1g}^+$	1.672	0
	4.729	0		3.157	0
	6.396	0		5.565	0
	6.821	0		5.906	0
	7.111	0		6.397	0
	9.140	0		8.963	0
$^1B_{2u}^-$	4.692	0	$^3B_{2u}^-$	4.692	0
	5.457	0		5.457	0
	8.051	0		8.051	0
$^1B_{2u}^+$	2.815	0.563	$^3B_{2u}^+$	0.793	Ref.
	4.133	0.286		2.671	0
	5.331	0.000		4.055	0
	6.132	0.364		5.703	0
	7.802			7.581	0
$^1B_{3u}^-$	3.514	0	$^3B_{3u}^-$	3.514	0
	5.351	0		5.351	0
	7.119	0		7.119	0
	8.094	0		8.094	0
$^1B_{3u}^+$	4.796	4.318	$^3B_{3u}^+$	3.453	0
	6.974	0.063		4.427	0
	7.329			7.030	0
	8.187			8.126	0

[a] See notes to Table V.

with a nonempirical calculation by Jacobs.[31] As in previous comparisons with the present theory,[1,34] the triplet state energies are much too low, the theoretical oscillator strengths are greater, and the effects of configuration interaction appear to be too large for the nonempirical calculation.

Table IX.[a] Intermediate singlets which can combine with triplets through spin-orbit coupling.

Triplets	σ_x	σ_y	σ_z
$^3A_{1g}$	$^1B_{3g}$	$^1B_{2g}$	$^1B_{:g}$
$^3B_{1g}$	$^1B_{2g}$	$^1B_{3g}$	$^1A_{1g}$
$^3B_{2u}$	$^1B_{1u}$	$^1A_{1u}$	$^1B_{3u}$
$^3B_{3u}$	$^1A_{1u}$	$^1B_{.u}$	$^1B_{2u}$

[a] Table IX is analogous to Mizushima and Koide's,[33] Table I for benzene. The meaning of σ_x, σ_y, σ_z is the same as given by these authors. x, y, z coordinates are defined by Fig. 1.

Some theoretical predictions can be made with regard to transition probabilities from the ground state to the triplet states. McClure[32] proposed a theory for singlet-triplet transitions based upon interactions through the spin-orbit coupling term. More recently Mizushima and Koide[33] have made a careful analysis of spin-orbit interactions in benzene. Applying their theory to polyacenes, one obtains Table IX, which summarizes the intermediate singlet states which can combine with the lower triplets.

Upon neglect of vibrational effects, only $^1B_{1u}$, $^1B_{2u}$, and $^1B_{3u}$ states can combine with the ground state through dipole transitions. Thus, of the triplets in Table IX, $^3B_{2u}$ and $^3B_{3u}$ states would have the best

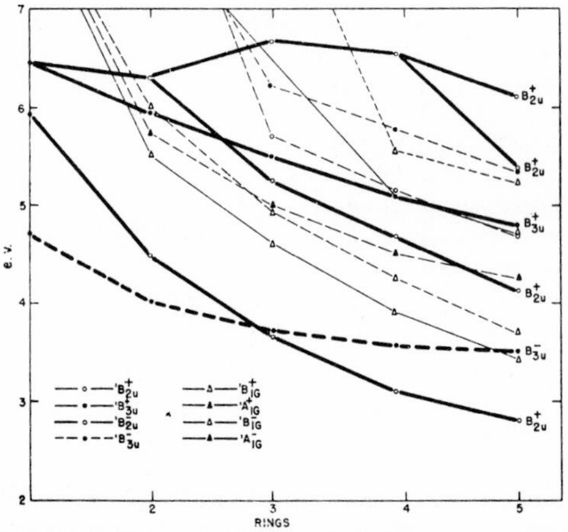

Fig. 2. Calculated polyacene lower singlet states. Heavy lines emphasize those states which should be more easily observed experimentally.

probability of transition with respect to the ground state.

A most difficult question to answer is: to what extent should configuration interaction be included, and what is the effect of changing the nature of the MO's? An informative discussion has very recently been given by Moser,[34] who has done a thorough calculation of butadiene by the present method. Moser points out the difficulty of interacting all the configurations for a large molecule, and from his results it appears that consideration of only singly excited configurations (as is done here) would lead to quite good results. Further limitation of configuration interaction to the very lowest singly excited configurations still gives good results for butadiene. For the polyacenes such limitation is prac-

[31] J. Jacobs, Proc. Phys. Soc. **A62**, 710 (1948). It should be noted that three and four center integrals were neglected; their effect is probably far from negligible in a nonempirical calculation.

[32] D. S. McClure, J. Chem. Phys. **17**, 665 (1949).

[33] M. Mizushima and S. Koide, J. Chem. Phys. **20**, 765 (1952).

[34] C. M. Moser, J. Chem. Soc. 3455, (1954).

tically a necessity. Even if one considers only the ground and all singly excited configurations for pentacene, there are in all 243 configurations. Factorization of these configurations according to spin, the four symmetry representations, and further factorization into *plus* and *minus* states eventually reduces the problem to 13 independent secular equations, each of approximately order 15. Although this problem is far from an impossible task for a modern high-speed computer, it nevertheless represents an excessively large amount of work for the benefits that may be forthcoming.

In order to arrive at some criterion for limiting the extent of configuration interaction, it is necessary to consider the nature and magnitude of its effect. Figure 4 illustrates the interaction of $^1A_{1g}$ configurations for naphthalene. It is clear that the general energy level spectrum is chiefly determined by interaction among the degenerate configurations pair by pair, i.e., factorization into *plus* and *minus* states. Further interaction among *plus* and *minus* states is of secondary importance, but not negligible.[35] The method for limiting the number of configurations, somewhat arbitrarily arrived at, was as follows: consider as a minimum all (singly excited) configurations which are within 3 ev of the lowest energy configuration of the particular symmetry representation. However, all singly excited configurations were taken into account for naphthalene. It was found that to within about one ev the conventional semi-empirical LCAO MO method could be used to estimate the configurational energy with respect to the ground state. That is,

$$\begin{aligned} E(V_{ij'})-E(V_0) &\sim 1.7+2.6(k_i-k_{j'}) \text{ ev}, \\ E(T_{ij'})-E(V_0) &\sim 2.9(k_i-k_{j'}) \text{ ev}, \end{aligned} \tag{80}$$

where $(k_{j'}-k_i)\beta$ would be the usual result of the conventional method. These equations, however, should not be used to extrapolate the results of the present method to infinitely long polyacenes.

The number of configurations which were eventually used can easily be counted in Tables V–VIII. This number for the singlets is approximately $15+5n$, where n is the number of rings ($n\neq 1$); for the triplets it is approximately $14+5n$.

Nevertheless, to remain consistent with the calculation for benzene, all, or nearly all, singly excited states should be interacted. Since this was not done for anthracene, naphthacene, and pentacene, the calculated energies for the lower states will be slightly high, i.e., by roughly 0.1–0.5 ev. However, interaction with the highest energy configuration in benzene, especially for $^3B_{1u}$, was neglected; hence, the corresponding results for the lowest $^3B_{2u}$ states of the polyacenes can be expected to be about right but perhaps too low for naphthalene by a few tenths ev. The calculated intensities are more sensitive than the energies to variation of the wave functions.[33] The extent of configuration interaction can influence these results considerably, by as much as a factor of two or three for the oscillator strength. Nevertheless, reasonably correct relative values should be expected from the calculation.

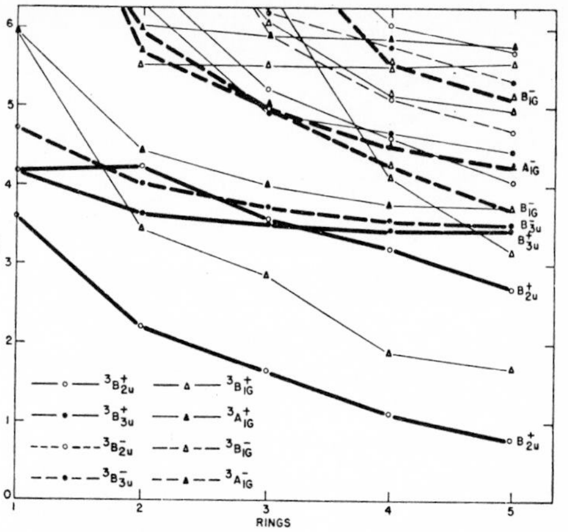

FIG. 3. Calculated polyacene lower triplet states. Heavy lines emphasize the states which are probably the more interesting from an experimental point of view.

It is of some interest that the lowering of the ground configuration energy by interaction with singly excited states is very small. For naphthalene, anthracene, naphthacene, and pentacene this lowering amounts to 0.0246 ev, 0.0501 ev, 0.0543 ev, and 0.0552 ev, respectively. This indicates that the conventional semi-empirical LCAO MO's are very close to Roothaan's self-consistent LCAO MO's,[14] where in the latter case all interaction of singly excited configurations with the ground configuration would vanish.[36] To test this as

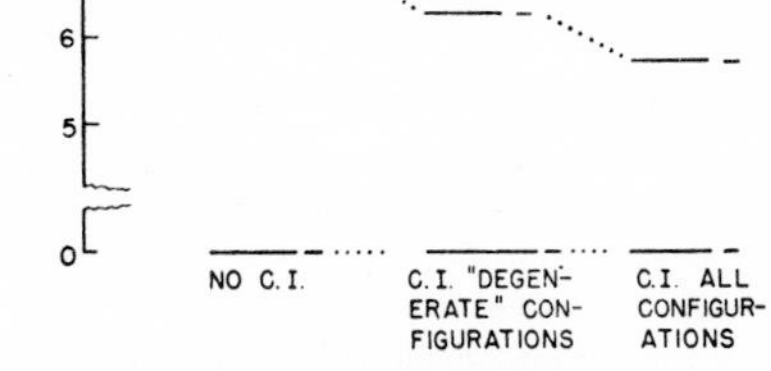

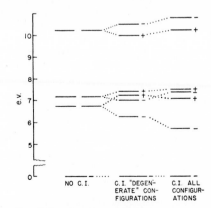

FIG. 4. The effect of configuration interaction on naphthalene $^1A_{1g}$ states.

[35] See also Moffitt,[28] who has called interaction with degenerate configurations "first-order configuration interaction" and that with higher energy configurations "second-order configuration interaction."

[36] R. Lefebvre, Compt. rend. **237**, 1158 (1953).

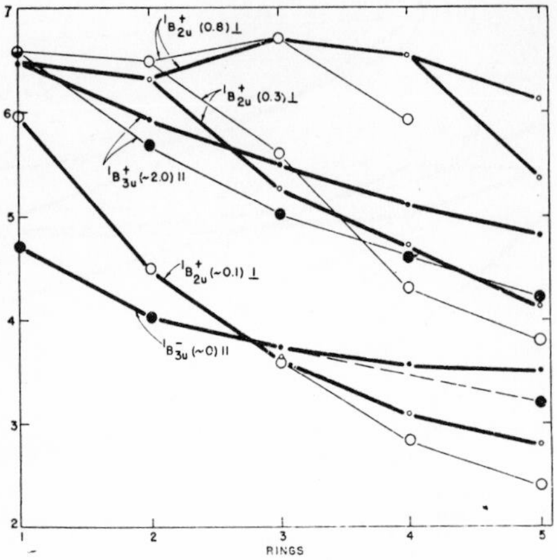

FIG. 5. Comparison of experimental and calculated singlet states. The experimental points (references in the text) are represented by large circles. Numbers in brackets are approximate average experimental oscillator strengths[23]; see Tables V through VIII for calculated oscillator strengths.

well as other hypotheses, the energy spectrum of naphthalene was recalculated by using all the same integrals, but employing perimeter MO's.[28] The most striking feature of the results, summarized in Table X, is the lowering of the ground states with respect to the ground configuration by as much as 0.9382 ev. The excited state energies are generally not altered by a corresponding amount. In fact, comparison of Tables V and X shows that agreement for the excited states is reasonably good, although a number of inversions in the order of states with energy occur. Perhaps, the most serious of these is the inverstion of the order of lower singlet "u" states: conventional MO's give, with increasing energy, $^1B_{3u}^-$, $^1B_{2u}^+$, $^1B_{3u}^+$, $^1B_{2u}^+$, whereas perimeter MO's give $^1B_{3u}^-$, $^1B_{2u}^+$, $^1B_{2u}^+$, $^1B_{3u}^+$. According to Sec. IX, experiment apparently supports the conventional MO result. It seems important to start with the best possible set of MO's in order to minimize the effects of configuration interaction. The interaction of all singly excited states in naphthalene fell considerably short of obliterating the difference between conventional and perimeter LCAO MO's. The conventional LCAO MO's appear as a good compromise and represent a type of "average" set of self-consistent MO's for the ground and singly excited states.

IX. COMPARISON WITH EXPERIMENTAL SPECTRA

In comparing theory with experiment, one should bear in mind the existing experimental, as well as theoretical, uncertainties. The observed emission or absorption bands are often several tenths ev wide. It is difficult to determine accurately the purely electronic transition energy and intensity. With a few exceptions the experimental polarizations are unknown. For the present discussion the position of the maximum of many of the experimental absorption bands is taken as a measure of the energy of the excited states, and the estimated total oscillator strength is taken as the purely electronic oscillator strength. Further experimental complications arise as a result of solvent interaction. To compensate partially for these uncertainties, the absorption spectrum of benzene in hexane was used in Sec. VII to evaluate the three empirical parameters. The theoretical uncertainties due to limited configuration interaction have been discussed in the last section. One should emphasize that the calculated energies and wave functions become less reliable as their energy increases.

Consider first the singlets; the calculated spectrum is quite complex. Upon closer examination one realizes, however, that the majority of states are forbidden by dipole transition with respect to the ground state. These are the triplet states, the g states, and the *minus* states, since the ground state is $^1A_{1g}^-$. The number of easily observable bands is therefore quite small. In Fig. 5 the absorption maxima as given by Clar[37] and by Klevens and Platt[23] are compared with theory.

Consider the two lowest band systems, the long axis polarized $^1B_{3u}^-$ and the short axis polarized $^1B_{2u}^+$.

TABLE X.[a] Calculated energies and intensities for naphthalene excited states (Perimeter MO's).

State	Energy (ev)	f	State	Energy (ev)	f
$^1A_{1g}^-$	−0.938	Ref.	$^3A_{1g}^-$		
	5.870	0		5.542	0.074
	7.425	0		7.060	0.370
	10.679	0		10.434	
$^1A_{1g}^+$	6.777	0	$^3A_{1g}^+$	4.440	0
	7.174	0		5.260	0
	9.984	0		9.175	0
$^1B_{1g}^-$	5.431	0	$^3B_{1g}^-$	5.431	0.361
	7.928	0		7.928	0.002
	12.409	0		12.409	
$^1B_{1g}^+$	5.155	0	$^3B_{1g}^+$	3.462	0
	7.500	0		5.179	0
	10.903	0		10.367	0
$^1B_{2u}^-$	8.901	0	$^3B_{2u}^-$	8.901	0
$^1B_{2u}^+$	4.142	0.301	$^3B_{2u}^+$	1.914	Ref.
	5.680	0.436		3.852	0
	7.519	0.990		6.060	0
	8.495			7.236	0
	10.744			10.095	0
	13.233			12.900	0
$^1B_{3u}^-$	3.627	0	$^3B_{3u}^-$	3.627	0
	7.796	0		7.796	0
	8.835	0		8.835	0
$^1B_{3u}^+$	6.338	2.495	$^3B_{3u}^+$	3.358	0
	7.733	0.038		5.736	0
	9.402			9.402	0

[a] See notes to Table V. Note that in this table the ground *configuration* V_0 is placed at the reference of zero energy.

[37] E. Clar, *Aromatische Kohlenwasserstoffe* (Springer-Verlag, Berlin, 1952), second edition.

The calculated and observed energies are in agreement. The calculated intensities are also satisfactory, although they are usually too high on an absolute basis. The corresponding assignment for benzene, i.e., in terms of the states $^1B_{1u}$ and $^1B_{2u}$, is also supported by other experimental evidence; a review has been given by Craig.[38]

Recently McClure[39] has been able to resolve the polarization of the two lowest singlet transitions in naphthalene. Using a mixed crystal of naphthalene in durene, he was able to orient the naphthalene molecule without inducing serious perturbations of its spectrum. He demonstrates convincingly that the lowest transition is long axis polarized ($^1B_{3u}^-$), while the second is short axis polarized ($^1B_{2u}^+$), being thus in complete agreement with theory. McClure further estimates $f=5\times10^{-4}$ for the electronic contribution to the $^1B_{3u}^-$ transition. Realization that the predicted $f=0$ strongly hinges on the assumption of zero differential overlap makes the agreement gratifying.

The very strong $^1B_{3u}^+$ bands also appear to be in agreement with experiment, both as to position and intensity. The calculated energy shows its largest deviation here for the case of pentacene, the predicted value being about 0.6 ev too high. However, this discrepancy should disappear when all singly excited states are interacted for pentacene as they have been for naphthalene. With regard to polarization recent experimental work by Craig *et al.*[40] on naphthalene suggests this band to be long axis polarized, in accordance with theory. The assignment for the lower $^1B_{3u}^-$, $^1B_{2u}^+$, and $^1B_{3u}^+$ band systems is thus completely in agreement with the inter-relations of these bands according to Klevens and Platt.[23]

The present calculations cannot be expected to yield accurate results for energies above about 7 ev. Nevertheless, an attempt is made here (Fig. 5) to assign some of the higher energy transitions to the predicted $^1B_{2u}^+$ states. The calculated energies and f numbers seem to be in acceptable agreement with experiment. The second lowest $^1B_{2u}^+$ system, which is predicted to cross the $^1B_{3u}^+$ system, corresponds to Clar's[37] α' bands for naphthacene and pentacene.

Figure 6 compares the experimental triplets chiefly with those theoretical triplets which are most likely by transition from the ground state, as well as those which correspond to allowed transitions with respect to the lowest triplet. These should be the most easily observable triplets.

The lowest triplets have been studied experimentally by many workers.[22,41] McGlynn, Padhye, and Kasha[42] have reconfirmed the position of the lowest anthracene triplet and have measured this transition for naphthacene. Their measurements agree with the theoretical values for the lowest $^3B_{2u}^+$ states. Using a different technique, Reid[43] has attempted to associate the emission from polyacene-trinitrobenzene complexes with the lowest triplet. This emission may be related to one of the higher triplets, such as $^3B_{3u}^+$, but it does not seem to be in simple correspondence with the lowest predicted $^3B_{2u}^+$ states.

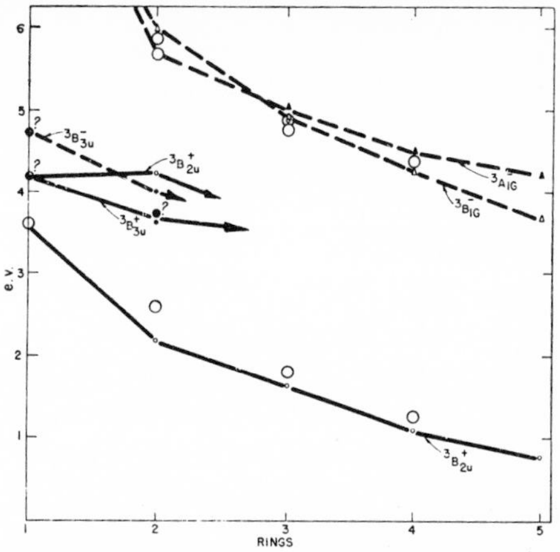

FIG. 6. Comparison of experimental and calculated triplet states. The experimental points (references in the text) are represented by large circles. See Tables V through VIII for calculated oscillator strengths of $T\rightarrow T$ transitions.

If one considers the higher energy triplets which might be observed by transition from the ground state, such as the second $^3B_{2u}^+$ and lowest $^3B_{3u}^+$ states, the experimental information is very scanty. It has been pointed out by Dr. J. S. Ham, of this laboratory, that the predicted $^3E_{1u}$ state of benzene is near the weak absorption at 4.2 ev, observed by Miss Pitts.[44] There is also some evidence for a singlet-triplet absorption in benzene at 4.9 ev,[45] which could be due to $^3B_{2u}$, which this theory places at 4.7 ev. McClure[46] has reported a very weak absorption in naphthelene crystal at 3.7 ev. He suspects this to be a triplet, and it is in accord with the calculated value for $^3B_{3u}^+$.

Triplet-triplet transitions in benzene, naphthalene, and anthracene in rigid glasses were first investigated by McClure[47] and also by Craig and Ross.[48] Very recently Porter and Windsor,[49] working with liquid system, have confirmed this earlier work and have extended the polyacene series to include naphthacene. In addition, they have been able to investigate a considerably wider spectral range. The lower $T\rightarrow T$ transi-

[38] D. P. Craig, Rev. Pure and Applied Chem. **3**, 207 (1953).
[39] D. S. McClure, J. Chem. Phys. **22**, 1668 (1954).
[40] Craig, Hobbins, and Walsh, J. Chem. Phys. **22**, 1616 (1954).
[41] McClure, Blake, and Hanst, J. Chem. Phys. **22**, 255 (1954); Ferguson, Iredale, and Taylor, J. Chem. Soc. 3160 (1954).
[42] McGlynn, Padhye, and Kasha, J. Chem. Phys. **23**, 593 (1955).
[43] C. Reid, J. Chem. Phys. **20**, 1212, 1214 (1952).
[44] A. C. Pitts, J. Chem. Phys. **18**, 1416 (1950).
[45] J. S. Ham, J. Chem. Phys. **21**, 756 (1953).
[46] D. S. McClure, private communication, letter May 10, 1954.
[47] D. S. McClure, J. Chem. Phys. **19**, 670 (1951).
[48] D. P. Craig and I. G. Ross, J. Chem. Soc. 1589 (1954).
[49] G. Porter and M. W. Windsor, Discussions Faraday Soc. **178**, (1954).

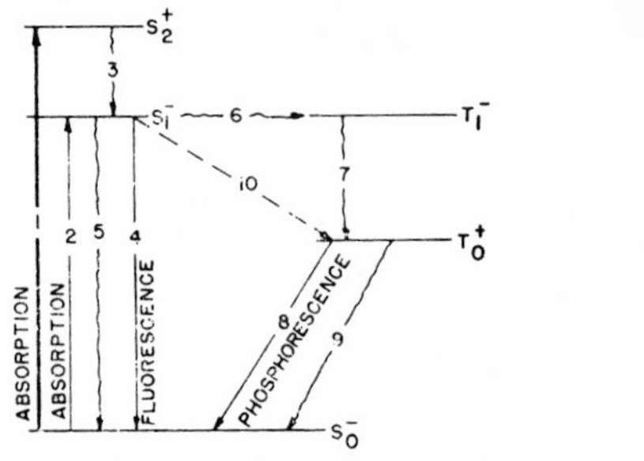

FIG. 7. Schematic representation of transition processes, illustrating the singlet-to-triplet radiationless transition through steps (6) and (7).

tions correspond well with the lowest theoretically allowed ${}^3B_{1g}{}^-$ and ${}^3A_{1g}{}^-$ states (Fig. 6). These transitions are established as being definitely allowed.[48,49] A doublet absorption band appears for both naphthalene and anthracene, but it has not as yet been experimentally established that this corresponds to two separate electronic states as would be compatible with the theory.[50] Experimentally the ratio of the extinction coefficients of the doublet bands is about 4, with the lower energy absorption always the stronger. Theoretically the ratio of oscillator strengths of ${}^3B_{1g}{}^-$ to ${}^3A_{1g}{}^-$ is also about 4, with the stronger ${}^3B_{1g}{}^-$ being lower in all polyacenes except naphthalene. This inversion, however, is not serious, since the two states are very close together. In fact, the use of perimeter MO's achieves the right order; see Table X. In naphthacene the lowest $T \rightarrow T$ transition is broad and complicated (since it overlies the singlet absorption), but it falls at the calculated energy. In benzene photochemical decomposition occurs preventing a precise study.

Higher $T \rightarrow T$ transitions were observed in naphthalene and anthracene, giving rise to continuous absorption below 2600 A and 2800 A, respectively. This locates the next higher allowed triplets for naphthalene and anthracene at about 7.4 ev and 6.3 ev above the ground state, which may be compared with the theoretical 7.351 ev and 6.799 ev, respectively, for the allowed transitions to the second ${}^3A_{1g}{}^-$ states.

[50] Craig and Ross[48] report *three* closely spaced absorption maxima for naphthalene, the third and highest energy band being very weak. If the view expressed here that these bands correspond to separate electronic transitions is correct, then this weak absorption may be a transition to ${}^3A_{1g}{}^+$ which is calculated to be at 6.020 ev (see Table V) above the ground state. Its intensity may be enhanced by "borrowing" from the allowed ${}^3A_{1g}{}^-$ and ${}^3B_{1g}{}^-$ states. In anthracene the corresponding ${}^3A_{1g}{}^+$ is further removed from the allowed system; similar reasons may account for the lack of observation of transitions to ${}^3B_{1g}{}^+$. However, some very recent results by Dr. Porter and Dr. Wright, reported to the author by private communication, indicate five bands for naphthalene in the vapor state. Porter and Wright point out that these may correspond to two electronic states located at about 5.75 ev and 6.25 ev above the ground state; this would also be in substantial agreement with the theory.

APPLICATION TO PHOSPHORESCENCE

A number of difficulties exist with regard to the interpretation of experimental results especially in the matter of transitions between singlet and triplet states. Porter and Windsor[49] emphasizes one such difficulty. This is caused by the observation that the radiationless transition probability in going from the lowest excited singlet state to the lowest triplet state is about 10^4 times greater than that in going from the lowest triplet to the singlet ground state. Since the two singlet-triplet energy intervals are about the same, one might expect the two transitions to take place with equally low probabilities. In actual fact, however, the transition from lowest excited singlet to lowest triplet must occur at a rate comparable with the singlet to singlet fluorescence process and radiationless transition. Otherwise, no phosphorescence would be observed. Bearing on this are the observations of Lewis and Kasha[22] on lycopene, a long chain polyene. The all *trans* form of lycopene shows very little phosphorescence or fluorescence. However, after producing some of the *cis* forms,[51] one observes a well-defined phosphorescence. Could it be that the isomerization in lycopene has greatly increased its singlet to lowest triplet transition rate? Lewis and Kasha report what may be a similar observation for stilbene, where the *trans* form exhibits a strong fluorescence but no phosphorescence, while the *cis* form shows phosphorescence, but no fluorescence. Also butadiene, probably a mixture of *trans* and *cis*, shows no detectable phosphorescence. However, in the case of *trans*-stilbene and butadiene, reasons other than a low singlet to triplet transition rate may account for their behavior.[22]

A possible explanation for the characteristics of the excited singlet to lowest triplet transition can be found through application of some of the rules advanced in Sec. IV. For alternant hydrocarbons one would expect that the lowest triplet, which is also the lowest excited state, is always a *plus* state, designated here by $T_0{}^+$. The ground state is always a *minus* state, designated by $S_0{}^-$. On the other hand, the lowest excited singlet state, S_1, may be either *plus* or *minus*. Now assume first that it is a *minus* state, or $S_1{}^-$. In the general result for *minus* states (Sec. IV), there exists a triplet state, $T_1{}^-$, which has the same energy as $S_1{}^-$.[52] One can now put forward the mechanism in Fig. 7, which includes the more important steps.

Absorption is chiefly by some higher singlet *plus* states, $S_2{}^+$ in step (1), since dipole transitions between the ground state and *minus* states are formally forbidden. Step (3), as well as (7), is assumed to take place very rapidly, i.e., $k_3 \sim k_7 \sim 10^{11}$ sec^{-1}. Both steps (4) and (5) are taken to be relatively slow, $k_4 \sim k_5 \sim 10^6$ sec^{-1}, for this type of transition; step (4) is formally forbidden

[51] Zechmeister, LeRosen, Schroeder, Polgár, and Pauling, J. Am. Chem. Soc. 65, 1940 (1943).

[52] This is true when self-consistent MO's are used. For an arbitrary set of MO's, $E(S_1{}^-) \geq E(T_1{}^-)$, since $S_1{}^-$ may interact with the ground state, $S_0{}^-$.

TABLE XI. Bond orders and bond distances for naphthalene.[a]

Bond[b]	1–2	3–3′	1–1′	2–3
Perimeter MO's, no C.I.	0.6472 (1.367)	0.1000 (1.485)	0.6472 (1.367)	0.6472 (1.367)
Perimeter MO's+C.I.[c]	0.7197 (1.368)	0.3841 (1.433)	0.6066 (1.389)	0.5628 (1.398)
Conv. LCAO MO's, no C.I.[d]	0.7246 (1.373)	0.5182 (1.413)	0.6032 (1.395)	0.5547 (1.405)
Conv. LCAO MO's+C.I.[c]	0.7434 (1.371)	0.5488 (1.407)	0.5867 (1.400)	0.5353 (1.410)
SCF MO's[e]	0.78 (1.366)	0.60 (1.398)	0.54 (1.410)	0.50 (1.418)
Observed[f]	(1.365)	(1.393)	(1.404)	(1.425)

[a] The bond distances in A are given in brackets, calculated as described in the text. Numbers not in brackets are the bond orders, as defined in this paper. 1 is often added to these bond orders to give the total bond order, including the σ electrons.
[b] Bonds are numbered according to Fig. 1.
[c] Includes interaction of all singly excited configurations with the ground configuration.
[d] Coulson's *et al.* results (reference 57) for the distance have been adjusted to give the experimental mean.
[e] See footnote 13.
[f] See footnote 54.

and (5) is over a relatively large energy separation between S_0^- and S_1^-. Competing with (3) and (4), is the important singlet to triplet transition expressed by (6) Compared to other singlet to triplet transitions, this one should be considerably more probable, caused by the degeneracy of S_1^- and T_1^-. Now, both (9) and (10) can be expected to proceed slowly, $k_9 \sim k_{10} \sim 10^2$ sec^{-1}, since they represent *direct* triplet to singlet transitions, separated by a large energy. Thus, it seems quite plausible that the *net* process of $S_1^- \rightarrow T_0^+$ proceeds at a considerably faster rate than the direct transition $T_0^+ \rightarrow S_0^-$.

If, on the other hand, S_1^+ should be the lowest excited singlet state and it is not nearly degenerate with some *minus* state or triplet state, then a mechanism similar to Fig. 7 would not apply. Phosphorescence in this case would probably not be observed, since in addition the transition probability of S_1^+ to the ground state would be relatively high.

The spectra of many condensed ring systems have been analyzed by Klevens and Platt.[23] They find that in the vast majority of cases the lowest excited singlet is a ^1L_b state, or a *minus* state by the present terminology. Possible exceptions occur only in "long" systems, such as anthracene, naphthacene, and pentacene; but even in these, the lowest excited minus singlet is very close to the lowest excited singlet state. Support for these assignments is also given by Moffitt's calculations[28] and by the results in Sec. IX. The effects of configuration interaction are of primary importance in determining whether the lowest excited singlet is a *plus* or *minus* state. In this connection, Platt's[53] discussion of "round field" and "long field" types of configuration interaction is illuminating. Thus, one would expect a *minus* state to be the lowest excited singlet in most condensed ring systems (i.e. "round field"). However, in all-*trans*-polyenes or in *trans*-stilbene (i.e. "long field") the *plus* excited singlet is definitely the lower. But as the field becomes rounder through some isomerization to *cis*, it seems likely that the energy of separation between the lowest *minus* and *plus* singlets would decrease, with the possibility that the *minus* state might even become the lowest excited singlet. More detailed experimental and theoretical work is needed to settle this point. An indication of the effect is evident in a calculation for butadiene.[1] The order of the excited singlets for *trans*-butadiene is $^1B_1^+$, $^1A_1^+$, $^1A_1^-$, while for *cis*-butadiene it is $^1B_1^+$, $^1A_1^-$, $^1A_1^+$. In both cases, however, $^1A_1^-$ is more than 1 ev above $^1B_1^+$.

Almost all of the hydrocarbon condensed ring systems tabulated by Lewis and Kasha,[22] Craig and Ross,[48] and Porter and Windsor[49] fall into the "round field" class, and the mechanism of Fig. 7 could be applicable. A slightly modified form of this mechanism could also apply to anthracene and naphthacene. Here the lowest excited singlet is probably a *plus* state, but it is nearly degenerate with a *minus* state. On the other hand, all-*trans*-lycopene, *trans*-stilbene, and butadiene may be examples where the triplet state is difficult to populate. The appearance of phosphorescence in some of the *cis* compounds may then be brought about through the change from the "long field" spectrum towards a "round field" spectrum.

In nonalternant hydrocarbons the degeneracy of *minus* singlet and triplet states is removed. For this reason the phosphorescence efficiency would be predicted to fall off. The introduction of hetero-atoms would also remove the singlet-triplet degeneracy, However, in this case compensating factors exist which help to increase the singlet to triplet transition probability.[54]

XI. BOND ORDER AND CHARGE DENSITY

As is pointed out in Sec. IV, the π electron charge density at each C atom is always unity within the present approximation when only singly excited configurations are considered in interaction with the ground configuration.

The bond orders, however, are different from those obtained by the conventional semiempirical LCAO MO method. Tables XI and XII compare the bond orders and distances for naphthalene and anthracene, computed by various procedures, with the experimental results.[55] All calculated bond distances are obtained

[53] J. R. Platt, J. Chem. Phys. 18, 1168 (1950).

[54] D. S. McClure, J. Chem. Phys. 17, 905 (1949); M. Kasha, J. Chem. Phys. 20, 71 (1952); M. Kasha, Discussions Faraday Soc. No. 9, 14 (1950).

[55] J. M. Robertson, *Organic Crystals and Molecules* (Cornell University Press, Ithaca, 1953), p. 192.

TABLE XII. Bond orders and bond distances for anthracene.[a]

Bond[b]	1–2	3–4	1–1′	2–3	3–3′
Conv. LCAO MO's, no C.I.[c]	0.7318 (1.379)	0.6014 (1.403)	0.5814 (1.407)	0.5313 (1.417)	0.4812 (1.427)
Conv. LCAO MO's+C.I.[d]	0.7666 (1.374)	0.6074 (1.402)	0.5552 (1.412)	0.5083 (1.422)	0.5047 (1.422)
Observed[e]	(1.370)	(1.396)	(1.408)	(1.423)	(1.436)

[a,b,c] See Table XI, references a, b, and d, respectively.
[d] Includes interaction of the ground configuration with all singly excited configurations except the two (degenerate) configurations of highest energy.
[e] See reference 54.

from Coulson's[56] formula,

$$\text{bond distance} = s - \frac{s-d}{1+0.765(1-b)/b}, \quad (81)$$

where b is the bond order as defined in this paper, $s=1.542$ A, and $d=1.340$ A; the values so obtained are then adjusted to give the experimental mean by subtracting a constant increment from each calculated distance.[13]

Consider naphthalene first (Table XI); better agreement with experiment is obtained upon inclusion of configuration interaction. Conventional LCAO MO's appear to be generally superior to perimeter MO's. Conventional MO's with configuration interaction predict the longest and shortest bonds correctly, although the order of bonds $3-3'$ and $1-1'$ is still inverted. On the other hand, Pople[13] has applied a theoretical method which is based on essentially the same approximations as the method employed here. However, he has used different numerical values for the integrals and rather than invoking configuration interaction, has calculated the self-consistent field MO's[12] for the ground state. His results place the bonds in their correct order. Whether this comes about through application of self-consistent MO's or as a result of different integral values is not clear at present.

In the case of anthracene (Table XII), little, if anything, is added to the conventional molecular orbital bond orders[57] through the inclusion of configuration interaction. The results in both cases are in good correspondence with experiment.

XII. CONCLUSION

The results of the present theoretical method as it is applied to the calculation of polyacene spectra appear to be in satisfactory quantitative agreement with the available experimental information. On this basis a number of existing assignments are confirmed, and some new assignments are proposed. It would seem that the theoretical results may now serve as a guide to the location of electronic bands which have, as yet, not been experimentally observed.

The general rules of Sec. IV for alternant hydrocarbons could possibly serve as a valuable tool for the qualitative interpretation of a variety of experimental observations. As an example, use is made of them in formulating a mechanism for singlet-triplet transitions which lead to phosphorescence and related phenomena. However, more experimental evidence is needed to put this hypothesis on a firm footing.

The present calculations clearly bring out the importance of starting with a reasonably good set of molecular orbitals if interaction is to be limited to singly excited configurations. The conventional LCAO MO's are satisfactory for the computation of spectra. They also appear to be close to the best possible (self-consistent) MO's for the ground state. Some of their deficiencies may be corrected by configuration interaction, as is exemplified by a considerably better correlation of bond order with distance for naphthalene.

Previously the present theory had been applied to the perturbation of the benzene and ethylene spectrum upon hetero-atom substitution.[58] There is good reason to believe that the calculated spectral effects of aza-substitution, for example, in the polyacenes would also be in agreement with experiment. However, the present method has, as yet, not been applied to the calculation of strong hetero-atom effects or to non-alternant conjugated systems. A test of this method applied to these more complex systems appears to be in order.

XIII. ACKNOWLEDGMENTS

The author is greatly indebted to Professor R. G. Parr and to Dr. J. S. Ham for numerous helpful discussions, their interest, and constant encouragement. He wishes to express his sincerest thanks to Professor D. S. McClure, Professor M. Kasha, Professor J. R. Platt, and Dr. G. Porter for discussing many of their experimental results and interpretations with him. He is sincerely grateful to Dr. P. Lykos, Professor W. Moffit, Professor C. C. J. Roothaan, Dr. K. Rüdenberg, and Professor H. Shull for informative discussions. Finally, it is a pleasure to thank the management and members of this laboratory, without whose cooperation and support this work would not have been possible.

[56] C. A. Coulson, Proc. Roy. Soc. (London) **A169**, 413 (1939).
[57] Coulson, Daudel, and Robertson, Proc. Roy. Soc. (London) **A207**, 306 (1951).
[58] See in particular the second and fourth papers under reference 1. The fourth paper also discusses the calculation of ionization potentials, where agreement with experiment is more difficult to attain.

APPENDIX: NUMERICAL RESULTS FOR NAPHTHALENE

The numerical calculations for naphthalene are summarized in Tables IA, IIA, and IIIA.

Table IIIA gives the final energies and wave functions after all singly excited configurations have been interacted. Energies and wave functions after factorization into *plus* and *minus* states according to Sec. IV are directly obtained from Table IIA. The energies of the various configurations before any configuration interaction and the interaction matrix elements are easily calculated. For example,

$$E(V_{ij'})=E(V_{ji'})=\{V_{ij'}|V_{ji'}\}$$
$$=\tfrac{1}{2}[\{{}^1\Omega_{ij'}{}^+|{}^1\Omega_{ij'}{}^+\}+\{{}^1\Omega_{ij'}{}^-|{}^1\Omega_{ij'}{}^-\}]$$
$$\{V_{ij'}|V_{ji'}\}=\tfrac{1}{2}[\{{}^1\Omega_{ij'}{}^+|{}^1\Omega_{ij'}{}^+\}-\{{}^1\Omega_{ij'}{}^-|{}^1\Omega_{ij'}{}^-\}].$$

As an illustration, for $V_{2,5'}$ from the first two matrices of Table IIA:

$$E(V_{2,5'})=E_{(5,2')}=\tfrac{1}{2}[7.3705+7.0013]=7.1859 \text{ ev.}$$
$$\{V_{2,5'}|V_{5,2'}\}=\tfrac{1}{2}[7.3705-7.0013]=0.1846 \text{ ev.}$$

Any other matrix element is readily obtained in a similar manner, through application of Eq. (41) and rules 1 and 2, Sec. IV.

TABLE IA.[a] *Naphthalene molecular orbitals.*

k	Symm.	$p \to$ / $\mu \to$; i, $\lambda\pm$ ↓	1 (1)	2 (2)	3 (3)	4 (4)	5 (5)	6 (5′)	7 (4′)	8 (3′)	9 (2′)	10 (1′)
2.30278	b_{1u}	1 (1+)	0.23070	0.30055	0.46140	0.30055	0.23070	0.23070	0.30055	0.46140	0.30055	0.23070
1.61803	b_{2g}	2 (2+)	0.42533	0.26287	0.00000	−0.26287	−0.42533	−0.42533	−0.26287	0.00000	0.26287	0.42533
1.30278	b_{3g}	3 (1−)	0.17352	0.39959	0.34705	0.39959	0.17352	−0.17352	−0.39959	−0.34705	−0.39959	−0.17352
1.00000	b_{1u}	4 (3+)	0.40825	0.00000	−0.40825	0.00000	0.40825	0.40825	0.00000	−0.40825	0.00000	0.40825
0.61803	a_{1u}	5 (2−)	0.26287	0.42533	0.00000	−0.42533	−0.26287	0.26287	0.42533	0.00000	−0.42533	−0.26287
−0.61803	b_{2g}	5′ (4+)	0.26287	−0.42533	0.00000	0.42533	−0.26287	−0.26287	0.42533	0.00000	−0.42533	0.26287
−1.00000	b_{3g}	4′ (3−)	0.40825	0.00000	−0.40825	0.00000	0.40825	−0.40825	0.00000	0.40825	0.00000	−0.40825
−1.30278	b_{1u}	3′ (5+)	0.17352	−0.39959	0.34705	−0.39959	0.17352	0.17352	−0.39959	0.34705	−0.39959	0.17352
−1.61803	a_{1u}	2′ (4−)	0.42533	−0.26287	0.00000	0.26287	−0.42533	0.42533	−0.26287	0.00000	0.26287	−0.42533
−2.30278	b_{3g}	1′ (5−)	0.23070	−0.30055	0.46140	−0.30055	0.23070	−0.23070	0.30055	−0.46140	0.30055	−0.23070

[a] p and μ label the AO's according to Secs. IV and V, respectively (see Fig. 2); i and $\lambda\pm$ number the MO's according to Secs. IV and V. Columns (5)–(14) list the MO coefficients C_{pi} or $C_{\mu\lambda}$.

TABLE IIA.[a,b] Naphthalene: configurational secular equations.

$^1A_{1g}{}^-$	(0)	(3,4′−4,3′)	(5,2′−2,5′)	(1,3′−3,1′)
	0.0000	−0.3889	0.0891	0.0973
$^3A_{1g}{}^-$		6.2534	−0.8552	−0.5709
			7.0013	0.6552
				10.4760

$^1A_{1g}{}^+$	(3,4′+4,3′)	(5,2′+2,5′)	(1,3′+3,1′)
	7.2136	−0.2024	0.3957
		7.3705	−0.3970
			10.0714

$^3A_{1g}{}^+$	(5,2′+2,5′)	(3,4′+4,3′)	(1,3′+3,1′)
	5.4702	−1.1758	−1.3379
		5.8723	0.8659
			8.5291

$^1B_{1g}{}^-$; $^3B_{1g}{}^-$	(5,3′−3,5′)	(4,2′−2,4′)	(2,1′−1,2′)
	6.0004	−0.0972	−0.4097
		8.5397	−1.1943
			12.1170

$^1B_{1g}{}^+$	(5,3′+3,5′)	(4,2′+2,4′)	(2,1′+1,2′)
	5.4918	−0.0900	−0.1763
		7.5347	−0.1329
			11.0284

$^3B_{1g}{}^+$	(5,3′+3,5′)	(4,2′+2,4′)	(2,1′+1,2′)
	3.6482	−0.2234	−1.0923
		5.6285	−1.0394
			10.2011

$^1B_{2u}{}^-$; $^3B_{2u}{}^-$	(4,1′−1,4′)
	9.2061

$^1B_{2u}{}^+$	(5,5′)	(4,4′)	(3,3′)	(4,1′+1,4′)	(2,2′)	(1,1′)
	4.6147	−0.4218	0.3234	0.1481	−0.0578	0.2722
		6.3051	−0.1637	0.4633	−0.5415	0.1861
			8.1419	−0.0013	0.1919	−0.1092
				9.3675	−0.9884	0.6133
					10.3284	−0.4342
						13.1119

$^3B_{2u}{}^+$	(5,5′)	(4,4′)	(3,3′)	(4,1′+1,4′)	(2,2′)	(1,10′)
	2.7320	−0.1820	−1.1761	−0.2059	−0.7655	−0.3758
		4.6123	−0.1950	0.5682	−1.4556	−0.5927
			6.7357	0.2086	−0.3163	−0.9734
				8.0208	−1.5794	1.1437
					9.2646	−0.9580
						12.1407

$^1B_{3u}{}^-$; $^3B_{3u}{}^-$	(4,5′−5,4′)	(5,1′−1,5′)	(3,2′−2,3′)
	4.2449	−0.5464	0.9525
		8.0504	−0.2456
			8.7618

$^1B_{3u}{}^+$	(4,5′+5,4′)	(5,1′+1,5′)	(3,2′+2,3′)
	6.1047	0.3348	−0.5165
		8.3598	0.8580
			8.9858

$^3B_{3u}{}^+$	(4,5′+5,4′)	(5,1′+1,5′)	(3,2′+2,3′)
	3.8808	0.2553	−1.0786
		7.2987	−1.7476
			8.1292

[a] All matrix elements are in ev. Since all matrices are real symmetric, e.g., $H_{mn}=H_{nm}$, only the "upper half" is tabulated.
Symbols of the type (0), ii', and $(ij'\pm ji')$ label the matrix elements; they stand, respectively, for V_0, $V_{ii'}$, or $T_{ii'}$, and ${}^1\Omega_{ij}{}^\pm \equiv 2^{-\frac{1}{2}}(V_{ij'}\pm V_{ji'})$ or ${}^3\Omega_{ij}{}^\pm = 2^{-\frac{1}{2}}(T_{ij'}\pm T_{ji'})$. Designation of the wave functions as + or −, singlet or triplet, is given by the two superscripts on the symmetry label for each matrix.
The diagonal elements are the expectation energies for V_0, $V_{ii'}$, $V_{ii'}$, or ${}^{1,3}\Omega_{ij}{}^\pm$, as the case may be; they are all expressed with reference to zero energy for V_0.
[b] First matrix is for $^1A_{1g}{}^-$; matrix with first row and column removed is for $^3A_{1g}{}^-$.

TABLE IIIA.[a] Naphthalene: state energies and wave functions.

$^1A_{1g}^-$	Energy (ev)	(0)	(3,4′−4,3′)	(5,2′−2,5)	(1,3′−3,1′)
Ψ_1	−0.0246	0.99813	0.06067	−0.00475	−0.00565
Ψ_2	5.7041	−0.04822	0.83828	0.54244	0.02679
Ψ_3	7.3344	0.03375	−0.51624	0.81385	−0.26459
Ψ_4	10.7167	0.01646	−0.16464	0.20828	0.96397

$^3A_{1g}^-$	Energy (ev)	(3,4′−4,3′)	(5,2′−2,5′)	(1,3′−3,1′)
Ψ_1	5.6906	0.84331	0.53674	−0.02711
Ψ_2	7.3260	−0.51202	0.81775	0.26292
Ψ_3	10.7138	0.16329	−0.20784	0.96444

$^1A_{1g}^+$	Energy (ev)	(3,4′+4,3′)	(5,2′+2,5′)	(1,3′+3,1′)
Ψ_1	7.0705	0.85430	0.51790	−0.04413
Ψ_2	7.3969	0.50048	−0.84254	−0.19911
Ψ_3	10.1881	−0.14030	0.14802	−0.97898

$^3A_{1g}^+$	Energy (ev)	(5,2′+2,5′)	(3,4′+4,3′)	(1,3′+3,1′)
Ψ_1	4.4104	0.81107	0.56688	0.14429
Ψ_2	5.9955	−0.43939	0.75324	−0.48946
Ψ_3	9.4657	0.38614	−0.33359	−0.86001

$^1B_{1g}^-$; $^3B_{1g}^-$	Energy (ev)	(5,3′−3,5′)	(4,2′−2,4′)	(2,1′−1,2′)
Ψ_1	5.9598	0.99393	0.07478	0.08064
Ψ_3	8.1978	−0.09466	0.95499	0.28112
Ψ_3	12.4995	−0.05599	−0.28704	0.95628

$^1B_{1g}^+$	Energy (ev)	(5,3′+3,5′)	(4,2′+2,4′)	(2,1′+1,2′)
Ψ_1	5.4819	0.99841	0.04590	0.03283
Ψ_2	7.5342	−0.04706	0.99826	0.03559
Ψ_3	11.0388	−0.03114	−0.03708	0.99883

$^3B_{1g}^+$	Energy (ev)	(5,3′+3,5′)	(4,2′+2,4′)	(2,1′+1,2′)
Ψ_1	3.3992	0.96610	0.18213	0.18297
Ψ_2	5.5012	−0.21260	0.96334	0.16364
Ψ_3	10.5773	−0.14646	−0.19699	0.96940

$^1B_{2u}^-$; $^3B_{2u}^-$	Energy (ev)	(4,1′−1,4′)
Ψ_1	9.2061	1.0000

$^1B_{2u}^+$	Energy (ev)	(5,5′)	(4,4′)	(3,3′)	(4,1′+1,4′)	(2,2′)	(1,1′)
Ψ_1	4.4688	0.96682	0.23643	−0.07683	−0.04265	0.02432	−0.03226
Ψ_2	6.2847	−0.23153	0.95596	0.11478	−0.10230	0.09427	0.00020
Ψ_3	8.1577	0.09883	−0.08973	0.97270	−0.11131	−0.15247	0.01980
Ψ_4	8.7529	0.02975	0.02716	0.17586	0.84430	0.50004	−0.06760
Ψ_5	10.8397	0.00630	−0.13614	0.05551	−0.46880	0.81908	0.29613
Ψ_6	13.3658	0.03091	0.05396	−0.02764	0.20666	−0.21529	0.95200

$^3B_{2u}^+$	Energy (ev)	(5,5′)	(4,4′)	(3,3′)	(4,1′+1,4′)	(2,2′)	(1,1′)
Ψ_1	2.1558	0.91929	0.20507	0.27354	0.03217	0.17192	0.08625
Ψ_2	4.1957	−0.26143	0.92986	0.02340	−0.09286	0.21889	0.09962
Ψ_3	6.6800	−0.13594	−0.06703	0.70356	−0.60251	−0.29202	0.18367
Ψ_4	7.2232	−0.25567	−0.12261	0.62169	0.61186	0.39768	0.02400
Ψ_5	10.2184	−0.05214	−0.27068	−0.17719	−0.39695	0.74517	0.42400
Ψ_6	13.0330	−0.00004	0.02247	−0.10829	0.30885	−0.35189	0.87667

$^1B_{3u}^-$; $^3B_{3u}^-$	Energy (ev)	(4,5′−5,4′)	(5,1′−1,5′)	(3,2′−2,3′)
Ψ_1	3.9935	0.97472	0.11987	−0.18853
Ψ_2	7.9850	−0.04670	0.93456	0.35274
Ψ_3	9.0786	0.21848	−0.33502	0.91653

$^1B_{3u}^+$	Energy (ev)	(4,5′+5,4′)	(5,1′+5,1′)	(3,2′+2,3′)
Ψ_1	5.9138	0.95369	−0.20707	0.21818
Ψ_2	7.9342	0.29268	0.80625	−0.51410
Ψ_3	9.6022	−0.06946	0.55414	0.82952

$^3B_{3u}^+$	Energy (ev)	(4,5′+5,4′)	(5,1′+1,5′)	(3,2′+2,3′)
Ψ_1	3.6144	0.96656	0.05212	0.25109
Ψ_2	6.0085	−0.19007	0.80291	0.56499
Ψ_3	9.6858	−0.17215	−0.59382	0.78597

[a] Columns (2)–(6) give the solution to the corresponding secular equations of Table IIA. Column (2) gives the eigenvalues with reference to zero energy for V_0. The row to the right of each eigenvalue is the corresponding eigenvector. The symbols (0), ii', and $(ij' \pm ji')$ label the coefficients multiplying the corresponding configurational functions (see Table IIA, footnote a) to give the final wave functions Ψ_m.

Reprinted from THE JOURNAL OF CHEMICAL PHYSICS, Vol. 25, No. 6, 1112–1116, December, 1956
Printed in U. S. A.

Electronic Spectrum and Structure of Azulene*

RUDOLPH PARISER
Jackson Laboratory, E. I. du Pont de Nemours and Co., Wilmington, Delaware
(Received January 12, 1956)

A previously given theoretical method is applied to the azulene molecule. π-electron energies, transtion moments, dipole moments, charge distributions, and bond orders are calculated for the ground state and for the lower singlet and triplet excited states.

The same detailed procedure which had previously given good results for the polyacenes is used here. Configuration interaction is included for all singly excited configurations. Two parallel calculations, one starting with conventional Hückel MOs and the other with perimeter MOs, are carried through.

Hückel MOs lead to numerical results in good agreement with available experimental spectral data. In this connection some previous assignments are confirmed and some new ones are proposed. For the π-electron dipole moment for the ground state, one calculates 1.88 D with Hückel MOs and 3.36 D with perimeter MOs; the experimental value is 1 D.

One may conclude that the present procedure gives results in substantial agreement with experiment provided that good MOs, e.g., Hückel MOs, are employed. For computation of excited state energies it is essential to include interaction among nearly degenerate configurations. More extensive configuration interaction, however, appears to improve the transition energies and especially the transition moments and dipole moments.

I. INTRODUCTION

AZULENE has received considerable attention from both a theoretical and experimental point of view. Although azulene is an isomer of naphthalene and like naphthalene has a bicyclic unsaturated structure, it differs greatly in its properties from aromatic molecules built up from six membered rings. In fact it is the geometry of this molecule, consisting, so to speak, of the fusion of a five and seven membered ring, which is chiefly responsible for its blue color and large dipole moment. It is the purpose of this note to add to the understanding of the spectral and other electronic properties of azulene through an attempt to calculate these by theoretical methods.

Early theoretical treatments[1–5] have achieved notable success in pointing out the basic causes for the dipole moment in azulene and for the bathochromic displacement of its spectrum relative to that of naphthalene, but quantitative agreement with experimental values has not been very satisfactory. Moffitt[6] has recently applied a semiempirical theory designed for catacondensed hydrocarbons to the lower excited singlet states in azulene, obtaining good results which are particularily valuable in giving a clear insight into the nature and origin of these states. Application of the nonempirical SCF LCAO method[7] by Julg[8,9] has been rather successful for the dipole moment but not for the energies of the lowest excited singlet and triplet; however, modification[10,12] of the one-center Coulomb integral improved these energies.

In the past few years a new theoretical method[11–13] has found considerable application to various problems in molecular spectra and structure. Very recently this method has produced good results for the polyacenes,[14] and its present application to azulene should serve as a further test of its validity and utility.

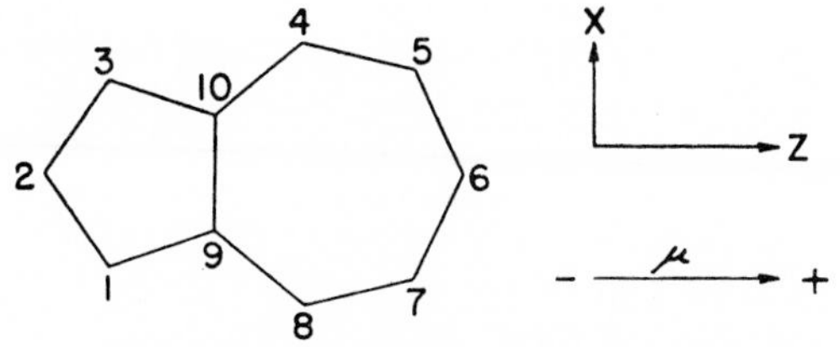

FIG. 1. The carbon skelton of azulene, the choice of axes, and the defined positive direction of the dipole moment.

II. METHOD AND PROCEDURE

The carbon skeleton structure of azulene is taken as in Fig. 1, with the sides of the regular pentagon and heptagon set equal to 1.390 A. The π-electronic states belong to the irreducible representations A_1 and B_1 of the symmetry group C_{2V}. Electronic transitions from the ground state, $^1A_1$, to other $^1A_1$ states will have the transition moment directed along the long, or z axis, whereas for transitions to $^1B_1$ states it will be directed along the short, or x axis.

The same detailed procedure which was used for naphthalene is used here.[14] As for naphthalene, two

* Presented at the Molecular Quantum Mechanics Conference, Austin, Texas, December 8, 1955.
[1] A. L. Sklar, J. Chem. Phys. **5**, 669 (1937).
[2] C. A. Coulson and H. C. Longuet-Higgins, Rev. Sci. Instr. **15**, 929 (1947).
[3] G. W. Wheland and D. E. Mann, J. Chem. Phys. **17**, 264 (1949).
[4] Mann, Platt, and Klevens, J. Chem. Phys. **18**, 481 (1949).
[5] R. D. Brown, Trans. Faraday Soc. **44**, 984 (1948).
[6] W. Moffitt, J. Chem. Phys. **22**, 320 (1954).
[7] C. C. J. Roothaan, Revs. Modern Phys. **23**, 69 (1951).
[8] A. Julg, Compt. rend. **239**, 1498 (1954).
[9] A. Julg, J. chim. phys. **52**, 377 (1955).
[10] R. Pariser, J. Chem. Phys. **21**, 568 (1953).
[11] R. Pariser and R. G. Parr, J. Chem. Phys. **21**, 466 (1953).
[12] R. Pariser and R. G. Parr, J. Chem. Phys. **21**, 767 (1953).
[13] J. A. Pople, Trans. Faraday Soc. **49**, 1375 (1953).
[14] R. Pariser, J. Chem. Phys. **24**, 250 (1956).

TABLE I. Azulene Hückel molecular orbitals.[a]

MO	Sym	(χ_2)	$(\chi_1 \pm \chi_3)$	$(\chi_9 \pm \chi_{10})$	$(\chi_4 \pm \chi_8)$	$(\chi_5 \pm \chi_7)$	(χ_6)	k
1	b_2	0.27988	0.32330	0.46703	0.28864	0.19981	0.17297	2.31028
2	a_2	0.00000	−0.22068	−0.29916	0.48406	0.35706	0.00000	1.35567
3	b_2	−0.32427	−0.26777	−0.11798	0.19090	0.43327	0.52467	1.65157
4	b_2	0.58294	0.25853	−0.35363	−0.21856	0.15978	0.36028	0.88698
5	a_2	0.00000	0.54285	0.25908	0.16012	0.33550	0.00000	0.47726
6	a_2	0.00000	−0.29916	0.22068	−0.35706	0.48406	0.00000	−0.73764
7	b_2	0.31575	−0.06321	−0.29044	0.46994	0.10228	−0.51089	−0.40039
8	b_2	−0.55268	0.43640	−0.13649	−0.08436	0.26971	−0.34157	1.57922
9	a_2	0.00000	0.25908	−0.54285	−0.33550	0.16012	0.00000	−2.09529
10	b_2	0.26749	−0.25000	0.19981	−0.32330	0.40450	−0.43280	−1.86921

[a] Note: By definition for the ith MO, $\phi_i = \Sigma\, C_{pi}\chi_p$. The C_{pi}'s are listed under the corresponding χ_p. + and − refer to MOs of symmetry b_2 and a_2, respectively. k's are eigenvalues of the resonance integral matrix, $\boldsymbol{\beta}$, which has the MOs as eigenvectors.

different sets of molecular orbitals are employed, perimeter MOs[6] and conventional semiempirical LCAO MOs, i.e., Hückel MOs, which are listed in Table I. The perimeter MOs are numbered so as to correspond to the Hückel MOs. The values for the one-center Coulomb integral, nearest neighbor two-center Coulomb integral, and the core resonance integral, β, are obtained from the benezene spectrum.[14] The other Coulomb integrals are calculated from Slater $2p$ AOs,[15] with $Z=3.18$, for the appropriate interatomic distances, and penetration integrals are neglected (or assumed to contribute equally to each C atom).

The maximum amount of configuration interaction which is included here mixes the ground and all singly excited configurations. This leads to a 14th-order secular equation for the singlet $^1A_1$ states, a 13th-order equation for the triplet $^3A_1$ states, and two 12th-order equations for $^1B_1$ and $^3B_1$ states, respectively. Since azulene is not an alternant hydrocarbon, further factorization of the secular equation into *plus* and *minus* states[14] is not possible. The numerical calculation of the matrix elements for the secular equations, as well as the solution of these equations, were performed on a high-speed digital computer, the International Business Machines Corporation's EDPM 701, with use of the same generalized program as for the polyacenes.[14]

Transition moments, dipole moments, bond orders, and charge densities are calculated according to the definitions which were given previously.[14]

III. RESULTS AND DISCUSSION

Solution of the secular equations for interaction among all singly excited and the ground configurations leads to a set of state energies and wave functions. Transition energies referred to the lowest energy state, or ground state, are listed in Table II. Referred to the lowest energy configuration (that is, the configuration expressed by a single determinantal wave function), the ground-state energy is lowered by 0.299 ev and by 0.782 ev for starting Hückel MOs and perimeter MOs, respectively. The oscillator strengths calculated from the wave functions are also listed in Table II, and the more important wave functions are presented in Table III.[16]

TABLE II. Calculated energies and oscillator strengths for azulene states.[a]

State		Hückel MOs Energy (ev)	Hückel MOs f	Perimeter MOs Energy (ev)	Perimeter MOs f
$^1A_1$:	1	0.000	Ref	0.000	Ref
	2	3.084	0.002	4.194	0.003
	3	4.692	1.243	6.250	1.673
	4	5.994	0.003	6.714	0.225
	5	6.867	0.215	7.194	0.343
	6	7.018	0.199	7.717	0.003
	7	7.385	0.350	8.075	0.111
$^1B_1$:	1	1.733	0.017	2.814	0.035
	2	4.112	0.116	5.095	0.080
	3	5.604	0.365	5.872	0.422
	4	6.191	0.014	6.881	0.847
	5	7.018	0.278	7.709	0.003
	6	7.271	0.870	7.864	0.151
$^3A_1$:	1	1.840	0.000	2.426	0.000
	2	2.440	0.006	3.211	0.001
	3	4.632	0.028	5.116	0.010
	4	4.752	0.082	5.329	0.095
	5	5.725	0.018	6.178	0.019
	6	5.929	0.000	6.846	0.010
$^3B_1$:	1	1.468	Ref	2.232	Ref
	2	3.496	0.008	4.249	0.028
	3	4.076	0.068	4.540	0.073
	4	4.881	0.259	5.232	0.161
	5	5.439	0.000	6.023	0.007
	6	6.533	0.100	7.210	0.045

Higher Energy States

Hückel MOs: $^1A_1$: 7.551, 8.122, 10.004, 10.851, 11.075, 11.561, 14.680; $^1B_1$: 8.129, 8.394, 9.185, 11.342, 11.716, 13.672; $^3A_1$: 6.831, 7.401, 9.323, 10.373, 10.567, 11.355, 14.666; $^3B_1$: 7.186, 7.526, 8.887, 10.449, 11.661, 13.519.

Perimeter MOs: $^1A_1$: 8.193, 8.616, 10.558, 11.207, 11.546, 12.796, 13.517; $^1B_1$: 8.749, 9.137, 10.025, 10.503, 11.740, 13.040; $^3A_1$: 7.774, 8.156, 9.377, 10.181, 10.784, 12.722, 13.416; $^3B_1$: 8.289, 8.502, 9.986, 10.191, 11.590, 12.627.

[a] For the singlets, oscillator strengths are calculated for transitions from the ground state; for the triplets, these are calculated for transitions from the lowest triplet state.

[15] See, for example, C. C. J. Roothaan, J. Chem. Phys. 19, 1445 (1951).

[16] Wave functions for all other excited states in Table II are available.

TABLE III. Wave functions for the ground and lower excited states of azulene by Hückel and perimeter MOs.[a]

State	0	5,6	4,7	2,6	3,7	4,8	5,9	3,8	2,9	1,7	4,10	1,8	3,10	1,10
Hückel MOs														
$^1A_1$: 1	0.97557	0.14158	−0.13497	0.03216	−0.03296	0.02319	−0.06368	−0.00160	0.01086	0.05456	−0.00506	−0.00782	0.00200	−0.00954
2	−0.00811	0.70808	0.67546	−0.12732	−0.12089	0.06517	0.06191	−0.00353	−0.00376	0.01512	−0.03478	−0.00375	0.02802	−0.03380
3	−0.14885	0.60514	−0.65722	−0.33110	0.19533	−0.13386	0.10040	0.01318	0.00342	−0.04528	0.03781	0.00663	−0.00623	−0.01348
$^3A_1$: 1	0.00000	0.76626	0.60044	0.03270	−0.03684	−0.02906	−0.03881	0.13394	0.11842	−0.04079	0.03632	−0.04579	0.07389	0.07105
Perim MOs:														
$^1A_1$: 1	0.94895	−0.06953	0.16215	0.14611	0.01688	0.07726	0.07170	0.01075	−0.11266	−0.07170	−0.11574	−0.02845	−0.01859	0.05596
2	−0.05295	0.69124	0.66951	−0.17493	−0.07353	0.05705	0.09337	0.00262	0.00076	0.07055	−0.12109	0.01254	0.03977	−0.04208
3	0.19341	0.53400	−0.62504	−0.42047	−0.05379	−0.03351	0.19200	−0.02812	−0.07078	−0.18917	0.15598	−0.04524	0.00919	0.03236
$^3A_1$: 1	0.00000	0.64902	0.70456	−0.05917	−0.02908	0.03334	0.05061	0.16940	0.16185	0.03918	−0.07323	0.00742	0.01572	0.11071
	5,7	4,6	2,7	3,6	5,8	4,9	2,8	3,9	1,6	5,10	1,9	2,10		
Hückel MOs:														
$^1B_1$: 1	0.97037	−0.13006	−0.17168	−0.03764	0.04606	0.02390	0.02835	−0.03454	0.03651	−0.05395	0.00783	0.03979		
2	0.04941	0.90379	−0.37615	−0.09188	0.00441	0.03337	−0.10087	0.05717	−0.01202	−0.12355	−0.02297	−0.01639		
$^3B_1$: 1	0.99040	−0.02006	0.08881	−0.04859	−0.02845	−0.03134	−0.02009	0.01894	−0.05782	−0.01814	0.04590	−0.01084		
Perim MOs:														
$^1B_1$: 1	0.91504	−0.25107	−0.24043	−0.01808	0.04531	−0.02640	0.05386	−0.05822	−0.01422	−0.17110	−0.00197	0.05482		
2	0.04923	0.76097	−0.60186	−0.00821	−0.10725	0.09271	−0.09663	0.07101	0.06613	−0.07784	0.03517	0.10027		
$^3B_1$: 1	0.95137	0.05411	−0.22983	−0.00945	0.05739	−0.01451	0.03483	−0.03818	−0.00463	−0.16959	0.01044	0.06320		

[a] Note: See Table II for energies of these states. For the singlet state $^1\Psi_a$, $^1\Psi_a = \sum A_{a,ij} V_{ij}$, where V_{ij} is the singlet configurational determinantal wave function (see reference 14), when one electron is excited from the ith to the jth MO; a similar definition applies to the triplets. The table lists A_{ij}'s under the heading i, j; MOs $k, j \cdots$ correspond to numbering in Table I.

TABLE IV. Comparison with experiment of Hückel MO calculation with interaction of all singly excited configurations.

State	Calculated E(ev)	Calculated f	Experimental[a] E(ev)	Experimental[a] f
$^1A_1$	0	0	0	0
$^1B_1$ ⊥	1.732	0.017	1.79	0.009
$^1A_1$ ‖	3.084	0.002	3.50	0.08
$^1B_1$ ⊥	4.112	0.116	4.05?	?
$^1A_1$ ‖	4.692	1.243	4.52	1.10
$^1B_1$ ⊥	5.604	0.365	5.24	0.38
$^1A_1$ ‖	5.994	0.003		
$^1B_1$ ⊥	6.191	0.014		
$^1A_1$ ‖	6.867	0.215	6.42	0.65
$^1B_1$ ⊥	7.018	0.278		
$^1A_1$ ‖	7.018	0.199		

[a] Experimental spectrum is based on Mann, Platt, and Klevens[4]; the zero-zero band is estimated for the lowest two excited states,[19] and the other bands are listed according to maximum absorption.

It is clear from inspection of Table II that agreement between the results calculated from the two different sets of molecular orbitals is only fair, even though a considerable amount of configuration interaction has been included. If one were to ignore the ground-state lowering in the perimeter MO calculation, agreement for the energies would be better. Nevertheless, the relative order of states given by the two calculations is not always in correspondence.

Experiment, however, appears to be in very satisfactory accord with the calculation based on Hückel MOs both with respect to energy and intensity[17] of transition. The comparison is made in Table IV. The calculated intensity for the lowest $^1A_1$ state appears to be considerably too low, but as Moffitt[6] has pointed out, this intensity can be readily enhanced through vibrational perturbations. This would add approximately 0.1 to the oscillator strength, that is, just the required amount. For the lowest $^1B_1$ state and the two lowest $^1A_1$ states the present assignment is thus in complete agreement with that of Mann, Platt, and Klevens.[4,6] However, the $^1B_1$ state at 4.112 ev is predicted to fall in between the two lowest $^1A_1$ states; a hump is present in the absorption spectrum at about 4.05 ev which is used for the present tentative assignment. Recent experimental work proves that the theoretical assignment for the two lowest excited singlets is correct,[18] and there exists indirect evidence that there may indeed be a perpendicularily polarized state, i.e., $^1B_1$, just above the lowest excited $^1A_1$ state.[19] The relationship between the naphthalene and azulene spectra has been discussed in detail previously[4,6] and will not be considered here.

The location of the triplet states in azulene is not known experimentally, but the two lowest triplets are

[17] No empirical factors are used here to reduce the oscillator strengths. An empirical correction factor between ½ and 1 would improve agreement with experiment. This correction may be due to polarization of the σ electrons.

[18] D. S. McClure, J. Chem. Phys. 22, 1256 (1954).

[19] J. Sidman and D. S. McClure, Symposium on Molecular Structure and Spectroscopy, Ohio State University, June, 1955.

TABLE V. Effect of configuration interaction on the lower singlets.

State	No. CI[a] E(ev)	f	Lim. CI[b] E(ev)	f	All CI[c] E(ev)	f	No. CI[a] E(ev)	f	Lim. CI[b] E(ev)	f	All CI[c] E(ev)	f
	←——— Perimeter MOs ———→						←——— Hückel MOs ———→					
$^1A_1$	0	0	0	0	(−0.782)	...	0	0	0	0	(−0.299)	...
$^1B_1$	2.710	0.238	2.468	0.086	2.814	0.035	1.742	0.077	1.673	0.042	1.733	0.017
$^1A_1$	4.690	1.205	3.626	0.000	4.194	0.003	3.774	0.796	2.937	0.002	3.084	0.002
$^1B_1$	4.607	0.405	4.849	0.648	5.095	0.080	4.208	0.382	4.277	0.470	4.112	0.116
$^1A_1$	4.629	1.124	5.693	2.845	6.250	1.673	3.835	0.747	4.672	1.892	4.692	1.243

[a] The corresponding configurations are, upon reading down: ground configuration V_0, $V_{5,7}$, $V_{5,6}$, $V_{4,6}$, and $V_{4,7}$. V_{ij} is the singlet determinantal wave function where an electron is excited from the ith to the jth MO; MOs are numbered as in Table I.
[b] Interaction is included only between the lowest two excited A_1 and B_1 configurations.
[c] Interaction is included among all singly excited configurations. Energies in brackets are relative to the ground configuration V_0. All other energies are relative to the ground state.

predicted to fall quite close to the lowest excited singlet; see Table II.

The effect of configuration interaction in azulene is usually large for configurations which are nearly degenerate, and for the lower excited states near degeneracy can be predicted from the conventional simple LCAO MO theory. This near degeneracy occurs in pairs among A_1 configurations. Thus the configuration with an electron excited from the 5th to the 6th molecular orbital (see Table I) is of about the same energy as the one obtained by excitation from the 4th to the 7th orbital. That these configurations are nearly degenerate is evident from inspection of the second and eighth columns of Table V. If one includes interaction only among those four configurations which are degenerate in the perimeter model, as advocated by Ham and Rüdenberg,[20] one obtains quite satisfactory results for the lower excited states; see Table V. Interaction among all singly excited states does, however, give better results compared to experiment, especially for the oscillator strengths.

The experimental dipole moment for azulene is about 1.0 D,[3] which may be compared to the calculated π electronic dipole moments for the ground state,[21] listed in the second column of Table VI. Configuration interaction greatly improves the dipole moment for the Hückel MO calculation, making it essentially the same as the SCF MO result.[8] This should be considered as satisfactory with respect to experiment, since σ-electron polarization effects would tend to reduce the total calculated dipole moment. The dipole moments for most of the excited states (see Table VI) are calculated to be opposed to the ground state dipole moment. From this one might expect that polar solvents would shift the azulene absorption spectrum to shorter wavelengths.

As may be seen in Table VI, the charge densities for the ground state are in fair agreement for SCF MOs, perimeter MOs plus configuration interaction, and Hückel MOs plus configuration interaction. The charge density at positions 1 and 3 is the largest, and this is consistent with the tendency of chemical electrophylic reactions to take place at these positions.[5,22,23]

The bond orders are brought into good accord by configuration interaction for the two sets of molecular orbitals; see Table VI. Application of Coulson's formula for bond order *vs* bond distance[24] predicts 1.39 A to

TABLE VI. Azulene dipole moments, charge densities, and bond orders, for ground and excited states.[a]

State	$\mu(D)$	$d_{2,2}$	$d_{1,1}$	$d_{10,10}$	$d_{4,4}$	$d_{5,5}$	$d_{6,6}$	$b_{1,2}$	$b_{1,10}$	$b_{4,10}$	$b_{4,5}$	$b_{5,6}$	$b_{9,10}$
Ground state:													
Perim. MOs, No. C.I.	0	1.0000	1.0000	1.0000	1.0000	1.0000	1.0000	0.6472	0.6472	0.6472	0.6472	0.6472	0.0000
Hückel MOs, No. C.I.	6.40	1.0466	1.1729	1.0274	0.8549	0.9864	0.8700	0.6561	0.5956	0.5858	0.6640	0.6389	0.4009
SCF MOs	1.7	0.997	1.049	1.042	0.908	1.034	0.938	...	...	...	...	...	...
Perim. MOs+C.I.	3.36	1.0011	1.1177	1.0157	0.8859	1.0148	0.9304	0.6620	0.6096	0.5915	0.6570	0.6481	0.2828
Hückel MOs+C.I.	1.88	0.9787	1.0960	1.0132	0.8785	1.0489	0.9482	0.6597	0.6098	0.6108	0.6513	0.6478	0.2882
Exc. states[b]:													
$^1B_1$: 1	−1.36	1.1175	0.8548	1.0246	1.0801	0.9275	1.1083	0.6468	0.4316	0.4612	0.6837	0.5936	0.5800
$^1A_1$: 2	−2.70	0.8791	0.9985	0.9902	1.0126	1.0770	0.9653	0.5602	0.5267	0.5239	0.5883	0.6024	0.4330
$^1B_1$: 2	−1.26	0.7454	1.1627	0.9618	0.9161	1.1626	0.8481	0.5157	0.6062	0.5336	0.5236	0.5917	0.2990
$^1A_1$: 3	−1.82	0.8874	1.0323	0.9950	0.9612	1.0894	0.9576	0.5606	0.4964	0.4901	0.6207	0.6002	0.5131
$^3B_1$: 1	−0.86	1.1264	0.8617	1.0363	1.0671	0.9076	1.1280	0.6374	0.4473	0.4748	0.6754	0.5942	0.5713
$^3A_1$: 1	0.60	0.9698	1.0416	1.0045	0.9588	1.0464	0.9283	0.5816	0.5113	0.5762	0.5520	0.5947	0.3745

[a] μ is the dipole moment in Debye, d_{pp} the charge density of the pth atom, and b_{pq} the bond order between atoms p and q: 1 is often added to b_{pq} for the total bond order. Atoms are numbered as in Fig. 1. Negative dipole moments are opposed to direction shown in Fig. 1.
[b] Results for excited states are computed via Hückel MOs. For analogous states via perimeter MOs the dipole moments, upon reading down, are: −2.49, −3.07, −1.72, −7.16, −2.65, and −1.00 D. For identification of states see Table II.

[20] N. S. Ham and K. Rüdenberg, J. Chem. Phys. 25, 1 (1956); *ibid.* 25, 13 (1956).
[21] If one assumes a dipole moment for $C^{-}-H^{+}$ of 0.6 D, this would contribute about +0.1 D to the total dipole moment.
[22] A. G. Anderson, Jr., and J. A. Nelson, J. Am. Chem. Soc. 72, 3824 (1950).
[23] Anderson, Nelson, and Tazuma, J. Am. Chem. Soc. 75, 4980 (1953).
[24] C. A. Coulson, Proc. Roy. Soc. (London) A169, 413 (1939).

TABLE VII. The effect of methyl substitution on the lowest azulene absorption band.

Position	2	3	4	5	6
$\Delta\lambda$ (mμ) exp	−21	41	−17	18	−16
$\Delta\lambda$ (mμ) calc	−22	41	−31	20	−25

1.41 A for the peripheral bonds and 1.47 A for the cross link.[25] Bond orders for the excited states, as well as the charge distributions, are considerably different from the ground-state values. If one assumes that the vibrational bond force constants are proportional to the bond orders, these might be used to consider the displacement of vibrational bands in excited states.

Application of a perturbation theory enables one to estimate the spectral shifts in azulene upon methyl substitution.[9] The change in energy difference between ground state and excited state is then proportional to the difference in charge density of the two states at the position of substitution. This calculation for the lowest $^1B_1$ state (as obtained through Hückel MOs plus configuration interaction) is compared with experiment[26] in Table VII. Substitution at the 3 position is used to calibrate the calculation. The results are on the average somewhat better than those of previous treatments,[27] but not too much significance should be attached to this. A similar calculation for the second excited state would predict (see Table VI) hypsochromic shifts for the 4, 5, and 6 positions and bathochromic shifts for the 2 and 3 positions, but experiment appears to indicate somewhat of a bathochromic shift for all positions.[28] Similar difficulties are encountered for the strong $^1A_1$ band at 4.5 ev. However, the present method for treatment of substitution effects is admittedly crude, and it does not seem profitable at present to speculate on the method's shortcomings.

[25] E. Heilbronner experimentally estimates 1.45 A for the cross link, as quoted by C. W. Scherr, J. Chem. Phys. **21**, 1582 (1953).

[26] P. A. Plattner and E. Heilbronner, Helv. Chim. Acta **30**, 910 (1947).

[27] See reference 9 for a summary of previous treatments.

IV. CONCLUSION

It appears evident that the present theoretical approach is applicable to azulene, a polar molecule, with about the same accuracy as to naphthalene,[14] a nonpolar molecule. This is most encouraging.

The present calculations also confirm the previous conclusion,[14] namely, that it is important to start with a reasonably good set of molecular orbitals if interaction is to be limited to singly excited configurations. In this connection Hückel MOs are considerably better than perimeter MOs. This is demonstrated by the results for the spectrum as well as for the dipole moment of azulene.

To calculate the spectrum, it is essential to include interaction among at least the nearly degenerate singly excited configurations. A general improvement, however, results from more extensive interaction. This is particularily true for the dipole moments and oscillator strengths. However, these still have a tendency to be somewhat too high, and it may well be necessary to consider the σ electrons explicitly in order to account for this discrepancy between experiment and the present theory.

[28] P. A. Plattner and E. Heilbronner, Helv. Chim. Acta **31**, 804 (1948).

Reprinted from THE JOURNAL OF CHEMICAL PHYSICS, Vol. 25, No. 1, 1–13, July, 1956
Printed in U. S. A.

Electronic Interaction in the Free-Electron Network Model for Conjugated Systems. I. Theory*†‡

NORMAN S. HAM§|| AND KLAUS RUEDENBERG¶
Laboratory of Molecular Structure and Spectra, Department of Physics, The University of Chicago, Chicago 37, Illinois

(Received August 1, 1955)

The free-electron network model for conjugated systems is extended to include electronic interaction. The free-electron wave functions are considered as molecular orbitals arising from an average one-electron potential, and a configuration interaction treatment with these MO's is developed. The integrals occurring in this procedure, in particular the electron interaction integrals, are analyzed and a convenient method for their computation in the FE model is suggested. The integral evaluation requires certain semiempirical parameters which are determined from the benzene spectrum.

INTRODUCTION

THE concept of π electrons as mobile electrons has long served to provide a qualitative understanding for many of the spectral and chemical properties of conjugated molecules. It leads to a description which assumes these electrons to move in the potential of the framework formed by the σ bonds.

As a quantitative formulation of this picture, E. Hückel suggested the simplified semiempirical molecular orbital theory,[1] which was further developed by Lennard-Jones,[2] and Coulson and Longuet-Higgins.[3,4] In this theory, which remains manageable for complicated molecules, the interactions between the π electrons are also included in an average potential acting equally on *all* of them. Thus with the ground state represented by a single Slater determinant of molecular orbitals, it has been possible to account quantitatively for many ground-state properties of these molecules.[5–7]

For the excited states however this simple orbital picture is incapable of furnishing a correct description. The degeneracy predicted for states of different multiplicity, for example, is in clear contradiction with experiment, and the correlation of the orbital transition energies with the spectra can only be qualitative.[8,9] A more realistic treatment of the interaction between π electrons is therefore required, i.e., the electron interaction operator in the Hamiltonian must be taken into account explicitly and superpositions of Slater determinants must be considered as wave functions (e.g., as in the method of configuration interaction). While the general formulation of such a treatment[10–12] is a straightforward matter, the real problem lies in simplifying it to the level of sophistication and manageability of the

* Presented in part at the Symposium on Molecular Structure and Spectroscopy held June 13–17, 1955 at The Ohio State University, Columbus, Ohio.

† This work was assisted by the Office of Naval Research under Task Order IX of Contract N6ori-20 with The University of Chicago.

‡ Part I of a thesis submitted by NSH to the Department of Chemistry, The University of Chicago, in partial fulfillment of the requirements for the degree of Ph.D.

§ Commonwealth Scientific and Industrial Research Organization, (Australia). Predoctoral Fellow 1952–1955; University of Chicago Predoctoral Fellow 1954–1955.

|| Present address: Division of Industrial Chemistry, Commonwealth Scientific and Industrial Research Organization, Box 4331, G.P.O. Melbourne, Australia.

¶ Present address: Department of Chemistry, Department of Physics, and Institute for Atomic Research, Iowa State College, Ames, Iowa.

[1] E. Hückel, Z. Physik **70**, 204 (1931); Z. Electrochem. **43**, 752, 827 (1937), review.

[2] J. E. Lennard-Jones, Proc. Roy. Soc. (London) **A158**, 280 (1937).

[3] C. A. Coulson and H. C. Longuet-Higgins, Proc. Roy. Soc. (London) **A191**, 39 (1947); **A192**, 16 (1947); **A193**, 447, 456 (1948).

[4] B. H. Chirgwin and C. A. Coulson, Proc. Roy. Soc. (London) **A201**, 196 (1950).

[5] E. Hückel, Z. Physik **72**, 310 (1931); **76**, 628 (1932).

[6] Coulson, Daudel, and Robertson, Proc. Roy. Soc. (London) **A207**, 306 (1951).

[7] H. C. Longuet-Higgins, J. Chem. Phys. **18**, 265, 275, 283 (1950).

[8] C. A. Coulson, Proc. Phys. Soc. (London) **A60**, 257 (1948).

[9] W. Moffitt, J. Chem. Phys. **22**, 1820 (1954), Fig. 2.

[10] M. Goeppert-Mayer and A. L. Sklar, J. Chem. Phys. **6**, 645 (1938).

[11] D. P. Craig, Proc. Roy. Soc. (London) **A200**, 474 (1950).

[12] C. C. J. Roothaan, Revs. Modern Phys. **23**, 61 (1951).

original Hückel theory. This implies the inclusion of semiempirical elements, which are all the more essential for success, since the "rigorous *a priori*" calculations which can be handled at present have been found unreliable for predictions of π-electronic spectra.[10,13–15]

Pariser and Parr[16–18] have developed an extension of the Hückel MO theory which meets these requirements and contains a semiempirical adjustment,[19] for which Moffitt[20] had earlier pointed out the need. They have applied it successfully to a number of aromatic systems.[17,21] Following Dewar and Longuet-Higgins,[22] Pople has recently made similar calculations.[23] A somewhat different approach based on the "perimeter" model[24] which gives good results for cata-condensed hydrocarbons, has been used by Moffitt.[25]

In all of the above methods the molecular orbitals are written as linear combinations of atomic ($2p\pi$) orbitals on the carbon atoms (LCAO MO's). More recently the free-electron theory[26–29] has been developed to serve the same purpose as the Hückel theory and it has been shown that LCAO MO's and free-electron MO's (FE MO's) furnish equivalent descriptions.[30–36] However the extension of the FE MO theory to include electron interaction has been hampered by the problem of evaluating the electron repulsion integrals. As a result of the present investigation a solution of this problem is proposed which will be successfully applied to a number of aromatic hydrocarbons in the following paper.[37]

This method turns out to be similar to that of Pariser and Parr so that the close resemblance between the LCAO and FE approach is also preserved when electronic interaction is included. We must admit however that we have not been uninfluenced by their work. On the other hand there are differences between the methods of Pariser and Parr, Pople, and the present one, which might be worthwhile to mention. All three approaches form the excited states by the method of configuration interaction, and they proceed similarly in the problem of streamlining the array of electron interaction integrals. They differ in the initial choice of molecular orbitals. Pariser and Parr for simplicity choose to start, with the LCAO MO's of the Hückel, Coulson, and Longuet-Higgins theory with neglect of overlap; Pople constructs from these, self-consistent field MO's with neglect of overlap[38]; we use FE MO's, which resemble more closely LCAO MO's with the inclusion of overlap.[34–35] Furthermore the LCAO and FE methods differ in the evaluation of the one-electron integrals over the kinetic energy operator and the framework potential. We hope that our derivations shed a new and perhaps illuminating light on the problem.

1. CONSTRUCTION OF ELECTRONIC-STATE FUNCTIONS

For an adequate description of the spectra of aromatic molecules, we require wave functions for the ground and excited states. Restriction of our treatment to the π electrons of a conjugated hydrocarbon with N atoms still leaves us with an N-electron problem. The wave functions of these π electrons are determined by the Hamiltonian[39]

$$\mathcal{H}=\sum_i^N f_i+\sum_{i<j}^N g_{ij}, \tag{1.1}$$

with

$$f_i=-(\hbar^2/2m)\Delta_i+U(x_i,y_i,z_i), \tag{1.1'}$$

and

$$g_{ij}=e^2/r_{ij}, \tag{1.1''}$$

where $U(x,y,z)$ is the potential of the molecular framework which is held together by the σ electrons. In order to simplify this N-electron problem, one proceeds on the assumption, as in atomic spectra, that the electronic interaction can be divided into a large average

[13] C. C. J. Roothaan and R. G. Parr, J. Chem. Phys. **17**, 1001 (1949).
[14] J. Jacobs, Proc. Phys. Soc. (London) **A62**, 710 (1949).
[15] Parr, Craig, and Ross, J. Chem. Phys. **18**, 1561 (1950).
[16] R. Pariser and R. G. Parr, J. Chem. Phys. **21**, 466 (1953).
[17] R. Pariser and R. G. Parr, J. Chem. Phys. **21**, 767 (1953).
[18] R. G. Parr and R. Pariser, J. Chem. Phys. **23**, 711 (1955).
[19] R. Pariser, J. Chem. Phys. **21**, 568 (1953).
[20] W. Moffitt, Proc. Roy. Soc. (London) **A210**, 244 (1951).
[21] R. Pariser, Symposium on Molecular Structure and Spectroscopy, The Ohio State University, Columbus, Ohio (June 1954), and J. Chem. Phys. **24**, 250 (1956).
[22] M. J. S. Dewar and H. C. Longuet-Higgins, Proc. Phys. Soc. (London) **A67**, 795 (1954).
[23] J. A. Pople, Proc. Phys. Soc. (London) **A68**, 81 (1955).
[24] J. R. Platt, J. Chem. Phys. **17**, 484 (1949).
[25] W. Moffitt, J. Chem. Phys. **22**, 320 (1954).
[26] N. S. Bayliss, J. Chem. Phys. **16**, 287 (1948); Quart. Revs. **6**, 319 (1952).
[27] H. Kuhn, J. Chem. Phys. **16**, 840 (1948); **17**, 1198 (1949); Helv. Chim. Acta **31**, 1441 (1948).
[28] W. T. Simpson, J. Chem. Phys. **16**, 1124 (1948).
[29] K. Ruedenberg and C. W. Scherr, J. Chem. Phys. **21**, 1565 (1953).
[30] W. T. Simpson, J. Chem. Phys. **17**, 1218 (1949).
[31] J. S. Griffith, J. Chem. Phys. **21**, 174 (1953); Trans. Faraday Soc. **49**, 345 (1953).
[32] H. H. Jaffé, J. Chem. Phys. **21**, 1287 (1953).
[33] C. W. Scherr, J. Chem. Phys. **21**, 1582 (1953).
[34] K. Ruedenberg, J. Chem. Phys. **22**, 1878 (1954).
[35] N. S. Ham and K. Ruedenberg, Technical Report, Laboratory of Molecular Structure and Spectra, The University of Chicago, (1953–1954), Part I, p. 97, and J. Chem. Phys. (to be published).
[36] A. A. Frost, J. Chem. Phys. **23**, 310 (1955).
[37] N. S. Ham and K. Ruedenberg, J. Chem. Phys. **25**, 13 (1956).

[38] J. A. Pople, Trans. Faraday Soc. **49**, 1375 (1953).
[39] Stationary problems contain as fundamental constants only a basic length and a basic energy. Instead of using the atomic constants $a=\hbar^2/e^2m=0.529151$ A = Bohr radius, and $E_H=\hbar^2/2ma^2=13.6035$ ev = ionization potential of hydrogen, π-electronic problems in the FE theory are best formulated in terms of the conjugated constants $D=2.64575a=1.400000$ A = an average internuclear distance in aromatics, and $E_C=\hbar^2/2mD^2=E_H(a/D)^2=1.9432$ ev, equivalent to 15.677 kk, where 1 kK = 1 kilo-Kayser = 1000 cm^{-1}. [These units are discussed in Eqs. (2.61)–(2.67) of reference 29, some misprints being corrected in J. Chem. Phys. **22**, 151 (1954).] For numerical calculations it is most convenient to use D and E_C as conjugated units. In the present paper these units are used in Eqs. (1.12), (5.3), (5.9), Fig. 2, and Table III, as explicitly mentioned. In these units the electron interaction term of Eq. (1.1″) becomes

$$E_C^{-1}(e^2/D)/r_{12}=(2D/a)/r_{12}=5.29150/r_{12}.$$

shielding effect, expressible as an effective potential, and a small effect which cannot be expressed as a sum of one-electron potentials, i.e., one assumes

$$\sum_i U(x_i,y_i,z_i)+\sum_{i<j} e^2/r_{ij}=\sum_i U_0(x_i,y_i,z_i)$$
$$+U_1(x_1,y_1,z_1,\cdots x_N,y_N,z_N), \quad (1.2)$$

where $U_0(x,y,z)$ is the total effective one-electron potential, and $U_1(x_1\cdots z_N)$ is of perturbative magnitude. The orthonormal solutions of the one-electron Schrödinger equation

$$\{-(\hbar^2/2m)\Delta+U_0(x,y,z)\}\varphi_n=\epsilon_n\varphi_n, \quad (1.3)$$

are called molecular orbitals (MO's).[40]

As a first step in forming electronic state functions, electrons are "assigned to these MO's," i.e., antisymmetrized products (AP's) are formed with the MO's. They represent zeroth-order approximations to the eigenfunctions of $\mathcal{H}$, and are therefore taken as a basis of expansion for the construction of such eigenfunctions. The best linear combinations of these AP's are determined by the variational procedure.

As in atomic spectra, we understand a *configuration* to comprise all AP's which are *degenerate for symmetry reasons*, and mixing of these is called *inner-configurational* interaction. Mixing of AP's which are *non-degenerate* or *accidentally* degenerate is called *inter-configurational* interaction.

Since U_1 is a perturbation, one expects that properly chosen superpositions of AP's which are degenerate or not too far from being degenerate, are already useful state function approximations. This limitation of configuration interaction will be adopted.

Ground State

The hydrocarbons considered here have an even number ($N=4M+2$) of electrons, and the one-electron problem of Eq. (1.3) is such that there are $\frac{1}{2}N$ ground-state (bonding) orbitals clearly separated in energy from the excited (antibonding) orbitals. With configuration interaction limited as in the foregoing, the ground state is therefore expressible as the single closed shell AP

$$\Phi_0=\mathcal{A}\{(\varphi_0\alpha)^1(\varphi_0\beta)^2\cdots(\varphi_{2M}\alpha)^{N-1}(\varphi_{2M}\beta)^N\}, \quad (1.4)$$

where

$$\varphi_0,\ \varphi_1,\ \cdots\ \varphi_{2M} \quad (1.4')$$

are the $\frac{1}{2}N$ ground-state orbitals and

$$\mathcal{A}=(N!)^{-\frac{1}{2}}\sum_P(-1)^P P$$

is the antisymmetrizer. The ground-state energy is

$$H_0=(\Phi_0|\mathcal{H}|\Phi_0),$$
$$=2\sum_{n=0}^{2M}(\varphi_n|f|\varphi_n)+\sum_{n=0}^{2M}\sum_{m=0}^{2M}\{2[\varphi_n\varphi_n|\varphi_m\varphi_m]$$
$$-[\varphi_n\varphi_m|\varphi_n\varphi_m]\}, \quad (1.5)$$

where[41]

$$[\varphi_i\varphi_j|\varphi_k\varphi_l]$$
$$=\int dV(1)\int dV(2)\varphi_i(1)\varphi_j(1)e^2/r_{12}\varphi_k(2)\varphi_l(2). \quad (1.6)$$

Excited States for One-Electron Excitations

The lower excited states are superpositions of AP's which differ from Φ_0 by the excitation of *one* electron from one of the ground-state orbitals to one of the excited orbitals. For each single excitation there exist four AP's corresponding to the four different spin orientations of the excited electron and the electron left behind. To begin with, linear combinations of these four AP's are formed so that they are eigenfunctions for the total spin, i.e., the singlet and triplet combinations. Thus one obtains for the excitation $\varphi_n\rightarrow\varphi_\nu$, the following four orthonormal linear combinations of AP's (LCAP's)

$$^{s\sigma}\Phi(\varphi_n,\varphi_\nu)=\mathcal{A}\{\cdots(\varphi_n\varphi_\nu\eta_{s\sigma})^{2n+1,2n+2}\cdots\}, \quad (1.7)$$

where φ_n (Roman suffix) is any one of the $2M+1$ ground-state orbitals, φ_ν (Greek suffix) is any one of the excited orbitals, and $\eta_{s\sigma}$ is one of the singlet, triplet spin eigenfunctions.[42] The dotted part in Eq. (1.7) is identical with the corresponding part in the ground state AP of Eq. (1.4). LCAP's of the type of Eq. (1.7) for different single excitations are then superposed, and the variation procedure leads to the eigenvalue problem of the matrix,

$$(^{s\sigma}\Phi(\varphi_n,\varphi_\nu)|\mathcal{H}|^{s'\sigma'}\Phi(\varphi_m,\varphi_\mu))$$
$$={}^sH(\varphi_n\varphi_\nu,\varphi_m\varphi_\mu)\delta_{ss'}\delta_{\sigma\sigma'}. \quad (1.8)$$

As indicated, only functions with the same index pair (s,σ) interact, and the three triplet cases are identical since the Hamiltonian is spin-free. The matrix elements for the singlet and triplet cases are given by

$$^sH(\varphi_n\varphi_\nu,\varphi_m\varphi_\mu)={}^s\{\varphi_n\varphi_\nu,\varphi_m\varphi_\mu\}+\{\varphi_\nu,\varphi_\mu\}\delta_{nm}$$
$$-\{\varphi_n,\varphi_m\}\delta_{\nu\mu}+H_0\delta_{nm}\delta_{\nu\mu}, \quad (1.9)$$

[40] There exist of course other kinds of molecular orbitals which are defined differently.

[41] This symbol was defined and used by C. C. J. Roothaan, J. Chem. Phys. 19, 1445 (1951); K. Ruedenberg, J. Chem. Phys. 19, 1459 (1951); Ruedenberg, Roothaan, and Jaunzemis, J. Chem. Phys. 24, 201 (1956).

[42] By s we denote the multiplicity, thus $\eta_{10}=2^{-\frac{1}{2}}(\alpha\beta-\beta\alpha)$, $\eta_{31}=\alpha\alpha$, $\eta_{30}=2^{-\frac{1}{2}}(\alpha\beta+\beta\alpha)$, $\eta_{3,-1}=\beta\beta$.

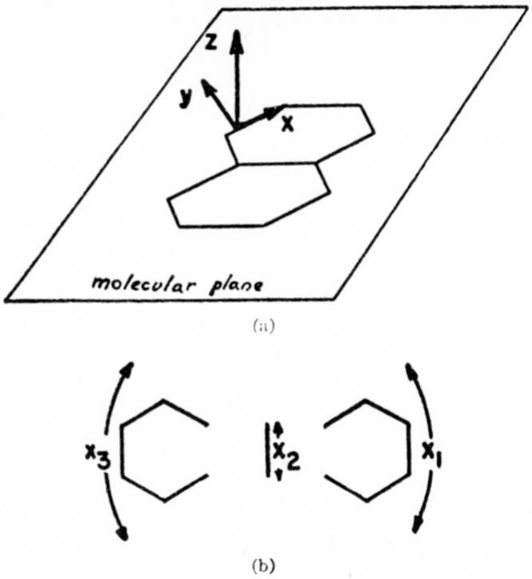

FIG. 1. (a) Orthogonal coordinate system along the bond path, shown on an outer bond in naphthalene. (b) Branches of the bond path in naphthalene.

where

$$^s\{\varphi_i\varphi_j,\varphi_k\varphi_l\}=(1-p_s)[\varphi_i\varphi_j|\varphi_k\varphi_l]-[\varphi_i\varphi_k|\varphi_j\varphi_l], \quad (1.10)$$

and

$$\{\varphi_i,\varphi_j\}=(\varphi_i|f|\varphi_j)+\sum_{n=0}^{2M}\{2[\varphi_n\varphi_n|\varphi_i\varphi_j]-[\varphi_n\varphi_i|\varphi_n\varphi_j]\}. \quad (1.11)$$

In these equations, H_0 is the ground-state energy, p_s is the parity of spin eigenfunction: −1 for singlets and 1 for triplets. The matrix elements of Eq. (1.9) are applicable to the interaction of any two single excitations[43] but in actual practice we shall limit the number of excitations to degenerate or almost degenerate ones. Methods for evaluating these matrix elements will be discussed in Secs. 2 and 3. The eigenvectors and eigenvalues of the matrices of Eq. (1.8) determine the final states and their energies. In the calculation of the energies of the transitions to these states, the ground-state energy H_0 cancels out.

Dipole Matrix and Intensities

The intensities of the transitions are most conveniently measured in terms of the oscillator strength. If Φ_0 is the ground state and Φ_S is an excited state, then the oscillator strength f_s[44,45] corresponding to this transition can be written

$$f_S=\tfrac{1}{3}\Delta E_S\mathbf{Q}_S^2, \quad (1.12)$$

where $\mathbf{Q}_S$ is the dipole matrix element or transition moment, in units of D,[39] and ΔE_S is the transition energy measured in the unit E_C.[39] The transition moment $\mathbf{Q}_S$ is defined by

$$\mathbf{Q}_S=(\Phi_0|\sum_i\mathbf{R}_i|\Phi_S), \quad (1.13)$$

where $\mathbf{R}_i$ is the position vector of the ith electron measured from an arbitrary origin. Since the state Φ_S is a linear combination of the LCAP's of Eq. (1.7), its transition moment $\mathbf{Q}_S$ is the same linear combination of the transition moments

$$^s\mathbf{Q}(\varphi_n,\varphi_\nu)=(\Phi_0|\sum_i\mathbf{R}_i|^{s0}\Phi(\varphi_n,\varphi_\nu)). \quad (1.14)$$

These vanish for the triplet states; for the singlet states they are found to be

$$^1\mathbf{Q}(\varphi_n,\varphi_\nu)=\sqrt{2}\,\mathbf{q}(\varphi_n,\varphi_\nu), \quad (1.15)$$

where

$$\mathbf{q}(\varphi_n,\varphi_\nu)=\int dV\varphi_n\mathbf{R}\varphi_\nu, \quad (1.16)$$

is the orbital transition moment.

This section has formulated the apparatus of configuration interaction based on the assumption that π electrons can be approximately described by molecular orbitals. It enables us to construct approximate state functions for the lower electronic states of a conjugated hydrocarbon. In order to calculate the transition energies, oscillator strengths and polarizations, we must now specify the molecular orbitals and the Hamiltonian appropriate for conjugated systems.

2. MOLECULAR ORBITALS AND HAMILTONIAN

For the construction of good many-electron wave functions, skillful choice of the one-electron MO's is paramount in order to reduce the computational work to a minimum. In particular, for the large molecules considered here, it is essential to have π-electronic MO's which combine simplicity with a good representation of the essential features of more exact MO's. Now in planar conjugated systems, the contributing carbon $2p\pi$ atomic orbitals overlap each other in such a way that the main stream of electrons is directed along the "bond path."[46] *Hence excitation of these electrons also occurs mainly along the bond path and different MO's are primarily distinguished by their different longitudinal profiles along the bond path while their transverse profiles remain essentially unchanged.* The LCAO MO's[1–4] and FE MO's[29,33] mentioned in the introduction both satisfy this "*principle of bond path excitation.*"

The present investigation is based on the FE MO's.

[43] The general matrix element for the interaction of the ground state with an excited singlet function of Eq. (1.7) is given by

$$(\Phi_0|\mathcal{H}|^{10}\Phi(\varphi_n,\varphi_\nu))=2^{\frac{1}{2}}\{\varphi_n,\varphi_\nu\}.$$

[44] See, for example, A. Sommerfeld, *Atomic Structure and Spectral Lines II, Wavemechanics* (Vieweg, Braunschweig, 1939), p. 365, Eq. (22).

[45] R. S. Mulliken and C. A. Rieke, Repts. Progr. Phys. **VIII**, 231 (1941).

[46] See reference 29, Sec. 1.

Choice of these MO's amounts to making the following assumptions for the potential U_0 in Eq. (1.3): the electrons are confined in a potential well which has certain aspects of a tube following the bond path. To be specific this potential must be such that the MO's are *quasi*-separable in x, y, z, the orthogonal curvilinear coordinate system following the bonds in such a way that x is tangential to the bond path and z perpendicular to the plane of the molecule [see Fig. 1(a)]. Furthermore the "tube width" is restricted by the condition that the lowest transverse excitation energies (for y, z motions) are larger than all the longitudinal excitation energies considered. Finally the potential must be nearly constant in the longitudinal (x) direction. Thus the resulting FE MO's have the approximate form

$$\varphi_n(x,y,z)=f(y,z)\phi_n(x). \tag{2.1}$$

The factor $f(y,z)$ is the same for all orbitals, "vanishes on the tube wall," and since we are discussing π electrons it is antisymmetric to the molecular plane. The functions $\phi_n(x)$ are eigenfunctions of the free-electron network equations and they have the form[29,34]

$$\phi_n(x)\begin{cases}=a_{1n}\cos(\kappa_n x_1+\delta_{1n}) \text{ on branch 1,}\\ =a_{2n}\cos(\kappa_n x_2+\delta_{2n}) \text{ on branch 2,}\\ \cdots\cdots\cdots\cdots\\ \cdots\cdots\cdots\cdots\end{cases}, \tag{2.2}$$

where x_B is the x coordinate on branch B; Fig. 1(b) shows how the framework of a molecule is divided into branches.[46] A particular orbital ϕ_n is characterized by a *set* of amplitudes a_{Bn} and phases δ_{Bn} and *one* wave constant κ_n which is related to the orbital energy by[47]

$$\epsilon_n=E_C\kappa_n^2+E^{tr}+E^t, \tag{2.3}$$

where the first term is the kinetic energy of the longitudinal motion (E_C is defined in reference 39), E^{tr} is the kinetic energy of the transverse motion and E^t the constant potential inside the tube.

Having chosen the effective potential U_0 of Eq. (1.3) and so the molecular orbitals, we must now formulate expressions, suitable for the FE model, for the terms in the Hamiltonian of Eq. (1.1), namely, the kinetic energy operator, the framework potential and the electron-interaction operator.

By virtue of Eq. (2.3) and subsequent remarks, the kinetic energy operator will lead to integrals

$$\begin{aligned}(\varphi_i|-(\hbar^2/2m)\Delta|\varphi_i)&=(E_C\kappa_i^2+E^{tr})\delta_{ij},\\ &=(\epsilon_i-E^t)\delta_{ij}.\end{aligned} \tag{2.4}$$

We next discuss the electron-interaction operator. Inserting the FE MO's of Eq. (2.1) into the electronic-interaction integral of Eq. (1.6), one obtains

$$[\varphi_i\varphi_j|\varphi_k\varphi_l]=\int dx_1\int dx_2\phi_i(x_1)\phi_j(x_1) \times G(x_1,x_2)\phi_k(x_2)\phi_l(x_2), \tag{2.5}$$

[47] See reference 34, Eqs. (A.3) and (A.4).

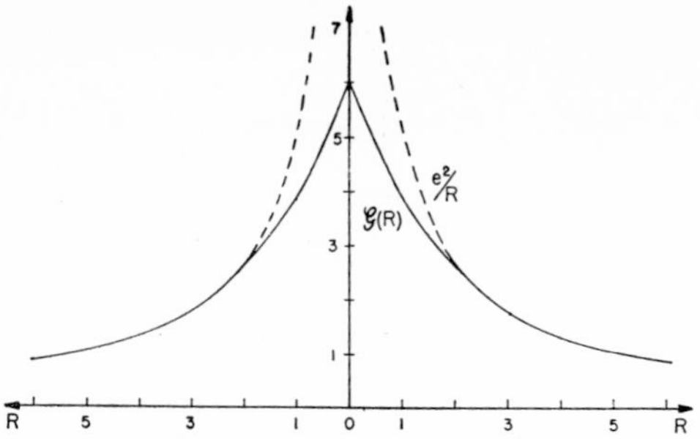

FIG. 2. Electron interaction function $\mathcal{G}(R)$. R in units of D and $\mathcal{G}$ in units of E_C (see reference 39).

with

$$G(x_1,x_2)=\int_{Q(x_1)}dQ_1\int_{Q(x_2)}dQ_2 f^2(y_1,z_1) \times(e^2/r_{12})f^2(y_2,z_2), \tag{2.5'}$$

where $Q(x_i)$ is the cross section of the tube of x_i and dQ_i the area element on this cross section. $G(x_1,x_2)$ represents the mutual electrostatic energy of two area charge distributions of the form $f^2(y,z)$ on the two areas $Q(x_1)$ and $Q(x_2)$. Clearly, for large distances one has

$$G(x_1,x_2)=e^2/R_{12}, \tag{2.6}$$

where $R_{12}=R(x_1,x_2)$ is the distance between the points (x_1, $y_1=0$, $z_1=0$) and (x_2, $y_2=0$, $z_2=0$). When the two areas $Q(x_i)$ coincide, i.e., for $x_1=x_2$, $G(x_1,x_1)$ has a finite value.[48] Thus $G(x_1,x_2)$ will be approximately described by the functional dependence

$$G(x_1,x_2)=\mathcal{G}[R(x_1,x_2)], \tag{2.7}$$

where $\mathcal{G}(R)$ has the general form indicated in Fig. 2. For large distances it approaches Eq. (2.6), while for small distances it goes over into a cusp-like shape.[49] The precise form for small R will depend on the "tube width," ϵ say, and on the explicit form of the transverse factor $f(y,z)$ in the MO's of Eq. (2.1). There is no point however in dwelling on this; for while the existence of ϵ and $f(y,z)$ is conceptually necessary and important, it is difficult to specify them beyond the fact that ϵ is small in comparison with the width of the ring and that $f(y,z)$ is antisymmetric with respect to z, symmetric with respect to y and the same for all MO's. A semiempirical procedure therefore must be adopted to determine the shape of $\mathcal{G}(R)$ for small R.

Finally the framework potential $U(x,y,z)$ of Eq. (1.1)'

[48] It is well known that the mutual electrostatic energy of two two-dimensional charge distributions on the same surface (similar to the self-energy of a surface charge distribution) is finite (see reference 49), whereas the mutual electrostatic energy of two one-dimensional charge distributions (similar to the self-energy of a line distribution) is logarithmically infinite.

[49] See, e.g., J. Jeans, *The Mathematical Theory of Electricity and Magnetism* (Cambridge University Press, Cambridge, 1946), p. 69.

will lead to the integral

$$(\varphi_i|U|\varphi_j)=\int dV\varphi_i(x,y,z)U(x,y,z)\varphi_j(x,y,z), \quad (2.8)$$

$$=\int dx\phi_i(x)V(x)\phi_j(x), \quad (2.8')$$

with

$$V(x)=\int_{Q(x)} dQf^2(y,z)U(x,y,z). \quad (2.9)$$

The framework potential represents the Coulomb attraction on an electron due to the carbon nuclei shielded by the σ electrons so that there is about one electronic charge per nucleus. Therefore we expect the electrostatic interaction between a nucleus and an electron to have a form very close to the one found above to represent the interaction of two electrons. Thus we take as an approximation to the "FE-framework potential" V

$$V(x)=-\sum_P G(P,x), \quad (2.10)$$

where the function G[50] is the one defined in Eq. (2.7) and the summation extends over all atoms P of the molecule. It is likely that the screening has been overestimated in Eq. (2.10) so that there probably exists a somewhat stronger attraction to the nuclei than that expressed by $V(x)$.

The considerations of this section have been carefully made so that the transformation of the Hamiltonian of Eq. (1.1) into a one-dimensional form, keeping only the dependence on the coordinate along the network (x), correctly retains the finite character of a three-dimensional formulation. Any effort to include electronic interaction in a one-dimensional formulation by using the operator $G=e^2/R(x_1,x_2)$ for *all* distances will lead to an insurmountable infinity at $(x_1-x_2)=0$. Two attempts which have been made to work with such a function will be discussed in Sec. 6.

3. METHOD OF EVALUATING MATRIX ELEMENTS

Electron-Interaction Integrals

An exact evaluation of the integral of Eq. (2.5) involving the function $G(x_1,x_2)$ as defined in Eq. (2.7) is obviously quite complicated. One has therefore to look for an approximate method of evaluation which is comparable in simplicity with the remainder of the model.

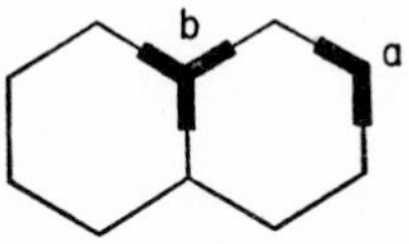

FIG. 3. Bond-path sections. (a) Bond path of a nonjoint atom, $L_P=D$. (b) Bond path of a joint atom, $L_P=3/2D$.

[50] By the symbol $G(P,Q)$ we mean the value of the function $G(x_1,x_2)$ at the points $x_1=x_P$ and $x_2=x_Q$ where x_P, x_Q are the x coordinates of the atoms P and Q.

This purpose is achieved by carrying out the double integration of Eq. (2.5) numerically and using the atoms as grid points for the numerical integration. Thus one obtains

$$[\varphi_i\varphi_j|\varphi_k\varphi_l]=\sum_P\sum_Q L_PL_Q\phi_i(P)\phi_j(P) \times G(P,Q)\phi_k(Q)\phi_l(Q), \quad (3.1)$$

where L_P or L_Q is the length of the bond path "belonging" to the atom P or Q as shown in Fig. 3. Thus L_P is D if P is a nonjoint atom and $\frac{3}{2}D$ if P is a joint atom.

As discussed in Sec. 2, the $G(P,Q)$ values are obtained from the R_{PQ}^{-1} dependence of Eq. (2.6) if the distance between the atoms P and Q is large. We shall assume it to hold for distances larger than the benzene diameter. The $G(P,Q)$ values for the separations within one benzene ring will be determined semiempirically so that the theory reproduces the benzene spectrum; this will be discussed in Sec. 5. It is reassuring that the $G(P,Q)$ values so determined in the two regions do indeed fall on a curve of the type given in Fig. 2.[51]

Framework Potential Integrals

A similar numerical integration is used to evaluate the matrix elements of the framework potential of Eqs. (2.8′), (2.10) yielding

$$(\varphi_i|U|\varphi_j)=-\sum_P\sum_Q L_Q\phi_i(Q)\phi_j(Q)G(P,Q). \quad (3.2)$$

General Matrix Element

The general matrix element of Eq. (1.9) contains the expressions (1.10) and (1.11). The former is calculated directly by using Eq. (3.1). For the latter one obtains, taking into account Eqs. (1.1′), (2.4), (3.1), and (3.2),

$$\{\varphi_i,\varphi_j\}=(\epsilon_i-E')\delta_{ij} +\sum_{PQ} L_Q[a(P)-1]G(P,Q)\phi_i(Q)\phi_j(Q) -\tfrac{1}{2}\sum_{PQ}(L_PL_Q)^{\frac{1}{2}}p(PQ)\phi_i(P)\phi_j(Q)G(P,Q), \quad (3.3)$$

with

$$a(P)=L_P\sum_{n=0}^{2M}2\phi_n^2(P), \quad (3.4)$$

$$p(PQ)=(L_PL_Q)^{\frac{1}{2}}\sum_{n=0}^{2M}2\phi_n(P)\phi_n(Q). \quad (3.5)$$

[51] The evaluation of electron interaction integrals by Eq. (3.1) is similar to Pariser and Parr's method in the LCAO theory (see references 16 and 17). The atom values of the wave functions $\phi_n(P)$ correspond to the expansion coefficients of the MO's in terms of the AO's and the quantities $L_PL_QG(P,Q)$ correspond to the Coulomb integrals between AO's. Thus the neglect of hybrid and exchange integrals in LCAO theory is an approximation comparable to the numerical integration method in the FE theory introduced here.

The quantity $a(P)$ represents the ground state population on atom P.[34] The quantity $p(PQ)$ for atoms P and Q is similar to the ground-state bond orders used in LCAO theory.

Orbital Transition Moments

Upon use of the MO's of Eq. (2.1), the orbital transition moments defined in Eq. (1.16) become

$$\mathbf{q}(\varphi_i,\varphi_j)=\int dx\phi_i(x)\phi_j(x)\{X,Y,Z\}, \qquad (3.6)$$

where

$$\{X,Y,Z\}=\int_{Q(x)} dQf^2(y,z)\mathbf{R}(x,y,z). \qquad (3.7)$$

The vector $\mathbf{R}(x,y,z)$ points from an arbitrary origin to the volume element $dQ\cdot dx=dy\cdot dz\cdot dx$. Its components are taken with respect to a fixed Cartesian system (X, Y in the molecular plane and Z perpendicular to it), and are functions of the integration variables x, y, z of the curvilinear orthogonal system along the bond path. The vector $\{X,Y,Z\}$ is a function of x and represents the average [weighted with $f^2(y,z)$] of $\mathbf{R}$ over the cross section $Q(x)$. Because of the symmetry of $f^2(y,z)$, the Z component vanishes and $\pi-\pi$ transitions are always polarized in the plane of the molecule. We assume we can approximate the X and Y components by the value of $\mathbf{R}(x,y,z)$ along the bond path, i.e., for $y=0$, $z=0$ so that

$$\mathbf{q}(\varphi_i,\varphi_j)=\int dx\phi_i(x)\phi_j(x)\mathbf{R}(x,0,0). \qquad (3.8)$$

Applying now the same numerical integration procedure as before, one obtains

$$\mathbf{q}(\varphi_i,\varphi_j)=\sum_P L_P\phi_i(P)\phi_j(P)\mathbf{R}_P, \qquad (3.9)$$

where $\mathbf{R}_P$ is the position vector of the Pth atom.

Alternant Hydrocarbons

The properties of "alternant hydrocarbons" lead to a number of theoretical simplifications when coupled with the numerical integration procedure for the evaluation of the integrals.

The atoms in an alternant hydrocarbon can be divided into a starred class and an unstarred class so that no two neighbors belong to the same class.[52] To each bonding orbital ϕ_n there exists a "paired" antibonding orbital ϕ_n' characterized by the relation

$$\left.\begin{aligned}\phi_n'(P)&=\phi_n(P)\quad \text{if } P=\text{starred atom},\\ \phi_n'(P)&=-\phi_n(P)\quad \text{if } P=\text{unstarred atom}.\end{aligned}\right\} \qquad (3.10)$$

These relations can profitably be used to simplify the integral evaluation of Eqs. (3.1), (3.3), and (3.9). Two theoretical results[3,4,52] which follow from these relations are

$$p(PQ)=0 \quad \text{if } P \text{ and } Q \text{ belong to the same class} \qquad (3.11)$$

and

$$a(P)=1$$
$$\text{for all atoms of an alternant hydrocarbon.} \qquad (3.12)$$

When applied to Eq. (3.3), the first of these equations halves the work of computing the exchange integrals and the second leads immediately to a cancellation of the Coulomb integrals against the framework integrals.

4. CYCLIC POLYENES

Before applying the foregoing methods to benzene, we wish to consider the more general case of the hypothetical cyclic polyenes $C_{4M+2}H_{4M+2}$, of which benzene is the first member. From these molecules one may "form," by cross-linking carbon atoms, the catacondensed hydrocarbons $C_{4M+2}H_{2M+4}$ (M being the number of rings) since no one carbon atom belongs to more than two rings, and in correlating the spectra of these latter molecules Platt[24] and Moffitt[25] have made illuminating use of the cyclic polyenes.

Since here the inner-configurational interaction is determined by symmetry alone, we can discuss the lower energy levels independently of the particular model and the particular form of the electron-interaction operator, merely by specifying the symmetry properties of the orbitals. Let us therefore forget for the moment the free-electron model and return to the general formulation of Sec. 1. Certainly the total effective potential U_0 of Eq. (1.3) has the polygonal symmetry of the cyclic polyene, and it is instructive to imagine the departure from cylindrical symmetry as a perturbation. Thus we suppose

$$U_0=U_c+U_p, \qquad (4.1)$$

where U_c has cylindrical symmetry and belongs to $D_{\infty h}$ and U_p has the symmetry of $D_{4M+2,h}$ the spatial symmetry group of the molecule.[53] Since with an even number of electrons, any product of π-like orbitals must be symmetric with respect to the molecular plane, we can limit the discussion to $C_{\infty v}$ and $C_{4M+2,v}$, i.e., we can suppress the g, u labels.

[52] The properties of the molecular orbitals of alternant hydrocarbons in (a) free-electron theory, are discussed in reference 29, Eqs. (2.72); (b) LCAO theory, are discussed by C. A. Coulson and G. S. Rushbrooke, Proc. Cambridge Phil. Soc. 36, 193 (1940). The properties of the lower excited states of alternant hydrocarbons have been discussed on the basis of the simplified LCAO theory (with neglect of overlap) by W. Moffitt (see reference 9); M. J. S. Dewar and H. C. Longuet-Higgins (see reference 22); R. Pariser (see reference 21). Similar arguments requiring only minor modifications will apply to the free-electron treatment. We only mention here those results which are relevant for the evaluation of matrix elements. Some other results will be discussed in the next paper (see reference 37).

[53] A qualitative discussion along similar lines has been given by D. P. Craig, J. Chem. Soc. 3175 (1951).

Molecular Orbitals in $C_{\infty v}$

The molecular orbitals furnished by Eq. (1.3) for the cylindrical potential U_c occur in degenerate pairs which have the following θ dependence:

$$\left.\begin{array}{l}\varphi_{2\lambda-1}\sim\cos\lambda\theta,\\ \varphi_{2\lambda}\ \sim\sin\lambda\theta,\end{array}\right\}\tag{4.2}$$

where $\lambda=1, 2, \cdots 2M$. The lowest orbital φ_0 is independent of θ. Here θ is the angle around the axis which goes through the center of the molecule, and is perpendicular to the molecular plane. It is always measured from a plane bisecting a bond. The two degenerate functions of Eq. (4.2) span the representation

$$\Delta_\lambda(\Delta_0=\Sigma,\ \Delta_1=\Pi,\ \Delta_2=\Delta\cdots)$$

of the two-dimensional rotation-reflection group $C_{\infty v}$.

The excitations which we expect to correspond to the long wavelength spectra are from the two highest degenerate ground-state orbitals, which are called

$$\left.\begin{array}{l}b_1\sim\cos M\theta,\\ b_2\sim\sin M\theta,\end{array}\right\}\tag{4.3}$$

to the lowest degenerate unfilled orbitals, called

$$\left.\begin{array}{l}c_1\sim\cos(M+1)\theta,\\ c_2\sim\sin(M+1)\theta.\end{array}\right\}\tag{4.4}$$

Molecular Orbitals in $C_{4M+2,v}$

When the polygonal perturbation U_p is added, the degeneracy of the pair of orbitals of Eq. (4.2) is not removed, and they then span the irreducible representation E_λ of the group $C_{4M+2,v}$.[54] φ_0 belongs to A_1. In the group $C_{4M+2\ v}$, there are two kinds of symmetry planes, σ_v planes which pass through atoms and σ_d planes which pass through bonds; in line with the convention stated above, the angle θ is, therefore, measured from a σ_d plane.

Molecular States in $C_{\infty v}$ and $C_{4M+2,v}$

The four excitations $b_1\to c_1$, $b_1\to c_2$, $b_2\to c_1$, and $b_2\to c_2$ give 16 degenerate AP's forming *one* configuration which spans a reducible representation of the symmetry group. The inner-configurational interaction leads to states[55] which span irreducible representations and can be found as follows.

TABLE I. Transformation properties of two-electron functions.

$p_{\Gamma\gamma}$	Transforms like	Representation spanned in $C_{\infty v}$	$C_{4M+2,v}$
$p_{1,1}$	$\cos\theta$	Δ_1	E_1
$p_{1,2}$	$\sin\theta$		
$p_{2M+1,1}$	$\cos(2M+1)\theta$	Δ_{2M+1}	B_2
$p_{2M+1,2}$	$\sin(2M+1)\theta$		B_1

[54] If λ is a multiple of $2M+1$ (a case not arising here), the degeneracy of a pair of orbitals *is* removed and they span separately the one dimensional representations B_1 and B_2.

The two-electron functions

$$\left.\begin{array}{l}p_{1,1}\ \ \ =2^{-\frac{1}{2}}(b_1c_1+b_2c_2),\\ p_{1,2}\ \ \ =2^{-\frac{1}{2}}(b_1c_2-b_2c_1),\\ p_{2M+1,1}=2^{-\frac{1}{2}}(b_1c_1-b_2c_2),\\ p_{2M+1,2}=2^{-\frac{1}{2}}(b_1c_2+b_2c_1),\end{array}\right\}\tag{4.5}$$

(where in each product the first orbital is a function of electron 1 and the second orbital is a function of electron 2) form a basis for irreducible representations of the groups $C_{\infty v}$ and $C_{4M+2,v}$. Their transformation properties are given in Table I. We further note that the two-electron function,

$$b_1(1)b_1(2)+b_2(1)b_2(2),\tag{4.6}$$

is invariant in both groups. It follows then that the normalized LCAP's defined by [see also Eq. (1.7)][42]

$$^{s\sigma}\Phi_{\Gamma\gamma}=\mathcal{A}\{\cdots(b_1{}^{N-3}b_1{}^{N-2}+b_2{}^{N-3}b_2{}^{N-2})\alpha^{N-3}\beta^{N-2}\times(p_{\Gamma\gamma}\eta_{s\sigma})^{N-1,N}\},\tag{4.7}$$

(where the dots indicate the $2M-1$ lowest orbitals which are doubly occupied) subtend simultaneously the same irreducible representations as the $p_{\Gamma\gamma}$ and $\eta_{s\sigma}$ and therefore perform the following reductions:

$$^2\Delta_M\times{}^2\Delta_{M+1}={}^1\Delta_1+{}^3\Delta_1+{}^1\Delta_{2M+1}+{}^3\Delta_{2M+1}\quad\text{in } C_{\infty v},$$

$$^2E_M\times{}^2E_{M+1}={}^1E_1+{}^3E_1+{}^1B_1+{}^3B_1+{}^1B_2+{}^3B_2\quad\text{in } C_{4M+2,h}.$$

Since each representation occurs only once, the state functions given in Eq. (4.7) are directly the solutions of the variation problem.

The energies of the different states, i.e., the diagonal elements of these state functions with respect to the Hamiltonian in Eq. (1.1), are found to have the form

$$H_0+H_e+H_h+{}^sH_{eh},\tag{4.8}$$

where H_0 is the energy of the closed-shell ground state; H_e comprises the kinetic and framework potential energy of the excited electron *and* its interaction energy with the closed shell; H_h is the analogous energy of the hole created in the closed shell by the excitation; and $^sH_{eh}$ is the interaction energy between the excited electron and the hole. Using the bracket symbol of Eq. (1.11), one finds

$$\left.\begin{array}{l}H_e=\frac{1}{2}\sum_i\{c_i,c_i\},\\ H_h=-\frac{1}{2}\sum_i\{b_i,b_i\}.\end{array}\right\}\tag{4.9}$$

[55] For benzene, these states were given first by Goeppert-Mayer and Sklar (see reference 10) and for the cyclic polyenes the singlet functions were given by Moffitt (see reference 25). They are also implicit in the work of Araki and Murai (see reference 68).

TABLE II. Energy level separations for cyclic polyenes.

$$
\begin{aligned}
s_0 &= \mathcal{E}_{M+1} - \mathcal{E}_M + [b_1b_2|c_1c_2] - [b_1b_1|c_2c_2] \\
s_1 &= 2[b_1c_1|b_1c_1] + 2[b_1c_1|b_2c_2] = 2[b_1c_2|b_1c_2] - 2[b_1c_2|b_2c_1] \\
s_{2M} &= 4[b_1b_2|c_1c_2] \\
s_{2M+1} &= 2[b_1c_1|b_1c_1] - 2[b_1c_1|b_2c_2] \\
\bar{s}_{2M+1} &= 2[b_1c_2|b_1c_2] + 2[b_1c_2|b_2c_1]
\end{aligned}
$$

with

$$\mathcal{E}_M = -H_h = \tfrac{1}{2}\sum_{i=1}^{2}\left\{(b_i|f|b_i) + \sum_{n=0}^{2M}\left(2[\varphi_n\varphi_n|b_ib_i] - [\varphi_nb_i|\varphi_nb_i]\right)\right\}$$

$$\mathcal{E}_{M+1} = H_e = \tfrac{1}{2}\sum_{i=1}^{2}\left\{(c_i|f|c_i) + \sum_{n=0}^{2M}\left(2[\varphi_n\varphi_n|c_ic_i] - [\varphi_nc_i|\varphi_nc_i]\right)\right\}$$

The only part of the energy which depends on the spatial and spin representations, thereby distinguishing the states, is ${}^sH_{eh}$. One has

$$\left.\begin{aligned}
&\left.\begin{aligned}&{}^sH_{eh}(1,1)\\ &{}^sH_{eh}(2M+1,1)\end{aligned}\right\} = \mp{}^s\{b_1c_1,b_2c_2\} - \tfrac{1}{2}{}^s\{b_1c_1,b_1c_1\} - \tfrac{1}{2}{}^s\{b_2c_2,b_2c_2\},\\
&\left.\begin{aligned}&{}^sH_{eh}(1,2)\\ &{}^sH_{eh}(2M+1,2)\end{aligned}\right\} = \pm{}^s\{b_1c_2,b_2c_1\} - \tfrac{1}{2}{}^s\{b_1c_2,b_1c_2\} - \tfrac{1}{2}{}^s\{b_2c_1,b_2c_1\},
\end{aligned}\right\} \tag{4.10}$$

where the arguments of ${}^sH_{eh}$ refer to the functions of Eq. (4.5) and the singlet-triplet dependence of the bracket symbol is given in their definition in Eq. (1.10). Between the two-electron integrals occurring in Eq. (4.10), there exist a number of identities which are due to the fact that certain linear combinations of the orbital products b_ib_j, c_kc_l, b_ic_k, have the transformation properties of irreducible representations of the group. Using these identities, one obtains the energy level spacings shown schematically in Fig. 4, the formulas for the separations being given in Table II. The left-hand side of Fig. 4 shows the levels in the cylindrical potential and the right-hand side indicates the additional splits of the B_1 and B_2 levels induced by the polygonal potential of the actual framework, when added to the hypothetical cylindrical potential. The split of the triplets is symmetrical, with ${}^3E_{1u}$ lying half-way between ${}^3B_{1u}$ and ${}^3B_{2u}$. The ordering of the levels in Fig. 4 has been drawn to correspond to the experimental assignment which will be made for benzene.

5. BENZENE SPECTRUM—THEORY AND EXPERIMENT

Theoretical Spectrum

As indicated in the discussion of Secs. 2 and 3, the values $G(P,Q)$ of the electron interaction function for the distances encountered within one benzene ring must be evaluated semiempirically by fitting the theory to the benzene spectrum.

The theoretical separations between the levels are indicated in Fig. 4 and their formulas are given in Table II. When these are evaluated for benzene by the method outlined in Sec. 3, they are[56]

$$\left.\begin{aligned}
s_0 &= \epsilon_c - \epsilon_b - \tfrac{1}{6}(G_1-G_4) + \tfrac{1}{3}(G_2-G_3),\\
s_1 &= \tfrac{1}{3}(G_1-G_4) + \tfrac{1}{3}(G_2-G_3),\\
s_2 &= \tfrac{1}{3}(G_1+G_4) - \tfrac{1}{3}(G_2+G_3),\\
\bar{s}_3 &= \tfrac{2}{3}(G_1-G_4) - \tfrac{4}{3}(G_2-G_3),\\
s_3 &= 0,
\end{aligned}\right\} \tag{5.1}$$

where ϵ_n are the orbital energies defined in Eq. (2.3) and $G_J = G(1,J)$ with $J = 1, 2, 3, 4$, are the values of $G(P,Q)$ for the four interatomic distances $(0, D, \sqrt{3}D, 2D)$ occurring within one benzene ring. Most conspicuous is the fact that $s_3 = 0$, i.e., ${}^1B_{2u}$ and ${}^3B_{2u}$ coincide, a

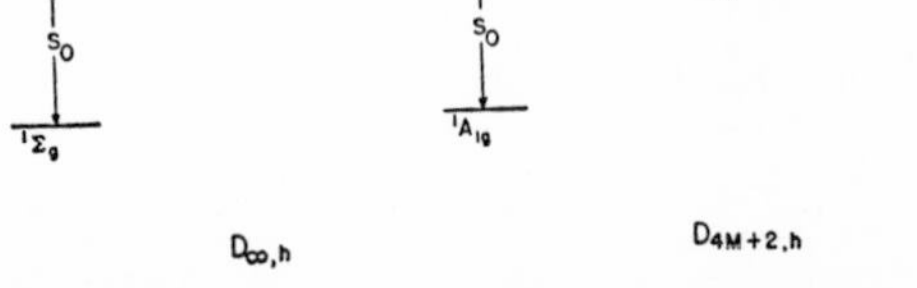

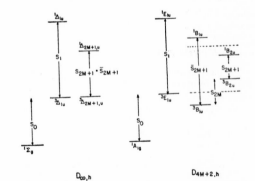

FIG. 4. Energy levels for cyclic polyenes. $D_{\infty h}$: Levels for cylindrical potential. $D_{4M+2,\,h}$: Levels for cylindrical potential with polygonal perturbation.

[56] This system of equations is formally identical with that derived by Pariser and Parr (see reference 17). In their case the place of the G_J's is taken by the Coulomb integrals between the $2p\pi$ atomic orbitals.

result which is due to the use of the properties of paired orbitals in conjunction with our method of integral evaluation as discussed in Eqs. (3.10). In benzene the orbitals b_1 and c_2, as well as b_2 and c_1, are paired.

Experimental Spectrum

The experimental values for the separations s_i depend on the assignment of the spectrum of benzene. This has been critically reviewed recently by Craig.[57] While the assignment of only one transition $({}^1B_{2u})$[58] can be taken as experimentally verified, a combination of theoretical and experimental evidence probably gives the correct assignment. Of the three observed singlet transitions, the analysis of the lowest one at 39.5 kK (kilo-Kayser) shows it to be ${}^1B_{2u}$[59] and the intensity[60] of the one at 56.5 kK leaves little doubt that it is the allowed transition to ${}^1E_{1u}$.[61] It seems likely that the 50-kK transition is to the other singlet, ${}^1B_{1u}$.[57] In our model with ${}^1B_{2u}\equiv{}^3B_{2u}$, the phosphorescent triplet state[62] (corrected to 30.6 kK for the absorption transition) must be assigned to ${}^3B_{1u}$, the lowest theoretical triplet. That ${}^3B_{1u}$ is the lowest triplet is one point of agreement common to most theories.[57] J. S. Ham has found a very weak transition underlying ${}^1B_{2u}$, which could be interpreted as a triplet[63] and on the basis of the zero value of s_3, we assign it as ${}^3B_{2u}$. In support of this, most other theories place ${}^3B_{2u}$ within 2.5 kK of ${}^1B_{2u}$.[13,15,17,57] Another very weak absorption has been observed by A. C. Pitts at 35 kK[64] and could possibly be ${}^3E_{1u}$. The assumed assignment, which agrees with that of Pariser,[21] and the experimental separations are given in Table III.

[57] D. P. Craig, Rev. Pure and Appl. Chem. **3**, 207 (1953).

[58] Ingold *et al.*, J. Chem. Soc. 406 (1948).

[59] Measurements of ${}^1B_{2u}$ band: Sponer, Nordheim, Sklar, and Teller, J. Chem. Phys. **7**, 207 (1939), vapor and solid, absorption and fluorescence; H. Sponer, J. Chem. Phys. **8**, 705 (1940), vapor spectrum; Ingold *et al.*, J. Chem. Soc. 406 (1948), vibrational analysis of absorption and fluorescence spectra; E. Clar, Spectrochim. Acta. **4**, 116 (1950), low temperature rigid glass absorption; A. Kronenberger, Z. Physik **63**, 494 (1930), low temperature solid spectrum.

[60] Part of the intensity of the ${}^1E_{1u}$ band seems to belong to another transition, possibly a molecular Rydberg series. This sharp structure has been removed in the low temperature study of Potts (see reference 61) and Craig (reference 57).

[61] Measurements of ${}^1E_{1u}$ band: E. P. Carr and H. Stücklein, J. Chem. Phys. **6**, 55 (1938), qualitative vapor spectrum; J. R. Platt and H. B. Klevens, Chem. Revs. **41**, 301 (1947), quantitative heptane solution spectrum; W. J. Potts, Jr., J. Chem. Phys. **23**, 73 (1955), quantitative low temperature rigid glass absorption; Pickett, Muntz, and McPherson, J. Am. Chem. Soc. **73**, 4862 (1951), V. J. Hammond and W. C. Price, Trans. Faraday Soc. **51**, 605 (1955), quantitative vapor spectrum; J. Romand and B. Vodar, Compt. rend. **223**, 930 (1951), low temperature solid spectrum.

[62] Phosphorescent emission: G. N. Lewis and M. Kasha, J. Am. Chem. Soc. **66**, 2100 (1944); H. Shull, J. Chem. Phys. **17**, 295 (1949). Singlet-triplet absorption: G. N. Lewis and M. Kasha, J. Am. Chem. Soc. **67**, 994 (1945); A. C. Pitts, J. Chem. Phys. **18**, 1416 (1950).

[63] J. S. Ham, J. Chem. Phys. **21**, 756 (1953)

[64] A. C. Pitts, J. Chem. Phys. **18**, 1416 (1950).

Determination of G_J's

With these experimental separations one might think that the first four equations of Eq. (5.1) determine G_1 to G_4, if the orbital energies are given. However, the combinations of G's occurring in the first and fourth equations are proportional, which leads to the condition on the orbital energies,

$$\epsilon_c-\epsilon_b=s_0+\tfrac{1}{4}\bar{s}_3=2.55E_C. \quad (5.2)$$

This leaves only three equations for the four unknown quantities G_1, G_2, G_3, and G_4. To reduce the redundancy, the additional postulate is made that the R_{PQ}^{-1} dependence of $G(P,Q)$, assumed for distances larger than the benzene diameter, holds also for the R_{14}, the distance apart of a pair of *para*-atoms, so that G_4 is identical with e^2/R_{14}. Inserting this value and the experimental separations from Table III into the system (5.1), one easily obtains the values below. The complete form of the interaction function $G(P,Q)$, in units of E_C and D is thus[39]

$$\left.\begin{array}{ll} G(1,1)=G_1=5.99 & \text{for } R_{11}=0,\text{ i.e., } P=Q,\\ G(1,2)=G_2=3.98 & \text{for } R_{12}=1,\text{ i.e., an } \textit{ortho}\text{-pair } PQ,\\ G(1,3)=G_3=2.97 & \text{for } R_{13}=\sqrt{3},\text{ i.e., a } \textit{meta}\text{-pair } PQ,\\ G(1,4)=G_4=5.30/2=2.65 & \\ & \text{for } R_{14}=2,\text{ i.e., a } \textit{para}\text{-pair } PQ,\\ G(P,Q)\quad =5.30/R_{PQ} & \text{for } R_{PQ}\geqslant R_{14}. \end{array}\right\} \quad (5.3)$$

The curve given in Fig. 2 actually represents these values.[65] It is remarkable that the empirical values G_1, G_2, G_3, which are uniquely computed from spectroscopic data, do fall on such a curve. In fact G_3 even turns out to be very close to the value, which the R^{-1} law would yield, i.e.,

$$e^2/R_{13}=5.30/\sqrt{3}=3.06. \quad (5.4)$$

That these three experimentally determined constants, in conjunction with the R^{-1} function for $R\geqslant R_{14}$, form such a smooth curve of the theoretically predicted shape lends considerable confidence to the basic assumptions.

Necessity for an Effective Mass

It is readily found that the consistency condition (5.2) is not satisfied by the FE orbital energies as determined from the FE network model. They must be reduced by the factor 0.75 in order to fulfill Eq. (5.2). Hence we replace Eq. (2.3) for the FE orbital energies by

$$\epsilon_n=\tfrac{3}{4}E_C\kappa_n^2+E^{tr}+E^t, \quad (5.5)$$

[65] These values for G_1, G_2, G_3, and G_4 are to be compared with Pariser's Coulomb integral values, $(11|11)=5.64E_C$, $(11|22)=3.55E_C$, $(11|33)=2.92E_C$, and $(11|44)=2.56E_C$ (see references 51 and 56). The differences presumably arise because we assume a theoretical value for G_4 and fit the experimental separations s_0, s_1, s_2, and $\bar{s}_3$, whereas Pariser assumes theoretical values for $(11|44)$ and $(11|33)$ and fits the separations s_0, s_2, and $\bar{s}_3$. A further small difference is that Pariser uses a slightly more complicated R dependence than we, for the theoretical values.

which may be written

$$\epsilon_n = E_C^* \kappa_n^2 + E^{tr} + E^t, \tag{5.5'}$$

with[39]

$$E_C^* = \hbar^2/2m^*D^2 = E_C(m/m^*), \tag{5.5''}$$

$$m^* = \tfrac{4}{3}m. \tag{5.5'''}$$

I.e., these new ϵ_n are the FE energies corresponding to the effective electron mass m^*. The appearance of an effective mass is common in theories which approximate a complicated molecular or crystal potential by an average free-electron potential.

Omission of the factor $\frac{3}{4}$ would not affect the separations between the levels but it would place the whole spectrum too high. The necessity for this correction possibly indicates that the framework potential introduced in Eq. (2.10) is not sufficiently negative. This was already anticipated there and perhaps adoption of Eq. (5.5) compensates for this overshielding.[65a]

Alternative Determination of G_J's

An alternative method of determining the G_J's proceeds on the assumption that the orbital energies of the simplified MO theories should be identified with self-consistent field energies,[66] i.e., with the quantities $\mathcal{E}_n$ in Table II. If this is done, the first equation of the system (5.1) becomes

$$s_0 = \epsilon_c - \epsilon_b - \tfrac{1}{6}(G_1 + G_4) - \tfrac{1}{3}(G_2 + G_3). \tag{5.6}$$

The new system of equations is now linearly independent and hence the orbital energies of Eq. (2.3) can be inserted unaltered, thereby *uniquely* determining all G_J's. Curiously it turns out that[67]

$$G_1 = \epsilon_c - \epsilon_b, \tag{5.7}$$

$$G_4 = 0, \tag{5.8}$$

and one obtains the values, in units of E_C,[39]

$$G_1 = 3.34, \quad G_2 = 1.19, \quad G_3 = 0.44, \quad G_4 = 0.00. \tag{5.9}$$

Consequently one has to put $G(P,Q) = 0$ for all distances larger than the separation of two *para*-atoms. A consistent application of this scheme to the polyacenes leads however to energies which are much too low.

[65a] A similar adjustment was found necessary by Pariser and Parr: They had to choose an unusually low β value.

[66] L. Goodman and H. Shull, J. Chem. Phys. **23**, 33 (1955).

[67] Solution of this system of equations yields *uniquely*

$$G_1 = \epsilon_c - \epsilon_b - (s_0 - s_1 - s_2 - \tfrac{1}{4}\bar{s}_3),$$
$$G_4 = \epsilon_c - \epsilon_b + (s_0 - s_1 - s_2 - \tfrac{1}{4}\bar{s}_3) - 2(s_0 - s_2).$$

Equation (5.7) results because of the experimental identity

$$s_0 - s_1 - s_2 - \tfrac{1}{4}\bar{s}_3 = 0;$$

Eq. (5.8) results from the additional coincidence

$$\epsilon_c - \epsilon_b = 2(s_0 - s_2),$$

where the left-hand side contains the theoretical FE orbital energies of Eq. (2.3) and the right-hand side experimental separations.

TABLE III. Assumed benzene assignment.

Excited state	Transition energy[a]	Experimental separations[b]		
$^1E_{1u}$	56.5 kK[c]			
		s_0	35.1 kK[c]	2.24 E_C[c]
$^1B_{1u}$	50.0			
		s_1	21.4	1.36
$^1B_{2u}$	39.5			
		s_2	8.9	0.57
		$\bar{s}_3$	19.4	1.23
$^3B_{2u}$	39.5			
		s_3	0	0
$^3E_{1u}$	35.1			
$^3B_{1u}$	30.6			

[a] These transition energies are for vibrationless, vertical absorptions in the vapor state. The necessary corrections to be applied to the experimental data will be discussed in the following paper, see reference 37.
[b] For the definitions of the separations, see Fig. 4.
[c] See reference 39.

6. OTHER ELECTRON-INTERACTION OPERATORS

It has sometimes been thought that the one-dimensional electron-interaction operator of the FE theory should be e^2/R_{12} for *all* distances. The infinity of this function at $R=0$ gives divergent integrals and several devices which have been designed to cope with this are discussed in this section.

I.

Araki and Murai[68] have attempted to calculate the spectra of the polyacenes starting from one-dimensional free-electron molecular orbitals on a circle.

They observe that the distance R_{12} of two electrons can be expressed in terms of their azimuthal angles θ_1 and θ_2 and the circle circumference L:

$$R_{12} = \pi^{-1} L \sin\tfrac{1}{2}(\theta_1 - \theta_2). \tag{6.1}$$

Hence any electron-interaction function $\mathcal{G}(R_{12})$ can be expanded in a Fourier series,

$$\mathcal{G}(R_{12}) = \sum_k g_k \cos k(\theta_1 - \theta_2). \tag{6.2}$$

The levels obtained will have the arrangement of the $D_{\infty h}$ spectrum of Fig. 4. Since the molecular orbitals have the trigonometric form of Eqs. (4.3), (4.4), calculation of the separations by the formulas of Table II leads to

$$\left.\begin{aligned} s_0 &= \mathcal{E}_{M+1} - \mathcal{E}_M + g_0, \\ s_i &= g_i \quad (i \geq 1). \end{aligned}\right\} \tag{6.3}$$

In order to obtain with the function $\mathcal{G} = e^2/R_{12}$ a finite result for the Fourier coefficients g_i, Araki and Murai use a "cutoff," i.e., in the integrals they put $\mathcal{G}(R) = 0$ in a small domain around $R=0$ adjusted so that the strongest transitions of the polyacenes are predicted correctly. Thus, for benzene with $L = 6D$,

[68] G. Araki and T. Murai, J. Chem. Phys. **22**, 954 (1954).

they obtain

$$\left.\begin{aligned} g_0 &= (e^2/D)\tfrac{1}{3}\ln\cot\tfrac{1}{4}\rho, \\ g_k &= (e^2/D)\tfrac{2}{3}\Big[\ln\cot\tfrac{1}{4}\rho \\ &\quad -\sum_{\nu=1}^{k}(\nu-\tfrac{1}{2})^{-1}\cos(\nu-\tfrac{1}{2})\rho\Big], \end{aligned}\right\} \quad (6.4)$$

where ρ is the cut-off angle. With ρ chosen so that g_1 yields the benzene ${}^1E_{1u}$ level, the value of g_3 is negative so that the other two singlets are placed entirely incorrectly, below the triplets.

II.

In view of the arguments of Sec. 2 concerning the general form of $\mathcal{G}(R)$, we modified their function in the cut-off region by putting it equal to a constant, whose value was such that the function was everywhere continuous.[69] Its Fourier coefficients differ from Eq. (6.4) by the additional terms

$$\left.\begin{aligned} g_0 &: +(e^2/D)(\rho_0/6\sin\tfrac{1}{2}\rho_0), \\ g_k &: +(e^2/D)(\sin k\rho_0/3k\sin\tfrac{1}{2}\rho_0), \end{aligned}\right\} \quad (6.5)$$

and g_3 now becomes positive in qualitative agreement with experiment. However the range of ρ, in the vicinity of $\pi/3$, which gives the experimental separation s_1 correctly, yields a ratio s_1/s_3 of 10/1, whereas the experimental value[70] is 2/1.

III.

In order to pass from the $D_{\infty h}$ spectrum to the D_{6h} spectrum one has to add an hexagonal perturbation. Such a perturbation will lead to an additional N-electron potential U_{hex} in the Hamiltonian of Eq. (1.1) *and to another* additional effective one-electron potential $U_{0,\,hex}$ in Eq. (1.3).[71] The latter equation will yield then the first-order perturbations terms $\phi_{n,\,hex}$ to the zeroth-order circular MO's ϕ_n. Correspondingly one has perturbations $\Phi_{i,\,hex}$ to the zeroth-order state functions Φ_i. The energy perturbation is then given by

$$(\Phi_i|U_{hex}|\Phi_i)+(\Phi_{i,\,hex}|\mathcal{H}|\Phi_{i,\,hex}) + (\Phi_{i,\,hex}|U_{hex}|\Phi_{i,\,hex}), \quad (6.6)$$

where $\mathcal{H}$ is the Hamiltonian of Eq. (1.1). The first term will not split the degeneracies of the $D_{\infty h}$ spectra since U_{hex} is a sum of hexagonal one-electron potentials which do not split the orbital degeneracies. The last term is of second order and will be neglected. Thus the perturbations of the separations are obtained from the middle term by using the formulas of Table II. Now s_2 will be different from zero and s_3 will no longer equal $\bar{s}_3$. These perturbations are determined solely by the sixth Fourier coefficient, u_6, of the perturbation $U_{0,\,hex}$ of the effective potential U_0.[71] The higher Fourier coefficients u_{12}, u_{18} $\cdots$ occur in the MO's but drop out when energy perturbations are formed. Although the resulting energy levels tended to lie in the right order we found it impossible to adjust u_6 and ρ (within the range 0 to $2\pi/3$) to yield anything close to the observed separations, since the ratio g_1/g_3 always remained too large. It is not quite clear whether this is due to an incorrect form for $\mathcal{G}(R)$ or whether it is a poor approximation to consider benzene as a perturbed circular system.

IV.

If one considers that the infinity in the interaction function e^2/R_{12} results from the assumption of zero width for the free-electron tube, one might think of coping with this infinity in a different fashion. When ϵ is very small but not zero, then the region around the origin will be the main contributor and one might try to approximate $\mathcal{G}(R_{12})$ by a Dirac delta function[72]

$$\mathcal{G}(R_{12})=\text{const}\ \delta(R_{12}). \quad (6.7)$$

This eliminates the distinction between Coulomb and exchange integrals, since now

$$\int dx_1\int dx_2\phi_1(x_1)\phi_2(x_1)\mathcal{G}(R_{12})\phi_3(x_2)\phi_4(x_2) = \text{const}\int dx\phi_1(x)\phi_2(x)\phi_3(x)\phi_4(x). \quad (6.8)$$

Thus the separations in benzene become (by virtue of Table II)

$$\left.\begin{aligned} {}^1E_{1u}-{}^3E_{1u} &= A+B, \\ {}^1B_{1u}-{}^3E_{1u} &= 2B, \\ {}^1B_{2u}-{}^3E_{1u} &= 2A, \\ {}^3B_{2u}-{}^3B_{1u} &= 2(B-A), \end{aligned}\right\} \quad (6.9)$$

---

[69] It was Professor J. R. Platt who pointed out that g_3 was negative as given by Araki and Murai and suggested this modification.

[70] The experimental separations referred to here are those of the $D_{\infty h}$ part of the benzene spectrum. In first order, the hexagonal potential leaves the E states unchanged, and splits B_{1u} and B_{2u} symmetrically (for both singlet and triplet). Thus for $D_{\infty h}$, s_1 is the value in Table III and s_3 is the mean value of s_3 and $\bar{s}_3$ in Table III.

[71] In fact one has

$$U_{hex}=\sum_{\text{all electrons }\nu} U_{hex}{}^{\nu},$$

where $U_{hex}{}^{\nu}$ is a hexagonal one-electron potential. By combining Eqs. (2.10) and (6.2) one obtains easily

$$U_{hex}{}^{\nu}=-6\sum_{j=0}^{\infty} g_{6j}\cos 6j(\theta-\pi/6).$$

A similar Fourier expansion exists for the hexagonal perturbation of the effective MO potential:

$$U_{0,\,hex}=\sum_{j=0}^{\infty} u_{6j}\cos 6j(\theta-\pi/6).$$

It must be noted that the coefficients in these two expansions are not identical. The g's are fixed by Eq. (6.4) but the u's are open to adjustment.

[72] Independently, A. A. Frost has recently advanced the same suggestion. A. A. Frost, J Chem. Phys. 22, 1613 (1954).

where

$$\left.\begin{aligned} A &= \text{const} \int dx b_1 b_1 c_1 c_1, \\ B &= \text{const} \int dx b_1 b_1 c_2 c_2. \end{aligned}\right\} \quad (6.10)$$

The results are unsatisfactory in that the strong transition $^1E_{1u}$ is placed between the other two singlets. The delta function assumption, therefore, seems unrealistic.

CONCLUSION

In this paper we have extended the free-electron theory to include electron interaction and in a subsequent paper, we will apply the general method developed here to a number of conjugated hydrocarbons. The present semiempirical procedure can be partly justified on the grounds that by forcing the theory to reproduce the benzene spectrum, we have compensated somewhat for the approximations made along the way. Thus we might hope that similar compensations will occur in a consistent application of this method to related molecules.

ACKNOWLEDGMENTS

Throughout this investigation we have been fortunate in enjoying stimulating discussions with Professor J. R. Platt and we wish to thank him sincerely. As already mentioned the new ideas in the first three parts of Sec. 6 are his. Further we gratefully acknowledge our indebtedness for fruitful contacts with Professor R. G. Parr and Dr. R. Pariser.

Reprinted from THE JOURNAL OF CHEMICAL PHYSICS,
Vol. 29, No. 1, 237, July, 1958
Printed in U. S. A.

Errata: Electronic Interaction in the Free-Electron Network Model for Conjugated Systems. I. Theory

[J. Chem. Phys. 25, 1 (1956)]

NORMAN S. HAM, *Division of Industrial Chemistry, Commonwealth Scientific and Industrial Research Organization, Melbourne, Australia*

AND

KLAUS RUEDENBERG, *Institute for Atomic Research, Iowa State College, Ames, Iowa*

THE numerical values in Eq. (5.3) of the paper referred to in the title should read as follows:

$$G_1 = 5.981$$

$$G_2 = 3.831$$

$$G_3 = 3.086$$

$$G_4 = 2.646.$$

Reprinted from
MOLECULAR PHYSICS, Vol. 2, No. 3, p. 271, July 1959

The pairing of electronic states in alternant hydrocarbons

by A. D. McLACHLAN
Department of Theoretical Chemistry, University Chemical Laboratory, Lensfield Road, Cambridge, England

(*Received* 3 *March* 1959)

The pairing of Hückel molecular orbitals in an alternant hydrocarbon holds in a more general sense for wave functions which make complete allowance for the correlation of π electrons within the atomic orbital scheme. The new pairing property holds exactly in the scope of Pariser, Parr, and Pople's approximations, and leads to an exact correspondence between every detail of the excited states, the electronic spectra and electron resonance spectra of positive and negative hydrocarbon ions. Neutral molecules have a half-filled electron shell in which electrons and holes are on an equal footing. This causes the electron distribution to be uniform in every electronic state, and leads to two kinds of excited state—' even ' and ' odd '—as Pariser first suggested. Transitions between states of the same parity are forbidden. In neutral radicals the spin density vanishes in all the bonds, and in both radicals and molecules the bond orders vanish between atoms of the same set (starred or unstarred).

1. INTRODUCTION

The electron resonance spectra of the positive and negative ions of an alternant hydrocarbon are often remarkably similar in hyperfine structure. Examples are anthracene, tetracene, and perylene [1, 2], which form negative ions in solutions containing free sodium or potassium and positive ions in strong sulphuric acid. The spectra of corresponding ions match in every detail and, as Carrington's experimental data in table 1 illustrate, the splitting constants from corresponding hydrogen atoms are almost equal. On the other hand there is no such spectral resemblance in the positive and negative ions of non-alternant hydrocarbons like acepleiadylene [1]. Hoijtink and Weijland [3] have found another interesting similarity between positive and negative ions of alternant hydrocarbons in the electronic spectra of perylene ions. The two spectra are almost indistinguishable, not only in the energies of the transitions, but also in their intensities, down to the smallest detail.

The similarity of these ions arises from a close correspondence between their electronic structures, which is peculiar to alternant hydrocarbons and is lost if the molecule contains odd-membered rings or if the aromatic system includes other atoms such as nitrogen.

In the molecular orbital theory of alternant hydrocarbons these peculiar electronic relationships arise from a pairing property between the energies and wave functions of the bonding and antibonding π orbitals. This accounts for all the observed similarities between corresponding positive and negative ions, and leads to many other interesting general properties of neutral molecules and radicals. However, the molecular orbital method has a serious limitation. No wave function constructed from a single configuration of orbitals can allow fully for the effect of the Coulomb forces between the electrons. Yet one has to use a wave function containing several configurations to interpret the electronic spectra in detail, or to account for the negative spin densities [4] which play an important part in the electron resonance spectra of many radicals.

Molecule	Ion	Splitting constants (gauss)		
		α	β	γ
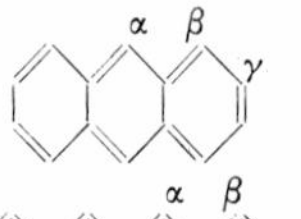	+	6·65	3·11	1·40
	−	5·56	2·74	1·57
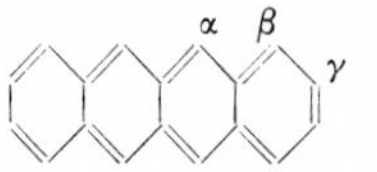	+	5·17	1·74	1·17
	−	4·25	1·49	1 03
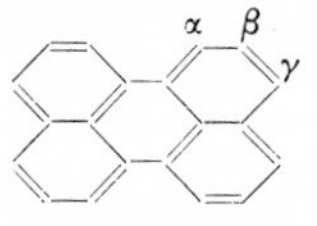	+	3·09	0 46	4·11
	−	3·09	0 46	5·53

Table 1. Hyperfine splitting constants in corresponding positive and negative ions.

The special result of the molecular orbital theory is by itself too crude to account for the closeness of the resemblance between positive and negative ions. We therefore suggest that the pairing property of the states in an alternant hydrocarbon holds in a more general sense, even when the wave functions include every possible configuration. In this paper we shall show that the wave function for each electronic state of a positive alternant ion is paired in this extended sense with a corresponding state of the negative ion. In the scope of the L.C.A.O. and π-electron approximations and the semi-empirical theory of Pople [5, 6] the new pairing theorem holds exactly. This is true even when the ground configuration is allowed to mix with every excited configuration, so that the effects of electron correlation are treated as exactly as possible. The new theorem confirms and extends many predictions of the simple molecular orbital theory, including those about the spectra of hydrocarbon ions.

Pairing relations arise in their simplest form in the Hückel molecular orbital theory [7, 8]. In an alternant hydrocarbon the aromatic system contains only even-membered rings of atoms, and alternate carbon atoms round the ring then divide into two groups called the starred and unstarred.

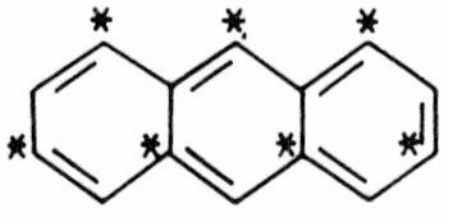

Each molecular orbital

$$\psi_i = \sum_{1}^{n} C_{ri}\phi_r \tag{1.1}$$

now has an image orbital ψ_i' with the opposite energy and with coefficients C'_{ri}.

$$\left.\begin{aligned} C'_{ri} &= C_{ri} \text{ on starred atoms,} \\ C'_{ri} &= -C_{ri} \text{ on unstarred atoms,} \\ \epsilon_i' &= -\epsilon_i. \end{aligned}\right\} \tag{1.2}$$

For this pairing relation to hold three conditions are necessary:

(*a*) the atomic orbitals $\phi_1 \ldots \phi_n$ are orthogonal;

(*b*) the 'Coulomb integrals' α_r are all equal;

(*c*) the 'resonance integral' β_{rs} vanishes if the two atoms do not form a bond.

Figure 1 (*a*), (*b*) and (*c*) shows the relations between the electronic structures of the neutral molecule, the monopositive ion, and the mononegative ion. The neutral molecule has two electrons in each of the bonding orbitals $\psi_1 \ldots \psi_m$, while the ions have a vacancy in ψ_m or an extra electron in ψ'_m. The excited states of the positive and negative ions are also related in pairs. The promotion of an electron from ψ_i to ψ'_j is matched by one from ψ_j to ψ'_i, and the excitation energies are both equal to $(\epsilon_j + \epsilon_i)$. Thus it is better to regard the pairing property in ions as a relation between the occupied orbitals of one ion and the empty ones of the other (figure 1 (*b*), (*c*)).

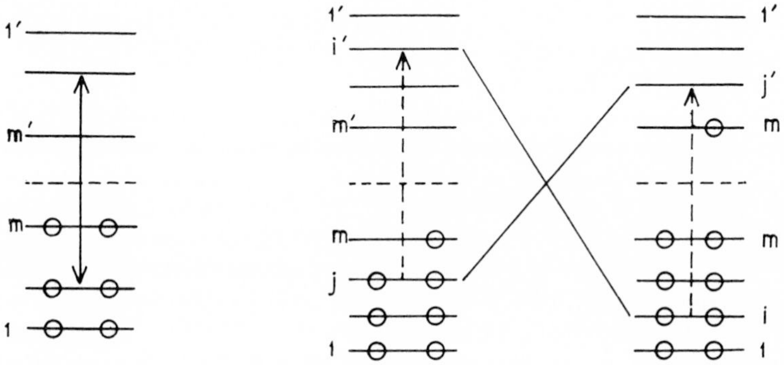

(*a*) (*b*) (*c*)

Figure 1. Electronic structure of alternant hydrocarbons according to Hückel theory

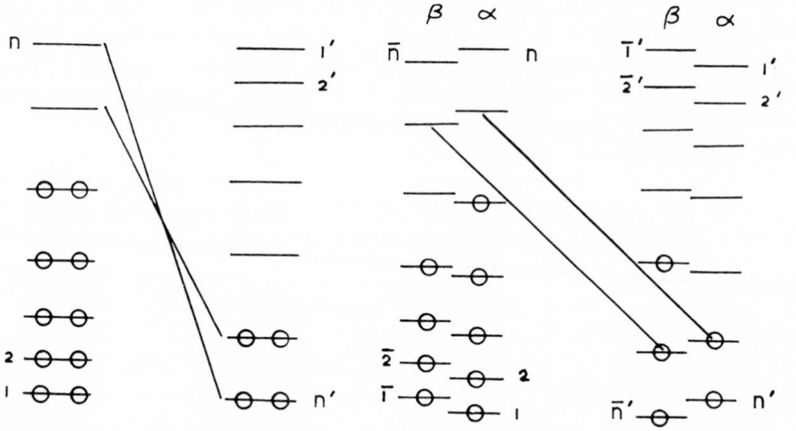

(*a*) (*b*)

Figure 2. Pairing of self-consistent orbitals in (*a*) closed shell ions; (*b*) radical ions.

Pople [6] found that the self-consistent orbitals calculated according to the Pariser and Parr method are paired in neutral molecules, and Hush and Pople [9] were able to deduce a relation

$$I + A = \text{const.} \tag{1.3}$$

between their ionization potentials and electron affinities. Pople and Brickstock [10] went further, showing that the occupied self-consistent orbitals of a positive closed shell ion are the images of the vacant orbitals in the negative ion (figure 2 (*a*)). Two approaches have been adopted in the self-consistent molecular orbital theory of radicals. In Pople and Longuet-Higgins' method [11] the $(2m+1)$ electrons occupy m orbitals in pairs and one other, to give a single determinant of the form

$$\psi = \| \psi_1^\alpha \psi_1^\beta \ldots \psi_m^\alpha \psi_m^\beta \psi_0^\alpha \|. \tag{1.4}$$

Lefèbvre [12] showed that the bonding and antibonding orbitals in (1.4) are paired so that $\psi_{n-r+1} = \psi'_r$, $\psi_0 = \psi'_0$. In Pople and Nesbet's theory [13] the electrons of α and β spin occupy two parallel but slightly different sets of self-consistent orbitals $\psi_1 \ldots \psi_n$ and $\bar{\psi}_1 \ldots \bar{\psi}_n (\psi_r \simeq \bar{\psi}_r)$, and the wave function is

$$\psi = \| \psi_1^\alpha \bar{\psi}_1^\beta \ldots \psi_m^\alpha \bar{\psi}_m^\beta \psi_0^\alpha \|. \tag{1.5}$$

In radical ions ψ_r for the negative ion is the image of $\bar{\psi}_{n-r}$ from the positive ion [10], as shown in figure 2 (*b*).

2. The pairing of configurations

The pairing convention which we shall adopt for the general method is a simple extension of that illustrated in figure 2 (*a*). In an alternant hydrocarbon with n carbon atoms we begin by forming a basic set of n orthonormal molecular orbitals $\psi_1 \ldots \psi_n$ which are linear combinations of the n atomic orbitals $\phi_1 \ldots \phi_n$. (Since we are going to include every possible configuration it does not matter how we choose the set $\psi_1 \ldots \psi_n$.) There need not be any pairing relations between the coefficients of the ψ's, but we note that $\psi'_1 \ldots \psi'_n$, the set of images of ψ, is another equally good orthonormal basic set of molecular orbitals. The molecular orbitals give rise to a basic set of $2n$ orthonormal spin-orbitals $\psi_1^\alpha \psi_1^\beta \ldots \psi_n^\alpha \psi_n^\beta$ which we denote by $\bar{\psi}_1 \ldots \bar{\psi}_{2n}$. Similarly the images ψ' give spin orbitals $\psi'^\beta_1 \psi'^\alpha_1 \ldots \psi'^\beta_n \psi'^\alpha_n$, which we write $\bar{\psi}'_1 \ldots \bar{\psi}'_{2n}$. Each $\bar{\psi}$ has the opposite spin to its image.

Suppose now that we have a positive ion with $(n-r)$ electrons, and the corresponding negative ion with $(n+r)$. The wave function Φ of any electronic state of the positive ion will be built up as a sum of Slater determinants χ_λ, each of $(n-r)$ spin-orbitals

$$\Phi = \sum_\lambda a_\lambda \chi_\lambda, \tag{2.1}$$

where

$$\chi_\lambda = \langle abc \ldots d| = \|abc \ldots d\|. \tag{2.2}$$

In the configuration represented by χ_λ an electron occupies each of the spin-orbitals $a, b, c, \ldots, d$ and $\|abc \ldots d\|$ is a normalized Slater determinant. The remaining $(n+r)$ spin-orbitals $e, f, \ldots, g$ are all vacant, and we could use them to form a corresponding configuration of the negative ion. Such a configuration would have a very different energy; so instead we take their images $e', f', \ldots, g'$ and form

$$\chi'_\lambda = |e'f' \ldots g'\rangle = \pm \|e'f' \ldots g'\|. \tag{2.3}$$

The corresponding complete wave function is

$$\Phi' = \sum_\lambda a_\lambda \chi'_\lambda. \tag{2.4}$$

This definition is perfectly general. If $\psi_1, \ldots, \psi_n$ are Hückel orbitals it agrees with the usual interpretation of figure 1, and it includes all the pairing relations between different types of self-consistent orbitals. The wave function (1.5) with different orbitals for different spins also pairs according to (2.4) if it is expanded in terms of configurations from a single set of orbitals $\psi_1, \ldots, \psi_n$.

Suppose that Φ_x is the correct wave function for the positive ion in a particular electronic state. We now wish to show that the negative ion has a corresponding electronic state Φ'_x, and further, that the excitation energies of the two states from their respective ground states are equal.

$$\left.\begin{aligned} &\Phi_x \to \Phi'_x;\ E_x \to E_{x'}, \\ &E_x - E_0 = E'_x - E'_0. \end{aligned}\right\} \qquad (2.5)$$

This can only be true if the matrix elements of the energy satisfy the equations

$$\begin{aligned} &\langle\chi_\lambda|H|\chi_\mu\rangle = \langle\chi'_\lambda|H|\chi'_\mu\rangle, \qquad \lambda \neq \mu, \\ &\langle\chi_\lambda|H|\chi_\lambda\rangle = \langle\chi'_\lambda|H|\chi'_\lambda\rangle + \text{const.} \end{aligned} \qquad (2.6)$$

for all corresponding pairs of configurations. In establishing (2.6) there are two points to consider. First are the approximations we make in the Hamiltonian so that corresponding matrix elements are equal in magnitude. This is discussed in the next section. Second are the signs of the matrix elements. We must be sure that it is possible to choose the sign of χ'_λ in (2.3) so that (2.6) is internally consistent. Suppose that $ab \ldots c$ or $\alpha\beta \ldots \gamma$ are the spin-orbitals which

$$\left.\begin{aligned} &\chi_\lambda = \langle ab.p..q..c| \\ \text{and} \qquad &\chi_\mu = \langle \alpha\beta..r..s.\gamma| \end{aligned}\right\} \qquad (2.7)$$

have in common, though not necessarily in the same order, and those which are not common occur in the order $p \ldots q$ and $r \ldots s$ respectively. Then we can derive χ_μ from χ_λ in two stages. First apply a permutation P^+ to the orbitals of χ_λ which puts the common orbitals $ab \ldots c$ into the order $\alpha\beta \ldots \gamma$, p in the position of $r, \ldots$, and q in the position of s.

$$P^+\chi_\lambda = \langle \alpha\beta..p..q.\gamma|. \qquad (2.8)$$

Then perform a substitution $T(p \ldots q \to r \ldots s)$ which replaces spin-orbital p of χ_λ by the spin-orbital r of χ_μ, q by s, and so on. We write

$$\chi_\mu = TP^+\chi_\lambda. \qquad (2.9)$$

In the corresponding negative ion

$$\left.\begin{aligned} &\chi'_\lambda = |d'e'.r'..s'..f'\rangle, \\ &\chi'_\mu = |\delta'\epsilon'..p'..q'.\zeta'\rangle, \end{aligned}\right\} \qquad (2.10)$$

and we have a permutation P^- which rearranges the common orbitals of χ'_λ:

$$P^-\chi'_\lambda = |\delta'\epsilon'..r'..s'.\zeta'\rangle. \qquad (2.11)$$

The substitution corresponding to T is $T^{-1} = T(r' \ldots s' \to p' \ldots q')$, so that

$$\chi'_\mu = T^{-1}P^-\chi'_\lambda. \qquad (2.12)$$

We now define the symbol $(p \ldots q|H|r \ldots s)$ to stand for the energy matrix element between two determinants like χ_μ and $P^+\chi_\lambda$ whose common orbitals are matched in the correct order and which differ by the substitution $T(p \ldots q \to r \ldots s)$. The corresponding matrix element for the states of the negative ion is

$$(r' \ldots s'|H|p' \ldots q').$$

It is here that the difficulty of sign arises, because the approximations we make later on show that

$$(p \ldots q|H|r \ldots s) = (-)^t(r' \ldots s'|H|p' \ldots q') \qquad (2.13)$$

where t is the number of orbitals which differ in χ_λ and χ_μ. To reconcile equations (2.13) and (2.6) we have to show that if the signs of one corresponding pair of states are chosen arbitrarily so that $\langle ab\ldots c| = \|ab\ldots c\|$ corresponds to $|d'e'\ldots f'\rangle = +\|d'e'\ldots f'\|$, then $\langle \alpha\beta\ldots\gamma| = \|\alpha\beta\ldots\gamma\|$ must correspond to $|\delta'\epsilon'\ldots\zeta'\rangle = (-)^P\|\delta'\epsilon'\ldots\zeta'\|$ where $(-)^P$ is the sign of the permutation

$$\langle \alpha\beta\ldots\gamma|\delta\epsilon\ldots\zeta\rangle = P\langle ab\ldots c|de\ldots f\rangle. \tag{2.14}$$

To see this we note that P is the product of the three permutations P^+, P^-, and the transpositions $t=(pr)\ldots.(qs)$:

$$P = tP^+P^-. \tag{2.15}$$

Then

$$\begin{aligned}\langle ab\ldots c|H|\alpha\beta\ldots\gamma\rangle &= \|ab\ldots c|H|\alpha\beta\ldots\gamma\| \text{ by (2.2)}\\ &= (-)^{P^+}(p\ldots q|H|r\ldots s),\\ &= (-)^{P^-}(-)^t(-)^P(p\ldots q|H|r\ldots s) \text{ by (2.15)}\\ &= (-)^P(-)^{P^-}(r'\ldots s'|H|p'\ldots q') \text{ from (2.13)}\\ &= (-)^P\|d'e'\ldots f'|H|\delta'\epsilon'\ldots\zeta'\|\\ &= \langle d'e'\ldots f'|H|\delta'\epsilon'\ldots\zeta'\rangle \text{ by hypothesis,}\end{aligned} \tag{2.16}$$

so that our conclusion is indeed self-consistent.

3. Matrix elements of the energy

We shall base our treatment on the Pariser and Parr theory of π electron molecules. In this theory it is assumed that the main features of the electronic spectra of hydrocarbons depend solely on the π electrons. Their energy is described by a Hamiltonian of the type

$$H = \sum_\mu U(\mathbf{r}_\mu) + \sum_{\mu\nu}\frac{e^2}{r_{\mu\nu}}, \tag{3.1}$$

in which the first term is the energy of the electron in the averaged field of a core of nuclei and σ electrons, while the last is the mutual Coulomb repulsion of the π electrons. The wave function for the π electrons is always assumed to be formed from combinations of n $2pz$ atomic orbitals $\phi_1\ldots\phi_n$, one from each carbon atom, so that the expectation value of H is expressed in terms of integrals over atomic orbitals. These may be core integrals

$$\left.\begin{aligned}\beta_{rs} &= \int \phi_r U \phi_s d\tau \quad (r\neq s),\\ E_r &= \int \phi_r U_r \phi_r d\tau,\\ g_{rt} &= -\int \phi_r U_t \phi_r d\tau \quad (r \neq t),\\ \alpha_r &= E_r - \sum_t g_{rt}\end{aligned}\right\} \tag{3.2}$$

(in which U_t stands for the potential energy of an electron in the field of atom t), or electron repulsion integrals

$$\left.\begin{aligned}\langle rs|tu\rangle &= \int \phi_r\phi_t(1)\frac{e^2}{r_{12}}\phi_s\phi_u(2)d\tau_1\,d\tau_2,\\ \langle rs|rs\rangle &\equiv \gamma_{rs}.\end{aligned}\right\} \tag{3.3}$$

Up to this point the theory is perfectly general except for the assumption of only one atomic orbital per atom. But several further approximations are usually made to simplify the method, and these are all necessary for proving the pairing theorem. The assumptions are:

(1) The orbitals $\phi_1 \ldots \phi_n$ are exactly orthogonal.

(2) We neglect electron repulsion integrals which arise from the overlap of two orbitals;

$$\langle rs|tu\rangle = \delta_{rt}\delta_{su}\gamma_{rt}. \tag{3.4}$$

This is the assumption of 'zero differential overlap'.

(3) An electron is perfectly shielded from the nuclear charges of other atoms when the other atom bears a π electron;

$$g_{rt} = \gamma_{rt} \text{ when } r \neq t. \tag{3.5}$$

(4) The effective potential energy of a π electron is the same on each carbon atom;

$$E_r + \tfrac{1}{2}\gamma_{rr} = \text{const.} = K \text{ for all atoms.} \tag{3.6}$$

(5) An alternant hydrocarbon is characterized by the division of its atoms into the starred and unstarred sets. $\beta_{rs} = 0$ when atoms r, s belong to the same set (in which case they cannot be neighbours).

Let $\psi_1 \ldots \psi_n$ be a complete set of real orthogonal molecular orbitals of the form $\psi_i = \sum C_{ri}\phi_r$. Their coefficients then have the property

$$\sum_{i=1}^{n} C_{ri}C_{si} = \delta_{rs}. \tag{3.7}$$

We form pairs of configurations χ_λ, χ'_λ, and define bond orders and electron densities for electrons of α and β spins in any configuration of a positive ion, and the corresponding configuration of the negative ion by summation over the occupied orbitals in each system.

$$\left.\begin{aligned} q_r^{+\alpha} &= \sum_i{}^{\alpha} C_{ri}^2, & q_r^{+\beta} &= \sum_i{}^{\beta} C_{ri}^2, \\ p_{rs}^{+\alpha} &= \sum_i{}^{\alpha} C_{ri}C_{si}, & p_{rs}^{-\beta} &= \sum_i{}^{\beta} C_{ri}C_{si}. \end{aligned}\right\} \tag{3.8}$$

We may also use the total bond orders and electron densities p_{rs} and q_r. The orthogonality relations (3.7) and the definitions (1.2) and (2.3) of the pairing property show that

$$\left.\begin{aligned} q_r^{+\alpha} + q_r^{-\beta} &= 1, \\ p_{rs}^{+\alpha} &= p_{rs}^{-\beta} \text{ if } r, s \text{ are in different sets} \\ &= -p_{rs}^{-\beta} \text{ if } r, s \text{ are in the same sets.} \end{aligned}\right\} \tag{3.9}$$

The matrix elements of the energy for corresponding pairs of configurations are now expressed in terms of integrals over molecular orbitals. The diagonal elements ϵ_λ and ϵ'_λ for χ_λ and χ'_λ are

$$\left.\begin{aligned} \epsilon_\lambda &= \sum_i (A_{ii} + B_{ii}) + \sum_{ij} \{\langle ij|ij\rangle - \sigma_{ij}\langle ij|ji\rangle\} \\ \epsilon'_\lambda &= \sum_i{}' (A'_{ii} + B'_{ii}) + \sum_{ij}{}' \{\langle i'j'|i'j'\rangle - \sigma_{ij}\langle i'j'|j'i'\rangle\}, \end{aligned}\right\} \tag{3.10}$$

where

$$\left.\begin{aligned} A_{ii} &= \sum_r C_{ri}^2\alpha_r = \sum_r C'^2_{ri}\alpha_r = A'_{ii}, \\ B_{ii} &= \sum_{rs} C_{ri}C_{si}\beta_{rs} = -\sum_{rs} C'_{ri}C'_{si}\beta_{rs} = -B'_{ii}, \end{aligned}\right\} \tag{3.11}$$

$$\langle ij|ij\rangle = \langle i'j'|i'j'\rangle = \sum_{rs} C_{ri}^2 C_{sj}^2 \gamma_{rs}, \tag{3.12}$$

$$\langle ij|ji\rangle = \langle i'j'|j'i'\rangle = \sum_{rs} (C_{ri}C_{si})(C_{rj}C_{sj})\gamma_{rs}, \tag{3.13}$$

and $\sigma_{ij} = 1$ or 0 when the spin orbitals $\bar{\psi}_i$, $\bar{\psi}_j$ have the same or opposite spins.

When these substitutions and summations are made the total π-electron energy of χ is

$$\epsilon = U + G, \tag{3.14}$$

with

$$U = \sum_r q_r(E_r - \sum_t{}' g_{rt}) + 2\sum_{r<s} p_{rs}\beta_{rs}, \tag{3.15}$$

$$G = \sum_{r<s} [(q_r q_s - (p^{\alpha}_{rs})^2 - (p^{\beta}_{rs})^2)]\gamma_{rs} + \sum_r q^{\alpha}_r q^{\beta}_r \gamma_{rr}. \tag{3.16}$$

The term G may be rearranged into the form

$$G = \sum_{r<s} [(q_r - 1)(q_s - 1) - 1 - (p^{\alpha}_{rs})^2 - (p^{\beta}_{rs})^2]\gamma_{rs}$$
$$+ \sum_r q_r(\tfrac{1}{2}\gamma_{rr} + \sum_t{}' \gamma_{rt}) + \sum_r [(q^{\alpha}_r - \tfrac{1}{2})(q^{\beta}_r - \tfrac{1}{2}) - \tfrac{1}{4}]\gamma_{rr}. \tag{3.17}$$

It is now evident from (3.9), and the fact that β_{rs} vanishes for atoms of the same set, that many of the terms in (3.15) and (3.17) are unchanged when we pass from the positive to the negative ion. The difference between the energies of the two molecules is

$$\epsilon^+ - \epsilon^- = \sum_r 2(q^+_r - 1)[E_r + \tfrac{1}{2}\gamma_{rr} + \sum_t (\gamma_{rt} - g_{rt})]. \tag{3.18}$$

This is equal to $\sum_r 2(q^+_r - 1)K$ by the assumptions (3) and (4), so that

$$\epsilon^+ - \epsilon^- = -2rK = \text{const.} \tag{3.19}$$

for all electronic states of an ion with $(n-r)$ electrons, and we have proved the second result of (2.6).

The off-diagonal elements of H are between states which differ by the excitation of either one or two electrons. For one-electron excitations we wish to show that, in the notation of (2.10)

$$(p|H|q) = -(q'|H|p'). \tag{3.20}$$

Now

$$\left.\begin{aligned} (p|H|q) &= U_{pq} + \sum_x \{\langle px|qx\rangle - \sigma_{px}\langle px|xq\rangle\} \\ (q'|H|p') &= U_{p'q'} + \sum_{x'}{}' \{\langle p'x'|q'x'\rangle - \sigma_{p'x'}\langle p'x'|x'q'\rangle\} \end{aligned}\right\} \tag{3.21}$$

where $\sum$, $\sum'$ stand for summation over all the other occupied spin orbitals x, x' of their respective ions. It is easy to show from the pairing relations that

$$\langle px|qx\rangle = \langle p'x'|q'x'\rangle; \quad \langle px|xq\rangle = \langle p'x'|x'q'\rangle \tag{3.22}$$

and the coefficients of β_{rs} in $(U_{pq} + U_{p'q'})$ vanish. Thus

$$(p|H|q) + (q'|H|p') = \sum_r 2C_{rp}C_{rq}(E_r - \sum_t{}' g_{rt})$$
$$+ \sum_1^{2n} \{\langle px|qx\rangle - \tfrac{1}{2}\langle px|xq\rangle\}. \tag{3.23}$$

The electrostatic integrals may now be written

$$\sum_{x=1}^{2n} \sum_{rs} \{C_{rp}C_{rq}C^2_{xs} - \tfrac{1}{2}C_{rp}C_{sq}C_{xr}C_{xs}\}\gamma_{rs} \tag{3.24}$$

which the orthogonality relations reduce to

$$\sum_r C_{rp}C_{rq}(2\sum_{r\neq s}\gamma_{rs} + \gamma_{rr}). \tag{3.25}$$

Hence finally

$$(p|H|q)+(q'|H|p')=2\sum_r C_{rp}C_{rq}[E_r+\tfrac{1}{2}\gamma_{rr}+\sum_t(\gamma_{rt}-g_{rt})]$$
$$=2\sum_r C_{rp}C_{rq}K$$
$$=0, \text{ by (3.7).} \tag{3.26}$$

The matrix elements $(pq|H|rs)$ for a double excitation depend only on electron repulsion integrals like $\langle pq|rs\rangle$ between molecular orbitals. Since

$$\langle p'q'|r's'\rangle=\langle pq|rs\rangle,$$

because of (2.3), it follows that

$$(pq|H|rs)=(r's'|H|p'q') \tag{3.27}$$

and the result anticipated in the previous section is proved. There is therefore an exact parallel between every detail of the electronic energy levels and excited states of corresponding alternant hydrocarbon positive and negative ions. This theorem holds under assumptions which are physically reasonable and have proved useful for understanding the electronic spectra of these molecules. They also appear to be the most general ones within which the desired result is true. Assumptions (3) and (4) together are essential to (3.19) and (3.26)—the pairing property does not hold if the ring contains nitrogen atoms. Assumption (1) is necessary for the orthogonality relations (3.7), and (2) is responsible for the special form of the Coulomb energy in (3.16). If we allow overlap, and form new orthogonal orbitals from the original set, they will have resonance integrals β_{rs} between atoms of the same set, and the hydrocarbon will no longer be truly 'alternant'. Any extension of this pairing theorem would require special and purely coincidental relations between the values of overlap integrals, Coulomb integrals $\langle rs|tu\rangle$, and resonance integrals β_{rs}.

4. Electrons and holes

One can regard the motion of $(n+r)$ electrons over n atomic orbitals as the motion of $(n-r)$ positive holes in a closed shell of 2n electrons. On going from a positive to a negative ion electrons are replaced by holes, and the holes have their own wave functions and effective Hamiltonian. In this view the special properties of alternant hydrocarbons arise because the neutral molecule has a half-filled shell of electrons, and there is a special symmetry between the Hamiltonians of holes and electrons in the ions. The results of the previous section can be interpreted in this way. Corresponding to the configuration

$$\chi=||ab\ldots c|| \tag{4.1}$$

for the electrons, (2.2) we define

$$\bar{\chi}=(-)^P||\ de..f|| \tag{4.2}$$

for the holes. The bond orders $\bar{p}^\chi_{rs}$, $\bar{q}^\chi_r$ for the holes are then

$$\bar{p}^\chi_{rs}=-p^\chi_{rs},\ \bar{q}^\chi_r=1-q^\chi_r; \tag{4.3}$$

and the energy of χ can be written in terms of quantities derived from $\bar{\chi}$ by substituting (4.3) into (3.17). The result is that

$$E=2\sum_r[E_r+\tfrac{1}{2}\gamma_{rr}+\sum_{r\neq t}(\gamma_{rt}-g_{rt})]+\langle\bar{\chi}|\bar{H}|\bar{\chi}\rangle$$
$$=2nK+\langle\bar{\chi}|\bar{H}|\bar{\chi}\rangle, \tag{4.4}$$

where $\bar{H}$ is now an effective Hamiltonian for the holes, of the form

$$\bar{H}=\sum_{\mu}\bar{U}(\mathbf{r}_{\mu})+\sum_{\mu\nu}\frac{e^2}{r_{\mu\nu}}, \tag{4.5}$$

representing the sum of a core energy $\bar{U}$ and the mutual Coulomb repulsions of the holes. The expectation value of the Coulomb repulsions is to be calulated with the same integrals γ_{rs} as before. The core energy is determined by the new integrals

$$\left.\begin{aligned}\bar{\alpha}_r&=-[E_r+\gamma_{rr}+\sum_t{}'(2\gamma_{rt}-g_{rt})],\\ \bar{\beta}_{rs}&=-\beta_{rs},\end{aligned}\right\} \tag{4.6}$$

which are closely related to those for electrons since

$$\left.\begin{aligned}\bar{\alpha}_r&=-K-(\tfrac{1}{2}\gamma_{rr}+\sum_t{}'\gamma_{rt}),\\ \alpha_r&=K-(\tfrac{1}{2}\gamma_{rr}+\sum_t{}'\gamma_{rt}).\end{aligned}\right\} \tag{4.7}$$

Hence, apart from a constant,

$$\left.\begin{aligned}\alpha_r&=+\bar{\alpha}_r,\\ \beta_{rs}&=-\bar{\beta}_{rs}.\end{aligned}\right\} \tag{4.8}$$

To establish a complete parallel between electrons and holes we need to consider the off-diagonal matrix elements of $\bar{H}$. Adapting the notation of § 3 we find that

$$\left.\begin{aligned}(p|H|q)+(q|\bar{H}|p)&=0,\\ (pq|H|rs)&=(rs|\bar{H}|pq),\end{aligned}\right\} \tag{4.9}$$

so that the correspondence between the wave functions of electrons and holes is defined similarly to that between paired configurations of positive and negative ions. If, for example, the spin orbitals are $abcdef$ and $\chi=\|abc\|$ corresponds to $\bar{\chi}=\|def\|$, then $\|\alpha\beta\gamma\|$ corresponds to $(-)^P\|\delta\epsilon\zeta\|$, where P is the permutation

$$P=\begin{pmatrix}a & b & c & d & e & f\\ \alpha & \beta & \gamma & \delta & \epsilon & \zeta\end{pmatrix}. \tag{4.10}$$

(4.10) shows that it is possible to speak consistently of the holes in any closed shell system whatsoever having a definite wave function and Hamiltonian. The special feature of alternant hydrocarbons is the connection (4.8) between the Hamiltonians of the electrons and the effective Hamiltonian of the holes. This leads to the result that the wave function Φ' of the $(n+r)$ electrons in a negative ion is identical with $\bar{\Phi}$ for the $(n+r)$ holes in the corresponding state Φ of the positive ion, provided that each spin-orbital $\bar{\psi}$ is replaced by its image $\bar{\psi}'$. Thus for

$$\left.\begin{array}{lll}\text{electrons in the positive ion,} & \chi=\langle ab\ldots c| & ;\\ \text{for holes in the positive ion,} & \bar{\chi}= & |de\ldots f\rangle;\\ \text{for electrons in the negative ion,} & \chi'= & |d'e'\ldots f'\rangle.\end{array}\right\} \tag{4.11}$$

5. The electronic spectra of ions

The intensities of corresponding transitions

$$\Phi_x\to\Phi_y \;:\; \Phi'_x\to\Phi'_y \tag{5.1}$$

are determined by the dipole moments $\mathbf{M}_{xy}$ and $\mathbf{M}'_{xy}$:

$$\mathbf{M}_{xy}=\langle\Phi_x|\mathbf{M}|\Phi_y\rangle,\ \mathbf{M}=\sum-e(\mathbf{r}_i). \tag{5.2}$$

These can be expressed in terms of integrals over single configurations by substituting

$$\Phi_x = \sum a_{\lambda x}\chi_\lambda,\ \Phi_y = \sum a_{\mu y}\chi_\mu, \tag{5.3}$$

and finally reduced to integrals over the atomic orbitals $\phi_1 \ldots \phi_n$;

$$\langle \chi_\lambda | \mathbf{M} | \chi_\mu \rangle = \mathbf{M}_{\lambda\mu} = \sum_r (q_r)^{\lambda\mu}\mathbf{M}_r + 2\sum_{r<s}(p_{rs})^{\lambda\mu}\mathbf{M}_{rs}, \tag{5.4}$$

where

$$\left.\begin{aligned} \mathbf{M}_r &= \int \phi_r \mathbf{M} \phi_r d\tau, \\ \mathbf{M}_{rs} &= \int \phi_r \mathbf{M} \phi_s d\tau. \end{aligned}\right\} \tag{5.5}$$

Here $(q_r)^{\lambda\mu}$ and $(p_{rs})^{\lambda\mu}$ are generalized electron densities and bond orders, which have the usual meaning when $\lambda = \mu$, and when $\lambda \neq \mu$ are defined as the coefficients of α_r and β_{rs} in $H_{\lambda\mu}$. Similarly we can define $(q_r)^{xy}$ and $(p_{rs})^{xy}$ to be the coefficients of α_r and β_{rs} in $\langle \Phi_x | H | \Phi_y \rangle$ so that

$$(q_r)^{xy} \equiv \frac{\partial H_{xy}}{\partial \alpha_r} \quad \text{and} \quad (p_{rs})^{xy} \equiv \frac{\partial H_{xy}}{\partial \beta_{rs}}. \tag{5.6}$$

Their values are found from (5.3) to be

$$\left.\begin{aligned} (q_r)^{xy} &= \sum a_{\lambda x} a_{\mu y} (q_r)^{\lambda\mu}, \\ (p_{rs})^{xy} &= \sum a_{\lambda x} a_{\mu y} (p_{rs})^{\lambda\mu}. \end{aligned}\right\} \tag{5.7}$$

The pairing theorem leads to special relations between the bond orders of corresponding transitions.

and

$$\left.\begin{aligned} (q_r^\alpha)^x + (q_r'^\beta)^x = 1,\ (q_r^\alpha)^{xy} + (q_r'^\beta)^{xy} = 0, \\ (p_{rs}^\alpha)^x = \pm (p_{rs}'^\beta)^x,\ (p_{rs}^\alpha)^{xy} = \pm (p_{rs}'^\beta)^{xy}, \end{aligned}\right\} \tag{5.8}$$

for bonds between atoms of different or the same sets respectively. The dipole moments of the transitions reduce to

$$\mathbf{M}_{xy} = \sum_r (q_r)^{xy}\mathbf{M}_r + 2\sum_{r<s}(p_{rs})^{xy}\mathbf{M}_{rs} \tag{5.9}$$

and

$$\mathbf{M}'_{xy} = -\sum_r (q_r)^{xy}\mathbf{M}_r + 2\sum_{r<s}(p_{rs})^{xy}\mathbf{M}_{rs}, \tag{5.10}$$

since all the bonds are between atoms of different sets. We have already neglected the effects of overlap, so in the same spirit we neglect the contributions to **M** from bonds. Then

$$\mathbf{M} \simeq -\mathbf{M}';\ |\mathbf{M}|^2 = |\mathbf{M}'|^2 \tag{5.11}$$

and the equality of transition moments and transition energies leads to identical electronic spectra for the two hydrocarbon ions. Some further consequences of the relations (5.8) are of interest.

(1) The charge densities at each atom of the two ions are complementary in every state; $q_r + q_r' = 2$.

(2) The bond orders are equal between bonded atoms, and opposite in magnitude between atoms of the same sets; $p_{rs} = \pm p_{rs}'$.

(3) The spin densities $\rho_r = (q_r^\alpha - q_r^\beta)$ are the same on each atom in a radical or triplet molecule; $\rho_r = \rho_r'$. In the bonds $\rho_{rs} = (p_{rs}^\alpha - p_{rs}^\beta)$ is equal but opposite to ρ_{rs}'. This explains the resemblance of the electron resonance spectra of the two species.

(4) The result of (3.19) that $\epsilon-\epsilon'=-2rK$, applied to both ions in their ground states, leads to the relation

$$I+A=-2K=(E^{+}-E^{-})$$

between the first ionization potential and electron affinity of a neutral hydrocarbon. In theory the second ionization potential and electron affinity should be similarly related by

$$I_2+A_2=-4K,$$

but in this case the validity of the approximation is more doubtful.

6. The electronic states of neutral molecules and radicals

If the pair of a negative ion is the positive one, the pair of a neutral molecule is itself, and for this reason its electronic structure is especially simple. If Φ_x and Φ_x' represent one electronic state and its pair, they are both states of the same molecule, and both have the same energy, according to (3.19). Thus

$$\Phi_x=\pm\Phi_x' \tag{6.1}$$

except when there is an accidental degeneracy. The pairing operation commutes with the energy operator in all neutral alternant hydrocarbons and every state is either 'even' or 'odd' to this operation. The ground configuration χ_0 of a neutral molecule, which is shown in figure 1 (a), is its own pair

$$\chi_0=\chi_0' \tag{6.2}$$

but all other configurations give rise to even and odd combinations

$$(\chi_i+\chi_i'),\quad (\chi_i-\chi_i'); \tag{6.3}$$

and the two kinds of electronic state are of characteristic form

$$\Phi_e=2a_0\chi_0+\sum a_i(\chi_i+\chi_i'),\quad \text{even};$$
$$\Phi_o=\sum b_i(\chi_i-\chi_i'),\quad \text{odd}. \tag{6.4}$$

One may easily show from the results of § 3 that, as anticipated, the energy has no matrix elements between even and odd terms, so that this classification of states is indeed legitimate. Pariser's [14] classification of the singly-excited states into plus and minus types is a special example of the more general theorem. His minus states are even. Pariser's discovery that transitions are only allowed between states of opposite type is also confirmed; for example, between two even states the transition moment is

$$\langle\Phi_x+\Phi_x'|\mathbf{M}|\Phi_y+\Phi_y'\rangle$$
$$=(\mathbf{M}_{xy}+\mathbf{M}_{x'y'})+(\mathbf{M}_{x'y}+\mathbf{M}_{xy'})=0, \tag{6.5}$$

and vanishes according to (5.11). Pariser's third result that the singly-excited even singlets and triplets ${}^1\Omega_{ij}$ and ${}^3\Omega_{ij}$ have the same energy does not hold in general, because only the singlets can mix with the ground term.

In a neutral molecule with $2m$ carbon atoms the ground state configuration is

$$\chi_0=||\psi_1^2\ldots\ldots\psi_m^2||. \tag{6.6}$$

The corresponding configuration for a radical is

$$\chi_0=||\psi_1^2\ldots\ldots\psi_m^2\psi_0^\alpha|| \tag{6.7}$$

and in the singly excited configurations $\chi(i \to j')$ the spin-orbital $\bar{\psi}_i$ of χ_0 is replaced by $\bar{\psi}_j$. According to our sign convention in (2.15)

$$\chi'(i \to j') = -\chi(j \to i'), \tag{6.8}$$

so that we classify the excited states of molecules according to the scheme of table 2. The parity is the same for triplets as for singlets.

	Even	Odd
Molecule	χ_0 $\chi(i \to j') - \chi(j \to i')$	$\chi(i \to i')$ $\chi(i \to j') + \chi(j \to i')$
Radical	χ_0 $\chi(0 \to i') - \chi(i \to 0)$ $\chi(i \to j') - \chi(j \to i')$	$\chi(i \to i')$ $\chi(0 \to i') + \chi(i \to 0)$ $\chi(i \to j') - \chi(j \to i')$

Table 2. Even and odd states of alternant hydrocarbons.

Many of the special results derived by Coulson and Longuet-Higgins [15] from the Hückel molecular orbital theory still hold, and follow from (6.4) taken with the bond order relations (5.8).

(1) The charge density on each atom is 1 in every electronic state, whether even or odd; so that one is justified in using the same self-consistent field molecular orbitals to describe the ground and excited states.

(2) Bond orders vanish between pairs of atoms in the same set (starred or unstarred).

(3) The law of alternating polarity does not hold rigorously, but should do if the long range Coulomb repulsion integrals are not too large. (This is true in self-consistent molecular orbital theory.)

(4) In a neutral radical the spin densities should vanish in all the real bonds. This confirms McConnell's [16] calculation of the spin density matrix of allyl.

Two other general theorems may be true. One is the alternation of bond-bond polarizabilities deduced by Coulson and Longuet-Higgins. The other is that the spin densities in a neutral radical alternate in sign, being always positive on the starred atoms and negative on the unstarred ones. I have proved that this is true for a valence-bond wave function without any polar structures, but cannot extend the result.

7. Conclusions

The most important consequence of these theorems is that they thoroughly confirm the previous predictions of the Hückel molecular orbital theory, and show that their validity does not depend on any special approximate treatment of the electron correlation problem. The success of the Hückel theory depends more on the special geometrical structure of alternant molecules than on the reasonableness of its physical assumptions. In this paper the most unreasonable assumptions we made were the neglect of overlap between atomic orbitals at the ends of a bond, and a concealed assumption that the same set of atomic orbitals is used by the electrons in both positive and negative ions. However the theoretical framework used here is probably the most general one within which a pairing theorem holds exactly, and one must justify the method by its excellent agreement with the experimental facts.

I would like to thank Professor H. C. Longuet-Higgins, F.R.S. for discussions and suggestions throughout this problem; Mr. J. S. Griffith for first raising the discussion of the signs of configurations in § 3; and the Department of Scientific and Industrial Research for a maintenance grant.

L'apparîment des orbitales moléculaires de Hückel dans un hydrocarbure alternant est valable dans un sens plus général pour des fonctions d'onde qui tiennent compte de façon complète de la corrélation des électrons π dans la molécule. La nouvelle propriété d'apparîment est parfaitement valable dans la limite des approximations de Pariser, Parr, et Pople, et conduit à une correspondance exacte entre chaque détail des états excités, des spectres électroniques, et des spectres de résonance électronique des ions hydrocarbonés positifs et négatifs. Les molécules neutres ont une couche électronique à demi-saturée dans laquelle les électrons et les trous sont sur un pied d'égalité. Ceci entraîne une distribution électronique uniforme dans chaque état électronique et conduit à deux types d'état excité—pair ou impair—comme l'avait d'abord suggéré Pariser. Les transitions entre états de parité semblable sont défendues. Dans les radicaux neutres, la densité de spin est nulle dans touts les liaisons, et dans les radicaux aussi bien que les molécules l'indice de liaison est nul pour les atomes d'un même ensemble (atomes à astérisque ou atomes sans astérisque).

Die paarweise Zuordnung Hückelscher *molecular orbitals* in einem alternierenden Kohlenwasserstoff bleibt in einem allgemeineren Sinne auch für solche Wellenfunktionen gültig, die die Korrelation der Elektronen in der Molekel vollständig berücksichtigen. Die neue Form der paarweisen Zuordnung gilt genau innerhalb der Näherungen von Pariser, Parr und Pople und führt zu einer exakten Korrespondenz zwischen jeder Einzelheit in den angeregten Zuständen, den Elektronenspektren und den Elektronenresonanzspektren von positiven und negativen Kohlenwasserstoffionen. Neutrale Molekeln haben eine halbgefüllte Elektronenschale, in der Elektronen und Löcher gleichberechtigt sind. Hieraus folgt eine gleichförmige Elektronenverteilung für jeden Elektronenzustand; ausserdem müssen zwei Arten angeregter Zustände existieren, nämlich gerade und ungerade, wie Pariser erstmalig vorschlug. Übergänge zwischen Zuständen gleicher Parität sind verboten. In neutralen Radikalen verschwindet die Spindichte in allen Bindungen, und in Radikalen, sowie Molekeln verschwinden die Bindungsordnungen zwischen Atomen der gleichen Klasse (mit bzw. ohne Stern).

References

[1] de Boer, E., and Weissman, S. I., 1958, *J. Amer. chem. Soc.*, **80,** 4549; 1957, *J. chem. Phys.*, **26,** 963.
[2] Carrington, A., 1959, *J. chem. Soc.*, 947.
[3] Hoijtink, G. J., and Weijland, W. P., 1957, *Rec. Trav. chim. Pays-Bas*, **76,** 836.
[4] McConnell, H. M., and Chesnut, D. B., 1957, *J. chem. Phys.*, **27,** 984.
[5] Pariser, R., and Parr, R. G., 1953, *J. chem. Phys.*, **21,** 466, 767.
[6] Pople, J. A., 1953, *Trans. Faraday Soc.*, **49,** 1375.
[7] Hückel, E., 1932, *Z. Phys.*, **76,** 628.
[8] Coulson, C. A., and Rushbrooke, G. S., 1940, *Proc. camb. Phil. Soc.*, **36,** 193.
[9] Hush, N. S., and Pople, J. A., 1955, *Trans. Faraday Soc.*, **51,** 600.
[10] Pople, J. A., and Brickstock, A., 1954, *Trans. Faraday Soc.*, **50,** 901.
[11] Pople, J. A., and Longuet-Higgins, H. C., 1955, *Proc. phys. Soc. Lond.*, A, **68,** 591.
[12] Lefèbvre, R., 1957, *J. Chim. phys.*, **54,** 168.
[13] Pople, J. A., and Nesbet, R. K., 1954, *J. chem. Phys.*, **22,** 571.
[14] Pariser, R., 1956, *J. chem. Phys.*, **24,** 250.
[15] Coulson, C. A., and Longuet-Higgins, H. C., 1947, *Proc. roy. Soc.* A, **191,** 39; 1947, *Ibid.*, **192,** 16.
[16] McConnell, H. M., 1958, *J. chem. Phys.*, **28,** 1188.

Reprinted from the JOURNAL OF CHEMICAL PHYSICS, Vol. 33, No. 4, 1184–1199, October, 1960
Printed in U. S. A.

Three Remarks on Molecular Orbital Theory of Complex Molecules*

ROBERT G. PARR†
Department of Chemistry, Carnegie Institute of Technology, Pittsburgh, Pennsylvania

(Received March 10, 1960)

Three suggestions are made and discussed concerning the generalized Hückel and related methods for treating the quantum chemistry of complex unsaturated molecules: (1) Justification for the assumptions of zero overlap and zero differential overlap resides in two facts: (a) For many molecules the atomic orbitals in the LCAO molecular orbitals may be replaced by the corresponding orthogonalized atomic orbitals of Löwdin, without effect on the molecular orbitals. (b) Integrals involving charge distributions which are products of orthogonalized atomic orbitals are small. (Observations previously made by several authors.) (2) Molecules isoelectronic with benzene are conveniently handled making use of molecular orbitals appropriate to the full benzene symmetry, for then deviations from benzene symmetry can be classified and treated systematically using symmetry combinations of basic integrals. (Formulas are given.) (3) The two-center coulomb repulsion integrals, previously dealt with by rather arbitrary semiempirical procedures, may be expanded by multipole expansion methods, leaving the independent multipoles of each atomic orbital as its defining theoretical or semiempirical characteristics.

I. INTRODUCTION

RECENT research in the theory of the electronic structure of complex unsaturated molecules[1–9] has produced a fundamentally more satisfactory theory and improved agreement between theory and experiment, but the methods that have been developed have admittedly been in need of further modification and clarification. The comments in the present paper are intended to provide insight into certain theoretical aspects of these methods, to suggest techniques for carrying out calculations with these methods on certain classes of molecules, and to propose for study a new way of looking at certain integrals basic in these methods.

More specifically, in Sec. II the point is made and amplified that when zero overlap and zero differential overlap[3] properties are ascribed to atomic orbitals in the semiempirical LCAO molecular orbital method called the generalized Hückel method,[7] the most satisfactory interpretation is that these atomic orbitals are orbitals that have been orthogonalized by the method of Löwdin[10]; and further, that this assumption produces no error whatsoever in certain important cases. In Sec. III formulas for handling molecules isoelectronic with benzene are displayed in a convenient format. Finally, in Sec. IV the idea is broached of using multipole expansion formulas for two-center electronic repulsion integrals of the simple coulomb type.

II. REMARK CONCERNING THE USE OF ORTHOGONALIZED ATOMIC ORBITALS

Sometime ago Löwdin[10] proposed using in molecular calculations orthogonalized atomic orbitals ($\overline{\text{AO}}$) built from the ordinary atomic orbitals (AO) by a certain orthogonalization process, and he indicated various formal advantages proffered by such functions. Later McWeeny[11] actually employed such orthogonalized orbitals in some calculations by a rigorous valence bond method. While he obtained interesting numerical results and developed various significant theorems, he found that the individual "contributing structures" in the orthogonalized atomic orbital scheme, which he labeled the $\overline{\text{VB}}$ scheme, do not have the same physical significance as the corresponding structures in the usual nonorthogonalized or VB scheme—a rather disappointing circumstance.

It will be shown in the following that the situation is often much more satisfactory when the LCAO molecular orbital scheme is used: Quite arbitrary replacement of AO with $\overline{\text{AO}}$ may not change the physical signficance of a molecular orbital configurational wave function at all.

Hydrogen Molecule

The hydrogen molecule illustrates well what is involved. To obtain an approximate wave function for its ground state by the valence bond method, starting from the usual nonorthogonal atomic orbitals $1s_a$ and $1s_b$, with overlap integral S, one would ordinarily merely linearly mix the two (unnormalized) structures,

$$\Phi_{\text{covalent}} = 1s_a(1)1s_b(2) + 1s_a(2)1s_b(1),$$

$$\Phi_{\text{ionic}} = 1s_a(1)1s_a(2) + 1s_b(1)1s_b(2), \qquad (1)$$

* Supported in part by research grants from the National Science Foundation, the Office of Ordnance Research, U. S. Army, and the Petroleum Research Fund of the American Chemical Society.

† Alfred P. Sloan Fellow.

1 R. Pariser and R. G. Parr, J. Chem. Phys. **21**, 466, 767 (1953).

2 J. A. Pople, Trans. Faraday Soc. **49**, 1375 (1953).

3 R. G. Parr, J. Chem. Phys. **20**, 1499 (1952).

4 R. Pariser, J. Chem. Phys. **21**, 568 (1953).

5 F. G. Fumi and R. G. Parr, J. Chem. Phys. **21**, 1864 (1953).

6 R. G. Parr and R. Pariser, J. Chem. Phys. **23**, 711 (1955).

7 R. G. Parr and F. O. Ellison, Ann. Rev. Phys. Chem. **6**, 171 (1955).

8 R. Pariser, J. Chem. Phys. **24**, 250 (1956); **25**, 1112 (1956).

9 P. G. Lykos and R. G. Parr, J. Chem. Phys. **24**, 1166 (1956), **25**, 1301 (1956).

10 P. O. Löwdin, J. Chem. Phys. **18**, 365 (1950).

11 R. McWeeny, Proc. Roy. Soc. (London) **A223**, 63, 306 (1954); **A227**, 288 (1955).

to give a covalent-plus-ionic function of the form

$$\Psi = A_c\Phi_{\text{covalent}} + A_i\Phi_{\text{ionic}}. \tag{2}$$

Alternatively, however, one could start from the orthogonal atomic orbitals

$$\lambda_a = [\tfrac{1}{2}(1+S)^{-\frac{1}{2}} + \tfrac{1}{2}(1-S)^{-\frac{1}{2}}](1s_a) + [\tfrac{1}{2}(1+S)^{-\frac{1}{2}} - \tfrac{1}{2}(1-S)^{-\frac{1}{2}}](1s_b),$$
$$\lambda_b = [\tfrac{1}{2}(1+S)^{-\frac{1}{2}} - \tfrac{1}{2}(1-S)^{-\frac{1}{2}}](1s_a) + [\tfrac{1}{2}(1+S)^{-\frac{1}{2}} + (1-S)^{-\frac{1}{2}}](1s_b). \tag{3}$$

One would then mix the two structures

$$\bar{\Phi}_{\text{covalent}} = \lambda_a(1)\lambda_b(2) + \lambda_a(2)\lambda_b(1),$$
$$\bar{\Phi}_{\text{ionic}} = \lambda_a(1)\lambda_a(2) + \lambda_b(1)\lambda_b(2), \tag{4}$$

and obtain

$$\Psi = \bar{A}_c\bar{\Phi}_{\text{covalent}} + \bar{A}_b\bar{\Phi}_{\text{ionic}}. \tag{5}$$

Equations (2) and (5) give the final wave function in the VB and $\overline{\text{VB}}$ procedures, respectively. These are naturally the same. However, and this is the essential point which vitiates the $\overline{\text{VB}}$ procedure,

$$\Phi_{\text{covalent}} \not\equiv \bar{\Phi}_{\text{covalent}}$$

and

$$\Phi_{\text{ionic}} \not\equiv \bar{\Phi}_{\text{ionic}}, \tag{6}$$

which means that any truncation of the covalent-ionic mixing (as, for example, by restriction of the structures to be mixed to the single one covalent in type) will give different results in the VB and $\overline{\text{VB}}$ methods. Indeed, as Slater first showed,[12] the single $\overline{\text{VB}}$ structure Φ_{covalent} is a poor approximation indeed for the ground state of the hydrogen molecules, whereas Φ_{covalent} is the original description of Heitler and London.

The molecular orbital situation is different. In the customary LCAO form of this method, starting from the same atomic orbitals $1s_a$ and $1s_b$ one defines molecular orbitals

$$\phi_1 = [2(1+S)]^{-\frac{1}{2}}(1s_a + 1s_b),$$
$$\phi_2 = [2(1-S)]^{-\frac{1}{2}}(1s_a - 1s_b), \tag{7}$$

builds configurational wave functions,

$$\Phi_1 = \phi_1(1)\phi_1(2), \qquad \Phi_2 = \phi_2(1)\phi_2(2), \tag{8}$$

and mixes these to give the final approximate wave function

$$\Psi = B_1\Phi_1 + B_2\Phi_2. \tag{9}$$

This is the MO method, including configuration interaction. Alternatively, in what may be termed the $\overline{\text{MO}}$ method, one would start from molecular orbitals

$$\bar{\phi}_1 = 2^{-\frac{1}{2}}(\lambda_a + \lambda_b),$$
$$\bar{\phi}_2 = 2^{-\frac{1}{2}}(\lambda_a - \lambda_b), \tag{10}$$

build configurational wave functions

$$\bar{\Phi}_1 = \bar{\phi}_1(1)\bar{\phi}_2(2), \qquad \bar{\Phi}_2 = \bar{\phi}_2(1)\bar{\phi}_2(2), \tag{11}$$

and mix these to give

$$\Psi = \bar{B}_1\bar{\Phi}_1 + \bar{B}_2\bar{\Phi}_2. \tag{12}$$

Again the final result is the same (and the same as in either the VB or $\overline{\text{VB}}$ methods), but this time one has a more detailed identity, namely,

$$\phi_1 \equiv \bar{\phi}_1 \quad \text{and} \quad \phi_2 \equiv \bar{\phi}_2. \tag{13}$$

From this it follows that

$$\Phi_1 \equiv \bar{\Phi}_1 \quad \text{and} \quad \Phi_2 \equiv \bar{\Phi}_2. \tag{14}$$

That is, the MO and $\overline{\text{MO}}$ methods are identical "step by step": they give identical descriptions whether or not configuration interaction is carried to its full limit.

General Case of High Symmetry[13]

In the case of the hydrogen molecule it thus turns out that the coefficients of the $\overline{\text{AO}}$ in the $\overline{\text{MO}}$ are in the same ratios as the coefficients of the AO in the MO. This result is of more practical interest than the simple identity between the MO and the $\overline{\text{MO}}$, for it implies that, for such a case, the LCAO coefficients themselves, as well as later results of calculations, are essentially the same in the MO and $\overline{\text{MO}}$ methods. For purely theoretical work this is not so helpful, because precise orbital forms must be specified before purely theoretical calculations can be carried out, but the advantages are definite for semiempirical schemes, in which integrals are evaluated by more devious means.

The MO and $\overline{\text{MO}}$ methods unfortunately are not always identical in this "complete sense." The simplest case when they are is when the molecular symmetry is high enough to determine the LCAO coefficients uniquely, that is, when each molecular orbital is a symmetry orbital for the problem. (Hydrogen falls in this class of molecules, as do ethylene, cyclobutadiene, and benzene, but not butadiene.)

To lay the argument out precisely, in the usual MO method one sets out to determine the coefficients C_{pj} in the expansions,

$$\phi_j = \sum_p \chi_p C_{pj}, \tag{15}$$

of the molecular orbitals ϕ in terms of overlapping atomic orbitals χ. But alternatively, one can write as well the molecular orbitals in terms of the orthogonalized orbitals λ of Löwdin,[10]

$$\bar{\phi}_j = \sum_q \lambda_q D_{qj}. \tag{16}$$

[12] J. C. Slater, J. Chem. Phys. **19**, 220 (1951).

[13] Compare F. Peradejordi, Compt. rend. **243**, 276 (1956).

Here,

$$\lambda_q=\sum_p \chi_p T_{pq}$$

and

$$C_{pj}=\sum_q T_{pq}D_{qj}, \qquad (17)$$

where T_{pq} is the element in the pth row and qth column of the matrix

$$T=(S)^{-\frac{1}{2}}=\begin{bmatrix} 1 & S_{12} & S_{13} & \cdots \\ S_{12} & 1 & S_{23} & \cdots \\ \cdot & \cdot & \cdot & \cdots \end{bmatrix}^{-\frac{1}{2}}, \qquad (18)$$

in which

$$S_{p'p}=\int \chi_{p'}^{*}\chi_p dv.$$

The question now is, are the D_{qj} of Eq. (16) the same as the C_{pj} of Eq. (15)?

In general, the answer to this question is no, but in case the C_{pj} are determined by symmetry the D_{qj} are also, and the two sets of coefficients differ at most by constants N_j:

$$\bar{\phi}_j=\sum_p \lambda_p D_{pj}\equiv N_j\sum_p \chi_p D_{pj}=\phi_j. \qquad (19)$$

This follows from the fact that the transformation to Löwdin orbitals, Eq. (17), leaves the symmetry properties of the orbitals unchanged.

The outside identity of Eq. (19), $\bar{\phi}_j\equiv\phi_j$ is not so surprising, for any reasonable method for arriving at LCAO molecular orbitals would be expected to give results unaffected by an intermediate linear transformation of the starting orbitals. It is the inside equality that is interesting and important; it shows that in determining the coefficients C_{pj} (up to constants) one can work as well with the λ as with the χ.

What this means becomes clear when one considers the example of the benzene molecule. In the usual rigorous treatment of the pi electrons in this molecule,[14] one starts with molecular orbitals

$$\phi_j=(1/6\sigma_j)^{\frac{1}{2}}\sum_{p=1}^{6}\omega^{jp}\chi_p, \qquad (20)$$

where $\omega=\exp(2\pi i/6)$ and the σ_j are normalizing factors; the χ_p are overlapping. One then builds various many-electron wave functions and mixes them variationally to give approximations for the wave functions for the several molecular states.[15] The calculation is very tedious, mainly because of the host of integrals of several kinds which enter the formulas.

One could start from the molecular orbitals expressed more simply in terms of Lowdin orbitals λ derived from the χ by the transformation of Eq. (17). By Eq. (19), one would have

$$\bar{\phi}_j=(1/6)^{\frac{1}{2}}\sum_{p=1}^{6}\omega^{jp}\lambda_p\equiv\phi_j. \qquad (21)$$

The many-electron functions consequently are expressible as well in terms of the $\bar{\phi}$ as in terms of the ϕ, and *the various integrals that enter the final formulas may be interpreted as over orthogonalized orbitals* λ *just as well as over nonorthogonal orbitals* χ, *with no error.* Overlap integrals may be struck out identically, and integrals involving electron distributions divided between different orthogonal orbitals may be set equal to zero as a reasonable approximation. Explicit calculations verify that this last, which is no more or less than the approximation of zero differential overlap, is a good approximation in this problem.[16]

Equation (21) has already been written down by Löwdin for Bloch orbitals in a crystal[10]; its implications for calculations on benzene have, however, not been pointed out so explicitly before.

Alternant Hydrocarbons and Similar Cases

Consider now a case in which the molecular orbital coefficients C_{pj} are determined not by symmetry alone but by solution of secular equations of the type

$$\sum_p[{}^{\chi}M_{rp}-S_{rp}\mu_j]C_{pj}=0. \qquad (22)$$

Here,

$${}^{\chi}M_{rp}=\int \chi_r^{*}\mu\chi_p dv, \qquad (23)$$

where μ is an approximate one-electron operator, as, for example, the LCAO SCF operator in Roothaan's method[17]; the μ_j are constants. Solution of these equations provides molecular orbitals ϕ from which many-electron wave functions can be built.

Alternatively, molecular orbitals $\bar{\phi}$ are defined by the coefficients D_{qj} which are solutions of the secular equations of simpler form,

$$\sum_q[{}^{\lambda}M_{sq}-\delta_{sq}\mu_j]D_{qj}=0, \qquad (24)$$

where

$${}^{\lambda}M_{sq}=\int \lambda_s^{*}\mu\lambda_q dv, \qquad (25)$$

and the δ_{sq} are Kronecker deltas.

The ϕ and the $\bar{\phi}$ are identical, so again the MO and $\overline{\text{MO}}$ methods are identical step by step. This time, however, the coefficient C_{pj} and D_{qj} will in general be different.

Suppose, though, that the matrices ${}^{\chi}M=({}^{\chi}M_{rp})$ and $S=(S_{rp})$ happened to commute. Then ${}^{\lambda}M$ and T

[14] M. Goeppert-Mayer and A. L. Sklar, J. Chem. Phys. **6**, 645 (1938).

[15] R. G. Parr, D. P. Craig, and I. G. Ross, J. Chem. Phys. **18**, 1561 (1950).

[16] R. McWeeny, Proc. Roy. Soc. (London) **A227**, 288 (1955). See also G. G. Hall, Trans. Faraday Soc. **50**, 773 (1954).

[17] C. C. J. Roothaan, Revs. Modern Phys. **23**, 69 (1951).

would commute,

$$\sum_s T_{rs}\,{}^{\lambda}M_{sq} = \sum_s {}^{\lambda}M_{rs} T_{sq}. \tag{26}$$

Therefore, multiplying Eq. (24) by T_{rs}, summing over s, and using Eqs. (26) and (17), one finds

$$\sum_s [{}^{\lambda}M_{rs} - \delta_{rs}\mu_j] C_{sj} = 0. \tag{27}$$

That is, the C_{pj} satisfy the same secular equations as do the D_{qj}. Or: For a given j, the set D_{pj} differs from the set C_{pj} by a common constant factor at most, the MO and MO methods are equivalent in the complete sense, no error is incurred if the assumption is made in semiempirical calculations that the atomic orbitals of the problem are orthogonal.

As was first suggested by Löwdin,[10] alternant hydrocarbons are an important large class of molecules for which the assumption that the matrices S and ${}^{x}M$ commute, with μ the LCAO SCF operator, should be very good.[18]

General Case

No matter what the molecule is, the MO and $\overline{\text{MO}}$ methods would be equivalent step by step if the operator μ were taken to be the same in Eqs. (23) and (25), although the C_{pj} and D_{qj} would be different.

Furthermore, the approximation that the matrices S and ${}^{x}M$ commute may often be a good one, with μ the LCAO SCF operator, in which case the D_{qj} and C_{pj} will be nearly the same. (Peradejordi has demonstrated this for butadiene.[13]) It may then prove expeditious to solve Eq. 24 and make up for the minor deficiencies in the molecular orbitals obtained by a later configuration interaction calculation. Or, the operator μ might be slightly modified in order to make S and ${}^{x}M$ commute and the D_{qj} and C_{pj} be the same, again with configuration interaction included later.[19]

Discussion

One may conclude from this discussion that purely theoretical $\overline{\text{MO}}$-type methods have advantages that could be explored further. Probably more important is the inference that semiempirical $\overline{\text{MO}}$-type methods have good justification; the atomic orbitals in the generalized Hückel method, for example, may be thought of as Löwdin orthogonalizations of ordinary atomic orbitals. The approximation of zero differential overlap then is the approximation that charge distributions which are products of orthogonalized atomic orbitals may be ignored. Further numerical calculations, checking this, would be helpful.

Interpretation of the basic integrals in the generalized Hückel method as over orthogonalized atomic orbitals has one consequence that has not yet been mentioned: The orthogonalized analog of each atomic orbital will have a form which varies from one molecule to the next. Because of this, the invariance of the basic integrals from one molecule to another, which has been postulated,[1–8] will require verification and perhaps modification.[20] A careful comparative study of the naphthalene and benzene molecules could shed much light on this question.

On the other hand, there is a final strong argument that can be given in favor of these semiempirical procedures.[21] The form of the "ordinary" atomic orbitals has not been specified anywhere in this discussion—it is a degree of freedom which one should recognize. Thus the precise values for the overlap integrals $S_{p'p}$ can be considered variable. (It has already been pointed out that the integrals ${}^{x}M_{p'p}$ can be adjusted by changes in μ). Or, one can transform back from very good molecular orbitals to an orthogonalized atomic basis; this would make the orthogonalized atomic orbitals identical with what Lennard-Jones and Hall have termed equivalent orbitals.[16]

III. REMARK CONCERNING THE TREATMENT OF BENZENE-LIKE MOLECULES

In an earlier paper[6] equations were given for treating by the generalized Hückel method molecules like ethylene which have two π electrons, and it was demonstrated how setting up such a problem in a certain way gives formulas in which theoretical electronegativity differences appear perspicuously. Here the same sort of procedure will be applied to analogs of the benzene molecule.

A *benzene-like molecule* is defined as a molecule such as benzene, toluene, or pyridine, the properties of which may be well described in terms of the behavior of six π electrons which have available six $2\pi p$ atomic orbitals arranged more or less hexagonally. In toluene a better description requires explicit consideration of two extra π electrons from the CH_3 group (hyperconjugation); in the terminology that has been suggested[6] this would involve "mesomeric effects" of a substituent. The problem treated in the present paper is just the six-electron one—only "inductive effects" of substituents are covered.[22]

Encouraging results for the spectra of several nitrogen heterocyclic analogs of benzene have already been reported.[23] The present more systematic development will deal with all benzene-like molecules; it should provide

---

[18] See also B. H. Chirgwin, and C. A. Coulson, Proc. Roy. Soc. (London) **A201**, 196 (1950).

[19] For example, Mulliken-type approximations in the LCAO SCF operator probably reduce its commutator with S.

[20] Professor K. Ruedenberg has informed the author that he has developed a theory explicitly dealing with overlap of nearest neighbors. Also see work cited in footnote reference 29.

[21] Compare the introductory remarks in R. McWeeny, Proc. Roy. Soc. (London) **A237**, 355 (1956).

[22] See however Sec. 5 of footnote reference 6.

[23] Work cited in footnote 1, p. 767. R. C. Hirt, F. Halverson, and R. G. Schmitt, J. Chem. Phys. **22**, 1148 (1954); R. McWeeny and T. E. Peacock, Proc. Phys. Soc. (London) **A60**, 41 (1957); J. N. Murrell, Mol. Phys. **1**, 384 (1958).

TABLE I. Character table for the group C_6.[a]

$^6C_6$ Representation	Operation[b] E	C_6	C_6^2	C_6^3	C_6^4	C_6^5
Γ_0 or A	1	1	1	1	1	1
Γ_1 or E_{1+}	1	ω	ω^2	-1	ω^4	ω^5
Γ_{-1} or E_{1-}	1	ω^5	ω^4	-1	ω^2	ω
Γ_2 or E_{2+}	1	ω^2	ω^4	1	ω^2	ω^4
Γ_{-2} or E_{2-}	1	ω^4	ω^2	1	ω^4	ω^2
Γ_3 or B	1	-1	1	-1	1	-1

[a] The two degenerate representations of the group C_6 can be treated as made up of two one-dimensional representations each if complex characters are used, as shown: $\omega=\exp(2\pi i/6)$.

[b] Here $C_6{}^n$ is the symmetry operation: rotate the molecule the angle $60n°$ about its sixfold axis of symmetry.

a useful framework for studying many properties of many such molecules.

Starting Wave Functions

The key to a simple and general treatment of benzene-like molecules is to set up the problem unprejudiced as to the type or location of the perturbation from the parent "standard" molecule benzene. With six π electrons and six $2p\pi$ overlapping atomic orbitals χ_0, χ_1, χ_2, χ_3, χ_4, χ_5 arranged hexagonally, the orthonormal molecular orbitals appropriate for the full benzene symmetry may be written, according to Eq. (21) (changing the numbering of the orbitals for convenience),

$$\phi_j=6^{-\frac{1}{2}}\sum_{p=0}^{5}\omega^{jp}\lambda_p, \qquad j=0, \pm1, \pm2, 3, \qquad (28)$$

where $\omega=\exp(2\pi i/6)=\cos(2\pi/6)+i\sin(2\pi/6)$ and the λ_p are the orthonormal Löwdin analogs of the χ_p, expressible in terms of the χ_p by Eq. (17).

The subscript j which labels a molecular orbital indicates the irreducible representation of the group C_6 to which the orbital belongs. The character table for this group is given in Table I; the determination of the ϕ_j from this table and the transformation properties of the χ_p or λ_p follows the usual standard procedure.

Now the molecular orbitals of Eq. (28) will not be quite the best ones for the ground state of the arbitrary benzene-like molecule. For each molecule an LCAO SCF calculation could be performed to improve them,[17] but an alternative method is better. This is to make up for deficiencies in the Eq. (28) orbital description for a given state of a given molecule by linearly mixing in corresponding functions for other states—the configuration interaction procedure. Symmetry present in benzene itself will make many of the configuration interaction matrix elements zero for benzene itself; nonzero values of these elements in a molecule which does not have full benzene symmetry produce the same effects as would alteration of the linear coefficients in the LCAO MO. This method takes advantage of the uniquely simple form of the linear coefficients in the benzene orbitals, and it gives formulas which are quite general.

Of the great many "states" that could be admixed, only the most important will be considered here: the "ground state" coming from assignment of two electrons each to the lowest-energy molecular orbitals ϕ_0, ϕ_1, and ϕ_{-1} and the "singly excited states" coming from promotion of one electron from one of these orbitals to a higher orbital. Every such "one-electron jump" gives rise to one singlet and one triplet state, so that ten starting singlet wave functions and nine starting triplet wave functions are thus defined. In Table II these "set A starting functions are explicitly given in terms of Slater determinants formed from the basic one-electron orbitals of Eq. (28). The notation adopted is that V_{jk} represents the singlet state (or its wave function) arising from excitation of one electron from the orbital ϕ_j to the orbital ϕ_k from the (singlet) ground state N; T_{jk} represents the corresponding triplet.

The assumption now is that the ground-state π-electronic wave function of a benzene-like molecule and the wave functions for its lower π-excited states are expressible in the form

$$\Psi=A_1\Phi_1+A_2\Phi_2+\cdots, \qquad (29)$$

where the Φ are the starting functions of Table II, or suitable combinations of them. This would in fact give for the ground state a function equivalent to the LCAO SCF function, provided the SCF MO differed only infinitesimally from the MO of Eq. (28). (Just such a procedure has been effectively used by Brion and others[24] to generate SCF MO by successive approximations.) To get comparable accuracy for excited states one should include two-electron as well as one-electron jumps,[25] which will not be done here; nevertheless, the results for the lower excited states should be reasonably good.

The problem then is a linear variational one of some magnitude; in the general case determination of the coefficients A in Eq. (29) requires computation of a large number of matrix elements and solution of equations of high order.

The secular equations would be the more easily dealt with the more completely diagonal they were for the special case of full benzene symmetry. If the set A functions were used, the symmetry characteristics,

$$V_{jk} \text{ and } T_{jk} \subset \text{Representation } \Gamma_{k-j} \text{ of } C_6, \qquad (30)$$

[24] H. Brion, R. Lefebvre, and C. M. Moser, J. Chem. Phys. **23**, 1972 (1955). See also J. A. Pople, Proc. Roy. Soc. (London) **A233**, 233 (1955), and J. A. Pople and P. Schofield, idem **A233**, 241 (1955).

[25] The importance of two-electron jumps has been emphasized by J. N. Murrell and K. L. McEwen, J. Chem. Phys. **25**, 1143 (1956).

TABLE II. Starting wave functions for benzene-like molecules: set A.

Configuration[a]	Starting state[b,c]	Starting wave function[d,e]
$0^2 1^2 -1^2$	$N \equiv V_{00}$	$(0\bar{0}1\bar{1}-1-\bar{1})$
$0^2 1 -1^2 2$	V_{12} and T_{12}	$2^{-\frac{1}{2}}[(0\bar{0}1\bar{2}-1-\bar{1}) \pm (0\bar{0}2\bar{1}-1-\bar{1})]$
$0^2 1^2 -1-2$	V_{-1-2} and T_{-1-2}	$2^{-\frac{1}{2}}[(0\bar{0}1\bar{1}-1-\bar{2}) \pm (0\bar{0}1\bar{1}-2-\bar{1})]$
$0^2 1 -1^2 -2$	V_{1-2} and T_{1-2}	$2^{-\frac{1}{2}}[(0\bar{0}1-\bar{2}-1-\bar{1}) \pm (0\bar{0}-2\bar{1}-1-\bar{1})]$
$0^2 1^2 -12$	V_{-12} and T_{-12}	$2^{-\frac{1}{2}}[(0\bar{0}1\bar{1}-1\bar{2}) \pm (0\bar{0}1\bar{1}2-\bar{1})]$
$01^2 -1^2 2$	V_{02} and T_{02}	$2^{-\frac{1}{2}}[(0\bar{2}1\bar{1}-1-\bar{1}) \pm (2\bar{0}1\bar{1}-1-\bar{1})]$
$01^2 -1^2 -2$	V_{0-2} and T_{0-2}	$2^{-\frac{1}{2}}[(0-\bar{2}1\bar{1}-1-\bar{1}) \pm (-2\bar{0}1\bar{1}-1-\bar{1})]$
$0^2 1 -1^2 3$	V_{13} and T_{13}	$2^{-\frac{1}{2}}[(0\bar{0}1\bar{3}-1-\bar{1}) \pm (0\bar{0}3\bar{1}-1-\bar{1})]$
$0^2 1^2 -13$	V_{-13} and T_{-13}	$2^{-\frac{1}{2}}[(0\bar{0}1\bar{1}-1\bar{3}) \pm (0\bar{0}1\bar{1}3-\bar{1})]$
$01^2 -1^2 3$	V_{03} and T_{03}	$2^{-\frac{1}{2}}[(0\bar{3}1\bar{1}-1-\bar{1}) \pm (3\bar{0}1\bar{1}-1-\bar{1})]$

[a] Here $0^2 1^2 -1^2$, for example, denotes the configuration $\phi_0^2\phi_1^2\phi_{-1}^2$.

[b] These starting states do not necessarily correspond to actual molecular states. See text.

[c] V_{jk} and T_{jk} denote singlet and triplet starting states arising from the one-electron excitation $\phi_k \leftarrow \phi_j$ from the ground starting state N.

[d] Here $(0\bar{0}1\bar{1}-1-\bar{1})$, for example, denotes the normalized Slater determinant $(6!)^{-\frac{1}{2}}\Sigma^P(-1)^P[(\phi_0\alpha)^1(\phi_0\beta)^2(\phi_1\alpha)^3(\phi_1\beta)^4(\phi_{-1}\alpha)^5(\phi_{-1}\beta)^6]$.

[e] The upper sign goes with V, the lower sign with T. Only one component of the three degenerate components of each triplet state is listed.

plus the fact that nonzero interaction between two functions for benzene requires that their product have symmetry Γ_0, show that one would have nothing worse than a 3×3 equation for benzene, but one can in fact do much better than this if one replaces the set A functions of Table II with the set B functions of Table III.

The set B functions are, up to constant factors, sums and differences of set A functions which are degenerate because they are complex conjugates of each other. Regardless of the molecular symmetry,

$$V_{jk} = V_{-j-k}^* \quad \text{and} \quad T_{jk} = T_{-j-k}^*, \tag{31}$$

so that replacement of V_{jk} and V_{-j-k} by $V_{jk}^+ = 2^{-\frac{1}{2}}(V_{jk}+V_{-j-k})$ and $V_{jk}^- = i2^{-\frac{1}{2}}\,(V_{jk}-V_{-j-k})$ gives two real orthonormal functions, and similarly with the triplets. And, as will be shown, in the case of full benzene symmetry, $^+$ and $^-$ functions do not interact. Consequently in the case of full benzene symmetry the only interactions among the set B functions which are not zero are between V_{1-2}^+ and V_{03}, between V_{02}^+ and V_{13}^+, between V_{02}^- and V_{13}^-, and between the corresponding triplets.

The V_{02} and V_{13} states, and the T_{02} and T_{13} states, are accidentally almost degenerate in the benzene case, which suggests that a final transformation of the basic functions would bring the secular equations still closer to a completely diagonal form for the case of full benzene symmetry:

$$\begin{aligned}
V_{02}^{++} &= 2^{-\frac{1}{2}}(V_{02}^+ + V_{13}^+), & T_{02}^{++} &= 2^{-\frac{1}{2}}(T_{02}^+ + T_{13}^+),\\
V_{02}^{+-} &= 2^{-\frac{1}{2}}(V_{02}^+ - V_{13}^+), & T_{02}^{+-} &= 2^{-\frac{1}{2}}(T_{02}^+ - T_{13}^+),\\
V_{02}^{-+} &= 2^{-\frac{1}{2}}(V_{02}^- + V_{13}^-), & T_{02}^{-+} &= 2^{-\frac{1}{2}}(T_{02}^- + T_{13}^-),\\
V_{02}^{--} &= 2^{-\frac{1}{2}}(V_{02}^- - V_{13}^-), & T_{02}^{--} &= 2^{-\frac{1}{2}}(T_{02}^- - T_{13}^-).
\end{aligned} \tag{32}$$

TABLE III. Starting wave functions for benzene-like molecules: set B.[a]

Starting state[b,c]	Starting wave function[c,d,e]
N	N
V_{12}^+ and T_{12}^+	$V_{12}^+ = 2^{-\frac{1}{2}}(V_{-1-2}+V_{12})$ and $T_{12}^+ = 2^{-\frac{1}{2}}(T_{-1-2}+T_{12})$
V_{1-2}^+ and T_{1-2}^+	$V_{1-2}^+ = 2^{-\frac{1}{2}}(V_{1-2}+V_{-12})$ and $T_{1-2}^+ = 2^{-\frac{1}{2}}(T_{1-2}+T_{-12})$
V_{02}^+ and T_{02}^+	$V_{02}^+ = 2^{-\frac{1}{2}}(V_{0-2}+V_{02})$ and $T_{02}^+ = 2^{-\frac{1}{2}}(T_{0-2}+T_{02})$
V_{13}^+ and T_{13}^+	$V_{13}^+ = 2^{-\frac{1}{2}}(V_{-13}+V_{13})$ and $T_{13}^+ = 2^{-\frac{1}{2}}(T_{-13}+T_{13})$
V_{03} and T_{03}	V_{03} and T_{03}
V_{12}^- and T_{12}^-	$V_{12}^- = i2^{-\frac{1}{2}}(V_{-1-2}-V_{12})$ and $T_{12}^- = i2^{-\frac{1}{2}}(T_{-1-2}-T_{12})$
V_{1-2}^- and T_{1-2}^-	$V_{1-2}^- = i2^{-\frac{1}{2}}(V_{1-2}-V_{-12})$ and $T_{1-2}^- = i2^{-\frac{1}{2}}(T_{1-2}-T_{-12})$
V_{02}^- and T_{02}^-	$V_{02}^- = i2^{-\frac{1}{2}}(V_{0-2}-V_{02})$ and $T_{02}^- = i2^{-\frac{1}{2}}(T_{0-2}-T_{02})$
V_{13}^- and T_{13}^-	$V_{13}^- = i2^{-\frac{1}{2}}(V_{-13}-V_{13})$ and $T_{13}^- = i2^{-\frac{1}{2}}(T_{-13}-T_{13})$

[a] The final, set C, starting functions are these set B function modified as indicated in the text, Eq. (32).

[b] See Table II, note b.

[c] The symbols N, V, and T denote both states and wave functions for states.

[d] The wave functions are given in terms of the set A starting functions of Table II.

[e] In D_{6h} symmetry, the symmetries of these starting functions are as follows: $N \subset A_{1g}$; V_{12}^+, V_{12}^-, $\subset E_{1u}$; V_{1-2}^+, $V_{03} \subset B_{1u}$; $V_{1-2}^- \subset B_{2u}$; V_{02}^+, V_{13}^+, V_{02}^-, $V_{13}^- \subset E_{2g}$; triplets same as corresponding singlets.

TABLE IV. Integrals over molecular orbitals for benzene-like molecules.

Symmetry classification[a]	Core integrals[b,d]	Electronic repulsion integrals[c,d]
Γ_0	$I_{00}=I_0=\epsilon_0$	$L_{00}=J_{ij}=J=\gamma_{ij}$
	$I_{1-1}=I_1=\epsilon_1$	$L_{1-1}=K_{01}=\delta_{01}$
	$I_{2-2}=I_2=\epsilon_2$	$L_{2-2}=K_{02}=\delta_{02}$
	$I_{3-3}=I_3=\epsilon_3$	$L_{3-3}=K_{03}=\delta_{03}$
Γ_1 or Γ_{-1}	I_{10} and $I_{-10}=I_{10}^*$	L_{10} and $L_{-10}=L_{10}^*$
	I_{2-1} and $I_{-21}=I_{2-1}^*$	L_{2-1} and $L_{-21}=L_{2-1}$
	I_{3-2} and $I_{-32}=I_{3-2}^*$	L_{3-2} and $L_{-32}=L_{3-2}^*$
Γ_2 or Γ_{-2}	I_{11} and $I_{-1-1}=I_{11}^*$	L_{11} and $L_{-1-1}=L_{11}^*$
	I_{20} and $I_{-20}=I_{20}^*$	L_{20} and $L_{-20}=L_{20}^*$
	I_{3-1} and $I_{-31}=I_{3-1}^*$	L_{3-1} and $L_{-31}=L_{3-1}^*$
	I_{4-2} and $I_{-42}=I_{4-2}^*$	L_{4-2} and $L_{-42}=L_{1-2}^*$
Γ_3	I_{21} and $I_{-21}=I_{21}^*$	L_{21} and $L_{-2-1}=L_{21}^*$
	I_{30} and $I_{-30}=I_{30}^*=I_{30}$	L_{30} and $L_{-30}=L_{30}^*=L_{30}$
	$I_{4-1}=I_{-2-1}$ and $I_{-41}=I_{21}=I_{4-1}^*$	$L_{4-1}=L_{-2-1}$ and $L_{-41}=L_{21}=L_{4-1}^*$

[a] Irreducible representation of group C_6, see Table I.

[b] For definition of I_{jk} see Eq. (35) of text. The contraction $I_j=I_{jj}$ is convenient; the notation $\epsilon_j=I_{jj}$ has also been used by certain authors.

[c] For definition of $L_{\mu\nu}$ see Eqs. (37) and (39) of text. The J, K notation for the first four of these integrals is more standard; the γ, δ notation has also been used by certain authors.

[d] For full benzene symmetry, all integrals vanish except those having symmetry Γ_0, leaving four distinct integrals of each type. In the general case, the number of *independent* integrals of each type is 21; the integrals, I_{-30}, I_{4-1}, I_{-41}, L_{-30}, L_{4-1} and L_{-41}, are redundant but are included for convenience.

These functions together with the other unmodified set B functions of Table III, N, V_{12}^+, V_{12}^-, V_{1-2}^+, V_{1-2}^-, V_{03}, T_{12}^+, T_{12}^-, T_{1-2}^+, T_{1-2}^-, T_{03}, are the final, set C, starting wave functions for the problem.

Secular Equations

The Hamiltonian operator for the π electrons has the form[9]

$$H=\sum_{\mu=1}^{6}H_{\text{core}}(\mu)+\tfrac{1}{2}\sum_{\mu,\nu=1}^{6}{}'\,(e^2/r_{\mu\nu});\qquad(33)$$

the problem is to determine S-matrix elements,

$$S_{mn}=\int\Phi_m^*\Phi_n dv,$$

and H-matrix elements

$$H_{mn}=(\Phi_m\,||\,\Phi_n)=\int\Phi_m^*H\Phi_n dv,\qquad(34)$$

where the Φ are the set C starting functions of Table III and Eq. (32). The secular equations for the singlet and triplet states then are 10×10 and 9×9 equations of the form $|(H_{mn}-S_{mn}E)|=0$, where E is the total π-electron energy; the corresponding wave functions are of the form of Eq. (29), with $\sum_n A_n(H_{mn}-S_{mn}E)=0$.

The set C functions are orthonormal by construction; hence $S_{mn}=\delta_{mn}$. The H matrix presents more difficulty. Rules for obtaining matrix elements between Slater determinants for an operator of the form of Eq. (33) are available, however,[26] and each set C function is a linear combination of Slater determinants. Such matrix elements always are expressible as linear combinations of two kinds of integrals over the molecular orbitals ϕ_j, integrals arising from the terms H_{core} in Eq. (33) and integrals arising from the terms $e^2/r_{\mu\nu}$.

The first class of integrals are the core integrals,

$$I_{jk}=\int\phi_j(1)H_{\text{core}}(1)\phi_k(1)dv(1).\qquad(35)$$

There are 21 distinct ones of these, since from Eqs. (28) and (35) one has the identities

$$I_{jk}=I_{kj}=I_{-j-k}^*=I_{j,k+6}=I_{j+6,k}.\qquad(36)$$

In Table IV are listed those of these integrals, which are taken here as independent, and their symmetry classifications.

The second class of integrals are the electronic repulsion integrals,

$$(ij\,|\,kl)$$

$$=\iint\phi_i^*(1)\phi_k^*(2)(e^2/r_{12})\phi_j(1)\phi_l(2)dv(1)dv(2).\qquad(37)$$

There are a great many of these. If, however, one assumes *zero differential overlap*,

$$\lambda_p(1)\lambda_q(1)dv(1)=0\quad\text{for}\quad p\neq q,\qquad(38)$$

one can see that two indices, $\mu=j-i$ and $\nu=l-k$, suffice to define these integrals, so that a more compact notation suffices for them:

$$L_{\mu\nu}=(i,\,i+\mu\,|\,k,\,k+\nu).\qquad(39)$$

Further, one has the identities,

$$L_{\mu\nu}=L_{\nu\mu}=L_{-\mu-\nu}^*=L_{\mu,\nu+6}=L_{\mu+6,\nu}.\qquad(40)$$

[26] For example, E. U. Condon and G. H. Shortley, *Theory of Atomic Spectra* (Cambridge University Press, Cambridge, England, 1935).

Consequently the number independent of these integrals also is 21; in Table IV are listed those here chosen as basic and their symmetries.

In Table V the H matrices for the singlet and triplet states of benzene-like molecules are given in terms of real parts, I_{jk}^r and $L_{\mu\nu}^r$, and imaginary parts, I_{jk}^i and $L_{\mu\nu}^i$, of the integrals $I_{jk}=I_{jk}^r+iI_{jk}^i$ and $L_{\mu\nu}=L_{\mu\nu}^r+iL_{\mu\nu}^i$ listed in Table IV.

Three sample calculations of H-matrix elements may be given without detailed comment:

$$(N\,||\,N)=[(00\bar{1}\bar{1}-1-\bar{1})\,||\,(00\bar{1}\bar{1}-1-\bar{1})]$$
$$=2I_{00}+2I_{-11}+2I_{1-1}+J_{00}+(4J_{01}-2K_{01})$$
$$+(4J_{0-1}-2K_{0-1})+J_{11}+(4J_{1-1}-2K_{1-1})+J_{-1-1}$$
$$=2I_0+4I_1+15J-4K_{01}-2K_{02},$$
$$(N\,||\,V_{12}^+)=2^{-\frac{1}{2}}[(N\,||\,V_{-1-2})+(N\,||\,V_{12})]$$
$$=2^{-\frac{1}{2}}[(N\,||\,V_{12})^*+(N\,||\,V_{12})]$$
$$=2^{\frac{1}{2}}\,\mathrm{Re}(N\,||\,V_{12})$$
$$=\mathrm{Re}\{[(00\bar{1}\bar{1}-1-\bar{1})\,||\,(00\bar{1}\bar{2}-1-\bar{1})]$$
$$+[00\bar{1}\bar{1}-1-\bar{1})\,||\,(00\bar{2}\bar{1}-1-\bar{1})]\}$$
$$=2\,\mathrm{Re}[(00\bar{1}\bar{1}-1-\bar{1})\,||\,(00\bar{1}\bar{2}-1-\bar{1})]$$
$$=2\,\mathrm{Re}[I_{-12}+2(12\,|\,00)-(10\,|\,02)$$
$$+(12\,|\,11)+2(12\,|\,-1-1)-(1-1\,|\,-12)]$$
$$=2(I_{2-1}+5L_{10}-L_{2-1}-L_{3-2})^r,$$
$$(V_{12}^+\,||\,V_{12}^-)=\tfrac{1}{2}i[V_{-1-2}+V_{12})\,||\,(V_{-1-2}-V_{12})]$$
$$=-\tfrac{1}{2}i\{[V_{12}\,||\,V_{12})-(V_{12}\,||\,V_{12})^*]$$
$$+[(V_{-1-2}\,||\,V_{12})-(V_{-1-2}\,||\,V_{12})^*]\}$$
$$=\mathrm{Im}[(V_{12}\,||\,V_{12})+(V_{-1-2}\,||\,V_{12})]$$
$$=\mathrm{Im}(V_{-1-2}\,||\,V_{12})$$
$$=\tfrac{1}{2}\,\mathrm{Im}\{[(00\bar{1}\bar{1}-1-\bar{2})+(00\bar{1}\bar{1}-2-\bar{1})]\,||$$
$$\times[(00\bar{1}\bar{2}-1-\bar{1})+(00\bar{2}\bar{1}-1-\bar{1})]\}$$
$$=\mathrm{Im}\{[(00\bar{1}\bar{1}-1-\bar{2})\,||\,(00\bar{1}\bar{2}-1-\bar{1})]$$
$$+[(00\bar{1}\bar{1}-1-\bar{2})\,||\,(00\bar{2}\bar{1}-1-\bar{1})]\}$$
$$=\mathrm{Im}[(12\,|\,-2-1)-(1-1\,|\,-22)$$
$$+(12\,|\,-2-1)]$$
$$=(2L_{11}-L_{4-2})^i.$$

Here Re and Im refer to real and imaginary parts of the quantities indicated; other notations are explained in Table IV.

Reduction to Integrals over Atomic Orbitals

The matrix elements in Table V are expressible in terms of integrals over orthogonalized atomic orbitals λ_p, through the use of Eq. (28). These integrals again involve either the core Hamiltonian or electron repulsion, and there are again 21 independent ones of each type. These are listed in Table VI.

The matrix elements can be classified by their symmetry, according to the rules

$$I_{jk}\subset\text{Representation }\Gamma_{j+k}\text{ of }C_6,$$
$$L_{\mu\nu}\subset\text{Representation }\Gamma_{\mu+\nu}\text{ of }C_6. \qquad (41)$$

It, therefore, is expedient to introduce as the entities to be algebraically manipulated in the problem *symmetry combinations* of the basic atomic integrals; these are listed in Table VII.

One then has, in the notation of the tables,

$$I_{jk}=A_{j+k}+2B_{j+k}^{01}\cos[(j-k)\pi/6]$$
$$+2B_{j+k}^{02}\cos[(j-k)\pi/3]+B_{j+k}^{03}\cos[(j-k)\pi/2] \qquad (42)$$

and

$$L_{\mu\nu}=C_{\mu+\nu}^{00}+2C_{\mu+\nu}^{01}\cos[(\mu-\nu)\pi/6]$$
$$+2C_{\mu+\nu}^{02}\cos[(\mu-\nu)\pi/3]+C_{\mu+\nu}^{03}\cos[(\mu-\nu)\pi/2]. \qquad (43)$$

From these two basic formulas one can determine any desired I_{jk} or $L_{\mu\nu}$ for any given values of the integrals in Table VII, and hence determine all secular equation elements in Table V for given values of the integrals.

Simplification: Introduction of Atomic Electronegativities

The quantities A_j, which enter the secular equations through the dependence of the I_{jk} on them, Eq. (42), are symmetry combinations of the α_p; each α_p in turn is a one-electron energy in the field of the molecular core, for an electron in a Löwdin orbital λ_p. An approximate treatment of these terms much simplifies the secular equations.

The first approximation is that in those combinations of the α_p which vanish for full benzene symmetry; the Löwdin orbitals λ can be replaced by the nonorthogonal atomic orbitals χ, that is,

$$A_j\approx{}^{\chi}A_j=(1/6)\sum_p\omega^{jp\chi}\alpha_p,\qquad j\neq0, \qquad (44)$$

where

$${}^{\chi}\alpha_p=\int\chi_p^*(1)H_{\text{core}}(1)\chi_p(1)dv(1). \qquad (45)$$

Strictly speaking the α_p contain not only terms ${}^{\chi}\alpha_p$ but also terms ${}^{\chi}\beta_{pq}$, but it is reasonable to suppose that these last cancel in the A_j having $j\neq0$. (In A_0, which would enter importantly the theoretical expression for the ionization potential, for example, this approximation would not be so good.)

TABLE V. H matrices for singlet and triplet states of benzene-like molecules in terms of integrals over molecular orbitals.

Matrix element[a]	Formula[b,c,d]	Corresponding triplet element[c,e]
$(N \parallel N)$	$2I_0+4I_1+15J-4K_{01}-2K_{02}$	—
$(V_{12}^+ \parallel V_{12}^+)$	$-I_1+I_2+2K_{01}-K_{03}+[2L_{11}-L_{4-2}]^r$	$-2K_{01}-[2L_{11}]^r$
$(V_{1-2}^+ \parallel V_{1-2}^+)$	$-I_1+I_2-K_{02}+3K_{03}$	$-4K_{03}$
$(V_{02}^{++} \parallel V_{02}^{++})$	$-\frac{1}{2}(I_0+I_1)+\frac{1}{2}(I_2+I_3)+3K_{02}-K_{03}+\frac{1}{2}[I_{4-2}+I_{11}-2L_{3-1}+7L_{4-2}-L_{11}]^r$	$-4K_{02}-[4L_{4-2}]^r$
$(V_{02}^{+-} \parallel V_{02}^{+-})$	$-\frac{1}{2}(I_0+I_1)+\frac{1}{2}(I_2+I_3)+2K_{01}-K_{02}-K_{03}+\frac{1}{2}[I_{4-2}-I_{11}-2L_{3-1}-L_{4-2}+3L_{11}]^r$	same
$(V_{03} \parallel V_{03})$	$-I_0+I_3+2K_{01}-2K_{02}+K_{03}$	$-2K_{03}$
$(V_{12}^- \parallel V_{12}^-)$	$-I_1+I_2+2K_{01}-K_{03}-[2L_{11}-L_{4-2}]^r$	$-2K_{01}+[2L_{11}]^r$
$(V_{1-2}^- \parallel V_{1-2}^-)$	$-I_1+I_2+K_{02}-K_{03}$	same
$(V_{02}^{-+} \parallel V_{02}^{-+})$	$-\frac{1}{2}(I_0+I_1)+\frac{1}{2}(I_2+I_3)+3K_{02}-K_{03}-\frac{1}{2}[I_{4-2}-I_{11}-2L_{3-1}+7L_{4-2}-L_{11}]^r$	$-4K_{02}+[4L_{4-2}]^r$
$(V_{02}^{--} \parallel V_{02}^{--})$	$-\frac{1}{2}(I_0+I_1)+\frac{1}{2}(I_2+I_3)+2K_{01}-K_{02}-K_{03}-\frac{1}{2}[I_{4-2}-I_{11}-2L_{3-1}-L_{4-2}+3L_{11}]^r$	same
$(N \parallel V_{12}^+)$	$2[I_{2-1}+5L_{10}-L_{2-1}-L_{3-2}]^r$	0
$(N \parallel V_{1-2}^+)$	$2[I_{21}+5L_{30}-2L_{21}]^r$	0
$(N \parallel V_{02}^{++})$	$2^{\frac{1}{2}}[I_{20}+I_{3-1}+10L_{20}-2L_{3-1}-L_{11}-L_{4-2}]^r$	0
$(N \parallel V_{02}^{+-})$	$2^{\frac{1}{2}}[I_{20}-I_{3-1}-L_{11}+L_{4-2}]^r$	0
$(N \parallel V_{03})$	$2^{\frac{1}{2}}[I_{30}+5L_{30}-2L_{21}]^r$	0
$(N \parallel V_{12}^-)$	$2[I_{2-1}+5L_{10}-L_{2-1}-L_{3-2}]^i$	0
$(N \parallel V_{1-2}^-)$	$2[I_{21}+5L_{30}-2L_{21}]^i$	0
$(N \parallel V_{02}^{-+})$	$2^{\frac{1}{2}}[I_{20}+I_{3-1}+10L_{20}-2L_{3-1}-L_{11}-L_{4-2}]^i$	0
$(N \parallel V_{02}^{--})$	$2^{\frac{1}{2}}[I_{20}-I_{3-1}-L_{11}+L_{4-2}]^i$	0
$(V_{12}^+ \parallel V_{1-2}^+)$	$[I_{4-2}-I_{11}+L_{11}+2L_{3-1}-L_{4-2}]^r$	$-[4L_{3-1}]^r$
$(V_{12}^+ \parallel V_{02}^{++})$	$2^{-\frac{1}{2}}[I_{3-2}-I_{10}-2L_{3-2}+4L_{2-1}-2L_{4-1}+4L_{21}]^r$	$-2^{-\frac{1}{2}}[4L_{2-1}+4L_{21}]^r$
$(V_{12}^+ \parallel V_{02}^{+-})$	$-2^{-\frac{1}{2}}[I_{3-2}+I_{10}+10L_{10}-2L_{3-2}-2L_{2-1}]^r$	same
$(V_{12}^+ \parallel V_{03})$	$2^{\frac{1}{2}}[2L_{3-1}-L_{11}]^r$	$-2^{-\frac{1}{2}}[2L_{3-1}]^r$
$(V_{12}^+ \parallel V_{12}^-)$	$[2L_{11}-L_{4-2}]^i$	$-[2L_{11}]^i$
$(V_{12}^+ \parallel V_{1-2}^-)$	$-[I_{4-2}+I_{11}+10L_{20}-2L_{3-1}-L_{4-2}-L_{11}]^i$	same
$(V_{12}^+ \parallel V_{02}^{-+})$	$2^{-\frac{1}{2}}[I_{3-2}-I_{10}-2L_{3-2}+4L_{2-1}-2L_{4-1}+4L_{21}]^i$	$-2^{-\frac{1}{2}}[4L_{2-1}+4L_{21}]^i$
$(V_{12}^+ \parallel V_{02}^{--})$	$-2^{-\frac{1}{2}}[I_{3-2}+I_{10}+10L_{10}-2L_{3-2}-2L_{2-1}]^i$	same
$(V_{1-2}^+ \parallel V_{02}^{++})$	$2^{-\frac{1}{2}}[I_{3-2}-I_{10}+6L_{3-2}-2L_{2-1}]^r$	$-2^{-\frac{1}{2}}[8L_{3-2}]^r$
$(V_{1-2}^+ \parallel V_{02}^{+-})$	$-2^{-\frac{1}{2}}[I_{3-2}+I_{10}+10L_{10}-2L_{3-2}-2L_{2-1}]^r$	same
$(V_{1-2}^+ \parallel V_{03})$	$2^{\frac{1}{2}}(2K_{03}-K_{01})$	$-2^{-\frac{1}{2}}[2K_{03}]$
$(V_{1-2}^+ \parallel V_{12}^-)$	$-[I_{4-2}-I_{11}+L_{11}+2L_{3-1}-L_{4-2}]^i$	$+[4L_{3-1}]^i$
$(V_{1-2}^+ \parallel V_{1-2}^-)$	0	same
$(V_{1-2}^+ \parallel V_{02}^{-+})$	$-2^{-\frac{1}{2}}[I_{3-2}-I_{10}+6L_{3-2}-2L_{2-1}]^i$	$+2^{-\frac{1}{2}}[8L_{3-2}]^i$
$(V_{1-2}^+ \parallel V_{02}^{--})$	$2^{-\frac{1}{2}}[I_{3-2}+I_{10}+10L_{10}-2L_{3-2}-2L_{2-1}]^i$	same

TABLE V.—*Continued.*

Matrix elements[a]	Formula[b,c,d]	Corresponding triplet element[c,e]
$(V_{02}^{++} \Vert V_{02}^{+-})$	$-\frac{1}{2}(I_0-I_1-I_2+I_3)+[I_{4-2}+I_{11}+10L_{20}-2L_{3-1}-L_{4-2}-L_{11}]^r$	same
$(V_{02}^{++} \Vert V_{03})$	$[I_{3-2}-I_{10}+2L_{3-2}]^r$	$-[4L_{3-2}]^r$
$(V_{02}^{++} \Vert V_{12}^{-})$	$-2^{-\frac{1}{2}}[I_{3-2}-I_{10}-2L_{3-2}+4L_{2-1}+2L_{4-1}-4L_{21}]^i$	$+2^{-\frac{1}{2}}[4L_{2-1}-4L_{21}]^i$
$(V_{02}^{++} \Vert V_{1-2}^{-})$	$-2^{-\frac{1}{2}}[I_{3-2}+I_{10}+10L_{10}-2L_{3-2}-2L_{2-1}]^i$	same
$(V_{02}^{++} \Vert V_{02}^{-+})$	$-\frac{1}{2}[I_{4-2}-I_{11}-2L_{3-1}+7L_{4-2}-L_{11}]^i$	$+[4L_{4-2}]^i$
$(V_{02}^{++} \Vert V_{02}^{--})$	$-\frac{1}{2}[I_{4-2}+I_{11}+10L_{20}-2L_{3-1}-L_{4-2}-L_{11}]^i$	same
$(V_{02}^{+-} \Vert V_{03})$	$[I_{3-2}+I_{10}+10L_{10}-2L_{3-2}-2L_{2-1}]^r$	same
$(V_{02}^{+-} \Vert V_{12}^{-})$	$2^{-\frac{1}{2}}[I_{3-2}+I_{10}+10L_{10}-2L_{3-2}-2L_{2-1}]^i$	same
$(V_{02}^{+-} \Vert V_{1-2}^{-})$	$2^{-\frac{1}{2}}[I_{3-2}-I_{10}+2L_{2-1}-2L_{3-2}]^i$	same
$(V_{02}^{+-} \Vert V_{02}^{-+})$	$-\frac{1}{2}[I_{4-2}+I_{11}+10L_{20}-2L_{3-1}-L_{4-2}-L_{11}]^i$	same
$(V_{02}^{+-} \Vert V_{02}^{--})$	$-\frac{1}{2}[I_{4-2}-I_{11}-2L_{3-1}-L_{4-2}+3L_{11}]^i$	same
$(V_{03} \Vert V_{12}^{-})$	$-2^{\frac{1}{2}}[2L_{3-1}-L_{11}]^i$	$+2^{\frac{1}{2}}[2L_{3-1}]^i$
$(V_{03} \Vert V_{1-2}^{-})$	0	same
$(V_{03} \Vert V_{02}^{-+})$	$-[I_{3-2}-I_{10}+2L_{3-2}]^i$	$+[4L_{3-2}]^i$
$(V_{03} \Vert V_{02}^{--})$	$-[I_{3-2}+I_{10}+10L_{10}-2L_{3-2}-2L_{2-1}]^i$	same
$(V_{12}^{-} \Vert V_{1-2}^{-})$	$-[I_{4-2}+I_{11}+10L_{20}-2L_{3-1}-L_{4-2}-L_{11}]^r$	same
$(V_{12}^{-} \Vert V_{02}^{-+})$	$2^{-\frac{1}{2}}[I_{3-2}-I_{10}-2L_{3-2}+4L_{2-1}+2L_{4-1}-4L_{21}]^r$	$-2^{-\frac{1}{2}}[4L_{2-1}-4L_{21}]^r$
$(V_{12}^{-} \Vert V_{02}^{--})$	$-2^{-\frac{1}{2}}[I_{3-2}+I_{10}+10L_{10}-2L_{3-2}-2L_{2-1}]^r$	same
$(V_{1-2}^{-} \Vert V_{02}^{-+})$	$-2^{-\frac{1}{2}}[I_{3-2}+I_{10}+10L_{10}-2L_{3-2}-2L_{2-1}]^r$	same
$(V_{1-2}^{-} \Vert V_{02}^{--})$	$2^{-\frac{1}{2}}[I_{3-2}-I_{10}+2L_{2-1}-2L_{3-2}]^r$	same
$(V_{02}^{-+} \Vert V_{02}^{--})$	$-\frac{1}{2}(I_0-I_1-I_2+I_3)-\frac{1}{2}[I_{4-2}+I_{11}+10L_{20}-2L_{3-1}-L_{4-2}-L_{11}]^r$	same

[a] $(\Phi_m \Vert \Phi_N)=\int\Phi_m{}^*H\Phi_n dv$, where the Φ are the real set C functions of Table III and Eq. (32).
[b] For definitions of I_{jk} and $L_{\mu\nu}$, see Eqs. (35), (37), and (39) of text.
[c] For full benzene symmetry, all terms in brackets [ ] vanish. For full benzene symmetry, therefore, the only nonzero off-diagonal matrix elements are

$$(V_{1-2}^{+} | V_{03}),\ (V_{02}^{++} \Vert V_{02}^{+-}),\ (V_{02}^{-+} \Vert V_{02}^{--}),$$

and the corresponding triplet elements.
[d] Except for $(N \Vert N)$ itself, diagonal elements are relative to $(N \Vert N)$.
[e] All elements relative to the corresponding singlet elements in the previous column, except those which are zero, which are so marked.

Elucidation of the ${}^{\chi}\alpha_p$ now follows familiar lines.[1,6,14] Breaking down H_{core}, one finds

$$^{\chi}\alpha_p=-I_p-P_p-\sum_{q\neq p}\gamma_{pq}, \tag{46}$$

where I_p is the ionization potential for a neutral atom p and P_p is the total attraction of the neutral atom p in the molecule for the rest of the molecule; the γ_{pq} strictly are electron repulsion integrals over the χ, but they may be supposed instead to be over the λ (actually, the corresponding terms in α_p involve both the χ and the λ). One also sets[1,4]

$$\gamma_{pp}=I_p-A_p, \tag{47}$$

where A_p is the electron affinity for atom p, and one defines the *effective electronegativity* of atom p in the molecule as[6]

$$y_p=\tfrac{1}{2}(I_p+A_p)+P_p. \tag{48}$$

Then one obtains

$$^{\chi}\alpha_p=-y_p-\tfrac{1}{2}\gamma_{pp}-\sum_{q\neq p}\gamma_{pq}, \tag{49}$$

and finally, for $j\neq0$,

$$A_j\approx-Y_j-6L_{j0}-\tfrac{1}{2}(\textstyle\sum L_{\mu\nu})_j. \tag{50}$$

Here $(\sum L_{\mu\nu})_j$ is the sum over $\mu-\nu=0, \pm2, \pm4, 6$ or $\pm1, \pm3, \pm5$ of all the $L_{\mu\nu}$ having $\mu+\nu=j$, and the

TABLE VI. Integrals over atomic orbitals for benzene-like molecules.

Core integrals[a,c]	Electronic repulsion integrals[b,c]
α_0	γ_{00}
α_1	γ_{11}
α_2	γ_{22}
α_3	γ_{33}
α_4	γ_{44}
α_5	γ_{55}
β_{01}	γ_{01}
β_{12}	γ_{12}
β_{23}	γ_{23}
β_{34}	γ_{34}
β_{45}	γ_{45}
β_{50}	γ_{50}
β_{02}	γ_{02}
β_{13}	γ_{13}
β_{24}	γ_{24}
β_{35}	γ_{35}
β_{40}	γ_{40}
β_{51}	γ_{51}
β_{03}	γ_{03}
β_{14}	γ_{14}
β_{25}	γ_{25}

[a] $\alpha_p=\int\lambda_p^*(1)H_{\text{core}}(1)\lambda_p(1)dv(1)$; $\beta_{pq}=\int\lambda_p^*(1)H_{\text{core}}(1)\lambda_q(1)dv(1)$.
[b] $\gamma_{pq}=\int\int\lambda_p^*(1)\lambda_p(1)(e^2/r_{12})\lambda_q^*(2)\lambda_q(2)dv(1)dv(2)$.
[c] For full benzene symmetry, only four core integrals are distinct, α_0, β_{01}, β_{02}, and β_{03}; and only four electronic repulsion integrals, γ_{00}, γ_{01}, γ_{02}, and γ_{03}.

quantities

$$Y_j=(1/6)\sum_p \omega^{jp}y_p \tag{51}$$

are generalized electronegativity differences—symmetry combinations of effective atomic electronegativities. Specifically, Eq. (50) gives the following approximate equations:

$$\begin{aligned} A_1+5L_{10}-L_{2-1}-L_{3-2}&\approx -Y_1,\\ A_2+5L_{20}-2L_{3-1}-L_{4-2}-L_{11}&\approx -Y_2,\\ A_3+5L_{30}-2L_{21}&\approx -Y_3. \end{aligned} \tag{52}$$

TABLE VII. Symmetry combinations of integrals over atomic orbitals for benzene-like molecules.[a,b]

Core integrals[c,d]	Electronic repulsion integrals[c,d]
$A_j=B_j^{00}=(1/6)\Sigma_p\omega^{jp}\alpha_p$	$C_j^{00}=(1/36)\Sigma_p\omega^{jp}\gamma_{pp}$
$B_j^{01}=(1/6)\Sigma_p\omega^{j(p+\frac{1}{2})}\beta_{p,p+1}$	$C_j^{01}=(1/36)\Sigma_p\omega^{j(p+\frac{1}{2})}\gamma_{p,p+1}$
$B_j^{02}=(1/6)\Sigma_p\omega^{j(p+1)}\beta_{p,p+2}$	$C_j^{02}=(1/36)\Sigma_p\omega^{j(p+1)}\gamma_{p,p+2}$
$B_j^{03}=(1/6)\Sigma_p\omega^{j(p+\frac{3}{2})}\beta_{p,p+3}$	$C_j^{03}=(1/36)\Sigma_p\omega^{j(p+\frac{3}{2})}\gamma_{p,p+3}$

[a] Sums over p are from 0 to 5; $\omega=\exp(2\pi i/6)$.
[b] The subscript j indicates the irreducible representation of the group C_6 to which a given symmetry combination belongs.
[c] For full benzene symmetry, all symmetry combinations not having $j=0$ vanish, leaving four distinct core integrals and four distinct electronic repulsion integrals: $A_0=\alpha_0$, $B_0^{01}=\beta_{01}$, $B_0^{02}=\beta_{02}$, and $B_0^{03}=\beta_{03}$; $C_0^{00}=1/6\gamma_{00}$, $C_0^{01}=1/6\gamma_{01}$, $C_0^{02}=1/6\gamma_{02}$ and $C_0^{03}=1/6\gamma_{03}$.
[d] In each case $j=0, \pm1, \pm2, 3$, with the $j=\pm1$ and $j=3$ integrals redundant for B_j^{03} and C_j^{03}. Thus the number of *independent* integrals of each type in the most general case is 21.

TABLE VIII. Simplified formulas for selected matrix elements.[a]

Matrix element[b]	Formula[b]	Corresponding triplet element[b]
$(N\,\|\,V_{12}^+)$	$-2Y_1^r$	0
$(N\,\|\,V_{1-2}^+)$	$-2Y_3^r$	0
$(N\,\|\,V_{02}^{++})$	$-8^{\frac{1}{2}}Y_2^r$	0
$(N\,\|\,V_{02}^{+-})$	$-2^{\frac{1}{2}}(-2B_2^{01}+L_{11}-L_{4-2})^r$	0
$(N\,\|\,V_{03})$	$-2^{\frac{1}{2}}Y_3^r$	0
$(N\,\|\,V_{12}^-)$	$-2Y_1^i$	0
$(N\,\|\,V_{1-2}^-)$	$-12^{\frac{1}{2}}(-B_3^{01})^i$	0
$(N\,\|\,V_{02}^{-+})$	$-8^{\frac{1}{2}}Y_2^i$	0
$(N\,\|\,V_{02}^{--})$	$-2^{\frac{1}{2}}(-2B_2^{01}+L_{11}-L_{4-2})^i$	0
$(V_{12}^+\,\|\,V_{1-2}^+)$	$(-4B_2^{01}+L_{11}+2L_{3-1}-L_{4-2})^r$	$-4L_{3-1}^r$
$(V_{12}^+\,\|\,V_{12}^-)$	$(2L_{11}-L_{4-2})^i$	$-2L_{11}^i$
$(V_{12}^+\,\|\,V_{1-2}^-)$	$2Y_2^i$	same
$(V_{1-2}^+\,\|\,V_{12}^-)$	$-(-4B_2^{01}+L_{11}+2L_{3-1}-L_{4-2})^i$	$+4L_{3-1}^i$
$(V_{1-2}^+\,\|\,V_{1-2}^-)$	0	same
$(V_{12}^-\,\|\,V_{1-2}^-)$	$2Y_2^r$	same

[a] From Table V and Eqs. (42), (52), and (53).
[b] See Table V, notes a, b, and e.

TABLE IX. H matrices for benzene-like molecules possessing a vertical plane of symmetry.[a,b]

Matrix element[c,d]	Formula[e]	Corresponding triplet element[f]
$(N\,\|\,N)$	$2I_0+4I_1+15J-4K_{01}-2K_{02}$	—
$(N\,\|\,V_{12}^+)$	$[-2Y_1]^r$	0
$(N\,\|\,V_{1-2}^+)$	$[-2Y_3]^r$	0
$(N\,\|\,V_{12}^-)$	0	0
$(N\,\|\,V_{1-2}^-)$	0	0
$(V_{12}^+\,\|\,V_{12}^+)$	$-I_1+I_2+2K_{01}-K_{03}+[2L_{11}-L_{4-2}]^r$	$-2K_{01}-[2L_{11}]^r$
$(V_{12}^+\,\|\,V_{1-2}^+)$	$[-4B_2^{01}+L_{11}+2L_{3-1}-L_{4-2}]^r$	$[-4L_{3-1}]^r$
$(V_{12}^+\,\|\,V_{12}^-)$	0	0
$(V_{12}^+\,\|\,V_{1-2}^-)$	0	0
$(V_{1-2}^+\,\|\,V_{1-2}^+)$	$-I_1+I_2-K_{02}+3K_{03}$	$-4K_{03}$
$(V_{1-2}^+\,\|\,V_{12}^-)$	0	0
$(V_{1-2}^+\,\|\,V_{1-2}^-)$	0	0
$(V_{12}^-\,\|\,V_{12}^-)$	$-I_1+I_2+2K_{01}-K_{03}-[2L_{11}-L_{4-2}]^r$	$-2K_{01}+[2L_{11}]^r$
$(V_{12}^-\,\|\,V_{1-2}^-)$	$[2Y_2]^r$	same
$(V_{1-2}^-\,\|\,V_{1-2}^-)$	$-I_1+I_2+K_{02}-K_{03}$	same

[a] From Tables V and VIII, from which matrix elements involving higher states also may be determined. To obtain matrix elements in terms of integrals over atomic orbitals, use Eqs. (42) and (43).
[b] Plane of symmetry through atoms 0 and 3, or bonds 0—1 and 3—4.
[c] See Table V, note a.
[d] For D_{6h} symmetries, see Table III, note e.
[e] See Table V, notes b to d.
[f] See Table V, note e.

A second approximation, of comparable accuracy, is that the nonneighbor β_{pq} may be neglected in those combinations of the β_{pq} which vanish for full benzene symmetry, that is,

$$B_j^{02}\approx 0 \quad\text{and}\quad B_j^{03}\approx 0 \quad\text{for}\quad j\neq 0. \tag{53}$$

Equations (52) and (53), together with Eq. (42), lead to considerable simplification in many of the matrix elements in Table V. Modified formulas for some of the most important are displayed in Table VIII.

Secular Equations for Molecules with a Vertical Plane of Symmetry

While the present purpose is not to perform specific calculations, it may be useful to display the formulas for one special case of very frequent occurrence, that in which the molecule retains one or more planes of symmetry in addition to the molecular plane. If such a plane passes through either atoms 0 and 3 (for example, any mono-substituted benzene) or through bonds 0—1 and 3—4 (for example, any ortho di-substituted benzene), all interactions between + and − states vanish, and one gets the simplified secular equation matrix elements listed in Table IX.

For such molecules the secular equations take factored forms, with further simplifications for cases of still greater symmetry. Table IX includes as special cases, among others, the secular equations for *s*-triazine, pyridine, pyrazine, and pyrimidine given in Tables VIII–XI of the second work cited in footnote 1, and the secular equations for borazole.

It will be noted that effects of perturbations are of two kinds, nonvectorial and vectorial, or symmetry-independent and symmetry dependent. A perturbation may affect one or more of the basic integrals of Table VI and hence change the integrals I_0, I_1, I_2, J, K_{01}, K_{02}, K_{03} which enter the formulas of Table IX even for full benzene symmetry. Or, depending on its symmetry, a perturbation may cause one or more of the bracketed quantities in Table IX to become nonzero, the $L_{\mu\nu}$ terms and the terms involving electronegativity differences. A spectroscopic shift relative to benzene in general thus is compounded from a part independent of symmetry and a part which depends on symmetry.

For actual numerical calculations, the suggested procedure is first to compute all integrals for benzene itself, and then to compute integral increments for the molecule(s) of interest relative to benzene. When the latter are small, perturbation techniques may suffice for determination of spectroscopic shifts.

Dipole and Transition Moments

To obtain formulas for dipole and transition moments, one may assume that all molecules have the regular hexagonal shape with side R. Assuming further a center of charge of the orbital λ_p at nucleus p and ignoring overlap effects, one then has the basic formula for determining pi-electron moments,

$$\int\phi_j\mathbf{r}\phi_k dv=(R/2)[\mathbf{i}(\delta_{j+k,1}+\delta_{j+k,-1}) + \mathbf{j}(\delta_{j+k,1}-\delta_{j+k,-1})i], \tag{54}$$

where $\mathbf{i}$ and $\mathbf{j}$ are unit vectors from the molecular center toward atom 0 and the 1—2 bond, respectively, and the δ are Kronecker deltas. From this formula follow the matrix elements $(\Phi_m \mid \mathbf{M}_\pi \mid \Phi_n)$ for the total pi-electron moment

$$\mathbf{M}_\pi=-e\sum_{\mu=1}^{6}\mathbf{r}\mu$$

among the set C starting functions of Table III and Eq. (32). Namely,

$$(N \mid \mathbf{M}_\pi \mid V_{12}^+)=-eR\mathbf{i}, \qquad (N \mid \mathbf{M}_\pi \mid V_{12}^-)=-eR\mathbf{j},$$
$$\text{all other matrix elements of } \mathbf{M}_\pi=0. \tag{55}$$

These simple results imply that all dipole and transition moments are zero except those involving both the starting function N and one of the functions V_{12}^+ and V_{12}^-.

Consider for example the question of the dipole moment of the ground state. If N is the main component of its wave function, with V_{12}^+, V_{12}^- and other states making small contributions only, the dipole moment will be given by the formula

$$(\mu_\pi/eR)=-(4/\Delta E)\mathbf{Y}_1. \tag{56}$$

Here the quantity

$$\mathbf{Y}_1=Y_1^r\mathbf{i}+Y_1^i\mathbf{j} \tag{57}$$

is an average of electronegativity vectors for the six atoms, the vector $\mathbf{y}_{p1}$ for atom p being directed from the molecular center toward atom p, as shown by Eq. (51). ΔE is the $^1A_{1g}-{}^1E_{1u}$ energy difference for benzene itself (+7.0 ev).[1,8]

Or, consider the moment for the $^1A-{}^1L_b$ transition in a benzene-like molecule,[27] the transition which for benzene itself is $^1A_{1g}-{}^1B_{2u}$ or $N-V_{1-2}^-$. For benzene itself this transition moment is zero, since V_{1-2}^- does not mix with V_{12}^+ or V_{12}^-, and neither does N. But in a perturbed benzene these mixings may occur. From assuming they are small, the formula for the transition moment is

$$\mathbf{m}(^1A-{}^1L_b)/eR=(2/\Delta E')\mathbf{Y}_2. \tag{58}$$

Here $\Delta E'$ is the $^1B_{2u}-{}^1E_{1u}$ energy difference in benzene itself (+2.1 ev)[1,8] and the quantity

$$\mathbf{Y}_2=Y_2^i\mathbf{i}+Y_2^r\mathbf{j} \tag{59}$$

is an average of electronegativity vectors $\mathbf{y}_{p2}$ on the six atoms, $\mathbf{y}_{p2}$ being perpendicular to the radius vector

[27] J. R. Platt, J. Chem. Phys. 19, 263 (1951). See also J. A. Petruska, Ph.D. thesis, University of Chicago, 1960.

to atom p, pointing in the clockwise direction if p is odd, in the counterclockwise direction if p is even, as required by Eq. (51).

Similar arguments could be given concerning other transition moments, or dipole moments of excited states.

Such vectorial constructions of transitions moments have been previously discussed at length by Platt.[27] Platt did not obtain explicit formulas from an orbital theory, but rather introduced empirical parameters for substituents which he called *spectroscopic moments.* Equation (58) is explicit; it makes clear the relation between spectroscopic moments and atomic electronegativities.

One simple example of the use of the foregoing equations will suffice to illustrate what may be done with them. For pyridine, a previous calculation gave, essentially through an equation like Eq. (58), an f value for the $^1A-{}^1L_b$ transition of 0.046, compared with an experimental 0.041.[28] The parameters used there give $Y_1=0.26$ ev, from which according to Eq. (56) the pi dipole moment for the ground state would be

$$\mu_\pi=4(0.26)(4.8)(1.4)/(7.0)=1.0\text{D}.$$

The experimental moment is more than twice this, but a substantial part of the total moment would be expected to be lone pair and/or sigma electron contributions.

Discussion

Many extensions of this analysis are possible, and there are many applications of it.

Among the properties that have not been considered here are ionization potential, electron affinity, resonance energy, electron densities, and bond orders. Formulas for these can be written out, although there are special problems associated with each of them.[29] It seems important to try to work more properties into a single coherent semiempirical scheme.

Among the further developments or extensions of the mathematical treatment that should be examined are: (1) The systematic cataloging of the various types of perturbations and their effects, using group theory. (2) The systematic simplification of the equations for the case that all perturbations are small. (3) The inclusion of two-electron jumps. (4) The extension to include mesomeric effects.[6] (5) The development of the equations for the LCAO SCF orbitals as obtained from this treatment.[24] (6) The further examination of the effective electronegativities y_p and the changes in them produced by charge transfer.[30]

Especially interesting would be the extension to the arbitrary cyclic polyene (which is essentially trivial).[29]

[28] Work cited in footnote reference 1, p. 767.

[29] P. G. Lykos, Ph.D. Thesis, Carnegie Institute of Technology, 1954.

[30] J. M. Parks and R. G. Parr, J. Chem. Phys. **28**, 335 (1958); **32**, 1657 (1960).

The cross-linking in molecules such as naphthalene can be viewed as a perturbation of corresponding cyclic polyenes. This approach was employed by Moffitt[31]; the present method would provide theoretical formulas for some elements treated by Moffitt as being purely empirical.

The most dubious point about the analysis is not the pi-electron approximation itself, which is quite securely based,[32] but the replacement of atomic orbitals by their orthogonalized counterparts and the subsequent neglect of overlap distributions. There seems to be no simple alternative to this last, however. The most general benzene-like molecule as here treated is a 42-parameter problem; treated without the zero differential overlap assumption it involves many hundreds of parameters.

It may be pointed out that formulas for various simpler theories of benzene-like molecules can be obtained from those given here. If one wished to neglect electron repulsion altogether, for example, one could merely strike out J, K_{01}, K_{02}, K_{03}, and all $L_{\mu\nu}$.

The most notable result of the analysis is the demonstration that the atomic electronegativities of Mulliken, modified as required by the molecular environment, determine in a simple way all charge distributions in benzene-like molecules.

IV. REMARK CONCERNING USE OF MULTIPOLE EXPANSION FORMULAS FOR ELECTRONIC REPULSION INTEGRALS

Following are reasons for considering evaluation of two-center coulomb repulsion integrals in the generalized Hückel method by multipole expansion methods:

(1) Pariser and Parr[1] introduced nonoverlapping uniformly charged sphere approximations for pi orbitals, which gave a formula for two-center coulomb integrals that involves reciprocal square roots of distances. Expanded in inverse powers of the internuclear distance R, this becomes an infinite series in $(1/R)$. Just the first term in this series, (e^2/R), was used by Pople,[2] but he later turned to the Pariser-Parr values.[33] Simpler than the complete Pariser-Parr series and yet more accurate than the simple Pople expansion, the multipole expansion formula involves only odd powers of $(1/R)$ up to the fifth, and the successive terms have simple physical interpretations.

(2) Mulligan[34] and Parr and Taylor[35] observed that multipole expansions formulas of a variety of purely theoretical electronic repulsion integrals over Slater orbitals are surprisingly accurate, even down to nearest neighbor distances, and that such expansions can be

[31] W. Moffitt, J. Chem. Phys. **22**, 320 (1954).

[32] P. G. Lykos and R. G. Parr, J. Chem. Phys. **24**, 1166 (1956); **25**, 1301 (1956).

[33] A. Brickstock and J. A. Pople, Trans. Faraday Soc. **50**, 901 (1954).

[34] J. F. Mulligan, J. Chem. Phys. **19**, 347 (1951).

[35] R. G. Parr and G. R. Taylor, J. Chem. Phys. **19**, 497 (1951).

obtained from purely theoretical formulas by merely striking out terms behaving as e^{-R}. As was shown in Sec. II the repulsion integrals in the generalized Hückel method may be regarded as over orthogonalized atomic orbitals. These might be expected to more closely follow multipole expansion formulas than do Slater orbitals, since they more closely obey the necessary condition for a multipole expansion formula to be an exact formula—detailed nonoverlapping of the electronic distributions (zero differential overlap).

(3) Adoption of multipole expansion formulas would allow the characterization of each pi orbital in a problem by specification of a value for its quadrupole moment, from which all two-center repulsion integrals involving it could be computed from simple classical formulas.

Multipole expansion formulas for electronic repulsion integrals between two electrons in two p orbitals on two atoms will be given and discussed later. Calculations testing the validity of such expansions will be performed, and an examination will be made of the effects of the Löwdin orthogonalization process. Finally, advantages and disadvantages of the multipole expansion formulation will be summarized.

Multipole Expansion Formulas for Two-Center Coulomb Repulsion Integrals Involving p Orbitals

An electron in a p orbital χ on an atom defines a distribution of electricity $e\Omega = e\chi^2$ which has a charge (monopole moment) e and quadrupole moments, but no dipole or other moments. This distribution is cylindrically symmetrical about some axis z, as a result of which the nonzero elements of the traceless quadrupole moment tensor can be expressed in terms of a single element,[36]

$$Q_{zz} = e\int (3z^2 - r^2)\Omega dv = eq. \qquad (60)$$

Indeed, $Q_{xx} = Q_{yy} = -\frac{1}{2}eq$. The quantity q is the *scalar quadrupole moment* of the distribution Ω.

Consider now two p orbitals χ_A and χ_B, centered at points A and B, a distance R apart. Let the corresponding distribution be Ω_A and Ω_B, with scalar quadrupole moments q_A and q_B. Then the coulomb repulsion integral,

$$\gamma_{AB} = \iint \Omega_A(1)(e^2/r_{12})\Omega_B(2)dv(1)dv(2), \qquad (61)$$

has a multipole expansion in powers of $(1/R)$ provided R is not zero. Namely, if θ_A, ϕ_A and θ_B, ϕ_B are polar coordinates of the axes of χ_A and χ_B with respect to the $A-B$ line of centers, one has the formula,[36]

$$\begin{aligned}\gamma_{AB} \sim e^2\{ R^{-1} &+ (4R^3)^{-1}[q_A(3\cos^2\theta_B - 1) + q_B(3\cos^2\theta_A - 1)] \\ &+ (3q_Aq_B/16R^5)[(1 - 5\cos^2\theta_A - 5\cos^2\theta_B - 15\cos^2\theta_A\cos^2\theta_B) + 2(\sin\theta_A\sin\theta_B\cos(\phi_A - \phi_B) \\ &- 4\cos\theta_A\cos\theta_B)^2]\}. \qquad (62)\end{aligned}$$

Here the successive terms represent charge-charge, charge-quadrupole, and quadrupole-quadrupole interactions.

The special case of most interest is the one in which χ_A and χ_B are parallel pi-type orbitals, a and b.[37] Here $\theta_A = \theta_B = \frac{1}{2}\pi$, $\phi_A - \phi_B = 0$, and Eq. (62) gives

$$\gamma_{ab} \sim e^2\{R^{-1} - [(q_A + q_B)/4R^3] + (9q_Aq_B/16R^5)\}. \qquad (63)$$

If χ_A and χ_B are pi-type but mutually perpendicular orbitals, a and b_s,[37] on the other hand, $\theta_A = \theta_B = \frac{1}{2}\pi$ but $\phi_A - \phi_B = \frac{1}{2}\pi$, and Eq. (62) gives

$$\gamma_{ab_s} \sim e^2\{R^{-1} - [(q_A + q_B)/4R^3] + (3q_Aq_B/16R^5)\}. \qquad (64)$$

If finally χ_A is a pi-type orbital a and χ_B a sigma-type orbital b_r,[37] $\theta_A = \frac{1}{2}\pi$, $\theta_B = 0$, $\phi_A - \phi_B = 0$, and Eq. (62) gives

$$\gamma_{ab_r} \sim e^2\{R^{-1} - [(q_A - 2q_B)/4R^3] - (3q_Aq_B)/16R^5)\}. \qquad (65)$$

For the homonuclear case $q_A = q_B = q$, these formulas reduce to the following:

$$\gamma_{ab} \sim e^2\{R^{-1} - (q/2R^3) + (9q^2/16R^5)\} \quad \text{(homonuclear case)}, \qquad (66)$$

$$\gamma_{ab_s} \sim e^2\{R^{-1} - (q/2R^3) + (3q^2/16R^5)\} \quad \text{(homonuclear case)}, \qquad (67)$$

$$\gamma_{ab_r} \sim e^2\{R^{-1} + (q/4R^3) - (3q^2/4R^5)\} \quad \text{(homonuclear case)}. \qquad (68)$$

All of these formulas would be exact for all R for distributions Ω_A and Ω_B which are point (ideal) charge-quadrupoles, or which are "spherically disconnected" and have the indicated moments[38]; for actual p functions they are asymptotically valid for large R.

Up to this point the radial factors in the p orbitals have not been specified. For $2p$ hydrogen-like orbitals, effective charge Z, one would have

$$q = 24a_0^2/Z^2 \quad (2p \text{ orbitals}), \qquad (69)$$

[36] J. O. Hirschfelder, C. F. Curtiss, and R. B. Bird, *Molecular Theory of Gases and Liquids* (John Wiley & Sons, Inc., New York, 1954), pp. 26–28, 839–840.

[37] R. G. Parr and B. L. Crawford, Jr., J. Chem. Phys. **16**, 1049 (1948).

[38] Per-Olov Löwdin, Phil. Mag. Suppl. **5**, 1 (1956).

TABLE X. Exact and asymptotic values for coulomb integrals involving $2p$ orbitals.[a]

ρ[b]	6	8	10	14
$Z^{-1}\gamma_{ab}$				
Exact[c]	0.1308	0.1080	0.0906	0.0676
Asymptotic[d]	0.1528	0.1115	0.0912	0.0677
Truncated Asymptotic[e]	0.1111	0.1016	0.0880	0.0671
Orthogonalized[f]	0.1216	0.1045	0.0895	0.0676
$Z^{-1}\gamma_{ab_s}$				
Exact[c]	0.1242	0.1047	0.0890	0.0673
Asymptotic[d]	0.1250	0.1049	0.0891	0.0673
$Z^{-1}\gamma_{ab_r}$				
Exact[c]	0.1422	0.1200	0.1003	0.0727
Asymptotic[d]	0.1389	0.1235	0.1017	0.0728

[a] Values in e^2/a_0 units.
[b] $\rho=ZR/a_0$.
[c] Footnote reference 39.
[d] From Eqs. (70) to (72) of text.
[e] Quadrupole-quadrupole term omitted. See text.
[f] From Eq. (75) of text and numerical values from footnote reference 39.

and in this case Eqs. (66) to (68) give, with $\rho=ZR/a_0$,

$$\gamma_{ab}\sim Z(e^2/a_0)[(1/\rho)-(12/\rho^3)+(324/\rho^5)] \quad \text{(homonuclear case, } 2p \text{ orbitals)}, \quad (70)$$

$$\gamma_{ab_s}\sim Z(e^2/a_0)[(1/\rho)-(12/\rho^3)+(108/\rho^5)] \quad \text{(homonuclear case, } 2p \text{ orbitals)}, \quad (71)$$

$$\gamma_{ab_r}\sim Z(e^2/a_0)[(1/\rho)+(6/\rho^3)-(432/\rho^5)] \quad \text{(homonuclear case, } 2p \text{ orbitals)}. \quad (72)$$

These formulas have been given previously by Mulligan.[34] Corresponding formulas for the heteronuclear case may be obtained by setting $q_A=24a_0^2/Z_A^2$ and $q_B=24a_0^2/Z_B^2$ in Eqs. (63) to (65).

Numerical Values. Effects of Orthogonalization

In Table X are given typical exact values of $Z^{-1}\gamma_{ab}$, $Z^{-1}\gamma_{ab_s}$ and $Z^{-1}\gamma_{ab_r}$, taken from the tables of Kopineck,[39] and approximate values calculated from Eqs. (70) to (72).

As would be expected, the approximate values are very good for large values of R. The remarkable feature is how good they remain for small values of R. For a carbon $2p\pi$ orbital with the Slater Z equal to 3.18, for instance, for R equal to the neighbor C—C distance in benzene, ρ is 8.37, and it can be seen from Table X that the asymptotic formulas are good to a few percent for this ρ value.

Also included in Table X are some integral values calculated from Eq. (70) with the quadrupole-quadrupole term deleted. Truncation produces considerable error for ρ equal to six, but only a few percent error for ρ equal to eight or higher.

Effects of transforming the atomic orbitals to a localized orthogonal set may be examined by explicitly carrying out the Löwdin orthogonalization procedure.[10] The Löwdin orthogonalized analogs of χ_a and χ_b are, by Eq. (3) of Sec. II,

$$\lambda_a=A\chi_a+B\chi_b$$

and

$$\lambda_b=B\chi_a+A\chi_b, \quad (73)$$

where

$$2A=(1+S)^{-\frac{1}{2}}+(1-S)^{-\frac{1}{2}},$$

$$2B=(1+S)^{-\frac{1}{2}}-(1-S)^{-\frac{1}{2}}, \quad (74)$$

and S is the $\chi_a-\chi_b$ overlap. The coulomb repulsion integral between λ_a and λ_b accordingly is given by the formula.

$${}^{\lambda}\gamma_{ab}=(A^4+B^4)\gamma_{ab}+2A^2B^2\gamma_{aa}+4AB(A^2+B^2)(aa\mid ab)+4A^2B^2(ab\mid ab), \quad (75)$$

where $(aa\mid ab)$ and $(ab\mid ab)$ are hybrid and exchange integrals.[37] All quantities in this formula may be found in the literature[39]; some values are included in Table X.

The orbitals λ_a and λ_b differ from the orbitals χ_a and χ_b by terms that become exponentially small for large R. This means that ${}^{\lambda}\gamma_{ab}$ has the same asymptotic expansion as γ_{ab}, namely, Eq. (70).[40] The numbers in Table X thus show that the discrepancies between asymptotic and exact values for ${}^{\lambda}\gamma_{ab}$ in fact are greater than the corresponding discrepancies for γ_{ab}, contrary to the supposition (2) at the beginning of this section. The errors remain small, however, so that one may say that multipole expansions are essentially as good for the coulomb integrals over orthogonalized orbitals as for these integrals over nonorthogonalized orbitals.

Discussion

The foregoing would appear to indicate that multipole expansion formulas might well be systematically studied in the context of the generalized Hückel method. They can reproduce purely theoretical integrals with a precision matching the inherent precision of the method as a whole. They involve a single parameter for each pi orbital, its quadrupole moment, which has a simple physical meaning, and *they accordingly provide a simple means for evaluating pi repulsions in heteropolar systems*.[41] They are independent of the form of the radial factors in the actual orbitals and so have an inherent accuracy which transcends the accuracy limit imposed by a particular orbital form. They are purely classical in nature and so have attraction as possible ingredients in a possible complete unified semi-quantum-mechanical theory of chemistry.

On the other side, use of multipole expansion formulas precludes use of a single formula for integrals γ_{ab}

[39] H. J. Kopineck, Z. Naturforsch. **5a**, 420 (1950).

[40] The moments of the distribution λ_a^2 actually differ from those of the distribution χ_a^2. These differences go to zero as S, however, and are here neglected.

[41] The prescription is provided by Eqs. (63)–(65). It may be noted that to the extent the quadrupole-quadrupole terms may be neglected, a heteropolar integral is an arithmetic mean of the corresponding homopolar integrals. Thus $\gamma_{cn}\approx\frac{1}{2}(\gamma_{cc}+\gamma_{nn})$.

for all distances, including $R=0$, which would have certain advantages. (Spectroscopic intervals depend on differences $\gamma_{aa}-\gamma_{ab}$, not on absolute values of γ_{ab}.[29]) The quadrupole-quadrupole terms tend to get suspiciously big for the small Z values required by attempts[29] to fit empirical γ_{ab} values[8] with purely theoretical integral values.[42]

V. ACKNOWLEDGMENTS

Section III was first written during 1953–1954 while the author was Guggenheim Fellow and Fulbright Scholar at the University of Cambridge. He is grateful for these fellowship awards, and he also would like to record his appreciation to the members of the Theoretical Chemistry Department at Cambridge for their gracious hospitality, most especially Dr. Frank S. Boys.

The author has profited from numerous discussions regarding the material in Secs. II and III with Professor Peter G. Lykos. Dr. Lykos has examined the application of some of these methods to the benzene and naphthalene molecules,[29] and plans to describe his results elsewhere. Discussions about Sec. II with Professor Klaus Ruedenberg and Dr. Rudolph Pariser also have been helpful.

[42] P. G. Lykos and R. G. Parr, J. Chem. Phys. **28**, 361 (1958).

Reprinted from the JOURNAL OF CHEMICAL PHYSICS, Vol. 34, No. 6, 1861–1913, June, 1961
Printed in U. S. A.

Quantum Mechanics of Mobile Electrons in Conjugated Bond Systems. I. General Analysis in the Tight-Binding Formulation*

KLAUS RUEDENBERG

Institute for Atomic Research, Department of Chemistry, Department of Physics, Iowa State University, Ames, Iowa

(Received March 16, 1959)

The quantum-mechanical treatment is carried through for a set of electrons in a homonuclear conjugated bond system of arbitrary size, including electronic interaction and including all overlap effects between neighbors. All framework contributions are obtained by explicit integration over the framework Hamiltonian, including the effect of nonconjugated neighbor atoms and differentiating between different types of conjugated atoms (joint, nonjoints, etc.). Expressions are given for the ground-state energy, ionization potential, electron affinity, electronegativity, and for the configuration interaction matrix for the calculation of excited states, assuming singly excited configurations. The results take simple forms permitting instructive interpretations. The partial additivity of one-electron binding-energy contributions, obtained as eigenvalues of topological molecular orbitals, and the approximate validity of the "neglect of differential overlap" is proved.

INTRODUCTION

SINCE its inception, the concept of mobile electrons in conjugated bond systems has provided a remarkably successful model in spite of many limitations, which must largely be attributed to the simplifying assumptions which usually have gone along with it. It is therefore surprising that no rigorous treatment of the quantum-mechanical problem has been carried through. The fruitfulness of the model indicates that it will always remain useful; it lends particular interest to the assumptions and invites a closer scrutiny of their relative significance. But a proper appreciation of the real foundations seems indispensable in order to assess and eliminate the limitations and inconsistencies. Certainly, after so much semi- and sesquiempirical work on the subject, steps towards rigorosity are not out of order.

While the developments given here are essentially written with the pi-electron systems of organic molecules in mind, the essential formulations apply equally to other conjugated bond systems which occur, e.g., in crystals and metals with mobile electrons.

I

The original work of Hückel,[1] which was further developed by Lennard-Jones,[2] Coulson,[3,4] Mulliken and Wheland,[5] Longuet-Higgins,[4,6] and others, is a *one-electron theory* with its shortcomings. The same holds for the free-electron theory, first suggested by Schmidt[7]; in particular the network formulation, developed by Platt,[8] Kuhn,[9] Ruedenberg and Scherr,[10] and others,[11] which was shown to be equivalent to the LCAO formulation,[12] has contributed an illuminating interpretation of the meaning of the model.

The beauty and usefulness of these approaches lies in the elegant simplicity of the mathematical formalism; a simplicity which prevails also when the system becomes arbitrarily large and, as Mulliken and Wheland first showed,[5] when all integrals between neighbor atoms are taken into account and only those involving the overlap between nonneighbors are neglected ("*tight-binding approximation*"). The latter circumstance is extremely gratifying since the quantitative examination of integrals between atomic orbitals shows that the neglect of integrals containing the overlap of nonneighbors can be honestly justified, whereas this is obviously not the case for integrals between neighbors. Thus, the tight-binding approximation is a bona fide first approximation, *whereas the outright neglect of neighbor overlap is not.*

The first step towards a rigorous approach beyond the one-electron model was taken by M. Goeppert-Mayer and A. L. Sklar,[13] who carried through the inclusion of the interaction between electrons in the case of benzene by means of a determinantal wave function. The treatment contained however, a theoretically inconsistent simplifying assumption: use is made, *in integrals between different atomic orbitals*, of

* Contribution No. 665. Work performed in the Ames Laboratory of the U. S. Atomic Energy Commission.

[1] E. Hückel, Z. Physik **70**, 204 (1931); Z. Electrochem. **43**, 752, 827 (1937), review; Z. Physik **72**, 310 (1931); **76**, 628 (1932).

[2] J. E. Lennard-Jones, Proc. Roy. Soc. (London) **A158**, 280 (1937).

[3] C. A. Coulson, Proc. Roy. Soc. (London) **A169**, 413 (1939); C. A. Coulson and G. S. Rushbrooke, Proc. Cambridge Phil. Soc. **36**, 193 (1940); B. H. Chirgwin and C. A. Coulson, Proc. Roy. Soc. (London) **A201**, 196 (1950); C. A. Coulson, R. Daudel, and D. M. Robertson, *ibid.* **A207**, 306 (1951).

[4] C. A. Coulson and H. C. Longuet-Higgins, Proc. Roy. Soc. (London) **A191**, 39 (1947); **A192**, 16 (1947); **A193**, 447, 456 (1948); **A195**, 188 (1948).

[5] R. S. Mulliken, C. Rieke, and S. Brown, J. Am. Chem. Soc. **63**, 41 (1941); see also R. S. Mulliken and C. Rieke, *ibid.* **63**, 1770 (1941); G. W. Wheland, *ibid.* 2025 (1941); P. O. Löwdin, J. Chem. Phys. **18**, 365 (1950).

[6] H. C. Longuet-Higgins, J. Chem. Phys. **18**, 265, 275, 283 (1950).

[7] O. Schmidt, Ber. deut. chem. Ges. **73A**, 97 (1940).

[8] J. R. Platt, J. Chem. Phys. **17**, 484 (1949).

[9] H. Kuhn, J. Chem. Phys. **16**, 840 (1948); **17**, 1198 (1949); Helv. Chim. Acta **31**, 1441 (1948).

[10] K. Ruedenberg and C. W. Scherr, J. Chem. Phys. **21**, 1565 (1953); C. W. Scherr, *ibid.* **21**, 1582 (1953).

[11] N. S. Bayliss, J. Chem. Phys. **16**, 287 (1948); Quart. Revs. **6**, 319 (1952); W. T. Simpson, J. Chem. Phys. **16**, 1124 (1948).

[12] K. Ruedenberg, J. Chem. Phys. **22**, 1878 (1954); N. S. Ham and K. Ruedenberg, *ibid.* **29**, 1199, 1215 (1958).

[13] M. Goeppert-Mayer and A. L. Sklar, J. Chem. Phys. **6**, 645 (1938); C. C. J. Roothaan and R. G. Parr, *ibid.* **17**, 1001 (1949); J. Jacobs, Proc. Phys. Soc. (London) **A62**, 710 (1949); R. G. Parr, D. P. Craig, and I. G. Ross, J. Chem. Phys. **18**, 1561 (1950).

the eigenvalue equation

$$(T+U_P)\chi_P=W_P\chi_P,$$

where T is the kinetic energy, U_P is the part of the framework potential originating from the carbon atom P, χ_P is the AO contributed from the same carbon atom towards the MO's, and W_P is the valence state ionization potential of carbon. Neither is this eigenvalue identity justifiable in principle, nor is it at all close to being satisfied by the particular U_P and χ_P chosen in practice. In spite of this adjustment and in spite of the high symmetry, causing many simplifications, the complexity of this treatment seemed to place it in a class different from the aforementioned models, discouraging its extension to large systems.

The inkling that this apprehension is probably unjustified has been the most important recent advance. It was observed by Parr and Pariser,[14] and also by Pople,[15] that the Goeppert-Mayer-Sklar approach can be cast in a form compatible in mathematical simplicity with the one-electron theories, *if neighbor overlap is neglected and all two-electron integrals, except the two-center Coulomb integrals, are neglected (neglect of differential overlap)*. Moreover Pariser and Parr showed that the results of such a treatment do not essentially deviate from those of the Goeppert-Mayer-Sklar formulation when the same integral values are used, and furthermore that much closer agreement with the experimental spectroscopic data of benzene can be achieved by introducing a semiempirical adjustment of the electron-interaction integrals and of the resonance integral.[14]

In extending the calculations to hydrocarbons larger than benzene, the question arose: how much configuration interaction is appropriate for the satisfactory understanding and prediction of the electronic spectra? Pariser[16] tested a *great* number of interacting one-electron excitations; Pople[17] chose only two such configurations (the "paired excitations," see Sec. 4); Ham and Ruedenberg included those four excited configurations which are analogous to those in benzene.[18] The latter choice, which goes back to J. R. Platt's pioneering interpretation of aromatic spectra,[8] seemed to be the most satisfactory one in comparison with experiment. The last-mentioned calculation was carried out in the free-electron network theory, demonstrating that here too the electronic interaction could be incorporated in a way quite similar to that used in the LCAO theory.

[14] R. G. Parr, J. Chem. Phys. **20**, 1499 (1952); R. Pariser and R. G. Parr, *ibid.* **21**, 466 (1953); **21**, 767 (1953); **23**, 711 (1955); R. Pariser, *ibid.* **21**, 568 (1953).

[15] J. A. Pople, Trans. Faraday Soc. **49**, 1375 (1953).

[16] R. Pariser, J. Chem. Phys. **24**, 250 (1956); **25**, 1112 (1956).

[17] J. A. Pople, Proc. Phys. Soc. (London) **A68**, 81 (1955).

[18] N. S. Ham and K. Ruedenberg, J. Chem. Phys. **25**, 13 (1956).

II

The present investigation would like to contribute some steps towards a more rigorous understanding of the problem. The main objective is to analyze the basic LCAO formulation of the pi-electronic approach with the help of such approximations as are *realistic and bona fide justifiable*, in particular without neglect of nonnegligible overlap terms.

The general formulations are arrived at in the first paper. Formulas are established for the ground-state energy, for ionization potential, electron affinity, electronegativity, and for the calculation of excited states—formulas which permit a simple interpretation and calculation. Concerning the ground state, an old controversy is settled by demonstrating that a major part of the binding energy can be expressed as a sum of the eigenvalues of a one-electron problem; they are of course different from the orbital energies.

These derivations are carried through including electronic interaction and all neighbor overlap effects and with an explicit analysis of the framework contributions. In the second paper the nonneighbor interactions are taken into account, and it is found that they add certain corrections, but will not alter the essential formulations.

For the contraction of the electron-interaction integrals two circumstances prove important. First, the effective Hamiltonian matrix, which determines the basic molecular orbitals, and the overlap matrix are both functions of the topological matrix (or, in the second paper, of a closely related matrix); hence the basic MO's are "topological" MO's and simultaneously eigenvectors of the overlap matrix. Second, the Mulliken approximation for electron interaction integrals is very accurate for $2p\pi$ AO's and therefore adopted. *The conjunction of these facts leads to essential simplifications and also emerges as the real reason for the rather good approximation achieved by the "neglect of differential overlap" under certain conditions.*

The third paper is devoted to a closer examination of the important molecular orbitals of the generalized Hückel type, which are based on the topological matrix. It is found that certain well-known regularities, like the Coulson-Rushbrooke theorem, are only special cases of a more general scheme of interesting cross-relations between bond-order-like quantities.

The last three papers deal with the quantitative aspects. Hitherto underived formulas for framework integrals are established in the fourth paper, and with their help a theoretical calculation of the framework energy contributions is carried out in the sixth paper without introducing unjustified relationships. These theoretical results are compared with the experimental conclusions deduced in the fifth paper. The application of the method to a number of large molecules is under way.

The degree of rigor introduced here shows new

aspects of the pi-electronic approach. A particular instructive part of the formulation is the somewhat intricate cancellation between attractive and repulsive terms, which can be traced in detail. This may lead to a better method for dealing with cases of less complete balancing, e.g., in the presence of hetero-atoms. Furthermore, the quantitative origin of the various energy contributions is established. Finally, certain fundamental quantitative difficulties are isolated, which will require further analysis.

1. HAMILTONIAN AND ATOMIC ORBITALS

General Formulation

The Hamiltonian for N pi electrons is

$$\mathcal{H}=f(\mathbf{r}_i)+\sum_{i<j}e^2/r_{ij}, \tag{1.1}$$

$$f(\mathbf{r})=(\hbar^2/2m)\Delta+U(\mathbf{r}). \tag{1.1'}$$

The potential energy U can be written as a sum over atomic contributions

$$U(\mathbf{r})=\sum_a V_a(\mathbf{r}), \tag{1.2}$$

where the sum goes over all atoms, carbons and hydrogens. For the hydrogen atoms, $a=h$, let

$$V_h(\mathbf{r})=U_h^{\mathrm{H}}(\mathbf{r})=U^{\mathrm{H}}(\mathbf{r}-\mathbf{r}_h), \tag{1.3}$$

where $\mathbf{r}_h$ is the position vector of the hydrogen nucleus, and the potential energy of an electron in the field of a neutral H atom is given by

$$U^{\mathrm{H}}(\mathbf{r})=-e^2/r+e^2[(1s)^2|, \tag{1.4}$$

where

$$[\Omega|=\int dV'\Omega(\mathbf{r}')/|\mathbf{r}-\mathbf{r}'|=f(\mathbf{r}) \tag{1.5}$$

defines the potential of a charge cloud $\Omega(\mathbf{r}')$.

The potential of a carbon atom, $a=P$, is considered as that of the neutral carbon atom minus that of the pi electron which has been contributed to the Schroedinger function of delocalized electrons. The energy of an electron in this potential is therefore

$$V_P=U^{\mathrm{C}}(\mathbf{r}-\mathbf{r}_P)-e^2\int dV'[\chi_P(\mathbf{r}')]^2/|\mathbf{r}-\mathbf{r}'|, \tag{1.6}$$

$$=U_P{}^{\mathrm{C}}-e^2[\chi_P{}^2|, \tag{1.6'}$$

where χ_P is the AO contributed to the pi-electronic wave function. The potential due to the neutral carbon in its valence state, is given by

$$U^{\mathrm{C}}(\mathbf{r})=-e^2(4/r)$$
$$+e^2[(2s)^2+(2px)^2+(2py)^2+(2pz)^2|, \tag{1.7}$$

i.e., the nucleus ($4e$) is shielded by the electrons in the four indicated orbitals. The division into short-range and long-range forces, implicit in Eq. (1.6), will be commented upon after Eq. (2.17′).

The potential proposed here differs from that introduced by Goeppert-Mayer and Sklar[13] in the following respects:

(1) The hydrogen atoms are taken into account.

(2) The orbital exponent ζ of the atomic orbital χ_P in Eq. (1.6) (AO *orbital exponent*) is not necessarily identical with the orbital exponent ζ_{C} of the four orbitals in Eq. (1.7) (*shielding orbital exponent*).

The following arguments suggest that the two orbital exponents may have to be chosen so that they are different from each other.

The Valence State of Carbon as Gauge

The integral

$$(\chi|(-\hbar^2/2m)\Delta+U^{\mathrm{C}}|\chi) \tag{1.8}$$

is the most sensitive one of the framework integrals, since it is the sum of two large terms (each about 35 ev) of opposite sign which cancel each other almost entirely. Hence a successful computation of framework energy contributions cannot be performed unless the two parts of Eq. (1.8) are properly balanced against each other.

The means for such balancing are the proper choice of the parameters ζ and ζ_{C}.

The criteria for the proper choice should be the known values for the ionization potential and the electron affinity of the valence state of carbon. According to Mulliken, one has[19]

$$\text{electron affinity}=A_{\mathrm{C}}=0.69\text{ ev}, \tag{1.9}$$

$$\text{ionization potential}=I_{\mathrm{C}}=11.22\text{ ev}. \tag{1.10}$$

Since the potential (1.7) corresponds to a neutral carbon, the expression (1.8) represents the energy of an additional electron, and hence it is related to the electron affinity by

$$-A_{\mathrm{C}}=(\chi|(-\hbar^2/2m)\Delta+U^{\mathrm{C}}|\chi). \tag{1.11}$$

Similarly, since Eq. (1.6) is the potential of the C^+ ion in the valence state, the energy of an electron in this potential must be related to the ionization potential; hence[20]

$$-I_{\mathrm{C}}=(\chi|(-\hbar^2/2m)\Delta+V|\chi)$$
$$=-A_{\mathrm{C}}-e^2\int dV_1\int dV_2\chi^2(1)\chi^2(2)/r_{12}. \tag{1.12}$$

That these two equations are consistent with each other can be seen by calculating the energy of *two* electrons,

[19] R. S. Mulliken, J. Chem. Phys. **2**, 782 (1934).

[20] That the one-center Coulomb integrals between the $2p\pi$AO's should equal the difference (I_C-A_C) was first postulated by Pariser. See the second and fourth paper of reference 14. See also W. Moffitt, Proc. Roy. Soc. (London) **A210**, 244 (1951).

occupying the orbital χ with opposing spins, under the influence of the potential (1.6). Their total energy becomes

$$-2I_C+e^2\int dV_1\int dV_2\chi^2(1)\chi^2(2)/r_{12}=-I_C-A_C,$$

i.e., the addition of the second electron lowers in fact the total energy by A_C.

The determination of the framework potential given here is not free of criticism. However, it is consistent and it leads to instructive formulations for the molecular energies. Independent support for this point of view is furnished by an examination of the benzene spectrum [see paper V, after Eq. (2.10)]. We therefore associate with A_C as defined by Eq. (1.11), and with I_C, as defined by Eq. (1.12), the proposed physical meanings, and relegate the analysis of the quantitative aspects to the fifth and sixth paper.

2. MATRIX ELEMENTS IN THE AO BASIS

Overlap Integrals

In the second paper, the error will be analyzed which is incurred when those integrals are neglected which involve the overlap between nonneighbor atomic orbitals. It will be seen that it is a valid approximation to neglect all contributions due to overlap between nonneighbors, but to take into account all contributions due to overlap between neighbors. This "tight-binding approximation" will be adhered to in the present paper.

If all atoms in the conjugated bond system are identical (carbon atoms), then all neighbor overlap integrals are equal, and the overlap matrix is

$$S_{PQ}=\delta_{PQ}+SM_{PQ}, \tag{2.1}$$

where

$$M_{PQ}=\begin{cases}1, & \text{if } P, Q \text{ are neighbors,}\\ 0, & \text{otherwise,}\end{cases} \tag{2.2}$$

is the "topological matrix" of the molecule. Certain properties of this matrix will become important in the subsequent derivations. A discussion of these properties is given in the third paper of this series.[21]

AO Integrals over Neutral Framework and Kinetic Energy

The following integrals have to be considered [see Eqs. (1.2–7)]

$$U_{PQ}=(\chi_P\mid \sum_R U_R{}^C+\sum_h U_h{}^H\mid\chi_Q)$$

$$=\int dV\chi_P\chi_Q\{\sum_R U_R{}^C(\mathbf{r})+\sum_h U_h{}^H(\mathbf{r})\}. \tag{2.3}$$

Since the integral contains the product of two AO's, it has an exponential decrease with distance similar to that of the overlap integral. Consequently only the case of P and Q being neighbors has to be taken into account, i.e.,

$$U_{PQ}=U_{PP}\delta_{PQ}+U_{PQ}M_{PQ}, \tag{2.4}$$

where M_{PQ} is given by Eq. (2.2).

Furthermore the potentials U^C and U^H, coming from neutral spherically symmetric charge distributions, decrease exponentially with distance, and the integral $(\chi_P\mid U_R{}^C\mid\chi_Q)$ decreases in fact more strongly with the distances (RP), (RQ), than do the corresponding overlap integrals. Consequently only those terms in the sum over R have to be kept for which [$R=P$ *or* (R, P) = neighbors] *and simultaneously* [$R=Q$ or (R, Q) = neighbors]. Similarly in the sum over h, only those terms have to be kept for which h is simultaneously a neighbor of P and Q.

Thus one obtains

$$U_{PP}=(\chi_1\mid U_1{}^C\mid\chi_1)+3(\chi_1\mid U_2{}^C\mid\chi_1), \tag{2.5}$$

if P is a joint atom;

$$U_{PP}=(\chi_1\mid U_1{}^C\mid\chi_1)+2(\chi_1\mid U_2{}^C\mid\chi_1)+(\chi_1\mid U_{h1}{}^H\mid\chi_1), \tag{2.5'}$$

if P is a nonjoint atom; and

$$U_{PP}=(\chi_1\mid U_1{}^C\mid\chi_1)+(\chi_1\mid U_2{}^C\mid\chi_1)+2(\chi_1\mid U_{h1}{}^H\mid\chi_1), \tag{2.5''}$$

if P is a free-end atom (end of a conjugated chain). Here the indices (1, 2) denote two neighboring C atoms, and the index ($h1$) denotes the H atom neighboring to the nonjoint C atom (1). For any pair (PQ) of C atoms one finds

$$U_{PQ}=2(\chi_1\mid U_1{}^C\mid\chi_2). \tag{2.6}$$

The kinetic energy integrals,

$$T_{PQ}=(\chi_P\mid(-\hbar^2/2m)\Delta\mid\chi_Q), \tag{2.7}$$

do *not* contain the *product* $\chi_P\chi_Q$. However, upon closer inspection[22] it is found that T_{PQ} decreases with the distance (PQ) almost exactly as the *square of the overlap integral*. Hence we are again entitled to write

$$T_{PQ}=(\chi_1\mid(-\hbar^2/2m)\Delta\mid\chi_1)\delta_{PQ}+(\chi_1\mid(-\hbar^2/2m)\Delta\mid\chi_2)M_{PQ}, \tag{2.8}$$

where the symbol of Eq. (2.2) is used.

It is expedient to write the matrices U and T together as follows

$$(\chi_P\mid(-\hbar^2/2m)\Delta+\sum_R U_R{}^C+\sum_h U_h{}^H\mid\chi_Q)=(\alpha+\delta\alpha_P)\delta_{PQ}+\beta M_{PQ}, \tag{2.9}$$

where

$$\beta=(\chi_1\mid(-\hbar^2/2m)\Delta\mid\chi_2)+2(\chi_1\mid U_1{}^C\mid\chi_2), \tag{2.10}$$

[21] K. Ruedenberg, J. Chem. Phys. **34**, 1878 (1961).

[22] See Eq. (2.5) of the fourth paper of this series, K. Ruedenberg, J. Chem. Phys. **34**, 1892 (1961).

and α is the mean value of *all* diagonal elements α_P, whereas $\delta\alpha_P$ are the deviations from this mean value for the three types of elements given in Eqs. (2.5, 5′, 5″). One finds for the mean value

$$\alpha = -A_C + (1+\tau)(\chi_1 \mid U_2^C \mid \chi_1) + (2-\tau)(\chi_1 \mid U_{h1}^H \mid \chi_1), \quad (2.11)$$

where

$$-A_C = (\chi_1 \mid (-\hbar^2/2m)\Delta \mid \chi_1) + (\chi_1 \mid U_1^C \mid \chi_1), \quad (2.11')$$

is the negative of the carbon electron affinity given by Eq. (1.11), and τ is defined as follows. Let

$$\left.\begin{aligned} \tau_N &= \text{fraction of nonjoint atoms,} \\ \tau_J &= \text{fraction of joint atoms,} \\ \tau_E &= \text{fraction of free-end atoms,} \end{aligned}\right\} \quad (2.12)$$

so that

$$\tau_N + \tau_J + \tau_E = 1,$$

then

$$\tau = \tau_N + 2\tau_J. \quad (2.12')$$

The deviations $\delta\alpha_P$ are found to be

$$\left.\begin{aligned} \delta\alpha_E &= -\tau\delta\alpha \\ \delta\alpha_N &= (1-\tau)\delta\alpha \\ \delta\alpha_J &= (2-\tau)\delta\alpha \end{aligned}\right\} \quad (2.13)$$

with

$$\delta\alpha = (\chi_1 \mid U_2^C \mid \chi_1) - (\chi_1 \mid U_{h1}^H \mid \chi_1). \quad (2.13')$$

It is easily verified that indeed

$$\sum_{P=1}^{N} \delta\alpha_P = 0.$$

AO Integrals of the Electron Interaction Type

The ionic part of the framework potential as well as electron interaction integrals lead to AO integrals of the form

$$[PQ \mid RS] = [\chi_P\chi_Q \mid \chi_R\chi_S], \quad (2.14)$$

with the definition

$$[\Omega \mid \Omega'] = \int dV_1 \int dV_2 \Omega(\mathbf{r}_1)\Omega(\mathbf{r}_2)/r_{12}. \quad (2.14')$$

Our postulate is that the evaluation of these integrals should be carried out to a degree of approximation comparable in quality to the tight-binding approximation. In the light of this criterion, the exact evaluation of the integrals would be too elaborate an approach, whereas the "neglect of differential overlap (between neighbors)," used by Pariser and Parr and by Pople, would be too great a simplification.

An adequate solution seems to be the approximation suggested by R. S. Mulliken.[23] Thereby automatically all those integrals will vanish which are proportional to the overlap of nonneighbors. Thus we put

$$[PQ \mid RS] = S_{PQ}S_{RS}[G(PR)+G(PS)+G(QR) + G(QS)]/4, \quad (2.15)$$

where S_{PQ} is defined by Eq. (2.1), and $G(PQ)$ is the Coulomb integral

$$G(PQ) = G(P,Q) = [PP \mid QQ] = \mathcal{G}(R_{PQ}). \quad (2.16)$$

Although the Mulliken approximation seems to be the most appropriate one for $2p\pi$ orbitals, it is also possible to use the Sklar-London approximation.[24] It is shown below, that the London approximation can be numerically reproduced[25] if one merely adds to the right-hand side of Eq. (2.15) the "correction term"

$$[PQ \mid RS]' = \tfrac{1}{2}S^2 g_2 M_{PQ} M_{RS}(\delta_{PR}\delta_{QS} + \delta_{PS}\delta_{QR}), \quad (2.17)$$

where

$$g_2 = G(1,1) - G(1,2). \quad (2.17')$$

This term is zero except for the two-center exchange integrals [12 | 12]. Its effect upon the final results is, however, small.

Short-Range and Long-Range Forces

Two kinds of energy terms can be clearly distinguished. Those due to the short-range forces which result from the neutral parts of the framework potential are given by Eq. (2.9). Those due to the Coulombic long-range forces, *viz.*, ionic attraction by the framework and interelectronic repulsion, are given by Eq. (2.15). It emerges that the short-range terms are essentially determined by the matrix **M** of Eq. (2.2), i.e., by the *topology* of the molecule. The *geometry* of the molecule is only introduced by the long-range terms, *viz.*, via the AO Coulomb integrals $G(PQ)$. It is a conceptual advantage of the tight-binding approximation that it makes the short-range forces strictly topological in character. This is the physical reason for the importance of the properties of the topological matrix **M** discussed in the third paper.[21] In the augmented tight-binding approximation defined in the second paper, the short-range forces are assumed to be determined by the overlap matrix.

AO Integrals for the Transition Moment

In order to calculate spectral intensities and dipole moments, one needs the integrals $(\chi_P \mid \mathbf{r} \mid \chi_Q)$. It is

---

[23] R. S. Mulliken, J. chim. phys. **46**, 500, 521 (1949); See also K. Ruedenberg, J. Chem. Phys. **19**, 1433 (1951).

[24] A. L. Sklar, J. Chem. Phys. **7**, 990 (1939); A. London, *ibid.* **13**, 417 (1945); See also C. Vroelant, J. chim. phys. **49**, 141 (1952).

[25] See the fifth paper of this series, K. Ruedenberg and E. M. Layton, J. Chem. Phys. **34**, 1897 (1961).

easily seen that

$$\int dV[\chi_P]^2\mathbf{r}=\mathbf{R}_P,$$

$$\int dV\chi_P\chi_Q\mathbf{r}=S\mathbf{R}_m,$$

where m denotes the midpoint between P and Q, and $\mathbf{R}_X$ is the vector from the origin to the point X. Thus the general result is

$$(\chi_P\mid\mathbf{r}\mid\chi_Q)=\tfrac{1}{2}S_{PQ}(\mathbf{R}_P+\mathbf{R}_Q) \qquad (2.18)$$

3. MOLECULAR ORBITALS AND CORRESPONDING MATRIX ELEMENTS

Molecular Orbitals

Since it is our intention to use the molecular orbitals for the ground state as well as for the excited states, the ground-state self-consistent field orbitals are not necessarily the most appropriate ones to use. In fact, the results of the calculations of Pariser[16] and Ham-Ruedenberg[18] with MO's of the type to be discussed below are at least as good as those made with self-consistent field MO's made by Pople.[17]

The point of view taken here is that the MO's should be used as the basis of a configuration interaction type of approach. Hence they should represent good zeroth-order "average" approximations for the several states to be calculated, and secondly they should offer a certain ease of manipulation in view of the configuration interaction calculation. Both requirements are met best by choosing the MO's as the solutions φ_n of a one-electron Schrödinger equation

$$h^{\text{eff}}\varphi_n=\{(-\hbar^2/2m)\Delta+U^{\text{eff}}\}\varphi_n=\epsilon_n^{\text{eff}}\varphi_n, \qquad (3.1)$$

with an effective potential U_{eff}. As will now be shown by a careful analysis, the general assumption (3.1) leads in effect to the Hückel orbitals including overlap between neighbors.

The effective potential U_{eff} must represent the average potential felt by any one electron, it must include the shielding of the carbon nuclei by the pi electrons, and thus represents essentially the field exerted by the neutralized atoms. Hence the effective Hamiltonian of Eq. (3.1) must have a form similar to that of the operator whose matrix elements were given in Eq. (2.9) above, i.e.,

$$h_{\text{eff}}=(-\hbar^2/2m)\Delta+\sum_R U_R^{\text{C,eff}}+\sum_h U_h^{\text{H,eff}}. \qquad (3.2)$$

While the potentials $U^{\text{C,eff}}$, $U^{\text{H,eff}}$ may be different from the neutral-atom potentials, given in Eqs. (1.4) and (1.7) for the many-electron Hamiltonian, they will share with those earlier potentials the property of falling of exponentially, i.e., they will not contain long-range electrostatic forces. The evaluation of AO matrix elements of h_{eff} therefore follows a pattern analogous to that given in Eqs. (2.3)–(2.13), whence

$$(\chi_P\mid h_{\text{eff}}\mid\chi_Q)=(\alpha^{\text{eff}}+\delta\alpha_P{}^{\text{eff}})\delta_{PQ}+\beta^{\text{eff}}M_{PQ}. \qquad (3.3)$$

The molecular orbitals φ_n have to be constructed from the atomic orbitals χ_P discussed in Sec. 1. If there are N carbon atoms, then there will be the ground-state MO's

$$\left.\begin{aligned} &\varphi_n=\sum_{P=1}^{N}c_{Pn}'\chi_P, \qquad n=1,2\cdots(N/2),\\ &\text{and the excited MO's}\\ &\varphi_\nu=\sum_{P=1}^{N}c_{P\nu}'\chi_P, \qquad \nu=(N/2)\cdots N.\end{aligned}\right\} \qquad (3.4)$$

According to the variation principle, the coefficients c_{Pk}' are determined by the eigenvalue problem characterized by the effective Hamiltonian matrix (3.3) and the overlap matrix (2.1).

In fact, the determination of the MO's (3.4) is the *only* purpose of the matrix (3.3); the matrix itself and the "effective orbital energies" ϵ_n^{eff} in Eq. (3.1) are not used at all in the further calculations. By virtue of this circumstance, it becomes entirely unnecessary to decide the precise nature of h^{eff} if, for the purpose of determining the MO's, one neglects the small terms $\delta\alpha_P$ in Eq. (3.3). This represents a slight adjustment of the initial molecular orbitals only, and is of little consequence for the further quantitative process. It has, however, the effect of reducing the matrix (3.3) to a function of the topological matrix $\mathbf{M}$ of Eq. (2.2), and therefore the eigenvectors of the effective Hamiltonian matrix (3.3) become those of the topological matrix $\mathbf{M}$.

Let $\{c_{Pn}\}$ be the eigenvectors of $\mathbf{M}$, normalized to unity, i.e.,

$$\left.\begin{aligned}&\sum_Q M_{PQ}c_{Qn}=m_nc_{Pn},\\ &\sum_P c_{Pn}^2=1,\end{aligned}\right\}, \qquad (3.5)$$

where the m_n are the eigenvalues of $\mathbf{M}$. For use in the further development we note that the overlap matrix $\mathbf{S}$, defined in Eq. (2.1), is also a function of the topological matrix $\mathbf{M}$ and, therefore, has the same eigenvectors, whence

$$\sum_Q S_{PQ}c_{Qn}=s_nc_{Pn}, \qquad (3.6)$$

where the eigenvalues s_n are given by

$$s_n=1+Sm_n. \qquad (3.7)$$

Under the conditions set forth above, the coefficients for the MO's (3.4) are proportional to the eigenvectors of $\mathbf{M}$. Since, in this case, the *wave functions* φ_n have to be normalized, one has to put[26]

$$c_{Pn}'=c_{Pn}(s_n)^{-\frac{1}{2}}, \tag{3.8}$$

so that indeed, by virtue of Eq. (3.6),

$$\int dV\varphi_m\varphi_n=\sum_{P,Q}c_{Pm}'S_{PQ}c_{Qn}'=\sum_P c_{Pm}'s_nc_{Qn}'=\delta_{mn}.$$

The MO's defined by Eqs. (3.4) and (3.8) are in fact exactly the Hückel-Wheland MO's. Clearly, the remarkable "power of survival" of these orbitals through all past refinements of the theory (albeit with a reinterpretation of their meaning and their use) is due to the fact that they represent in effect the appropriate "topological molecular orbitals" of the molecule. In view of the remarks made in Sec. 2 [see the section following Eq. (2.17′)] it is understandable that, under the present conditions, the best "compromise MO's" must be topological rather than geometrical in character, since the long-range forces between electrons and nuclei cancel each other out on the average.

Closely connected with this topological character is the fact that different orbitals are primarily distinguished by their different "longitudinal" profiles along the "bond path," while their "transverse" profiles perpendicular to the bond path remain essentially unchanged. Hence the excitations of electrons described by these orbitals are "*bond-path excitations*." [27] It is the merit of J. R. Platt[8] to have first shown that the spectra of aromatic systems can be understood in terms of what has been called the "principle of bond-path excitation,"[27] and that this represents the strongest experimental evidence for the appropriateness of the topological MO's. The topological character and the principle of bond-path excitation represent the common feature shared by the LCAO MO's discussed here and the free electron MO's used by Platt, Ham, and Ruedenberg.[12,27]

MO Integrals over Neutral Framework and Kinetic Energy

The matrix elements between MO's are found by expanding the MO's according to Eqs. (3.4) and (3.8) and then substituting the matrix elements between AO's given by Eq. (2.9). Thus, one finds

$$(\varphi_i\,|\,(-\hbar^2/2m)\Delta+\sum_R U_R{}^{\mathrm{C}}+\sum_h U_h{}^{\mathrm{H}}\,|\,\varphi_j)$$
$$=\sum_{P,Q}\sum c_{Pi}'[(\alpha+\delta\alpha_P)\delta_{PQ}+\beta M_{PQ}]c_{Qi}',$$

whence, by virtue of Eqs. (3.5) and (3.8)

$$=(\alpha+\beta m_i)(1+Sm_i)^{-1}\delta_{ij}+\sum_P(c_{Pi}'c_{Pj}')\delta\alpha_P,$$

and, by virtue of Eq. (2.13)

$$=\epsilon_i^{nf}\delta_{ij}+\delta\alpha[J,NJ,E]_{ij}, \tag{3.9}$$

with

$$\epsilon_i^{nf}=\alpha+\gamma m_i/(1+Sm_i),$$
$$\gamma=\beta-\alpha S \tag{3.10}$$

$$[N,NJ,E]_{ij}=(2-\tau)\sum_J c_{Pi}'c_{Pj}'+(1-\tau)\sum_{NJ}c_{Pi}'c_{Pj}'-\tau\sum_E c_{Pi}'c_{Pj}', \tag{3.10′}$$

where α, $\delta\alpha$, β, τ, are defined in Eqs. (2.10)–(2.13′). Furthermore, $\sum_J$, $\sum_{NJ}$, $\sum_E$ indicate summations over all joint atoms, all nonjoint atoms, and all free-end atoms, respectively. Because of the orthonormalization of the c_{Pn}', Eq. (3.10′) can be simplified to

$$[N,NJ,E]_{ij}=(\sum_J c_{Pi}'c_{Pj}'-\sum_E c_{Pi}'c_{Pj}')+(1-\tau)(1+Sm_i)^{-1}\delta_{ij}. \tag{3.10″}$$

In the sequel it will be seen that the quantity γ plays a role which somewhat resembles that attributed to the "empirical resonance integral" in the early semi-empirical approaches. Although the present formulation leads to considerably more complex results, we shall occasionally use the name *resonance integral* to denote γ. (It should be noted that Mulliken[5] uses the nomenclature differently: He calls β what we and most authors call γ; he calls γ what we and most authors call β.)

MO Integrals of the Electron Interaction Type

From Eq. (2.15) for the electron interaction integrals between AO's one finds

$$[\varphi_i\varphi_j\,|\,\varphi_k\varphi_l]$$
$$=\tfrac{1}{4}\sum_{P,Q}\sum_{R,S}[G(PR)+G(PS)+G(QR)+G(QS)]\times S_{PQ}c_{Pi}'c_{Qj}'S_{RS}c_{Rk}'c_{Sl}'. \tag{3.11}$$

This equation can be simplified *by taking into account that the c_{Pn}' are also eigenvectors of the overlap matrix*, as given by Eq. (3.6); the result is:

$$[\varphi_i\varphi_j\,|\,\varphi_k\varphi_l]=\tfrac{1}{4}(s_i+s_j)(s_k+s_l)\sum_{P,Q}G(PQ)\times c_{Pi}'c_{Pj}'c_{Qk}'c_{Ql}', \tag{3.12}$$

where the s_n are the eigenvalues of the orbitals φ_n for the overlap matrix $\mathbf{S}$, as given by Eq. (3.7). In this fashion the quadruple sum has been reduced to a double sum. When the coefficients c_{Pn}' are expressed in terms of the coefficients c_{Pn}, according to Eq. (3.8), then Eq. (3.12) takes, also, the form

$$[\varphi_i\varphi_j\,|\,\varphi_k\varphi_l]=s_{ij}s_{kl}\sum_{P,Q}G(P,Q)c_{Pi}c_{Pj}c_{Qk}c_{Ql}, \tag{3.13}$$

where

$$s_{nm}=\tfrac{1}{2}(s_m+s_n)/(s_ns_m)^{\frac{1}{2}} \tag{3.13′}$$

[26] For a more detailed discussion see K. Ruedenberg, J. Chem. Phys. **22**, 1874 (1954), Sec. 1.
[27] N. S. Ham and K. Ruedenberg, J. Chem. Phys. **25**, 1 (1956), Sec. 2.

is the ratio of the arithmetic and the geometric mean of the respective eigenvalues of the overlap matrix. This ratio becomes unity in the case $m=n$.

The electron interaction integrals between MO's can also be formulated for the case of the Sklar-London approximation. Since in this case the correction term (2.17) has to be added to the AO integrals, one finds for the MO integrals that in addition to the expression (3.12) and (3.13) one has the small correction term

$$[\varphi_i\varphi_j \mid \varphi_k\varphi_l]$$
$$=\tfrac{1}{2}S^2g_2\sum_B(c_{Pi}'c_{Qj}'+c_{Qi}'c_{Pj}')(c_{Pk}'c_{Ql}'+c_{Qk}'c_{Pl}'), \quad (3.14)$$

where $\sum_B$ means the summation over all "bonds," i.e., over all *pairs of neighbor atoms* (each pair taken once), and P, Q denote the two neighbors forming the bond B.

The "Neglect of Differential Overlap"

The formulation (3.13) is convenient to assess the meaning of the assumption of "neglect of differential overlap."[14,15] In the first place it must be noticed that the eigenvalues of **S** are positive, in order that the atomic orbitals be linearly independent. Let s_m be the smaller one and s_n be the larger one of the two; then one may write

$$s_{nm}=(1-\tfrac{1}{2}\eta)(1-\eta)^{-\frac{1}{2}}=1+\tfrac{1}{2}\eta^2+\tfrac{3}{2}\eta^3+\cdots$$

with

$$0<\eta=1-(s_m/s_n)<1.$$

Since

$$\eta=S(m_n-m_m)/(1+m_nS),$$

it is seen that the deviation of s_{nm} form unity is quadratic in the overlap integral. Thus, if one wishes to compute the MO integrals *formally* only up to terms linear in S, then one can put $s_{ij}=s_{kl}=1$ in Eq. (3.13). The resulting expression

$$[\varphi_i\varphi_j \mid \varphi_k\varphi_l]=\sum_{P,Q}G(PQ)c_{Pi}c_{Pj}c_{Qk}c_{Ql}$$

is exactly that obtained by the neglect of differential overlap.

Dependence upon the Absolute Magnitude of AO Coulomb Integrals

From Eq. (3.13) follows the interesting identity

$$s_{ij}s_{kl}\sum_{PQ}[G(PQ)+A]c_{Pi}c_{Pj}c_{Qk}c_{Ql}$$
$$=s_{ij}s_{kl}\sum_{PQ}G(PQ)c_{Pi}c_{Pj}c_{Qk}c_{Ql}+A\delta_{ij}\delta_{kl}. \quad (3.15)$$

It shows that the electronic interaction integral (3.13) between molecular orbitals is independent of the absolute value of the Coulomb integrals $G(PQ)$, unless $i=j$ *and* $k=l$. In the latter case, the addition of a constant to all Coulomb integrals changes the MO integrals exactly by the amount of this constant.

By virtue of Eq. (3.15), one obtains

$$s_{ij}s_{kl}\sum_{PQ}G(PQ)c_{Pi}c_{Pj}c_{Qk}c_{Ql}$$
$$=s_{ij}s_{kl}\sum_{PQ}G'(PQ)c_{Pi}c_{Pj}c_{Qk}c_{Ql}+G'\delta_{ij}\delta_{kl}, \quad (3.16)$$

where G' is an arbitrary constant and

$$G'(PQ)=G(PQ)-G'.$$

For G', three particular choices are of interest.

(1) $G'=G(1,1)$. This leads to the elimination of all diagonal elements in the first sum on the right-hand side of Eq. (3.16). Using this device in the calculation of the molecular energy states, it is possible to predict the dependence upon the interaction integral $G(1,1)=[11 \mid 11]$, as will be discussed later.

(2) $G'=G(R_{\max})$, where $R_{\max}$ is the largest internuclear distance in the molecule. This choice quasi-concentrates the effect of the longest range forces in the simple second term on the right-hand side of Eq. (3.16) and minimizes their effect in the complex first term.

(3) $G'=G(R_{mf})$, where R_{mf} is the internuclear distance occurring most frequently in the molecule under investigation. This choice would tend to minimize as much as possible the expected cancellation of Coulomb terms and therefore be computationally advantageous.

Orbital Transition Moments

The orbital transition moment matrix is defined by

$$\mathbf{q}(\varphi_n\varphi_\nu)=(\varphi_n \mid \mathbf{r} \mid \varphi_\nu). \quad (3.17)$$

Substitution of the expansion (3.4) and the AO integrals (2.18) yields

$$\mathbf{q}(\varphi_n\varphi_\nu)=\sum_{P,Q}\tfrac{1}{2}(\mathbf{R}_P+\mathbf{R}_Q)S_{PQ}c_{Pn}'c_{Q\nu}',$$

whence by a transformation similar to that leading to Eq. (3.13)

$$\mathbf{q}(\varphi_n\varphi_\nu)=s_{nm}\sum_P\mathbf{R}_Pc_{Pn}c_{P\nu}, \quad (3.18)$$

where the quantities s_{nm} are defined by Eq. (3.13′).

The off-diagonal elements are required for intensity calculations; the diagonal elements represent the dipole moment of the orbital,

$$\mathbf{q}(\varphi_n\varphi_n)=\sum_P\mathbf{R}_Pc_{Pn}^2.$$

The total dipole moment in the ground state becomes therefore, with $q(P)$ defined by Eq. (4.16′),

$$\mathbf{D}=\sum_P\mathbf{R}_Pq(P)$$

even when neighbor overlap is properly included.

4. ELECTRONIC STATES

Basic Formalism

I

The electronic-state wave functions are constructed as linear combinations of antisymmetrized products (LCAP's) of molecular orbitals. The ground state is given in first approximation by the "closed-shell" determinant containing the N electrons in the $(N/2)=G$ lowest orbitals, $n=1, 2, \cdots G$,

$$\Phi_0=\mathcal{A}\{(\varphi_1\alpha)^1(\varphi_1\beta)^2\cdots(\varphi_G\alpha)^{N-1}(\varphi_G\beta)^N\}, \quad (4.1)$$

where

$$\mathcal{A}=(N!)^{-\frac{1}{2}}\sum_P(-1)^P P$$

is the antisymmetrizer. It is assumed that the number of electrons is even and equal to the number of AO's. For each "one-electron orbital excitation" $\varphi_n\rightarrow\varphi_\nu$, there exist four excited wave functions which can be chosen as singlet and triplet states,

$$^{s\sigma}\Phi(\varphi_n, \varphi_\nu)=\mathcal{A}\{\cdots(\varphi_n\varphi_\nu\eta_{s\sigma})^{2n-1,2n}\cdots\}. \quad (4.2)$$

Here the dotted part is identical with the corresponding part in the ground state (4.1), the Roman suffix indicates a ground-state orbital, the Greek suffix indicates one of the exicted orbitals [see Eq. (3.4)], and $\eta_{s\sigma}$ is one of the four spin eigenfunctions

$$\eta_{10}=(\alpha\beta-\beta\alpha)/\sqrt{2},$$

$$\eta_{31}=\alpha\alpha, \qquad \eta_{30}=(\alpha\beta+\beta\alpha)/\sqrt{2}, \qquad \eta_{3,-1}=\beta\beta. \quad (4.3)$$

In general, the actual excited states of the molecule have to be constructed as superpositions of several one-orbital excitations of the type (4.2), whereas the actual ground state is expected to contain only a small admixture of the LCAP's given by Eq. (4.2). The determination of appropriate superpositions is based on the eigenvalue problems of the respective configuration interaction matrices.

II

The diagonal element of the Hamiltonian with respect to the ground state (4.1), i.e., the ground-state energy, becomes

$$\mathrm{H}_0=(\Phi_0\,|\,\mathcal{H}\,|\,\Phi_0)=\sum_{n=1}^{G}[(\varphi_n\,|f|\,\varphi_n)+\{\varphi_n, \varphi_n\}], \quad (4.4)$$

where f is the *total framework* Hamiltonian defined in Eq. (1.1′) and

$$\{\varphi_i, \varphi_j\}=(\varphi_i\,|\,f\,|\,\varphi_j)$$
$$+\sum_{n=1}^{G}\{2[\varphi_n\varphi_n\,|\,\varphi_i\varphi_j]-[\varphi_n\varphi_i\,|\,\varphi_n\varphi_j]\}. \quad (4.5)$$

For $i=j=$a ground-state orbital, this expression represents the energy of one electron in the orbital i due to the framework *and* the field of the $(N-1)$ *other* electrons in the $(N-1)$ other orbital, because of the cancellation occurring in the sum for $n=i$. If one forms the expression (4.5) for $i=j=$an excited orbital, the sum over n still covering the ground-state orbitals, no cancellation occurs. Hence, in this case Eq. (4.5) represents the energy of an electron in orbital i due to the framework and N other electrons occupying all ground-state orbitals.

If one wishes to improve the ground-state wavefunction by configuration interaction, one requires the matrix elements for the interaction of the ground state with the excited singlet functions of the type (4.2). They are[28] given by

$$(\Phi_0\,|\,\mathcal{H}\,|\,^{10}\Phi(\varphi_n, \varphi_\nu))=\{\varphi_n, \varphi_\nu\}/\sqrt{2} \quad (4.6)$$

and vanish if the φ_n happen to be solutions of the self-consistent field equations. For this reason they are expected to be small for the topological MO's.

The matrix elements describing the interaction between the various one-orbital excitations of the type (4.2) are given by[28]

$$[^{s\sigma}\Phi(\varphi_n, \varphi_\nu)\,|\,\mathcal{H}\,|^{s'\sigma'}\Phi(\varphi_m, \varphi_\mu)]$$
$$={}^s\mathrm{H}(\varphi_n\varphi_\nu, \varphi_m\varphi_\mu)\,\delta_{ss'}\delta_{\sigma\sigma'}, \quad (4.7)$$

As indicated, this matrix is already diagonal with respect to the spin angular momentum. Within one multiplicity the elements are given by

$$^sH(\varphi_n\varphi_\nu, \varphi_m\varphi_\mu)=H_0\delta_{nm}\delta_{\nu\mu}-\{\varphi_n, \varphi_m\}\delta_{\nu\mu}+\{\varphi_\nu, \varphi_\mu\}\delta_{nm}$$
$$-{}^s\{\varphi_n\varphi_\nu, \varphi_m\varphi_\mu\}. \quad (4.8)$$

Here H_0 and $\{\varphi_i, \varphi_j\}$ are given by Eqs. (4.4) and (4.5) and

$$^s\{\varphi_n\varphi_\nu, \varphi_m\varphi_\mu\}=[\varphi_n\varphi_m\,|\,\varphi_\nu\varphi_\mu]-(1+p_s)[\varphi_n\varphi_\nu\,|\,\varphi_m\varphi_\mu], \quad (4.9)$$

where p_r is the parity of the space function: $+1$ for singlets and -1 for triplets. Eq. (4.8) can be interpreted as follows: the one-electron excitation $\varphi_n\rightarrow\varphi_\nu$ can be represented as the addition of an electron in orbital φ_ν and a hole in orbital φ_n; then the first term in Eq. (4.8) is the ground-state energy, the second term is the interaction energy of the added hole and the ground state, the third term is the interaction energy of the added electron and the ground state, and the fourth term is the interaction energy of the added electron and the added hole. Another interpretation will be given later.

Only interactions between singly excited antisymmetrized products are taken into account. The inclusion of doubly excited configurations would seem to call for the simultaneous consideration of the sigma electrons.

III

Whereas the *energies* of the excited states are obtained as eigenvalues of the configuration interaction matrix, the *intensity* corresponding to the transition

[28] See reference 27, Sec. 1.

ΔE is characterized by the oscillator strength[29]

$$f=\tfrac{1}{3}\Delta E\mathbf{Q}^2/E_{\mathrm{H}}a^2, \tag{4.10}$$

($a=\hbar^2/e^2m=$ Bohr radius, $E_{\mathrm{H}}=e^2/2a=$ ionization potential of H) where

$$\mathbf{Q}=(\Phi_0\mid \sum_i \mathbf{R}_i \mid \Phi_{\text{excited}}) \tag{4.11}$$

is the dipole transition moment divided by e, the absolute value of the electronic charge. The latter is a superposition of the transition moments to the one-orbital excitations (4.2) which vanish for the triplets and, for the singlet states, are given by

$$[\Phi_0\mid \sum_i \mathbf{R}_i \mid {}^{10}\Phi(\varphi_n\varphi_\nu)]=\sqrt{2}\,\mathbf{q}(\varphi_n\varphi_\nu), \tag{4.12}$$

where the $\mathbf{q}$'s are the orbital transition moments discussed in Eqs. (3.17) and (3.18).

There are also no complications in applying the formulas of Eqs. (3.11), (3.12), and (3.13) to the calculation of the electron-hole interaction (4.9). The insertion of the electron-interaction integrals into the matrix $\{\varphi_i, \varphi_j\}$, as needed for Eq. (4.8), is a little more involved and will be discussed in the following.

Auxiliary Relations Concerning Bond Characteristics

Before carrying on the development it is useful to establish certain properties of quantities of the form

$$f_{PQ}=2\sum_{n=1}^{G} c_{Pn}c_{Qn}f(m_n), \tag{4.13}$$

(bond characteristics) where the m_n are the eigenvalues of $\mathbf{M}$, $\{c_{Pn}\}$ the corresponding eigenvectors [see Eq. (3.5)], and various functions will have to be considered for $f(x)$. The present discussion is based on the analysis given in the third note, to which the reader must be referred for some results.[21]

The following cases will occur in the term $\{\varphi_i, \varphi_j\}$:

$$p(PQ)=2\sum_{n=1}^{G} c_{Pn}c_{Qn}, \tag{4.14}$$

$$p'(PQ)=2\sum_{n=1}^{G} c_{Pn}'c_{Qn}'=2\sum_{n=1}^{G} c_{Pn}c_{Qn}/(1+Sm_n), \tag{4.15}$$

$$p''(PQ)=2\sum_{n=1}^{G} c_{Pn}'c_{Qn}'s_n=2\sum_{n=1}^{G} c_{Pn}c_{Qn}(1+Sm_n). \tag{4.16}$$

The quantities $p(PQ)$ form the Coulson bond-order matrix, whose diagonal elements

$$p(PP)=q(P) \tag{4.16'}$$

are Mulliken's "gross atomic populations." The quantities $p'(PQ)$ differ from the Mulliken bond orders merely by the factor $(1+S)$. The quantities $p''(PQ)$ have not been used before, but are also subject to the analysis given in the third paper.[21]

According to Eqs. (2.2), (2.6), and (2.19) of the third paper the following relations are valid,

$$p'(PQ)=\sigma^{-1}\{p(PQ)+\sigma'[\tfrac{3}{2}p(PQ)-(\mathbf{pM})_{PQ}]\}, \tag{4.17}$$

$$p''(PQ)=\sigma\{p(PQ)-\sigma'[\tfrac{3}{2}p(PQ)-(\mathbf{pM})_{PQ}]\}, \tag{4.17'}$$

where

$$\sigma=(1+\tfrac{3}{2}S),\qquad \sigma'=(S/\sigma). \tag{4.17''}$$

The identity (4.17′) is exact. The relation (4.17) results from an expansion in term of the small quantity $(\sigma')^2=0.03$, and is a very accurate approximation. The diagonal elements of the matrix $\mathbf{pM}$ are the usual bound valences; in alternant systems

$$(\mathbf{pM})_{PQ}=M_{PQ}, \tag{4.18}$$

if P, Q belong to different classes.

It can be shown that always

$$\mid \tfrac{3}{2}p(PQ)-(\mathbf{pM})_{PQ}\mid <1. \tag{4.19}$$

From Eq. (4.17), (4.17′) follows

$$p'(PQ)p''(PQ)=[p(PQ)]^2 -(\sigma')^2[\tfrac{3}{2}p(PQ)-(\mathbf{pM})_{PQ}]^2.$$

Because of Eq. (4.19), the second term can be neglected to the excellent degree of approximation used in Eq. (4.17), so that

$$p'(PQ)p''(PQ)\cong p(PQ)^2. \tag{4.20}$$

To the same degree of approximation one furthermore finds for a *ground-state orbital* φ_n:

$$s_np'(PQ) =[1+\sigma'(m_n-\tfrac{3}{2})]\{p(PQ)+\sigma'[\tfrac{3}{2}p(PQ)-(\mathbf{pM})_{PQ}]\},$$

$$s_n^{-1}p''(PQ) =[1-\sigma'(m_n-\tfrac{3}{2})]\{p(PQ)-\sigma'[\tfrac{3}{2}p(PQ)-(\mathbf{pM})_{PQ}]\},$$

and hence, in approximation,

$$\tfrac{1}{2}[s_np'(PQ)+p''(PQ)/s_n]\cong p(PQ), \tag{4.21}$$

where s_n is the eigenvalue of $\mathbf{S}$ (here, the fact $(m_n-\tfrac{3}{2})<1.5$ has been used).

As an example of the accuracy of the approximations, Table I gives the quantitative results for benzene, with $S=(\tfrac{1}{4})$ substituted in Eq. (4.17″). It is seen that Eq. (4.20), is a nontrivial statement, since p, p', and p'' can be very different from each other. An extensive test of the relation (4.17) was made by Ham and Ruedenberg.[30]

From the definitions (4.14), (4.15), (4.16), and the orthogonality relations for the eigenvectors of $\mathbf{M}$,

[29] See, for example, A. Sommerfeld, "Wave mechanics," *Atomic Structure and Spectral Lines* (Frederick Vieweg, Braunschweig, Germany, 1939), Vol. II, p. 365, Eq. (22). The formula-tion (4.10) has the advantage of being easily convertible to any units.

[30] N. S. Ham and K. Ruedenberg, J. Chem. Phys. **29**, 1215 (1958).

TABLE I. Numerical values for various bond-order definitions in benzene.

PQ	p	pM	p''	p'	$0.9256p$ -0.1322(pM)	p^2	$p'p''$
11	1	1.3333	1.3333	0.7579	0.7493	1	1.0105
12	0.6667	1	0.9167	0.4905	0.4848	0.4444	0.4496
13	0	0.3333	0.0833	0.0442	0.0441	0	0.0037
14	−0.3333	0	−0.3333	−0.3115	−0.3085	0.1111	0.1038

there furthermore follows without approximation the matrix relation

$$\sum_R p'(PR)p''(RQ)=\sum_R p(PR)p(RQ)=2p(PQ),$$

i.e.,

$$\mathbf{p}'\mathbf{p}''=\mathbf{p}^2=2\mathbf{p}. \tag{4.22}$$

Evaluation of the Matrix $\{\varphi_i,\varphi_j\}$

After Eqs. (1.1′), (1.2), (1.3), (1.6) and Eq. (3.12) have been inserted in the definition (4.5), this matrix is conveniently written as follows

$$\{\varphi_i,\varphi_j\}=[\varphi_i,\varphi_j]_1+\{\varphi_i,\varphi_j\}_2+\{\varphi_i,\varphi_j\}_3, \tag{4.23}$$

where

$$\{\varphi_i,\varphi_j\}_1=(\varphi_i\,|\,(-\hbar^2/2m)\Delta+\sum_R U_R{}^{\mathrm{C}}+\sum_h U_h{}^{\mathrm{H}}\,|\,\varphi_j), \tag{4.24}$$

$$\{\varphi_i,\varphi_j\}_2=-e^2\sum_R[\chi_R{}^2|\varphi_i\varphi_j]+e^2\sum_{n=1}^{G}2[\varphi_n\varphi_n|\varphi_i\varphi_j]^0, \tag{4.25}$$

$$\{\varphi_i,\varphi_j\}_3=-e^2\sum_{n=1}^{G}[\varphi_n\varphi_i\,|\,\varphi_n\varphi_j]^0. \tag{4.26}$$

Let us consider these three terms in turn.

The first can be taken over directly from Eq. (3.9),

$$\{\varphi_i,\varphi_j\}_1=\epsilon_i{}^{nf}\delta_{ij}+\delta\alpha[J,NJ,E]_{ij}, \tag{4.27}$$

and originates from the kinetic energy and the neutral part of the framework potential.

An expression for the second is obtained by substituting the Eqs. (2.15) and (3.12) in Eq. (4.25), whence

$$\{\varphi_i,\varphi_j\}_2=-\tfrac{1}{2}(s_i+s_j)\sum_{P,Q}G(PQ)c_{Pi}'c_{Pj}' +\tfrac{1}{2}(s_i+s_j)\sum_{P,Q}G(PQ)q(P)c_{Pi}'c_{Pj}',$$

where the $q(P)$ are the gross atomic populations of Eq. (4.16′). Since the terms $G(PQ)$ are symmetric in P and Q, one can write

$$\{\varphi_i,\varphi_j\}_2=\tfrac{1}{4}(s_i+s_j)\sum_{P,Q}G(PQ)\{[q(P)-1]c_{Qi}'c_{Qj}' +[q(Q)-1]c_{Pi}'c_{Pj}'\}. \tag{4.28}$$

This term contains the "ionic" part of the framework potential and the Coulomb part of the electronic interaction. It is small since the gross atomic populations are in general close to unity, and it vanishes altogether in alternant systems due to the Coulson-Rushbrooke theorem [$q(P)=1$ for all atoms].

The third term of the matrix $\{\varphi_i,\varphi_j\}$ represents the exchange part of the electronic interaction. Substituting Eqs. (3.12) and (3.13) into Eq. (4.26), one obtains

$$\{\varphi_i,\varphi_j\}_3=-\tfrac{1}{16}\sum_{P,Q}G(PQ)[(s_i+s_j)p(PQ)+s_is_jp'(PQ) +p''(PQ)](c_{Pi}'c_{Qj}'+c_{Qi}'c_{Pj}'), \tag{4.29}$$

where $p(PQ)$, $p'(PQ)$, and $p''(PQ)$ are the matrices defined in Eqs. (4.14), (4.15), and (4.16). While Eq. (4.29) is usable in practice, it can be simplified by virtue of the relations (4.17) and (4.17′), which are good approximations. From the computational point of view it seemed convenient to cast (4.29) in the form

$$\{\varphi_i,\varphi_j\}_3=-\tfrac{1}{16}\sum_{P,Q}G(PQ)[(2\sigma+s_i+s_j)p(PQ) +(s_is_j-\sigma^2)p'(PQ)](c_{Pi}'c_{Qj}'+c_{Qi}'c_{Pj}'), \tag{4.30}$$

$$p'(PQ)=2\sum_{n=1}^{G}c_{Pn}'c_{Qn}',$$

$$p(PQ)=2\sum_{n=1}^{G}c_{Pn}'c_{Qn}'s_n. \tag{4.30′}$$

If the Sklar-London approximation is used, the following additional term has to be included in the expression (4.23)

$$\{\varphi_i,\varphi_j\}'=\tfrac{1}{4}S^2g_2\sum_B\{3p'(PQ)[c_{Pi}'c_{Qj}'+c_{Qi}'c_{Pj}'] -p'(PP)c_{Qi}'c_{Qj}'-p'(QQ)c_{Pi}'c_{Pj}'\}. \tag{4.31}$$

Evaluation of H^0

The term H^0 given in Eq. (4.4) contains the expressions $\{\varphi_n,\varphi_n\}$, for which the result of the preceding subsection can be used. It also contains the terms $\{\varphi_n\,|\,f\,|\,\varphi_n\}$ which are in fact furnished by the expressions (4.24, 4.27) plus the first part of (4.25). When these expressions are inserted in Eq. (4.4), the following result is obtained for H^0:

$$H^0+G^0=2\sum_{n=1}^{G}\{\epsilon_n^{nf}+\delta\alpha[J, NJ, E]_{nn}\}$$
$$+\tfrac{1}{2}\sum_{P,Q}G(PQ)[q(P)-1][q(Q)-1]$$
$$-\tfrac{1}{8}\sum_{P,Q}G(PQ)\{[p(PQ)]^2+p'(PQ)p''(PQ)\}, \quad (4.32)$$

where the constant

$$G^0=\tfrac{1}{2}\sum_{P,Q}G(P,Q) \quad (4.32')$$

is separated out for convenience.[31]

The Sklar-London approximation would add the term

$$-\tfrac{1}{4}S^2g_2\sum_{B}\{3[p'(PQ)]^2-q'(P)q'(Q)\} \quad (4.33)$$

to H^0.

Dependence upon the Absolute Value of the Coulomb Integrals

In Eq. (3.15) it was shown that the MO electron-interaction integrals change in a very simple way if *all* AO Coulomb integrals $G(PQ)$ are increased by a constant amount, A. We shall now discuss the corresponding change of the total matrix elements.

By virtue of Eq. (3.15), the electron-hole interaction (4.9) will change by

$$+A\delta_{\nu\mu}\delta_{nm}. \quad (4.34)$$

By virtue of Eq. (3.15) the exchange term (4.26) will change by

$$-A\delta_{ij}\delta_{i,\text{ground state}}, \quad (4.35)$$

where

$$\delta_{i,\text{ground state}}=\begin{cases}1, & \text{if } i \text{ denotes a ground-state orbital,}\\ 0, & \text{if } i \text{ denotes an excited orbital.}\end{cases}$$

The change of the term $\{\varphi_i, \varphi_j\}_2$ can be inspected by making the substitution $G(PQ)\to G(PQ)+A$ directly in the expression (4.28). It is found that A is multiplied by the factor

$$\sum_P[q(P)-1]=N-N=0. \quad (4.36)$$

Thus the total configuration interaction matrix (4.8) contains the absolute value of the $G(PQ)$ only in H^0 and in the terms (4.34), (4.35). The latter two are, however, seen to cancel in Eq. (4.8) so that

$${}^s\mathrm{H}(\varphi_n\varphi_\nu, \varphi_m\varphi_\mu)-\mathrm{H}^0\delta_{nm}\delta_{\nu\mu}=\text{invariant under the substitution } G_{PQ}\to G_{PQ}+A. \quad (4.37)$$

In order to find the dependence of H^0 upon the absolute value of the $G(PQ)$ we make the substitution $G(PQ)\to G(PQ)+A$ directly in Eq. (4.32). The Coulomb terms give rise to vanishing terms of the type (4.36) and the exchange terms yield

$$-(A/8)\,\text{trace}\,(\mathbf{p}^2+\mathbf{p}'\mathbf{p}'')=-(A/2)\sum_P q(P)$$
$$=-NA/2,$$

where the identity (4.22) has been used. Hence the substitution changes the expression (H^0+G^0) by the amount

$$-(\tfrac{1}{2})NA. \quad (4.38)$$

The Ground-State Energy

I

The results of the preceding subsection can be used to bring the ground-state energy into an interpretable form.

Let us transform H^0, as given by Eq. (4.32), in the manner illustrated in Eq. (3.16) choosing $G'=G(1, 1)$. Furthermore, we express ϵ_n^{nf} by means of Eqs. (3.10) ff. and Eqs. (1.12) and (2.11). Thus we obtain

$$H^0=N\alpha'+2\sum_{n=1}^{G}\bar{\epsilon}_n+\bar{G}, \quad (4.39)$$

where

$$\alpha'=\alpha-G(1, 1)=-I_C+\bar{\alpha}, \quad (4.40)$$

with

$$-I_C=-A_C-G(1, 1), \quad (4.41)$$

$$\bar{\alpha}=(1+\tau)(\chi_1|U_2^C|\chi_1)+(2-\tau)(\chi_1|U_{h1}^H|\chi_1). \quad (4.42)$$

Furthermore,

$$\bar{\epsilon}_n=\{\gamma m_n+\delta\alpha[(1-\tau)+\sum_J c_{Pn}^2-\sum_E c_{Pn}^2]\}/(1+Sm_n), \quad (4.43)$$

with

$$\gamma=\beta-\alpha S. \quad (4.43')$$

Finally

$$\bar{G}=\sum_{P<Q}g(PQ)\bar{p}(PQ)-\sum_{P<Q}G(PQ), \quad (4.44)$$

with

$$g(PQ)=[G(1,1)-G(PQ)]>0, \quad (P,Q)\neq(1,1), \quad (4.45)$$

$$\bar{p}(PQ)=\tfrac{1}{4}\{[p(PQ)]^2+p'(PQ)p''(PQ)\}-[q(P)-1][q(Q)-1]\}. \quad (4.46)$$

The last equation can be simplified, when the approximation (4.20) is inserted, giving

$$\bar{p}(PQ)=\tfrac{1}{2}[p(PQ)]^2-[q(P)-1][q(Q)-1], \quad (4.46')$$

as a close approximation to (4.46).

The quantities α, β, $\delta\alpha$, τ are defined in Eqs. (2.10)–(2.13′), the quantities I_C, A_C are defined in Eqs. (1.11) and (1.12). In slight deviation from previous usage, we shall call $\bar{\alpha}$, γ, the Coulomb integral and the resonance integral, respectively.

[31] A similar separation was made in the case $S=0$ (neglect of differential overlap) by J. A. Pople, see reference 15.

II

Equation (4.39) has the following interpretation.

All terms involving G's originate from the attraction by the ionic part of the framework potential or from the interelectronic repulsion. It is to be expected that these two effects cancel each other to a large degree. This cancellation is described by the term $[q(Q)-1]\cdot[q(P)-1]$ in Eqs. (4.46) and (4.46′). The effect is largest for alternant systems, since in those one has $q(P)=1$ for all atoms; but also in other systems the term will be small, since it is quadratic in the small quantities $[q(P)-1]$. The cancellation of the two forces cannot be complete however, since, classically speaking, the attraction of N electrons by the N positive ionic charges would be $-\sum_P\sum_Q G(PQ)$, whereas the repulsion between the N electrons is only $+\sum_{P<Q}G(PQ)$. Thus there remains a sizable attraction, and this is described by the term $-G(1, 1)$ in Eq. (4.41) and the second sum in Eq. (4.44). There remains a relatively small term in $\bar{G}$, *viz.*, the first term in Eq. (4.46, 46′) which is due to exchange effects and the change in orbital self-energy.[32]

All other terms, containing no G's originate from the attraction of the neutral part of the framework potential and from the kinetic energy.

Another point of view is also instructive and has in fact determined the arrangements of terms in Eq. (4.39). From Eq. (1.12) it is seen that the term I_C of Eq. (4.41) is the ionization potential of C in its valence state, i.e., the energy of *one* electron in the field of *one* C^+ ion in the valence state. Hence $-(NI_C)$ is the bona fide energy of the pi electrons before the formation of the pi bonds so that

$$H^0+NI_C$$

is the energy lowering due to the bond formation. The lowering consists of three parts: $N\bar{\alpha}$=a general effect of the neutral framework on all orbitals, $2\Sigma_n\bar{\epsilon}_n$=an effect of the neutral framework specific for different orbitals, and $\bar{G}$=the effect of the ionic part of the framework minus the electron repulsion.

Thus, one finds again the division into short-range and long-range forces, which was commented upon after Eq. (2.17′). The former described by $\bar{\alpha}$ and $\bar{\epsilon}_n$, arise when atomic orbitals overlap and are responsible for covalent binding. The latter, described by $\bar{G}$, are responsible for ionic effects and electron-penetration effects.[32]

III

In order to assess the bonding power of the pi electrons properly, a further point must be taken into account, however. It must be remembered that the sigma framework contains a certain internal electrostatic-repulsion strain due to the fact that it is considered stripped of the pi electrons and therefore has excess positive charges, giving rise to the framework potential. This positive charge is represented by the last ("ionic") term in Eq. (1.6). The repulsion energy within the sigma framework, due to this ionic part, is therefore

$$E^{f+}=\sum_{P<Q}\{[\chi_P{}^2\,|\,\chi_Q{}^2]-(\chi_P\,|\,U_Q{}^{\mathrm{C}}\,|\,\chi_P)-(\chi_Q\,|\,U_P{}^{\mathrm{C}}\,|\,\chi_Q)\}-\sum_{P,h}\sum(\chi_P\,|\,U_h{}^{\mathrm{H}}\,|\,\chi_P). \qquad (4.47)$$

One must separate this energy from the framework and include it instead in the pi-electronic energy, in order to obtain a fair estimate of the strength of the pi-bonding.

By virtue of the arguments following Eq. (2.3), and using the definition (2.16), one finds from Eq. (4.47),

$$E^{f+}=\sum_{P<Q}G(PQ)-2N_B(\chi_1\,|\,U_2{}^{\mathrm{C}}\,|\,\chi_1)-(2N_E+N_N)(\chi_1\,|\,U_{h1}{}^{\mathrm{C}}\,|\,\chi_1),$$

where N_B is the number of bonds, N_N is the number of nonjoint atoms, and N_E is the number of free-end atoms. Now it can be shown that

$$2N_B=N(1+\tau), \qquad (2N_E+N_N)=N(2-\tau),$$

where τ is just the quantity defined in Eq. (2.12′). By virtue of the definition (4.42) of $\bar{\alpha}$, the internal ionic framework repulsion energy can therefore be written

$$E^{f+}=\sum_{P<Q}G(PQ)-N\bar{\alpha}. \qquad (4.48)$$

Let us call

$$E^0=H^0+E^{f+}=\textit{effective pi energy of the conjugated system}, \qquad (4.49)$$

and, in view of the meaning of (NI_C),

$$E_j=E^0+NI_C=\textit{effective bonding energy of pi electrons with respect to the carbon valence state.} \qquad (4.50)$$

Then one obtains for the latter, by combining Eqs. (4.39) and (4.48), finally

$$E_b=2\sum_{n=1}^{G}\bar{\epsilon}_n+\sum_{P<Q}g(PQ)\bar{p}(PQ), \qquad (4.51)$$

where all symbols are defined in Eqs. (4.40)–(4.46′). This expression could be used to compute delocalization energies, but this subject is not pursued here because of the well-known uncertainties of interpretation. However, Eq. (4.51) should give an idea of the comparative pi-electron binding in different molecules.

As an example of the energies which are involved and which cancel against each other, we give the quantitative results for benzene.[33]

[32] See K. Ruedenberg (to be published).

[33] The numerical results are taken from the sixth paper in this series, see K. Ruedenberg, J. Chem. Phys. **34**, 1907 (1961).

The binding energy contributions are:

$$2\sum_{n=1}^{G}\bar{\epsilon}_n = -2.1838\times(88/15) = -12.81 \text{ ev},$$

$$\sum_{P<Q} g(PQ)\bar{p}(PQ) = +6.80 \text{ ev [Eq. (4.46)]},$$

$$\approx +6.77 \text{ ev [Eq. (4.46')]}.$$

Canceled away are the following energy contributions to H^0, in total 260 ev.

One-center attraction (short-range and ionic) contained in the ionization potential of carbon,

$$-NI_C = -6\times(0.69+10.53) = -67.32 \text{ ev}.$$

Many-center attractions canceled by framework repulsion:

short-range:

$$N\bar{\alpha} = -6\times 5.516 = -33.10 \text{ ev}.$$

ionic:

$$-\sum_{P<Q} G(PQ) = -79.70 \text{ ev}.$$

Many-center ionic attraction, canceled by electronic repulsion:

$$-\sum_{P<Q} G(PQ)q(P)q(Q) = -\sum_{P<Q} G(PQ) = -79.70 \text{ ev}.$$

All large energy contributions have canceled out exactly in Eq. (4.51), and it emerges that the term which is finally responsible for the binding, i.e., the first term in Eq. (4.51), is a *sum over the one-electron energies* $\bar{\epsilon}_n$ *due to the neutral framework potential composed of short-range forces.* Thus $\bar{\epsilon}_n$ can be called the "*orbital contribution*" to the total energy. This additive orbital contribution must be clearly distinguished from the "*orbital energy,*" i.e., the energy of an electron which occupies this orbital. The latter is given by the expression $\{\varphi_n, \varphi_n\}$, as mentioned after Eq. (4.5), and is frequently denoted by ϵ_n, in particular when the ϵ_n's are self-consistent field orbitals.

IV

The original Hückel-Lennard-Jones-Coulson-Wheland theory assumed *ad hoc* and without any analysis the additivity of "one-electron energies," say $\bar{\epsilon}_n$. At the same time, these $\bar{\epsilon}_n$ were believed to be "orbital energies," it was in fact hoped that they would be close to the self-consistent field orbital energies. Critics then pointed out the inherent contradiction of these two expectations. The present analysis solves the puzzle by showing that there exist additive orbital energy contributions which are different from the orbital energies and, instead, obtained as eigenvalues of a *topological* one-electron problem. Thus there is an element of truth in the old formula

$$\text{binding energy} \propto 2\sum_{n=1}^{G} m_n/(1+Sm_n);$$

however, Eq. (4.51) provides the additional terms required by the theory.

Thus Eq. (4.51) also furnishes a rigorous justification for the distinction between bonding and antibonding pi orbitals: the orbital is *bonding* (*antibonding*) when the "*orbital energy contribution*" $\bar{\epsilon}_n$ is negative (positive). In contrast, the orbital is *bound* (*unbound*) if the "*orbital energy*" ϵ_n is negative (positive).

The present derivation furthermore affords understanding of the intricate balancing of energy terms and thereby gives hope for a better treatment of those cases in which the canceling is not complete, e.g., when heteroatoms and substituents enter in. In another investigation this aspect will be pursued further and in fact generalized to arbitrary molecular and crystal systems.[32]

Finally, we wish to comment on the remarkable fact that the electronic interaction terms as given by Eq. (4.46') are *exactly* identical with the ones obtained by Pople[15] under the radical assumption of neglecting *all* overlap integrals from the very beginning. It should be stressed that our Eq. (4.46') is not obtained by a *formal* expansion in S, but from a very accurate approximation, based on a quantitatively checked expansion in terms of the parameter σ' of Eq. (4.17''). As seen above, in benzene use of Eq. (4.46') leads to an error of 0.03 ev in the expression (4.44).

It must be pointed out however that the result (4.46') is *also heavily based on the fact that our MO's are eigenvectors of the topological matrix* **M**, i.e., that they are essentially the Hückel-Wheland orbitals. It may well be that Eq. (4.46') and others are unjustifiable for any other type of molecular orbital. It would seem that the execution of the self-consistent field mechanism, as proposed by Pople, is worth the effort only when it should be possible to establish, under the general assumptions adopted in the present analysis, the validity of Eq. (4.46') and the corresponding simplifications for the self-consistent field operator for the successive iterations in a self-consistent field sequence. Also the difference between joint and nonjoint atoms should be taken into account. The possibility exists that the execution of the self-consistent field formalism, while neglecting differential overlap, leads to results which are less reliable than those derived from Hückel-Wheland orbitals.

Ionization Potential, Electron Affinity, Electronegativity

It can be argued that in a large system the AO's do not change appreciably if only *one* electron out of $N\gg 1$ is removed or added, and for the same reason the topological Hückel-Wheland MO's should not be appreciably worse approximations than they were in the neutral molecule.

If an electron is removed from the ground-state orbital φ_n, the ground-state energy of the resulting positive ion becomes

$$H^0-\{\varphi_n,\varphi_n\}.$$

On the other hand, if an additional electron is placed in the excited orbital φ_ν, then the ground-state energy of the resulting negative ion is

$$H^0+\{\varphi_\nu,\varphi_\nu\}.$$

Hence one has

$$I=-\{\varphi_n,\varphi_n\}=\text{ionization potential of the molecule,} \tag{4.52}$$

$$A=-[\varphi_\nu,\varphi_\nu]=\text{electron affinity of the molecule,} \tag{4.53}$$

if φ_n is the highest ground-state orbital and φ_ν is the lowest excited orbital. Equation (4.52) is the Hartree-Slater-Koopmans[34] theorem; Mulliken explained its usually good agreement with experiment by a fortunate cancellation of errors. In the case of Eq. (4.53) the errors would tend to add, however.

The ionization potential is obtained from Eq. (4.23) by putting $i=j=n$. Again we make a transformation of the kind which led to Eq. (4.39). Noting Eqs. (4.35) and (4.36), we obtain

$$-I=\{\varphi_n,\varphi_n\}=-I_C+\bar{\alpha}+\bar{\epsilon}_n+\sum_{P<Q}g(PQ)\bar{p}_n(PQ), \tag{4.54}$$

with

$$\bar{p}_n(PQ)=\tfrac{1}{2}\{p(PQ)+\tfrac{1}{2}[s_np'(PQ)+s_n^{-1}p''(PQ)]\}c_{Pn}c_{Qn}$$
$$-\{[q(P)-1]c_{Qn}^2+[q(Q)-1]c_{Pn}^2\}, \tag{4.55}$$

where all symbols are defined in Eq. (4.39) ff and Eq. (3.7). Since φ_n is a ground-state orbital, the approximation (4.21) can be used, yielding in close approximation,

$$\bar{p}_n(PQ)=p(PQ)c_{Pn}c_{Qn}$$
$$-\{[q(P)-1]c_{Pn}^2+[q(P)-1]c_{Qn}^2\}. \tag{4.55'}$$

The electron affinity is obtained in the same way. However, in this case Eq. (4.35) gives the contribution zero, and furthermore approximation (4.21) is not applicable. Hence,

$$-A=\{\varphi_\nu,\varphi_\nu\}=-A_C+\bar{\alpha}+\bar{\epsilon}_\nu+\sum_{P<Q}g(PQ)\bar{p}_\nu(PQ), \tag{4.56}$$

with

$$\bar{p}_\nu(PQ)=\tfrac{1}{2}\{p(PQ)+\tfrac{1}{2}[s_\nu p'(PQ)+s_\nu^{-1}p''(PQ)]\}c_{P\nu}c_{Q\nu}$$
$$-\{[q(P)-1]c_{Q\nu}^2+[q(Q)-1]c_{P\nu}^2\}. \tag{4.57}$$

Again the derived equations have a sensible interpretation.

In Eq. (4.57), the electron affinity of the carbon valence state, A_C, appears. In Eq. (4.54) the corresponding ionization potential, $I_C=A_C+G(1,1)$, appears. In fact, we expect that the electron in the ground-state orbital φ_n, before its removal, had been subject to a net Coulombic attraction $-G(1,1)$ due to the incomplete shielding of the N nuclei by the $(N-1)$ other electrons, whereas this attraction is absent for the additional electron in the excited orbital φ_ν, which is completely shielded by the N ground-state electrons.

The term $(\bar{\alpha}+\bar{\epsilon}_n)$ in Eq. (4.54) describes the lowering of the orbital energy of the bonding orbital φ_n caused by the short-range, neutral part of the framework potential leading to bond formation. The last term in this equation is the remnant of the long-range Coulombic force, mostly of exchange character, since the appearance of $[q(P)-1]$ indicates that provision has been made for the intrinsic cancellation of ionic framework attraction and electronic repulsion. Again this cancellation is largest for alternants, since here $q(P)=1$.

It is of interest to examine the mean value of the ionization potential and the electron affinity, a quantity which Mulliken has defined as an appropriate measure of the electronegativity of the molecule. From Eqs. (4.54) and (4.56) follows

$$-\tfrac{1}{2}(I+A)=-\tfrac{1}{2}(I_C+A_C)+\bar{\alpha}+\tfrac{1}{2}(\bar{\epsilon}_n+\bar{\epsilon}_\nu)$$
$$+\sum_{P<Q}g(PQ)\tfrac{1}{2}[\bar{p}_n(PQ)+\bar{p}_\nu(PQ)]. \tag{4.58}$$

The quantitative behavior of this expression is best appreciated by considering the case of alternant systems. In this case φ_n and φ_ν are paired orbitals so that

$$m_\nu=-m_n,\qquad c_{P\nu}=J_Pc_{Pn},$$

$$J_P=\begin{cases}1, & \text{if } P \text{ is a starred atom,}\\ -1, & \text{if } P \text{ is an unstarred atom,}\end{cases}$$

$$q(P)=1, \tag{4.59}$$

$p(PQ)=0$,
$p'(PQ)$, $p''(PQ)$ are small. (see e.g. Table I for benzene) — if P and Q belong to the same class, but $P\neq Q$.

By virtue of these relations, one obtains

$$\tfrac{1}{2}(\bar{\epsilon}_n+\bar{\epsilon}_\nu)=\{-\gamma Sm_n^2+\delta\alpha[(1-\tau)$$
$$+\sum_J c_{Pn}^2-\sum_E c_{Pn}^2]\}/(1-S^2m_n^2), \tag{4.60}$$

and

$$\tfrac{1}{2}[\bar{p}_n(PQ)+\bar{p}_\nu(PQ)]=\tfrac{1}{4}\begin{Bmatrix}1\\ Sm_n\end{Bmatrix}$$
$$\times[p'(PQ)+J_QJ_Pp''(PQ)(1-S^2m_n^2)^{-1}]c_{Pn}c_{Qn}. \tag{4.61}$$

[34] T. Koopmans, Physica 1, 104 (1933). (Strictly Koopmans' theorem applies to SCF orbitals.)

The expression (4.61) will be small if P and Q belong to the same class, since then p' and p'' are small; if P and Q are of different class, then the minus sign in (4.61) in conjunction with the factor S will make it small. In benzene, e.g., one obtains about -0.15 ev for the total last sum in Eq. (4.58). In contrast the contribution from Eq. (4.60) is about 0.6 ev.

N. S. Hush and J. A. Pople[35] recently suggested that the quantity $(I+A)$ is a constant in alternant systems, basing their conclusions on a treatment neglecting all overlap integrals. However, while the neglect of neighbor overlap introduces only a moderate error in calculating the difference $(\bar{\epsilon}_n-\bar{\epsilon}_\nu)$, it introduces a considerable error, e.g., 1.2 ev in benzene, when the sum $(\bar{\epsilon}_n+\bar{\epsilon}_\nu)$ is computed. The reason for this is clearly seen from the discussion in the second paper of this series. In fact, the quantity m_n^2 in Eq. (4.60) can vary between 0 and 1 in considering several conjugated systems. As a result, the deviations of the electronegativities (4.58) from a constant value are of the same magnitude as the electronegativity values themselves and as the variations in the ionization potentials. The same is true for the few experimental values quoted by Hush and Pople.

Energies of Excited States

If an electron is promoted from a ground-state orbital φ_n to an excited orbital φ_ν, then the energies of the resulting triplet and singlet states are given by the diagonal element of the matrix (4.8), which we may write

$$^sH(\varphi_n\varphi_\nu, \varphi_n\varphi_\nu)=[H^0-\{\varphi_n, \varphi_n\}] +[\{\varphi_\nu, \varphi_\nu\}-{}^s\{\varphi_n\varphi_\nu, \varphi_n\varphi_\nu\}]. \quad (4.62)$$

In view of the remarks after Eq. (4.5) and of the discussion in the preceding subsection, the first bracket term in (4.62) represents the energy of the system after the electron in φ_n has been removed, and hence the second bracket term must represent the energy addition when the removed electron is now placed in orbital φ_ν, while the orbital φ_n remains empty. Indeed, the remarks after Eq. (4.5) and the discussion in the preceding subsection also show that $\{\varphi_\nu,\varphi_\nu\}$ is the energy of an electron in φ_ν when *all* ground-state orbitals are filled, and that subtracting the term $^s\{\varphi_n\varphi_\nu, \varphi_n\varphi_\nu\}$ amounts to subtracting out the energy of an electron in φ_ν with respect to an electron in φ_n.

This general interpretation is very visibly borne out by our formalism, if we carry out again a transformation of the kind that led to Eq. (4.39). According to Eq. (4.54), this transformation puts in evidence the net Coulomb attraction $-G(1, 1)$ in $\{\varphi_n, \varphi_n\}$, expressing shielding by $(N-1)$ other electrons only. Such a term did not appear in $\{\varphi_\nu, \varphi_\nu\}$, Eq. (4.56), indicating shielding by N other electrons. According to Eq. (4.34) our transformation does however put in evidence such a term in $^s\{\varphi_n\varphi_\nu, \varphi_n\varphi_\nu\}$, indicating that $\{\zeta_\nu, \zeta_\nu\}-{}^s[\varphi_n\varphi_\nu, \varphi_n\varphi_\nu\}$ is the energy of an electron shielded by $(N-1)$ other electrons only.

As a consequence, the integral $G(1, 1)$ cancels out in the excitation energy $^sH(\varphi_n\varphi_\nu,\varphi_n\varphi_\nu)-H^0$, as was already noticed in Eq. (4.37), so that all spectroscopic transitions depend only upon the differences defined in Eq. (4.45). *In view of this circumstance it is rather surprising that the proper adjustment of* $G(1, 1)$ *did play such an important role in the recent advances made in the calculations of spectra.*[20] *In the fourth paper*[25] *we shall in fact see that the primary point of the Pariser-Parr adjustment is the adjustment of the g's of Eq.* (4.45). *This latter adjustment goes considerably beyond changing* $G(1, 1)$ *and requires the adjustment of* $G(1, 1)$ *as a "secondary effect."*

As was discussed after Eq. (4.3), the excited molecular states are in general superpositions of several singly excited states with the configuration interaction matrix (4.8). In alternant systems, it was noted by Moffitt[36] and Pariser[16] that there exists a particularly strong interaction between the "paired one-orbital excitations," *if all overlap integrals are neglected.* Let

φ_ν = the excited orbital *paired* to the ground-state orbital φ_n,

φ_μ = the excited orbital *paired* to the ground-state orbital φ_m,

then the two paired one-orbital excitations are: $\varphi_n\rightarrow\varphi_\mu$ and $\varphi_m\rightarrow\varphi_\nu$, and the strong interaction originated from the fact that the difference of the diagonal elements, *viz.*,

$$\Delta^s\mathrm{H}(\mathrm{P})={}^s\mathrm{H}(\varphi_n\varphi_\mu, \varphi_n\varphi_\mu)-{}^s\mathrm{H}(\varphi_m\varphi_\nu, \varphi_m\varphi_\nu), \quad (4.63)$$

is zero when *all overlap integrals are set equal to zero.* We shall therefore examine this expression under our more rigorous assumptions.

From Eq. (4.62) follows, by changing indices,

$$\Delta^s\mathrm{H}(P)=\Delta_1-\Delta_2, \quad (4.64)$$

with

$$\Delta_1=[\{\varphi_m,\varphi_m\}+\{\varphi_\mu,\varphi_\mu\}]-[\{\varphi_n,\varphi_n\}+\{\varphi_\nu,\varphi_\nu\}], \quad (4.65)$$

$$\Delta_2={}^s\{\varphi_n\varphi_\mu, \varphi_n\varphi_\mu\}-{}^s\{\varphi_m\varphi_\nu, \varphi_m\varphi_\nu\}. \quad (4.65')$$

Thus, Δ_1 is composed of the electronegativities which were discussed in Eq. (4.58) ff. Hence the largest contribution to Δ_1 will come from the first term in

[35] N. S. Hush and J. A. Pople, Trans. Faraday Soc. **51**, 600 (1955).

[36] W. Moffitt, J. Chem. Phys. **22**, 1820 (1954). Pariser's independent results,[16] though published later, were communicated in June, 1954, at the Symposium for Molecular Structure and Spectra, Ohio State University, Columbus, Ohio. Subsequent applications were made by M. J. S. Dewar and H. C. Longuet-Higgins, Proc. Phys. Soc. (London) **A67**, 795 (1954), by Pople[17] and by Ham and Ruedenberg.[18]

Eq. (4.60), so that

$$\Delta_1 = -2\gamma S(m_{m}{}^2 - m_n{}^2)/(1-S^2 m_m{}^2)(1-S^2 m_n{}^2)+\cdots. \tag{4.66}$$

An expression for Δ_2 is obtained by substituting the expressions (4.9) and (3.13) in Eq. (4.65′) and taking into account the properties (4.59) for alternants. Thus results

$$\Delta_2 = -(s_{n\mu}{}^2 - s_{m\nu}{}^2)(1-p_s)\sum_{P<Q} J_P J_Q c_{Pn} c_{Qn} c_{Pm} c_{Qm}, \tag{4.67}$$

where p_s is defined after Eq. (4.9). For the multiplying factor, one finds from the definition (3.13′),

$$(s_{n\mu}{}^2 - s_{m\nu}{}^2) = \tfrac{1}{2}[(Sm_m) + (Sm_n)]$$
$$\times[(Sm_m)^2 - (Sm_n)^2]/[(1-(Sm_m)^2][1-(Sm_n)^2]. \tag{4.68}$$

In many cases, it seems practical to consider only one-orbital excitations from the 2–3 highest ground-state orbitals to the 2–3 lowest excited orbitals (see footnote 18). In the majority of these cases one has $0 \leq m_n \leq 1$, $0 \leq m_m \leq 1$. With $S=\frac{1}{4}$, it becomes evident that the difference (4.64) is then small in comparison to the diagonal matrix elements themselves.

It is furthermore seen that the two paired one-orbital excitations differ very little in their orbital transition moments. According to Eq. (3.18) and by virtue of Eq. (4.59), one obtains for the difference

$$\mathbf{q}(\varphi_n, \varphi_\nu) - \mathbf{q}(\varphi_m, \varphi_\nu) = (s_{n\mu} - s_{m\nu})\sum_P J_P \mathbf{R}_P c_{Pn} c_{Pm}, \tag{4.69}$$

and one can again show that the multiplying factor is small in many cases.

Consequently, the present theory including overlap effects appears to substantiate the result that in many cases there is a strong interaction between paired excitation, leading to a strong band and a weak band, in agreement with experiment. However, the interaction does not go quite to a 1:1 mixing, but it is rather of the kind analyzed by Ham and Ruedenberg.[18]

5. VALIDITY OF THE NEGLECT OF DIFFERENTIAL OVERLAP

The foregoing results show that differential overlap cannot be neglected uncritically. The following conclusions seem to be warranted.

Use for Two-Electron Integrals

The neglect of differential overlap represents a valid and effective approximation if the atomic orbitals satisfy Mulliken's approximation *and if* the molecular orbitals are simultaneously eigenvectors of the overlap matrix. Three cases of such orbitals are known so far:

(i) the topological MO's discussed in the present paper;

(ii) the MO's of the augmented tight-binding approximation discussed in the subsequent paper;

(iii) the MO's in cyclic systems, since the effective Hamiltonian and the overlap matrix commute in these systems for symmetry reasons.[37] An example is discussed in the subsequent paper.

To what degree neglect of differential overlap is a bona fide approximation in conjunction with a self-consistent-field procedure, in cases where the SCF MO's are not determined by symmetry, remains questionable. The use of neglect of differential overlap in this situation, and in others, is related to the question, to what degree and under what conditions neglect of differential overlap is a bona fide approximation for Löwdin orbitals.[38] A cogent mathematical analysis of this latter point would be desirable.

Use for One-Electron Integrals

It seems that the neglect of differential overlap introduces little error in the calculation of energy differences, as needed for electronic spectra.

The case of the electronegativities shows however that there are problems where the use of this approximation may have rather little meaning, and a more careful formulation is unavoidable.

[37] P. O. Löwdin, J. Chem. Phys. **18**, 365 (1950).

[38] For further references on this aspect, see R. G. Parr, J. Chem. Phys. **33**, 1184 (1960).

Reprinted from
Molecular Physics, Vol. 5, No. 1, p. 91, January 1962

Calculations on the ions and lowest π triplet states of some conjugated hydrocarbons

by A. T. AMOS
Department of Mathematics, Imperial College, London, S.W.7

(*Received* 10 *August* 1961)

A steepest descent procedure which can be used in an iterative calculation of the unrestricted bond order matrices for any system is described. The method is used to calculate unrestricted bond order matrices for the ions and lowest π triplet states of naphthalene, anthracene, phenanthrene and azulene. Spin densities and net charges on each carbon atom in these systems together with triplet excitation energies and ionization potentials are found and compared with experiment. Unrestricted wave functions are not in general eigenfunctions of the total spin operator but this situation can be improved by using projection operators and annihilators. Spin properties of the wave function both before and after a single annihilation are discussed together with the effect of annihilation on spin densities and energy values.

1. Introduction

The unrestricted Hartree–Fock method has recently received considerable attention in the literature [1, 2, 3, 4] since it has been realized that it can provide a more accurate treatment of electronic structure than the usual Hartree–Fock method without introducing the elaborate mathematics and lack of physical interpretation found in so many theories. The great disadvantage of the method is that the unrestricted wave function, built up by using different orbitals for electrons with different spins, is not an eigenfunction of S^2, but this can be remedied by using projection operators and annihilators [5, 6, 7]. On the other hand the unrestricted method does take the correlation between electrons with different spins more fully into account and is therefore likely to give good energy values. Also it predicts negative spin densities in π electron radicals in agreement with experiment whereas the usual Hartree–Fock method does not.

The main difficulty in any discussion of the unrestricted method is that there have been few calculations. One object of this paper, therefore, is to devise a method of calculation which can be applied even to systems with a large number of electrons. The main purpose of this paper is then to use this method to calculate some properties of the ions and lowest π triplet states of a number of conjugated hydrocarbons. The theoretical values of these properties can then be compared with the few available experimental values to determine how successful the unrestricted method is.

2. The unrestricted Hartree–Fock method

The unrestricted Hartree–Fock method is based on the single determinant wave function

$$\Psi=(n\,!)^{-1/2}\,\mathrm{Det}\,\{\psi_1(1)\alpha(1),\,\ldots,\,\psi_p(p)\alpha(p),\phi_1(p+1)\beta(p+1),\,\ldots,\,\phi_q(n)\beta(n)\},\quad(2.01)$$

where the functions ψ_i and ϕ_i form two different orthonormal sets. If ψ_i and ϕ_i are written in terms of a suitable set of $m(\geqslant n)$ orthonormal functions ω_r,

$$\psi_i = \sum_s^m \omega_s a_{si}, \quad \phi_i = \sum_s^m \omega_s b_{si} \tag{2.02}$$

the total energy will be given by

$$E = \mathrm{tr}(\mathbf{PH}) + \mathrm{tr}(\mathbf{QH}) + \tfrac{1}{2}\mathrm{tr}(\mathbf{PG}^{\alpha}) + \tfrac{1}{2}\,\mathrm{tr}(\mathbf{QG}^{\beta}), \tag{2.03}$$

where, in the notation of Amos and Hall [7],

$$\left.\begin{aligned} H_{us} &= \int \omega_u^*\Big(-\tfrac{1}{2}\nabla^2 - \sum_\alpha Z_\alpha/r_\alpha\Big)\omega_s\,d\mathbf{x}, \\ G_{su}{}^{\alpha} &= \sum_{vt} \{(P_{vt}+Q_{vt})(st|uv) - P_{vt}(st|vu)\} \\ \text{and}\quad G_{su}{}^{\beta} &= \sum_{vt} \{(P_{vt}+Q_{vt})(st|uv) - Q_{vt}(st|vu)\}. \end{aligned}\right\} \tag{2.04}$$

The unrestricted bond order matrices $\mathbf{P}$ and $\mathbf{Q}$ are defined by

$$P_{uv} = \sum_r^p a_{ur} a_{vr}^*, \quad Q_{uv} = \sum_r^q b_{ur} b_{vr}^* \tag{2.05}$$

and the orthonormality conditions imply that

$$\left.\begin{aligned} \mathbf{P}^2 = \mathbf{P}, &\quad \mathbf{Q}^2 = \mathbf{Q}, \\ \mathrm{tr}\,\mathbf{P} = p, &\quad \mathrm{tr}\,\mathbf{Q} = q. \end{aligned}\right\} \tag{2.06}$$

By minimizing E subject to the orthonormality conditions the equations determining the coefficients $\{a_{sr}\}$ and $\{b_{sr}\}$ can be found. For the unrestricted molecular orbitals these have eigenvalue form:

$$\left.\begin{aligned} \sum_t F_{st}{}^{\alpha} a_{tu} &= \sum_t (\mathbf{H}+\mathbf{G}^{\alpha})_{st} a_{tu} = a_{su} e_u, \\ \sum_t F_{st}{}^{\beta} b_{tu} &= \sum_t (\mathbf{H}+\mathbf{G}^{\beta})_{st} b_{tu} = b_{su} e_u', \end{aligned}\right\} \tag{2.07}$$

so that the eigenvectors of the matrices $\mathbf{F}^{\alpha}$ and $\mathbf{F}^{\beta}$ will be the molecular orbitals for electrons with α-spin and β-spin respectively. The orbital energies e_u for α-spin electrons and e_u' for β-spin electrons are the eigenvalues of $\mathbf{F}^{\alpha}$ and of $\mathbf{F}^{\beta}$ and can be associated with ionization potentials using an extension of Koopman's theorem [7].

Since the wave function (2.01) is built up using different orbitals for electrons with different spins it will not, in general, be an eigenfunction of the total spin operator S^2 but it can conveniently be written in the form

$$\Psi = c_0\Psi_{2s+1} + c_1\Psi_{2s+3} + c_2\Psi_{2s+5} + \dots, \tag{2.08}$$

where $s = \frac{1}{2}(p-q)$ and Ψ_{2s+1} is a spin eigenstate with eigenvalue $s(s+1)$. Thus, for example, if $p-q=2$, the main contribution to Ψ will be from the triplet Ψ_3 but mixed in with this will be a quintet Ψ_5, a septet Ψ_7 and so on.

Löwdin [5] and Amos and Hall [7] have discussed methods of using projection operators and annihilators to obtain from Ψ wave functions which are eigenfunctions of spin. The latter give examples to show that in the expansion (2.08) the coefficients $c_2, c_3, \dots$ are usually very small and only c_0 and c_1 are important. Consequently they suggest that a good approximation to a spin eigenfunction will be

$$\Psi' = A_s\Psi, \tag{2.09}$$

where A_s is the annihilator $S^2 - (s+1)(s+2)$.

Providing $c_2, c_3, \ldots$ are small, the energy corresponding to the new wave function will be

$$W=\int \Psi^* H A_s \Psi \, d\mathbf{x} \Big/ \int \Psi^* A_s \Psi \, d\mathbf{x}. \qquad (2.10)$$

The use of the annihilator also changes the first-order density matrix. For Ψ this has the form

$$\gamma(1 \mid 2)= \sum_{rs} P_{rs}\omega_s^*(1)\omega_r(2)\alpha^*(1)\alpha(2) + \sum_{rs} Q_{rs}\omega_s^*(1)\omega_r(2)\beta^*(1)\beta(2), \qquad (2.11)$$

whereas for Ψ' it becomes

$$\gamma(1 \mid 2)= \sum_{rs} R_{rs}\omega_s^*(1)\omega_r(2)\alpha^*(1)\alpha(2) + \sum_{rs} S_{rs}\omega_s^*(1)\omega_r(2)\beta^*(1)\beta(2), \qquad (2.12)$$

where

$$\mathbf{R}=\mathbf{P}-(\mathbf{PQP}-\tfrac{1}{2}\mathbf{PQ}-\tfrac{1}{2}\mathbf{QP})/x,$$

$$\mathbf{S}=\mathbf{Q}-(\mathbf{QPQ}-\tfrac{1}{2}\mathbf{QP}-\tfrac{1}{2}\mathbf{PQ})/x,$$

and

$$x=(s+1)(s+2)-\tfrac{1}{4}(p-q)^2-\tfrac{1}{2}(p+q)+\mathrm{tr}\,\mathbf{PQ}.$$

3. Calculation of the bond order matrices

In any actual calculation using the unrestricted method, one procedure is to apply the Roothaan technique to the eigenvalue equations (2.07) so as to obtain the unrestricted M.O.'s [1, 8]. Once these have been found the bond order matrices $\mathbf{P}$ and $\mathbf{Q}$ and any other required quantities can be calculated. However, since the first-order density matrix and consequently the density matrices of all other orders can be written in terms of $\mathbf{P}$ and $\mathbf{Q}$ only, it follows that the bond order matrices are the fundamental quantities in the theory and there is no real need to calculate the orbitals at all.

Therefore a second method of calculation is to find directly matrices $\mathbf{P}$ and $\mathbf{Q}$ which minimize E. Providing they also satisfy the conditions (2.06), they will be the bond order matrices. A similar situation in ordinary Hartree–Fock theory led McWeeny [9] to develop a steepest descent method of solution which it is possible to adapt to the present requirements. This gives an iteration procedure for calculating $\mathbf{P}$ and $\mathbf{Q}$ which takes into account second-order terms.

This can be seen by considering variations $\delta\mathbf{P}$ and $\delta\mathbf{Q}$ in $\mathbf{P}$ and $\mathbf{Q}$ with resulting changes $\delta\mathbf{G}^\alpha$ in $\mathbf{G}^\alpha$ and $\delta\mathbf{G}^\beta$ in $\mathbf{G}^\beta$. If the net result is a change δE then from equation (2.03),

$$\delta E=\mathrm{tr}(\delta\mathbf{P}\,.\,\mathbf{H})+\mathrm{tr}(\delta\mathbf{Q}\,.\,\mathbf{H})+\tfrac{1}{2}\mathrm{tr}(\delta\mathbf{P}\,.\,\mathbf{G}^\alpha)+\tfrac{1}{2}\mathrm{tr}(\delta\mathbf{Q}\,.\,\mathbf{G}^\beta)+\tfrac{1}{2}\mathrm{tr}(\delta\mathbf{P}\,.\,\delta\mathbf{G}^\alpha) + \tfrac{1}{2}\mathrm{tr}(\delta\mathbf{Q}\,.\,\delta\mathbf{G}^\beta)+\tfrac{1}{2}\mathrm{tr}(\mathbf{P}\,.\,\delta\mathbf{G}^\alpha)+\tfrac{1}{2}\mathrm{tr}(\mathbf{Q}\,.\,\delta\mathbf{G}^\beta). \qquad (3.01)$$

Because of the symmetry of the integrals in (2.04) it is clear that

$$\mathrm{tr}(\mathbf{P}\,.\,\delta\mathbf{G}^\alpha)+\mathrm{tr}(\mathbf{Q}\,.\,\delta\mathbf{G}^\beta)=\mathrm{tr}(\delta\mathbf{P}\,.\,\mathbf{G}^\alpha)+\mathrm{tr}(\delta\mathbf{Q}\,.\,\mathbf{G}^\beta) \qquad (3.02)$$

and therefore,

$$\delta E=\mathrm{tr}(\delta\mathbf{P}\,.\,\mathbf{F}^\alpha)+\mathrm{tr}(\delta\mathbf{Q}\,.\,\mathbf{F}^\beta)+\tfrac{1}{2}\mathrm{tr}(\delta\mathbf{P}\,.\,\delta\mathbf{G}^\alpha)+\tfrac{1}{2}\mathrm{tr}(\delta\mathbf{Q}\,.\,\delta\mathbf{G}^\beta). \qquad (3.03)$$

This implies that to first order the variation in E is equivalent to two separate independent variations in

$$\epsilon_1 = \mathrm{tr}(\mathbf{P} \,.\, \mathbf{F}^{\alpha}) \tag{3.04}$$

and

$$\epsilon_2 = \mathrm{tr}(\mathbf{Q} \,.\, \mathbf{F}^{\beta}), \tag{3.05}$$

where $\mathbf{F}^{\alpha}$ and $\mathbf{F}^{\beta}$ are to be regarded as fixed matrices. Thus the method analagous to Roothaan's is correct to first order, the dependence of $\mathbf{F}^{\alpha}$ and $\mathbf{F}^{\beta}$ on $\mathbf{P}$ and $\mathbf{Q}$ and of $\mathbf{P}$ and $\mathbf{Q}$ on each other appearing only as second-order terms. . Expressing this in terms of the method of steepest descents, equation (3.03) implies that for a direct descent of the E surface the initial direction and rate of descent for $\mathbf{P}$ is exacdly the same as for the descent of the ϵ_1 surface, and for $\mathbf{Q}$ exactly the same as for the descent of the ϵ_2 surfacc. The only difference is in the curvatures of the descents which differ due to the second order terms. However, these second-order terms are not trivial but have important effects on the rate of convergence of any iteration process and neglect of them can even lead to divergence (see reference [9]).

McWeeny (op. cit.) has used steepest descent methods to show that if $\mathbf{P}$ and $\mathbf{Q}$ are matrices which approximately minimize ϵ_1 and ϵ_2 respectively, then improvements $\delta\mathbf{P}$ in $\mathbf{P}$ and $\delta\mathbf{Q}$ in $\mathbf{Q}$ are given by

$$\left.\begin{aligned} \delta\mathbf{P} &= \left[\sum_{m=1}^{\infty}(-1)^m\lambda^{2m}(\mathbf{I}^2)^{m-1}\right]\mathbf{IJ} - \left[\sum_{m=0}^{\infty}(-1)^m\lambda^{2m+1}(\mathbf{I}^2)^m\right]\mathbf{I}, \\ \delta\mathbf{Q} &= \left[\sum_{m=1}^{\infty}(-1)^m\mu^{2m}(\mathbf{K}^2)^{m-1}\right]\mathbf{KL} - \left[\sum_{m=0}^{\infty}(-1)^m\mu^{2m+1}(\mathbf{K}^2)^m\right]\mathbf{K}, \end{aligned}\right\} \tag{3.06}$$

where

$$\begin{aligned} \mathbf{I} &= \mathbf{s}+\mathbf{s}^{\dagger}, & \mathbf{J} &= \mathbf{s}-\mathbf{s}^{\dagger}, \\ \mathbf{K} &= \mathbf{t}+\mathbf{t}^{\dagger}, & \mathbf{L} &= \mathbf{t}-\mathbf{t}^{\dagger}, \\ \mathbf{s} &= \mathbf{F}^{\alpha}\mathbf{P}-\mathbf{P}\mathbf{F}^{\alpha}\mathbf{P}, \\ \mathbf{t} &= \mathbf{F}^{\beta}\mathbf{Q}-\mathbf{Q}\mathbf{F}^{\beta}\mathbf{Q}, \end{aligned}$$

and λ and μ are parameters which represent the curvatures of the descents of the ϵ_1 and ϵ_2 surfaces respectively and which satisfy

$$\frac{\partial}{\partial\lambda}(\delta\epsilon_1) = 0 \quad \text{and} \quad \frac{\partial}{\partial\mu}(\delta\epsilon_2) = 0. \tag{3.07}$$

The same formulae can be used for the minimization of E since for the descent of the E surface, $\mathbf{P}$ and $\mathbf{Q}$ have the same directions and rates of descent as for descents of the ϵ_1 and ϵ_2 surfaces. However, the curvatures are not the same and λ and μ must now be chosen so that

$$\frac{\partial}{\partial\lambda}(\delta E) = 0 \quad \text{and} \quad \frac{\partial}{\partial\mu}(\delta E) = 0, \tag{3.08}$$

and in this way second-order terms are taken into account. It can hardly be emphasized too much that equation (3.08) allows for the changes in $\mathbf{G}^{\alpha}$ and $\mathbf{G}^{\beta}$ due to the small changes $\delta\mathbf{P}$ and $\delta\mathbf{Q}$ in $\mathbf{P}$ and $\mathbf{Q}$, whereas to obtain equation (3.07) $\mathbf{G}^{\alpha}$ and $\mathbf{G}^{\beta}$ are taken as constant.

To obtain values for λ and μ, equations (3.06) are substituted in (3.03) and if cubic and higher powers of λ and μ are neglected this gives

$$\delta E = -\lambda^2 \operatorname{tr}(\mathbf{I}\,.\,\mathbf{J}\,.\,\mathbf{F}^{\alpha}) - \lambda \operatorname{tr}(\mathbf{I}\,.\,\mathbf{F}^{\alpha}) - \mu^2 \operatorname{tr}(\mathbf{K}\,.\,\mathbf{L}\,.\,\mathbf{F}^{\beta}) - \mu \operatorname{tr}(\mathbf{K}\,.\,\mathbf{F}^{\beta})$$

$$+\tfrac{1}{2}\lambda^2 \sum_{stuv}^{m} I_{st} I_{uv}[(su|tv)-(su|vt)] + \tfrac{1}{2}\mu^2 \sum_{stuv}^{m} K_{st} K_{uv}[(su|tv)-(su|vt)]$$

$$+\lambda\mu \sum_{stuv}^{m} I_{st} K_{uv}(su|tv) = -\lambda^2 a - \lambda b - \mu^2 a' - \mu b' + \tfrac{1}{2}\lambda^2 c + \tfrac{1}{2}\mu^2 c' + \lambda\mu d \qquad (3.09)$$

with the obvious notation.

The conditions (3.08) give

$$\left.\begin{aligned} \{d^2-(2a-c)(2a'-c')\}\lambda &= (2a-c)b+b'd, \\ \{d^2-(2a'-c')(2a-c)\}\mu &= (2a'-c')b'+bd. \end{aligned}\right\} \qquad (3.10)$$

4. The iteration procedure

The iteration procedure to calculate the bond order matrices by the method just described starts with approximate matrices $\mathbf{P}$ and $\mathbf{Q}$ and then iterates using (3.06) until there is consistency. However, even though $\mathbf{P}$ and $\mathbf{Q}$ may minimize E, they will not be the correct bond order matrices unless the conditions (2.06) are also satisfied. Thus it is most important that the original approximate matrices should satisfy these conditions and after each iteration the new matrices should also be made to satisfy them. The idempotency condition arises also in McWeeny's original treatment and the difficulty can be solved here in the same way. In practice, the other condition does not prove very troublesome and can be satisfied by making minor alterations to the diagonal elements of the matrices after each iteration.

The complete iteration procedure can now be summarized as follows:

(i) Starting with approximate 'guessed' matrices $\mathbf{P}(0)$ and $\mathbf{Q}(0)$ the matrices $\mathbf{F}^{\alpha}(0)$ and $\mathbf{F}^{\beta}(0)$ are calculated.

(ii) The matrices $\mathbf{I}$, $\mathbf{J}$, $\mathbf{K}$, $\mathbf{L}$, are found and the constants λ and μ determined from (3.06) and (3.10).

(iii) The improvement $\delta\mathbf{P}(0)$ in $\mathbf{P}(0)$ and $\delta\mathbf{Q}(0)$ in $\mathbf{Q}(0)$ will be given by

$$\delta\mathbf{P}(0) = -\lambda(\mathbf{1}+\lambda^2\mathbf{I}^2)^{-1}(\mathbf{I}+\lambda\mathbf{I}\mathbf{J}).$$

$$\delta\mathbf{Q}(0) = -\mu(\mathbf{1}+\mu^2\mathbf{K}^2)^{-1}(\mathbf{K}+\mu\mathbf{K}\mathbf{L}).$$

which are equivalent to (3.06).

(iv) The improved bond order matrices will be

$$\boldsymbol{\sigma}(0) = \mathbf{P}(0)+\delta\mathbf{P}(0); \quad \boldsymbol{\rho}(0) = \mathbf{Q}(0)+\delta\mathbf{Q}(0)$$

but in general $\boldsymbol{\sigma}(0)$ and $\boldsymbol{\rho}(0)$ will not be idempotent nor will their traces be correct. Idempotent matrices will be given by

$$\boldsymbol{\sigma}(1) = [\boldsymbol{\sigma}(0)]^2\,[3-2\boldsymbol{\sigma}(0)],$$

$$\boldsymbol{\rho}(1) = [\boldsymbol{\rho}(0)]^2\,[3-2\boldsymbol{\rho}(0)] \text{ (see reference [9]).}$$

The final step is to obtain matrices $\mathbf{P}(1)$ and $\mathbf{Q}(1)$ whose traces are correct by writing

$$\mathbf{P}(1) = \boldsymbol{\sigma}(1)+a\mathbf{1}; \quad \mathbf{Q}(1) = \boldsymbol{\rho}(1)+b\mathbf{1},$$

where a and b are the usually very small quantities

$$a=[p-\mathrm{tr}\,\boldsymbol{\sigma}(1)]/m, \quad b=[q-\mathrm{tr}\,\boldsymbol{\rho}(1)]/m.$$

(v) With these new values of **P** and **Q** the whole process is repeated until consistency is obtained.

Ideally (iv) should be repeated several times in each iteration until (2.06) are exactly satisfied but, in practice, it seems that to use it just once is sufficient.

5. Simplifications for π electron systems

The preceding results are perfectly general and apply to any system, but since the main purpose of this paper is to discuss conjugated hydrocarbon molecules it is appropriate at this point to consider the simplifications which can be made for π electron systems.

The obvious one is that only π electrons need be considered so that n is the number of π electrons and **H** represents the field due to the atom cores. If the usual Pariser and Parr approximations [10] are used together with the simplifications of Pople and Brickstock [11] and McWeeny [12], then $\mathbf{F}^{\alpha}$ and $\mathbf{F}^{\beta}$ have the much simpler form.

$$\left.\begin{aligned} F_{rs}{}^{\alpha} &= \beta_{rs}-\delta_{rs}\sum_{t\neq r}\gamma_{rt}+\delta_{rs}\sum_{t}(P_{tt}+Q_{tt})\gamma_{rt}-P_{rs}\gamma_{rs},\\ F_{rs}{}^{\beta} &= \beta_{rs}-\delta_{rs}\sum_{t\neq r}\gamma_{rt}+\delta_{rs}\sum_{t}(P_{tt}+Q_{tt})\gamma_{rt}-Q_{rs}\gamma_{rs}. \end{aligned}\right\} \quad (50.1)$$

The use of these approximations implies that the functions ω_r are chosen to be localized around the atom cores so that $(\mathbf{P}+\mathbf{Q})_{rr}$ will represent the total π electron charge and $(\mathbf{P}-\mathbf{Q})_{rr}$ the spin density at the atom core r. If the annihilator is used to improve the wave function then the predicted values for the charge and spin densities will change to $(\mathbf{R}+\mathbf{S})_{rr}$ and $(\mathbf{R}-\mathbf{S})_{rr}$.

6. 'Pairing of orbitals' in alternants

It is well known that Hückel theory and self-consistent theory predict that there will be unit π-electron charge on each atom core for many states of alternant molecules. The underlying reason for this is that the atoms in each molecule can be divided into two sets which means that for every orbital $\{a_{is}\}$ there is also a 'paired orbital' $\{\pm a_{is}\}$, the plus sign being used for atoms in one set and the minus sign for atoms in the other.

Pople and Brickstock [11] have shown that similar results apply to unrestricted calculations of doublet ground states of odd alternants but the same is also true for many other states as a simple extension of their proof shows. Using their methods, it is clear that if the matrices $\mathbf{F}^{\alpha}$ and $\mathbf{F}^{\beta}$ satisfy the relations

$$\left.\begin{aligned} F_{rs}{}^{\alpha} &= -F_{rs}{}^{\beta}, \quad r, s \text{ in same set},\\ F_{rs}{}^{\alpha} &= F_{rs}{}^{\beta}, \quad r, s \text{ in different sets}, \end{aligned}\right\} \quad (6.01)$$

then there will be a pairing between the occupied α-spin orbitals and the unoccupied β-spin orbitals and vice versa. This imposes on **P** and **Q** the conditions:

$$\left.\begin{aligned} P_{rs}+Q_{rs} &= \delta_{rs}, \quad r, s \text{ in same set},\\ P_{rs} &= Q_{rs}, \quad r, s \text{ in different sets}, \end{aligned}\right\} \quad (6.02)$$

and so for states in which (6.01) is satisfied the unrestricted method predicts uniform atomic charges.

To decide for which states of an alternant (6.01) holds, the eigenvalue equations (2.07) together with the simplification (5.01) should be examined. These show that if **P** and **Q** are being calculated by an iteration process and at any stage (6.01) and (6.02) are satisfied, then any first-order correction will not change this. Since the second-order terms of equation (3.03) are based on first-order ones, it follows that the conditions will remain satisfied throughout the iteration. It is always possible to begin an iteration using matrices based on the appropriate Hückel or self-consistent ones and so, assuming convergence, if the self-consistent method gives results which satisfy (6.01) and (6.02) for any state, then so will the unrestricted method. This means in particular that the lowest triplet states of even alternants will have unit π-electron charge on each atom and will therefore be non-polar.

There is also a ' pairing of orbitals ' theorem associated with the positive and negative ions of alternants. McLachlan [13] has pointed out that there are pairings between the occupied α-spin orbitals of the positive ion and the unoccupied β-spin orbitals of the negative ion and so on. Therefore the spin densities of the positive and negative ions are the same and the charges differ only in sign.

7. Ambiguity in the unrestricted bond orders

Hall [14] has pointed out that there is an ambiguity in the determination of self-consistent bond orders due to the fact that the same equations can often be obtained for the bond orders of several different states. A similar situation is found in the unrestricted method and can be illustrated by a calculation of the ground state of allyl. If the orbitals are chosen to have the form:

$$\left.\begin{aligned} \psi_1 &= (2+K^2)^{-1/2}\omega_1 + K(2+K^2)^{-1/2}\omega_2 + (2+K^2)^{-1/2}\omega_3, \\ \psi_2 &= 2^{-1/2}\omega_1 - 2^{-1/2}\omega_3, \\ \phi_1 &= (2+L^2)^{-1/2}\omega_1 + L(2+L^2)^{-1/2}\omega_2 + (2+K^2)^{-1/2}\omega_3 \end{aligned}\right\} \qquad (7.01)$$

then from (3.01) it follows that $KL=2$. The equation determining L will be

$$L^4 + 2L^3(\gamma_1 - \gamma_{12}) + 2L(2\gamma_{12} - \gamma_{13} - \gamma_1) - 4 = 0, \qquad (7.02)$$

where all the β_{rs} integrals are taken to be zero except that $\beta_{12} = \beta_{23} = 0{\cdot}5$ (in units of $\beta = -4{\cdot}79$ ev). The quartic equation for L has two real roots and taking the reduced values of the Pariser and Parr integrals, the real roots will be

$$L = +2 \quad \text{or} \quad -1{\cdot}21,$$

which give (7.03)

$$K = +1 \quad \text{or} \quad -1{\cdot}65.$$

The positive values correspond to the ground state but the negative values satisfy the same equations. Thus there still remains ambiguity even though the form of the orbitals was specified very closely by (7.01). Denoting the orbitals in order of their energies as 1, 2, 3 for α-spin and 1′, 2′, 3′ for β-spin, the ground state will be [12, 1′] and the bond orders which satisfy the same equations as those of the ground state correspond to [23, 2′]. If this treatment had begun with the general equations while still retaining (6.02) there would be further ambiguity due to the state [13, 2′]. In a perfectly general treatment there would also be solutions associated with states such as [12, 2′] for which there is no pairing of orbitals.

8. Perturbation calculation of P and Q

It would be very desirable to have a method for calculating approximate unrestricted bond order matrices and at first sight the perturbation theory of Coulson and Longuett-Higgins [15] seems an obvious way to do this. In the ions and triplet states of alternant hydrocarbons, for example, the unrestricted M.O.'s might be expected to be close to the self consistent ones. If this were so the $\mathbf{P}$ and $\mathbf{Q}$ of the unrestricted method could be calculated from the self consistent M.O.'s with the exchange terms in $\mathbf{G}^{\alpha}$ and $\mathbf{G}^{\beta}$ treated as perturbations.

McLachlan [13] has used such a method to calculate spin densities in the ions of alternant hydrocarbons. Applying his method to a negative ion, the major contribution to the spin density is due to the lowest antibonding self-consistent M.O. but there will be a correction to this due to the difference in exchange terms in $\mathbf{G}^{\alpha}$ and $\mathbf{G}^{\beta}$ and this can be found using perturbation theory. Unfortunately, if Hückel polarizabilities are used, perturbation theory has to be applied several times since any changes in $\mathbf{P}$ and $\mathbf{Q}$ cause further changes in $\mathbf{G}^{\alpha}$ and $\mathbf{G}^{\beta}$ and these can be significant. This is not because they are very large but because they alter the relative magnitude of the perturbation at different atoms and their effect is accumulative.

For the negative ion of naphthalene, perturbation theory has to be applied at least six times before $\mathbf{P}$ and $\mathbf{Q}$ and $\mathbf{F}^{\alpha}$ and $\mathbf{F}^{\beta}$ are reasonably consistent and therefore McLachlan's calculations in which perturbation theory is used once only, while qualitatively correct, are not very accurate quantitatively. The situation may be improved by using self-consistent polarizabilities (they are usually very different from Hückel ones, see reference [9]) but these are not readily available. With Hückel polarizabilities, the calculations are really too tedious even though the final results are in fair agreement with the correct ones reported in § 10.

9. Parameters and Calculations

The iteration procedure of § 4 was used to obtain the unrestricted bond order matrices for the ions and triplet states of naphthalene, anthracene, phenenthrene and azulene. The whole calculation was programmed for the University of London 'Mercury' computer and the approximations of § 5 were used.

The parameters for the alternants were taken from previous papers [10, 13, 17, 18] and a few of these parameters were also satisfactory for azulene. In this molecule, some of the more distant integrals γ_{rs} were not available and had to be estimated using an inverse distance approximation, while for the integrals involving next-nearest neighbours which were also unavailable a rather more sophisticated approximation [19] was needed giving the values $-1{\cdot}222\beta$ in the five-membered ring; $-1{\cdot}105\beta$ in the seven-membered ring; and $-1{\cdot}132\beta$ between the two rings.

To begin the iterations, the initial matrices were based on the appropriate Hückel orbitals and to give accuracy to three decimal places took about 10 iterations and 30 min machine time for naphthalene and azulene and correspondingly longer for the larger molecules. The machine time used was about twice as much as for a corresponding ground state calculation (see [18]) as might be expected. The results of the calculations of the bond order matrices given in the following section are correct to three decimals for the ten membered rings but for the 14 membered rings, to conserve machine time, the iterations were stopped sooner, so there may be slight error in the third decimal place. This does not affect any other quantity since $\langle S^2 \rangle$, $\langle S^4 \rangle$ and energy values were given accurately to several decimals after a very few iterations.

Without doubt the amount of time used in these calculations could be reduced. For example, in the triplet states of the alternants, equation (6.01) shows that only one of the matrices $\mathbf{P}$ and $\mathbf{Q}$ is independent so that the iterations could proceed with one bond order matrix only, reducing the calculation time by about a half. Also the symmetrical properties of the matrices could be used to halve the number of matrix elements involved with a corresponding decrease in computing time. A further improvement would be to choose better initial matrices since those based on the Hückel orbitals do not turn out to be very good approximations.

Several checks and trial runs were made to test both the programme and method of calculation. In one of these the bond order matrices for the allyl radical were calculated and compared with the results of § 7. As a more complete check the bond order matrices of the naphthalene ion were computed to about four-figure accuracy and then used to form $\mathbf{F}^{\alpha}$ and $\mathbf{F}^{\beta}$. The eigenvectors of these matrices were then found and the appropriate number recombined to form $\mathbf{P}$ and $\mathbf{Q}$. The agreement between the initial and final bond order matrices was nowhere worse than 0·00005.

10. Charges and spin densities

The spin densities and net charges at the carbon atoms for the positive ions of naphthalene, anthracene and phenanthrene and for the positive and negative ions of azulene are given in the following tables. From § 6 it follows that the spin densities in the negative ions of the alternants will be the same as in the positive ions while the charges change only in sign. Azulene, however, is not an alternant and, as can be seen from results, its positive and negative ions are completely different. Two sets of spin densities are given for each molecule. Those before annihilation (B.A.) are associated with the wave function Ψ while those after a single annihilation (A.S.A.) are associated with Ψ' and are given by $(\mathbf{R}-\mathbf{S})_{rr}$.

Corresponding to these two sets of spin densities are two sets of charges but it is found that annihilation changes the charges hardly at all and so only the charges before annihilation are given.

The hydrogen hyperfine splittings at different ring positions in the naphthalene and anthracene ions have recently been measured by Carrington [20]. These are proportional to the spin density on the nearest carbon atom [21] and using the constant of proportionality suggested by work on the benzene negative ion [22] experimental values for the spin densities can be found. If these are compared with the theoretical values it will be seen that the qualitative agreement is good and the quantitative agreement less so. The main error occurs at position 2 in both molecules where the theoretical spin densities are much too low. It is interesting to note that in these two molecules the use of the annihilator improves the agreement with experiment.

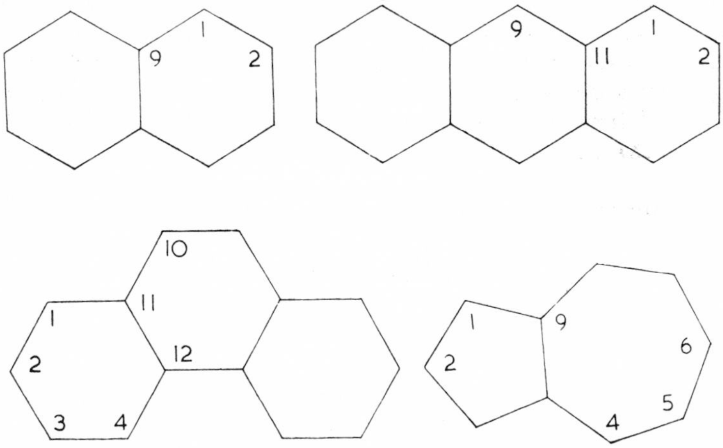

Numbering system for the molecules.

Naphthalene positive ion

Atom	1	2	9
Spin density B.A.	0·269	0·021	−0·081
Spin density A.S.A.	0·243	0·032	−0·055
Spin density Exp. [20]	0·218	0·081	−0·098
Net charge	+0·179	+0·101	−0·061

Anthracene positive ion

Atom	1	2	9	11
Spin density B.A.	0·143	0·010	0·328	−0·067
Spin density A.S.A.	0·126	0·018	0·298	−0·043
Spin density Exp. [20]	0·122	0·070	0·247	−0·065
Net charge	0·089	0·090	0·206	−0·031

Phenanthrene positive ion

Atom	1	2	3	4	10	11	12
Spin density B.A.	0·229	−0·118	0·178	−0·014	0·216	−0·039	0·047
Spin density A.S.A.	0·190	−0·079	0·147	0·005	0·209	−0·014	0·042
Net charge	0·111	0·038	0·134	0·058	0·176	−0·023	0·005

Azulene positive ion

Atom	1	2	4	5	6	9
Spin density B.A.	0·432	−0·195	−0·068	0·185	−0·111	0·104
Spin density A.S.A.	0·398	−0·133	−0·042	0·149	−0·075	0·099
Net charges	0·126	0·017	0·150	0·113	0·137	0·032

Azulene negative ion

Atom	1	2	4	5	6	9
Spin density B.A.	0·015	0·103	0·351	−0·229	0·457	0·083
Spin density A.S.A.	0·012	0·088	0·306	−0·154	0·416	0·084
Net charges	−0·165	−0·157	−0·027	−0·065	−0·139	−0·095

If the charges are considered, the theory predicts negative charges on all the carbon atoms in the azulene negative ion and positive charges in the positive ion. On the other hand, for the positive ions of the alternants the results rather surprisingly show negative charges at some positions. Nevertheless the general effect is for each atom to have positive charge as might be expected.

Results have also been obtained for the lowest π triplet states of the same molecules. The net charge on each carbon atom in the alternants is zero, as in the ground state, but the non-alternant azulene molecule has different charges in its ground and lowest triplet states. Spin densities both before and after a single annihilation are given but again it is found that annihilation does not change the charges.

Naphthalene triplet

Atom	1	2	9
Spin density B.A.	0·488	0·098	−0·174
Spin density A.S.A.	0·470	0·096	−0·132

Anthracene triplet

Atom	1	2	9	11
Spin density B.A.	0·184	0·060	0·658	−0·074
Spin density A.S.A.	0·170	0·057	0·648	−0·049

Phenanthrene triplet

Atom	1	2	3	4	10	11	12
Spin density B.A.	0·350	−0·194	0·292	−0·098	0·644	−0·178	0·184
Spin density A.S.A.	0·314	−0·147	0·254	−0·070	0·623	−0·133	0·159

Azulene triplet

Atom	1	2	4	5	6	9
Spin density B.A.	0·478	−0·136	0·355	−0·111	0·432	0·131
Spin density A.S.A.	0·457	−0·096	0·331	−0·076	0·407	0·133
Net charge	0·100	−0·132	−0·063	0·101	−0·100	−0·021
Ground state charges	−0·112	0·010	0·130	−0·044	0·084	−0·021

The results for the naphthalene ion and lowest triplet may be compared with recent open-shell calculations by Hoyland and Goodman [23]. The spin densities given by the two calculations are different of course, since the open-shell method cannot give rise to negative spin densities. In this sense, therefore, the unrestricted method is the better one. The net charges predicted by the two methods are in good agreement, the open-shell calculations also giving zero net charge on each carbon atom in the triplet state and negative charge at the γ position in the positive ion.

11. Spin properties

If the unrestricted wave function is written formally as in equation (2.08) then by using the normalizing condition and the expectation values of S^2 and S^4, upper bounds on the values of $c_1, c_2, \ldots$ can be obtained which in turn give a lower bound to c_0. In practice, for c_0, c_1 and c_2 these bounds will be almost exactly the actual values of the coefficients but the upper bounds to the remaining coefficients will not be so good. The estimated values of c_0^2, c_1^2, c_2^2 for the various unrestricted wave functions are given in table 1. The best estimate for c_3^2 which can be obtained from $\langle S^2 \rangle$ and $\langle S^4 \rangle$ is about a half of the value given for c_2^2 with correspondingly smaller values for the remaining coefficients. However, these are likely to overestimate the weights of the higher spin states.

Molecular state	c_0^2	c_1^2	c_2^2
Allyl radical	0·9628	0·0372	0
Naphthalene positive ion	0·9828	0·0170	0·0001
Anthracene positive ion	0·9792	0·0207	0·0001
Phenanthrene positive ion	0·9723	0·0273	0·0002
Azulene positive ion	0·9716	0·0280	0·0002
Azulene negative ion	0·9551	0·0441	0·0004
Naphthalene lowest π triplet	0·9805	0·0193	0·0001
Anthacene lowest π triplet	0·9866	0·0132	0·0001
Phenanthrene lowest π triplet	0·9469	0·0509	0·0011
Azulene lowest π triplet	0·9791	0·0207	0·0001

Table 1. Relative weights of spin states in single determinant wave functions.

From table 1 it can be seen that only c_0^2 and c_1^2 are large and c_2^2 is very small in comparison. Therefore except possibly for the lowest triplet state of phenanthrene the assumptions involved in equations (2.10) and (2.12) are satisfied for all the wave functions considered in this paper.

Table 2 shows the expectation values of S^2 corresponding to the wave function Ψ' and to the wave function after the annihilation of the spin state Ψ'_{2s+3}. The annihilation considerably improves the value of $\langle S^2 \rangle$ but it cannot reduce it completely to the correct value since Ψ'_{2s+5}, Ψ'_{2s+7}, etc. will still be present in the wave function.

Molecular state	S	$\langle S^2 \rangle$ for Ψ'	$\langle S^2 \rangle$ for Ψ''
Allyl radical	$\frac{1}{2}$	0·8612	0·75
Naphthalene positive ion	$\frac{1}{2}$	0·8011	0·7523
Anthracene positive ion	$\frac{1}{2}$	0·8160	0·7548
Phenanthrene positive ion	$\frac{1}{2}$	0·8320	0·7550
Azulene positive ion	$\frac{1}{2}$	0·8340	0·7547
Azulene negative ion	$\frac{1}{2}$	0·8822	0·7596
Naphthalene lowest π triplet	1	2·0770	2·0027
Anthracene lowest π triplet	1	2·0530	2·0025
Phenanthrene lowest π triplet	1	2·2038	2·0295
Azulene lowest π triplet	1	2·0828	2·0029

Table 2. $\langle S^2 \rangle$ before and after a single annihilation.

12. Energies

When the bond order matrices are known the total energy can be calculated from equation (2.03). If the ground-state energies are also known (for details of calculation see [18]), then triplet excitation energies and ionization potentials can be found. It is also interesting to use equation (2.10) to find the energy after a single annihilation and this will lead to different values for the excitation energies and ionization potentials.

The triplet excitation energies both before and after a single annihilation are shown in table 3 together with experimental values. The agreement with experiment is not particularly good but this is only to be expected when small differences between large quantities are being calculated. The results are in any case not noticably worse than those of other calculations [16, 24, 25] even though some of these were able to use adjustable parameters to improve agreement with experiment.

Molecule	Excitation energies (ev)		
	B.A.	A.S.A.	Experimental
Naphthalene	$2{\cdot}50_0$	$2{\cdot}38_0$	2·64[26]
Anthracene	$1{\cdot}44_2$	$1{\cdot}36_0$	1·82[26]
Phenanthrene	$2{\cdot}41_8$	$2{\cdot}29_2$	2·67[26]
Azulene	$1{\cdot}15_8$	$1{\cdot}08_5$	—

Table 3. Triplet excitation energies.

The ionization potentials cannot be obtained as directly as the excitation energies since the total energies for the ions and for the ground states are calculated using different zero energy levels. To allow for this β_{rr} should be added to the difference between the total energies in the ground state and in the ion. Although it would be possible to calculate β_{rr} it seems better to find it empirically. It has therefore been chosen to give the best agreement between the calculated ionization potentials of naphthalene, anthracene and phenanthrene and the recent experimental values obtained by Wacks and Dibeler [27]. In this way there will be two possible values of β_{rr} depending on whether energies before or after a single annihilation are used; the difference between them will of course represent the averaged lowering of the total energy of the ions obtained by using the annihilator. In table 4 the calculated and experimental ionization potentials are given. The agreement between them is good and is improved when energies after a single annihilation are used.

The value obtained for β_{rr} using energies before annihilation was 4·132 ev and using energies after a single annihilation, 4·242 ev.

Molecule	Ionization potentials (ev)		
	B.A.	A.S.A.	Experimental
Allyl	$8{\cdot}51_9$	$8{\cdot}72_3$	9·05[28]
Naphthalene	$8{\cdot}29_0$	$8{\cdot}22_8$	8·26[27]
Anthracene	$7{\cdot}47_4$	$7{\cdot}54_7$	7·55[27]
Phenanthrene	$8{\cdot}07_5$	$8{\cdot}06_4$	8·03[27]
Azulene	$7{\cdot}23_2$	$7{\cdot}27_9$	—

Table 4. Ionization potentials.

13. Conclusion

It is difficult to draw any general conclusions from the results presented in this paper since there are few experimental values available for comparison. It does seem clear, however, that the unrestricted Hartree–Fock method can give good qualitative agreement with experiment for various properties. In this, the unrestricted wave function is an improvement on other single determinant wave functions since it can give lower energy values and predicts negative spin densities at some atoms.

The quantitive agreement with experiment is quite good for most properties but the obvious exception is in the calculation of spin densities, some of which are predicted to be far too small. On reflection this is not very surprising for the unrestricted wave function is not an eigenfunction of spin and so it might be expected that spin properties would be predicted rather poorly. The fact that the use of a single annihilator improves the spin densities tends to confirm this view. Presumably if the bond order matrices were obtained by minimizing (2.10) instead of (2.03), i.e. if extended bond order matrices with A_s were found, then the calculated spin densities would be much better.

The author would like to express his thanks to Dr. G. G. Hall for much helpful advice and encouragement, to the Department of Scientific and Industrial Research for the award of a Research Grant and to Dr. R. A. Buckingham for permission to use the University of London computer.

References

[1] Pople, J. A., and Nesbet, R. K., 1954, *J. chem. Phys.*, **22,** 571.
[2] Löwdin, P. O., 1954, *Symposium on Molecular Physics, Nikko* (Tokyo: Maruzen), p. 13.
[3] Hurst, R. P., Gray, J. D., Brigman, G. H., and Matsen, F. A., 1958, *Mol. Phys.*, **1,** 189.
[4] Nesbet, R. K., 1960, *Phys. Rev.*, **107,** 1002.
[5] Löwdin, P. O., 1955, *Phys. Rev.*, **97,** 1509.
[6] Marshall, W., 1961, *Proc. phys. Soc., Lond.*, **78,** 113.
[7] Amos, A. T., and Hall, G. G., 1961, *Proc. roy. Soc.* A, **263,** 483.
[8] Roothaan, C. C. J., 1951, *Rev. mod. Phys.*, **23,** 69.
[9] McWeeny, R., 1956, *Proc. roy. Soc.* A, **235,** 496; **237,** 355.
[10] Pariser, R., and Parr, R. G., 1953, *J. chem. Phys.*, **21,** 466, 767.
[11] Brickstock, A., and Pople, J. A., 1954, *Trans. Faraday Soc.*, **50,** 901.
[12] McWeeny, R., 1955, *Tech. Rep.* No. 1, Solid State and Molecular Theory Group, M.I.T.
[13] McLachlan, A. D., 1960, *Mol. Phys.*, **3,** 233.
[14] Hall, G. G., 1960, *J. chem. Phys.*, **33,** 953.
[15] Coulson, C. A., and Longuet-Higgins, H. C., 1947, *Proc. roy. Soc.* A, **191,** 39; **192,** 16.
[16] Pariser, R., 1956, *J. chem. Phys.*, **24,** 250.
[17] McWeeny, R., and Peacock, T. E., 1957, *Proc. phys. Soc., Lond.*, A, **70,** 41.
[18] Amos, A. T., and Hall, G. G., 1961, *Mol. Phys.*, **4,** 25.
[19] Parr, R. G., 1960, *J. chem. Phys.*, **33,** 1184.
[20] Carrington, A., Dravnieks, F., and Symons, M. C. R., 1959, *J. chem. Soc.*, p. 947.
[21] McConnell, H. M., and Chesnut, D. B., 1958, *J. chem. Phys.*, **28,** 107.
[22] Weissman, S. I., Tuttle, T. R., and De Boer, E., 1957, *J. phys. Chem.*, **61,** 28; McConnell, H. M., and Dearman, H. H., 1958, *J. chem. Phys.*, **28,** 51.
[23] Hoyland, J. R., and Goodman, L., 1961, *J. chem. Phys.*, **34,** 1446.
[24] Pariser, R., 1956, *J. chem. Phys.*, **25,** 1112.
[25] Hall, G. G., 1952, *Proc. roy. Soc.* A, **213,** 113.
[26] McClure, D. S., 1949, *J. chem. Phys.*, **17,** 905.
[27] Wacks, M. E., and Dibeler, V. H., 1959, *J. chem. Phys.*, **31,** 1557.
[28] Evans, M. G., and Szwarc, M., 1951, *J. chem. Phys.*, **19,** 1322.

Communicated 7 June 1961 by Erik Hulthén and Oskar Klein

Different MO approximations applied to aniline

By Inga Fischer-Hjalmars

1. Introduction and summary

Theoretical investigations of the electronic structure of comparatively complicated molecules seem to be of increasing importance in widely differing contexts, from the small inorganic molecules and ions to the organic macromolecules of vital importance in biology. In these cases it cannot be hoped to carry through complete theoretical calculations in the near future. Approaches towards theoretical determination of structure may nevertheless be extremely valuable for the understanding of the behaviour of these molecules, cf. e.g. the interpretations of biological processes from theoretical considerations, given recently by Grabe [1] and by B. and A. Pullman *et al.* [2]. On account of the far-reaching importance of such interpretations it would be most useful to obtain as much information as possible about the accuracy and limitations of the approximations necessarily involved in such calculations.

The approximation most widely applied is the Hückel approximation, with or without inclusion of overlap. In a smaller number of cases the comparatively more elaborate Pariser-Parr-Pople treatment [3, 4] has been applied. A comparison between these semi-empirical methods and the purely theoretical π-electron approach has hitherto been carried out in only a few cases, e.g. for ethylene, butadiene and benzene by Pariser and Parr [3]. This comparison gives much insight into the merits and limitations of the different methods of calculating the spectrum. Such ground state properties as ionization potentials and bond orders have been investigated and thoroughly discussed by Pople [4] and others, who used the two above-mentioned semi-empirical methods for the calculations. However, there does not seem to exist any detailed comparison between ground state properties (e.g. ionization potential and dipole moment) calculated by the purely theoretical method, and by the semi-empirical methods. Furthermore, calculations of both ground state properties and spectrum for the same molecule by the same semi-empirical approach seem to be very scarce.

Previously, the present author carried out a purely theoretical study of the ground state of the aniline molecule, $C_6H_5NH_2$ [5]. It seemed appropriate therefore to supplement this investigation by semi-empirical calculations. Besides, it appeared to be of interest to extend the purely theoretical treatment of aniline to excited states, to make possible a comparison between the different methods with regard to the spectrum also. On account of the unwieldy numerical work, the purely theoretical calculations for the excited states of aniline could not be extended to include complete superposition of configurations. Only the two simplest cases, i.e. with one single configuration and with superposition of two configurations, could be included.

The present investigation shows that the Hückel method will give satisfactory results for several ground state properties, when the semi-empirical parameters are carefully chosen. It is found, however, that the finer details of the electron distribution in the ground state and of the spectrum are not given correctly by this method. On the other hand, the Pariser-Parr-Pople method is shown to give very promising agreement with experiment both for ground state properties and for the spectrum, with the same parameter choice.

Some interesting features of the electronic structure of aniline have also been obtained. It is, for example, shown that the *ortho* atom has twice as big a charge as the *para* atom, a property shared by most compounds of the form C_6H_5X, as shown elsewhere by the author [6]. Moreover, it has been found that the lowest excited state of aniline corresponds very closely to the $^1B_{2u}$ state of benzene and that the next higher state of aniline is composed of about 60 % of the $^1B_{1u}$ state of benzene and 40 % of a charge transfer state, in good agreement with the results of Murrell [7], obtained by other methods.

2. Methods of calculation

The particle system to be investigated in the present study is the π-electron system of the aniline molecule $C_6H_5NH_2$. Three different methods of calculation will be considered, i.e., in order of increasing complexity:

(I) the Hückel method;

(II) the Pariser-Parr-Pople method;

(III) the purely theoretical method.

All three methods are molecular orbital (MO) methods with different kinds of approximations introduced to make the calculations at all feasible. In all methods the LCAO (linear combination of atomic orbitals) approximation will be used.

The Hamiltonian operator for the π-electrons is, in atomic units:

$$H = \sum_t H_t^{\text{core}} + \sum_{t>s} r_{st}^{-1}, \tag{1}$$

where s,t indicate the number of an electron, and the sums are to be taken over all π-electrons of the system. The one-electron operator H_t^{core} of (1) is (subscript t dropped):

$$H^{\text{core}} = T + \sum_k U_k. \tag{2}$$

In (2) T is the kinetic energy operator. U_k stands for the potential from nucleus k plus the σ-electrons of atom k. According to methods I and II, the sum over k is to be taken over all atoms with π-electrons, i.e., in the present case, over the six carbon atoms (one π-electron each) and the nitrogen atom (two π-electrons). In accordance with the method III, as applied in the previous aniline investigation [5], the sum over k has to include the seven hydrogen atoms as well.

In the Hartree-Fock approximation the eigenfunction Ψ_0 of the ground state of (1) can be written as a Slater determinant of one-electron molecular orbitals $\varphi_i(t)$. According to the LCAO approximation it is supposed that $\varphi_i(t)$ can be written:

$$\varphi_i(t) = \sum_{\mu} \chi_\mu(t) c_{\mu i}, \tag{3}$$

where χ_μ is an atomic orbital, localized to the atom μ. In conformity with all three methods I, II and III the sum in (3) should be taken over all atoms with π-electrons, i.e., in the present case, over seven atoms. The coefficients $c_{\mu i}$ are determined by the Hartree-Fock equations:

$$\sum_{\nu} (F_{\mu\nu} - \varepsilon_i S_{\mu\nu}) c_{\nu i} = 0. \tag{4}$$

S is the overlap matrix with the elements

$$S_{\mu\nu} = \int \chi_\mu^* \chi_\nu \, d\tau. \tag{5}$$

According to methods I and II it is assumed that S is a unity matrix:

$$S_{\mu\nu} = \delta_{\mu\nu} \quad \text{(methods I and II)}. \tag{6}$$

F of (4) is the one-electron Fock operator, represented by a quadratic matrix $F_{\mu\nu}$, and the parameters ε_i are the eigenvalues of F. The matrix elements of F are (ground state with two electrons in all occupied space orbitals):

$$F_{\mu\nu} = H_{\mu\nu}^{\text{core}} + 2 J_{\mu\nu} - K_{\mu\nu}. \tag{7}$$

$H_{\mu\nu}^{\text{core}}$ are the matrix elements of the operator (2) in the atomic orbital representation. The operators J and K, representing the electronic interaction, have the following matrix elements:

$$J_{\mu\nu} = \sum_i J(\mu\nu \mid ii), \tag{8}$$

$$K_{\mu\nu} = \sum_i K(\mu i \mid i\nu), \tag{9}$$

where the sums are to be taken over all filled molecular space orbitals φ_i, i.e. four in the present case. The new symbols, introduced in (8) and (9), are defined as follows:

$$J(\varkappa\lambda \mid ij) = \int \psi_\varkappa^*(1)\, \psi_\lambda(1)\, r_{12}^{-1}\, \varphi_i^*(2)\, \varphi_j(2)\, d\tau_1\, d\tau_2, \tag{10}$$

$$K(\varkappa i \mid j\lambda) = \int \psi_\varkappa^*(1)\, \varphi_i(1)\, r_{12}^{-1}\, \varphi_j^*(2)\, \psi_\lambda(2)\, d\tau_1\, d\tau_2. \tag{11}$$

In the atomic orbital representation of (8) and (9) $\psi_\varkappa$ and ψ_λ of (10) and (11) are atomic orbitals χ_μ, χ_ν. When the expressions (10) and (11) are used below for the description of excited states, they will be given in a molecular orbital representation. In that context $\psi_\varkappa$, ψ_λ will be molecular orbitals φ_m, φ_n, making (10) and (11) identical in principle. However, provided $i = j$ or $m = n$, it will still be meaningful to distinguish between (10) and (11).

The coefficients $c_{\mu i}$ of (3) are determined by the variational principle, leading to the secular equation:

$$\mathrm{Det}\{F_{\mu\nu}-\varepsilon S_{\mu\nu}\}=0. \tag{12}$$

(12) is an equation of the seventh degree in ε. To each root ε_j corresponds one set of coefficients $c_{\mu j}$, i.e. one MO φ_j of (3).

To solve the equation (12) the matrix elements of (2) and the electron interaction integrals over atomic orbitals, occurring in (10) and (11), must be known. The way of determining these integrals is different for each of the three different methods. In the Hückel method (I) the operators J and K of (7) are not written down explicitly and the first term should be looked upon as an effective one-electron Hamiltonian operator H^{eff}. The matrix elements of this operator are as usual denoted in the following way:

$$\alpha_\mu=\int\chi_\mu^* H^{\text{eff}}\chi_\mu\,d\tau, \tag{13}$$

$$\beta_{\mu\nu}=\int\chi_\mu^* H^{\text{eff}}\chi_\nu\,d\tau, \tag{14}$$

and the values of α and β are determined semi-empirically. Knowing these values, one can solve (12) and directly obtain the MO's (3).

In both the Pariser-Parr-Pople method (II) and the purely theoretical method (III) the one-electron integrals,

$$W_\mu=\int\chi_\mu^* H^{\text{core}}\chi_\mu\,d\tau, \tag{15}$$

$$\beta_{\mu\nu}=\int\chi_\mu^* H^{\text{core}}\chi_\nu\,d\tau, \tag{16}$$

as well as the two-electron integrals over atomic orbitals,

$$(\varkappa\lambda\,|\,\mu\nu)=\int\chi_\varkappa^*(1)\,\chi_\lambda(1)\,r_{12}^{-1}\,\chi_\mu^*(2)\,\chi_\nu(2)\,d\tau_1\,d\tau_2, \tag{17}$$

must be known. Moreover, the matrix elements (8) and (9) of the operators J and K will be functions of the $c_{\mu i}$'s. So one has to apply a self-consistent field treatment to obtain the final solution of (12), giving the SCF MO's of (3).

3. Method I: the Hückel method

As mentioned above this method is a semi-empirical one, in which the values of the parameters α and β of (13) and (14) are obtained from experimental data. In the present investigation this parameter choice has been made as follows.

In the present study of aniline by semi-empirical methods, benzene has been chosen as a reference molecule. Consequently, the experimental values of the ionization potential (IP) and the spectrum of this molecule have been used to determine α_{C} and β_{CC}. As is well known, according to the Hückel method, the orbital energies of the benzene orbitals are given by the expressions listed in Table 1.

Table 1. Orbital energies of benzene according to the Hückel method.

Orbital	Orbital energy ε_i
φ_3	$\alpha_C - 2\beta_{CC}$
$\varphi_2, \varphi_{\bar{2}}$	$\alpha_C - \beta_{CC}$
$\varphi_1, \varphi_{\bar{1}}$	$\alpha_C + \beta_{CC}$
φ_0	$\alpha_C + 2\beta_{CC}$

In the ground state the three orbitals φ_0, φ_1, and $\varphi_{\bar{1}}$ are doubly occupied. The first vertical ionization potential IP is therefore given by:

$$-9.24 \text{ ev} = -\text{IP} = \varepsilon_1 = \alpha_C + \beta_{CC}. \tag{18}$$

Besides, the first excited state (fourfold degenerate) lies in this approximation $-2\beta_{CC}$ above the ground state. This energy should be equal to the position of the weighted mean value of the three lowest excited singlet and triplet states of benzene, cf. e.g. [8]:

$$-2\beta_{CC} = 5.20 \text{ ev}. \tag{19}$$

For the assignment of a value to β_{CN} it has been supposed that the ratio β_{CC}/β_{CN} should be the same in methods I and II, i.e., irrespective of whether (14) or (16) is used for the definition of β. In this way a value of β_{CN} for the Hückel method has been found by means of the corresponding value of Pariser-Parr-Pople method II. Both methods also include the assumption that $\beta_{\mu\nu} = 0$, when μ and ν are non-neighbours. Finally, it is supposed to be reasonable to put α_N equal to the value of W_N, determined by method II:

$$\alpha_N = W_N \text{ of (26)}. \tag{20}$$

The value of (20) is of course somewhat arbitrary, but the choice $\alpha_N = \alpha_C + \beta_{CC}$, for example, would lead to almost the same result. The values (18), (19), and (20) are supposed to be our best choices for the Hückel parameters, and in what follows, the Hückel method with these parameter values is denoted as method I*a*. Another choice of Hückel parameters has also been made, as discussed in Section 5 below. This second choice is denoted as method I*b*. The numerical values of the parameters of methods I*a* and I*b* are collected in Table 2.

Table 2. Semi-empirical parameter values, pertinent to Hückel methods I*a* and I*b*.

Parameter	Method I*a* (cf. formulae (18), (19), (20))		Method I*b* (cf. Section 5)	
	ev	a.u.	ev	a.u.
β_{CC}	−2.60	−0.0956	− 2.39	−0.088
α_C	−6.64	−0.2440	−11.28	−0.415
β_{CN}	−1.58	−0.0581	− 2.74	−0.101
α_N	−8.97	−0.3297	−16.55	−0.608

4. Method II: the Pariser-Parr-Pople method

This method is a semi-empirical one also, and here all the one-electron and some of the two-electron integrals are determined from experimental data. A possible way of choosing these integral values is discussed elsewhere by the present author [6]. These suggestions will now be applied to the case of aniline.

The two-electron integrals of interest are given by the common formula (17). As a consequence of the assumption in [3, 4] that the atomic orbitals satisfy not only (6), but also have vanishing differential overlap, only Coulomb integrals will be different from zero. The integrals (17) will therefore be of only two kinds, one-centre integrals $(\mu\mu|\mu\mu)$ and two-centre integrals $(\mu\mu|\nu\nu)$. In [6] it is suggested that the one-centre integral should be computed from the expression:

$$(\mu\mu|\mu\mu) = F_0 + 4\,F_2, \tag{21}$$

where the notations of Condon and Shortley [9] are used. F_2 should be determined from the spectrum of the neutral atom; F_0 from the ionization potential IP(μ) and the electron affinity EA(μ) of the atom in its ground state and the following relations in [6]:

$$\begin{aligned} \mathrm{IP(C)} - \mathrm{EA(C)} &= F_0 - 5\,F_2, \\ \mathrm{IP(N)} - \mathrm{EA(N)} &= F_0 + 10\,F_2. \end{aligned} \tag{22}$$

The two-centre integrals $(\mu\mu|\nu\nu)$ have been calculated in the way suggested by Pariser and Parr [3], i.e. for large distances by means of the uniformly charged sphere model and for the shortest distances by means of the polynomial formula

$$(\mu\mu|\nu\nu) = C_1 + C_2 r + C_3 r^2. \tag{23}$$

C_1 in (23) is the mean value of $(\mu\mu|\mu\mu)$ and $(\nu\nu|\nu\nu)$, determined from (21). C_2 and C_3 are determined by means of two large-distance integrals between the same kinds of atoms μ and ν, as in (23).

As mentioned in Section 3, benzene has been chosen as a reference substance for the present aniline investigation. Experimental data for benzene have therefore been used for the determination of the integrals W_C of (15) and β_{CC} of (16). Again, spectral data have been used for the determination of β_{CC}, and the ionization potential to determine W_C. In this approximation the excitation energy for the lowest singlet and triplet states of benzene are functions of β and the two-electron Coulomb integrals, cf. e.g. [3]. When using (21) and the uniformly charged sphere model, the best fit to all the experimental values of the excited states was obtained with

$$\left.\begin{aligned} \beta_{CC}(r = 1.397\ \text{Å}) &= -2.437\ \text{ev}, \\ (\mu\mu|\nu\nu)\ (r = 1.397\ \text{Å}) &= 6.972\ \text{ev}. \end{aligned}\right\} \tag{24}$$

The value of $(\mu\mu|\nu\nu)$ in (24), being slightly different from that computed according to (23), was adopted in order to obtain as good a reproduction of the benzene spectrum as possible.

To obtain W_C the expression for the orbital energy ε_1, corresponding to the degenerate pair of orbitals φ_1, $\varphi_{\bar{1}}$ of Table 1, should be calculated. It is easily found to be

$$\varepsilon_1 = W_C + \beta_{CC} + \tfrac{1}{6}\{3(11|11) - 2(11|22) - (11|44)\}, \tag{25}$$

with obvious notations for the Coulomb integrals $(\mu\mu|\nu\nu)$.

The integral W_N has been put equal to the negative of the first ionization potential of $C_2H_5NH_2$,

$$W_N = -\mathrm{IP}(C_2H_5NH_2), \tag{26}$$

since it is reasonable to suppose that this ionization corresponds to the removal of an electron from the lone pair of a nitrogen atom, bonded to a carbon atom.

The integral β_{CN}, finally, has been computed from the following formula:

$$\beta_{\mu\nu} = -S_{\mu\nu}\{k_1[(\mu\mu|\mu\mu)+(\nu\nu|\nu\nu)]+k_2\,(\mu\mu|\nu\nu)\}. \tag{27}$$

The formula (27) has been derived elsewhere [6] from the theoretical expression of $\beta_{\mu\nu}$, cf. (16) and (2), by application of the Mulliken approximation for the pertinent integrals and estimates of penetration integrals in terms of two-electron integrals. The constants k_1 and k_2 are independent of the kinds of atoms involved. These constants have been determined from the values of $\beta_{CC}(r = 1.397\ \text{Å})$ and $\beta_{CC}(r = 1.337\ \text{Å})$, the two β-values being determined from the spectra of benzene and ethylene respectively.

The integral values, obtained in the Pariser-Parr-Pople method as described above, are supposed to be our best parameter choices for this method and are listed in Table 3 under the heading of Method II*a*. When necessary, the carbon atoms are denoted C_1, C_2, etc., NH_2 being bonded to the carbon atom C_1. For the calculation of the

Table 3. Integral values, adopted in Pariser-Parr-Pople methods II*a* and II*b*.

Integral	Method II *a* (r_{CC} = 1.397 Å, r_{CN} = 1.47 Å)			Method II *b* (cf. Section 5) (r_{CC} = 1.40 Å, r_{CN} = 1.36 Å)	
	Procedure of calculation	ev	a.u.	ev	a.u.
(CC|CC)	Formula (21)	11.810	0.4340	11.08	0.4072
$(C_1C_1\|C_2C_2)$	(24)	6.972	0.2562	7.50	0.2757
$(C_1C_1\|C_3C_3)$	Charged sphere appr.	5.517	0.2027	5.53	0.2034
$(C_1C_1\|C_4C_4)$	Charged sphere appr.	4.856	0.1785	4.96	0.1820
(NN|NN)	Formula (21)	12.498	0.4593	13.46	0.4947
$(NN\|C_1C_1)$	(23)	7.743	0.2846	8.13	0.2989
$(NN\|C_2C_2)$	Charged sphere appr.	5.453	0.2004	5.78	0.2124
$(NN\|C_3C_3)$	Charged sphere appr.	3.715	0.1365	3.84	0.1410
$(NN\|C_4C_4)$	Charged sphere appr.	3.300	0.1213	3.37	0.1239
W_C	Formula (25)	− 9.574	−0.3519	−11.28	−0.4146
W_N	(26)	− 8.970	−0.3297	−16.55	−0.6081
β_{CC}	(24)	− 2.437	−0.0896	− 2.39	−0.0878
β_{CN}	(27)	− 1.452	−0.0534	− 2.74	−0.1007

two-centre integrals the geometry of the molecule must be known. Since there does not seem to exist any structure determination of aniline in the gas phase, it has been assumed that the C–C distances are the same as in benzene, i.e. the shortest r_{CC} = 1.397 Å, and that the C–N distance has its normal value for free molecules, i.e. r_{CN} = 1.47 Å. Another choice of parameters has also been made, as discussed in Section 5. This second choice is listed in Table 3 under the heading of Method II*b*.

5. Method III: the purely theoretical method

This method, including the parameter choice, is the one used by the author in the previous investigation of aniline [5]. For this π-electron approximation of the purely theoretical MO calculation the geometry of the molecule must be known. In [5] the atomic distances determined for the anilinium ion in the solid state were used, i.e. $r_{CN}=1.36$ Å and $r_{CC}=1.40$ Å. It should be noticed that these values are somewhat different from those used in Section 4. The only other parameters to be introduced are the orbital exponents of the atomic orbitals χ_μ and the integral W_μ of (15). All the other integrals, approximately two hundred, have been computed from the theoretical expressions, cf. [5]. The choice of the parameters (15), made in [5], was the following:

$$\left.\begin{aligned} W_C &= -11.28 \text{ ev} = -0.4146 \text{ a.u.}, \\ W_N &= -16.55 \text{ ev} = -0.6081 \text{ a.u.} \end{aligned}\right\} \qquad (28)$$

The values of (28) are seen to be rather different from those of method II*a*, given in Table 3. The reasons for the choice (28) were the following. The W_C-value had been used previously by other authors for similar calculations. The guide for the choice of W_N was the IP-value for the free nitrogen atom, IP(N) = 14.54 ev. Moreover, it was supposed that this value should be slightly increased on account of the positive charge on nitrogen in the aniline molecule.

Today, the author believes that the arguments leading to the values of method I*a* in Table 2 and of method II*a* in Table 3, are more appropriate for the choice of parameters concerning the free molecule than the arguments of [5]. However, the parameter values of [5] have bearing upon the aniline molecule, when interacting with its environment, e.g. in water solution. It would therefore be of interest to make a parameter choice other than I*a* and II*a* in methods I and II, i.e. values in better agreement with the values of method III. This second parameter choice is listed under the headings of Method I*b* and Method II*b* in Tables 2 and 3. Obviously, these latter parameters are also more appropriate for a comparison between the three methods than the parameters of methods I*a* and II*a*.

6. Observables of the ground state

The molecule $C_6H_5NH_2$ belongs to the symmetry group $\mathbf{C}_{2v}$ and the π-electron molecular orbitals belong to the irreducible representations b_1 and a_2. (The notations used here are the same as those of Herzberg [10].) The electron configuration of the parent molecule C_6H_6 in the notation of the symmetry group $\mathbf{C}_{2v}$ is given in Table 4,

Table 4. Electron configuration of the ground state of benzene C_6H_6.

Notation	Filled molecular orbitals			Unfilled molecular orbitals		
		degenerate		degenerate		
$\mathbf{C}_{2v}$	$(1b_1^0)^2$	$(2b_1^0)^2$	$(1a_2^0)^2$	$2a_2^0$	$3b_1^0$	$4b_1^0$
cf. Table 1	$(\varphi_0)^2$	$(\varphi_1)^2$	$(\varphi_{\bar{1}})^2$	φ_2	$\varphi_{\bar{2}}$	φ_3

together with the corresponding notations of Table 1. The orbitals have an index 0 to indicate that they belong to the unperturbed parent molecule.

The lone pair orbital of the nitrogen in the NH_2-group has the symmetry b_1, cf. [5*a*]. Thus, the electron configuration of the ground state of aniline is as follows:

$$\Psi_0 = (1b_1)^2\,(2b_1)^2\,(1a_2)^2\,(3b_1)^2, \tag{29}$$

which is an obvious short-hand notation for the determinant wave function to be used in the actual calculations.

The orbital energies ε_i, given in Table 5, have been calculated from (29) by the three different methods with comparable parameter values, i.e. methods I*b*, II*b*, and III. The orbital energies, obtained with the best parameter choice, i.e. by methods I*a* and II*a*, are listed in Table 6, together with the corresponding values for benzene. The experimental values of the first ionization potentials are also given in Table 6.

Table 5. The orbital energies ε_i of aniline, $C_6H_5NH_2$, calculated by the three different methods with comparable parameter values.

All values are given in electron volts.

Orbital φ_i	Orbital energy ε_i		
	Method I *b* (Hückel)	Method II *b* (Pariser--Parr-Pople)	Method III (Purely theoretical)
$5b_1$	− 6.36	+ 3.41	+ 7.38
$4b_1$	− 8.58	+ 0.29	+ 1.90
$2a_2$	− 8.89	+ 0.09	+ 1.56
$3b_1$	− 13.03	− 10.86	− 10.57
$1a_2$	− 13.67	− 11.35	− 10.93
$2b_1$	− 15.61	− 14.23	− 13.91
$1b_1$	− 18.10	− 18.16	− 20.17

It is seen that the energies of the filled orbitals (in the bottom halves of Tables 5 and 6) are almost equal by all methods with corresponding parameter choice. This is particularly true for the methods with the best parameter choice (cf. Table 6). As for the unfilled orbitals (in the top halves), there is good agreement between methods II*b* and III. According to methods I*a* and I*b*, however, the energies of the unfilled orbitals are found to be much lower than those of II*a* and II*b*, III respectively. It can thus be inferred that the Hückel method will give rather erroneous absolute values of electronegativities. It should also be noted that the aniline orbitals have almost the same ε-values as the corresponding benzene orbitals in cases where the coefficients $c_{\mu i}$ are found to be roughly equal (cf. Table 7 below).

The explicit forms of the molecular orbitals have been tabulated for the best parameter choice, where a comparison with the corresponding benzene orbitals can be made. The orbital coefficients for these cases are listed in Table 7. This table shows that the results from methods I*a* and II*a* are very similar both for filled and unfilled orbitals, despite of the different orbital energies of the latter. Comparison

Table 6. Orbital energies ε_i of aniline, $C_6H_5NH_2$, and of the parent molecule benzene, C_6H_6, calculated by methods with the best parameter choice, I*a* and II*a*. All values are given in electron volts. The experimental values of the first ionization potentials, IP, are also given.

Orbital φ_i		Orbital energy ε_i: Method I *a* (Hückel)		Method II *a* (Pariser-Parr-Pople)	
C_6H_6	$C_6H_5NH_2$	C_6H_6	$C_6H_5NH_2$	C_6H_6	$C_6H_5NH_2$
$4b_1^0$	$5b_1$	− 1.440	− 1.382	+ 5.044	+ 5.197
$3b_1^0$	$4b_1$	− 4.040	− 3.875	+ 1.901	+ 2.114
$2a_2^0$	$2a_2$	− 4.040	− 4.040	+ 1.901	+ 2.027
—	$3b_1$	—	− 8.261	—	− 8.188
$1a_2^0$	$1a_2$	− 9.240[a]	− 9.240	− 9.240[b]	− 9.122
$2b_1^0$	$2b_1$	− 9.240[a]	− 10.011	− 9.240[b]	− 10.226
$1b_1^0$	$1b_1$	− 11.840	− 12.001	− 12.383	− 12.455
IP, exp. [11, 12]:					
First		9.248	7.70	9.248	7.70
Second		11.489	—	11.489	—

[a] Cf. formula (18). [b] Cf. formula (25).

with the benzene orbitals shows that the unfilled orbitals $5b_1$ and $4b_1$ can easily be correlated with the benzene orbitals $4b_1^0$ and $3b_1^0$, respectively. The same holds true for the lowest filled orbital $1b_1$. On the other hand, the two remaining filled orbitals of aniline, $2b_1$ and $3b_1$, are both mixtures of about equal parts of the $2b_1^0$ benzene orbital and the lone pair orbital of the N atom. It is therefore quite arbitrary that the $2b_1^0$ orbital has been put on the same line as the $2b_1$ orbital in Tables 6 and 7. Table 6 also

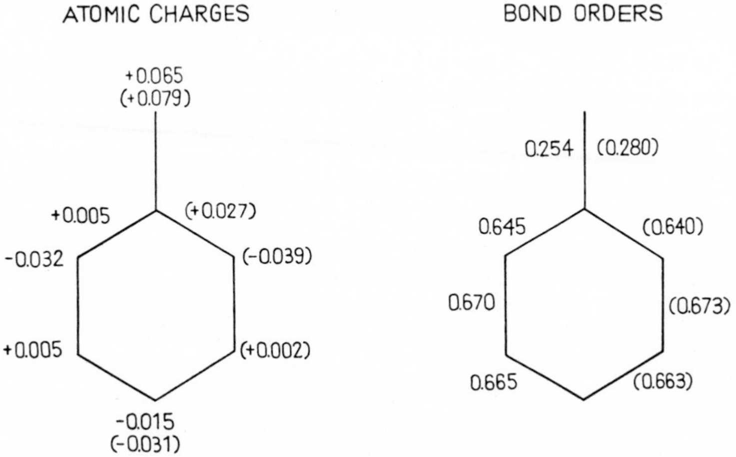

Fig. 1. Atomic charges and bond orders of aniline by method II*a*. The values in brackets refer to Hückel method I*a*.

Table 7. Orbital coefficients $c_{\mu i}$ of aniline, $C_6H_5NH_2$, and of the parent molecule benzene, C_6H_6, calculated from the methods with the best parameter choice: I*a* and II*a*.

MO φ_i	Atom μ for AO χ_μ	Coefficients $c_{\mu i}$ of (3), calculated for		
		benzene	aniline	
		Methods I *a*, II *a*	Method I *a*	Method II *a*
$4b_1^0$	N	—	+0.09006	+0.08679
or	C(1)	−0.40825	−0.43251	−0.41052
$5b_1$	C(2) = C(2′)	+0.40825	+0.41000	+0.40339
	C(3) = C(3′)	−0.40825	−0.39669	−0.40654
	C(4)	+0.40825	+0.39229	+0.40982
$3b_1^0$	N	—	+0.17720	+0.15792
or	C(1)	−0.57735	−0.57134	−0.57781
$4b_1$	C(2) = C(2′)	+0.28868	+0.24990	+0.27156
	C(3) = C(3′)	+0.28868	+0.30562	+0.29098
	C(4)	−0.57735	−0.57486	−0.56953
$3b_1$	N	—	−0.71480	−0.66091
	C(1)	—	+0.32055	+0.36864
	C(2) = C(2′)	—	+0.31715	+0.31175
	C(3) = C(3′)	—	−0.12276	−0.16160
	C(4)	—	−0.39370	−0.42509
$2b_1^0$	N	—	+0.62561	+0.68496
or	C(1)	+0.57735	+0.41199	+0.36886
$2b_1$	C(2) = C(2′)	+0.28868	+0.07695	+0.04006
	C(3) = C(3′)	−0.28868	−0.31224	−0.30313
	C(4)	−0.57735	−0.48172	−0.45584
$1b_1^0$	N	—	+0.24117	+0.24810
or	C(1)	+0.40825	+0.46263	+0.47503
$1b_1$	C(2) = C(2′)	+0.40825	+0.40366	+0.40588
	C(3) = C(3′)	+0.40825	+0.36969	+0.36339
	C(4)	+0.40825	+0.35859	+0.34525

shows that the mean value of the two ε_i's, corresponding to $2b_1$ and $3b_1$, is almost equal to $\varepsilon(2b_1^0)$.

Population analyses [13] have been carried out for all the different cases. The gross atomic populations $N(\mu)$ and the atomic charges $Q(\mu)$ of aniline, calculated by the three comparable methods, I*b*, II*b* and III, are collected in Table 8. Table 9 lists the corresponding values, calculated by the methods with the best parameter choice, I*a* and II*a*. The bond orders $p_{\mu\nu}$ of [14] have been calculated for all methods I and II and the overlap populations $n(\mu, \nu)$ of [13] for method III. In order to compare these different quantities, the ratios between the values computed for aniline and for benzene have been given in Table 10. The atomic charges and bond orders for aniline, calculated by methods I*a* and II*a*, are also collected in Fig. 1.

Table 8. Population analyses of aniline: gross atomic populations $N(\mu)$ and atomic charges $Q(\mu)$, calculated by the three methods with corresponding parameter values, I*b*, II*b*, and III.

Atom μ	Gross atomic populations $N(\mu)$ by method			Atomic charges $Q(\mu)$ by method		
	I *b*	II *b*	III	I *b*	II *b*	III
N	1.89231	1.93791	1.95684	+0.10769	+0.06209	+0.04316
C(1)	0.91658	0.95062	0.93455	+0.08342	+0.04938	+0.06545
C(2) = C(2′)	1.07262	1.05894	1.05529	−0.07262	−0.05894	−0.05529
C(3) = C(3′)	0.99636	0.98173	0.98427	+0.00364	+0.01827	+0.01573
C(4)	1.05316	1.03011	1.02949	−0.05316	−0.03011	−0.02949

Table 9. Population analyses of aniline: gross atomic populations $N(\mu)$, calculated by the methods with the best parameter choice, I*a* and II*a*.

Atom μ	Gross atomic populations $N(\mu)$ by method	
	I *a*	II *a*
N	1.92098	1.93506
C(1)	0.97302	0.99522
C(2) = C(2′)	1.03890	1.03201
C(3) = C(3′)	0.99846	0.99517
C(4)	1.03128	1.01537

Table 10. Ratios of bond orders $p_{\mu\nu}$ and overlap populations $n(\mu, \nu)$ between corresponding bonds in aniline and benzene.

μ, ν in $p_{\mu\nu}$ or $n(\mu,\nu)$	$p_{\mu\nu}$-aniline/$p_{\mu\nu}$-benzene		$n(\mu,\nu)$-aniline / $n(\mu,\nu)$-benzene
	Method I *b*	Method II *b*	Method III
C(1), C(2)	0.93694	0.96553	0.99873
C(2), C(3)	1.01234	1.00435	0.99743
C(3), C(4)	0.99218	0.99729	1.00104

From Tables 8, 9, 10 and Fig. 1 it is obvious that the population of the π-electrons is very similar for all methods. There is, however, one interesting difference between the methods, viz. the ratio between the charges Q on the atoms C(2) and C(4). In methods II*a,b* and III the charge on the atom C(2) is twice as large as that on C(4). As discussed elsewhere [6], this result seems to be typical for mono-substituted benzenes, C_6H_5X. This is remarkable, since it has often been claimed that the charge on the *para* atom C(4) should be larger than that on the *ortho* atom C(2). This latter view has been supported both by theoretical calculations according to the Hückel method and by experimental results from reaction kinetics. However, the present more accurate calculations, II*a*, *b* and III, as well as recent NMR measurements [15], show unambiguously that the *ortho* atom has the larger charge.

It should also be noticed that the atomic charges are all very small. This result is emphasized by the computed values of the π-electronic part of the dipole moment, shown in Table 11. It is seen that all values, except that of I*b*, are of the correct magnitude, some of them being in excellent agreement with the experimental value which has been obtained by the present author from dipole moment measurements for a series of substituted aniline derivatives [16].

Table 11. π-electronic part of the dipole moment of aniline.

All values are given in Debye units.

Dipole moment calculated by method					Exptl. value [16]
I *a*	I *b*	II *a*	II *b*	III	
1.21	1.83	0.78	0.84	0.72	0.7

7. The electronic spectrum of aniline

For the present study of the electronic spectrum we are going to use the approximation of describing the electron configuration of an excited state by promotion of one electron from a filled MO to one of the empty MO's, leaving all the other MO's unchanged. The energy ${}^1E(i\to m)$ of an excited singlet state, obtained by promotion of an electron from the MO φ_i to the MO φ_m, is known to be:

$$ {}^1E(i\to m) = E_0 - \varepsilon_i + \varepsilon_m - J(mm\,|\,ii) + 2\,K(mi\,|\,im). \tag{30}$$

E_0 in (30) is the energy of the ground state. The electron interaction integrals J and K of (30) are defined by (10) and (11), respectively.

For the description of excited states by superposition of several configurations ${}^1\Psi(i\to m)$, ${}^1\Psi(j\to n)$, ... the off-diagonal matrix elements of the Hamiltonian (1) must be calculated. These elements are found to be as follows, cf. e.g. [17]:

$$\int {}^1\Psi^*(i\to m)\,H\,{}^1\Psi(j\to n)\,d\tau = -J(mn\,|\,ij) + 2K(mj\,|\,in). \tag{31}$$

As mentioned above, the distinction between J and K of (31) disappears when $m \neq n$ and $i \neq j$. The probability for an electronic transition between the ground state Ψ_0 and the excited state ${}^1\Psi(i\to m)$ is known to be proportional to the square of the modulus of the off-diagonal matrix element of the dipole moment, cf. [18]:

$$\mathbf{R} = \int \Psi_0^* \sum_t \mathbf{r}_t\, {}^1\Psi(i\to m)\,d\tau = \sqrt{2}\int \varphi_i^*\,\mathbf{r}\,\varphi_m\,d\tau. \tag{32}$$

The oscillator strength f of the transition is

$$f = 3.039 \times 10^{-6} \nu |\mathbf{R}|^2, \tag{33}$$

where ν is the wave number in cm^{-1} and $\mathbf{R}$ is measured in a.u.

The possible configurations of the lower excited states of benzene are, in the notation of the $\mathbf{C}_{2v}$ symmetry group:

$$\left.\begin{array}{l} \Psi_1^0(2b_1^0 \to 2a_2^0),\ B_2, \\ \Psi_2^0(1a_2^0 \to 3b_1^0),\ B_2, \\ \Psi_4^0(2b_1^0 \to 3b_1^0),\ A_1, \\ \Psi_5^0(1a_2^0 \to 2a_2^0),\ A_1. \end{array}\right\} \tag{34}$$

The four wave functions of (34) are all degenerate. The linear combinations of the functions (34), describing the observed energy levels of benzene, have been given by Dewar and Longuet-Higgins [8], and are reproduced in the present notation in Table 12, where also the $\mathbf{D}_{6h}$ and the Clar notations of the levels are given.

Table 12. Wave functions of the lower excited states of C_6H_6.

Wave function (cf. (34))	Notations of the corr. energy level			Transition from ground state
	$\mathbf{C}_{2v}$	$\mathbf{D}_{6h}$	Clar	
$\Psi_\alpha^0 = 0.707\{{}^1\Psi_1^0 - {}^1\Psi_2^0\}$	${}^1B_2$	${}^1B_{2u}$	α	forbidden
$\Psi_p^0 = 0.707\{{}^1\Psi_4^0 + {}^1\Psi_5^0\}$	${}^1A_1$	${}^1B_{1u}$	p	forbidden
$\Psi_\beta^0 = 0.707\{{}^1\Psi_1^0 + {}^1\Psi_2^0\}$	${}^1B_2$	${}^1E_{1u}$	β	allowed
$\Psi_{\beta'}^0 = 0.707\{{}^1\Psi_4^0 - {}^1\Psi_5^0\}$	${}^1A_1$	${}^1E_{1u}$	β'	allowed

For the discussion of the aniline spectrum we have to consider not only the states corresponding to the wave functions (34), but also the states describing a charge transfer from the lone pair orbital b_1^x of the NH_2-group to the benzene ring. The wave functions for such transitions are:

$$\left.\begin{array}{l} \Psi_3^0(b_1^x \to 2a_2^0),\ B_2, \\ \Psi_6^0(b_1^x \to 3b_1^0),\ A_1. \end{array}\right\} \tag{35}$$

Both (34) and (35) refer to a description of $C_6H_5NH_2$ by means of unperturbed orbitals of C_6H_6 and the NH_2-group. Using the SCF orbitals of aniline for the description of the electron configurations of the excited states, we obtain:

$$\left.\begin{array}{l} \Psi_1(2b_1 \to 2a_2),\ B_2, \\ \Psi_2(1a_2 \to 4b_1),\ B_2, \\ \Psi_3(3b_1 \to 2a_2),\ B_2, \\ \Psi_4(2b_1 \to 4b_1),\ A_1, \\ \Psi_5(1a_2 \to 2a_2),\ A_1, \\ \Psi_6(3b_1 \to 4b_1),\ A_1. \end{array}\right\} \tag{36}$$

The wave functions of (36) do not correspond uniquely to the unperturbed functions of (34) and (35). As shown by Tables 5, 6 and 7, the degeneracy between them is removed. Furthermore, all states of (36) correspond to symmetry-allowed transitions from the ground state. However, an approximate degeneracy between the states will still be found. So, the excited states of aniline should preferably be described by superpositions of all the states of (36) belonging to the same irreducible representation, B_2 or A_1.

The expressions for the matrix elements, (30) and (31), are referred to the SCF orbital representation. Consequently, the transitions have been calculated primarily in this representation. Afterwards, a transformation to a representation corresponding to (34) and (35) has been carried out to facilitate a comparison between the excited states of aniline and those of benzene. However, this kind of transformation has only been applied to the results of the calculation according to method II. In the case of method III, only two configurations of each representation have been included, since the parameter choice (28) shifts the transitions (35) to the remote ultraviolet part of the spectrum. Besides, the extremely tedious calculations involved in this method prohibit any extensive superposition of configurations.

The energies of excited states calculated from one single configuration by methods I*b*, II*b* and III are collected in Table 13. Table 14 shows the energy values obtained from superposition of two or more configurations in accordance with the same methods. This table also gives the energy values for the excited states of benzene calculated by method II*b*, and by Parr, Craig, and Ross [19] from superposition of several configurations according to a purely theoretical MO method comparable with the present method III.

Table 13. The lower excited states of aniline, calculated from one single configuration by methods I*b*, II*b* and III.

All energy values are given in ev.

Wave function (cf. (36))	Excitation energy, calculated by method		
	I *b*	II *b*	III
Ψ_3, $^1B_3$	4.14	5.69	7.15
Ψ_6, $^1A_1$	4.45	6.07	7.98
Ψ_2, $^1B_2$	5.10	6.18	7.61
Ψ_5, $^1A_1$	4.78	6.25	8.00

It should be noted that all excitation energies obtained by Hückel method I*b* (cf. Table 13) are considerably smaller than both the energies obtained by methods II*b* and III, and the experimental values, given in Table 14. The values obtained by method III are too large, although the discrepancy with experiment is considerably reduced by superposition of two configurations (cf. Table 14). These values are to be compared with the values calculated for benzene by Parr *et al.* [19]. All the values calculated for aniline by method III are somewhat lower than those calculated for benzene [19]. The differences between these energy values for aniline and the corresponding values for benzene are fairly close to the differences between the experimental values (cf. Table 16).

Table 14. The lower excited states of benzene and of aniline, calculated from superposition of two or more configurations.

All energy values are given in ev.

State	Calculated excited energy of benzene		Excitation energy of aniline: Calculated from superposition of two config. by method		five config. by method	seven config. by method	Experimental values [20]
	II *b*	[19]	III	II *b*	II *b*	II *b*	
$^1B_2$	4.91	5.9	5.33	4.83	4.80	—	4.32
$^1A_1$	5.38	7.3	6.59	5.29	—	5.14	5.31
$^1A_1$	7.11	9.8	9.38	7.03	—	7.00	6.32
$^1B_2$	7.11	9.8	9.44	7.03	7.02	—	6.32
$^1A_1$	—	—	—	—	—	7.89	> 7.06
$^1B_2$	—	—	—	—	8.06	—	> 7.06

Table 15 shows the excitation energies for benzene, calculated by methods I*a* and II*a*, and the corresponding experimental values. It should be noted that the values of the integrals β_{CC} and $(C_1C_1|C_2C_2)$ have been chosen so as to obtain the best possible fit to all the six experimental values (cf. (24)). The excitation energies of aniline, calculated by the same methods I*a* and II*a*, are collected in Table 16. The experimental values of both aniline and benzene are also listed in this table to facilitate a comparison between the spectra of the two molecules.

The excitation energies of aniline, calculated by methods I*a*, II*a* and II*b*, are comparatively close to the experimental values. Method I*a* gives, however, too small a separation between the two lowest levels. The values of method II*a* are seen to agree well with the experimental values, although they are all about 0.4 ev higher than the latter. A comparison between the aniline and the benzene spectrum shows that all benzene bands are shifted towards longer wave lengths (smaller excitation energies) in aniline. This shift is found to be largest for the lowest excited $^1A_1$ state and smallest for the lowest $^1B_2$ state, both from experiment and from calculations by method II*a*. According to method II*b*, however, all shifts are found to be almost equal. So, the present calculations indicate that the spectrum of the anilinium ion should have a closer correspondence to the benzene spectrum than has the spectrum of aniline. In the present calculations we have only considered the conjugative effect, although the inductive effect is likely to be of some importance, especially for the spectrum of the anilinium ion. Since this effect is likely to change the A_1 levels more than the B_2 levels the above prediction about the spectrum of the anilinium ion may possibly need a slight modification.

The wave function corresponding to an excitation energy, calculated by superposition of several configurations, can be written:

$$\Psi = C_1\Psi_1(i \to m) + C_2\Psi_2(j \to n) + \dots \quad (37)$$

When $\varphi_m = \varphi_n = \dots$, (or $\varphi_i = \varphi_j = \dots$) the expression (37) can be simplified by a transformation of the SCF MO's $\varphi_i, \varphi_j, \dots$ to natural spin orbitals ψ_k, cf. Löwdin [22], the

Table 15. Spectrum of benzene. Calculations by methods Ia and IIa (cf. formula (24)).
All energy values are given in ev.

State	Values of excitation energy, obtained from			
	calculations with			experiment [21]
	one configuration		superpos. of two config.	
	I a	II a	II a	
$^1B_2$	5.200	6.602	4.897	4.89
$^1A_1$	5.200	6.602	6.200	6.14
$^1B_2$, $^1A_1$	5.200	6.602	7.004	6.74
$^3A_1$	5.200	3.852	3.504	3.8
$^3B_2$, $^3A_1$	5.200	3.852	4.201	4.7
$^3B_2$	5.200	3.852	4.897	4.9

Table 16. Spectrum of aniline, calculated by methods Ia and IIa, compared to experimental values of aniline and benzene.
All energy values are given in ev.

State	Values of excitation energy, obtained from					
	calculations for aniline with				experiment	
	one configuration			Superpos. of three config.		
	Wawe fctn. of (36)	I a	II a	II a	aniline [20]	benzene [21]
$^1B_2$	Ψ_3	4.221	5.428	4.699	4.32	4.89
$^1A_1$	Ψ_6	4.386	5.749	5.581	5.31	6.14
$^1B_2$	Ψ_2	5.365	6.032	6.503	6.32	6.74
$^1A_1$	Ψ_5	5.200	6.609	6.668	6.32	6.74
$^1A_1$	Ψ_4	6.135	7.287	7.396	> 7.06	—
$^1B_2$	Ψ_1	5.971	7.239	7.496	> 7.06	—

transformation matrix being obtained by diagonalization of the one-electron density matrix. (37) then takes the form

$$\Psi = C_k \Psi(\psi_k \rightarrow \varphi_m) + \dots \qquad (38)$$

This kind of transformation can be applied to the linear combinations of Ψ_1 and Ψ_3 of the B_2 representation and to Ψ_4 and Ψ_6 of the A_1 representation, cf. (36). In both cases the MO's $2b_1$ and $3b_1$ will be transformed into two natural spin orbitals, ψ_1 and ψ_2. Only one of them, ψ_2 say, will appear explicitly in the wave function (38), ψ_1 being doubly occupied both before and after the transition. The transformation of the MO's can be written:

$$\left.\begin{array}{c} \psi_2 = k_2(2b_1) + k_3(3b_1) = k_x(b_1^x) + k_0(2\tilde{b}_1^0), \\ 2\tilde{b}_1^0 \approx 2b_1^0. \end{array}\right\} \qquad (39)$$

The second transformation of ψ_2 is introduced in order to find an approximate correspondence between the benzene spectrum and the aniline spectrum. The molecular orbital $2\tilde{b}_1^0$ of aniline has approximately the same coefficients as the benzene orbital $2b_1^0$. Analogously, the notation $\tilde{\Psi}'^0_k$ will be used for determinant wave functions composed of $n\tilde{b}_1^0$ orbitals. For the sake of simplicity, however, the wave functions corresponding to Ψ'^0_α, etc. from Table 12, will be denoted Ψ'_α instead of $\tilde{\Psi}'^0_\alpha$.

The above-mentioned transformations have been applied to the wave functions of method IIa, corresponding to the four lower excited states of aniline (cf. Table 16). The natural spin orbitals calculated for these four states are reproduced in Table 17.

Table 17. Natural spin orbitals ψ_2 of (39) calculated by method IIa.

State	Energy, ev	Natural spin orbital (39)			
		k_2	k_3	k_x	k_0
$^1B_2$	4.699	+ 0.2628	+ 0.9648	− 0.3970	+ 0.9178
$^1A_1$	5.581	− 0.0902	+ 0.9959	− 0.6719	+ 0.7406
$^1B_2$	6.503	+ 0.3745	− 0.9272	− 0.8362	+ 0.5485
$^1A_1$	6.668	+ 0.6512	− 0.7589	+ 0.9343	− 0.3565

The different transforms of the total wave functions are collected in Table 18. The last transform permits a direct comparison with the spectrum of benzene.

Table 18. Total wave functions for the lower excited states of aniline, according to method IIa. Ψ'_k are defined in (36) and Ψ'^0_k in (34), (35), and Table 12.

State	Energy, ev	Total wave function
$^1B_2$	4.699	$0.208\ \Psi'_1 - 0.610\ \Psi'_2 + 0.765\ \Psi'_3 =$ $0.727\ \tilde{\Psi}'^0_1 - 0.610\ \tilde{\Psi}'^0_2 - 0.315\ \tilde{\Psi}'^0_3 = 0.946\ \Psi'_\alpha + 0.083\ \Psi'_\beta - 0.315\ \tilde{\Psi}'^0_3$
$^1A_1$	5.581	$-0.083\ \Psi'_4 + 0.391\ \Psi'_5 + 0.917\ \Psi'_6 =$ $0.682\ \tilde{\Psi}'^0_4 + 0.391\ \tilde{\Psi}'^0_5 - 0.619\ \tilde{\Psi}'^0_6 = 0.758\ \Psi'_p + 0.206\ \Psi'_{\beta'} - 0.619\ \tilde{\Psi}'^0_6$
$^1B_2$	6.503	$-0.260\ \Psi'_1 + 0.719\ \Psi'_2 + 0.644\ \Psi'_3 =$ $0.381\ \tilde{\Psi}'^0_1 + 0.719\ \tilde{\Psi}'^0_2 - 0.581\ \tilde{\Psi}'^0_3 = -0.239\ \Psi'_\alpha + 0.778\ \Psi'_\beta - 0.581\ \tilde{\Psi}'^0_3$
$^1A_1$	6.668	$0.301\ \Psi'_4 + 0.887\ \Psi'_5 - 0.351\ \Psi'_6 =$ $-0.165\ \tilde{\Psi}'^0_4 + 0.887\ \tilde{\Psi}'^0_5 + 0.432\ \tilde{\Psi}'^0_6 = 0.511\ \Psi'_p - 0.744\ \Psi'_{\beta'} + 0.432\ \tilde{\Psi}'^0_6$

The table shows that the lowest excited state of aniline, $^1B_2$, corresponds very closely to the lowest excited state of benzene, the $^1B_{2u}$ or α state. The lowest $^1A_1$ state is composed of about 60 per cent of the benzene B_{1u} or p state and of 40 per cent of the charge transfer state $\tilde{\Psi}'^0_6$. In the two higher aniline states, the contributions from the benzene E_{1u} states, β and β', dominate, but the contributions from the charge

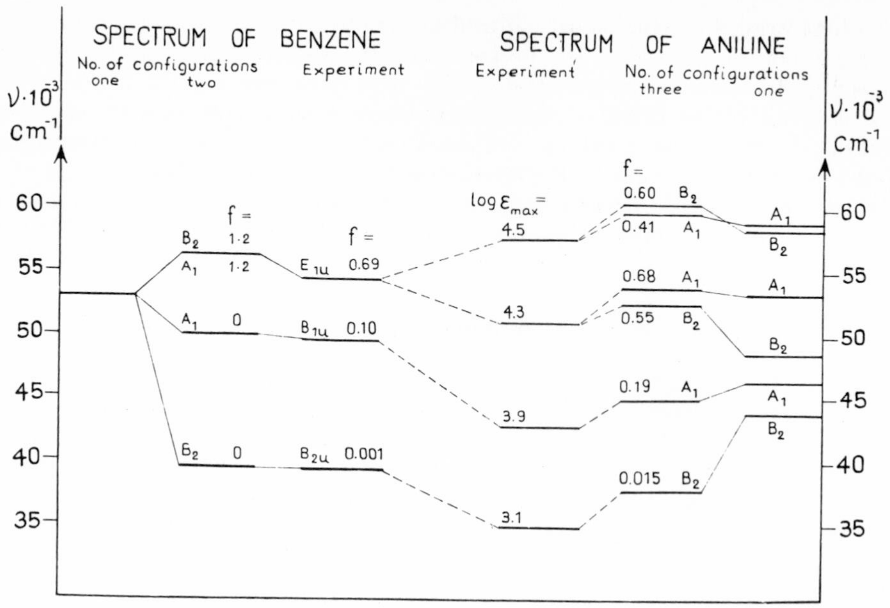

Fig. 2. Spectra of benzene and aniline from calculations by method II*a* with one or more configurations, and from experiment. The broken lines indicate connections according to the last transforms of the total wave functions given in Table 18.

transfer states, $\tilde{\Psi}_3^0$ and $\tilde{\Psi}_6^0$, are also considerable. The wave functions of Table 18 agree very well with those calculated for the same states of aniline by Murrell [7], using a perturbation method.

The correspondence between the benzene levels and the aniline levels is also confirmed by calculations of the oscillator strength f of (33) by method II*a*. The results of these calculations are shown by the f-values given in Fig. 2. In this figure the spectral levels (in wave numbers) of benzene and aniline are plotted along the ordinate. Both experimental and calculated values are shown (cf. Tables 15 and 16). The probable connections between different levels are indicated by continuous or broken lines.

Table 19. Spectrum of aniline, calculated by the present method II*a*, compared with calculations by Murrell [7] and Peacock [23].

All energy values E are given in ev.

State	Murrell [7]		Peacock [23]	Present method II *a*		Experiment [20]	
	$E-E_0$	f	$E-E_0$	$E-E_0$	f	$E-E_0$	$\log \varepsilon_{max}$
$^1B_2$	4.91	very weak	4.3	4.699	0.015	4.32	3.1
$^1A_1$	5.16	weak	4.3	5.581	0.19	5.31	3.9
$^1B_2$	6.34	medium	6.1	6.503	0.55	6.32	4.3
$^1A_1$	6.67	medium	7.6	6.668	0.68		
$^1A_1$	7.39	strong	10.1	7.396	0.41	> 7.06	4.5
$^1B_2$	7.58	strong	8.3	7.496	0.61		

The results of the present calculation by method IIa of the aniline spectrum are listed in Table 19 together with the spectrum, previously calculated by Murrell [7], and the recent calculations by Peacock [23], who also used a perturbation method. In view of the rather different methods the agreement of the present results with those of [7] are very satisfactory. The results of [23] do not agree so well with [7] and the present results. It is, however, difficult to discuss the significance of this disagreement, since [23] does not give any comparison with the benzene levels or any estimate of transition probabilities.

8. Conclusions

The present investigation shows that the Hückel method will give results satisfactory in several respects when the semi-empirical parameters are chosen carefully (Method Ia). Thus, very reasonable values have been obtained for such ground state properties as ionization potentials (Table 6), atomic charges (Table 9), bond orders (Table 10) and the π-electronic part of the dipole moment (Table 11). In addition, the molecular orbitals of the Hückel method appear to be a good starting point for the calculation of self-consistent field orbitals (Table 7). Some of these points have been stressed previously in an interesting comparison between Hückel and SCF methods, carried out by McWeeny and Peacock [17, 24]. On the other hand, the Hückel values of electron affinities are found to be less satisfactory. Also, the finer details of the charge distribution, e.g. the ratio between the charges on the *ortho* and the *para* atoms, have not been correctly reproduced by the Hückel method. With regard to the spectrum, the Hückel method can give an approximate agreement with experiment (Table 16), but again, the finer details, e.g. the separation between the excited states, are not given correctly.

For an appropriate parameter choice in the Hückel method one must make use of experimental values for a suitable parent molecule (benzene in the present case). Thus, a successful application of the Hückel method could be expected only for series of rather similar molecules. When the parameter choice is made without reference to a parent molecule (Method Ib) the results should be interpreted very cautiously. Calculated values of both ionization potentials and electron affinities might be rather erroneous (Table 5), the atomic charges might be too big (Table 8), and the order of the excited states could easily be rearranged (Table 13).

The results obtained by the Pariser-Parr-Pople method (Method II) are very promising. In the first place, the results from this method are not so sensitive to the parameter choice as are the results from the Hückel method. Both dipole moment (Table 11) and spectrum (Tables 14, 16) are found to be roughly equal for the two parameter choices, called method IIa and IIb. Thus, minor changes in the geometry of the molecule (for example the deviation from planarity in case of aniline) and the corresponding changes of the semi-empirical parameters will only give rise to immaterial changes in the calculated values of physical observables. The parameter choice, subject to the prescriptions given elsewhere [6] (Method IIa), is found to give results in very satisfactory agreement with experiment both for ground state properties (Tables 6, 9, 11, Fig. 1) and for the spectrum (Tables 16, 19, Fig. 2). Consequently, it would seem that the Pariser-Parr-Pople method could be used with great confidence for all kinds of calculations involving the electronic properties of complicated molecules.

ACKNOWLEDGEMENTS

This investigation was made possible by grants from the Swedish Natural Science Research Council. Part of the numerical work has been carried out by use of free machine time on the Swedish electronic computer Besk, which is gratefully acknowledged. My best thanks are due to Mr. L. Norén, who carried out most of the remaining, still rather tedious numerical work.

Division of Mathematical Physics, Royal Institute of Technology, Stockholm 70, June 1961.

REFERENCES

1. Grabe, B., Exp. Cell Res. *13,* 588 (1957); Biochim. Biophys. Acta *30,* 560 (1958); Ark. Fys. *17,* 97 (1960).
2. Pullman, B., and Pullman, A., Rev. Mod. Phys. *32,* 428 (1960), and further references given there.
3. Pariser, R., and Parr, R. G., J. Chem. Phys. *21,* 466 (1953); ibid. *21,* 767 (1953).
4. Pople, J. A., Trans. Faraday Soc. *49,* 1375 (1953); J. Phys. Chem. *61,* 6 (1957).
5. Fischer, I., Ark. Fys. *5,* 377 (1952); (*a*) pp. 378–9.
6. Fischer-Hjalmars I., (unpublished).
7. Murrell, J. N., Proc. Phys. Soc. A *68,* 969 (1955).
8. Dewar, M. J. S., and Longuet-Higgins, H. C., Proc. Phys. Soc. A *67,* 795 (1954).
9. Condon, E. U., and Shortley, G. H., The Theory of Atomic Spectra. Cambridge, 1953.
10. Herzberg, G., Molecular Spectra and Molecular Structure. II. Infrared and Raman Spectra of Polyatomic Molecules. New York, 1945, p. 106.
11. Amr El-Sayed, M. F., Kasha, M., and Tanaka, Y., J. Chem. Phys. *34,* 334 (1961).
12. Watanabe, K., J. Chem. Phys. *26,* 542 (1957).
13. Mulliken, R. S., J. Chem. Phys. *23,* 1833 (1955).
14. Coulson, C. A., and Longuet-Higgins, H. C., Proc. Roy. Soc. A *191,* 39 (1947).
15. Hoffman, R. A., and Gronowitz, S., (Uppsala, private communication).
16. Fischer, I., Acta Chem. Scand. *4,* 1197 (1950).
17. McWeeny, R., Proc. Phys. Soc. A *70,* 593 (1957).
18. Mulliken, R. S., and Rieke, C. A., Rep. Phys. Soc. Progr. Phys. *8,* 231 (1941).
19. Parr, R. G., Craig, D. P., and Ross, I. G., J. Chem. Phys. *18,* 1561 (1950).
20. Platt, J. R., J. Chem. Phys. *19,* 101 (1951).
21. Klevens, H. B., and Platt, J. R., Technical Report of the Laboratory of Molecular Structure and Spectra, University of Chicago, 1953–1954.
22. Löwdin, P.-O., Phys. Rev. *97,* 1474 (1955).
23. Peacock, T. E., Molecular Phys. *3,* 453 (1960).
24. McWeeny, R., and Peacock, T. E., Proc. Phys. Soc. A *70,* 41 (1957).

Reprinted from THE JOURNAL OF CHEMICAL PHYSICS, Vol. 28, No. 2, 335–345, February, 1958
Printed in U. S. A.

Theory of Separated Electron Pairs*

JOE M. PARKS† AND ROBERT G. PARR
Department of Chemistry, Carnegie Institute of Technology, Pittsburgh, Pennsylvania
(Received March 25, 1957)

Electron pairs in a molecule are said to be *separated* if (i) the molecular electronic wave function is accurately expressible as an antisymmetrized product of individual pair wave functions, and (ii) the individual pair functions are mutually exclusive in the sense that if all pair functions are linearily expressed in terms of Slater determinants built from some orthogonal one-electron spin orbitals, no spin orbital enters the description of more than one pair function. It is shown that the electronic energy of a system of separated electron pairs may be written in a particularly simple form, and the problem of determining the best separated electron-pair description of a particular molecule is discussed.

The *best orbital description* of an electron-pair bond is defined to be the best wave function for the pair that can be built from two atomic orbitals, one on each of two atoms. Systematic adjustment of individual pair descriptions one at a time is shown to provide a rigorous yet practicable procedure for obtaining best orbital descriptions for several separated electron-pair bonds in a molecule.

The equations obtained are shown to simplify considerably when Mulliken approximations are introduced for certain electronic repulsion integrals. Under these approximations a single property of each bond is shown to dominate its effect on other bonds, the net charge transferred from one atom to the other in the bond. This charge is called the *bond polarity parameter*. The equations are rewritten in terms of polarity parameters, and a scheme is thereby obtained which is convenient for discussion of *intrabond charge transfer effects* in a molecule. Formulas are given for the terms to be added to the absolute electronegativity of an atom in a bond to correct for charge transfers in other bonds.

It is shown that the total molecular energy of a system of separated electron-pair bonds can be expressed quite rigorously as a sum of bond energies, and the approximate invariance of bond energy to molecular environment is verified.

Limitations of the assumption of separability and methods for transcending it are discussed.

I. INTRODUCTION

THERE are many situations in which two or more chemical bonds are at least approximately "separated" in the sense that the spatial parts of the wave functions describing different bonds do not overlap. Two bonds at opposite ends of a long molecule provide one example, the sigma and pi bonds in a double bond provide another.

No nontrivial case occurs in practice in which separability of electron pairs in this sense holds exactly, because interelectronic correlations make such a resolution of the electronic structure of a molecule into parts impossible. Nevertheless, the approximation[1] of separability is certainly very good in some cases (e.g., the first example above), and it is probably very good in others (e.g., the second example above). In the present paper, some of the consequences of the approximation of separability are examined. The results should be useful both for testing the approximation in specific cases and as a basis for development of theory in better approximations.

For a given two-electron bond, the chemist likes to think in terms of a simple covalent wave function of the Heitler-London type, a simple molecular orbital wave function, or (better) a covalent wave function modified to include a suitable amount of ionic character. This description is a rather good one, worth testing fully. It includes a good deal of the correlation correction implicit in an exact description, and it enables one to relate the description of a molecule to the description of its constituent atoms, after the manner of Moffitt,[2] Arai,[3] and Hurley.[4] Such a "best orbital description" for each of several separated electron-pair bonds is introduced in this paper, and the effects of charge transfer from atom to atom in one bond on the other bonds are studied. Bond energies and the valence bond theory also are considered.

In two previous communications, a theory of generalized antisymmetrized product wave functions has been outlined[5,6] and applied to the problem of sigma-

* Supported in part by research grants from the National Science Foundation and the Office of Ordnance Research, U. S. Army. Based on part of a thesis submitted by Joe M. Parks in partial fulfillment of the requirements for the degree of Doctor of Philosophy at the Carnegie Institute of Technology, 1956.

† National Science Foundation Predoctoral Fellow, 1954–1955. Present address: Chemical Department, Experimental Station, E. I. du Pont de Nemours and Company, Wilmington 98, Delaware.

1 The term "approximation" as used here does not imply any necessary loss of either accuracy or precision. Correct quantum-mechanical operators are being employed, and expectation values for observables are being correctly calculated from precisely specified wave functions. The "approximations" come in the constraints that are imposed on the forms of the wave functions. These define a *model* which may or may not be good enough for a particular purpose; by the variational principle, one can always get a better result by removing one or more of the constraints.

2 W. Moffitt, Proc. Roy. Soc. (London) **A210**, 245 (1951).

3 T. Arai, J. Chem. Phys. **26**, 435 (1957).

4 A. C. Hurley, Proc. Phys. Soc. (London) **A69**, 49, 301 (1956).

5 Parr, Ellison, and Lykos, J. Chem. Phys. **24**, 1106 (1956). In Eqs. (2) and (3) of this paper, delete the signs ×; in the line after Eq. (4), read $d\tau_{n_a}$ for $d\tau n_a$; in Eq. (7) read $\frac{1}{2}\Sigma'_{IJ}$ in place of Σ_{IJ}; in line 4 above Eq. (12), delete the sign −; in Eq. (17), delete $\Lambda_{\mathrm{peel}}^*$.

6 P. G. Lykos and R. G. Parr, J. Chem. Phys. **24**, 1166 (1956). See also the erratum for this paper, J. Chem. Phys. **25**, 1301 (1956). On line 1, page 1169, read (30) instead of (3).

pi separability in unsaturated molecules[6]; the present paper extends these. A discussion similar to the present one both in method and in scope has been given by Hurley, Lennard-Jones, and Pople.[7]

II. DEFINITION AND ELEMENTARY PROPERTIES OF SEPARATED ELECTRON PAIRS[8]

The following three *conditions of separability for electron pairs* may be taken as defining a case of *separated electron pairs:*

(A) The total electronic wave function for the $2n$-electron system has the form

$$\Lambda=[\Lambda_A(1,2)\Lambda_B(3,4)\cdots\Lambda_M(2n-1,\,2n)], \tag{1}$$

where each Λ_I is an antisymmetric function of the space and spin coordinates of two electrons and the brackets denote the normalized partial antisymmetrization operator which generates a completely antisymmetric Λ from the simple products of the individually antisymmetric Λ_I:

$$[\Lambda_A\Lambda_B\cdots]\equiv[(2n)!/2^n]^{-\frac{1}{2}}\textstyle\sum_P(-1)^P P(\Lambda_A\Lambda_B\cdots). \tag{2}$$

Here the permutations P interchange electrons only among *different* Λ_I.[9]

(B) The pair functions Λ_I are well behaved and normalized to unity:

$$\int\int|\Lambda_I(1,2)|^2 d\tau_1 d\tau_2=1 \text{ for all } I. \tag{3}$$

(C) There is a complete set of one-electron functions λ, called spin orbitals, which can be partitioned into subsets

$$\lambda_{a1},\,\lambda_{a2},\,\lambda_{a3},\,\cdots;\,\lambda_{b1},\,\lambda_{b2},\,\lambda_{b3},\,\cdots;\,\cdots;\,\lambda_{i1},\,\lambda_{i2},\,\lambda_{i3},\,\cdots;\,\cdots$$

such that the pair function Λ_I may be accurately expressed in terms of Slater determinants built from the subset I orbitals only, for all I. That is,

$$\Lambda_I=A_{I1}\Lambda_{I1}+A_{I2}\Lambda_{I2}+A_{I3}\Lambda_{I3}+\cdots, \tag{4}$$

where the A_{Ij} are constants and the Λ_{Ij} are Slater determinants built from the spin orbitals $\lambda_{i1}, \lambda_{i2}, \lambda_{i3}, \cdots$.

As a consequence of condition C, the individual Λ_I are mutually orthogonal in a generalized sense,[10,11]

$$\int\Lambda_I^*(1,2)\Lambda_J(1,4)d\tau_1\equiv0 \quad\text{for}\quad I\neq J, \tag{5}$$

$$\int\int\Lambda_I^*(1,2)\Lambda_J(1,2)d\tau_1 d\tau_2=0 \quad\text{for}\quad I\neq J. \tag{6}$$

From these orthogonality relations and condition B, it follows that the total wave function Λ is normalized,

$$\int\int\cdots\int|\Lambda|^2 d\tau_1 d\tau_2\cdots d\tau_{2n}=1. \tag{7}$$

III. TOTAL ELECTRONIC ENERGY OF A SYSTEM OF SEPARATED ELECTRON PAIRS

Consider a $2n$-electron system with a fixed nuclear framework consisting of various nuclei α with charges $Z_\alpha e$. The Hamiltonian determining the electronic motions may be written

$$\mathbf{H}^{\text{el}}(1,2,\cdots 2n)=\sum_{\zeta=1}^{2n}\mathbf{H}_N(\zeta)+\tfrac{1}{2}\sum_{\zeta,\eta=1}^{2n}{}'(e^2/r_{\zeta\eta}), \tag{8}$$

where

$$\mathbf{H}_N(\zeta)\equiv\mathbf{T}(\zeta)+\mathbf{U}_N(\zeta), \tag{9}$$

$$\mathbf{U}_N(\zeta)\equiv-\textstyle\sum_\alpha(Z_\alpha e^2/r_{\zeta\alpha}). \tag{10}$$

Here $\mathbf{U}_N(\zeta)$ gives the potential energy of attraction between electron ζ and the bare nuclei and $T(\zeta)$ is the kinetic energy operator for electron ζ; $\mathbf{H}_N(\zeta)$ thus would be the total Hamiltonian operator for electron ζ if the other electrons were absent.

Suppose now that the system can be described by a wave function Λ satisfying the separability conditions A, B, and C of Sec. II. The expectation value for the total electronic energy then is given by the formula[5]

$$E_\Lambda^{\text{el}}=\textstyle\sum_I I_I+\tfrac{1}{2}\sum_I\sum_{J\neq I}(J_{IJ}-K_{IJ}), \tag{11}$$

where the sums are over the distinct electron pairs $A, B, \cdots, M$. Here the quantity I_I is the electronic energy electron pair I would have if the other pairs were absent, that is

$$I_I\equiv\int\int\Lambda_I^*(1,2)\mathbf{H}^0(1,2)\Lambda_I(1,2)d\tau_1 d\tau_2, \tag{12}$$

where

$$\mathbf{H}^0(1,2)\equiv\mathbf{H}_N(1)+\mathbf{H}_N(2)+(e^2/r_{12}). \tag{13}$$

The quantity J_{IJ} is the total Coulomb repulsion between

---

[7] Hurley, Lennard-Jones, and Pople, Proc. Roy. Soc. (London) **A220**, 446 (1953). Compare the discussion by J. C. Slater, Quarterly Progr. Rept. No. 16 (Solid-State and Molecular Theory Group, Massachusetts Institute of Technology, Cambridge, Massachusetts, April 15, 1955), p. 5.

[8] The argument in this and the following section is given in a somewhat abbreviated form. For more detailed discussion see references 7; for a more general discussion see reference 5.

[9] Alternatively, one may write the normalizing factor simply as $(n!)^{-\frac{1}{2}}$ and sum over *all* permutations of electrons—see the appendix of reference 2.

[10] While Eq. (6) follows from Eq. (5), the reverse is not true. With the present model this is immaterial, but it should be well worth examining a model in which Eq. (6) is assumed, but not Eq. (5). One would then have what could be called *almost separated* or *almost orthogonal* electron pairs. Work on this type of model is in progress.

[11] As an alternative to the present condition C, one may *postulate* Eqs. (5) and (6), from which Dr. T. Arai of this laboratory has shown condition C can be proved.

electron pair I and electron pair J, that is,

$$J_{IJ}\equiv\iiiint \Lambda_I^*(1,2)\Lambda_J^*(3,4)\times[(e^2/r_{13})+(e^2/r_{14})+(e^2/r_{23})+(e^2/r_{24})]\times\Lambda_I(1,2)\Lambda_J(3,4)d\tau_1d\tau_2d\tau_3d\tau_4. \quad (14)$$

K_{IJ} is a corresponding exchange repulsion:

$$K_{IJ}\equiv\iiiint \Lambda_I^*(1,2)\Lambda_J^*(3,4)\times[(e^2/r_{13})\Lambda_I(3,2)\Lambda_J(1,4)+(e^2/r_{14})\Lambda_I(4,2)\Lambda_J(3,1)+(e^2/r_{23})\Lambda_I(1,3)\Lambda_J(2,4)+(e^2/r_{24})\Lambda_I(1,4)\Lambda_J(3,2)]d\tau_1d\tau_2d\tau_3d\tau_4. \quad (15)$$

It should be noted that in general $J_{II}\neq K_{II}$,[12] so that terms with $I=J$ necessarily must be left out of Eq. (11).

The fundamental Eq. (11) may be recast in several ways. Thus, if one defines

$$E_I\equiv I_I+\sum_{J\neq I}(J_{IJ}-K_{IJ}), \quad (16)$$

one may write

$$E_\Lambda{}^{\rm el}=\sum_I E_I-\tfrac{1}{2}\sum_I\sum_{J\neq I}(J_{IJ}-K_{IJ}). \quad (17)$$

Or, taking the average of Eqs. (12) and (18), one has

$$E_\Lambda{}^{\rm el}=\sum_I \tfrac{1}{2}(I_I+E_I)=\sum_I \bar{E}_I, \quad (18)$$

where

$$\bar{E}_I\equiv\tfrac{1}{2}(I_I+E_I) \quad (19)$$

or

$$\bar{E}_I\equiv I_I+\tfrac{1}{2}\sum_{J\neq I}(J_{IJ}-K_{IJ}). \quad (20)$$

Equations (11), (17), and (18) may be termed the *additive*, *subtractive*, and *median partitions* of the energy, respectively.[13]

Still another way of writing the energy is useful if one wishes to treat the electron pairs one at a time, each moving in the average field of the others. Suppose that attention is to be focused on pair K. Then Eq. (11) may be rewritten

$$E_\Lambda{}^{\rm el}=E_{\Lambda-K}{}^0+E_K. \quad (21)$$

Here $E_{\Lambda-K}{}^0$ is the total electronic energy of all the pairs but K, including their interactions with each other, *viz.*,

$$E_{\Lambda-K}{}^0\equiv\sum_{I\neq K} I_I+\tfrac{1}{2}\sum_{I\neq K}\sum_{J\neq K,I}(J_{IJ}-K_{IJ}). \quad (22)$$

The quantity E_K, on the other hand, is the energy of pair K *including all the interactions between pair K and other pairs*. That is, E_K is just the quantity defined by Eq. (16):

$$E_K=I_K+\sum_{J\neq K}(J_{KJ}-K_{KJ}). \quad (23)$$

Furthermore, this quantity E_K may be expressed in the form

$$E_K=\iint \Lambda_K^*(1,2)\mathbf{H}_K(1,2)\Lambda_K(1,2)d\tau_1d\tau_2. \quad (24)$$

Here

$$\mathbf{H}_K(1,2)\equiv[\mathbf{H}_N(1)+\mathbf{G}_{\Lambda-K}(1)]+[\mathbf{H}_N(2)+\mathbf{G}_{\Lambda-K}(2)]+(e^2/r_{12})=\mathbf{H}^0(1,2)+\sum_{I\neq K}[\mathbf{G}_I(1)+\mathbf{G}_I(2)], \quad (25)$$

where the $\mathbf{G}_{\Lambda-K}$ are Coulomb-exchange operators which take care of the mutual interactions of the pair K with the other pairs. Specifically,

$$\mathbf{G}_{\Lambda-K}(1)\equiv\mathbf{J}_{\Lambda-K}(1)-\mathbf{K}_{\Lambda-K}(1)=\sum_{I\neq K}[\mathbf{J}_I(1)-\mathbf{K}_I(1)]\equiv\sum_{I\neq K}\mathbf{G}_I(1), \quad (26)$$

where

$$\mathbf{J}_I(1)[\varphi(1)]\equiv\iint \Lambda_I^*(3,4)[(e^2/r_{13})+(e^2/r_{14})]\times\Lambda_I(3,4)\varphi(1)d\tau_3d\tau_4 \quad (27)$$

and

$$\mathbf{K}_I(1)[\varphi(1)]\equiv\iint \Lambda_I^*(3,4)[(e^2/r_{13})\Lambda_I(1,4)\varphi(3)+(e^2/r_{14})\Lambda_I(3,1)\varphi(4)]d\tau_3d\tau_4. \quad (28)$$

Here $\varphi(1)$ is an arbitrary well-behaved one-electron function. Each of the bracketed operators in Eq. (26) is a well-defined one-electron operator which is fixed for a fixed description of the electron pairs other than K.

The operators $\mathbf{J}_I$ and $\mathbf{K}_I$, and hence the operators $\mathbf{G}_I$ and $\mathbf{G}_{\Lambda-K}$, may be resolved into parts, making use of the expansion of Λ_I in terms of Slater determinants, Eq. (4). Thus

$$\mathbf{G}_I(1)=\sum_k\sum_l A_{Ik}^*A_{Il}\mathbf{G}_{kl}{}^I(1). \quad (29)$$

The component operators $\mathbf{G}_{kl}{}^I$ in turn are expressible in terms of operators $\mathbf{J}_{\lambda\lambda'}$ and $\mathbf{K}_{\lambda\lambda'}$ defined by

$$\mathbf{J}_{\lambda\lambda'}(1)[\varphi(1)]\equiv\int\lambda^*(2)\lambda'(2)(e^2/r_{12})\varphi(1)d\tau_2 \quad (30)$$

and

$$\mathbf{K}_{\lambda\lambda'}(1)[\varphi(1)]\equiv\int\lambda^*(2)\varphi(2)(e^2/r_{12})\lambda'(1)d\tau_2. \quad (31)$$

In fact,

$$\mathbf{G}_{kl}{}^I(1)=\sum_\lambda[\mathbf{J}_{\lambda\lambda}(1)-\mathbf{K}_{\lambda\lambda}(1)], \quad (32a)$$

$$\mathbf{G}_{kl}{}^I(1)=(\pm1)[\mathbf{J}_{\lambda\lambda'}(1)-\mathbf{K}_{\lambda\lambda'}(1)], \quad (32b)$$

$$\mathbf{G}_{kl}{}^I(1)=0, \quad (32c)$$

according as (a) $\Lambda_{Ik}\equiv\Lambda_{Il}$, the sum being over all spin orbitals occupied in Λ_{Ik}, (b) Λ_{Ik} can be transformed by an even (+1) or odd (−1) number of column interchanges into a determinant differing from Λ_{Il} in only one spin orbital, λ appearing in the transformed Λ_{Ik} where λ' appears in Λ_{Il}, or (c) neither (a) nor (b) applies. These equations give the explicit functional dependence of the operators $\mathbf{G}_{\Lambda-K}$ of Eq. (25) on the expansion coefficients A_{Ik} of Eq. (4), for a given

[12] For an antisymmetrized product Λ of one-electron functions Λ_I one does have $J_{II}=K_{II}$, but this case apparently is unique.

[13] Compare R. G. Parr, J. Chem. Phys. 19, 799 (1951).

partitioning into subsets of a given complete set of one-electron spin orbitals λ.

IV. MINIMIZATION OF THE TOTAL ELECTRONIC ENERGY OF A SYSTEM OF SEPARATED ELECTRON PAIRS

Procedures now will be described for finding a *best* separated electron-pair wave function for the ground electronic state of a particular nuclear configuration of a particular molecule.

First Method

In the method which most frequently would be employed in practice, one starts with some *specific* set of orthonormal one-electron spin orbitals λ partitioned into nonoverlapping subsets, λ_a, λ_b, $\cdots$, λ_m, in some *specific* way. One then asks, what is the best function $\Lambda\equiv(\Lambda_A\Lambda_B\cdots\Lambda_M)$ describing the system such that Λ_A can be expanded in terms of the λ_a, Λ_B in terms of the λ_b, and so on. This is a well-defined variational problem.

To obtain the solution one may use an iterative procedure. One first assumes some approximate zeroth order wave functions for all the electron pairs save one, say the pair K. These fix the value of the quantity $E_{\Lambda-K}{}^0$ of Eq. (21) and fix the operators $\mathbf{G}_{\Lambda-K}$ of Eq. (25). One then obtains a best pair K function Λ_K by minimizing, through constrained variation of Λ_K, the pair K energy E_K as computed from Eq. (24). The constrained variations of Λ_K are those variations which do not destroy the pair separability conditions, which amount to all variations of the coefficients A_{Kj} in the linear expansion

$$\Lambda_K=A_{K1}\Lambda_{K1}+A_{K2}\Lambda_{K2}+\cdots, \qquad (33)$$

where the Λ_{Kj} are the (fixed) set of all Slater determinants of order two that can be built from the (fixed) set of spin orbitals λ_k. The problem of finding the best such $\Lambda_K(1,2)$ thus is a two-electron linear variational problem of the conventional kind, with Hamiltonian operator $\mathbf{H}_K(1,2)$ of Eq. (25) and linear variation function $\Lambda_K(1,2)$ of Eq. (33).

Having found a best Λ_K, one turns to some other pair and adjusts its description. One then continues to adjust the individual pair descriptions one at a time but repeatedly until no further improvements are obtained. There will result the best possible such electron-pair description of the system of interest.

This method will be further elaborated below. It has been used by the authors and found to converge satisfactorily.

Second Method

A more general method results if the restriction is lifted that the one-electron orbitals be a specific set of functions partitioned in a specific way. One can (in principle at least) seek the *best* set of one-electron functions and the *best* partitioning of them. By the variational principle, results so obtained must always be at least as good, energy-wise, as results obtained with specific functions specifically partitioned.

If one does not wish to try one set after another of partitioned one-electron functions, *ad* double *infinitum*, one might hope to deal directly with the two-electron functions. The mathematical procedure required for this would seem to amount to a direct generalization of the familiar Hartree-Fock technique for determining molecular orbital wave functions.[14] This *generalized self-consistent field procedure* will not be further considered here, since its practicability is questionable.[15]

V. BEST ORBITAL DESCRIPTION OF A SYSTEM OF SEPARATED ELECTRON-PAIR BONDS

In actual molecules there frequently are a number of electron pairs separated in space from one another, each pair localized between two atoms—"electron-pair bonds." Further, in constructing wave functions for such electron pairs one frequently employs just one atomic orbital (two atomic spin orbitals) on each of the bonded atoms, supposing that a good enough description results from mixing the "covalent" and "ionic" functions that can be built from these orbitals. Thus it is pertinent to examine what the equations in the previous sections give when this particular restricted orbital base is used.

A single *electron-pair bond in orbital description* may be defined as an electron pair accurately describable by a singlet[16] antisymmetrized wave function that can be built from the two atomic orbitals (normalized but not necessarily orthogonal) χ_a and χ_b and the two spin functions α and β. Equivalently, it is a pair describable by a singlet wave function that can be built from the two molecular orbitals (normalized and orthogonal)

$$\begin{aligned}\phi_1&=[2(1+S)]^{-\frac{1}{2}}(\chi_a+\chi_b),\\ \phi_2&=[2(1-S)]^{-\frac{1}{2}}(\chi_a-\chi_b),\end{aligned} \qquad (34)$$

and the spin functions α and β, where $S\equiv S_{ab}$ is the overlap integral between χ_a and χ_b. That is, if

$$\Phi_1\equiv(\phi_1\bar{\phi}_1)\equiv(1/\sqrt{2})\begin{vmatrix}(\phi_1\alpha)^1 & (\phi_1\beta)^1\\ (\phi_1\alpha)^2 & (\phi_1\beta)^2\end{vmatrix}, \qquad (35)$$

$$\Phi_2\equiv(1/\sqrt{2})[(\phi_1\bar{\phi}_2)+(\phi_2\bar{\phi}_1)], \qquad (36)$$

$$\Phi_3\equiv(\phi_2\bar{\phi}_2), \qquad (37)$$

then an electron-pair bond in orbital description is an electron pair described by a wave function Λ having the form

$$\Lambda=A_1\Phi_1+A_2\Phi_2+A_3\Phi_3. \qquad (38)$$

[14] C. C. J. Roothaan, Revs. Modern Phys. 23, 69 (1951).

[15] The fact that $J_{II}\neq K_{II}$ in the two-electron case (cf. footnote 12) prevents one from obtaining a two-electron generalized Hartree-Fock equation of the simple form $\mathbf{F}\Lambda=E\Lambda$. Instead, one obtains equations of the form $\mathbf{F}_K'\Lambda_K=\sum_L E_{KL}\Lambda_L$, with the operators $\mathbf{F}_K'$ dependent on K.

[16] Consideration is here given only to the case in which the spins of the two electrons in each pair are antiparallel. See however Sec. X.

If the coefficients A_1, A_2 and A_3 are such as to minimize the electronic energy, the wave function Λ may be said to be the *best orbital description* of the given electron-pair bond.[17]

More generally, one may have several electron-pair bonds, A, B, $\cdots$, M, having orbital descriptions, Λ_A, Λ_B, $\cdots$, Λ_M, each of the form of Eq. (38):

$$\begin{aligned}\Lambda_A &= A_{A1}\Phi_{A1}+A_{A2}\Phi_{A2}+A_{A3}\Phi_{A3},\\ \Lambda_B &= A_{B1}\Phi_{B1}+A_{B2}\Phi_{B2}+A_{B3}\Phi_{B3},\\ &\cdots\\ \Lambda_M &= A_{M1}\Phi_{M1}+A_{M2}\Phi_{M2}+A_{M3}\Phi_{M3}.\end{aligned} \tag{39}$$

If, in addition, the (singlet) many-pair function,

$$\Lambda=[\Lambda_A\Lambda_B\cdots\Lambda_M], \tag{40}$$

satisfies the separability conditions A, B, and C of Sec. II, then one has a *system of separated electron-pair bonds in orbital description*. If the coefficients A_{Im} of Eq. (39) are such as to minimize the total electronic energy, one has in the function Λ of Eq. (40) the *best orbital description* of the given system of separated electron-pair bonds.

A sufficient condition that a system of electron-pair bonds in orbital description be separated in this sense is that the pair I atomic orbitals χ_{Ia} and χ_{Ib} be orthogonal to the pair J atomic orbitals χ_{Ja} and χ_{Jb}, for any two distinct pairs I and J. Such orthogonality does hold strictly for the atomic orbitals in common use in some cases of interest (e.g., sigma with pi orbitals in planar molecules); it does not hold strictly in others (e.g., bonding orbitals on nonneighbor carbon atoms in a saturated hydrocarbon). The latter circumstance does not reduce the value of following out the consequences of exact separability, however. The general analysis will be valid as long as the precise form of the atomic orbitals is not specified; and even if at some time orbitals are introduced which do not satisfy the orthogonality requirement exactly, orthogonality may still be a useful approximation.[18]

Variational determination of the coefficients A_{Im} may be carried out with the formulas of Sec. III and the iterative procedure of Sec. IV. The idea is to minimize the total energy by adjusting the pair descriptions one at a time. To determine the best pair K function, Λ_K, at a given stage, all other pair functions being specified at that stage, one must solve a linear variational problem with Hamiltonian operator $\mathbf{H}_K(1,2)$ of Eq. (25). This leads to the secular equations for the coefficients,

$$\sum_{m=1}^{3} A_{Km}[H_{mn}{}^K-\delta_{mn}E_K]=0, \quad n=1,2,3 \tag{41}$$

and the determinantal equation for the energy,

$$\begin{vmatrix} H_{11}-E_K & H_{12} & H_{13}\\ H_{12} & H_{22}-E_K & H_{23}\\ H_{13} & H_{23} & H_{33}-E_K\end{vmatrix}=0, \tag{42}$$

where

$$H_{mn}\equiv H_{mn}{}^K=\int\int \Phi_{Km}\mathbf{H}_K(1,2)\Phi_{Kn}d\tau_1 d\tau_2. \tag{43}$$

Here and henceforth for simplicity all orbitals are assumed real.

The wave functions for the other pairs enter these equations through the operators G_I in Eq. (25). Application of Eqs. (29) and (32) to the present case will give these operators in terms of Coulomb and exchange operators $J_{\lambda\lambda'}$ and $K_{\lambda\lambda'}$. Introducing the notations (subscripts I suppressed on λ's for brevity), $\lambda_1\equiv(\phi_{I1}\alpha)$, $\langle\lambda_1\rangle\equiv(\phi_{I1}\beta)$, $\lambda_2\equiv(\phi_{I2}\alpha)$, $\langle\lambda_2\rangle\equiv(\phi_{I2}\beta)$, one thus obtains[19]

$$\begin{aligned}\mathbf{G}_I=&(A_{I1}{}^2+\tfrac{1}{2}A_{I2}{}^2)\\ &\times[(\mathbf{J}_{\lambda_1\lambda_1}-\mathbf{K}_{\lambda_1\lambda_1})+(\mathbf{J}_{\langle\lambda_1\rangle\langle\lambda_1\rangle}-\mathbf{K}_{\langle\lambda_1\rangle\langle\lambda_1\rangle})]\\ &+(A_{I3}{}^2+\tfrac{1}{2}A_{I2}{}^2)\\ &\times[(\mathbf{J}_{\lambda_2\lambda_2}-\mathbf{K}_{\lambda_2\lambda_2})+(\mathbf{J}_{\langle\lambda_2\rangle\langle\lambda_2\rangle}-\mathbf{K}_{\langle\lambda_2\rangle\langle\lambda_2\rangle})]\\ &+\sqrt{2}A_{I2}(A_{I1}+A_{I3})\\ &\times[(\mathbf{J}_{\lambda_1\lambda_2}-\mathbf{K}_{\lambda_1\lambda_2})+(\mathbf{J}_{\langle\lambda_1\rangle\langle\lambda_2\rangle}-\mathbf{K}_{\langle\lambda_1\rangle\langle\lambda_2\rangle})].\end{aligned} \tag{44}$$

This is a fairly complex expression for $\mathbf{G}_I$, which contains spin. It is possible to express $\mathbf{G}_I$ in a somewhat simpler, *spin-free form*. Indeed, if one defines the operator

$$\mathbf{G}_{\phi\phi'}\equiv\mathbf{J}_{\phi\phi'}-\tfrac{1}{2}\mathbf{K}_{\phi\phi'}, \tag{45}$$

where ϕ and ϕ' are any two one-electron *space* functions, then one may write

$$\begin{aligned}\mathbf{G}_I=&(A_{I1}{}^2+\tfrac{1}{2}A_{I2}{}^2)2\mathbf{G}_{\phi_1\phi_1}+(A_{I3}{}^2+\tfrac{1}{2}A_{I2}{}^2)2\mathbf{G}_{\phi_2\phi_2}\\ &+\sqrt{2}A_{I2}(A_{I1}+A_{I3})2\mathbf{G}_{\phi_1\phi_2}.\end{aligned} \tag{46}$$

This formula is spin-free, yet it is exact.

A final reduction of $\mathbf{G}_I$ can be achieved through use of the Eqs. (34), which give the molecular orbitals ϕ_{I1} and ϕ_{I2} in terms of atomic orbitals χ_{Ia} and χ_{Ib}. Straightforward expansion yields (subscripts I and symbols χ suppressed)

$$\begin{aligned}2\mathbf{G}_{\phi_1\phi_1}&=(1+S)^{-1}(\mathbf{G}_{aa}+\mathbf{G}_{bb}+2\mathbf{G}_{ab}),\\ 2\mathbf{G}_{\phi_2\phi_2}&=(1-S)^{-1}(\mathbf{G}_{aa}+\mathbf{G}_{bb}-2\mathbf{G}_{ab}),\\ 2\mathbf{G}_{\phi_1\phi_2}&=(1-S^2)^{-\frac{1}{2}}(\mathbf{G}_{aa}-\mathbf{G}_{bb}).\end{aligned} \tag{47}$$

These expressions may be inserted into Eq. (46) to give a general working formula for $\mathbf{G}_I$.

Returning to the Eqs. (41)–(43) determining the pair

[17] A pair of nonbonding electrons in an atomic orbital on an atom may be treated as a case of an "electron pair bond" through the device of setting $A_2=A_3=0$ in Eq. (38) and interpreting ϕ_1 as the atomic orbital.

[18] Compare footnote 1 and the discussions in references 7.

[19] Note that the functions Φ_2 of Eq. (36) are not single determinants but normalized sums of two determinants.

K function, one may now rewrite Eq. (25) in the form

$$\mathbf{H}_K(1,2)=\mathbf{H}_{\Lambda-K}(1)+\mathbf{H}_{\Lambda-K}(2)+(e^2/r_{12}), \quad (48)$$

where

$$\mathbf{H}_{\Lambda-K}(1)\equiv\mathbf{H}_N(1)+\sum_{I\neq K}\mathbf{G}_I(1) \quad (49)$$

is a well-behaved spin-free one-electron operator. Reduction of the matrix elements $H_{mn}{}^K$ then proceeds by standard means.[20] The results are as follows (superscripts K suppressed):

$$\begin{aligned} H_{11}&=2I_{11}+(11|11),\\ H_{22}&=I_{11}+I_{22}+(11|22)+(12|12),\\ H_{33}&=2I_{22}+(22|22),\\ H_{12}&=\sqrt{2}[I_{12}+(12|11)],\\ H_{23}&=\sqrt{2}[I_{12}+(12|22)],\\ H_{13}&=(12|12). \end{aligned} \quad (50)$$

Here[21]

$$I_{ij}\equiv I_{ij}{}^K\equiv\int\phi_{Ki}(1)H_{\Lambda-K}(1)\phi_{Kj}(1)dv_1 \quad (51)$$

and

$$(ij|kl)\equiv(ij|kl)^K$$

$$\equiv\int\int\phi_{Ki}(1)\phi_{Kj}(1)(e^2/r_{12})\phi_{Kk}(2)\phi_{Kl}(2)dv_1dv_2 \quad (52)$$

are integrals over molecular orbitals, as indicated, readily expressible in terms of corresponding integrals over atomic orbitals.

The electronic repulsion integrals in Eqs. (52) involve the pair K orbitals only. In Eqs. (51), on the other hand, there arise, through the operators $\mathbf{G}_I$, electronic repulsion integrals representing Coulomb and exchange interactions between the pair K orbitals and the orbitals in the other pairs.

VI. APPROXIMATIONS AND SIMPLIFICATIONS

To work with the above equations in a given problem, one must be willing to compute a large array of two-electron electronic repulsion integrals. This is perfectly feasible in principle and in some cases in practice. Considerable interest attaches to semiquantitative treatment of these equations however. It is only sensible to do first calculations with simpler equations, and the simpler equations also are more likely to correspond to the pictorial theories of the chemist.

To simplify the evaluation of the pair K electronic repulsions in Eqs. (52), it is convenient to make the *Mulliken approximation*,[22,23]

$$2a(1)b(1)=S_{ab}[a^2(1)+b^2(1)]. \quad (53)$$

Or, in operator language,

$$2\mathbf{J}_{ab}=S_{ab}(\mathbf{J}_{aa}+\mathbf{J}_{bb}). \quad (54)$$

With this assumption, Eqs. (34) and (52) yield

$$\begin{aligned} 4(11|11)&=4(22|22)=4(11|22)\\ &=[(aa|aa)+(bb|bb)+2(aa|bb)],\\ 4(11|12)&=4(12|22)\\ &=(1-S^2)^{-\frac{1}{2}}[(aa|aa)-(bb|bb)],\\ 4(12|12)&=(1-S^2)^{-\frac{1}{2}}[(aa|aa)+(bb|bb)-2(aa|bb)]. \end{aligned} \quad (55)$$

There remain in these equations only Coulomb integrals, which are comparatively easy to evaluate.

To simplify the evaluation of the Coulomb-exchange interactions between the pair K electrons and the electrons in the other pairs, which interactions are present in the integrals of Eq. (51) through the $\mathbf{G}_I$ terms in Eq. (49), it is convenient to make the *generalized Mulliken approximation*,[24]

$$2\mathbf{G}_{ab}=S_{ab}(\mathbf{G}_{aa}+\mathbf{G}_{bb}). \quad (56)$$

With this approximation, Eqs. (47) become

$$\begin{aligned} 2\mathbf{G}_{\phi1\phi1}&=2\mathbf{G}_{\phi2\phi2}=(\mathbf{G}_{aa}+\mathbf{G}_{bb}),\\ 2\mathbf{G}_{\phi1\phi2}&=(1-S^2)^{-\frac{1}{2}}(\mathbf{G}_{aa}-\mathbf{G}_{bb}), \end{aligned} \quad (57)$$

and Eq. (46) yields (note that $\sum_m|A_{Im}|^2=1$)

$$\mathbf{G}_I=\mathbf{G}_{aa}(1+Q_I)+\mathbf{G}_{bb}(1-Q_I), \quad (58)$$

where

$$Q_I\equiv\sqrt{2}(1-S^2)^{-\frac{1}{2}}A_{I2}(A_{I1}+A_{I3}). \quad (59)$$

The quantity Q_I has a physical meaning which can be read from Eq. (58): it is essentially the positive charge, in units of e, which in bond I is transferred from atom Ia to atom Ib as a result of bond formation in the molecule, or the negative charge transferred from Ib to Ia. Q_I may be termed the bond I *polarity parameter*.

The ultimate meaning of Eqs. (53) and (56) will not be discussed in detail here. Equation (53) has been put to quantitative test when used in conjunction with Slater orbitals; the results are reasonably satisfactory.[25] The extension of Eq. (53) involved in Eq. (56) probably is percentagewise not as good, but this extension here will be used only for estimating terms which, to begin with, are rather small. And it is not the final test of Eq. (53), or of Eq. (56), to test it with Slater orbitals. In the present discussion the precise form of the atomic orbitals has not yet been specified—this provides a degree of freedom which is not commonly recognized. *Orbitals better for molecular calculations than Slater orbitals quite possibly may obey equations such as Eq. (53) more closely than do Slater orbitals.*[26]

[20] E. U. Condon and G. H. Shortley, *Theory of Atomic Spectra* (Cambridge University Press, New York, 1935).

[21] Volume elements $d\tau$ imply integrations over space and spin; volume elements dv imply integrations over space only.

[22] R. S. Mulliken, J. Chem. Phys. **46**, 497 (1949).

[23] K. Ruedenberg, J. Chem. Phys. **19**, 1433 (1951).

[24] This generalization of Mulliken's approximation also is covered by the discussion in reference 23.

[25] For example, R. S. Barker and H. Eyring, J. Chem. Phys. **22**, 2072 (1954), or F. O. Ellison, *ibid.* **23**, 2358 (1955).

[26] To explore this further, one could attempt to show, by some sort of variational analysis, that an improvement in orbital form would result in a closer compliance with Eq. (53). A rudimentary

Under these assumptions, the equations in the previous section simplify considerably. With the definitions,

$$\alpha_a \equiv \alpha_{Ka} \equiv I_{aa}{}^K, \quad \alpha_b \equiv \alpha_{Kb} \equiv I_{bb}{}^K, \tag{60}$$

$$\beta \equiv \beta_K \equiv (1-S^2)^{-1}[I_{ab}{}^K - S(I_{aa}{}^K + I_{bb}{}^K)], \tag{61}$$

$$\gamma_{aa} \equiv \gamma_{KaKa} \equiv (aa|aa)^K, \quad \gamma_{bb} \equiv \gamma_{KbKb} \equiv (bb|bb)^K, \tag{62}$$

$$\gamma_{ab} \equiv \gamma_{KaKb} \equiv (aa|bb)^K, \tag{63}$$

the Eqs. (50) become (superscripts and subscripts K suppressed)

$$\begin{aligned} H_{11} &= \alpha_a + \alpha_b + 2(1-S)\beta + \tfrac{1}{4}(\gamma_{aa} + \gamma_{bb} + 2\gamma_{ab}), \\ H_{22} - H_{11} &= -2\beta + \tfrac{1}{4}(1-S^2)^{-\frac{1}{2}}(\gamma_{aa} + \gamma_{bb} - 2\gamma_{ab}), \\ H_{33} - H_{11} &= -4\beta, \\ H_{12} = H_{23} &= [2(1-S^2)]^{-\frac{1}{2}} \times [(\alpha_a - \alpha_b) + \tfrac{1}{2}(\gamma_{aa} - \gamma_{bb})], \\ H_{13} &= \tfrac{1}{4}(1-S^2)^{-\frac{1}{2}}(\gamma_{aa} + \gamma_{bb} - 2\gamma_{ab}). \end{aligned} \tag{64}$$

These are the matrix elements of the Eqs. (41) and (42) which determine the pair K coefficients A_{Km} and the pair K energy E_K.

The other pairs enter Eqs. (64) only through the quantities α_{Ka}, α_{Kb} and β_K. For α_{Ka} and α_{Kb} one has, from Eqs. (49), (51), (58), and (60),

$$\begin{aligned} \alpha_{Ka} = \alpha_{NKa} + \textstyle\sum_{I \neq K} \Big[& (1+Q_I) \int \chi_{Ka}(1) \mathbf{G}_{IaIa}(1) \chi_{Ka}(1) dv_1 \\ & + (1-Q_I) \int \chi_{Ka}(1) \mathbf{G}_{IbIb}(1) \chi_{Ka}(1) dv_1 \Big], \\ \alpha_{Kb} = \alpha_{NKb} + \textstyle\sum_{I \neq K} \Big[& (1+Q_I) \int \chi_{Kb}(1) \mathbf{G}_{IaIa}(1) \chi_{Kb}(1) dv_1 \\ & + (1-Q_I) \int \chi_{Kb}(1) \mathbf{G}_{IbIb}(1) \chi_{Kb}(1) dv_1 \Big], \end{aligned} \tag{65}$$

where

$$\alpha_{NKa} \equiv \int \chi_{Ka}(1) \mathbf{H}_N(1) \chi_{Ka}(1) dv_1,$$
$$\alpha_{NKb} \equiv \int \chi_{Kb}(1) \mathbf{H}_N(1) \chi_{Kb}(1) dv_1. \tag{66}$$

More compactly, if one defines

$$\zeta_{pq} \equiv (pp|qq) - \tfrac{1}{2}(pq|pq), \tag{67}$$

then one has

$$\begin{aligned} \alpha_{Ka} &= \alpha_{NKa} + \textstyle\sum_{I\neq K}[(\zeta_{KaIa} + \zeta_{KaIb}) + Q_I(\zeta_{KaIa} - \zeta_{KaIb})], \\ \alpha_{Kb} &= \alpha_{NKb} + \textstyle\sum_{I\neq K}[(\zeta_{KbIa} + \zeta_{KbIb}) + Q_I(\zeta_{KbIa} - \zeta_{KbIb})]. \end{aligned} \tag{68}$$

argument of this sort goes as follows: If $\delta \equiv (ab) - (S/2)[(aa) + (bb)]$ is the "error" function for atomic orbitals a and b, then for the semilocalized orbitals $a + \lambda b \equiv a'$ and $b + \lambda a \equiv b'$ the corresponding error function δ' is less than δ, provided λ is positive.

The formula for β_K is even simpler; if one uses Eq. (56) one finds[27]

$$\beta_K = \beta_{NK} \tag{69}$$

where

$$\beta_{NK} \equiv \tfrac{1}{2}(1-S^2)^{-1}\Big[\int \chi_{Ka}(1)\mathbf{H}_N(1)\chi_{Kb}(1)dv_1 + \int \chi_{Kb}(1)\mathbf{H}_N(1)\chi_{Ka}(1)dv_1 - S(\alpha_{NKa} + \alpha_{NKb})\Big]. \tag{70}$$

According to Eq. (69), *the quantity β_K is independent of the polarities of the other bonds;* it is even independent of whether the other electron pairs are present or not! This fact is very helpful in actual calculations.

This completes a prescription for carrying out a determination of the best orbital description of a system of separated electron-pair bonds. In a given problem first all of the basic integrals, S, α_N, β, γ, and ζ, must be calculated (or otherwise obtained); the calculation then may proceed iteratively as described in Sec. IV above.

VII. BOND MOMENTS

Before considering what can be said about the effects of the various polarity parameters Q_I on each other, it is convenient to examine the dependence of the charge distribution in bond K on its own polarity parameter Q_K:

$$Q_K \equiv \sqrt{2}(1-S_{ab}{}^2)^{-\frac{1}{2}} A_{K2}(A_{K1} + A_{K3}). \tag{71}$$

An appropriate measure of the asymmetry in the pair K distribution is the contribution to the molecular dipole moment due to it, along the bond axis—the *bond moment*. This may be taken as

$$\mu_K = -e \int\int \Lambda_K(1,2)[z(1)+z(2)]\Lambda_K(1,2) d\tau_1 d\tau_2, \tag{72}$$

where z is measured along the bond axis, with nucleus Ka at $z = -\frac{1}{2}R_K$ and nucleus Kb at $z = +\frac{1}{2}R_K$. Or,

$$\mu_K = -e \sum_{m=1}^{3} \sum_{n=1}^{3} A_{Km} A_{Kn} M_{mn}{}^K, \tag{73}$$

where

$$M_{mn} \equiv M_{mn}{}^K \equiv \int\int \Phi_{Km}(1,2) \times [z(1)+z(2)] \Phi_{Kn}(1,2) d\tau_1 d\tau_2. \tag{74}$$

Evaluation of the $M_{mn}{}^K$ is reasonably straightforward. One defines quantities δ_{Ka}, δ_{Kb}, δ_{Kab} by the

[27] It should be noted that Mulliken's approximation, Eq. (63), is *not* used in the integrals involving $H_N(1)$.

formulas

$$\int \chi_{Ka}(1)z(1)\chi_{Ka}(1)dv_1 \equiv -\tfrac{1}{2}R_K(1-2\delta_{Ka}),$$

$$\int \chi_{Kb}(1)z(1)\chi_{Kb}(1)dv_1 \equiv +\tfrac{1}{2}R_K(1-2\delta_{Kb}), \quad (75)$$

$$\int \chi_{Ka}(1)z(1)\chi_{Kb}(1)dv_1 \equiv \tfrac{1}{2}R_K\delta_{Kab}.$$

One then finds

$$\begin{aligned} M_{11} &= (1+S)^{-1}(\delta_{Ka}-\delta_{Kb}+\delta_{Kab})R_K,\\ M_{22} &= (1-S^2)^{-1}(\delta_{Ka}-\delta_{Kb}-S\delta_{Kab})R_K,\\ M_{33} &= (1-S)^{-1}(\delta_{Ka}-\delta_{Kb}-\delta_{Kab})R_K, \quad (76)\\ M_{12} &= M_{23}{}^K = [2(1-S^2)]^{-\frac{1}{2}}(\delta_{Ka}+\delta_{Kb}-1)R_K,\\ M_{13} &= 0. \end{aligned}$$

Here δ_{Ka} is the fractional displacement toward atom Kb from atom Ka of the center of charge of the orbital χ_{Ka}, δ_{Kb} is the fractional displacement toward atom Ka from atom Kb of the center of charge of the orbital χ_{Kb}, and δ_{Kab} is the fractional displacement toward Kb from the geometric center of the $Ka-Kb$ bond of the center of charge of the overlap distribution $\chi_{Ka}\chi_{Kb}$.

Combination of Eqs. (71), (73), and (76) gives the formula,

$$\begin{aligned} -(\mu_K/eR_K) = (1-S^2)^{-1}(\delta_{Ka}-\delta_{Kb})[1-S(A_{K1}{}^2-A_{K3}{}^2)]\\ +(1-S^2)^{-1}\delta_{Kab}[(A_{K1}{}^2-A_{K3}{}^2)-S]\\ -Q_K(1-\delta_{Ka}-\delta_{Kb}). \quad (77) \end{aligned}$$

The first term on the right represents the contribution to the bond moment of *atomic dipoles;* the second term represents the *homopolar moment.* The third term represents the contribution to the moment due to charge transfer—the *heteropolar moment.*

Equation (77) gives the pair K moment accurately if the pair K wave function is accurately given by Eq. (39). An approximate formula results if the homopolar dipole is expressed in terms of atomic dipoles using Eq. (53):

$$\delta_{Kab} = S_{ab}(\delta_{Ka}-\delta_{Kb}). \quad (78)$$

Then

$$-(\mu_K/eR_K) = (\delta_{Ka}-\delta_{Kb}) - Q_K(1-\delta_{Ka}-\delta_{Kb}). \quad (79)$$

If in addition the atomic dipoles may be neglected, a very simple form is obtained,

$$\mu_K = eR_KQ_K. \quad (80)$$

This should make clear the physical significance and importance of the polarity parameters Q_K.

VIII. INTRABOND CHARGE TRANSFER EFFECTS AND ELECTRONEGATIVITIES

The quantities Q_I, for $I\neq K$, enter the equations determining the pair K function, Eqs. (41) and (42), only through the quantities α_{Ka} and α_{Kb} of Eqs. (68), and they appear in these quantities linearly. How do the values of the several Q_I affect the value of Q_K?

Solution of the equations in a given case always will provide the answer to this question for that case. Considerable general insight can be obtained by an inspection of one key equation, however. If one substitutes the second of Eqs. (41), namely,

$$A_{K2} = -H_{12}{}^K(H_{22}{}^K-E_K)^{-1}(A_{K1}+A_{K3}), \quad (81)$$

in Eq. (71), one obtains

$$\begin{aligned} Q_K = -\sqrt{2}H_{12}{}^K(1-S^2)^{-\frac{1}{2}}\\ \times(H_{22}{}^K-E_K)^{-1}(A_{K1}+A_{K3})^2, \quad (82) \end{aligned}$$

where E_K is an appropriate root of Eq. (42). This equation is very useful for examining intrabond charge transfer effects.

Consider, for example, the molecular ground state in a case where no bond is very polar (as for a saturated hydrocarbon). Then

$$A_{K1}+A_{K3} \doteq 1. \quad (83)$$

Also

$$1-S^2 \doteq 1, \quad (84)$$

and if it is supposed for simplicity that the contribution of Φ_3 is small,

$$H_{22}{}^K-E_K \doteq H_{22}{}^K-H_{11}{}^K. \quad (85)$$

Then Eq. (82) gives

$$Q_K \doteq -\sqrt{2}H_{12}{}^K(H_{22}{}^K-H_{11}{}^K)^{-1}. \quad (86)$$

According to Eqs. (64), (68), and (69), $H_{22}{}^K-H_{11}{}^K$ is Q_I independent and $H_{12}{}^K$ depends linearly on the Q_I, for $I\neq K$. Equation (86) thus is a linear relation among the n distinct Q_I. There being an equation of the same form for every K, one has n simultaneous linear equations in n unknowns, which can be solved in the usual way.

More generally, one must consider the Q_I dependence of the factors $H_{22}{}^K-E_K$ and $A_{K1}+A_{K3}$ in Eq. (82), which will not always be negligible. That the factor $H_{12}{}^K$ usually will dominate is clear, however. This, plus the form of Eq. (80), suggests that the quantity $H_{12}{}^K$ plays the role of what one would like to call an electronegativity difference.

One is thus motivated to define Y_K, an *electronegativity difference* of *atomic orbital electronegativities* y_{Ka} and y_{Kb}, as follows:

$$\begin{aligned} Y_K \equiv y_{Ka}-y_{Kb} \equiv -\sqrt{2}(1-S_{ab}{}^2)^{\frac{1}{2}}H_{12}{}^K\\ = (\alpha_{Kb}-\alpha_{Ka})+\tfrac{1}{2}(\gamma_{KbKb}-\gamma_{KaKa}). \quad (87) \end{aligned}$$

One then has Q_K *essentially* proportional to Y, μ *essentially* proportional to Y, and Y *strictly* linear in the Q_I.

Equation (87) contains the essence of a definition of

electronegativity. It can be related to Mulliken's definition of an electronegativity,[28]

$$x_{Ka}=\tfrac{1}{2}(\mathcal{I}_{Ka}+A_{Ka}), \qquad (88)$$

where $\mathcal{I}_{Ka}$ is the orbital Ka ionization potential and A_{Ka} is its electron affinity, in the following manner. One defines quantities U_{Kb} and U_{Kb}^0 by the formulas

$$\mathbf{U}_{Kb}(1)\equiv-(e^2/r_{1Kb})\equiv\mathbf{U}_{Kb}^0(1)-\mathbf{G}_{KbKb}(1), \qquad (89)$$

and similarly $\mathbf{U}_{Ka}$, $\mathbf{U}_{Ia}$, $\mathbf{U}_{Ia}^0$, $\mathbf{U}_{Ib}$, $\mathbf{U}_{Ib}^0$. One further defines

$$P_{Ka}\equiv-\int\chi_{Ka}(1)\{\mathbf{U}_{Kb}^0(1)+\textstyle\sum_{I\neq K}[\mathbf{U}_{Ia}^0(1)+\mathbf{U}_{Ib}^0(1)]\}\chi_{Ka}(1)dv_1, \qquad (90)$$

and similarly P_{Kb}. One sets

$$-\mathcal{I}_{Ka}\equiv\int\chi_{Ka}(1)[\mathbf{T}(1)+\mathbf{U}_{Ka}(1)]\chi_{Ka}(1)dv_1, \qquad (91)$$

and similarly with $-\mathcal{I}_{Kb}$. One then finds, from Eqs. (9), (10), (66), and (68),

$$\alpha_{Ka}=-\mathcal{I}_{Ka}-P_{Ka}-\textstyle\sum_{I\neq K}Q_I(\zeta_{KaIa}-\zeta_{KaIb})-\zeta_{KaKb}, \qquad (92)$$

$$\alpha_{Kb}=-\mathcal{I}_{Kb}-P_{Kb}-\textstyle\sum_{I\neq K}Q_I(\zeta_{KbIa}-\zeta_{KbIb})-\zeta_{KaKb}.$$

Hence Eq. (87) gives

$$y_{Ka}-y_{Kb}=[-\mathcal{I}_{Ka}-\tfrac{1}{2}\gamma_{KaKa}+P_{Ka}+\textstyle\sum_{I\neq K}Q_I(\zeta_{KaIa}-\zeta_{KaIb})]-[-\mathcal{I}_{Kb}-\tfrac{1}{2}\gamma_{KbKb}+P_{Kb}+\textstyle\sum_{I\neq K}Q_I(\zeta_{KbIa}-\zeta_{KbIb})]. \qquad (93)$$

One now further takes

$$\gamma_{KaKa}=\mathcal{I}_{Ka}-A_{Ka}, \qquad (94)$$

and similarly γ_{KbKb}, and one sets each of the bracketed terms in Eq. (93) equal to the corresponding y. One then obtains, finally,

$$y_{Ka}=x_{Ka}+P_{Ka}+\textstyle\sum_{I\neq K}Q_I(\zeta_{KaIa}-\zeta_{KaIb}), \qquad (95)$$

and similarly y_{Kb}. This provides two corrections to Mulliken's formula—the "neutral penetration" term P_{Ka} and the intrabond charge transfer terms involving the Q_I.[29]

The critical step in going from Eq. (87) to Eq. (95) is Eq. (94)—the rest are matters of definition. A detailed discussion of the correctness (or incorrectness!) of Eq. (94) will not be given here. It is the simplest possible expression of Moffitt's atoms-in-molecules idea,[30] a device to insure that molecular energies come out right at least at infinite interatomic distances.[31] Actually, from the theoretical point of view Eqs. (91) and (94) are not entirely compatible[32]; whether both should be retained in semiempirical schemes (which has been done with great success)[33] remains problematical.

Equation (93), it should be noted, gives the $Ka-Kb$ electronegativity difference *before* charge transfer in bond K—a sort of potential difference furnishing a driving force for charge transfer.

IX. BOND ENERGIES

The problem now to be considered is whether the total molecular energy, including the nuclear repulsions, can be written as a sum of bond energies, with the energy of a bond independent of the presence of other bonds.

One equation is already at hand that bodes well for a favorable situation, Eq. (18) for the total electronic energy,

$$E^{\text{el}}=\textstyle\sum_K\bar{E}_K, \qquad (96)$$

where

$$\bar{E}_K\equiv\tfrac{1}{2}(E_K+I_K). \qquad (97)$$

Here E_K is the pair K electronic energy taking cognizance of other pairs, and I_K is the pair K electronic energy if the other pairs were absent. The basic questions are whether addition of nuclear repulsion energies will destroy additivity and to what extent the various pair K energy terms are "other-pair" dependent.

To take the second question first, the best orbital approximation to E_K, as determined by solution of Eq. (42), may be written

$$E_K=H_{11}^K+A_{K2}^2(H_{22}^K-H_{11}^K)+A_{K3}^2(H_{33}^K-H_{11}^K)+2(A_{K1}+A_{K3})A_{K2}H_{12}^K+2A_{K1}A_{K3}H_{13}^K, \qquad (98)$$

where the matrix elements H_{mn}^K are given by Eqs. (64). These matrix elements depend on the other pairs only through α_{Ka} and α_{Kb}, which enter H_{11}^K and H_{12}^K but not $H_{22}^K-H_{11}^K$, $H_{33}^K-H_{11}^K$ and H_{13}^K. Using Eq. (71), Eq. (98) thus may be rewritten in the form

$$E_K=\alpha_{Ka}(1+Q_K)+\alpha_{Kb}(1-Q_K)+F_K, \qquad (99)$$

where F_K (defined by these equations) and Q_K depend on the other pairs only through the dependence of the coefficients A_{K1}, A_{K2}, A_{K3} on the other pairs. Similarly, the pair K energy in the absence of the other pairs is given by the formula

$$I_K=\alpha_{NKa}(1+Q_K)+\alpha_{NKb}(1-Q_K)+F_K, \qquad (100)$$

where F_K and Q_K are just the same as in Eq. (99). The other-pair dependence of $\bar{E}_K$ then can be obtained from

[28] R. S. Mulliken, J. Chem. Phys. **2**, 782 (1934).
[29] The neutral penetration correction was suggested by R. G. Parr and R. Pariser, J. Chem. Phys. **23**, 711 (1955).
[30] W. Moffitt, Proc. Roy. Soc. (London) **A210**, 245 (1951).
[31] R. Pariser, J. Chem. Phys. **21**, 568 (1953).
[32] See references 3 and 4.
[33] R. Pariser and R. G. Parr, J. Chem. Phys. **21**, 767 (1953); F. G. Fumi and R. G. Parr, J. Chem. Phys. **21**, 1864 (1953).

the formula

$$\bar{E}_K = \tfrac{1}{2}[(\alpha_{Ka}+\alpha_{Kb}+\alpha_{NKa}+\alpha_{NKb}) + Q_K(\alpha_{Ka}-\alpha_{Kb}+\alpha_{NKa}-\alpha_{NKb})]+F_K, \quad (101)$$

and Eqs. (68) and (92) for the α_K and α_{NK}.

In order to obtain the *total* energy, one must add to Eq. (96) the potential energy of repulsion between nuclei,

$$E^n = \sum_\alpha \sum_{\beta\neq\alpha} (Z_\alpha Z_\beta e^2/r_{\alpha\beta}). \quad (102)$$

In this expression one may replace the sums over distinct nuclei by sums over bond pair nuclei Ka, Kb and Ia, Ib. Thus, assuming $2n=\sum_\alpha Z_\alpha$,

$$E^n = \sum_K (e^2/r_{KaKb}) + \sum_K \sum_{I\neq K}[(e^2/r_{KaIa})+(e^2/r_{KaIb}) + (e^2/r_{KbIa})+(e^2/r_{KbIb})]. \quad (103)$$

Here any term with $r_{KaIa}=0$ is to be omitted, or any term with $r_{KaKb}=0$, $r_{KaIb}=0$, $r_{KbIa}=0$ or $r_{KbIb}=0$. With this understanding, one thus may write

$$E^n = \sum_K (V_K+W_K), \quad (104)$$

where

$$V_K = e^2/r_{KaKb}, \quad (105)$$

$$W_K = \tfrac{1}{2}\sum_{I\neq K}[(e^2/r_{KaIa})+(e^2/r_{KaIb}) + (e^2/r_{KbIa})+(e^2/r_{KbIb})]. \quad (106)$$

The terms V_K are other-pair independent, the terms W_K other-pair dependent.

The total energy is the sum of Eqs. (96) and (104):

$$E^{\mathrm{tot}} = E^{\mathrm{el}} + E^n = \sum_K B_K, \quad (107)$$

where the *bond energy* B_K is defined by

$$B_K \equiv \bar{E}_K + V_K + W_K = \tfrac{1}{2}(E_K+I_K)+V_K+W_K. \quad (108)$$

The total energy thus is expressible as the sum of contributions from the several bonds.

That the bond energies B_K in general are *not* independent of other pairs follows from the complicated indirect other-pair dependences of Q_K, F_K and W_K, as well as the explicit other-pair dependences of the α_K and α_{Nk}. There is one case in which the quantities B_K are essentially other-pair independent, however. Suppose that

$$Q_I \doteq 0 \text{ for all } I \quad (109)$$

and that

$$P_{Ia} \doteq P_{Ib} \doteq 0 \text{ for all } I; \quad (110)$$

that is, that all bonds are essentially homopolar and that the neutral penetration terms are negligible. Only the first term in Eq. (101) for $\bar{E}_K$ then is other-pair dependent, and from Eqs. (68) and (92) one obtains a result of the form

$$\bar{E}_K \doteq -\tfrac{1}{2}\sum_{I\neq K}(\zeta_{KaIa}+\zeta_{KaIb} + \zeta_{KbIa}+\zeta_{KbIb})+E_K^0, \quad (111)$$

where E_K^0 is other-pair independent. Hence Eqs. (106) and (108) yield

$$B_K \doteq B_K^0 + \tfrac{1}{2}\sum_{I\neq K}\{[(e^2/r_{KaIa})-\zeta_{KaIa}] + [(e^2/r_{KaIb})-\zeta_{KaIb}]+[(e^2/r_{KbIa})-\zeta_{KbIa}] + [(e^2/r_{KbIb})-\zeta_{KbIb}]\}, \quad (112)$$

where B_K^0 is other-pair independent. Therefore to the (often good) approximations that

$$\zeta_{KaIa} = (KaKa|IaIa)-\tfrac{1}{2}(KaIa|KaIa) \doteq (e^2/r_{KaIa}),$$
$$\zeta_{KaIb} \doteq (e^2/r_{KaIb}), \quad \zeta_{KbIa} \doteq (e^2/r_{KbIa}), \quad \zeta_{KbIb} \doteq (e^2/r_{KbIb}), \quad (113)$$

one has

$$B_K = B_K^0. \quad (114)$$

That is, not only are the bond energies additive, but they are true molecular invariants.[34]

Equations (113) are badly in error for two bonds K and I which involve the same atom, for then by the conventions adopted in Eq. (103) some one of the e^2/r terms in Eqs. (113) must be set equal to zero. Bond energies for such bonds will be interdependent.

When bond polarities are significant, violating Eq. (109), or when neutral penetrations are large, violating Eq. (110), the bond energies also lose their invariance property. Additivity itself only breaks down when the separability assumptions of Sec. II break down—when the orbitals describing one bond are not orthogonal to those describing the others.

X. DISCUSSION

It is perhaps worth emphasizing that the model of an electron pair bond that has here been elucidated is not a "simple valence bond" model or a "simple molecular orbital" model but is more general than either. A *simple valence bond theory of a system of separated electron pair bonds* may be obtained from the present development by setting

$$A_{I1}=A_{I3}=2^{-\frac{1}{2}}, \quad A_{I2}=0, \text{ for all } I. \quad (115)$$

Similarly, a *simple molecular orbital theory of a system of separated electron pair bonds* may be obtained by setting

$$A_{I1}=1, \quad A_{I2}=A_{I3}=0, \text{ for all } I. \quad (116)$$

These special cases will not be discussed here. One related happy circumstance may be mentioned, however.[35] Equation (58) shows that the operator G_I which governs the influence of bond I on other bonds is the same (under Mulliken approximations) for the simple valence bond description of Eq. (115) as for the simple molecular orbital description of Eq. (116). This means that as far as its effects on other bonds are concerned the description taken of a homopolar bond is immaterial,

[34] The discussion of bond energies given by J. C. Slater in reference 7 is similar to the present one. In effect, Slater derives Eq. (114) under the same assumptions as here, plus the assumption that $A_{K1}=A_{K3}$, here shown to be unnecessary.

[35] The valence bond case is discussed at some length in the two references 7, where the relationships with classical valence bond theory are also indicated.

while for a heteropolar bond almost all that matters is the amount of charge transferred—the quantity Q_I.

The argument in this paper has been concerned in the main with the case in which each electron pair is in a singlet state and the molecule is in its ground state, but triplet states of the pairs (which enter the exact molecular wave functions)[36] and excited states of the molecule also can be handled. A single electron can be treated, as can a group of three.[37]

That electron pairs in practice are not often separated in the technical sense of the present paper is proper cause for concern. However, the model often should be a good approximation, and its treatment here has followed a rigorous variational pattern. Furthermore, the way is open for systematic incorporation of improvements.[38]

In purely theoretical treatments of molecules integrals conventionally are broken down to integrals involving bare nuclei. In treatments of large molecules with many electrons an alternative procedure seems more desirable, referring matters where possible to integrals involving neutral atoms or ions of small charge. As has been demonstrated in this and a preceding paper,[6] one then can treat electrons one pair at a time or one group at a time, from the outside in, so to speak. Furthermore, purely theoretical and semiempirical theories alike then can be put in the same language, and this language is closer to the everyday language of ordinary chemists.

Extensive quantitative calculations with the equations of this paper and appropriate extensions and generalizations of them have been carried out by the authors on the formaldehyde molecule, H_2CO, yielding information about the charges transferred in and between the various bonds in several molecular and ionic states, their effects on one another, and so on.[37] The results will be presented elsewhere.

[36] See Sec. VI of reference 6.

[37] J. M. Parks, Ph.D. Thesis, Carnegie Institute of Technology, 1956.

[38] See Sec. V of reference 6, and reference 10.

Reprinted without change of pagination from the
Proceedings of the Royal Society, A, *volume* 253, pp. 242–259, 1959

The density matrix in many-electron quantum mechanics
I. Generalized product functions. Factorization and physical interpretation of the density matrices

By R. McWeeny

Departments of Mathematics, Physics and Chemistry, University College of North Staffordshire

(*Communicated by H. C. Longuet-Higgins, F.R.S.—Received* 8 *June* 1959)

Many-electron wave functions are usually constructed from antisymmetrized products of one-electron orbitals (determinants) and energy calculations are based on the matrix element expressions due to Slater (1931). In this paper, the orbitals in such a product are replaced by 'group functions', each describing any number of electrons, and the necessary generalization of Slater's results is carried out. It is first necessary to develop the density matrix theory of N-particle systems and to show that for systems described by 'generalized product functions' the density matrices of the whole system may be expressed in terms of those of the component electron groups. The matrix elements of the Hamiltonian between generalized product functions are then given by expressions which resemble those of Slater, the 'coulomb' and 'exchange' integrals being replaced by integrals containing the one-electron density matrices of the various groups. By setting up an 'effective' Hamiltonian for each electron group in the presence of the others, the discussion of a many-particle system in which groups or 'shells' can be distinguished (e.g. atomic $K, L, M, \ldots$, shells) can rigorously be reduced to a discussion of smaller subsystems.

A single generalized product (cf. the single determinant of Hartree–Fock theory) provides a convenient first approximation; and the effect of admitting 'excited' products (cf. configuration interaction) can be estimated by a perturbation method. The energy expression may then be discussed in terms of the electon density and 'pair' functions. The energy is a sum of group energies supplemented by interaction terms which represent (i) electrostatic repulsions between charge clouds, (ii) the polarization of each group in the field of the others, and (iii) 'dispersion' effects of the type defined by London. All these terms can be calculated, for group functions of any kind, in terms of the density matrices of the separate groups.

Applications to the theory of intermolecular forces and to π-electron systems are also discussed.

1. Introduction

The wave functions employed in many-electron quantum mechanics are almost invariably linear combinations of basis functions of the type

$$\Phi_{Aa,Bb,\ldots}(1,2,\ldots,N) = M\sum_{\mathscr{P}}(-1)^p \mathscr{P}\Phi_{Aa}(1,\ldots,N_A)\,\Phi_{Bb}(\overline{N_A+1},\ldots,\overline{N_A+N_B})\ldots \quad (1\cdot1)$$

We shall call $\Phi_{Aa}(1,\ldots,N_A)$ a 'group function' for the N_A electrons of group A and use the subscript a to indicate the particular 'state' of this group: similarly Φ_{Bb} describes the next electron group in state b etc., and M is simply a normalizing factor for the totally antisymmetrical sum. It is obvious that a Slater determinant (antisymmetrized spin-orbital product) is a particular form of (1·1) in which each group consists of just *one* electron whose 'state' is described by a single spin-orbital: and (1·1) will accordingly be called a '*generalized* product function'. In using linear combinations of such functions, a variety of states will be permitted for each electron group and the wave function will be

$$\Psi(1,\ldots,N) = \sum_{a,b,\ldots} C_{ab\ldots}\Phi_{Aa,Bb,\ldots}(1,\ldots,N). \quad (1\cdot2)$$

This 'mixing'—again analogous to that employed in orbital theories—will be referred to as 'configuration interaction', where now any specification of group states $(a, b, \ldots)$ defines a 'configuration'. We shall be concerned with approximate solutions of the wave equation of type (1·1) and more generally (1·2).

It will be assumed that the group functions are individually antisymmetric in the (space-spin) variables of the particles to which they refer; and in this case a completely antisymmetrical function results when the summation in (1·1) excludes the subgroup of permutations which leave every electron in its original group. If there are ν permutations in the remaining distinct cosets, the normalizing factor will then be $\nu^{-\frac{1}{2}}$ *provided* the group functions are normalized and orthogonal in the sense

$$\int \Phi^*_{Rr}(1, i, j, \ldots)\, \Phi_{Ss}(1, k, l, \ldots)\, \mathrm{d}\tau_1 = \delta_{RS}\, \delta_{rs} \quad (Rr \neq Ss), \tag{1·3}$$

where the functions contain one common set of variables, indicated by 1‡ (and written in the 'first place' since—owing to antisymmetry—any set may be brought to this place with at most a sign change) and $\int \mathrm{d}\tau_1$ indicates integration over these variables. This condition, which resembles those proposed by Hurley, Lennard-Jones & Pople (1953) and by Parr *et al.* (1956), is clearly a natural generalization of that usually assumed for orbitals and will provisionally be adopted. With $R \neq S$ the functions are orthogonal because they belong to *different groups*, while for $R = S$ but $r \neq s$ they are orthogonal because they represent *different states* of the same group.

In this paper we examine quite generally the mathematical and physical implications of using wave functions of type (1·2), without any restriction on the individual group functions other than that implied by (1·3). An *exact* wave function cannot be expressed in the form (1·2) since the set of functions of type (1·1) cannot be complete unless all partitions of $N = N_A + N_B + \ldots$ are allowed (cf. Parr *et al.* 1956), but (1·2) appears to be the most promising generalization of the Hartree–Fock approximation consistent with the need for a simple physical picture, and obviously has a direct appeal in the many problems where 'loosely coupled' electron groups can be distinguished. Density matrix theory (McWeeny 1955*a*, *b*, 1956; Löwdin 1955), besides providing a powerful mathematical tool, is particularly useful in facilitating a clear physical interpretation.

2. The density matrix

The *density* (or *statistical*) *operator* ρ for a system in stationary state Ψ may be defined symbolically§ by

$$\left.\begin{aligned} \rho &= \Psi\Psi^*, \\ \rho\Phi &= (\Psi\Psi^*)\,\Phi = \Psi(\Psi^*\Phi), \end{aligned}\right\} \tag{2·1}$$

‡ The numbers which indicate the co-ordinates describing the various electrons are of course arbitrary: 1, 2, ..., N merely refer to N different points of configuration space. When we refer to a single electron (and it is meaningless to ask 'which?') we shall usually indicate its co-ordinates by 1; when we refer to a pair we use 1, 2; etc.

§ The reader accustomed to Dirac notation will notice that $\Psi \equiv |\rangle$ and $\Psi^* \equiv \langle|$. The statistical operator in state $|\rangle$ is $\rho = |\rangle\langle|$ and has representative $\langle q|\rho|q'\rangle = \langle q|\rangle\langle|q'\rangle$: these statements compare with $\rho = \Psi\Psi^*$ (starred symbol on the *right*) and $\rho(q; q') = \Psi(q)\,\Psi^*(q')$. The Dirac-type scalar product notation $\langle\Psi|\Psi\rangle$ or $(\Psi|\Psi)$ may also consistently be replaced by where Φ is any state vector and $\Psi^*\Phi$ its scalar product with Ψ. Since ρ always produces a multiple of Ψ it is a 'projection operator' and (assuming Ψ normalized) it is 'idempotent', $\rho^2 = \rho$. In the Schrödinger representation Ψ is represented by a function $\Psi(q)$, q standing for a whole set of variables, and $\Psi^*\Phi = \int \Psi^*(q)\,\Phi(q)\,dq$. The density operator is then represented by an integral operator:

$$\left.\begin{aligned} \rho \to \rho(q;q') &= \Psi(q)\,\Psi^*(q') \\ \text{and} \qquad \rho\Phi(q) &= \int \rho(q;q')\,\Phi(q')\,dq' = \Psi(q)\,\Psi^*\Phi, \end{aligned}\right\} \tag{2·2}$$

$\rho(q;q')$ is the density 'matrix' in the continuous representation, and $\Psi(q)$ may always be eliminated in favour of $\rho(q;q')$. Thus, the expectation value of any quantity A, with operator $\mathscr{A}$, in state Ψ becomes:

$$\bar{A} = (\Psi\,|\,\mathscr{A}\,|\,\Psi) = \int \Psi^*(q)\mathscr{A}\Psi(q)\,dq = \int [\mathscr{A}\rho(q;q')]_{q'\to q}\,dq, \tag{2·3}$$

where the prime is removed *after* operation with $\mathscr{A}$. This procedure is analogous to taking the trace of a matrix and will often be abbreviated to

$$(\Psi\,|\,\mathscr{A}\,|\,\Psi) = \mathrm{tr}\,\mathscr{A}\rho(q;q'). \tag{2·4}$$

An *off*-diagonal element of $\mathscr{A}$, between states Ψ_K and Ψ_L, may similarly be written

$$(\Psi_L\,|\,\mathscr{A}\,|\,\Psi_K) = \mathrm{tr}\,\mathscr{A}\rho(KL\,|\,q;q'), \tag{2·5}$$

where

$$\rho(KL\,|\,q;q') = \Psi_K(q)\,\Psi_L^*(q') \tag{2·6}$$

is a 'transition density matrix'.

We shall follow the usual practice of expressing $\Psi(q)$ in terms of a discrete set of functions $\Phi_1(q)$, $\Phi_2(q)$, ... $\Phi_\kappa(q)$, ...,

$$\Psi(q) = \sum_\kappa C_\kappa \Phi_\kappa(q), \tag{2·7}$$

and in this case it follows that

$$\rho(q;q') = \sum_{\kappa,\lambda} \rho_{\kappa\lambda}\Phi_\kappa(q)\Phi_\lambda^*(q'), \quad \rho_{\kappa\lambda} = C_\kappa C_\lambda^* \tag{2·8}$$

and that, with the usual definition of the matrix elements,

$$(\Psi\,|\,\mathscr{A}\,|\,\Psi) = \sum_{\kappa,\lambda} A_{\lambda\kappa}\rho_{\kappa\lambda} = \mathrm{tr}\,\mathbf{A}\boldsymbol{\rho}, \quad \boldsymbol{\rho} = \mathbf{C}\mathbf{C}^\dagger \tag{2·9}$$

where the components C_κ are collected into a column matrix $\mathbf{C}$. The 'tr' in (2·4) therefore becomes a literal matrix trace in the discrete basis. We are concerned mainly with a single state but note that the transition density matrix (2·6) may be expressed similarly:

$$(\Psi_L|\mathscr{A}|\Psi_K) = \mathrm{tr}\,\mathbf{A}\boldsymbol{\rho}^{KL}, \quad \boldsymbol{\rho}^{KL} = \mathbf{C}^K\mathbf{C}^{L\dagger}. \tag{2·10}$$

$\Psi^*\Psi$ (starred symbol on the *left*). The notation is otherwise familiar —A, a dynamical quantity: $\mathscr{A}$, its associated operator: $\mathbf{A}$, the matrix representing $\mathscr{A}$ in some discrete basis: $A_{\kappa\lambda}$ or $(\Phi_\kappa|\mathscr{A}|\Phi_\lambda)$ the $\kappa\lambda$-element of $\mathbf{A}$: $A(q;q')$ the 'matrix element' of $\mathscr{A}$ in a continuous representation. The density operator itself does not represent any dynamical variable and we use ρ (operator), $\boldsymbol{\rho}$ (matrix), $\rho_{\kappa\lambda}$ (matrix element), $\rho(q;q')$ (continuous form).

We note also that the individual matrix elements, $A_{\kappa\lambda}$, may be written in terms of *formal* transition density matrices for 'states' Φ_κ, Φ_λ. (2·5) and (2·6) become

$$\left.\begin{aligned} A_{\lambda\kappa} &= (\Phi_\lambda|\mathscr{A}|\Phi_\kappa) = \operatorname{tr}\mathscr{A}\rho(\kappa\lambda\,|\,q;q'),\\ \rho(\kappa\lambda\,|\,q;q') &= \Phi_\kappa(q)\,\Phi_\lambda^*(q'). \end{aligned}\right\} \tag{2·11}$$

In an N-particle system it is convenient to introduce, besides the *system* density matrix,

$$\rho(q;\,q') = \rho(1,2,\ldots,N;\;1',2',\ldots,N'),$$

particle density matrices. Renormalizing, we define an N-electron density matrix by

$$\rho_N(1,2,\ldots,N;\;1',2',\ldots,N') = N!\Psi(1,2,\ldots,N)\,\Psi^*(1',2',\ldots,N') \tag{2·12}$$

and we also introduce a whole series of *reduced* density matrices (cf. Husimi 1940; Born & Green 1947) by

$$\rho_n(1,\ldots,n;\;1',\ldots,n') = N(N-1)\ldots(N-n+1) \times\int\Psi(1,\ldots,N)\,\Psi^*(1',\ldots,n',\overline{n+1},\ldots,N)\,\mathrm{d}\tau_{n+1}\ldots\mathrm{d}\tau_N \tag{2·13}$$

these being related successively by

$$(N-n)\,\rho_n(1,\ldots,n;\;1',\ldots,n') = \int\rho_{n+1}(1,\ldots,n,\overline{n+1}\,;\;1',\ldots,n',\overline{n+1})\,\mathrm{d}\tau_{n+1}. \tag{2·14}$$

The diagonal element $\rho_n(1,\ldots,n;1,\ldots,n)$ is then the probability density function for simultaneously finding any n particles with co-ordinates (and spins) indicated by $1,2,\ldots,n$. The expectation value of any n-electron operator,‡ $\mathscr{A}(1,2,\ldots,n)$, is independent of the labelling of the particles and any symmetrical sum,

$$\sum_{(n)}{}'\mathscr{A} = \sum_{i,j,\ldots=1}^{N}{}'\,\mathscr{A}(i,j,\ldots),$$

in which there are $N(N-1)\ldots(N-n+1)$ selections of the n different variables $i,j,\ldots$ has an expectation value

$$\begin{aligned}(\Psi|\textstyle\sum_{(n)}'\mathscr{A}|\Psi) &= \operatorname{tr}\mathscr{A}\rho_n(1,\ldots,n;\;1',\ldots,n')\\ &= \int[\mathscr{A}(1,\ldots,n)\rho_n(1,\ldots,n;\;1',\ldots,n')]_{1'\to1,\ldots n'\to n}\,\mathrm{d}\tau_1\ldots\mathrm{d}\tau_n.\end{aligned} \tag{2·15}$$

The usual Hamiltonian operator

$$\mathscr{H}(1,\ldots,N) = \sum_{i=1}^{N}h(i)+\tfrac{1}{2}\sum_{i,j=1}^{N}{}'\,g(i,j),$$

where $$h(i) = -\frac{\hbar^2}{2m}\nabla^2(i)+V(i),\quad g(i,j) = \frac{e^2}{r_{ij}}, \tag{2·16}$$

contains two such sums and accordingly

$$E = (\Psi|\mathscr{H}|\Psi) = \operatorname{tr}h(1)\rho_1(1;\;1')+\tfrac{1}{2}\operatorname{tr}g(1,2)\rho_2(1,2;\;1',2'), \tag{2·17}$$

‡ It is convenient to use the notation $\mathscr{A}(1,2,\ldots,n)$ for an operator which works on the variables $1,2,\ldots,n$: for example $\nabla^2(i)$ will be used in preference to ∇_i^2. Script may be discarded when the operation is simply *multiplication* by the given *function*.

where the primes in the second term may in fact be omitted immediately since g is simply a multiplier, $g(1,2) = g(1,2)$.

It is of course possible to reduce transition density matrices in exactly the same way. When Ψ is given by (2·7) the energy follows from (2·9) and (2·11) as

$$E = \operatorname{tr} \mathbf{H\rho} = \sum_{\kappa,\lambda} H_{\lambda\kappa}\, \rho_{\kappa\lambda} \tag{2·18}$$

where

$$H_{\lambda\kappa} = (\Phi_\lambda | \mathscr{H} | \Phi_\kappa) = \operatorname{tr} h(1)\, \rho_1(\kappa\lambda \,|\, 1; 1') + \tfrac{1}{2} \operatorname{tr} g(1,2)\, \rho_2(\kappa\lambda \,|\, 1,2; 1',2') \tag{2·19}$$

and $\rho_1(\kappa\lambda \,|\, 1;\, 1')$, $\rho_2(\kappa\lambda \,|\, 1,2;\, 1',2')$ arise from reduction of

$$\rho_N(\kappa\lambda \,|\, 1, \ldots, N;\, 1', \ldots, N') = N!\,\Phi_\kappa(1, \ldots, N)\, \Phi^*_\lambda(1', \ldots, N'). \tag{2·20}$$

In general

$$\rho_n(\kappa\lambda \,|\, 1, \ldots, n;\, 1', \ldots, n') = N(N-1) \ldots (N-n+1)$$
$$\times \int \Phi_\kappa(1, \ldots, N)\, \Phi^*_\lambda(1', \ldots, n', \overline{n+1}, \ldots N)\, \mathrm{d}\tau_{n+1} \ldots \mathrm{d}\tau_N \tag{2·21}$$

and in state Ψ

$$\rho_n(1, \ldots, n;\, 1', \ldots, n') = \sum_{\kappa,\lambda} \rho_{\kappa\lambda}\, \rho_n(\kappa\lambda \,|\, 1, \ldots, n;\, 1', \ldots, n'). \tag{2·22}$$

The reduced density matrices are defined without reference to any specific operator but are conveniently calculated by evaluating the matrix element of a symmetrical operator such as $\sum_{i,j=1}^{N}{}' g(i,j)$. Thus $\rho_2(\kappa\lambda \,|\, 1,2;\, 1',2')$ is simply the coefficient of $g(1,2)$ in the integrand of

$$\left(\Phi_\lambda \left| \sum_{i,j=1}^{N}{}' g(i,j) \right| \Phi_\kappa\right) = \int \Phi^*_\lambda(1, \ldots, N) \sum_{i,j=1}^{N}{}' g(i,j)\, \Phi_\kappa(1, \ldots, N)\, \mathrm{d}\tau_1 \ldots \mathrm{d}\tau_N$$
$$= \int g(1,2)\, \rho_2(\kappa\lambda \,|\, 1,2;\, 1,2)\, \mathrm{d}\tau_1\, \mathrm{d}\tau_2 \tag{2·23}$$

with the primes restored to the variables in those factors which come from Φ^*_λ.

For many purposes the simultaneous values of particle spins are of secondary importance and it is convenient to introduced spinless density matrices (McWeeny 1955 *a*, *b*). These are defined simply by

$$P_n(1, \ldots, n;\, 1', \ldots, n') = \int [\rho_n(1, \ldots, n;\, 1', \ldots, n')]_{\omega_1' \to \omega_1, \ldots \omega_n' \to \omega_n}\, \mathrm{d}\omega_1 \ldots \mathrm{d}\omega_N, \tag{2·24}$$

where $\int \mathrm{d}\omega_i$ indicates integration over the ith spin variable and the arguments in P_n are now spatial co-ordinates only. The diagonal elements $P_n(1, \ldots, n;\, 1, \ldots, n)$ are simply distribution functions: if $\mathrm{d}v_i$ be the ordinary 3-dimensional volume element for the ith set of spatial co-ordinates

$$P_n(1, \ldots, n;\, 1, \ldots, n)\, \mathrm{d}v_1 \ldots \mathrm{d}v_n = \begin{cases} \text{probability of finding any } n \text{ particles, in} \\ \text{any order, in volume elements} \\ \mathrm{d}v_1, \ldots, \mathrm{d}v_n \text{ at points } 1, \ldots, n. \end{cases} \tag{2·25}$$

Thus $P_1(1;\, 1)$ is the charge density function and $P_2(1,2;\, 1,2)$ the 'pair function'.

Provided all operators are spinless, the spin integrations are immediate and all the previous results may be rewritten with ρ_n replaced by P_n and $d\tau_i$ by dv_i. Thus (2·17) becomes (cf. McWeeny 1954, 1955*a*)

$$\begin{aligned} E &= \operatorname{tr} h(1)\, P_1(1;1') + \tfrac{1}{2}\operatorname{tr} g(1,2)\, P_2(1,2;1',2') \\ &= \int\left[-\frac{\hbar^2}{2m}\nabla^2(1)\, P_1(1;1')\right]_{1'\to 1} dv_1 + \int V(1)\, P_1(1;1)\, dv_1 + \tfrac{1}{2}\int g(1,2)\, P_2(1,2;1,2)\, dv_1\, dv_2 \\ &= T + V_e + V_{ee}, \end{aligned} \tag{2·26}$$

where T is the expectation value of the kinetic energy; V_e is the total potential energy of the individual electrons in the given field and is identical with that of a static 'charge cloud' of density P_1; and V_{ee} has a corresponding classical interpretation as the average interaction energy of particles distributed with pair function P_2. This immediate pictorial interpretation, which will be developed later, is characteristic of a density matrix approach.

3. Matrix elements between generalized product functions

Matrix elements of the Hamiltonian between antisymmetrized *orbital* products were first given by Slater (1931) and corresponding contributions to the 1- and 2-electron density matrices then follow readily (cf. McWeeny 1955*a*, *b*) as in (2·23). In this case each 'group' comprises a single electron described by a spin-orbital. We now generalize these results to functions of type (1·1) in which each group comprises any number of electrons described by one of a variety of antisymmetrical group functions, the latter being subject to the requirement (1·3) but otherwise unspecified.

To do this we simply determine $\left(\Phi_\lambda \middle| \sum_{i,j=1}^{N}{}' g(i,j) \middle| \Phi_\kappa\right)$ by standard methods (e.g. Slater 1931; Condon & Shortley (1935)) remembering that each group function is individually antisymmetric and that the number of permutations which lead to non-vanishing contributions is severely limited by (1·3). The results take their neatest form on introducing the density matrices for each separate group, these being defined in the usual way (cf. 2·21):

$$\begin{aligned} \rho_n^R(rr' \mid 1, \ldots, n;\, 1', \ldots, n') &= N_R(N_R-1)\ldots(N_R-n+1) \\ &\times \int \Phi_{Rr}(1, \ldots, N_R)\, \Phi_{Rr'}(1', \ldots, n', \overline{n+1}, \ldots, N_R)\, d\tau_{n+1}\ldots d\tau_{N_R}, \end{aligned} \tag{3·1}$$

where the labelling of the variables, is, of course, arbitrary.

To give one example, when $\kappa = (a, b, \ldots)$—giving the function (1·1)—it is found that

$$\begin{aligned} \left(\Phi_\kappa \middle| \sum_{i,j=1}^{N}{}' g(i,j) \middle| \Phi_\kappa\right) &= \sum_R \int g(1,2)\, \rho_2^R(rr \mid 1,2;1,2)\, d\tau_1\, d\tau_2 \\ &+ \sum_{R,S}{}' \int g(1,2)\, \rho_1^R(rr \mid 1;1)\, \rho_1^S(ss \mid 2;2)\, d\tau_1\, d\tau_2 \\ &- \sum_{R,S}{}' \int g(1,2)\, \rho_1^R(rr \mid 2;1)\, \rho_1^S(ss \mid 1;2)\, d\tau_1\, d\tau_2 \end{aligned}$$

and, by analogy with (2·23), this implies that

$$\rho_2(\kappa\kappa \mid 1,2;\ 1',2') = \sum_R \rho_2^R(rr \mid 1,2;\ 1',2') + \sum_{R,S}{}' \rho_1^R(rr \mid 1;\ 1')\,\rho_1^S(ss \mid 2;\ 2') - \sum_{R,S}{}' \rho_1^R(rr \mid 2;\ 1')\,\rho_1^S(ss \mid 1;\ 2'). \quad (3\cdot 2)$$

The two-particle density matrix for an antisymmetrized product of orthogonal group functions can be expressed in terms of the one- and two-particle density matrices of the individual groups. This is a fundamental result: from it, using (2·14) and remembering (1·3), it follows at once that

$$\rho_1(\kappa\kappa \mid 1;\ 1') = \sum_R \rho_1^R(rr \mid 1;\ 1'). \quad (3\cdot 3)$$

This means, in particular, that the electron densities of the separate groups are additive.

The general results may now be summarized. As in Slater's analysis, non-vanishing terms arise only for configurations, κ and λ, which differ in not more than *two* group functions. There are thus three distinct cases:

(*a*) $\kappa = \lambda = (a, b, \ldots, r, \ldots, s, \ldots)$

$$\left.\begin{aligned} \rho_2(\kappa\kappa \mid 1,2;\ 1',2') &= \sum_R \rho_2^R(rr \mid 1,2;\ 1',2') + \sum_{R,S}{}' \rho_1^R(rr \mid 1;\ 1')\,\rho_1^S(ss \mid 2;\ 2') \\ &\quad - \sum_{R,S}{}' \rho_1^R(rr \mid 2;\ 1')\,\rho_1^S(ss \mid 1;\ 2'), \\ \rho_1(\kappa\kappa \mid 1;\ 1') &= \sum_R \rho_1^R(rr \mid 1;\ 1'). \end{aligned}\right\} \quad (3\cdot 4a)$$

(*b*) $\kappa = (a, b, \ldots, r, \ldots, s, \ldots)$, $\lambda = (a, b, \ldots, r', \ldots, s, \ldots)$

$$\left.\begin{aligned} \rho_2(\kappa\lambda \mid 1,2;\ 1',2') &= \rho_2^R(rr' \mid 1,2;\ 1',2') \\ &\quad + \sum_{S(\neq R)} \rho_1^R(rr' \mid 1;\ 1')\,\rho_1^S(ss \mid 2;\ 2') - \sum_{S(\neq R)} \rho_1^R(rr' \mid 2;\ 1')\,\rho_1^S(ss \mid 1;\ 2') \\ &\quad + \sum_{S(\neq R)} \rho_1^S(ss \mid 1;\ 1')\,\rho_1^R(rr' \mid 2;\ 2') - \sum_{S(\neq R)} \rho_1^S(ss \mid 2;\ 1')\,\rho_1^R(rr' \mid 1;\ 2'), \\ \rho_1(\kappa\lambda \mid 1;\ 1') &= \rho_1^R(rr' \mid 1;\ 1'). \end{aligned}\right\} \quad (3\cdot 4b)$$

(*c*) $\kappa = (a, b, \ldots, r, \ldots, s, \ldots)$, $\lambda = (a, b, \ldots, r', \ldots, s', \ldots)$

$$\left.\begin{aligned} \rho_2(\kappa\lambda \mid 1,2;\ 1',2') &= \rho_1^R(rr' \mid 1;\ 1')\,\rho_1^S(ss' \mid 2;\ 2') - \rho_1^R(rr' \mid 2;\ 1')\,\rho_1^S(ss' \mid 1;\ 2') \\ &\quad + \rho_1^S(ss' \mid 1;\ 1')\,\rho_1^R(rr' \mid 2;\ 2') - \rho_1^S(ss' \mid 2;\ 1')\,\rho_1^R(rr' \mid 1;\ 2'). \end{aligned}\right\} \quad (3\cdot 4c)$$

The formal similarity with Slater's results is more obvious in the actual matrix element expressions. From (2·19) we obtain

(*a*) $$H_{\kappa\kappa} = \sum_R H^R(rr) + \tfrac{1}{2} \sum_{R,S}{}' [J^{RS}(rr, ss) - K^{RS}(rr, ss)]; \quad (3\cdot 5a)$$

(*b*) $$H_{\lambda\kappa} = H^R(rr') + \sum_{S(\neq R)} [J^{RS}(rr', ss) - K^{RS}(rr', ss)]; \quad (3\cdot 5b)$$

(*c*) $$H_{\lambda\kappa} = J^{RS}(rr', ss') - K^{RS}(rr', ss'); \quad (3\cdot 5c)$$

where $$H^R(rr') = \operatorname{tr} h(1)\,\rho_1^R(rr' \mid 1;\,1') + \tfrac{1}{2}\operatorname{tr} g(1,2)\,\rho_2^R(rr' \mid 1,2;\,1',2'); \tag{3·6}$$

$$J^{RS}(rr',ss') = \operatorname{tr} g(1,2)\,\rho_1^R(rr' \mid 1;\,1')\,\rho_1^S(ss' \mid 1;\,2')$$
$$= \int g(1,2)\,\rho_1^R(rr' \mid 1;\,1)\,\rho_1^S(ss' \mid 2;\,2)\,d\tau_1\,d\tau_2; \tag{3·7}$$

$$K^{RS}(rr',ss') = \operatorname{tr} g(1,2)\,\rho_1^R(rr' \mid 2;\,1')\,\rho_1^S(ss' \mid 1;\,2')$$
$$= \int g(1,2)\,\rho_1^R(rr' \mid 2;\,1)\,\rho_1^S(ss' \mid 1;\,2)\,d\tau_1\,d\tau_2. \tag{3·8}$$

These quantities are the analogues of one-electron, two-electron 'coulomb', and two-electron 'exchange' integrals, respectively; but they contain density matrices instead of orbitals and a matrix element notation for (3·7) and (3·8) (e.g. $(rs\,|g|\,r's')$) would therefore be inappropriate. The analogue of the one-electron integral, $H^R(rr')$, can however be regarded as a matrix element of a *many*-electron Hamiltonian for group R *alone* in the field of the nuclei. Comparison of (3·6) with (2·19) shows that

$$H^R(rr') = (\Phi_{Rr'}\,|\mathscr{H}^R|\,\Phi_{Rr}), \tag{3·9}$$

where $$\mathscr{H}^R(1,\ldots,N_R) = \sum_{i=1}^{N_R} h(i) + \tfrac{1}{2}\sum_{i,j=1}^{N_R}{}' g(i,j). \tag{3·10}$$

In particular, $H^R(rr)$ is a 'group energy' of the electrons described by Φ_{Rr}, with all other electrons removed.

It is clear from (3·7) that $J^{RS}(rr',ss')$ is simply the mutual repulsion of two electron distributions, whose densities—at points 1 and 2 respectively—are $\rho_1^R(rr' \mid 1;\,1)$ and $\rho_1^S(ss \mid 2;\,2)$: this interpretation is not affected by elimination of the spin for the spin integrations are immediate and give (cf. 2·24)

$$J^{RS}(rr',ss') = \int g(1,2)\,P_1^R(rr' \mid 1;\,1)\,P_1^S(ss \mid 2;\,2)\,dv_1\,dv_2 \tag{3·11}$$

in which the two density factors are now ordinary 3-dimensional charge densities associated with the transition $r \to r'$ in group R and $s \to s'$ in group S, respectively. Transition densities of this kind play an important part in the theory of radiation, their moments determining the transition probabilities. The interpretation of $K^{RS}(rr',ss')$ is less obvious and depends on the spin states of the two groups: it will appear later that when these each correspond to zero z component of total spin

$$K^{RS}(rr',ss') = \frac{1}{2}\int g(1,2)\,P_1^R(rr' \mid 2;\,1)\,P_1^S(ss' \mid 1;\,2)\,dv_1\,dv_2, \tag{3·12}$$

where the integrand is small unless groups R and S overlap considerably.

4. Coulomb and exchange operators for general electron groups

It is possible to write Slater's results in an alternative form by introducing 'coulomb' and 'exchange' operators: exactly similar one-electron operators can be defined in the more general case by using the natural interpretation of $\rho_1^R(rr \mid 1;\,1')$ as the kernel of an integral operator. If $\sum_{i=1}^{N_R} \mathscr{A}(i)$ is any symmetrical sum $\left(\text{cf. } \sum_{i=1}^{N_R} h(i)\right)$

of one-electron *integral* operators, $\mathscr{A}(1)$ having kernel $A(1;1')$, we can write (cf. (2·15))

$$\left(\Phi_{Rr}\left|\sum_{i=1}^{N_R}\mathscr{A}(i)\right|\Phi_{Rr}\right) = \mathrm{tr}\,\mathscr{A}(1)\,\rho_1^R(rr' \mid 1;\,1') = \int A(1;\,1'')\,\rho_1^R(rr' \mid 1'';\,1)\,\mathrm{d}\tau_{1''}\,\mathrm{d}\tau_1. \quad (4{\cdot}1)$$

This enables us to express $K^{RS}(rr', ss)$ as the matrix element of a sum of one-electron operators associated with group S. For, from (3·8)

$$K^{RS}(rr', ss) = \int g(1, 1'')\,\rho_1^S(ss \mid 1;\,1'')\,\rho_1^R(rr' \mid 1'';\,1)\,\mathrm{d}\tau_{1''}\,\mathrm{d}\tau_1$$

and therefore by (4·1)

$$K^{RS}(rr', ss) = \int K^S(1;\,1')\,\rho_1^R(rr' \mid 1';\,1)\,\mathrm{d}\tau_1\,\mathrm{d}\tau_{1'} = \left(\Phi_{Rr'}\left|\sum_{i=1}^{N_R}\mathscr{K}^S(i)\right|\Phi_{Rr}\right), \quad (4{\cdot}2)$$

where the typical operator is $\mathscr{K}^S(1)$ with kernel $K^S(1;1')$

$$\mathscr{K}^S(1) \to K^S(1;\,1') = g(1, 1')\,\rho_1^S(ss \mid 1;\,1'). \quad (4{\cdot}3)$$

On the other hand, $J^{RS}(rr', ss)$ can be regarded as the matrix element of an operator sum whose terms are merely multipliers: from (3·7)

$$J^{RS}(rr', ss) = \mathrm{tr}\,J^S(1)\,\rho_1^R(rr' \mid 1;\,1') = \left(\Phi_{Rr'}\left|\sum_{i=1}^{N_R}\mathscr{J}^S(1)\right|\Phi_{Rr}\right), \quad (4{\cdot}4)$$

where the typical operator is $\mathscr{J}^S(1) = J^S(1)$, a simple multiplier

$$\mathscr{J}^S(1) \to J^S(1) = \int g(1, 1')\,\rho_1^S(ss \mid 1';\,1')\,\mathrm{d}\tau_{1'}. \quad (4{\cdot}5)$$

We shall refer to $\mathscr{J}^S(1)$ and $\mathscr{K}^S(1)$, defined by (4·5) and (4·3), as the Coulomb and exchange operators for an electron in the field of the electrons of group S. $J^{RS}(rr', ss)$ and $K^{RS}(rr', ss)$ are therefore the matrix elements of the interaction between the N_R electrons of group R and the field produced by the electrons of group S. The coulomb and exchange operators for an electron in the field of group S apparently have the following effect upon an arbitrary function

$$\mathscr{J}^S(1)\,\psi(1) = J^S(1)\,\psi(1) = \left\{\int g(1, 1')\,\rho_1^S(ss \mid 1';\,1')\,\mathrm{d}\tau_{1'}\right\}\psi(1), \quad (4{\cdot}6)$$

$$\mathscr{K}^S(1)\psi(1) = \int K^S(1;\,1')\,\psi(1')\,\mathrm{d}\tau_{1'} = \int g(1, 1')\,\rho_1^S(ss \mid 1;\,1')\,\psi(1')\,\mathrm{d}\tau_{1'}. \quad (4{\cdot}7)$$

The exchange operator is seen from (4·3) to be simply the one-electron density operator weighted with an inverse distance factor. It is also useful to introduce a *total* Coulomb operator and a *total* exchange operator to describe the Coulomb-exchange field felt by an electron of group R at point 1 in the presence of *all* groups *except* R—these are simply

$$\mathscr{J}_{(R)}(1) = \sum_{S(\neq R)} \mathscr{J}^S(1), \quad \mathscr{K}_{(R)}(1) = \sum_{S(\neq R)} \mathscr{K}^S(1). \quad (4{\cdot}8)$$

The 'effective one-electron Hamiltonian' for an electron of group R in the field of the nuclei and all other groups may then be defined as

$$h^R_{\text{eff.}}(1) = h(1) + \mathscr{J}_{(R)}(1) - \mathscr{K}_{(R)}(1) \tag{4·9}$$

and the 'effective total Hamiltonian' for group R as (cf. 3·10)

$$\mathscr{H}^R_{\text{eff.}}(1, \ldots, N_R) = \sum_{i=1}^{N_R} h^R_{\text{eff.}}(i) + \frac{1}{2} \sum_{i,j=1}^{N_R}{}' g(i,j). \tag{4·10}$$

The matrix elements of $\mathscr{H}^R_{\text{eff.}}$ will be written, by analogy with (3·9)

$$H^R_{\text{eff.}}(rr') = (\Phi_{Rr'} | \mathscr{H}^R_{\text{eff.}} | \Phi_{Rr}) = H^R(rr') + \sum_{S(\neq R)} [J^{RS}(rr', ss) - K^{RS}(rr', ss)] \tag{4·11}$$

and it then follows easily that (3·5a, b) may be written in the alternative forms

$$(a) \qquad H_{\kappa\kappa} = \sum_R H^R_{\text{eff.}}(rr) - \frac{1}{2} \sum_{R,S}{}' [J^{RS}(rr, ss) - K^{RS}(rr, ss)]; \tag{4·12}$$

$$(b) \qquad H_{\kappa\lambda} = H^R_{\text{eff.}}(rr'). \tag{4·13}$$

These forms are useful because contributions to $\mathscr{H}^R_{\text{eff.}}$ from distant nuclei are offset by the screening effect of their associated electrons, giving an operator which (in an electrically neutral system) should depend appreciably only upon the *local* environment of group R.

5. Approximate solution of the configuration interaction problem

It is now necessary to examine in general terms the effect of configuration interaction. For this purpose (1·2) is conveniently abbreviated to

$$\Psi = \sum_\kappa C_\kappa \Phi_\kappa, \tag{5·1}$$

where $\kappa = (a, b, \ldots)$ indicates a whole set of group states. By (2·9) the corresponding energy expression is

$$E = \operatorname{tr} \mathbf{H}\boldsymbol{\rho} \left(= \frac{\mathbf{C}^\dagger\mathbf{H}\mathbf{C}}{\mathbf{C}^\dagger\mathbf{C}} \right), \quad \boldsymbol{\rho} = \frac{\mathbf{C}\mathbf{C}^\dagger}{\mathbf{C}^\dagger\mathbf{C}}. \tag{5·2}$$

Written in this form, the coefficients in (5·1) need not be normalized. The general element of $\mathbf{H}$ is given by (2·19) and upper bounds to the exact eigenvalues (cf. MacDonald 1933) are usually determined, along with corresponding optimum sets of coefficients C_κ, by solution of

$$\mathbf{H}\mathbf{C} = E\mathbf{C}. \tag{5·3}$$

It is, however, useful to start from a one-configuration approximation, Φ_0, to the desired state (taking $C_0 = 1, C_\kappa = 0$ $(\kappa > 0)$) and to obtain the density matrix associated with the corresponding accurate solution of (5·3) in the form of a series. The standard Rayleigh–Schrödinger perturbation theory is unwieldy for this purpose and frequently diverges: we therefore use a method developed by Löwdin (1951) which is free from these defects.

We write (5·3) in partitioned form

$$\begin{pmatrix} \mathbf{H}^{AA} & \mathbf{H}^{AB} \\ \mathbf{H}^{BA} & \mathbf{H}^{BB} \end{pmatrix} \begin{pmatrix} \mathbf{A} \\ \mathbf{B} \end{pmatrix} = E \begin{pmatrix} \mathbf{A} \\ \mathbf{B} \end{pmatrix}, \tag{5·4}$$

where A labels the functions of the initial approximation and B those whose effect is to be admitted as a perturbation. For a non-degenerate one-configuration approximation (which we shall assume),$\mathbf{H}^{AA} = H_{00}$, the 'unperturbed' energy. (5·4) is then equivalent to

$$E = \mathbf{H}^{AA} + \mathbf{H}^{AB}(E\,.\,\mathbf{1} - \mathbf{H}^{BB})^{-1}\mathbf{H}^{BA} = f(E) \tag{5·5}$$

which gives the Brillouin–Wigner series (Brillouin 1932; Wigner 1935; see also Löwdin 1951) on expansion of the inverse matrix. If we take $C_0 = 1$ (normalization arbitrary), the coefficients $C_\kappa (\kappa > 0)$ are contained in the column matrix

$$\mathbf{B} = (E\,.\,\mathbf{1} - \mathbf{H}^{BB})^{-1}\mathbf{H}^{BA} = \mathbf{B}(E). \tag{5·6}$$

Since E occurs on the right-hand side of (5·5) and (5·6) it is necessary to solve iteratively: one could, for example, form the sequence $E^{(0)}, E^{(1)}, E^{(2)}, \ldots$ with

$$E^{(k)} = \mathbf{H}^{AA} + \mathbf{H}^{AB}\mathbf{B}^{(k)}, \tag{5·7}$$

$$\mathbf{B}^{(k+1)} = \mathbf{B}(E^{(k)}) = (E^{(k)}.\mathbf{1} - \mathbf{H}^{BB})^{-1}\mathbf{H}^{BA}, \tag{5·8}$$

but this would be a first-order process (see, for example, Hartree 1949) with poor convergence properties. Moreover, $E^{(k)} \neq \mathbf{C}^{(k)\dagger}\mathbf{H}\mathbf{C}^{(k)}/\mathbf{C}^{(k)\dagger}\mathbf{C}^{(k)}$ and the approximate energy and density matrix *in any given order of iteration* are not, therefore, mutually compatible; $E^{(k)}$ is *not* an energy expectation value for state $\Psi' = \sum_\kappa C_\kappa^{(k)}\Phi_\kappa$. Both difficulties are removed by going over to a *second order* process (Löwdin 1958); for when this is done the sequence $E^{(0)}, E^{(1)}, E^{(2)}, \ldots$ is replaced by $E^{(0)}, \bar{E}^{(1)}, \bar{E}^{(2)}, \ldots$ where $\bar{E}^{(k)}$ is found to be just the expectation energy associated with the coefficients determined by (5·8), We therefore discard (5·7) and adopt the second order process (dropping the bars) which leads immediately to

$$E^{(k)} = \operatorname{tr} \mathbf{H}\boldsymbol{\rho}^{(k)}, \quad \boldsymbol{\rho}^{(k)} = [1 + \mathbf{B}^{(k)\dagger}\mathbf{B}^{(k)}]^{-1} \begin{pmatrix} 1 & \mathbf{B}^{(k)\dagger} \\ \mathbf{B}^{(k)} & \mathbf{B}^{(k)}\mathbf{B}^{(k)\dagger} \end{pmatrix}, \tag{5·9}$$

where $\mathbf{B}^{(k)}$ is defined by (5·8). The sequence $E^{(0)}, E^{(1)}, \ldots$ nearly always converges rapidly (even when the first-order process diverges—Löwdin 1958) and its limit is an upper bound to an exact eigenvalue. Usually, taking $E^{(0)} = H_{00}$, the approximation $\boldsymbol{\rho} = \boldsymbol{\rho}^{(1)}$ will be adequate and $E = E^{(1)}$ remains an upper bound for the *lowest* eigenvalue.

The Rayleigh–Schrödinger series can be obtained by iteration if the inverse matrix in (5·8) is expanded in powers of its off-diagonal part; but this expansion converges only under certain well-defined conditions (e.g. Ferrar 1951). When the usual series diverges it is generally because these conditions are not fulfilled; but (5·9) is still valid provided the inverse matrix in (5·8), which always exists, is determined by other methods. When the usual series does converge it is of considerable value and leads to corresponding series expansions of the density matrices. On putting $H_{\kappa\lambda} = \xi H_{\kappa\lambda} (\xi \to 1)$ for $\kappa \neq \lambda$, it is a simple matter to show that the first iterate corresponds to the inclusion of the *exact* first- and second-order terms of the usual theory plus *parts* of all the higher order terms. We record here the results up to ξ^2

$$\left.\begin{aligned} \rho_{00}(=\rho_{00}^{AA}) &= \left[1-\xi^2\sum_{\kappa>0}\frac{H_{0\kappa}H_{\kappa 0}}{(H_{00}-H_{\kappa\kappa})^2}+\ldots\right], \\ \rho_{0\kappa}(=\rho_{0\kappa}^{AB}) &= \left[\xi\frac{H_{0\kappa}}{(H_{00}-H_{\kappa\kappa})}+\xi^2\sum_{\lambda(\neq\kappa)}\frac{H_{0\lambda}H_{\lambda\kappa}}{(H_{00}-H_{\lambda\lambda})(H_{00}-H_{\kappa\kappa})}+\ldots\right]=\rho_{\kappa 0}^{*}, \\ \rho_{\kappa\lambda}(=\rho_{\kappa\lambda}^{BB}) &= \left[\xi^2\frac{H_{\kappa 0}H_{0\lambda}}{(H_{00}-H_{\kappa\kappa})(H_{00}-H_{\lambda\lambda})}+\ldots\right]. \end{aligned}\right\} \quad (5\cdot 10)$$

The energy in this order may be found directly from (5·9)

$$E = \operatorname{tr}\mathbf{H}\boldsymbol{\rho} = H_{00}\rho_{00}+\sum_{\kappa>0}H_{\kappa\kappa}\rho_{\kappa\kappa}+\sum_{\kappa>0}\xi H_{0\kappa}\rho_{\kappa 0}+\sum_{\kappa>0}\xi H_{\kappa 0}\rho_{0\kappa}+\sum_{\kappa,\lambda>0}{}'\,\xi H_{\kappa\lambda}\rho_{\kappa\lambda}$$

$$= H_{00}\left[1-\xi^2\sum_{\kappa>0}\frac{H_{0\kappa}H_{\kappa 0}}{(H_{00}-H_{\kappa\kappa})^2}\right]+\xi^2\sum_{\kappa>0}H_{\kappa\kappa}\frac{H_{\kappa 0}H_{0\kappa}}{(H_{00}-H_{\kappa\kappa})^2}+2\xi^2\sum_{\kappa>0}\frac{H_{0\kappa}H_{\kappa 0}}{(H_{00}-H_{\kappa\kappa})}+O(\xi^3).$$

Thus
$$E = H_{00}+\xi^2\sum_{\kappa>0}\frac{H_{0\kappa}H_{\kappa 0}}{(H_{00}-H_{\kappa\kappa})}+0(\xi^3) \quad (\xi\to 1). \qquad (5\cdot 11)$$

Evidently the ξ^2-terms in the off-diagonal elements of $\boldsymbol{\rho}$ have no effect on the *energy* in this order, for they occur only with off-diagonal elements of **H**: but in discussing electron distribution functions and expectation values of operators other than the Hamiltonian, these terms cannot consistently be discarded. We shall now find that when the basis functions are generalized products the terms in (5·11) can be given a valuable physical interpretation.

6. Physical interpretation of the energy expression

Although the expression (2·26) permits a quite general interpretation of the energy expression in terms of the charge density and pair functions (which, in a many-configuration theory, may be approximated in any order by means of (5·9) and (2·22)), it is instructive in the present case to analyse the energy into terms associated with the separate electron groups. This is conveniently done, up to second order, by inserting the results of §§3 and 4 in (5·11). To order ξ^2 it is necessary to admit only configurations which differ from Φ_0 in not more than *two* group functions; and if the summation in (5·11) is split into parts referring to single and double excitations it follows that

$$E = E_{\text{elec.}}+E_{\text{pol.}}+E_{\text{disp.}}, \qquad (6\cdot 1)$$

where
$$E_{\text{elec.}} = H_{00} = \sum_{R}H^{R}(rr)+\sum_{R<S}[J^{RS}(rr,ss)-K^{RS}(rr,ss)], \qquad (6\cdot 2)$$

$$E_{\text{pol.}} = -\sum_{R}\sum_{r'(\neq r)}\frac{|H^{R}_{\text{eff.}}(rr')|^2}{E(r\to r')}, \qquad (6\cdot 3)$$

$$E_{\text{disp.}} = -\sum_{R<S}\sum_{r'(\neq r)}\sum_{s'(\neq s)}\frac{|J^{RS}(rr',ss')-K^{RS}(rr',ss')|^2}{E(r\to r',s\to s')} \qquad (6\cdot 4)$$

and the 'excitation energies' in the denominators are

$$\left.\begin{aligned} E(r \to r') &= H_{\kappa\kappa} - H_{00}, \quad \kappa = (a, b, \ldots, r', \ldots), \\ E(r \to r', s \to s') &= H_{\kappa\kappa} - H_{00}, \quad \kappa = (a, b, \ldots, r', \ldots, s', \ldots). \end{aligned}\right\} \tag{6·5}$$

The description of the energy terms as 'electrostatic', 'polarization' and 'dispersion' will presently be justified. Each will be considered in turn.

The first approximation

$E_{\text{elec.}}$ is simply the energy in the one-configuration approximation and, as such, has a special importance. Although the terms in (6·2) admit an immediate description in terms of the charge densities of the separate groups (cf. (3·11) and (3·12)) it is important to remember that they originate in the reduction of $\rho_1(\kappa\kappa \mid 1;\, 1')$ and $\rho_2(\kappa\kappa \mid 1, 2;\, 1', 2')$ according to (3·3) and (3·2) and that $E_{\text{elec.}}$ results when these one-configuration approximations are substituted in the general expression (2·17). It is then useful to obtain the corresponding spinless quantities which appear in (2·26), but to do this some assumption about spin states is necessary. The most widely useful assumption is that each electron group has zero z-component of total spin and for illustration we consider this case. Every term in an expansion over spin space of a typical function Φ_{Rr} must then contain equal numbers of α and β factors and it readily follows that the most general one-electron density matrix is

$$\rho_1^R(rr \mid 1;\, 1') = P_1^R(rr \mid \overset{+}{1};\, \overset{+}{1'})\alpha(1)\,\alpha^*(1') + P_1^R(rr \mid \overset{-}{1};\, \overset{-}{1'})\beta(1)\,\beta^*(1'), \tag{6·6}$$

where, from (2·24),

$$P_1^R(rr \mid \overset{+}{1};\, \overset{+}{1'}) = P_1^R(rr \mid \overset{-}{1};\, \overset{-}{1'}) = \tfrac{1}{2} P_1^R(rr \mid 1;\, 1')$$

Consequently, when the spin integrations are performed in (3·3) and (3·2) we obtain (with $\kappa = 0$)

$$\left.\begin{aligned} P_2(00 \mid 1, 2;\, 1', 2') = \sum_R P_2^R(rr \mid 1, 2;\, 1', 2') &+ \sum_{R,S}{}' P_1^R(rr \mid 1;\, 1')\, P_1^S(ss \mid 2;\, 2') \\ &- \tfrac{1}{2} \sum_{R,S}{}' P_1^R(rr \mid 2;\, 1')\, P_1^S(ss \mid 1;\, 2'), \\ P_1(00 \mid 1;\, 1') = \sum_R P_1^R(rr \mid 1;\, 1'). \end{aligned}\right\} \tag{6·7}$$

The distribution functions, which determine the potential energy terms in the energy expression (2·26) follow, of course, on removing the primes in (6·7).

The charge density is simply a sum of the charge densities associated with the separate groups, irrespective of the forms of the group functions. But the pair function has the simplest interpretation when each Φ_{Rr}—and hence $P_n^R(rr \mid 1, \ldots, n;\, 1' \ldots, n')$—is *localized*, becoming small when any of the variables $1, \ldots, n, 1', \ldots, n'$ refer to a point outside some fairly definite region (figure 1). For in this case

$$\left.\begin{aligned} P_2(00 \mid 1, 2;\, 1', 2') &\simeq P_2^R(rr \mid 1, 2;\, 1, 2) \quad \text{for points 1 and 2 within region } R \\ &\simeq P_1^R(rr \mid 1;\, 1)\, P_1^S(ss \mid 2;\, 2) \quad \text{for 1 in region } R, \text{ 2 in region } S. \end{aligned}\right\} \tag{6·8}$$

In other words, when two particles are close together in the same group region (figure 1*a*) they are described by the pair function for that group—which in principle may allow accurately for correlation effects since the group function has not been specified. It is only for two particles in *different* group regions (figure 1*b*) that the pair function is unable to admit full correlation, reducing to the product of two one-particle probabilities. The wave function is thus flexible enough to admit correlation in regions where it is most important and yet recognizes in a simple way the independence of parts of the system which are remote from one another.

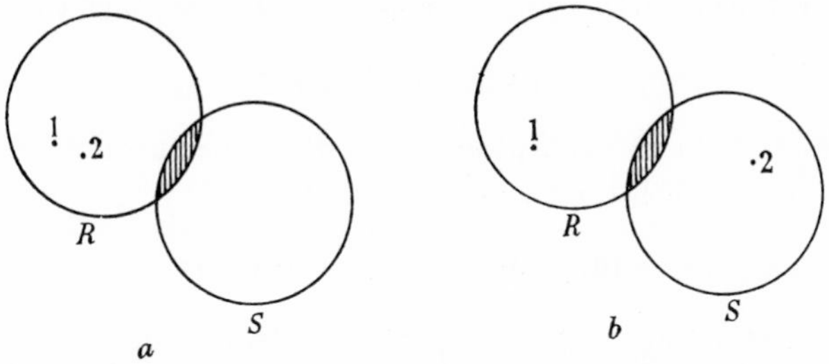

FIGURE 1. Localized electron groups (overlap region shaded). Correlation is taken into account for electrons 1 and 2 in *a*, but not in *b*: it is partially accounted for when 1 and 2 are in the overlap region.

On inserting (6·7) in (2·26) we retrieve (6·2) with the interaction terms reduced according to (3·11) and (3·12): but now it is clear that J^{RS} corresponds to neglect of *correlation* between the particles in group R and those in group S, each group being regarded as a *static* charge cloud, while K^{RS} admits some degree of inter-group correlation because it arises from inter-group terms which are not of simple product form. Closer investigation shows that the associated correlation terms are completely analogous to those which, in one-determinant theory, describe the 'Fermi hole': they describe the reduced probability of approach of particles with the *same spin*.

To summarize, $E_{\text{elec.}}$ is a sum of the energies of the different groups (each taken separately in the field of all nuclei), supplemented by the electrostatic interactions between their separate charge clouds. There remains a correlation correction—but this will be very small if the separate groups are substantially localized in different regions of space.

Polarization energy

$E_{\text{pol.}}$ arises from admixture of singly-excited configurations, those in which the R group is described by $\Phi_{Rr'}$ being incorporated with a weight depending on $H^R_{\text{eff.}}(rr')$ and giving rise (by 3·4*b*) to a change of *electron density* within group R. Since $H^R_{\text{eff.}}(rr')$ is a matrix element of $\mathscr{H}^R_{\text{eff.}}$, which contains the effective field produced by the nuclei and all electron groups other than R (each group in the state indicated in Φ_0), this modification of charge density is conditioned by the presence of other electron groups and is aptly described as a *polarization*. A given one-configuration approximation may thus be improved by admitting the polarization of each group in the

Coulomb-exchange field of the others—the latter being calculated using the group functions assigned in the one-configuration approximation. It is clear from (4·11) and (3·11) that the dominant potential energy terms in $H^R_{\text{eff.}}(rr')$ may be visualized in terms of a transition charge cloud, of density $P^R_1(rr' \mid 1;\, 1)$, in the field of the nuclei and other electron groups. The exchange effect will again be of secondary importance, being associated with a correlation correction.

There is one case in which the polarization energy vanishes and the charge density in each group is unaffected (to order ξ^2 in the perturbation expansion) by the admission of configuration interaction. This will occur when $(\Phi_{Rr'} | \mathscr{H}^R_{\text{eff.}} | \Phi_{Rr}) = 0$ for all single excitations $(r \rightarrow r')$ in each group R. But when this is so

$$(\Phi \,|\mathscr{H}^R_{\text{eff.}}|\, \Phi_{Rr}) = 0$$

for any function Φ in the subspace spanned by the functions of group R and orthogonal to Φ_{Rr}: and this in turn implies that

$$(\Phi_{Rr} \,|\mathscr{H}^R_{\text{eff.}}|\, \Phi_{Rr}) = \text{stationary} \tag{6·9}$$

against any variation $\Phi_{Rr} \rightarrow \Phi_{Rr} + \sum_{r'(\neq r)} C_r \, \Phi_{Rr'}$. This is also the condition that a normalized single product Φ_{Rr} shall be a *best approximation* to the wave function for a system with Hamiltonian $\mathscr{H}^R_{\text{eff.}}$, in the usual sense of variation theory. It follows that the best one-configuration approximation occurs when each group function Φ_{Rr} is an approximate eigenfunction of an effective group Hamiltonian $\mathscr{H}^R_{\text{eff.}}$ and that in this case the polarization energy vanishes.

Dispersion energy

$E_{\text{disp.}}$ involves double excitations and clearly represents the effect of mixing due to electrostatic interaction between *pairs* of transition densities; for that part which refers to groups R and S depends upon $J^{RS}(rr', ss')$ and $K^{RS}(rr', ss')$, the first being the interaction energy between charge clouds whose densities at points 1 and 2 are $P^R_1(rr' \mid 1;\, 1)$ and $P^S_1(ss \mid 2;\, 2)$ respectively, and the second being the associated correlation correction. When the electron groups R and S belong to distant molecules $K^{RS}(rr', ss')$ will become quite negligible; and the coulomb interaction of the two transition densities is then the well-known 'dispersion energy' of London's theory of intermolecular forces (London 1930); see also Longuet-Higgins 1956).

7. Remarks on applications

It has now been established that whenever a system contains a number of orthogonal electron groups it is useful to distinguish interaction terms analogous to those recognized in the theory of intermolecular forces. It is meaningful, at a certain level of approximation, to speak of polarization and dispersion interactions between, say, two CH_3 groups in the same molecule; between the σ and π electrons of a conjugated system; and even between the K and L shells of a single atom. In conclusion two limiting situations to which the analysis is immediately applicable are briefly discussed.

Separate systems. Intermolecular forces

Systems may be described as 'separate' if the *nuclei* fall into groups, each with its own complement of electrons described by a substantially localized group function. Van der Waals forces and the cohesive energies of ionic and molecular crystals would be amenable to discussion using this model. For such a system we put

$$V(1) = V_A(1) + V_B(1) + \dots \tag{7·1}$$

—a sum of contributions from the separate groups of nuclei—and define a one-electron Hamiltonian for group R in the field of its *own nuclei alone*;

$$h^R(1) = -\frac{\hbar^2}{2m}\nabla^2(1) + V_R(1) \tag{7·2}$$

and an associated N_R-electron Hamiltonian for system R,

$$\mathscr{H}_0^R(1, \dots, N_R) = \sum_{i=1}^{N_R} h^R(i) + \frac{1}{2}\sum_{i,j=1}^{N_R}{}' g(i,j). \tag{7·3}$$

If matrix elements of this Hamiltonian are distinguished by subscript zero, the one-configuration energy (6·2) takes the explicit form

$$\begin{aligned} E_{\text{elec.}} = \sum_R H_0^R(rr) + \sum_{R<S} \Big\{ & \int V_S(1)\,\rho_1^R(rr \mid 1;\, 1)\,\mathrm{d}\tau_1 + \int V_R(1)\,\rho_1^S(ss \mid 1;\, 1)\,\mathrm{d}\tau_1 \\ & + \int g(1,2)\,\rho_1^R(rr \mid 1;\, 1)\,\rho_1^S(ss \mid 2;\, 2)\,\mathrm{d}\tau_1\,\mathrm{d}\tau_2 \\ & - \int g(1,2)\,\rho_1^R(rr \mid 2;\, 1)\,\rho_1^S(ss \mid 1;\, 2)\,\mathrm{d}\tau_1\,\mathrm{d}\tau_2 \Big\}. \end{aligned} \tag{7·4}$$

If the functions Φ_{Rr} were exact wave functions for the separate systems, the first sum would be the total electronic energy at infinite separation: generally, it is the total electronic energy of separate systems whose wave functions are appropriately perturbed by their mutual approach. If the exchange correlation is neglected, the typical interaction term in (7·4) reduces, on eliminating spin, to

(energy of R-group charge distribution in field of nuclei of system S)

+ (energy of S-group charge distribution in field of nuclei of system R)

+ (interaction energy of charge densities of group R and group S).

The first-order interactions between all pairs of groups are thus basically Coulombic until their electron distributions begin to overlap—in which case the exchange terms can no longer be neglected.

The polarization and dispersion terms follow from (6·3) and (6·4). In particular, the polarization of system R by the other systems is now determined by the matrix element

$$\begin{aligned} H_{\text{eff.}}^R(rr') = H_0^R(rr') + \sum_{S(\neq R)} \Big\{ & \int V_S(1)\,\rho_1^R(rr' \mid 1;\, 1)\,\mathrm{d}\tau_1 \\ & + \int g(1,2)\,\rho_1^R(rr' \mid 1;\, 1)\rho_1^S(ss \mid 2;\, 2)\,\mathrm{d}\tau\,\mathrm{d}\tau_2 \\ & - \int g(1,2)\,\rho_1^R(rr' \mid 2;\, 1)\,\rho_1^S(ss \mid 1;\, 2)\,\mathrm{d}\tau_1\,\mathrm{d}\tau_2 \Big\}. \end{aligned} \tag{7·5}$$

The first term will vanish if Φ_{Rr} and $\Phi_{Rr'}$ are exact wave functions for the isolated system R, but not otherwise. The second term is mainly the energy of a transition charge cloud, $P_1^R(rr' \mid 1; 1)$, in the field of all other systems in their ground states.

Electrostatic and polarization forces will clearly be large if the systems bear a net charge (ionic crystals), small if they are neutral (molecular crystals) and very small if they possess high symmetry and small multipole moments (inert gases). As Longuet-Higgins (1956) has pointed out, however, multipole expansions are neither an integral part of the London theory nor, at short distances appropriate.

Superimposed groups. Inner and outer shells

The second extreme situation occurs when all electron groups surround the *same* set of nuclei. It is sufficient to consider the case of two groups—an 'inner shell' and an 'outer shell'. An important example is a conjugated molecule, and in this case the first approximation yields the theory of Lykos & Parr (1956).

From (6·2) the one-configuration energy is

$$H_{00}(=E_{\text{elec.}}) = H^A(aa) + H^B(bb) + J^{AB}(aa, bb) - K^{AB}(aa, bb). \qquad (7\cdot6)$$

But if A is a tightly bound inner shell it is preferable to associate it with the nuclei to form a 'framework' in whose field the B electrons move. In this case we use the effective Hamiltonian $\mathscr{H}^B_{\text{eff.}}$ (4·10) for group B and rewrite (7·6) as

$$H_{00} = H^A(aa) + H^B_{\text{eff.}}(bb) \qquad (7\cdot7)$$

—the energy of an inner shell in the field of the nuclei alone, plus that of an outer shell in the effective field of the 'framework'. This result was first given, in essence, by Lykos & Parr (1956); but the definition of the effective Hamiltonian is greatly simplified by the density matrix reduction of the Coulomb and exchange operators.

The polarization and dispersion interactions between different shells have not previously been recognized. Very often (e.g. in π-electron theory) the B-shell function is determined variationally and the B-term in (6·3) disappears: the next step would evidently be to recognize the polarization of the inner shell by the outer by estimating the remaining A-term. Finally, the dispersion energy is given by (6·4).

The work reported in this paper forms part of a research programme sponsored and supported partly by the Department of Scientific and Industrial Research and partly by the U.S. Department of the Army, through its European Research Office.

The author is grateful to Professor H. C. Longuet-Higgins, F.R.S. for useful comments and criticism.

References

Born, M. & Green, H. S. 1947 *Proc. Roy. Soc.* A, **191**, 168.
Brillouin, L. 1932 *J. Phys. Radium* (7) **3**, 373.
Condon, E. U. & Shortley, G. H. 1935 *The theory of atomic spectra.* Cambridge University Press.
Ferrar, W. L. 1951 *Finite matrices.* Oxford University Press.
Hartree, D. R. 1949 *Proc. Camb. Phil. Soc.* **45**, 230.
Hurley, A. C., Lennard-Jones, J. E. & Pople, J. A. 1953 *Proc. Roy. Soc.* A, **220**, 446.
Husimi, K. 1940 *Proc. Phys.-Math. Soc. Japan* **22**, 264.

London, F. 1930 *Z. Phys.* **63**, 245.
Longuet-Higgins, H. C. 1956 *Proc. Roy. Soc.* A. **235**, 537.
Löwdin, P.-O. 1951 *J. Chem. Phys.* **19**, 1396.
Löwdin, P.-O. 1955 *Phys. Rev.* **97**, 1474.
Löwdin, P.-O. 1958 *Tech. Note (23 April, 1958), Quantum Chemistry Group.* Uppsala University.
Lykos, P. G. & Parr, R. G. 1956 *J. Chem. Phys.* **24**, 1166.
MacDonald, J. K. L. 1933 *Phys. Rev.* **43**, 830.
McWeeny, R. 1954 *Proc. Roy. Soc.* A, **223**, 63.
McWeeny, R. 1955*a* *Tech. Rep. No. 7, Solid-State and Mol. Theory Gp. Mass. Inst. Tech.* (1st May, 1955).
McWeeny, R. 1955*b* *Proc. Roy. Soc.* A, **232**, 114.
McWeeny, R. 1956 *Proc. Roy. Soc.* A, **235**, 496.
Parr, R. G., Ellison, J. & Lykos, P. G. 1956 *J. Chem. Phys.* **24**, 1106.
Slater, J. C. 1931 *Phys. Rev.* **38**, 1109.
Wigner, E. P. 1935 *Math. naturw. Anz. ung. Akad, Wiss.* **53**, 477.

Reprinted from the JOURNAL OF CHEMICAL PHYSICS, Vol. 35, No. 5, 1644–1651, November, 1961
Printed in U. S. A.

The Chemical Bond in Molecular Quantum Mechanics*

THOMAS L. ALLEN† AND HARRISON SHULL

Chemistry Department, Indiana University, Bloomington, Indiana

(Received March 30, 1961)

It is postulated that a properly antisymmetrized product function over geminals (electron-pair wave functions) is adequate for discussion of the principal chemical properties of molecules. By application of the virial theorem it is shown that such a wave function has both of the properties essential to the bond-energy concept; namely (a) the energy of a molecule is the sum of the energies of its individual bonds and (b) the bond energies are invariant from one molecule to another. Within the framework of this approximation, bond energies become identified in magnitude with the kinetic energies associated with the respective geminals. The concepts are sufficiently general to include both localized and nonlocalized bonds, unshared electron pairs, odd electrons, and states of various multiplicities.

INTRODUCTION

IT has become evident in recent years that electronic correlation is of fundamental importance in chemical binding, and therefore the one-electron approximation is inherently too inaccurate to provide a suitable basis for the discussion of systems of chemical interest. Electronic correlation is usually introduced by means of a superposition of configurations. Although this method can lead to results of any desired accuracy, for many-electron systems the wave functions are very complicated. It is then extremely difficult to see what factors are significant in stabilizing a particular configuration of electrons and nuclei, and how these factors change in going to a related molecule. This has led to a natural trend toward obtaining results of high numerical accuracy, and an atrophy of the kind of activity traditionally associated with "understanding" chemistry. There appears to be little hope, however, that reasonably accurate wave functions will be calculated in the foreseeable future even for such a relatively simple molecule as, for example. propane.[1] Thus it is still important to utilize accurate calculations on simple molecules to gain an insight into chemical binding which can be applied to more complex molecules. The fundamental problem is to construct molecular wave functions which approximate closely the exact wave functions and which are at the same time of a form sufficiently simple to be comprehensible.

TWO-ELECTRON APPROXIMATION

What kind of wave function will best meet these specifications may be inferred from the molecular model used so successfully in chemistry. The electron pair is the fundamental structural unit, and it is used to form the various chemical bonds, unshared pairs, and inner shells necessary for a complete description of a molecule. For our purposes two properties of the electron pairs in this model should be emphasized. They are localized in nonconjugated systems, and many of them are localized even in conjugated molecules. They are independent of one another to a very high degree, as shown by the remarkable invariance of bond properties in going from one molecule to another.

A wave function appropriate to this model can be constructed from electron-pair functions.[2–12] (To distinguish these two-electron functions from the conventional orbitals, which are one-electron functions, the term *geminal* is useful.[8]) A product is formed from the geminals appropriate to the various chemical bonds and unshared electron pairs (and an orbital if the molecule contains an odd number of electrons). Application of an antisymmetrization operator gives a molecular wave function satisfying the Pauli principle. Further projection operators can be used, if necessary, to construct the desired symmetry properties of the resultant function. As the two electrons in a geminal need not have antiparallel spins, the function may have whatever multiplicity is appropriate to the state being represented.

Simply because the electron-pair concept has been so successful in chemistry, the best wave function of this form will almost certainly be a very satisfactory approximation to the exact wave function. This conjecture is supported by an examination of the correlation properties of an antisymmetrized product of geminals. No

† On leave from the Department of Chemistry, University of California, Davis, California, for 1959–1960.

* Supported in part by grants from the National Science Foundation to each of the authors and in part by a contract with Indiana University by the U.S. Air Force Office of Scientific Research.

[1] G. G. Hall, Repts. Progr. in Phys. **22**, 14 (1959).

[2] L. Pauling, Proc. Roy. Soc. (London) **A196**, 343 (1949).

[3] A. C. Hurley, J. E. Lennard-Jones, and J. A. Pople, Proc. Roy. Soc. (London) **A220**, 446 (1953).

[4] L. A. Schmid, Phys. Rev. **92**, 1373 (1953).

[5] J. C. Slater, Solid-State and Molecular Theory Group Massachusetts Institute of Technology, Cambridge, Massachusetts, Quart. Progr. Rept. No. 16 (1955), p. 5.

[6] J. M. Parks and R. G. Parr, J. Chem. Phys. **28**, 335 (1958).

[7] E. Kapuy, Acta Phys. Acad. Sci. Hung. **9**, 237 (1958); **10**, 125 (1959); **11**, 409 (1960); **12**, 185 (1960).

[8] H. Shull, J. Chem. Phys. **30**, 1405 (1959).

[9] M. Karplus and D. M. Grant, Proc. Natl. Acad. Sci. U.S. **45**, 1269 (1959).

[10] R. McWeeny and K. A. Ohno, Proc. Roy. Soc. (London) **A255**, 367 (1960).

[11] J. M. Parks and R. G. Parr, J. Chem. Phys. **32**, 1657 (1960).

[12] T. Arai, J. Chem. Phys. **33**, 95 (1960).

limit is placed on the complexity of the individual geminals, and therefore the two electrons in each electron pair may be correlated with one another to any desired degree of accuracy. Thus the principal deficiency in the one-electron approximation is overcome.

For two electrons in different geminals with antiparallel spins we have a case analogous to that of "different orbitals for different electrons" which has been found an effective method of introducing correlation. In addition to this effect, of course, two electrons in different geminals with parallel spins are correlated by the Fermi hole.

One can construct a conceptual process by which an optimum geminal-product wave function could be found for a given molecular system. One might, for example, following the analogy of the familiar self-consistent field process in the orbital scheme, use an energetic criterion for this first optimum term. Such a process has been outlined in detail by Parks and Parr.[6] Or, alternatively, one could imagine the existence of a transformation of the second-order density matrix that would make the first term optimum with respect to overlap with the true function, much as the first natural orbital is in a two-electron system.[13]

We assume that a suitable optimization process exists which leads to a unique optimum geminal product function. From the viewpoint of electron-electron interaction (or correlation), the repulsion effects will be minimized when the optimum geminals are essentially localized in different regions of space. We can expect, therefore, that optimum geminals will be localized, at least in nonconjugated systems. [In conjugated systems the best π geminals will likely have a semi-localized character, corresponding to benzene π equivalent orbitals (see Appendix A).] They should be even more localized than optimum localized orbitals, because in the one-electron approximation, repulsion between electrons in the same orbital hinders localization.

A related argument has been given by Hurley, Lennard-Jones, and Pople to show that the optimum forms of the paired electron functions are of a localized nature.[3] These authors also point out that the transformation properties which make molecular orbitals (delocalized) and equivalent orbitals (localized) mathematically equivalent to each other are not applicable in the two-electron approximation. This observation has interesting consequences regarding the best description of the double bond in ethylene and related molecules. It has been shown that, in the one-electron approximation, the wave function constructed from σ and π orbitals and the wave function constructed from bent-bond (or "banana-bond") orbitals are identical.[14,15] As the equivalence of the two descriptions does not hold in the two-electron approximation, and as the more localized form is expected to be the better function, the optimum electron-pair functions will correspond to a bent-bond description rather than to a σ, π description.

The high degree of invariance of bond properties suggests that geminals will be transferable from one molecule to another to a very good approximation. If essentially the same geminal describes the electron pair of a particular chemical bond in a variety of molecules, the observation that the energy, internuclear distance, force constant, etc., of this bond are essentially the same in each molecule is not an unreasonable consequence. On the other hand, this fact would be very difficult to understand if we were to suppose that the geminal corresponding to the bond varied widely among the different molecules.

Transferability would greatly simplify the construction of good wave functions for complex molecules, as one could then utilize the results obtained with simpler systems. In fact, belief in the existence of this property would seem to be essential to any optimistic view of the application of quantum mechanics to complex molecules. It is rather clear that geminals will be transferable in a qualitative sense, and the question is really one of degree—how large are the differences between the optimum geminals corresponding to a chemical bond in different molecules? This question will be discussed more fully in connection with molecular energies.

BOND ENERGY CONCEPT

While the bond energy method is an approximate one, its relative accuracy is often underestimated. The usual reference state is the enthalpy of the separated atoms in their ground electronic states at 25°C. If excited states (e.g., valence states) are chosen for points of reference, each bond energy is increased by some constant, but the additivity of bond energies is unaffected.[16,17] Therefore one may equally well use the reference state common in quantum-mechanical calculations, the energy of separated electrons and nuclei. This permits a direct comparison of the accuracy of quantum-mechanical calculations and the bond energy method.

The calculation of the energy of propane from the energies of methane and ethane may be taken as a representative example of the accuracy of the bond energy method. Using data for the molecules in the ideal gas state at 0°K with fixed nuclei,[18] and the basic assumption that bond energies are constant, the result is in error by 1.68 kcal/mole. But the energy of propane in this state with respect to separated electrons and nuclei is 74 698 kcal/mole. The relative error of the bond energy method is thus only 0.002%, which is two orders of magnitude better than the accuracy of recent

[13] P. O. Löwdin and H. Shull, Phys. Rev. **101,** 1730 (1956).
[14] G. G. Hall and J. E. Lennard-Jones, Proc. Roy. Soc. (London) **A205,** 357 (1951).
[15] J. E. Lennard-Jones and J. A. Pople, Discussions Faraday Soc. **10,** 9 (1951).
[16] C. T. Zahn, J. Chem. Phys. **2,** 671 (1934).
[17] The relation between bond energies and bond dissociation energies changes, and this is involved in one method of estimating valence state energies [L. Pauling, Proc. Natl. Acad. Sci. U.S. **35,** 229 (1949)].
[18] T. L. Allen, J. Chem. Phys. **31,** 1039 (1959).

quantum-mechanical calculations for much simpler molecules. And even this small error can be almost completely eliminated by including the interactions between next-nearest neighbors.[18]

In attempting to account for the remarkable accuracy of the bond energy method, it is important to note the twofold nature of this concept, according to which (a) the energy of a molecule is the sum of the energies of its individual bonds, and (b) the bond energies are invariant from one molecule to another. Inasmuch as the bond energies are calculated empirically from molecular energies, (a) without (b) is a mere tautology.

Difficulty in explaining additivity of bond energies arises from the complexity of the Hamiltonian operators, which include the Coulomb interaction of every particle with every other particle, and which differ for each molecule. Several authors have investigated the problem of writing expectation values of molecular Hamiltonian operators as the sums of bond energies. It has been shown by Brown,[19] and Dewar and Pettit,[20] that when certain approximations are made in the form of the wave functions and in the integrations, then the total electronic energy is given as a sum of bond energies. But the empirical bond energy concept applies to total molecular energies, and these include the internuclear-repulsion terms. Repulsions between nonbonded nuclei, which are large quantities, cannot be represented by a sum of bond terms (see Appendix B). Therefore the bond energy concept is not valid for electronic energies, and the proposed explanations account for a nonexistent phenomenon.

Hall has shown that in the one-electron approximation the total energy of a saturated molecule (including internuclear repulsions) can be expressed as the sum of suitably defined orbital energies.[21,22] In these quantities potential-energy terms arising from the interactions of distant particles are grouped so that terms of opposite sign tend to cancel. As a consequence of localization, the equivalent orbitals are primarily determined by the atom or atoms around which they are concentrated. It then follows that the orbital energies are approximately invariant. In an investigation of the valence-bond formulation of the two-electron approximation, Slater has given a somewhat similar argument showing that the energy of a molecule can be approximated by a constant part plus a sum of bond energies.[5] The questions of transferability and invariance of bond energies from one molecule to another were not considered.

Bond energies in the two-electron approximation have been studied in greater detail by Parks and Parr.[6] They find that the total molecular energy is rigorously expressible as a sum of bond energies. The bond energies are invariant only when the bonds are essentially homopolar and the "neutral-penetration terms" are negligible.

[19] R. D. Brown, J. Chem. Soc. **1953,** 2615.

[20] M. J. S. Dewar and R. Pettit, J. Chem. Soc. **1954,** 1625.

[21] G. G. Hall, Proc. Roy. Soc. (London) **A205,** 541 (1951).

[22] G. G. Hall, Proc. Roy. Soc. (London) **A213,** 113 (1952).

Even in this particular case the bond energies still depend indirectly on one another through the dependence of the A_k coefficients on the other electron pairs. Furthermore, they find that their approximations are badly in error for two bonds which involve the same atom, so that bond energies for such bonds are interdependent. However, different polyatomic molecules (the only kind to which bond energy additivity can apply) necessarily involve a difference in at least one pair of adjacent bonds. If the energies of such bonds are interdependent to a significant extent, bond energies will not be additive, unless the bond energy changes compensate one another. This has not been shown. Also, it is known that additivity of bond energies is not limited to homopolar bonds (for example, it holds extremely well for the chlorinated methanes). Therefore part (b) of the bond energy concept has not been explained, and we have seen that part (a) without (b) is essentially meaningless from an empirical point of view.

APPLICATION OF THE VIRIAL THEOREM

The high relative accuracy of the bond energy concept suggests that it is a direct consequence of some fundamental quantum-mechanical theorem, rather than the result of a somewhat fortuitous cancellation of terms. We demonstrate in the following that application of the very fundamental virial theorem gives a sound theoretical basis to the bond energy concept.

Let L be the class of all functions Λ which are products of geminals, each geminal being normalized and one-electron orthogonal to every other geminal in the same Λ. Using the notation and defining equations introduced by Parks and Parr[6]:

$$\Lambda = [\Lambda_A(1,2)\Lambda_B(3,4)\cdots\Lambda_M(2n-1,2n)], \qquad (1)$$

$$\iint |\Lambda_I(1,2)|^2 d\tau_1 d\tau_2 = 1, \qquad (2)$$

$$\int \Lambda_I^*(1,2)\Lambda_J(1,4)\,d\tau_1 = 0, \qquad (I \neq J). \qquad (3)$$

That trial function of class L which gives the lowest expectation value of the energy for a particular molecule will be termed the best function of class L for that molecule.[23] The Born-Oppenheimer approximation is assumed, and therefore the best wave function of class L describes the molecule with the nuclei fixed at their equilibirum positions.[24]

[23] When each geminal is constructed from only two spin-orbitals, the total wave function consists of a single determinant. The Hartree-Fock or SCF function is the best function of this special type. In general the functions of class L are many-determinant wave functions, and therefore the Hartree-Fock energy is an upper limit to the energy of the best function of class L.

[24] It is known that additivity of bond energies is somewhat improved by replacing conventional bond energies with bond energies calculated from data for the hypothetical state with fixed nuclei. In either case next-nearest neighbor interactions satisfactorily account for the deviations from additivity.[18]

It is also assumed that this wave function is a satisfactory approximation to the exact wave function. Our argument in a preceding section strongly suggests that molecules may be represented to chemical accuracy by a simple antisymmetrized geminal product function. It is not yet clear, however, what auxiliary conditions (for example, orthogonality conditions) can be placed on these geminals and still permit an adequate representation of a chemical system. That one-electron orthogonality [Eq. (3)], which is the orthogonality condition usually placed on electron-pair functions, is not too strong a condition, can perhaps be inferred from some unpublished calculations we have done on the ground state of the beryllium atom. A function of class L has been obtained which has an overlap of 0.99989 with one of the best published wave functions, Watson's 37-configuration function.[25] By contrast, the SCF function has an overlap with the latter of only 0.95758.

The kinetic energy of the molecule in this state then consists solely of electronic kinetic energy and is

$$T=\sum_I T_I, \tag{4}$$

where the summation is taken over all of the geminals in the appropriate Λ, and

$$T_I=2\iint \Lambda_I^*(1,2)\mathbf{T}(1)\Lambda_I(1,2)d\tau_1 d\tau_2. \tag{5}$$

The best wave function is necessarily correctly scaled and obeys the quantum-mechanical virial theorem,[26] which takes a particularly simple form when the nuclei are at their equilibrium positions.[27] In this case the total energy of the molecule (including the internuclear repulsion energy) E, is just the negative of the kinetic energy, so that

$$E=-\sum_I T_I. \tag{6}$$

Thus the total molecular energy is precisely given by a sum of terms, one for each electron pair. This takes care of part (a) of the bond energy concept. If now the geminals are transferable from one molecule to another (and we have already considered one reason for believing that they are at least approximately so), then the geminal energies are invariant. This takes care of part (b). The energy of a chemical bond relative to separated electrons and nuclei is therefore very simply interpreted: It is exactly equal to the negative of the kinetic energy of the geminal or geminals which describe the bond.

[25] R. E. Watson, Phys. Rev. **119**, 170 (1960).

[26] The virial theorem is satisfied by the true wave function, but not necessarily by an approximate wave function. If a trial function does not satisfy the virial theorem, application of the scaling procedure leads to a new approximate wave function which is of lower energy than the unscaled function and which also satisfies the virial theorem. This point has been recently emphasized by P. O. Löwdin [J. Mol. Spectroscopy **3**, 46 (1959); Advances in Chem. Phys. **2**, 207 (1959)].

[27] J. C. Slater, J. Chem. Phys. **1**, 687 (1933).

It is not suggested, of course, that the kinetic energy is the fundamental cause of chemical binding. But the kinetic energy is directly connected to the potential energy and the total energy through the virial theorem, and therefore it is justifiable and illuminating to analyze the latter quantities, which are very complex, in terms of the much simpler kinetic energy.

The bond energies so defined are identical with empirical bond energies, except that the latter quantities include *pro rata* contributions from inner shells and unshared pairs. There are also the arbitrary differences in reference states previously noted, and the sign conventions are opposite. Empirical bond energies are primarily defined for symmetrical molecules of formula AB_n. Except for the changes in reference states and sign convention necessary to provide a common basis, the empirical bond energy is

$$E(\mathrm{A-B})=E/n. \tag{7}$$

By analogy with equivalent orbitals, the functions for the different bonds differ only in their position in space, and therefore have the same kinetic energy. Let T_{AB} denote the kinetic energy of the geminal(s) describing a bond, and let T_{A} and T_{B} denote the kinetic energies of any inner shells or unshared electron pairs on atoms A and B, respectively, T_{B} being the same for each atom B. Then

$$E=-nT_{\mathrm{AB}}-T_{\mathrm{A}}-nT_{\mathrm{B}}, \tag{8}$$

$$E(\mathrm{A-B})=-T_{\mathrm{AB}}-T_{\mathrm{B}}-T_{\mathrm{A}}/n. \tag{9}$$

The argument may readily be extended to more complex molecules.

TRANSFERABILITY OF GEMINALS

We shall now obtain a connection between the concept of transferability and the potential energy terms. For this purpose we note that in the class of molecules obeying bond energy additivity, the energy of one molecule may be expressed as a linear combination of other molecular energies. A simple but quite general example is the sequence of molecules BAB, CAC, and BAC, where A, B, and C are atoms and/or radicals. If the molecular energies are E_1, E_2, and E_3, respectively, then

$$E_3=\tfrac{1}{2}(E_1+E_2). \tag{10}$$

Let the best wave functions of class L for these molecules be Λ_1, Λ_2, and Λ_3, respectively, where

$$\Lambda_1=[\beta\beta' abb'], \tag{11}$$

$$\Lambda_2=[\gamma\gamma' acc'], \tag{12}$$

$$\Lambda_3=[\beta\gamma' abc']. \tag{13}$$

The symbols β and γ denote the geminals or products of geminals describing the bonds connecting A and B, and A and C, respectively. Unprimed symbols refer to the left, primed symbols to the right members of each molecule, and a, b, and c are the geminal products describing all inner shells, unshared pairs, and internal bonds in the corresponding radicals A, B, and C. It is assumed that the nuclear frameworks of the BA and CA groupings are the same in each molecule.

The potential energy of a molecule described by a function of class L is

$$V=\sum_I\sum_p U_I(p)+\sum_I S_I+\tfrac{1}{2}\sum_I\sum_{J\neq I} W_{IJ}+\tfrac{1}{2}\sum_p\sum_{q\neq p}(Z_pZ_q/r_{pq}), \quad (14)$$

where we are using atomic units and

$$U_I(p)=-2Z_p\iint \Lambda_I^*(1,2)(1/r_{1p})\Lambda_I(1,2)d\tau_1 d\tau_2, \quad (15)$$

$$S_I=\iint \Lambda_I^*(1,2)(1/r_{12})\Lambda_I(1,2)d\tau_1 d\tau_2, \quad (16)$$

$$W_{IJ}=J_{IJ}-K_{IJ}. \quad (17)$$

The symbols J_{IJ} and K_{IJ}, defined by Eqs. (14) and (15) of Parks and Parr[6] (except for the change to atomic units), involve electron repulsions between different geminals.

Let

$$U_\beta(B)=\sum_{I\epsilon\beta}\sum_{p\epsilon B} U_I(p), \quad (18)$$

that is, the sum of all terms representing the attraction of the electrons in every geminal contained in the bond β to every nucleus contained in the atom or radical B. Also, let

$$S_\beta=\sum_{I\epsilon\beta} S_I, \quad (19)$$

$$W_{\beta\beta'}=\sum_{I\epsilon\beta}\sum_{J\epsilon\beta'} W_{IJ}, \quad (20)$$

and

$$Z_BZ_A/r_{BA}=\sum_{p\epsilon B}\sum_{q\epsilon A}(Z_pZ_q/r_{pq}). \quad (21)$$

Other terms of these same types are defined similarly. The potential energy of molecule BAB is then:

$$\begin{aligned}V_1=&2U_\beta(\mathrm{B})+2U_\beta(\mathrm{A})+2U_\beta(\mathrm{B}')+2U_a(\mathrm{B})+U_a(\mathrm{A})\\&+2U_b(\mathrm{B})+2U_b(\mathrm{A})+2U_b(\mathrm{B}')+2S_\beta+S_a+2S_b\\&+W_{\beta\beta}+W_{bb}+\tfrac{1}{2}W_{aa}+W_{\beta\beta'}+2W_{\beta a}+2W_{\beta b}\\&+2W_{\beta b'}+2W_{ab}+W_{bb'}+2Z_BZ_A/r_{BA}\\&+Z_\mathrm{B}Z_{\mathrm{B}'}/r_{\mathrm{BB}'}. \quad (22)\end{aligned}$$

In deriving this expression we have utilized equations of the type $U_\beta(\mathrm{B})=U_{\beta'}(\mathrm{B}')$, which follow from the supposed equivalence of β to β', and of b to b'.

Analogous equations can be written for V_2 and V_3. From Eq. (10) and the virial theorem, the potential energies are related by

$$V_3=\tfrac{1}{2}[V_1+V_2]. \quad (23)$$

When the detailed expressions for V_1, V_2, and V_3 are substituted into this equation, most of the terms cancel. The terms which remain involve the interactions between the ends of each molecule. To represent these interactions concisely, let $\nu(XYZ)$ be the sum of all potential energy terms arising from the interactions of the electrons and nuclei in X and the bond joining X to Y, with the electrons and nuclei in Z and the bond joining Z to Y. Thus we have

$$\begin{aligned}\nu(\mathrm{BAC})=&U_b(\mathrm{C}')+U_{c'}(\mathrm{B})+U_\beta(\mathrm{C}')+U_{\gamma'}(\mathrm{B})+W_{bc'}\\&+W_{\beta\gamma'}+W_{\beta c'}+W_{\beta\gamma'}+Z_\mathrm{B}Z_{\mathrm{C}'}/r_{\mathrm{BC}'}, \quad (24)\end{aligned}$$

with similar expressions for the other molecules. The relationship between these interactions, obtained from Eq. (23), is then simply

$$\nu(\mathrm{BAC})=\tfrac{1}{2}\{\nu(\mathrm{BAB})+\nu(\mathrm{CAC})\}. \quad (25)$$

To summarize the argument, if we assume that (a) geminals are transferable, then it follows that (b) bond energies are additive, and (c) the interaction between the ends of molecule BAC is the arithmetic mean of the interactions between the ends of molecules BAB and CAC, as expressed by Eq. (25).

Conversely, (a) is a necessary consequence of (b) and (c). Instead of assuming transferability,[28] let the best wave function of class L for molecule BAC be some function Λ'_3. Let the total energies associated with Λ_3 and Λ'_3 be E_3 and E'_3, respectively, with corresponding designations for the kinetic and potential energies. By the virial theorem and the assumption of (b) and (c),

$$E_3'=\tfrac{1}{2}\{E_1+E_2\}, \quad (26)$$

$$T_3'=\tfrac{1}{2}\{T_1+T_2\}=T_3, \quad (27)$$

$$\begin{aligned}V_3-V_3'=V_3-\tfrac{1}{2}\{V_1+V_2\}=&\nu(\mathrm{BAC})\\&-\tfrac{1}{2}\{\nu(\mathrm{BAB})+\nu(\mathrm{CAC})\}=0. \quad (28)\end{aligned}$$

Therefore $E_3'=E_3$ and $\Lambda_3'=\Lambda_3$.

While it would be of interest to show that transferability of geminals is a necessary consequence of additivity of bond energies *per se*, this has not been possible without some auxiliary assumption such as Eq. (25), or the assumption that Λ_3 is correctly scaled. However, Eq. (25) expresses a plausible relationship. In $\nu(\mathrm{BAC})$, the terms representing attraction between electrons and nuclei will largely cancel the interelectronic and internuclear repulsion terms. Colloquially, the electrons effectively screen the nuclei. The only remaining term is that part of $W_{\beta\gamma'}$ representing the repulsion between the bonding electrons at the central atom or group, and even here the repulsion will be relatively small because of the orthogonality of the bond geminals. Similar considerations apply to $\nu(\mathrm{BAB})$ and $\nu(\mathrm{CAC})$. As A increases in size, and the end groups become further separated, each term in Eq. (25) tends to zero. There

[28] However, it must be noted that it has been necessary to assume that the a function is the same in Λ_1 and Λ_2.

is a corresponding improvement in the accuracy of Eq. (10), in accordance with the general limiting law of Benson and Buss.[29]

Empirical treatments of molecular energies have led to a system of postulates somewhat analogous to (a), (b), and (c) above.[16,18] It is assumed that molecular energies are the sums of bond energies and the energies of interaction between next-nearest neighbors and/or adjacent bonds, designated $\alpha'(BAC)$, etc. In the following set of statements, given (a), then (b) is a necessary and sufficient condition for (c):

(a) these intrinsic bond energies are constant from one molecule to another;

(b) Eq. (10) is valid; that is, conventional bond energies are additive;

(c) $$\alpha'(BAC)=\tfrac{1}{2}\{\alpha'(BAB)+\alpha'(CAC)\}. \quad (29)$$

In concluding this section, we wish to note that transferability of geminals is not to be confused with the usual assumption that matrix elements of the Hamiltonian operator with respect to a particular function are the same throughout a series of molecules. Also, it is not anticipated that geminals will be transferable between molecules of different valence types, or even between different states of the same molecule. For example, the C—H bond geminals in ethane, ethylene, and acetylene will certainly differ significantly from one another. As is well-known, the identity of the C—H bond energies in these molecules is a common, convenient, but completely arbitrary assumption.

DEVIATIONS FROM ADDITIVITY

Although the deviations from strict additivity of bond energies are quite small with respect to total molecular energies, they are still sufficiently large to be of great interest in chemistry. We have seen that transferability of geminals leads to bond energy additivity, and therefore the deviations from additivity necessarily reflect deviations from transferability, or inadequacies in the kind of wave function under consideration, or both.

It is not hard to see why the geminals might vary to some extent. Each is an approximate eigenfunction of an effective Hamiltonian which includes the effective field created by the other electron-pair functions and the nuclei.[30] In going from one molecule to another the change in the effective field is bound to affect the optimum form of a particular geminal. It seems appropriate to call this an inductive effect.[22] The inductive effect should be particularly pronounced when there are changes in nearby nuclei and in geminals localized in the same region of space.

What is perhaps more difficult to understand is why inductive effects do not produce much larger deviations from additivity. There appear to be several factors, however, which restrict inductive changes in molecular energies:

(1) A geminal energy is not affected directly, but only to the extent that the form of the geminal itself responds to changes in nearby geminals and nuclei.

(2) The different bonds of the same valence type are perhaps more alike than is usually supposed. For example, substitution of a chlorine atom for a hydrogen atom in methane may not greatly alter the effective field in which the electrons of the remaining C—H bonds move.

(3) The kinetic energy seems to be relatively insensitive to changes in the wave function. Thus in the reaction $2H=H_2$, the wave function undergoes a drastic change. But whereas the electronic potential energy decreases by 1.062 Hartree atomic units, the kinetic energy increases by only 0.174 H. Because of their connection with the kinetic energy terms, the same will be true for the geminal energies.

(4) Considering once again the sequence of molecules BAB, CAC, and BAC, the wave function for molecule BAC obtained by transferring geminals, Λ_3, may be treated as an unperturbed function. The perturbation on β and b, to a first approximation, consists in replacing β' and b' by γ' and c', and the nuclei of the other B by the nuclei of C. For γ' and c' the perturbation consists in replacing γ and c by β and b, and the nuclei of the other C by those of B. As the perturbations are thus equal in magnitude and opposite in sign, the corresponding changes in the geminal energies will largely cancel.

The same conclusion is reached by consideration of the simple picture of hybridization at the central atom or group. Changes in hybridization which strengthen one bond will be accompanied by changes which weaken other bonds.

The deviations from additivity might also be connected with the difference between the best wave functions of class L and the exact wave functions. An improvement in accuracy can be obtained by dropping the requirement of one-electron orthogonality, Eq. (3), while retaining the less restrictive two-electron orthogonality condition,[31]

$$\iint \Lambda_I^*(1,2)\Lambda_J(1,2)d\tau_1 d\tau_2=0, \qquad (I\neq J). \qquad (30)$$

The expression for the kinetic energy is now much more complex, including terms such as

$$\iiiint \Lambda_I^*(1,2)\Lambda_J^*(3,4)\mathbf{T}(1)\Lambda_I(3,2)\Lambda_J(1,4) \times d\tau_1 d\tau_2 d\tau_3 d\tau_4,$$

which formerly vanished because of the one-electron orthogonality condition. It is reasonable to class these terms as interactions between the electron-pair func-

[29] S. W. Benson and J. H. Buss, J. Chem. Phys. **29**, 546 (1958).

[30] R. McWeeny, Proc. Roy. Soc. (London) **A253**, 242 (1959); Revs. Modern Phys. **32**, 335 (1960).

[31] See footnote 10 of reference 6.

tions. Besides this complication there will still be inductive effects in going from one molecule to another.

GENERALIZATION OF THE BOND ENERGY CONCEPT

One of the most inviting features of the use of wave functions of class L and the application of the virial theorem outlined above is the possibility of generalizing the concept of bond energies. For any system of chemical interest, a unique energy can be assigned to each electron pair and odd electron, and by Eq. (6) the total energy is precisely given by the sum of these components. Thus energies can be assigned not only to chemical bonds but to unshared pairs, inner shells, and odd electrons. In a multiple bond the several parts will have distinct energies. Furthermore, the generalization broadens the field of systems to include atoms, ions, transition states, excited states, etc.

It will then be possible to obtain detailed descriptions of the differences between related molecules. As comparative studies have proved so fruitful in chemistry, it is to be expected that investigations along these lines will lead to a better understanding of the electronic changes involved in chemical phenomena. A simple example is the question of the extent to which the lithium K shell affects the dissociation energy of the lithium hydride molecule. By comparing the energy of the K shell electron pair in the lithium atom and LiH, it will now be possible to give a definite, quantitative answer to this question.

It should be mentioned that the virial theorem can also yield interesting results when applied to SCF wave functions. Provided that a set of mutually orthogonal orbitals is used, the total energy is then given by a sum of orbital energies, each equal in magnitude and opposite in sign to the expectation value of the kinetic energy operator with respect to the orbital. These orbital energies will differ from the conventional ones, which do not have the property that their sum is equal to the total energy of the system.

Finally, we note that the individual geminals, which are postulated here to be sufficiently accurate to describe most properties of chemical interest, may be subjected to further analysis by the usual natural orbital techniques applicable to such two-electron systems. There is nothing in what has been written above which inherently requires that any given geminal be an eigenfunction of $\mathbf{S}^2$ for example, and we can expect that each one will be a mixture (probably only to a very small extent) of various spin states. But by suitable projection operator techniques and natural orbital transformations, one should be able to find excellent representations of each geminal that would permit discussion of its electron distribution, etc., in ordinary chemical language. We therefore have in principle an orderly scheme solidly based upon the principles of quantum mechanics which will enable us in the future to give a coherent and satisfying description of the nature of the chemical bond.

ACKNOWLEDGMENT

One of the authors (T.L.A.) wishes to express his appreciation to the members of the Chemistry Department at Indiana University for their generous hospitality and for many stimulating discussions.

APPENDIX A. BENZENE π EQUIVALENT ORBITALS

It has been shown by Hall and Lennard-Jones[14] that the three π molecular orbitals of lowest energy in benzene can be transformed into three equivalent orbitals with C_{3v} symmetry. The appropriate transformation is the same as that used in sp^2 hybridization.[32] Expressions for the a_g, e_x, and e_y molecular orbitals as linear combinations of p atomic orbitals are given by Coulson in Eqs. (20), (21a), and (21b), respectively.[33] Substituting a_g for ψ_{2s}, e_x for ψ_{2px}, and e_y for ψ_{2py}, the following expressions are obtained for the equivalent orbitals:

$$\chi_1 = \{\psi_1 + (1+\surd 3)(\psi_2+\psi_3) + \psi_4 + (1-\surd 3)(\psi_5+\psi_6)\}/3\surd 2, \tag{31}$$

$$\chi_2 = \{\psi_5 + (1+\surd 3)(\psi_6+\psi_1) + \psi_2 + (1-\surd 3)(\psi_3+\psi_4)\}/3\surd 2, \tag{32}$$

$$\chi_3 = \{\psi_3 + (1+\surd 3)(\psi_4+\psi_5) + \psi_6 + (1-\surd 3)(\psi_1+\psi_2)\}/3\surd 2. \tag{33}$$

These orbitals fit the description given by Hall and Lennard-Jones.

A simpler set of equivalent orbitals can be derived by interchanging the roles of e_x and e_y in this transformation. Substituting a_g for ψ_{2s}, e_y for ψ_{2px}, and e_x for ψ_{2py}, we obtain:

$$\chi_1' = \{2\psi_6 + 3\psi_1 + 2\psi_2 - \psi_4\}/3\surd 2, \tag{34}$$

$$\chi_2' = \{2\psi_2 + 3\psi_3 + 2\psi_4 - \psi_6\}/3\surd 2, \tag{35}$$

$$\chi_3' = \{2\psi_4 + 3\psi_5 + 2\psi_6 - \psi_2\}/3\surd 2. \tag{36}$$

The charge distributions associated with these orbitals, each doubly occupied, are as follows:

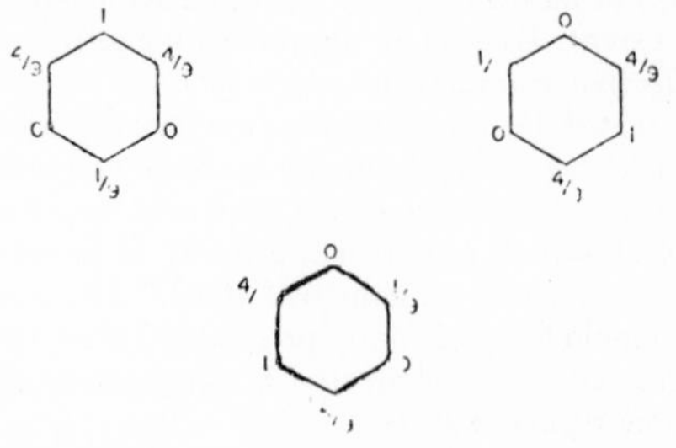

[32] H. Eyring, J. Walter, and G. E. Kimball, *Quantum Chemistry* (John Wiley & Sons, Inc., New York, 1944), p. 224.

[33] C. A. Coulson, *Valence* (Oxford Universitv Press, New York, 1952), p. 240.

The importance of this truncation of the basis in ICC calculations lies in the treatment of highly ionized states of the dissociation products. Thus the full valence-bond basis (2.18) includes many states of the ions C^{2-}, C^{3-}, C^{4-}. It is clearly impossible to obtain reliable experimental estimates of the energies of these states. In a previous calculation of the binding energy of N_2 [Hurley (1956b)], this difficulty was circumvented by using an extrapolation technique to dispense with empirical estimates of the energies of various states of the ions N^{2-} and N^{3-}. Nevertheless, the presence of these states in the total wave function led to some uncertainty in the final results.

Here it is possible to eliminate these troublesome states entirely. First it is shown that they have a negligible effect on the total energy in the orbital calculation. These states are then omitted from the ICC calculations by truncating the bases in accordance with Eq. (2.23).

Of course, it is always possible to truncate the basis in an ICC calculation after transforming the full energy matrix explicitly into the valence-bond basis, regardless of what process of orthogonalization is employed. However, this is a much less efficient procedure than exploiting the properties of Schmidt orthogonalization.

(c) Energy Matrix

The energy matrix $\tilde{H}(\Theta)$ in the basis of orthogonalized valence-bond functions (2.19) was evaluated by using McWeeny's (1954) generalization of the cycle-diagram method. This somewhat arduous task was greatly simplified by taking full advantage of the special reductions in the formulas which result from the factorization of the wave functions into antisymmetrized products of Θ_i^{σ} $(i=1\cdots8)$ and Θ_j^{π} $(j=1\cdots6)$ [Eq. (2.20)]. In this way the 48×48 matrix $\tilde{H}(\Theta)$ may be evaluated with little more work than is required for one 8×8 matrix and one 6×6 matrix. As these special reductions are simple examples of McWeeny's (1960) recent analysis of density matrices for generalized product functions, they are not discussed further.

(d) Total Energy and Binding Energy

The total molecular wave function $\tilde{\Omega}$ and energy $\tilde{E}$ in the orbital calculation are now given by the usual secular equations,

$$\tilde{\Omega}=\tilde{\Theta}\tilde{\Gamma}$$

$$\det\{\tilde{H}(\Theta)-\tilde{E}1\}=0 \quad \text{(lowest root)} \qquad (2.24)$$

$$\{\tilde{H}(\Theta)-\tilde{E}1\}\tilde{\Gamma}=0.$$

The binding energy $\tilde{D}_e$ is obtained from the equation

$$\tilde{D}_e=\tilde{W}_G-\tilde{E}, \qquad (2.25)$$

where $\tilde{W}_G$ is the total energy of the ground state $O(s^2p^4, {}^3P)C(s^2p^2, {}^3P)$ of the dissociation products calculated by using the atomic orbitals (2.1).

TABLE II. Total energy and binding energy (orbital calculation).

Basis functions	$\tilde{E}$ (a.u.)	$\tilde{D}_e$(ev)[b]
23 terms[a] $C^{2+}O^{2-}$, C^+O^-, CO, C^-O^+	−112.437	7.45
39 terms $C^{2+}O^{2-}\cdots C^{2-}O^{2+}$	-112.438_4	7.50
48 terms $C^{2+}O^{2-}\cdots C^{4-}O^{4+}$	-112.438_5	7.50
SCFMO [Moser (1960)]	−112.343	4.9
SCFMO [Ransil (1960)]	−112.344	4.9[c]

[a] See Table III.
[b] 1 a.u. = 27.210 ev.
[c] Relative to $C(s^2p^2,{}^3P)$, $O(s^2p^4,{}^3P)$ calculated with optimum Slater functions [Hurley (1959)].

The results obtained from Eqs. (2.24) and (2.25) by using different numbers of functions in the basis (2.19) are shown in Table II. The results of self-consistent field molecular orbital calculations [Moser (1960), Ransil (1960)] are shown for comparison. The orbital exponents ($\zeta_1=7.7$, $\zeta_3=\zeta_5=2.275$, $\zeta_2=5.7$, $\zeta_4=\zeta_6=1.625$) used by Ransil differ slightly from those of Eq. (2.2), which were also used by Moser.

We see from Table II that the binding energy obtained by Ransil and Moser is increased by about 2.5 ev by the 23-term valence-bond calculation. However, the further reduction in energy brought about by all the chemically unreasonable structures involving more than one negative charge on the carbon nucleus is very small. The 23-term basis, which was used in the subsequent calculations, is specified in detail in Sec. 3 (Table III).

(e) Validity of Valence Coupling

Even the full valence-bond basis (2.18) contains only a small fraction of the total number of ${}^1\Sigma^+$ wave functions which can be constructed from the basic atomic orbitals (2.1). Indeed, an application of the correlation rules of Wigner and Witmer (1928) to all possible states of the dissociation products (subject to the restriction that the inner-shell orbitals k_O, k_C are both doubly occupied) shows that a complete basis for the ${}^1\Sigma^+$ ground state of carbon monoxide contains 177 terms. The additional functions are of two types:

(i) Functions with the same orbital assignments as the functions (2.18) but with different spin couplings. In the valence-bond basis, the spin coupling is always between electrons in orbitals of the same symmetry type (σ, x, or y). The relaxation of this restriction leads to a large number of additional functions which show spin couplings between orbitals of different symmetries.

Additional functions of this type must be included if we wish to resolve the valence-bond basis functions in terms of approximate composite functions [Moffitt (1954)]. This would be important for a calculation at large nuclear separations since it would lead to dissociation products in true stationary states rather than in the valence states which result from the basis (2.18) (cf. Table III).

However, the effect of these extra functions on the energy of the ground state at the equilibrium nuclear

TABLE III. Wave functions for the 23-term calculations.

Basis functions[a] Ψ_i	$\Psi_i^\sigma, \Psi_i^\pi$	Dissociation products Ionicity C^{n+}	Valence states[b] C	O	$(W_i - \tilde{W}_i')$[c]	Coefficients in total wave function Orbital calculation $\tilde{\Gamma}(\Theta)$	$\tilde{\Gamma}(\Psi)$	$\tilde{\nu}$	ICC calculation $\Gamma(\Theta)$	$\Gamma(\Psi)$	ν
1	1,1	2	s^2V_0	$s^2p^6V_0$	−0.6184	0.3883	−0.0025	−0.001	0.5063	0.0566	0.020
2	2,1	1	s^2pV_1	$s^2p^5V_1$	−0.2453	0.2804	0.0904	0.029	0.2868	0.1283	0.048
3	3,1	2	spV_0	$s^2p^6V_0$	−0.5992	−0.1301	−0.0225	0.007	−0.2002	−0.0922	0.037
4	4,1	0	$s^2x^2V_0$	$s^2x^2y^2V_0$	−0.0746	0.0722	0.0677	0.012	0.0708	0.0503	0.010
5	5,1	1	s^2pV_1	sp^6V_1	−0.4784	0.0547	0.0322	0.011	0.0591	0.0720	0.033
6	6,1	1	sx^2V_1	$s^2p^5V_1$	−0.2505	0.0643	0.0524	0.013	0.0701	0.0875	0.026
7	7,1	0	$s^2x^2V_0$	sp^5V_0	−0.2087	−0.0146	−0.0338	0.010	−0.0208	−0.0146	0.005
8	1,2	1	s^2pV_1	$s^2p^5V_1$	−0.2454	0.6350	0.1490	0.085	0.6092	0.2805	0.168
9	2,2	0	s^2xyV_2	$s^2x^2yzV_2$	−0.0102	0.3434	0.3053	0.188	0.2793	0.1642	0.099
10	3,2	1	$sp^2V_1^*$	$s^2p^5V_1$	−0.2658	−0.2025	−0.1342	0.083	−0.2289	−0.2346	0.154
11	4,2	−1	$s^2x^2yV_1$	$s^2x^2yV_1$	0.0027	0.0515	0.0392	0.012	0.0506	0.0503	0.015
12	5,2	0	s^2xyV_2	sp^5V_2	−0.1393	0.0608	0.1035	0.075	0.0421	0.0305	0.023
13	6,2	0	sx^2yV_2	$s^2x^2yzV_2$	−0.0574	0.0646	0.1565	0.071	0.0549	0.1040	0.047
14	7,2	−1	$s^2x^2yV_1$	$sp^4V_1^*$	−0.1031	−0.0033	−0.0090	0.005	−0.0272	−0.0749	0.040
15	1,3	0	$s^2x^2V_0$	$s^2x^2y^2V_0$	−0.0746	0.1691	0.1184	0.035	0.1392	0.0836	0.024
16	2,3	−1	$s^2x^2yV_1$	$s^2x^2yV_1$	0.0027	0.0516	0.0666	0.020	0.0454	0.0546	0.015
17	3,3	0	$sp^3V_0^*$	$s^2x^2y^2V_0$	−0.1419	−0.0475	−0.0891	0.028	−0.0467	−0.0840	0.025
18	5,3	−1	$s^2x^2yV_1$	$sx^2y^2V_1$	−0.0754	0.0049	0.0107	0.004	0.0085	0.0186	0.006
19	1,4	0	s^2xyV_2	$s^2x^2yzV_2$	−0.0102	0.3333	0.2360	0.114	0.2420	0.1483	0.064
20	2,4	−1	s^2xyzV_3	s^2xyzV_3	0.0702	0.1100	0.1489	0.071	0.0804	0.0946	0.039
21	3,4	0	$sp^3V_2^*$	$s^2x^2yzV_2$	−0.0959	−0.0924	−0.1690	0.084	−0.0853	−0.1542	0.071
22	5,4	−1	s^2xyzV_3	sx^2yzV_3	−0.0132	0.0139	0.0304	0.018	0.0149	0.0326	0.017
23	1,5	−1	$s^2x^2yV_1$	$s^2x^2yV_1$	0.0027	0.0550	0.0886	0.026	0.0407	0.0656	0.016

[a] There are 30 ι.unctions in the bases (2.18) (2.19) which show not more than one negative charge on the carbon atom. However, some of these are mixed with states of higher ionicity by the transformations (2.21) and are omitted from the Table. This mixing could be avoided by changing the order of ϕ_4 and ϕ_5 in the Schmidt orthogonalization.

[b] $sp^2V_1^* = \frac{1}{4}\,{}^2D + \frac{3}{4}\,{}^2P$, $sp^3V_0^* = \frac{1}{2}\,{}^1D^0 + \frac{1}{2}\,{}^1P^0$, $sp^3V_2^* = \frac{1}{4}\,{}^3D^0 + \frac{1}{2}\,{}^3S^0 + \frac{1}{4}\,{}^1D^0$, $sp^4V_1^* = \frac{1}{4}\,{}^2D + \frac{3}{4}\,{}^2P$, all other valence states are listed in terms of stationary states by Moffitt (1954).

[c] Relative to the ground state dissociation products $C(s^2p^2, {}^3P)$, $O(s^2p^4, {}^3P)$ for which $W_G - \tilde{W}_G' = -0.8013$.

separation is certainly small and probably very small (<0.05 ev). The effect on the total energy of three states of this type, derived by altering the spin coupling in the most important valence-bond functions (Table III), was estimated by second-order perturbation theory to be less than 0.01 ev.

(ii) Functions with orbital assignments which differ from those of the valence-bond functions (2.18). These functions arise from the molecular orbital configurations $\sigma^4\pi^6$, $\sigma^8\pi^2$, and $\sigma^2\pi^8$ and also from the functions Ψ_9^σ and Ψ_{10}^σ, which we have discarded. The effect of these functions on the total energy will be very small, except for those functions which represent atomic configuration interaction; for example, interaction between $C(s^2p^2, {}^3P)$, $C(p^4, {}^3P)$ or $O^+(s^2p^3, {}^2P)$, $O^+(p^5, {}^2P)$. This atomic configuration interaction will have an appreciable effect (~0.5 ev) on the total energy in the orbital calculation but almost no effect on the results of the ICC calculation [Hurley (1959)].

It appears therefore, that as far as the ICC calculation is concerned, the 23-term valence-bond basis for the ground state of carbon monoxide (Table III) is almost complete in the sense that additional functions constructed from the atomic orbitals (2.1) would affect the calculated total energy by less than 0.1 ev. However, this result has not been established as unequivocally as in the much simpler case of the first-row hydrides [Hurley (1958b, 1959), Krauss and Wehner (1958)].

3. INTRA-ATOMIC CORRELATION CORRECTION

In the ICC theory, the energy matrix H in the valence bond basis Ψ (2.18) is given by the equation [Hurley (1958a)]

$$H = \tilde{H} + \tfrac{1}{2}[\tilde{M}(W - \tilde{W}') + (W - \tilde{W}')\tilde{M}] \quad (\Psi \text{ basis}). \quad (3.1)$$

Here $\tilde{H}$, $\tilde{M}$ are the energy and overlap matrices calculated directly from the orbital wave functions, W is a diagonal matrix whose elements are the empirical energies of the appropriate dissociation products, and $\tilde{W}'$ is a similar matrix formed from the energies calculated for the dissociation products by using the orbital wave functions (2.18) with optimum values of the parameters $\zeta_1, \zeta_2, \zeta_3, \zeta_4, \zeta_5, \zeta_6$. That is, in calculating $\tilde{W}'$, these parameters are varied to minimize the energy of each state of the dissociation products.

In Eq. (3.1) the valence-bond basis is restricted to the 23 functions shown in Table III; the functions are specified by the values of i and j in Eq. (2.17) (column 2). The valence state corresponding to each function and the numerical value of the correction term $W_i - \tilde{W}_i'$ [Eq. (3.1)] are given in columns 3 and 4. The evaluation of these correction terms is described in Appendix I.

To simplify the calculations, Eq. (3.1) is transformed into the orthogonal valence-bond basis Θ (2.19), which in virtue of Eqs. (2.23) also contains just 23 functions with the same values of i and j as for the Ψ basis:

$$H(\Theta)=\tilde{H}(\Theta)+\tfrac{1}{2}\{(W-\tilde{W}')^0+(W-\tilde{W}')^{0\dagger}\}, \quad (3.2)$$

where

$$(W-\tilde{W}')^0=S(W-\tilde{W}')T. \quad (3.3)$$

Here and in all subsequent matrix equations, the matrices are for the truncated 23×23 basis of Table III; S and T are the transformation matrices of Eqs. (2.22); the symbol † denotes the Hermitian conjugate.

The coefficients of the total wave function in the orthogonal basis Θ are listed in Table III, column 5 (orbital calculation) and column 8 (ICC calculation). For the orbital calculation these coefficients $\tilde{\Gamma}(\Theta)$ are given by Eqs. (2.24), whilst for the ICC calculation, $\Gamma(\Theta)$ is given by the corresponding equations with $H(\Theta)$ replacing $\tilde{H}(\Theta)$:

$$\Omega=\Theta\Gamma(\Theta)$$
$$\det\{H(\Theta)-E1\}=0 \quad \text{(lowest root)} \quad (3.4)$$
$$\{H(\Theta)-E1\}\Gamma(\Theta)=0.$$

The remaining columns of Table III give the coefficients of the total wave function in the valence-bond basis and the occupation numbers $\tilde{\nu}$, ν of the valence-bond structures. These quantities are determined from the equations

$$\tilde{\Gamma}(\Psi)=T\tilde{\Gamma}(\Theta), \quad \Gamma(\Psi)=T\Gamma(\Theta), \quad (3.5)$$

$$\tilde{\nu}_i=\sum_j \tilde{\Gamma}_i(\Psi)\tilde{M}_{ij}\tilde{\Gamma}_j(\Psi)=\tilde{\Gamma}_i(\Psi)\sum_j S_{ji}\tilde{\Gamma}_j(\Theta),$$
$$\nu_i=\sum_j \Gamma_i(\Psi)\tilde{M}_{ij}\Gamma_j(\Psi)=\Gamma_i(\Psi)\sum_j S_{ji}\Gamma_j(\Theta). \quad (3.6)$$

In practice, the second form of Eqs. (3.6), which derives from the equation $\tilde{M}=S^\dagger S$, is the more convenient since the matrix S is triangular.

The values of the occupation numbers ν_i enable us to estimate the effect ΔE on the ICC total energy of any uncertainties ΔW_i in the empirical values of the valence-state energies. To first order, we have

$$\Delta E=\sum_i \nu_i \Delta W_i.$$

In the present calculation the only appreciable uncertainty of this kind arises from the states of O^{2-} (Ψ_1 and Ψ_3). For these states, the value -6.63 ± 0.3 ev [Morris (1957)] was used for the double-electron affinity of oxygen. The small values of ν_1 and ν_3 (Table III, final column) indicate that this uncertainty will have a very small effect (<0.05 ev) on the calculated total energy.

The total energy E and the binding energy D_e which result from the 23-term ICC calculation are given in Table IV together with three spectroscopic values

TABLE IV. Total energy and binding energy (23-term ICC calculation).

ICC calculation	Total energy (a.u.) −113.368	Binding energy D_e(ev) >11.00
Spectroscopic	−113.377[a]	11.24[a]
	−113.322[b]	9.74[b]
	−113.305[c]	9.28[c]

[a] Gaydon (1947). [b] Hagstrum (1947). [c] Herzberg (1950).

which have been put forward. The total energy is given by Eq. (3.4) and the binding energy by the equation

$$D_e=W_G-E, \quad (3.7)$$

where W_G is the experimental energy of the ground state dissociation products $O(^3P)$, $C(^3P)$. Since the ICC binding energy is calculated relative to the experimental energy of the dissociation products, it is a lower limit to the true value to within the accuracy of the approximation underlying the basic equation of the ICC theory (3.1). For the simple systems, H_2 [Hurley (1955, 1956a), Pauncz (1954), Arai (1957)], HeH^+ [Hurley (1956c), Evett (1956)], and Li_2 [Arai and Sakamoto (1958)], it has been shown that the errors underlying Eq. (3.1) are very small (<0.02 ev). Furthermore, calculations on the ground state of N_2 [Hurley (1956b)] and on a large number of states of the first-row hydrides LiH, BH, CH, NH, OH, and FH [Hurley (1958b, 1959), Krauss and Wehner (1958)] each lead to a total molecular energy which is above the experimental value, that is, to a binding energy D_e which is a lower limit to the true value.

However, more refined calculations on the ground state of FH [Krauss and Ransil (1960), Hurley (1960)], in which the orbital exponents are varied to minimize the total energy, show that under certain circumstances Eq. (3.7) may give binding energies which exceed the true value by 0.2–0.8 ev. This implies an error of at least this amount in Eq. (3.1). These calculations on HF have been analyzed, and it has been shown that the errors arise from discrepancies between Slater-type functions such as (2.1) and atomic and ionic Hartree-Fock functions. Such discrepancies, which are negligible for the simple systems mentioned above, sometimes lead to an overestimate of the correction for ionic states.

On the basis of this analysis, it is concluded that the uncertainty in the lower limit to the binding energy of carbon monoxide given in Table IV should not exceed 0.5 ev. Since a much larger uncertainty is needed to reconcile the ICC binding energy with either of the lower spectroscopic values, the present calculations indicate that the high value $D_e=11.24$ ev is correct.

This result is in accord with a direct determination of the heat of sublimation of graphite [Chupka and Inghram (1955)], which is linked to D_0(CO) by well-established thermochemical quantities. Until recently it was thought that this high value for D_0(CO) was inconsistent with electron-impact data [Hagstrum (1951)]. However, when these data were reanalyzed [Hagstrum (1955)] using a new value (1.45 ev) for the electron affinity of oxygen [Branscomb and Smith (1955)], most of the discrepancies disappeared and the high value for $D_0(CO)$ became generally accepted.

4. ANALYSIS OF THE TOTAL WAVE FUNCTION

The specification of the total wave functions by the coefficients $\bar{\Gamma}(\Theta)$, $\bar{\Gamma}(\Psi)$, $\Gamma(\Theta)$, and $\Gamma(\Psi)$ is not very convenient for physical interpretation or for the calculation of further properties. The most useful derived quantities for this purpose are the first-order density matrices $[\bar{\rho}_{pq}]$, $[\rho_{pq}]$ for the orbital and ICC calculations, respectively. These may be defined from the expressions for the total charge densities $\bar{\rho}$, ρ in terms of the basic atomic orbitals (2.1) [Löwdin (1955)]:

$$\bar{\rho}=\sum_p\sum_q \bar{\rho}_{pq}\phi_p\phi_q, \tag{4.1}$$

$$\rho=\sum_p\sum_q \rho_{pq}\phi_p\phi_q. \tag{4.2}$$

These density matrices were evaluated for the total wave functions of Table III and are given by the following equations:

$$[\bar{\rho}_{pq}]=\begin{bmatrix}\bar{\rho}^\sigma & 0 & 0\\ 0 & \bar{\rho}^x & 0\\ 0 & 0 & \bar{\rho}^y\end{bmatrix},\quad [\rho_{pq}]=\begin{bmatrix}\rho^\sigma & 0 & 0\\ 0 & \rho^x & 0\\ 0 & 0 & \rho^y\end{bmatrix}, \tag{4.3}$$

where[2]

$$\bar{\rho}^\sigma=\begin{Bmatrix}2.0040, & 0.0038, & 0.0119, & -0.0409, & -0.0553, & -0.0229\\ & 2.0109, & -0.0646, & 0.0178, & -0.0919, & -0.0571\\ & & 2.0015, & -0.3846, & -0.4296, & 0.0875\\ & & & 1.8764, & 0.0181, & -0.6283\\ & & & & 1.3645, & 0.6344\\ & & & & & 0.6364\end{Bmatrix},$$

$$\bar{\rho}^x=\bar{\rho}^y=\begin{bmatrix}1.1472, & 0.6664\\ & 0.4923\end{bmatrix},$$

and

$$\rho^\sigma=\begin{Bmatrix}2.0028, & 0.0039, & 0.0028, & -0.0275, & -0.0507, & -0.0168\\ & 2.0117, & -0.0639, & 0.0127, & -0.1021, & -0.0549\\ & & 1.9329, & -0.2871, & -0.3966, & 0.1364\\ & & & 1.7587, & 0.0204, & -0.7144\\ & & & & 1.4675, & 0.5787\\ & & & & & 0.6163\end{Bmatrix},$$

$$\rho^x=\rho^y=\begin{bmatrix}1.2667, & 0.6504\\ & 0.3814\end{bmatrix}.$$

The matrices (4.3) enable us to calculate the expectation values $\langle\bar{f}\rangle$, $\langle f\rangle$ of any one electron operator f for the ground state wave functions given by the orbital and ICC calculations

$$\langle\bar{f}\rangle=\sum_p\sum_q \bar{\rho}_{pq}f_{pq}, \tag{4.4}$$

$$\langle f\rangle=\sum_p\sum_q \rho_{pq}f_{pq}, \tag{4.5}$$

where

$$f_{pq}=\int\phi_p f\phi_q dv.$$

The net and gross atomic populations $[\bar{N}(p), \bar{n}(p); N(p), n(p)]$ and the overlap populations $[\bar{n}(pq), n(pq)]$ for the orbital and ICC wave functions were derived from the matrices (4.3) by using the following equations [Mulliken (1955), Hurley (1958b)]:

$$\bar{n}(p)=\bar{\rho}_{pp},\quad n(p)=\rho_{pp},$$

$$\bar{n}(pq)=2m_{pq}\bar{\rho}_{pq},\quad n(pq)=2m_{pq}\rho_{pq},$$

$$\bar{N}(p)=\bar{n}(p)+\tfrac{1}{2}\sum_{q\neq p}\bar{n}(pq),\quad N(p)=n(p)+\tfrac{1}{2}\sum_{q\neq p}n(pq),$$

where

$$m_{pq}=\int\phi_p\phi_q dv.$$

Since these populations are obtained so simply from the matrices (4.3) and the overlap integrals m_{pq} (Appendix II), they are not listed separately. The alternative expressions for the gross atomic populations $\bar{N}(p)$, $N(p)$ in terms of the occupation numbers $\bar{\nu}_i$, ν_i of the valence-bond structures [Hurley (1958b)],

$$\bar{N}(p)=\sum_i \bar{\nu}_i n_i(p),\quad N(p)=\sum_i \nu_i n_i(p), \tag{4.6}$$

provide a very useful check on the evaluation of the density matrices (4.3) and on the electron-population analysis. In Eqs. (4.6), $n_i(p)$ is the occupation number (0, 1 or 2) of the atomic orbital p in the valence-bond function Ψ_i (Table III, column 3).

The natural orbitals for the two calculations and their occupation number $\mathfrak{N}$ were obtained as the latent vectors and latent roots of the matrices (4.3) [Löwdin (1955)]. They are shown in Table V together with the self-consistent field molecular orbitals of Moser (1960).

[2] These matrices are all symmetrical.

TABLE V. Natural orbitals and self-consistent field molecular orbitals.

Natural orbital	Occupation number $\mathfrak{N}$	Coefficients of atomic orbitals							
		k_O	k_C	s_O	s_C	σ_O	σ_C	$x_O(y_O)$	$x_C(y_C)$
$\tilde{\sigma}_1$	2	1	...	...	...	...	...	...	...
$\tilde{\sigma}_2$	2	...	1	...	...	...	...	...	...
$\tilde{\sigma}_3$	1.9998	−0.0069	−0.0302	0.8886	0.2573	−0.1722	−0.0712	...	...
$\tilde{\sigma}_4$	1.9967	−0.0320	−0.0118	−0.4230	0.8436	0.3970	−0.1240	...	...
$\tilde{\sigma}_5$	1.9809	−0.0258	−0.0650	0.1354	−0.3907	0.7000	0.5305	...	...
$\tilde{\sigma}_6$	0.0225	−0.1596	0.1347	−1.1317	0.9530	−0.9383	1.2994	...	...
$\tilde{x}_1(\tilde{y}_1)$	1.9424	...	...	...	...	...	...	0.7587	0.4777
$\tilde{x}_2(\tilde{y}_2)$	0.0576	...	...	...	...	...	...	−0.7094	0.9224
σ_1	2	1	...	...	...	...	...	...	...
σ_2	2	...	1	...	...	...	...	...	...
σ_3	1.9996	−0.0084	−0.0355	0.8991	0.2244	−0.1145	−0.0337	...	...
σ_4	1.9962	−0.0335	−0.0494	−0.2718	0.4475	−0.7581	0.1273	...	...
σ_5	1.9894	−0.0054	−0.0450	0.2740	−0.7907	0.3764	0.5289	...	...
σ_6	0.0149	−0.1612	0.1330	−1.1447	0.9813	−0.9101	1.3013	...	...
x_1	1.9717	...	...	...	...	...	...	0.7976	0.4249
x_2	0.0283	...	...	...	...	...	...	−0.6655	0.9478
SCFMO[a]									
$\phi_{1\sigma}$		1	...	...	...	...	...	...	...
$\phi_{2\sigma}$		...	1	...	...	...	...	...	...
$\phi_{3\sigma}$		−0.0245	−0.0573	0.7477	0.2198	0.2380	0.1558	...	...
$\phi_{4\sigma}$		−0.0320	−0.0209	−0.6355	0.5254	0.6349	0.0603	...	...
$\phi_{5\sigma}$		−0.0106	−0.0355	−0.0400	−0.7430	0.4515	0.5613	...	...
$\phi_{6\sigma}$		−0.1597	0.1358	−1.1416	0.9811	−0.9455	1.2836	...	...
$\phi_{1x}(\phi_{1y})$								0.7709	0.4617
$\phi_{2x}(\phi_{2y})$								−0.6962	0.9305

[a] Moser (1960).

The occupation numbers of the higher natural orbitals ($\tilde{\sigma}_6$, $\tilde{x}_2$, $\tilde{y}_2$; σ_6, x_2, y_2) provide an absolute measure of the departure of the total wave function from the form of a single determinant, that is, a measure of the irreducible configuration interaction which cannot be eliminated by a transformation of the one-electron functions. We see that, as in previous calculations, configuration interaction is much less important in the ICC calculation than in the orbital calculation.

The approximate equality of the higher natural orbitals $\tilde{\sigma}_6$, $\tilde{x}_2$, $\tilde{y}_2$ to the unoccupied molecular orbitals $\phi_{6\sigma}$, ϕ_{2x}, ϕ_{2y} ensures that the first term in the natural expansion of the total orbital wave function, namely,

$$|\tilde{\sigma}_1\alpha, \tilde{\sigma}_1\beta, \tilde{\sigma}_2\alpha, \tilde{\sigma}_2\beta, \tilde{\sigma}_3\alpha, \tilde{\sigma}_3\beta, \tilde{\sigma}_4\alpha, \tilde{\sigma}_4\beta, \tilde{\sigma}_5\alpha, \tilde{\sigma}_5\beta, \times \tilde{x}_1\alpha, \tilde{x}_1\beta, \tilde{y}_1\alpha, \tilde{y}_1\beta|, \quad (4.7)$$

is very similar to the self-consistent field function

$$|\phi_{1\sigma}\alpha, \phi_{1\sigma}\beta, \phi_{2\sigma}\alpha, \phi_{2\sigma}\beta, \phi_{3\sigma}\alpha, \phi_{3\sigma}\beta, \phi_{4\sigma}\alpha, \phi_{4\sigma}\beta, \times \phi_{5\sigma}\alpha, \phi_{5\sigma}\beta, \phi_{1x}\alpha, \phi_{1x}\beta, \phi_{1y}\alpha, \phi_{1y}\beta|. \quad (4.8)$$

Indeed, by using the techniques developed by Löwdin (1955), it is readily shown that the overlap between the functions (4.7) and (4.8) is simply

$$\left(\int \tilde{\sigma}_6\phi_{6\sigma}dv\right)^2 \left(\int \tilde{x}_2\phi_{2x}dv\right)^2 \left(\int \tilde{y}_2\phi_{2y}dv\right)^2 = (0.99949)^2(0.99985)^2(0.99985)^2 = 0.9984. \quad (4.9)$$

A close similarity between the functions (4.7) and (4.8) is expected on general grounds [Lödwin (1955)]. Thus, the large values of the overlap integrals (4.9) provide a valuable check on the consistency of the present orbital calculation with Moser's self-consistent field calculation.

On the other hand, there are quite large differences between the occupied self-consistent field orbitals $\phi_{1\sigma}\cdots\phi_{5\sigma}$ and the corresponding natural orbitals $\tilde{\sigma}_1\cdots\tilde{\sigma}_5$. This suggests that the orbital energies of self-consistent field functions are not very reliable guides in setting up a simple wave function to allow for configuration interaction. For example, it is to be expected that the double substitution $\phi_{5\sigma}^2 \rightarrow \phi_{6\sigma}^2$ would be considerably less effective than $\tilde{\sigma}_5^2 \rightarrow \tilde{\sigma}_6^2$ in lowering the total energy of the single determinant wave function.

5. DIPOLE MOMENT

Perhaps the simplest qualitative picture of the wave functions is that of resonance between the structures $C^{2+}O^{2-}$, $C^+{-}O^-$, $C{=}O$, $C^- \equiv O^+$ (Table VI). The occupation numbers of these structures are obtained from Table III by summing $\tilde{\nu}_i$ and ν_i for states of the same ionicity.

These results may be compared with the picture of Pauling (1940), which leaves out the structure $C^{2+}O^{2-}$ and gives equal weight to each of the other three. In constructing this picture Pauling made use of the fact that the dipole moment of carbon monoxide is almost zero. He considered only the formal moment μ_f, and it is clear that this will be zero if these three structures have equal weight. However, as Moffitt (1949) has pointed out, there is a large contribution to the moment from the carbon atomic dipole—so that a zero formal moment does not correspond to a zero total moment.

TABLE VI. Resonating structure and dipole moment (C^-O^+).

Structure	Orbital calculation	ICC calculation	Pauling
$C^{2+}O^{2-}$	0.006	0.057	0
C^+-O^-	0.221	0.428	$\frac{1}{3}$
$C=O$	0.617	0.367	$\frac{1}{3}$
$C^-\equiv O^+$	0.156	0.148	$\frac{1}{3}$
Dipole			
μ_f	$-0.42D$	$-2.13D$	0
μ_C	$2.94D$	$3.34D$	
μ_O	$-1.43D$	$-1.32D$	
μ_{CO}	$-0.08D$	$-0.25D$	
μ_t	$1.00D$	$-0.37D$	
μ_{SCFMO}[a] $=0.73D$, $\mu_{exptl.}=0.12D$			

[a] Ransil (1960).

We see this clearly from the present results (Table VI). For both calculations, the carbon atomic dipole μ_C is the largest single contribution. The oxygen atomic dipole μ_O is also fairly large, whilst the covalent dipole μ_{CO} is small. These dipole moments were evaluated by using the expressions (4.4), (4.5), the density matrices (4.3), and the dipole moment integrals (Appendix II). The contributions μ_f, μ_C, μ_O, μ_{CO} are obtained by an obvious grouping of the terms in Eqs. (4.4) and (4.5) [Hurley (1958)].

For the orbital calculation, the total moment is of the right sign but much too large; its value fits in well with that obtained by Ransil (1960) in a self-consistent field molecular orbital calculation.

The total moment from the ICC calculation is small but of the wrong sign. The relative values of the orbital and ICC moments are consistent with the results for the first-row hydrides [Hurley (1958b)]. Here also, the effect of the intra-atomic correlation correction is to alter the orbital moment in the right direction but by an amount which is rather too large. This overcorrection of the dipole moment is attributable, at least in part, to errors arising from the discrepancies between the Slater-type functions (2.1) and Hartree-Fock atomic orbitals [Hurley (1960)].

6. ACKNOWLEDGMENTS

This work was made possible by the generous hospitality and assistance of Professor Slater and the Solid State and Molecular Theory Group (Massachusetts Institute of Technology) and the Laboratory of Molecular Structure and Spectra (University of Chicago). The two-electron exchange integrals were evaluated on the Whirlwind digital computer using a program written by Mr. Merriman. The remaining two-electron integrals were evaluated at the Laboratory of Molecular Structure and Spectra, University of Chicago, by Dr. Ransil. The author is also indebted to Dr. Moser and Dr. Krauss for the communication of their results before publication, to Dr. Maslen for checking the matrix elements of the Hamiltonian, and to the staff of the Adolph Basser Computation Laboratory (University of Sydney) for assistance with the numerical computations.

BIBLIOGRAPHY

T. Arai, J. Chem. Phys. **26**, 451 (1957).
T. Arai and M. Sakômoto, J. Chem. Phys. **28**, 32 (1958).
L. M. Branscomb, D. S. Burch, S. J. Smith, and S. Geltman, Phys. Rev. **111**, 504 (1958).
W. A. Chupka and M. G. Inghram, J. Chem. Phys. **21**, 1313 (1953); J. Phys. Chem. **59**, 100 (1955).
A. A. Evett, J. Chem. Phys. **24**, 150 (1956).
A. G. Gaydon, *Dissociation Energies* (Chapman and Hall, Ltd., London, 1947).
H. G. Hagstrum, Phys. Rev. **72**, 947 (1947); Revs. Modern Phys. **23**, 185 (1951); J. Chem. Phys. **23**, 1178 (1955).
G. Herzberg, *Spectra of Diatomic Molecules* (D. Van Nostrand Company, Inc., Princeton, New Jersey, 1950).
A. C. Hurley, Proc. Phys. Soc. (London) **A68**, 149 (1955); **A69**, 49 (1956) (a); **A69**, 767 (1956) (b); **A69**, 868 (1956) (c); J. Chem. Phys. **28**, 532 (1958) (a); Proc. Roy. Soc. (London) **A248**, 119 (1958) (b); **A249**, 40 (1959); (unpublished) (1960).
M. Krauss and B. Ransil, (Boulder Conference, unpublished) (1960).
M. Krauss and J. F. Wehner, J. Chem. Phys. **29**, 1287 (1958).
P. O. Löwdin, J. Chem. Phys. **18**, 365 (1950); Phys. Rev. **97**, 1474 (1955).
R. McWeeny, Proc. Roy. Soc. (London) **A223**, 306 (1954); (Boulder Conference, unpublished) (1960).
W. Moffitt, Proc. Roy. Soc. (London) **A196**, 524 (1949); **A210**, 245 (1951); Repts. Progr. Phys. **17**, 173 (1954).
C. M. Moore, Natl. Bur. Standards (U. S.) Circ. 467 (1949).
D. F. C. Morris, Proc. Roy. Soc. (London) **A242**, 116 (1957).
C. Moser, (Boulder Conference, unpublished) (1960).
L. Pauling, *The Nature of the Chemical Bond* (Cornell University Press, Ithaca, New York, 1940).
R. Pauncz, Acta Phys. Acad. Sci. Hung. **4**, 237 (1954).
B. Ransil (Boulder Conference, unpublished) (1960).
C. C. J. Roothaan, Tech. Rept. Laboratory of Molecular Structure and Spectra, University of Chicago (unpublished) (1955).
E. Wigner and E. E. Witmer, Z. Physik **51**, 859 (1928).

APPENDIX I

The calculated and experimental energies of the stationary states of the atoms C and O and of the positive ions C^+, C^{2+}, O^+ were obtained from the tables of Roothaan (1955). The calculated and experimental energies of the stationary states of the negative ions C^-, O^-, and O^{2-} are given in Table VII. In all cases the calculated energies are those obtained by using the orbitals (2.1) with optimum values of the parameters $\zeta_1 \cdots \zeta_6$ for each state.

The experimental energies of the negative ion states were obtained from the electron affinities EA(O) = 1.465 ±0.005 ev, EA(C) = 1.12±0.05 ev given by Branscomb, Burch, Smith, and Geltman (1958), the value −6.63 ±0.3 ev for the double-electron affinity of oxygen [Morris (1957)], and spectroscopic intervals extrapolated from the tables of Moore (1949).

TABLE VII. Energies of stationary states of the ions C^-, O^-, O^{2-} (a.u.).

State	Calc energy $\tilde{W}'$	Exptl. energy W
$C^-(s^2p^3, {}^4S^0)$	−37.5742	−37.8962
$, {}^2D^0)$	−37.4899	−37.8446
$, {}^2P^0)$	−37.4349	−37.8202
$O^-(s^2p^5, {}^2P^0)$	−74.3043	−75.1628
$O^-(sp^6, {}^2S)$	−73.5290	−74.6206
$O^{2-}(s^2p^6, {}^1S)$	−73.6202	−74.8653

The calculated and empirical energies of the valence states of Table III (column 4) are now obtained from the expressions for these states in terms of stationary states (Table III, footnote a). Since the additional valence-bond functions required to resolve the basis functions $\tilde{\Psi}_i$ in terms of approximate composite functions are all orthogonal to the functions $\tilde{\Psi}_i$, this procedure is equivalent to using a basis of approximate composite functions throughout the calculations [Hurley (1958b, Appendix)].

APPENDIX II

Atomic Integrals

(a) One-Electron Integrals (Table VIII)

Notation. Overlap integrals: $(ab) = \int ab dv$,

Core integrals: $(afb) = \int afb dv$,

$$f = -\tfrac{1}{2}\nabla^2 - (6/r_C) - (8/r_O).$$

Dipole moment integrals: $(a\mu b) = \int a\mu b dv$.

TABLE VIII. One-electron integrals.

p,q	$(\phi_p\phi_q)$	$(\phi_p f \phi_q)$[a]	$(\theta_p f \theta_q)$	$(\phi_p \mu \phi_q)$
1,1	1	−34.75659	−34.75659	−1.06595
1,2	0.00009	−0.00297	0.00002	−0.00004
1.3	0	−7.69622	0.35259	0
1,4	0.05050	−1.65416	−0.10150	−0.05010
1,5	0	−0.07029	−0.03414	0.05324
1,6	0.08579	−2.87949	−0.12450	−0.08550
2,2	1	−21.69807	−21.69807	1.06595
2,3	0.05011	−1.03235	0.02690	0.04312
2,4	0	−4.51873	0.25395	0
2,5	0.08313	−1.75901	−0.05195	0.07252
2,6	0	−0.11806	−0.06660	−0.06708
3,3	1	−10.95760	−9.75262	−1.06595
3,4	0.43044	−4.45051	0.13422	−0.12875
3,5	0	−0.82671	−0.90416	0.64963
3,6	0.50815	−5.53923	0.46304	−0.34175
4,4	1	−8.02746	−6.96866	1.06595
4,5	0.32824	−3.48869	−0.68772	0.17787
4,6	0	−1.36060	−0.65810	−0.91495
5,5	1	−9.57767	−9.36043	−1.06595
5,6	0.28880	−3.17960	0.41650	0.08235
6,6	1	−7.77696	−7.03055	1.06595
7,7	1	−9.06222	−9.06222	−1.06595
7,8	0.28880	−2.25027	0.20894	−0.06476
8,8	1	−6.74949	−6.68430	1.06595

[a] In this column only the integrals with $p, q = 3, 4$ are for the nodeless 2S functions ϕ_{3*}, ϕ_{4*}.

Here μ is the z coordinate of the electron relative to the center of the CO bond.

Orbitals: ϕ_p defined by Eqs. (2.1).

θ_p defined by Eqs. (2.9) and (2.15) (Table I).

(b) Two-Electron Integrals (Table IX)

Notation. $[ab,cd] = \int\int a(1)b^*(1)(1/r_{12}) \times c(2)d^*(2)dv_1dv_2$,

$$\phi_{3*} = (\zeta_3{}^5/3\pi)^{\frac{1}{2}} r_O \exp(-\zeta_3 r_O), \quad \theta_{3*} = \theta_3,$$

$$\phi_{4*} = (\zeta_4{}^5/3\pi)^{\frac{1}{2}} r_C \exp(-\zeta_4 r_C), \quad \theta_{4*} = \theta_4,$$

$$\phi_{7*} = 2^{-\frac{1}{2}}(\phi_7 + i\phi_9), \quad \theta_{7*} = 2^{-\frac{1}{2}}(\theta_7 + i\theta_9),$$

$$\phi_{9*} = 2^{-\frac{1}{2}}(\phi_7 - i\phi_9), \quad \theta_{9*} = 2^{-\frac{1}{2}}(\theta_7 - i\theta_9),$$

$$\phi_{8*} = 2^{-\frac{1}{2}}(\phi_8 + i\phi_{10}), \quad \theta_{8*} = 2^{-\frac{1}{2}}(\theta_8 + i\theta_{10}),$$

$$\phi_{10*} = 2^{-\frac{1}{2}}(\phi_8 - i\phi_{10}), \quad \theta_{10*} = 2^{-\frac{1}{2}}(\theta_8 - i\theta_{10}).$$

TABLE IX. Electron repulsion integrals.

pq,rs	$[\phi_p\phi_q,\phi_r\phi_s]$	$[\theta_p\theta_q,\theta_r\theta_s]$
11,11	4.78750	4.78750
12,11	0.00017	−0.00024
13*,11	0.67556	−0.44432
14*,11	0.15396	0.11929
15,11	0.00000	−0.04913
16,11	0.26991	0.19060
22,11	0.46907	0.46906
23*,11	0.02552	0.00272
24*,11	0.10275	−0.00130
25,11	0.04322	0.00509
26,11	0.01476	0.01545
3*3*,11	1.11739	1.12232
3*4*,11	0.35748	−0.14168
3*5,11	0.00000	0.05847
3*6,11	0.50408	−0.19522
4*4*,11	0.45309	0.43135
4*5,11	0.23360	0.10522
4*6,11	0.16903	0.11563
55,11	1.10765	1.13448
56,11	0.26100	−0.23597
66,11	0.53558	0.58787
12,12	0.00000	0.00000
13*,12	0.00003	0.00003
14*,12	0.00001	−0.00001
15,12	0.00001	0.00001
16,12	0.00001	−0.00002
22,12	0.00006	0.00002
23*,12	0.00000	−0.00000
24*,12	0.00001	−0.00000
25,12	0.00001	0.00000
26,12	0.00000	0.00000
3*3*,12	0.00008	−0.00002
3*4*,12	0.00003	0.00001
3*5,12	0.00002	0.00002
3*6,12	0.00005	0.00001
4*4*,12	0.00005	0.00001
4*5,12	0.00003	−0.00000
4*6,12	0.00002	0.00001
55,12	0.00009	−0.00001
56,12	0.00003	0.00001
66,12	0.00006	0.00001
13*,13*	0.12149	0.06895
14*,13*	0.02650	−0.01874
15,13*	0.00000	0.00771
16,13*	0.04636	−0.03009
22,13*	0.10849	−0.00001
23*,13*	0.00590	−0.00001
24*,13*	0.02377	0.00002
25,13*	0.00999	−0.00000
26,13*	0.00341	0.00000
3*3*,13*	0.24929	−0.01763
3*4*,13*	0.08080	0.00484
3*5,13*	0.00000	−0.00199
3*6,13*	0.11330	0.00779
4*4*,13*	0.10437	−0.00137
4*5,13*	0.05359	0.00001
4*6,13*	0.03835	−0.00192
55,13*	0.24731	−0.01043
56,13*	0.05963	0.00550
66,13*	0.12257	−0.00559
14*,14*	0.00588	0.00517
15,14*	0.00117	−0.00070
16,14*	0.01029	0.00755
22,14*	0.02398	0.00097
23*,14*	0.00131	0.00001
24*,14*	0.00525	−0.00001
25,14*	0.00222	0.00002
26,14*	0.00078	0.00006
3*3*,14*	0.05312	0.00457
3*4*,14*	0.01760	−0.00078
3*5,14*	0.00229	0.00287
3*6,14*	0.02464	−0.00245
4*4*,14*	0.02289	0.00079
4*5,14*	0.01221	−0.00040

pq,rs	$[\phi_p\phi_q,\phi_r\phi_s]$	$[\theta_p\theta_q,\theta_r\theta_s]$
4*6,14*	0.00854	0.00079
55,14*	0.05285	0.00299
56,14*	0.01385	−0.00174
66,14*	0.02697	0.00244
15,15	0.02500	0.02885
16,15	0.00196	−0.01623
22,15	0.01172	0.01226
23*,15	0.00071	0.00015
24*,15	0.00257	−0.00007
25,15	0.00120	0.00029
26,15	0.00074	0.00078
3*3*,15	0.00000	−0.00193
3*4*,15	0.00577	0.00711
3*5,15	0.03840	0.03518
3*6,15	0.00762	−0.00653
4*4*,15	0.00928	0.00522
4*5,15	0.01222	−0.00645
4*6,15	0.00533	0.00386
55,15	0.00000	0.00333
56,15	0.01812	−0.00543
66,15	0.01220	0.01358
16,16	0.01800	0.01909
22,16	0.04164	−0.00481
23*,16	0.00227	−0.00006
24*,16	0.00912	0.00003
25,16	0.00385	−0.00011
26,16	0.00136	−0.00031
3*3*,16	0.09257	0.00721
3*4*,16	0.03062	−0.00467
3*5,16	0.00378	−0.01412
3*6,16	0.04289	0.00008
4*4*,16	0.03978	−0.00154
4*5,16	0.02118	0.00279
4*6,16	0.01483	−0.00089
55,16	0.09213	0.00247
56,16	0.02402	0.00047
66,16	0.04687	−0.00357
22,22	3.54375	3.54375
23*,22	0.11009	−0.06451
24*,22	0.47079	−0.31667
25,22	0.19063	0.01270
26,22	0.00000	−0.07193
3*3*,22	0.46648	0.46506
3*4*,22	0.27694	0.08448
3*5,22	0.13706	0.11337
3*6,22	0.29523	0.04453
4*4*,22	0.80007	0.79968
4*5,22	0.30097	−0.03627
4*6,22	0.00000	0.03869
55,22	0.52276	0.50531
56,22	0.25542	0.08111
66,22	0.78055	0.83981
23*,23*	0.00426	0.00206
24*,23*	0.01802	0.00931
25,23*	0.00734	−0.00005
26,23*	0.00159	0.00412
3*3*,23*	0.02498	0.00222
3*4*,23*	0.01434	−0.00032
3*5,23*	0.00772	0.00121
3*6,23*	0.01606	−0.00013
4*4*,23*	0.03760	−0.00322
4*5,23*	0.01540	0.00128
4*6,23*	0.00325	0.00204
55,23*	0.02816	0.00254
56,23*	0.01424	−0.00078
66,23*	0.03721	−0.00154
24*,24*	0.08006	0.04736
25,24*	0.03106	−0.00236
26,24*	0.00000	0.01016
3*3*,24*	0.10182	−0.00167
3*4*,24*	0.05942	−0.00229
3*5,24*	0.02940	−0.00067
3*6,24*	0.06408	−0.00129
4*4*,24*	0.16940	−0.01131

pq,rs	$[\phi_p\phi_q,\phi_r\phi_s]$	$[\theta_p\theta_q,\theta_r\theta_s]$
4*5,24*	0.06378	0.00014
4*6,24*	0.00000	−0.00369
55,24*	0.11345	−0.00167
56,24*	0.05496	−0.00095
66,24*	0.16559	−0.00872
25,25	0.01265	0.00085
26,25	0.00269	0.00327
3*3*,25	0.04238	0.00444
3*4*,25	0.02440	0.00037
3*5,25	0.01312	0.00236
3*6,25	0.02727	0.00033
4*4*,25	0.06430	−0.00104
4*5,25	0.02625	0.00215
4*6,25	0.00535	0.00498
55,25	0.04781	0.00503
56,25	0.02419	−0.00091
66,25	0.06360	0.00094
26,26	0.01556	0.02498
3*3*,26	0.01378	0.01442
3*4*,26	0.00733	0.00127
3*5,26	0.00719	0.00738
3*6,26	0.01158	0.00220
4*4*,26	0.00000	−0.00747
4*5,26	0.00825	0.00857
4*6,26	0.02474	0.02225
55,26	0.01754	0.01539
56,26	0.01340	−0.00362
66,26	0.00000	−0.00108
3*3*,3*3*	0.81738	0.79659
3*4*,3*3*	0.29183	−0.06214
3*5,3*3*	0.00000	0.02518
3*6,3*3*	0.39355	−0.07265
4*4*,3*3*	0.43290	0.40348
4*5,3*3*	0.20717	0.08272
4*6,3*3*	0.13704	0.08778
55,3*3*	0.81373	0.80078
56,3*3*	0.21954	−0.10336
66,3*3*	0.48343	0.47870
3*4*,3*4*	0.12402	0.02860
3*5,3*4*	0.04250	0.03913
3*6,3*4*	0.15829	0.01807
4*4*,3*4*	0.22439	0.03610
4*5,3*4*	0.10617	−0.01718
4*6,3*4*	0.05497	0.00299
55,3*4*	0.29762	−0.05751
56,3*4*	0.11084	0.02611
66,3*4*	0.23725	0.03148
3*5,3*5	0.17984	0.16440
3*6,3*5	0.04948	−0.01919
4*4*,3*5	0.09442	0.05924
4*5,3*5	0.07833	−0.02123
4*6,3*5	0.03781	0.03058
55,3*5	0.00000	0.03459
56,3*5	0.10287	−0.00566
66,3*5	0.10585	0.09624
3*6,3*6	0.20842	0.03166
4*4*,3*6	0.25432	0.01253
4*5,3*6	0.12996	−0.00456
4*6,3*6	0.08415	0.00050
55,3*6	0.39947	−0.06824
56,3*6	0.14180	0.03205
66,3*6	0.27935	−0.00276
4*4*,4*4*	0.58488	0.56765
4*5,4*4*	0.21894	−0.02874
4*6,4*4*	0.00000	−0.01191
55,4*4*	0.45644	0.42492
56,4*4*	0.19557	0.03928
66,4*4*	0.57748	0.57238
4*5,4*5	0.10731	0.03255
4*6,4*5	0.04728	0.03428
55,4*5	0.22313	0.08780
56,4*5	0.11389	−0.02360
66,4*5	0.22689	−0.01597
4*6,4*6	0.12757	0.09503

TABLE IX.—*Continued.*

pq,rs	$[\phi_p\phi_q,\phi_r\phi_s]$	$[\theta_p\theta_q,\theta_r\theta_s]$
55,4*6	0.14556	0.08185
56,4*6	0.07240	−0.02701
66,4*6	0.00000	−0.00414
55,55	0.87284	0.87286
56,55	0.23864	−0.11512
66,55	0.51034	0.51105
56,56	0.13159	0.05339
66,56	0.21412	0.02486
66,66	0.61451	0.63325
77,11	1.10765	1.10765
78,11	0.18434	−0.11975
88,11	0.40899	0.42112
77,12	0.00008	−0.00002
78,12	0.00002	0.00001
88,12	0.00004	0.00001
77,13*	0.24731	−0.00914
78,13*	0.04231	0.00222
88,13*	0.09458	−0.00055
77,14*	0.05261	0.00211
78,14*	0.00918	−0.00031
88,14*	0.02069	0.00067
77,15	0.00000	−0.00088
78,15	0.00262	0.00307
88,15	0.00752	0.00684
77,16	0.09168	0.00310
78,16	0.01597	−0.00194
88,16	0.03595	−0.00254
77,22	0.43810	0.43810
78,22	0.15391	0.03677
88,22	0.78055	0.78692
77,23*	0.02336	0.00204
78,23*	0.00795	−0.00010
88,23*	0.03653	−0.00180
77,24*	0.09594	−0.00102
78,24*	0.03344	−0.00027
88,24*	0.16559	−0.00558
77,25	0.03961	0.00386
78,25	0.01352	−0.00005
88,25	0.06247	−0.00080
77,26	0.01184	0.01264
78,26	0.00345	0.00037
88,26	0.00000	−0.00172
77,3*3*	0.81373	0.80217
78,3*3*	0.16445	−0.05561
88,3*3*	0.40426	0.40297
77,3*4*	0.28757	−0.06678
78,3*4*	0.07137	0.01967
88,3*4*	0.21472	0.04151
77,3*5	0.00000	0.02768
78,3*5	0.02278	0.01740
88,3*5	0.08547	0.06813
77,3*6	0.03837	−0.08190
78,3*6	0.08968	0.01630
88,3*6	0.23868	0.01592

pq,rs	$[\phi_p\phi_q,\phi_r\phi_s]$	$[\theta_p\theta_q,\theta_r\theta_s]$
77,4*4*	0.42053	0.39411
78,4*4*	0.13355	0.01868
88,4*4*	0.57748	0.56943
77,4*5	0.19847	0.07800
78,4*5	0.06050	−0.01170
88,4*5	0.21046	−0.02651
77,4*6	0.13192	0.08603
78,4*6	0.02985	−0.00021
88,4*6	0.00000	0.01321
77,55	0.77876	0.77933
78,55	0.16336	−0.05092
88,55	0.42442	0.42068
77,56	0.20891	−0.10507
78,56	0.06133	0.01993
88,56	0.18233	0.03604
77,66	0.46886	0.46782
78,66	0.13738	0.01076
88,66	0.54827	0.56322
71,71	0.02500	0.02500
81,71	0.00086	−0.00613
72,71	0.00005	0.00005
82,71	0.00037	0.00037
73*,71	0.03840	0.03357
83*,71	0.00448	−0.00487
74*,71	0.00934	−0.00685
84*,71	0.00415	0.00450
75,71	0.00000	0.00285
85,71	0.00262	0.00261
76,71	0.01470	−0.01044
86,71	0.00304	0.00381
81,81	0.00003	0.00151
72,81	0.00000	−0.00001
82,81	0.00002	−0.00008
73*,81	0.00169	−0.00784
83*,81	0.00024	0.00118
74*,81	0.00046	0.00165
84*,81	0.00025	−0.00102
75,81	0.00021	−0.00046
85,81	0.00017	−0.00065
76,81	0.00070	0.00241
86,81	0.00018	−0.00086
72,72	0.00005	0.00005
82,72	0.00076	0.00077
73*,72	0.00051	0.00050
83*,72	0.00045	0.00030
74*,72	0.00037	0.00016
84*,72	0.00156	0.00139
75,72	0.00031	0.00027
85,72	0.00060	−0.00003
76,72	0.00040	0.00010
86,72	0.00035	0.00064
82,82	0.01556	0.01635
73*,82	0.00423	0.00426
83*,82	0.00539	0.00382

pq,rs	$[\phi_p\phi_q,\phi_r\phi_s]$	$[\theta_p\theta_q,\theta_r\theta_s]$
74*,82	0.00377	0.00208
84*,82	0.02474	0.02273
75,82	0.00253	0.00187
85,82	0.00760	−0.00252
76,82	0.00345	0.00144
86,82	0.00000	0.00519
73*,73*	0.17984	0.17303
83*,73*	0.03363	−0.01339
74*,73*	0.05372	−0.02444
84*,73*	0.04295	0.03980
75,73*	0.00000	0.01038
85,73*	0.02278	0.01140
76,73*	0.07857	−0.03374
86,73*	0.02605	0.02658
83*,83*	0.01337	0.00846
74*,83*	0.01553	0.00818
84*,83*	0.03166	0.01857
75,83*	0.00929	0.00721
85,83*	0.01365	−0.00221
76,83*	0.01967	0.00738
86,83*	0.01060	0.00763
74*,74*	0.02063	0.00916
84*,74*	0.02891	0.01003
75,74*	0.00980	0.00821
85,74*	0.01392	−0.00269
76,74*	0.02794	0.00814
86,74*	0.01285	0.00396
84*,84*	0.12757	0.12548
75,84*	0.01806	0.01000
85,84*	0.03816	−0.01592
76,84*	0.02985	0.00550
86,84*	0.00000	0.02106
75,75	0.04704	0.04679
85,75	0.01351	−0.00363
76,75	0.01201	−0.00996
86,75	0.01060	0.01017
85,85	0.01604	0.00748
76,85	0.01645	−0.00025
86,85	0.01070	0.00646
76,76	0.03918	0.01536
86,76	0.01762	0.00165
86,86	0.03312	0.03545
7*7*,7*7*	0.82580	0.82580
7*8*,7*7*	0.16444	−0.06123
8*8*,7*7*	0.39393	0.39424
7*8*,7*8*	0.04259	0.01516
8*8*,7*8*	0.13004	0.02263
8*8*,8*8*	0.58139	0.58463
9*7*,7*9*	0.09408	0.09408
9*8*,7*9*	0.01459	−0.01128
10*8*,7*9*	0.01164	0.01147
9*8*,7*10*	0.00471	0.00399
10*8*,7*10*	0.01029	0.00664
10*8*,8*10*	0.06624	0.06699

Reprinted from the Proceedings of the NATIONAL ACADEMY OF SCIENCES
Vol. 47, No. 8, pp. 1217–1226. August, 1961.

MANY-ELECTRON THEORY OF ATOMS AND MOLECULES

BY OKTAY SINANOĞLU

STERLING CHEMISTRY LABORATORY, YALE UNIVERSITY

Communicated by R. M. Fuoss and read before the Academy, April 24, 1961

Orbital theories of atoms and molecules work quite well in a qualitative or semi-empirical way but fail when put to a quantitative test. The error, which is so large that often even molecule formation is not predicted, is generally attributed to electron correlation. Its importance has been stressed in several reviews.[1, 2]

Since electrons affect one another through their instantaneous potentials and not just by their average potentials as in the Hartree-Fock method,[1] we do have a many-electron problem. But what sort of a many-body problem? Does the long range of coulomb repulsions cause all electrons to be involved in one complicated motion? If this were the case to the extent of overcoming the effects of the exclusion principle, shell structure would be wiped out, and an atom or molecule would be more like a drop of electron liquid. Actual shell structure and electron densities are close to those given by the Hartree-Fock method. For example, densities from the latter agree quite well with X-ray results.[3]

The situation of the many-electron problem in atoms and molecules is compared with related many-body problems in Figure 1. Inside nuclei, strong, short-range forces cause only local nucleon pair correlations to dominate. Brueckner theory[4] considers these for the idealized infinite nuclear "matter." Due to the strength of repulsions, each particle moves in an environment it is constantly polarizing. In finite systems,[5] difficulties arise. This "polarized sea" potential is strongly dependent on particle state, so that orthogonal ground-state orbitals cannot be obtained easily. The basis is discrete, and the difficulties of evaluating slowly convergent infinite sums as in ordinary perturbation theory[1] appear.

In the infinite electron gas, Hartree-Fock orbitals being plane waves, there is no electron localization. As we shall see below, correlation is determined by the difference of the instantaneous coulomb potential $g_{ij} = r_{ij}^{-1}$ between two electrons i, j and the average, i.e., Hartree-Fock (H.F.), potential they would exert on one

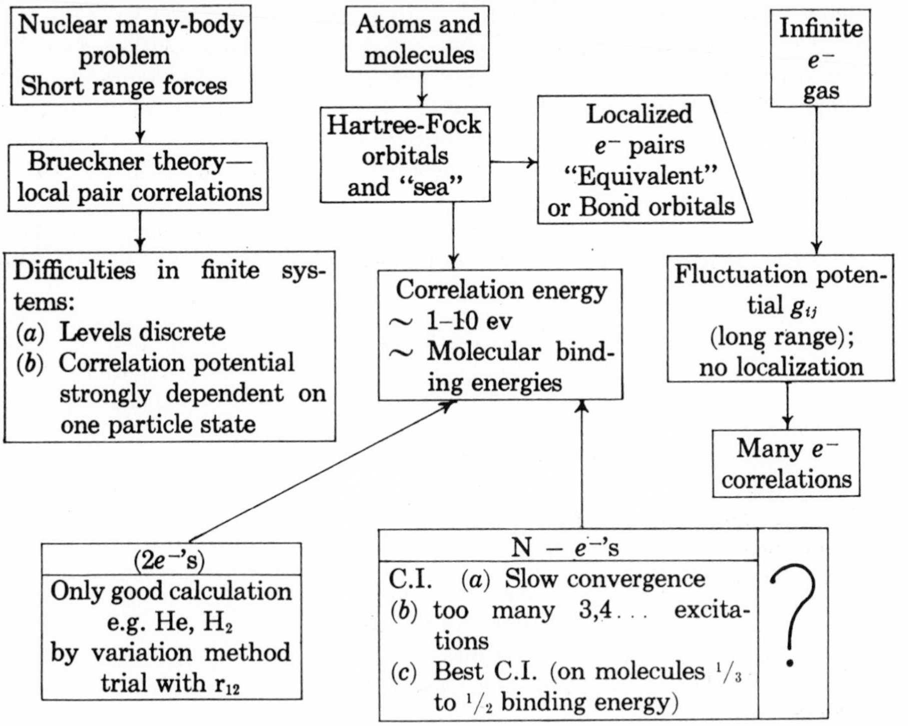

FIG. 1.—The situation of the many-electron problem in atoms and molecules and related many-body problems.

another. But due to complete delocalization, this H.F. part, $\bar{S}_i(j) + \bar{S}_j(i)$ is uniform and nearly zero for a very large box, and the fluctuation potential is the full g_{ij} with its long range. Thus *many* electrons correlate at the same time.

Fortunately, in atoms and molecules (except dyes, etc., where metallic behavior is approached), the problem is very different from that of the electron gas. The symmetry, the nuclear wells, and the exclusion principle localize electrons with paired spins in the Hartree-Fock wave function. As shown by Linnett and Pöe,[6] the configuration of maximum probability given by a determinental function, e.g., for Ne, is four electron pairs tetrahedrally arranged. Such spatial arrangements, bonds, etc., are better represented by transforming the H.F. orbitals to "equivalent orbitals" which leave the determinant unchanged.[7]

The only accurate calculations on atoms and molecules so far[8] are still those on two-electron systems based on the classical works[1] of Hylleraas on He, and James and Coolidge on H_2 using trial functions containing r_{12}. This method not having been extended to the case of N electrons, for such systems configuration-interaction (C.I.) is used. The latter is often slowly convergent (except when used for degeneracy or "resonance"), the number of multiple excitations increases very rapidly with N, and best C.I. on small molecules so far has given only about $^1/_3$ to $^1/_2$ of the binding energies.

We have developed an extensive theory for the N-electron atom or molecule (a) to get a quantitative scheme of the order of the difficulty of the He, H_2 case, (b) to understand the physical behavior of many-electron motion and to relate the "chemical" picture to correlation. In our initial work, rigorous solutions were obtained in perturbation theory.[9] We have now gone far beyond those results and completed the picture in several directions. In this communication, we summarize our latest findings with emphasis on the physical basis and the over-all structure that emerges. The full mathematical theory will be published in the *Journal of Chemical Physics*.

Physical Aspects of Correlation in Atoms and Molecules.—The principal features of the many-electron problem in atoms and molecules are shown in Figure 2. The

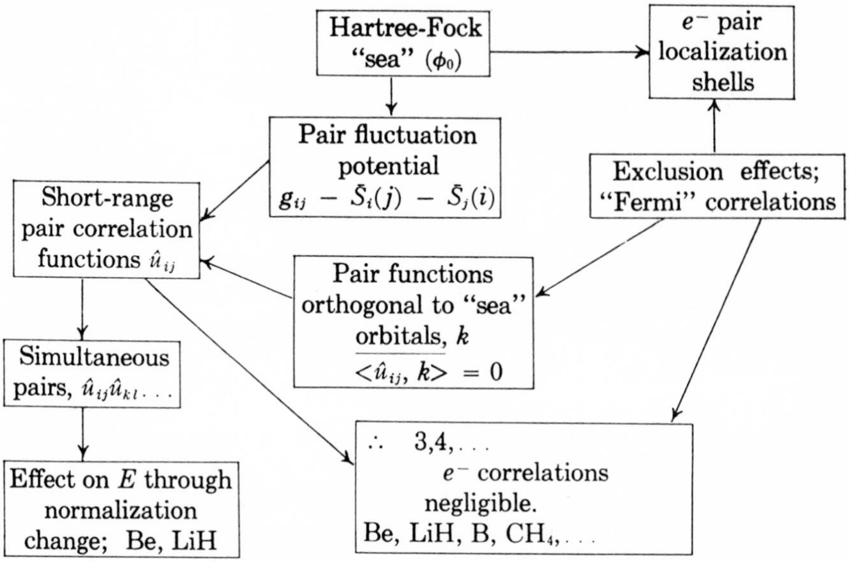

FIG. 2.—Main physical aspects of electron correlation in atoms and in molecules with no strong delocalization.

long-range effects of coulomb repulsions are well taken care of by the Hartree-Fock potential and orbitals. We start with the Hartree-Fock solution, ϕ_0. The reason for the choice of this "sea" in which electrons move will become more and more apparent as we go along. The effects of using a polarized "sea" as in the Brueckner method would come up only to quite high orders and would be negligible aside from the cumbersome self-consistency procedures[4, 5] that it would require.

If we write

$$\psi = \phi_0 + \chi \tag{1}$$

for the exact wave function with ϕ_0 the single H.F. determinant and χ the correction for correlation, the energy is separated into an H.F. and a correlation part.

$$E = \frac{<\chi, H\psi>}{<\chi, \chi>} = E_{\text{H.F.}} + \frac{2 < \phi_0, (H - E_{\text{H.F.}})\chi > + < \chi, (H - E_{\text{H.F.}})\chi>}{1 + 2 < \phi_0, \chi > + <\chi, \chi>}, \tag{2}$$

$$E_{\text{H.F.}} = < \phi_0, H\phi_0>,$$

and
$$H = \sum_{i=1}^{N} h_i^0 + \sum_{i>j} g_{ij} = H_0 + H_1, \tag{3}$$

with h_i^0 the bare nuclei hamiltonian of electron i and $g_{ij} \equiv 1/r_{ij}$. We separate H into a

$$H_0 = \sum_{i=j}^{N} (h_i^0 + V_i) \tag{4}$$

part for independent electrons in the H.F. potential V_i and a residual "fluctuation" potential part

$$H_1 = \sum_{i>j}^{N} [g_{ij} - \bar{S}_i(j) - \bar{S}_j(i)], \tag{5}$$

writing[9] $\sum_{i=1}^{N} V_i$ as $\sum_{i>j}^{N} [\bar{S}_i(j) + \bar{S}_j(i)]$. An $\bar{S}_i(j)$ is the coulomb plus exchange potential of orbital i acting on electron j. Then

$$E_{\text{H.F.}} = E_0 + E_1 = \sum_{i=1}^{N} \epsilon_i - \sum_{i>j}^{N} (J_{ij} - K_{ij}) \tag{6}$$

with ϵ_i the H.F. orbital energies, J_{ij}, K_{ij} the coulomb and exchange integrals. $(H - E_{\text{H.F.}})$ becomes

$$(H - E_{\text{H.F.}}) = \sum_{i=1}^{N} e_i + \sum_{i>j} m_{ij}, \tag{7a}$$

where
$$e_i \equiv h_i^0 + V_i - \epsilon_i$$

and
$$m_{ij} = g_{ij} - \bar{S}_i(j) - \bar{S}_j(i) + J_{ij} - K_{ij}. \tag{7b}$$

A Hartree-Fock spinorbital occupied by electron i before antisymmetrization is denoted by i also so that

$$e_i i = 0 \quad \text{from} \quad H_0\phi_0 = E_0\phi_0.$$

Equation (2) becomes

$$E - E_{\text{H.F.}} = \frac{2 < \phi_0, \sum_{i>j} m_{ij}\chi > + < \chi, (\sum_{j>j} e_i + \sum_{i} m_{ij})\chi >}{1 + 2 < \phi_0, \chi > + < \chi, \chi >} \tag{8}$$

Fluctuation Potential.—Correlation behavior is determined (a) by the pairwise fluctuation potentials m_{ij}, and (b) by the electron distribution in the "sea," ϕ_0, which depends strongly on its antisymmetric character.[6,7]

An m_{ij} is usually of short range in directions going from orbital to orbital. Take a (1s) electron and another in the *Be* atom for example. An electron placed at r_2 sees the average coulomb potential $S_1(r_2)$ of the (1s) electron with opposite spin as shown in Figure 3 (taking a Slater (1s) orbital with exponent 3.70 as sufficiently close to *H.F.*). The (1s) electron is most likely to be found at $r_1 = 0.27$ a.u. (Bohr orbit in Be^{+2}). If it were there instantaneously, electron two would see the $g_{12} = r_{12}^{-1}$, also shown in Figure 3.

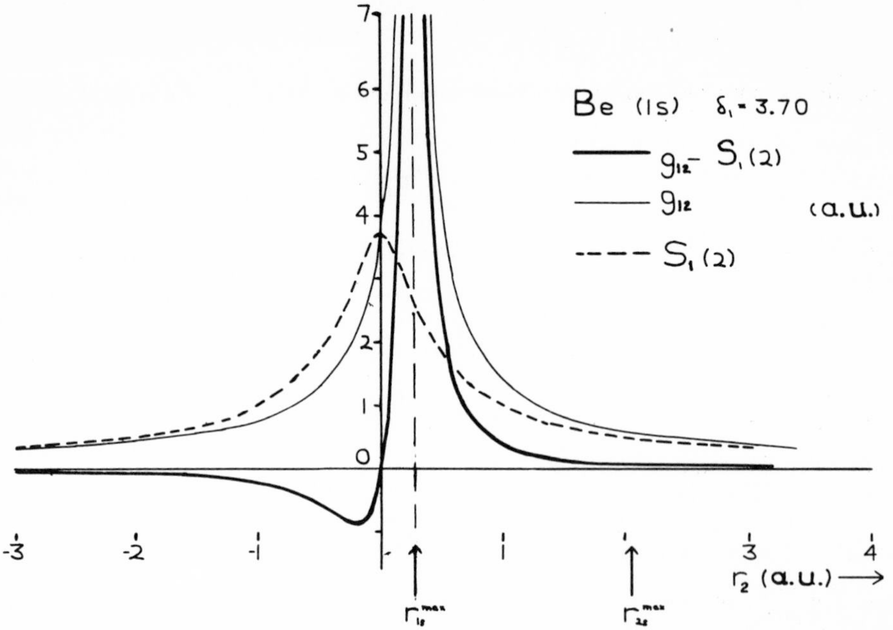

FIG. 3.—Fluctuation potential (g_{12}–$S_1(2)$) as seen by an electron at r_2 due a (1s) electron with opposite spin instantaneously at its Bohr radius and in line with r_2. Note that this potential which determines the correlation, is of short range through $g_{12} = r_{12}^{-1}$ and the Hartree-Fock potential, $S_1(2)$, are long range.

The difference, $g_{12} - S_1(2)$, differing from m_{12} by the constant value 0.39 a.u., is the fluctuation potential, which shows where electron two (r_2) would want to be if electron one were at $r_{1s}^{max.} = 0.27$ a.u. Both g_{12} and $S_1(2)$ are of long range, but $m_1(2)$ has a short range. It has died off before reaching a distance of 2.1 a.u., about the Bohr radius of (2s) in *Be*. The singularity of g_{12} at $r_{12} = 0$ is the main feature left in m_{12}. Note also the minimum in $m_1(2)$ on the other side of the nucleus. Similar curves and surfaces can be drawn by varying r_1 and θ_{12} (angle between r_1 and r_2) also. These would aid the selection of trial functions to give maximum charge density at the dips and zero at singularity.

The exclusion principle, by putting the third and fourth electrons in a different shell, keeps them at a safe distance from the fluctuation potentials of the $(1s)^2$ electrons. As the discussion of other cases below will show, this phenomenon is quite general and even in more subtle cases leads to local pair correlations as the main effects, making the "collisions" of three, four, . . . electrons usually negligible.

This fact manifests itself in the equation:

$$\chi \sim \chi_s = \sum_{i>j}^{N} \frac{\mathcal{A}}{\sqrt{2}} \left(1,2,3 \ldots N \frac{\hat{u}_{ij}}{ij}\right) \tag{9}$$

where 1, 2, . . . N are the spin-orbitals in ϕ_0 occupied by electrons with the same numerals before the antisymmetrizer $\mathcal{A}$ makes them indistinguishable. The $\hat{u}_{ij}$ is the antisymmetric correlation wave function of i and j which shows how they are thrown out of each other's way by m_{ij}. In the orbital representation, $\hat{u}_{ij}$ contains all double excitations of orbitals i, j from the "sea," ϕ_0. The two electrons cannot go into regions already occupied by other electrons, and this effect of the exclusion principle is reflected in the orthogonality[9] of $\hat{u}_{ij}$ to the *orbitals* of ϕ_0, i.e.

$$<\hat{u}_{ij}(x_i, x_{xj}), k(x_i)>_{xi} = 0 \qquad (k = 1,2, \ldots N) \tag{10}$$

where integration is performed over x_i only. The $\hat{u}_{ij}$ does not contain any single excitations either[9] ($k = i$ or j), because any further adjustment of the orbitals in the "sea" (Brueckner method) is negligible. The major adjustment has been done already in the Hartree-Fock method.

Equations (9) and (10) come out exactly[9] in first-order perturbation χ_1 beyond H.F., i.e., if only part of the energy, equation (8), is minimized.[10] Then $\hat{u}_{ij}$ would be the solution, $\hat{u}_{ij}^{(1)}$, of the first-order part of the Schrödinger equation[11] of two electrons in the H.F. "sea":

$$(e_i + e_j)\hat{u}_{ij}^{(1)} + \hat{m}_{ij}\mathcal{B}(ij) = 0. \tag{11}$$

$\mathcal{B}$ antisymmetrizes i and j. The $(\hat{m}_{ij}Bij)$ is $m_{ij}B(ij)$ made orthogonal to all k as in equation (10); thus $\hat{m}_{ij}$ is even more localized than m_{ij}.

We shall now leave equations (9) and (10) quite general and not confine $\hat{u}_{ij}$ to any order of approximation. Various ways of obtaining the pair correlations exactly will be discussed later.

Unlinked Clusters versus Many-Electron Correlations.—The complete χ would contain in addition to equation (9), "clusters" of three, four, etc., electrons at a time ($\hat{U}_{123}$, $\hat{U}_{1234}$, etc.). In addition to these terms, just the substitution of χ_s, equation (9), into the energy, equation (8), introduces three-electron correlations. The analysis is carried out easily with diagrams giving the energy of χ_s as

$$E - E_{\text{H.F.}} \leqslant \frac{1}{D}\left(\sum_{i>j} \tilde{\epsilon}_{ij} + 4 \sum_{ijk} \begin{array}{c} i \quad j \\ \circ\!\!-\!\!\circ \\ \diagdown \ \ | \\ \circ\, k \end{array}\right) \tag{12}$$

$$\tilde{\epsilon}_{ij} = 2 < \mathcal{B}(ij), m_{ij}\, \hat{u}_{ij} > + < \hat{u}_{ij}, (e_i + e_j + m_{ij})\hat{u}_{ij}> \tag{13}$$

$$D = 1 + <\chi_s, \chi_s> = 1 + \sum_{i>j} <\hat{u}_{ij},\hat{u}_{ij}> \tag{14}$$

The triangle is the three-electron correlation involving the product of $\hat{u}_{kj}$, $\hat{u}_{ij}$, and m_{ki}. Because of the physical effects described, $\hat{u}_{kj}$ and $\hat{u}_{ji}$ will not both be large in the same region of space, so that only pair energies in equation (12) are significant.

In the recent configuration-interaction study[12] of the Be atom starting with H.F., single and triple excitations were found entirely negligible. But important quadruple excitations appeared—at first sight a surprising result, since the probability of a four-electron "collision" ought to be smaller than that of a three-body one.

Equation (9) represents only two electrons correlating at one time. Actually, it is very likely that when two electrons "collide," somewhere else in the system other binary "collisions" will be taking place independently but simultaneously. To account for these, all possible products of independent pair functions must be added to χ_s; e.g., for Be:

$$\chi_{ss} = \frac{\mathcal{A}}{2}\,(\hat{u}_{12}\hat{u}_{34} + \hat{u}_{13}\hat{u}_{24} + \hat{u}_{14}\hat{u}_{23}). \tag{15}$$

As in the theory of imperfect gases, these are "unlinked clusters" and have played an important role in other many-body problems.[4, 13]

If in *Be*, true four-electron correlations, $\hat{U}_{1234}$, are negligible; the coefficients of quadruple excitations should be given only by those of double excitations. In Table 1, such coefficients from equation (15) are compared with those from the

TABLE 1

UNLINKED CLUSTERS VERSUS FOUR-ELECTRON CORRELATIONS IN BE ATOM

Four-excited configuration	Coefficient from 37-configuration wave function*	Calc'd. [Eq. (15)] Unlinked cluster coefficient
$P_I^2(^1S)p_{II}^2(^1S)$	0.00706	0.0073
$P_I^2(^1S)s_I^2(^1S)$	0.00565	0.00647
$P_I^2(^1S)d_{II}^2(^1S)$	0.00159	0.00168
$P_{II}^2(^1S)d_I^2(^1S)$	0.000464	0.000478
Energy contribution	−0.075 ev	−0.074 ev

* From Watson.[12]

37 configuration[12] C.I. The agreement is indeed satisfactory. We have obtained similar results upon examining recent C.I. results[14] on *LiH*.

Effect on Energy.—The energy effect of unlinked clusters such as in Equation (15), is again analyzed with diagrams. One gets from equation (8).

$$E - E_{\text{H.F.}} \leq \sum_{i>j}^{N} \tilde{\epsilon}_{ij} \frac{D_{ij}}{D'} + \frac{R}{D'}. \tag{16a}$$

$D' \cong D$ and R contains all triangles, squares, and other joint four- or more-electron correlation effects.

$$D_{ij} = 1 + \sum_{k,l \neq i,j} < \hat{u}_{kl}, \hat{u}_{kl} > + \ldots \tag{16b}$$

As N tends to infinity, D_{ij}/D approaches 1.[4, 13] In atoms and molecules if D is sufficiently different from unity due to some "resonance" as in *Be* (large $2s^2 - 2p^2$ mixing which makes *Be* a metal not an inert gas), unlinked clusters affect the energy by canceling part of D'. This energy change agrees perfectly with the 37 C.I. result in Table 1, showing also that R in equation (16*a*) is negligible as anticipated. Thus,

$$E - E_{\text{H.F.}} \cong \sum_{i>j} \tilde{\epsilon}_{ij} D_{ij}/D. \tag{17}$$

One reason for the smallness of many-particle effects is the smallness of $\hat{u}_{ij}$. Even with the $2s^2 - 2p^2$ "resonance" in *Be*, D gets only as large as 1.09. Usually $D \cong D_{ij} \cong 1$. Equation (17) will usually be a good approximation, but if need be, the neglected terms, R, can also be estimated with $\hat{u}_{ij}$ and an upper limit obtained to E.

Exlusion effect in boron.—We have seen how and why three-, four-, and more-electron correlations become unimportant when electrons are localized in radially different regions of space as in *Be* and *LiH*. What about cases, however, which involve say $2s$, $2p$ electrons which are radially all in the same vicinity?

To see how three-electron correlations are expected to behave in such cases, we examine the boron atom. Almost all of the $(2s)^2$ correlation, $\hat{u}_{34}$, in *Be* is due to $(2p)^2$ mixing.[12] There, $\hat{u}_{34}$ is ^1S, a combination of three $(2p)^2$ determinants. When a $(2p_z\alpha)$, i.e., spinorbital 5, is put on top of the $(2s)^2$ shell as in boron however, $\hat{u}_{34}$ becomes orthogonal to it, i.e. $<\hat{u}_{34}, 5> = 0$. Instead of the whole sphere, $\hat{u}_{34}$ will now be large only on the xy-plane as shown in Figure 4. To make the three-electron $(2s_\alpha 2s_\beta 2p_z\alpha \equiv 345)$ correlation, *i.e.*, the triangle of equation (12), appreciable, the product $\hat{u}_{34}\hat{u}_{45}$ must be large. But $\hat{u}_{45}$ is large where its fluctuation potential m_{45} and $B(45)$ are large [see equation (11)]. The fluctuation potential, $(g_{45} - S_5(4))$, that electron 4 sees when 5 is at its most likely place (Fig. 4) is shown

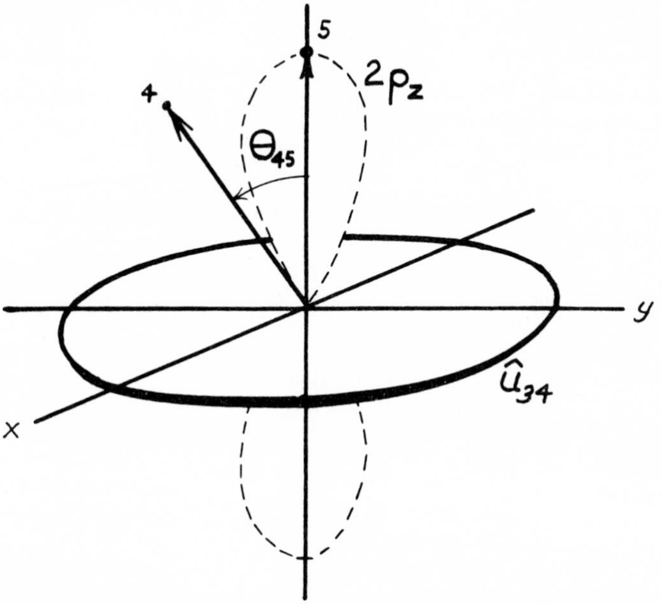

FIG. 4.—Exclusion effect in Boron $(1s^2 2s^2 2p_z)$. The two (2s) electrons while correlating are kept away from the $(2p_z)$ electron which has the same spin as one or the other (2s). Thus $(2s)^2$ correlation, $\hat{u}_{34}$, is confined to the vicinity of the xy-plane.

in Figure 5 for a fixed radius.

Note that m_{45}, hence $\hat{u}_{45}$, is very small just where $(\sim 90°)$ $\hat{u}_{34}$ is large. Thus, the product $\hat{u}_{34}\hat{u}_{45}$ will be small everywhere, again exhibiting the combined behavior of m_{ij} and exclusion to make many-electron correlations unimportant.

How to Get the Pair Functions.—Having a sum of pair energies in equation (17), each pair function can be obtained separately in several ways, depending on the magnitude of (D_{ij}/D). These ways and the over-all picture that comes out of our theory is shown in Figure 6.

Each $\tilde{\epsilon}_{ij}$, equation (13), varied subject to orbital orthogonality, equation (10), yields Schrödinger equations of electron pairs in a Hartree-Fock "sea."

$$(e_i + e_j + \hat{m}_{ij})\phi_{ij} = 0 \tag{18a}$$

where $\phi_{ij} = \mathcal{B}(ij) + \hat{u}_{ij}$. When this equation is satisfied, $\tilde{\epsilon}_{ij}$ becomes

$$\epsilon_{ij} = <\mathcal{B}(ij), g_{ij}\hat{u}_{ij}>. \tag{18b}$$

Minimization of smaller parts[10] of $\tilde{\epsilon}_{ij}D_{ij}/D$ leads to first-order pairs,[9] equation (11). On the other hand, a more complete Schrödinger equation than equation

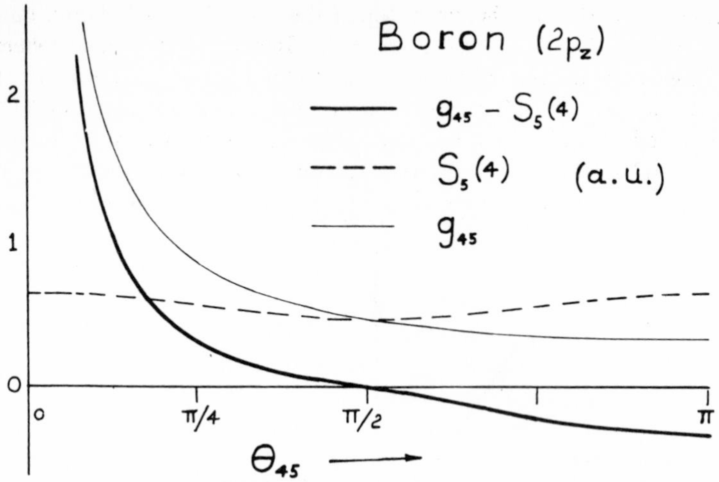

FIG. 5.—Reason for expecting $(2s)^2(2p_z)$ three e^- correlation to be small. The fluctuation potential, $[g_{45}-S_5(4)]$, seen by the (2s) electron, 4, due to electron 5 at the maximum of $(2p_z)$ is *ca.* zero on the *xy*-plane ($\pi/2$) where $\hat{u}_{34}$ was largest (Fig. 4).

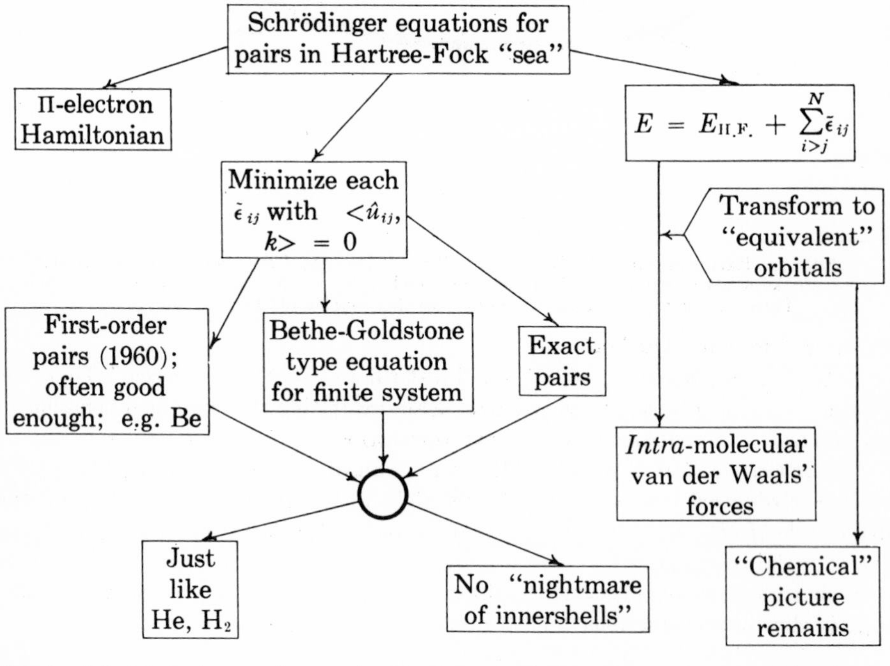

FIG. 6.—Principle features and ways of using the many-electron theory of atoms and molecules as reported in text.

(18*a*) is obtained by minimizing $\tilde{\epsilon}_{ij}/(1 + <\hat{u}_{ij},\hat{u}_{ij}>)$ instead of ϵ_{ij} alone. Equation (18*a*) differs from the closed form of the Bethe-Goldstone[15]–Brueckner equation in containing $\hat{m}_{ij}$ instead of $\hat{g}_{ij}$. The results we have obtained in this connection should also be useful for finite nuclei.

Now the variational *minimum* principle can be applied to each $\tilde{\epsilon}_{ij}$, equation (13), separately subject to equation (10) and with trial functions that may contain r_{12} explicitly as in He and H_2 for shells with a strong "correlation hole.[1]" For others, e.g., those with "resonance" as in the $(2s)^2$ of Be, a small secular equation need be solved mixing a few configurations. The number of independent pair functions that are needed[9] is much smaller than $N(N-1)/2$ due to the multiplicity of many pair states such as ^3S, ^1D, etc. Only 9 pair functions of which 6 are singlets must be obtained for Ne, instead of 45. Because of orbital orthogonality, equation (10), the *minimization* procedure can be applied even to outer shell pairs with no fear of converging to the wrong shell ("the nightmare of inner shells" which plagued the quantum chemistry of the thirties).[16]

The "Chemical" Picture.—Equation (18) for an outer pair with $V_i + V_j - \bar{S}_i - \bar{S}_j = V_{\text{core}}$ (Eq. 7b) has the form of a "Π-electron Hamiltonian" thus providing a basis for such semiempirical schemes.[17] Moreover, $\tilde{\epsilon}_{ij}$ can be added to $(J_{ij} - K_{ij})$, equation (6), explaining the successes of semiempirical M.O. calculations.

In molecules with no strong electron delocalization, the Hartree-Fock orbitals in ϕ_0 can be transformed[7] into "equivalent orbitals." Then $\sum_{i<j} \tilde{\epsilon}_{ij}$ becomes simply the sum of "bond" correlation energies and "Van der Waals" attractions between non-bonded regions. The latter were discussed semi-empirically by Pitzer.[2] One can use the theory both ways and (a) calculate such Van der Waals forces having C.I. etc. type correlation results starting with Hartree-Fock, or (b) estimate correlation energies of pairs of H.F. orbitals from estimates of bond energies and London dispersion type forces.[2]

Thus the "chemical" picture with its bonds, Lewis-Langmuir octets[6] and orbitals remains *in spite of correlation.*

It is my great pleasure to thank Raymond M. Fuoss and Lars Onsager for the kind interest they showed in this work.

[1] Löwdin, P. O., in *Advances in Chemical Physics* (New York: Interscience Publishers, 1959), vol. 2.

[2] Pitzer, K. S., in *Advances in Chemical Physics* (New York: Interscience Publishers, 1959), vol. 2.

[3] See, e.g., Daudel, R., R. LeFebvre, and C. Moser, *Quantum Chemistry* (New York: Interscience Publishers, 1959).

[4] Brueckner, K. A., in *The Many Body Problem*, ed. C. De Witt and P. Nozières (New York: John Wiley and Sons, 1959).

[5] Bethe, H. A., *Phys. Rev.*, **103,** 1353 (1956).

[6] Linnett, J. W., and A. J. Pöe, *Trans. Faraday Soc.*, **47,** 1033 (1951).

[7] See e.g., Pople, J. A., *Quart. Revs. (London)*, **11,** 291 (1957).

[8] The next best calculation is the recent one on Be (reference 12). Here $(2s)^2$–$(2p)^2$ "resonance" is of utmost importance and corrects for much of the correlation.

[9] Sinanoğlu, O., *Proc. Roy. Soc. (London)*, **A260,** 379 (1961).

[10] Sinanoğlu, O., *J. Chem. Phys.*, **34,** 1237 (1961).

[11] As shown in reference 9, for a general pair $\mathcal{B}(ij)$ is replaced by a pure symmetry state combination.

[12] Watson, R. E., *Phys. Rev.*, **119,** 170 (1960).

[13] Brout, R., *Phys. Rev.*, **111,** 1324 (1958).

[14] Ebbing, D. D., Ph.D. Thesis, Department of Chemistry, Indiana University (June 1960).

[15] Bethe, H. A., and J. Goldstone, *Proc. Roy. Soc. (London)*, **A238,** 551 (1956).

[16] Van Vleck, J. H., and A. Sherman, *Revs. Modern Phys.*, **7,** 167 (1935).

[17] Pariser, R., and R. G. Parr, *J. Chem. Phys.*, **21,** 466 (1953).

Corrections

Dr. Ross has requested that the following correction to his paper be noted:

page 237

In Table II, footnote d, the clause beginning with "after changing" should be deleted.

Professor Fischer-Hjalmars has requested that the following correction to her paper be noted:

page 425

Formula (15) should read:

$$W_\mu = \int \chi_\mu^* (T + U_\mu) \chi_\mu \, d\tau$$

Dr. Pariser asks that the following statements regarding his papers be noted:

page 247

Equation (19) should read $\beta(r) = -2517.5 \exp(-5.007r)$ ev

page 249

See note (2), *J. Chem. Phys.*, **23**, 711 (1955)

page 325

In Eq. (10) for $(V_{ik'} | V_{jk'})$, the third term following the equals sign should be $[ij|jj]$ instead of $[ij|ii]$. In Eq. (12), the summation should be over $f \neq i$.

---

*Page numbers refer to the numbers added to pages in this volume.

Index